THE FLORA OF H.

THE
FLORA OF
HAMPSHIRE

ANNE BREWIS
PAUL BOWMAN
FRANCIS ROSE

IN COLLABORATION WITH THE
HAMPSHIRE FLORA COMMITTEE

a continuation of the work of Alick Westrup and Phoebe Yule

IN ASSOCIATION WITH THE
HAMPSHIRE AND ISLE OF WIGHT WILDLIFE TRUST
1996

Published by Harley Books
(B. H. & A. Harley Ltd),
Martins, Great Horkesley,
Colchester, Essex, CO6 4AH, England

in association with
The Hampshire & Isle of Wight Wildlife Trust,
8 Romsey Road, Eastleigh,
Hampshire SO50 9AL

Designed by Geoff Green

Text set in Ehrhardt by Saxon Graphics Ltd, Derby

Text printed in Great Britain by
St Edmundsbury Press Ltd, Bury St Edmunds, Suffolk

Colour plates printed by George Over Ltd,
Rugby, Warwickshire

Bound by Hartnolls Ltd, Bodmin, Cornwall

British Library Cataloguing-in-Publication Data applied for

hardback ISBN 0 946589 34 8
paperback ISBN 0 946589 53 4

CONTENTS

Colour Plates I–XVI are bound between pages 84 and 85.

FOREWORD

RICHARD MABEY

Hampshire is to botanists what Norfolk is to birdwatchers – a great melting-pot of habitats, a migration cross-roads, a Mecca. Chalk hills arch in from the north-east and meet the hot Wessex heathlands. There are bogs and beech-hangers, water-meadows and sweeps of cryptic ancient woodland – and the New Forest, the last place in lowland England where you can have the illusion of wilderness.

This was where plants began to enter my bloodstream in a new way, too. Savouring bog-myrtle on the summer breeze in the New Forest was a different kind of experience from sniffing cowslips on a Chiltern roadside. It was primaeval, sensual, oddly stirring. So were the craggy beech-pollards of the Ancient and Ornamental Woodlands, and the sight of shoals of bog pimpernel, unfenced and un-fussed-about.

Yet the Forest – and the rest of Hampshire beyond it – is also a human landscape, and part of the fascination of botany is discovering the disposition of plants – their 'fit', if you like – in local geography and culture. This is the theme at the heart of county Floras, and one that the many plant-lovers who have lived or travelled in Hampshire have all been in thrall to: Thomas Johnson, William How, William Curtis, William Gilpin, the great John Goodyer, to whom this book is dedicated (and how reassuring to read of him excited by finding 5- and 6-leaved Herb Paris at Chawton, just like any modern botanophile), and, of course, Gilbert White.

Working on White's life introduced me to another part of Hampshire, and for a while the hangers and the hollow-ways became a second home for me. I do not know any other habitat in which natural luxuriance and human history combine so redolently as in Selborne's hollow-lanes, worn down, as White put it, 'by the traffic of ages, and the fretting of water', especially in spring when ramsons and golden-saxifrage are drifting amongst the ferns.

White's sense of the intimate detail of those lanes – of, in the best sense, parochial ecology – is the precursor of almost all that is special and characterful in modern Floras. He found wall lettuce and hart's-tongue fern 'in a most shady part of the hollow lane under the cover of the rock as you first enter the lane ... on the right-hand side before you come to Nine-acre lane'. They are still where White recorded them today – as, until a couple of years ago, was the clump of green hellebore that he found in flower 'in the stony lane towards Alton' on 23 April 1766. Nearly two-and-a-half centuries in the same patch of rubble-strewn track!

The fragile but persistent continuity of nature that local Floras document in such vivid detail is what makes them of value beyond the world of botany. It is also the best possible answer to those who believe that diligent recording may, in some way, lessen their sheer delight in plants. Who could fail to be beguiled and heartened by the thought that the Christmas-leafing oak at Castle Malwood near the Rufus Stone was first recorded by William How in the 1650s?

Not that Hampshire people need any such persuading to take their part in narrating this continuing story. With more than 1300 contributors, a fascination with local history and lore, and an open-minded acceptance of exotic colonists, this must be the most democratic of modern county Floras, in the great tradition started by *The Ecological Flora of the Shropshire Region* in 1985.

It is a chastening reminder to me, though – a pilgrim to Hampshire and an avid disciple of its natural history who has not always paid his dues. So I will begin to put that right now with a proper record of one of the most beautiful plants I have ever seen in the county: '*Veronica chamaedrys*, Germander Speedwell. A variety of tufted habit with dove-grey flowers. Hedgebank near Hawkley Mill, 1981'. I hope it is still there when the next edition of this inspirational Flora appears.

Dedicated to the memory of John Goodyer (1592–1664)
of Petersfield, Hampshire –
'an incomparable botanist, of sound judgement
and of immense industry'

An approximately 150-year-old specimen of
Goodyer's Elm (*Ulmus minor* ssp. *angustifolia*)
in a hedge at Rockford Green, near Ringwood (*Photo:* R. P. Bowman)

PREFACE

This is an account of the established flora of Hampshire (exclusive of the Isle of Wight). Those alien species that are no more than temporary casuals, such as many of the annuals from wool shoddy unlikely to survive frosts, are not included as this would have made the book too long.

The area covered is principally that defined by the two Watsonian vice-counties of North and South Hampshire, VCs 11 and 12 respectively. However, the frequent boundary changes since the date when the vice-county system was devised last century have led to certain former parts of Hampshire being transferred to adjacent counties and likewise certain parts of neighbouring counties belonging to other vice-counties being incorporated in present-day Hampshire. All of these portions which are – or have been at some time – part of Hampshire, as defined in Chapter VIII, are covered by this book.

There has been no Flora of Hampshire since Townsend's second edition of 1904 which J. F. Rayner's supplement of 1929 augmented but did not supersede. Our new work aims to provide a more balanced coverage of the County than Townsend was able to achieve, his treatment of some areas being decidedly more thorough than that of others. He also gave considerable emphasis to the less rich flora of the Isle of Wight which lies outside the scope of this book (and for which, incidentally, a new Flora has been produced only recently). As described in the chapter 'Earlier Workers on the Hampshire Flora', the seeds of the present work were sown in the 1950s, when Alick Westrup was collecting data not only for the new national mapping scheme but also for his proposed, more detailed, tetrad-based County atlas. Sadly, in 1964, just as this was progressing well, Westrup died prematurely and the project was set back severely. In his will he bequeathed all material for his Flora to the Hampshire and Isle of Wight Naturalists' (now Wildlife) Trust, which he had been instrumental in setting up, and on this foundation all future work was built.

Mrs Phoebe Yule, a lifelong field botanist, then in her early 70s, nobly and with no little trepidation accepted the invitation to pick up the pieces and began co-ordinating the renewed gathering and assembling of records. The original base map was produced at this time at the instigation of our friend and original adviser, the late Dr John Dony. However, in 1974, by then in her eighties and following a motor accident, Phoebe Yule was obliged to give up this immense task and hand it over to another.

The final phase in the preparation of the Flora began when the Hampshire Trust invited me to take it over. This I agreed to do, on condition that the task would be shared with Mr Paul Bowman, an able and active botanist from the south of the County who was later appointed the Botanical Society of the British Isles recorder for VC11. In 1969, Dr Francis Rose, one of the most knowledgeable all-round field botanists and plant ecologists in Britain, came to live in the County. He was soon invited to contribute his considerable expertise to the project, an invitation which he accepted, thus completing the trio of principal authors.

Another invaluable recruit to the team with a keen interest in the history of natural history was Dr D. E. Allen, the author of another county Flora, who moved to Winchester in 1972. He not only succeeded Dr Dony as our adviser, but has also written the fascinating historical account and as a national authority on *Rubus* – so well represented in the County – has contributed the outstandingly excellent account of this group.

In the mid-1970s, a Hampshire Flora Committee was established under the initial chairmanship of Mr W. M. M. Baron. Other founding members, in addition to the three principal authors were Mr M. Bryant, Dr R. B. Gibbons, Dr R. R. Page (as

Secretary) and Mr N. Phillips. This Committee lapsed in the late 1970s, shortly after Dr Allen had joined it, and a new one was formed in December 1984 comprising the authors, a few of the original Committee members and 'new blood' in the persons of Mrs Alison E. Bolton, Dr. P. R. Brough and Mr A. R. G. Mundell. In 1985, Dr Brough succeeded Mr Baron as Chairman on the latter's retirement and has skilfully steered our meetings over the long period since. In the same year Mr A. J. P. Branson, Mr G. D. Field (who acted as Minuting Secretary on the retirement from the Committee of Dr Page the following year) and Mr A. J. Rackham were additionally recruited. Mr C. R. Hall, who had been specially commissioned in 1989 to extract plant records from the Hampshire County Council Habitat Assessment Team Survey and from data obtained from the Nature Conservancy Council (now English Nature), was subsequently co-opted on to the Committee as well. This remained the composition until the completion of the text for publication, all members making valuable contributions to discussions over the years, during which many difficult problems and conflicting views on the presentation were sorted out. At this point Tony Mundell should be singled out for special mention. He was sent the entire text piecemeal by the individual authors and typed it on to disk – not once but countless times, in various orders, as the systematic arrangement was revised – first on a borrowed word-processor and later on one purchased out of his own pocket. This was an almost superhuman effort which occupied most of his spare time over several years and without which the Flora would still remain unpublished. We are enormously indebted to him.

For their contributions to Chapters IV and VI of the Introduction, we would like to express our particular gratitude to Messrs A. J. P. Branson, C. Chatters, C. R. Hall, A. R. G. Mundell, N. A. Sanderson and P. J. Wilson, and to Dr P. R. Brough; also, respectively, to Mr K. A. Sandell and Mr A. C. Crundwell for their co-operation and assistance in compiling the Lichen and Bryophyte Floras.

The preparation of the distribution maps had been initiated in the time of Mrs Yule, who organized the production of neatly drawn species' maps on standard master graph outlines. These were the basis for many of the draft maps and we are grateful to the late Miss R. Hartas Jackson, the late Mr J. L. S. Lansley and, above all, to Miss W. M. Keens for their long hours of work on these. The original base-map was drawn by Dr P. D. Coker following Dr Dony's recommendations. Computer-

ization of the maps was initially undertaken by Mr A. J. Rackham, assisted by Mr J. Procter and Mr and Mrs A. R. Welstead, with the support of Brockenhurst College who permitted the use of their computer and printer. After joining the Committee, Mr C. R. Hall continued work on the computerization of the maps, until they were very satisfactorily completed by Mr R. A. Barrett. Before they were computerized, each map was rigorously checked for accuracy by the three principal authors. During the two years while computer work was in progress, the maps were continuously updated so that all reliable records up to the end of October 1993 could be included and then afterwards checked again by Paul Bowman – another mammoth task. Miss Ann Hutchinson, Recorder for S. Wilts, was very helpful in sorting out some of the vice-county boundary problems. The drafts of maps used in the introductory chapters were vetted by Francis Rose and Paul Bowman and then skilfully drawn by Mr D. P. J. Smith, to whom we are most grateful for the infinite pains he took to refine them to our requirements.

Gathering the records for tetrad mapping has been spread over nearly thirty years, and it can well be appreciated that the number of botanists who have 'square-bashed' or helped with records is immense. Their names are among those listed at the end of the book, and many are also cited by their initials in the text of the Flora. To any who may inadvertently have been omitted we sincerely apologize.

Not only were records gathered by botanists in the field; many more were abstracted from published and unpublished accounts. The authors themselves have all contributed records culled from the literature – fully cited in the text. In addition to Mr Hall's sterling work already mentioned, we are grateful to Mr Neil Sanderson who collated many later records; to Messrs Clive Chatters (Conservation Officer), Ian Ralphs and John Rowe (habitat surveyors) of Hampshire Wildlife Trust, who all provided numerous records; to Mr Bill Shepard, Recorder for the Isle of Wight, who helped greatly by, among other things, extracting Hampshire records from the Bromfield Herbarium; to Dr H. J. M. Bowen (Recorder for Dorset) who kindly contributed many records for VCs 11 and 12; to Mr George Forster who passed on all his records for the New Forest; to Mr Paul Goriup who provided many records for aquatic plants (e.g. *Ranunculus* and *Potomageton*); and to the late Mr A. F. Mitchell for his interesting anecdotal information on trees.

We are also most grateful to Mrs F. A. Woodhead, who kindly gave us access to her records for her then unpublished *Flora of the Christchurch Area*; to Martin Jenkinson for allowing use of his orchid records; and to the Revd J. T. Tyler for letting us study the beautiful flower paintings by Miss C. R. May, from the catalogue of which we extracted many first records.

For help and advice on the treatment of certain genera and for determinations of material of these, we offer our special thanks to the following referees: Dr R. H. Roberts (*Polypodium, Mimulus*); Dr Sarah Webster and Prof. C. D. K. Cook (*Ranunculus*); the late Dr R. Melville (*Ulmus, Rosa*); Mr R. D. Meikle (*Salix*); the late Mr E. S. Edees and Mr A. Newton (*Rubus*); Mrs Jeanette Fryer (*Cotoneaster*); Dr R. M. Harley (*Mentha*); Dr A. J. Silverside (*Euphrasia*); Dr A. J. Richards and the late Mr C. C. Haworth (*Taraxacum*); Dr N. T. H. Holmes (*Potamogeton* and other aquatic plants); Mr C. R. Tubbs (*Zostera*); Prof. C. A. Stace (*Juncus, Festuca, Vulpia*); the late Mr R. W. David, Mr A. C. Jermy and Mr A. O. Chater (*Carex*); Mr P. J. O. Trist (*Festuca, Bromus* and other grasses); Dr A. J. Gray (*Spartina*); the late Dr D. P. Young (*Epipactis*); Mr E. J. Clement, Mr J. M. Mullin and the late Mr A. L. Grenfell (alien vascular plants); Dr B. J. Coppins and Dr T. D. V. Swinscow (lichens); and Mr H. W. Matcham (bryophytes). Our thanks are also extended to Mr R. C. Stern who kindly checked the text of 'The Bryophyte Flora' and to Dr Keith Barber, Dept. of Geography, Southampton University, who made very helpful and constructive comments on some of the introductory chapters.

We are extremely grateful to Mr R. G. Ellis of the Department of Botany, National Museum of Wales, not only for permitting us to use his computerized indexes to Clive Stace's *New Flora of the British Isles* and other works as the basis for our own index to the vascular plants but also for supplying it on disk. Mr A. C. Crundwell kindly compiled the index of names for the bryophyte flora and the index of lichen names was prepared by the publishers. The pagination of the index for the whole work has been assiduously undertaken by Annette Harley. The photographs used in the illustration of this work were generously provided by members of the committee and others and are individually acknowledged on the plates.

The tracking down of some of the private herbaria required considerable detective work. The authors and publishers were greatly assisted by the curators and staff of the Wiltshire Archaeological and Natural History Society Museum at Devizes Museum; Hampshire County Council Museum Services, Chilcomb House, Winchester; The Druce-Fielding Herbarium, Oxford; the Tolson Memorial Museum, Huddersfield; The Reading Museum & Art Gallery; and the University of Reading.

Assistance in checking literature references was generously given by the librarians and other members of staff of The Linnean Society of London; the General and Botany Libraries of The Natural History Museum, London; The Library, The Herbarium, Royal Botanic Gardens, Kew; The Geological Society; The Library, University of Southampton; Winchester Reference Library; The London Library; The United Oxford & Cambridge University Club; and also the Museum & Records Service, Portsmouth City Museum. To all of these we offer our sincere thanks.

We would also like to acknowledge the help given in various other ways by The Botanical Society of the British Isles; English Nature; The Game Conservancy; Hampshire County Council; the Hampshire County Council Museums Service; The Hampshire and Isle of Wight Wildlife Trust; The Haslemere Educational Museum; King's College, London; the National Rivers Authority; the Natural History Museum, London; Swindon Museum and Art Gallery; and the University of Southampton.

The preparation of a multi-author Flora by a committee has its problems, one of which is that there is a need for a co-ordinating editor to give an overview to the text and iron out inconsistencies between the various contributions. In the absence of such a person in our team, this task fell to the publishers, Basil and Annette Harley, who spent long hours over many months checking the text for accuracy and consistency from a variety of aspects. With the publication, after the completion of the text but during the editorial stage, of three important botanical works of reference, on nomenclature, authors' names and alien plants respectively (to which Paul Bowman refers in his chapter on 'Recording the Vascular Flora'), it was felt highly desirable to follow these 'state-of-the-art' works, making this the first county Flora to do so. We are particularly grateful to Mr D. H. Kent for help in clarifying a number of subsequent nomenclatural queries, which bring the work right up to date, and for advice on citing herbaria.

In addition to those kind donors, listed below, who have responded to the Hampshire Flora Appeal, we would like to thank the following benefactors who have supported the Flora financially at various stages of its production. Generous donations towards expenses were received from Mr and Mrs Peter Soanes and from the Portsmouth and District Natural History Society (including a contribution from the Westrup Memorial Fund); the Wild Flower Society contributed substantially to the cost of the colour of the jacket and cover illustrations; and the Botanical Society of the British Isles likewise to the publication costs. To all of these we are deeply indebted. With the aid of the donations to the Hampshire Flora Appeal and help from the Hampshire and Isle of Wight Wildlife Trust, the publishers have underwritten the balance of the heavy costs.

As can be seen, this Flora has been very much a composite effort over many years. It is sad that a number of those involved are no longer with us to see it in print at last. Without the immense contributions and the dedication of my co-authors, Paul Bowman and Francis Rose, it would certainly never have reached this stage and I express my considerable gratitude to them both. We and the publishers hope that the care and attention to detail that have been given to this project justify the unconscionable time it has taken to produce.

ANNE BREWIS
Blackmoor, Liss,
Hampshire
November, 1995

LIST OF SUBSCRIBERS

Donors to the Hampshire Flora Appeal whose generosity is most gratefully acknowledged are as follows:

Peter Billinghurst
Lady Anne Brewis
A. C. Crundwell
D. H. & J. M. Dell
Alan Dunkley
David and Madge Goodall
Dorothy Jean Herlihy

John Hills
Rosemary Horne
Joy and Peter Rollinson
Ann Rutherford
Dr J. E. Schubert
Alison Thompson
Elizabeth Young and the late Mrs Gertrude Young

INTRODUCTION

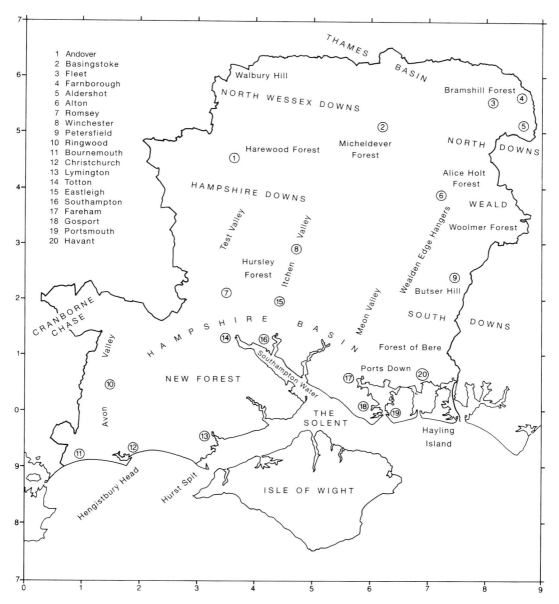

1 Andover
2 Basingstoke
3 Fleet
4 Farnborough
5 Aldershot
6 Alton
7 Romsey
8 Winchester
9 Petersfield
10 Ringwood
11 Bournemouth
12 Christchurch
13 Lymington
14 Totton
15 Eastleigh
16 Southampton
17 Fareham
18 Gosport
19 Portsmouth
20 Havant

Fig. 1   The main natural regions and principal towns of Hampshire

3

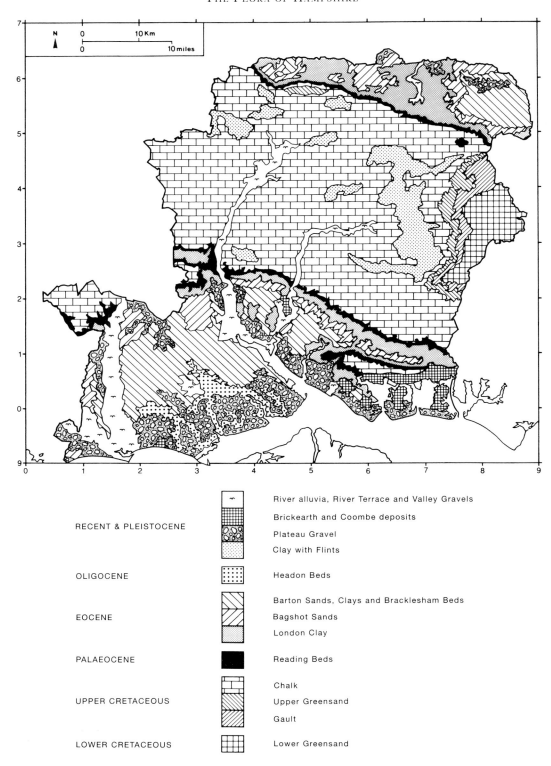

RECENT & PLEISTOCENE

River alluvia, River Terrace and Valley Gravels

Brickearth and Coombe deposits

RECENT & PLEISTOCENE

Plateau Gravel

Clay with Flints

OLIGOCENE — Headon Beds

Barton Sands, Clays and Bracklesham Beds

EOCENE — Bagshot Sands

London Clay

PALAEOCENE — Reading Beds

Chalk

UPPER CRETACEOUS — Upper Greensand

Gault

LOWER CRETACEOUS — Lower Greensand

Fig. 2   Simplified geological map showing the central area underlain by chalk, with younger, largely Tertiary deposits of sands, clays and gravels to the south and north, and older, Cretacean rocks exposed on the eastern margin

CHAPTER I

THE STRUCTURE AND GEOLOGY OF HAMPSHIRE

FRANCIS ROSE

Compared with some parts of England, Hampshire is comparatively simple in geological structure (Fig.2), falling broadly into four parts:

(i)   the Chalk of the centre and also of much of the northern two-fifths of the county;

(ii) the younger Tertiary rocks of the Hampshire (or Solent) Basin to the south of the Chalk;

(iii) the Tertiary rocks to the north-east of the Chalk, part of the Thames Basin; and

(iv) the more ancient, Lower Cretaceous rocks of the Wealden area to the east of the chalk massif.

Much of the chalk area is an undulating plateau, dissected by the river valleys of the chalk tributary streams of the Test, the Itchen and the Meon (Fig.3). This plateau is structurally the eastern extension of Salisbury Plain which is largely in Wiltshire; the Martin Down area in the far west, much of which is administratively in Hampshire, is typical Salisbury Plain country.

Most of the undulating chalk plateau is now under

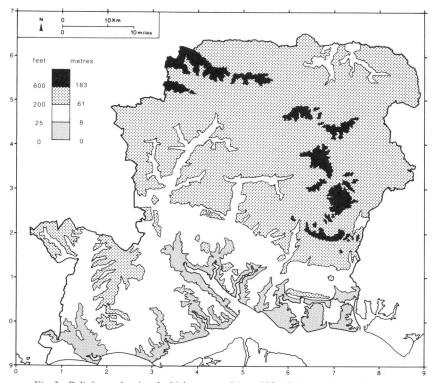

Fig. 3   Relief map showing the highest ground (over 183m) lying on the northern and eastern chalk, while the south of the county is mostly low-lying

arable (or grass ley) cultivation, but early Ordnance Survey maps make it quite clear that formerly it consisted largely of extensive, open sheepwalk downland, with an interesting vegetation that now survives in only a few places, mostly in nature reserves. Nevertheless, wherever steep slopes occur, such as on the sides of the main river-valleys or of the deeper dry coombes, relics of the former chalk-grassland may be found to have survived locally.

The dip-slope of the chalk passes gently southwards under the later Tertiary deposits of the Hampshire Basin, emerging again locally, due to folding, in the chalk ridge of Ports Down north of Portsmouth, and then much more extensively in the Isle of Wight on the south side of the Solent. In earlier times before the sea-levels rose, the Solent, now a sea strait, was a river valley that geomorphologists call the Solent River.

To the north of the main chalk outcrop, Tertiary beds occur again along Hampshire's northern boundary under which the chalk dips northwards to reappear in the Berkshire Downs and the Chilterns.

Along this north-western boundary of the Hampshire chalk, however, there is not the gradual dip under the Tertiary deposits that one sees to the south of the chalk country, and in north-eastern Hampshire from east of Kingsclere across to near Farnham; there is instead a steep 'false escarpment' of the chalk facing north, due again to folding and faulting caused by earth movements. This escarpment extends westwards from south of Wolverton across to the Wiltshire border south of Inkpen, and in its western part includes the highest chalk terrain in England, reaching an altitude of 297m at Walbury Hill (in VC12 but now in Berkshire).

To the east of the main block of the chalk, from south-east of Alton to the south-east of Petersfield, there is another major chalk escarpment. The northern part of this is known as the Hampshire Hangers, and reaches an altitude of 249m at Wheatham Hill. It runs roughly southwards, but the escarpment is much dissected by deep coombes. At a point south of East Meon, it turns abruptly eastwards to form the north-facing escarpment of the South Downs, which then extends far eastwards into Sussex to meet the sea at Beachy Head. On the west Hampshire part of this escarpment, there is another very high point at Butser Hill (270m).

To the east and north of this scarp, older rocks of Lower Cretaceous age appear, the Upper Greensand or Malmstone, the Gault, and the Lower Greensand beds. Structurally these form the western extremity of the Wealden system, which dominates the south-eastern counties of Sussex, Surrey and Kent. It is worth remarking here that the eastern extremity of the Weald is actually across the Straits of Dover in the Pas de Calais around Boulogne in the French Boulonnais, where the chalk scarp finally veers north from the line of the South Downs and then west to link up with the line of the North Downs of Kent – though of course since this feature was formed, the Channel and the Straits of Dover have been cut through it. This point is made here because those Hampshire naturalists who visit northern France will find there a 'mirror image' of the Hampshire Hangers and western Weald terrain.

Hampshire lies well to the south of the most extensive southerly spread of ice sheets during the Pleistocene glaciation. Hence its surface geology is relatively simple, not affected by major ice erosion or by glacial deposits, except for loessic brickearth – windblown silt from the outwash plains of the ice sheet to the north (Fisher, 1971; Catt, 1979). The underlying solid rocks are largely reflected in the surface exposures and their soils.

In places, however, there are recent deposits overlying the solid geology, particularly the so-called 'Clay-with-flints' over parts of the chalk, coombe deposits in the valleys and coombes of the chalk scarps, often of periglacial origin, and alluvial deposits (including peat) in basins and river valleys. There are also extensive plateau- and valley-gravels of Pleistocene origin, as spread over much of the Tertiary areas, deposited by former river flood-plains. All these affect soils and vegetation. There is no need here to go into detail about the origins and mode of formation of the various strata; this information is available in geological text books. See also Jones (1981); Melville & Freshney (1982). Only matters relevant to the vegetation are considered here.

The characteristics of the exposed soil-forming rocks

The Chalk

The Chalk strata are examined first as being the most extensive deposits in Hampshire. The **Upper Chalk** occupies most of the higher ground of the plateau; it is comparatively soft in Hampshire, and composed largely of precipitated calcium carbonate. It does, however, contain successive layers of flints, composed of very hard silica. Thus, when it has been weathered over long periods of time and the calcium carbonate dissolved, beds of flints may be left on the surface. The stratum immediately below is the **Middle Chalk**, which is harder and contains few or no flints; this is the formation which often forms the bulk of the chalk on steep escarpments or the sides of valleys, as it is generally more resistant to weathering

6

than the Upper Chalk. The lowest formation, the **Lower Chalk**, is often greyish in colour, much softer and with more marl, and usually contains more insoluble siliceous material. Its lowest beds, the **Chalk Rock**, are usually very hard, but the Lower Chalk generally weathers into a rather calcareous clay which can be very sticky and slippery when wet.

Strata older than the Chalk

Outcropping beneath the chalk, and exposed at the surface in east Hampshire is the **Upper Greensand**. This formation, particularly in its upper layers, contains beds of the hardest rock to be found in Hampshire, the **Malmstone**. Apart from flints from the chalk, this is the only hard building-stone present in the county. It is a calcareous sandstone which has been much used in the past for building in the Selborne and Buriton areas but, as it is porous, it readily absorbs water. When this freezes, the surface of the stone flakes away. Hence it is not an ideal building material. The lower layers of the Upper Greensand are usually softer and weather more rapidly to a glauconite-rich clayey soil which is very fertile.

The Upper Greensand forms a distinct escarpment of its own in east Hampshire, below that of the chalk, and in places the upper beds are hard enough to form steep cliffs, as at the Slip near Hawkley and Wick Hill Hanger north-east of Selborne. Above the escarpment, there is normally a flattish terrace bearing good arable land. A line of ancient settlements occurs on this terrace, of which Worldham, Selborne, and Hawkley are examples. The steep escarpment itself is still largely woodland of great botanical interest.

The Upper Greensand and its Malmstone beds are particularly well developed in east Hampshire: as it extends eastward into Sussex, the outcrop becomes narrower, and by the time Storrington is reached it ceases to be a feature.

Beneath the Upper Greensand there is the **Gault**, a stiff bluish clay with occasional beds of pebbles or iron-stones, fairly rich in phosphate nodules and gypsum but not of itself markedly calcareous. However, erosion of the chalk above during periglacial conditions in the later Pleistocene and early Flandrian has led in places to massive outwash fans of chalk rubble and sludge over the Gault. The effect has been to make the present-day soils much more calcareous locally than they would otherwise have been. The Malmstone also contributed to this calcareous influence. Solifluction of chalk rubble took place where thawing occurred in spring, moving it downhill over the permanently frozen

surface beneath. The Gault, even today as at Alice Holt, bears much woodland and poor pastureland.

Beneath the Gault there is the **Lower Greensand**, the oldest geological formation exposed in Hampshire. This formation is composed of three distinct beds (named after their coastal outcrops in east Kent): (i) the **Folkestone Beds** – a coarse, sterile, ferruginous sand, which underlies the former extent of the mediaeval Royal Forest of Woolmer; much of it is still heathland country; (ii) the **Sandgate Beds** – silty clays which weather to fertile soils and contain beds of **Bargate Stone**, a calcareous sandstone that occurs along the Upper Rother and Upper Wey valleys: the calcareous water from the spring-lines on the Sandgate Beds produces calcareous mires (as at Conford) in contrast to the acid mires on the Folkestone Beds; and (iii) the **Hythe Beds** – these, which in the western Weald are largely devoid of calcium carbonate, hence tending to produce acid soils, form alternating beds of hard, cherty, rubbly sandstone or gritstone, and of sandy loam. The Hythe Beds occur in only a limited area of Hampshire along the Surrey and Sussex borders from west of Churt, through Headley, to Whitmore Vale and Waggoners Wells. Formerly mostly barren heathland or sessile oak (*Quercus petraea*) woodland, much of the outcrop is now either under conifer forestry or partly built over, as about Grayshott.

Strata younger than the Chalk

The youngest geological deposits in Hampshire are the alluvial silts and muds of the coastline and the river valleys, and the various plateau and valley gravels already mentioned.

Deposits from the Tertiary period, which ran from c.60 million to 2 million years BP, are represented in Hampshire by those of two epochs: the Eocene (54–38 million years BP) and the Oligocene (38–24 million years BP). The deposits of the Hampshire Basin south of the chalk are partly Oligocene: these are the **Headon Beds**, which appear at the surface locally in the southern part of the New Forest. These clayey strata contain beds of fossil shells, so produce calcareous mires locally. However, in the New Forest, the Headon Beds are for the most part covered with Pleistocene gravels of the Quaternary period and, where this is the case, bear heathland.

Below the Oligocene occur the Eocene formations, much more extensively in the New Forest and also in south-east Hampshire from east of Southampton to the Sussex border. Most of the New Forest and the country north and east of Southampton is underlain by **Barton Sands**, and by **Bracklesham Beds**, so that the Forest is largely on a complex of sands (giving rise to lighter soils now to a great extent under heathland) or of clays (mostly bearing oak-woodland). The situation is, however, rendered much more complex by the overlying **Plateau Gravels**, which cover most of the higher ground and bear either heathland or dry acidic woodland. In the far north of the Forest, and in the Bournemouth area (extending far into Dorset), the coarse, nutrient-poor **Bagshot Sands** occur. The Plaitford Common area of National Trust heathland is mainly on the Bagshot Sands.

In south-east Hampshire, east of the River Hamble, the Barton and Bracklesham Beds come to an end; the Forest of Bere is largely on **London Clay**, a stiff heavy clay, with patches of Bagshot Sands overlying it in a number of places on higher ground. The northern edge of the Tertiary deposits in south Hampshire is marked by the outcrop of its oldest local formation, the **Reading Beds** of sands and clays of acidic character. In the Cranbury Park woods, west of the M3 motorway to the south-west of Winchester, these Reading Beds form a distinct north-facing escarpment over the edge of the chalk, mostly under mixed oak-woodland.

A similar pattern is to be seen in reverse in the Eocene rocks of the north-east of Hampshire. From East Woodhay south-west of Newbury, east to Farnborough and Aldershot, and north of the narrow continuous outcrop of the Reading Beds (which forms the southern boundary of this Eocene area over the edge of the gently dipping chalk) much of the terrain is floored by London Clay. Bagshot Sands occur about Burghclere and Highclere; at Silchester and Tadley, with overlying plateau gravels where heathy commons occur; and under Pamber Forest. In the far north-east, around Fleet, Farnborough and Aldershot, Bagshot Sands reappear extensively, extending into south-east Berkshire and north-west Surrey, but are overlaid in a wide area about Aldershot by Barton Sands. Until recently this area was mostly open heath, formerly part of Windsor Forest in its widest mediaeval extent, but much of it is now urbanized.

The superficial deposits that occur locally on the chalk plateau, the 'Clay-with-flints', were formerly regarded as a solution deposit, produced by the residue of the Upper Chalk left after weathering away of the soluble calcium carbonate by rain. Careful calculations have, however, shown that there is far too high a content of acid-insoluble material to represent simply a chalk residue; that is, there is too much residue in proportion to the depth of chalk that would have to be weathered to produce the quantity of flints present. It seems likely therefore that strong Tertiary elements are present in the reddish Clay-with-flints, which may represent the remains of a subtropical forest soil-profile, most of which was later eroded to expose the chalk surface, when early man cleared the 'wildwood' from the chalk uplands.

CHAPTER II

THE CLIMATE OF HAMPSHIRE

FRANCIS ROSE

Situated at a mid-point on the south coast of England, Hampshire has a relatively warm, mild climate, even compared with the Midlands and East Anglia, let alone north-east England or Scotland. Within the county, the New Forest and the area from Southampton south-eastwards has one of the best climates in England in terms of mildness, sunshine, low frost and incidence of snowfall. Not for nothing was Southampton a major English health resort in the late 18th and early 19th centuries.

The mildness and humidity of the New Forest has ensured that it has remained a stronghold of 'Oceanic-Southern' species, nearly as rich in some ways as South Devon and Cornwall, and limited only by the lack of the ravines in harder rocks required by many humidity-demanding ferns and bryophytes (some of which do however occur even further east, in the Sussex Weald).

Because of its situation adjacent to the south-west coast of Hampshire, the New Forest has a rather

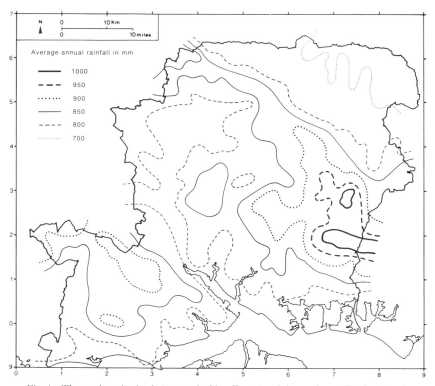

Fig. 4   The southern lowlands (except the New Forest) and the north-east Tertiary terrain have relatively low rainfall, while on the high chalk hills north and south of Petersfield the average rainfall exceeds 1000mm

9

higher rainfall than the eastern part of the Hampshire Basin. However, the highest rainfall in the county is on the high ground of the Butser Hill ridge and on the Hampshire Hangers north of Petersfield in both of which areas the average annual precipitation exceeds 1,000mm. This high rainfall area extends a little way eastwards along the South Downs into Sussex. No other area in southern England east of Devon reaches this level of precipitation (Metereological Office, 1977) (Fig.4).

Further inland, on the chalk plateau and still more so on the Tertiary region of the north-east of Hampshire, the climate becomes drier and more continental, with markedly colder winter weather and a greater mean daily range of temperature. Days with snowfall increase in number, as does the incidence of fogs.

The intermediate position of Hampshire, and the marked gradient from more oceanic to more continental conditions noticeable as one moves north-east from the New Forest to the inland chalk plateau, helps to account for the presence both of extreme oceanic species on the one hand, like *Pinguicula lusitanica*, *Cicendia filiformis* and *Dryopteris aemula* in the New Forest, and of Continental species on the other, like *Aceras anthropophora*, *Herminium monorchis*, *Galium pumilum*, *Gentianella germanica*, and *Astragalus danicus* on the chalk uplands further inland.

CHAPTER III

THE HISTORY OF THE VEGETATION OF HAMPSHIRE

FRANCIS ROSE

As a result of recent research (Barber, 1987), there is now valuable information available on the history of the Solent River, on the last interglacial (Ipswichian) vegetation in Hampshire, and on the early Holocene vegetation in the New Forest area.

Through much of at least the later Pleistocene epoch the Solent River flowed from the present Frome estuary eastwards, north of what is now the Isle of Wight, to reach the open sea somewhere off the present Sussex coast. R. J. Nicholls (1987) has published further information on this subject. When the sea-level was very low, the Solent River flowed in a channel across the sites of Poole and Christchurch Bays, and through the Solent and Spithead. At this time the Isle of Purbeck chalk headland must have been linked in a ridge of chalk with that of the central Isle of Wight. It seems likely that the Frome broke through to the sea at the latest during the last glacial (Devensian) period, but that the Avon, Stour and Yar (at the western end of the Isle of Wight) continued to flow eastward for much longer. It now seems probable that the Holocene rise in sea-level finally submerged the whole system, so perhaps for the first time separating the Isle of Wight from the mainland quite late in the early Holocene. Most of Hampshire's earlier Holocene flora would therefore have been able to spread easily to the island, but this probable sequence of events would also help to account for the absence in the Isle of Wight of some species such as *Paris quadrifolia*, *Polygonatum multiflorum*, *Geum rivale* and *Melittis melissophyllum*, all of which occur widely in mainland Hampshire today. Many are woodland species, and, by the time of the separation, the woodland flora might not have fully colonized the south Hampshire mainland. However, *Pulmonaria longifolia* was clearly able to colonize both banks of the Solent River before the sea-level rose and cut off the Isle of Wight – though whether it entered our area from the south (i.e. from France whilst the English Channel was largely dry land) or from the north (from the mainland) is not known. As it is so restricted on the British mainland, the first alternative seems more probable: *Pulmonaria longifolia* is frequent in north-west France.

Late- and Post-Devensian vegetation

The work of M. J. Clarke and K. E. Barber (1987) provides some interesting information on the vegetation of the New Forest area from Late Devensian Lateglacial times onwards. At Church Moor, a valley bog within Mark Ash Wood, there is a continuous peat-deposit undamaged by peat-cutting from its inception in Lateglacial times to the present day. The lowest levels (330–350cm below the present surface of the bog) are monocotyledonous (mainly *Carex*) peats, which apart from fruits of *Carex rostrata* and *C. paniculata* contain fruits and catkin scales of both *Betula nana* and *B. pendula*. A little higher up numerous leaves and rootlets of *Betula nana* are present, indicating that it was growing on the mire surface, with a high proportion of *B. nana* pollen compared to *B. pendula* agg. Associated with this are the mosses *Homalothecium nitens*, *Campylium stellatum*, and *Calliergon cuspidatum*, and remains too of *Saxifraga nivalis*. The three mosses are common in late-glacial assemblages in southern England, but while the *Calliergon* remains a common species in Hampshire, *Campylium stellatum* is now restricted to a few calcareous fens in the county, where it may well be a relic. The *Homalothecium*, apart possibly from a few surviving lowland sites in East Anglian valley fens and Shropshire, is largely now a species of northern or upland fens; it is a very common moss in arctic and sub-arctic regions. *Saxifraga nivalis*, still frequent in the arctic tundra, is now confined in Britain to moist ledges in mountain areas. This level is radiocarbon dated to 12,440 ± 60 years BP[1], placing it firmly in the Devensian Lateglacial Interstadial.

[1] In the case of radiocarbon dating, BP signifies pre-1950, i.e. before nuclear carbon spread into the atmosphere.

The vegetation at this time evidently comprised a tall-sedge and dwarf-birch fen with extensive fen-moss carpets, surrounded by birch-woodland with only small amounts of willows, herbs and grasses detectable.

There followed a clay layer with charcoal remains (indicating a fire at the site) in which no pollen was preserved. Peat accumulation above this black clay-layer is dated to 8,260 ± 50 years BP and the pollen in this peat shows the rise of a mixed oak–elm–hazel woodland.

From 118cm depth upwards (5,170 ± 50 years BP) *Alnus* woodland with *Myrica gale*, *Sphagnum* (mostly *S. palustre*) and *Erica tetralix* formed a mire community, with much *Molinia caerulea*. As this community has persisted to the present, it can safely be described as a primary woodland. Oak has remained prominent in the pollen record, with little evidence of any major deforestation, though there are brief rises in pollen of *Rumex* and grasses, suggesting local clearances of small areas by early man about 5,200 years ago. Clay inwashes containing charcoal also occur at this level. *Ulmus* declines and *Tilia* rises for a time, then disappears.

Radiocarbon dating and pollen analysis further show that, about 2,500 years ago, *Fagus* starts to expand (Mark Ash today is largely beech-dominated) and *Pinus sylvestris* decreases to low levels, indicative of long distance transport of its pollen only. It seems now fairly certain that *P. sylvestris*, until its reintroduction to the Forest in 1776 AD, was not part of the Forest flora in earlier historical times, nor indeed since about 6,000 years ago (Barber & Clarke, 1987), though this is still disputed by some workers (R. Scaife, pers.comm.).

The evidence outlined above indicates that at least some if not most of the 'Ancient and Ornamental Woodlands' of the New Forest, so-designated in the 1877 New Forest Act (see Tubbs, 1986, p.138), have a very long history, and may have been woodland since fairly early in the Holocene.

The study of pollen in embankments and buried soils at a number of New Forest sites suggests that an original 'Atlantic' forest-cover of oak–hazel woodland (with some *Tilia* and a little *Carpinus*) gave way to a patchy vegetation-pattern of deciduous woodland interspersed with open areas of bracken-rich grassland and heath, from at least 1,500 BC. Certainly, on the basis of historical evidence, this vegetation-pattern was established by Norman times. Much clearance occurred in the Bronze Age (Tubbs & Dimbleby, 1965). The buried soils beneath earthworks and barrows, and the later unburied soils from Bronze Age times onwards, indicate changes from fertile mull soils with oak, lime, and hazel to leached podsols (i.e. poor in humus) with heath vegetation. Similar changes probably occurred in the other areas of Hampshire which now carry or, until recent times, carried heathland on the north-east Tertiary sands and gravels and on the Lower Greensand.

The chalk-plateau areas would certainly have been largely afforested in early Atlantic times and, to judge from the intense prehistoric occupation of the chalk uplands, were presumably cleared from Neolithic times onwards (Waton, 1982). Dating the changes in the vegetation, and the interpretation of its nature are, however, more difficult on the chalk-lands because there are no acid peat-bogs to preserve a pollen record; pollen, moreover, largely decays in chalky soils or in alkaline peat.

There is very interesting evidence of vegetational transition, however, from successional changes in the molluscan fauna on the chalk at Butser Hill. Gordon & Shakesby (1973) studied the sub-fossil molluscs in the valley-floor deposits in the great coombe of Rake Bottom on the north-west side of Butser Hill. The lowest layers in the deposits were devoid of mollusc shells, or indeed of any biological remains, and were interpreted as solifluction deposits during periglacial conditions in the late Devensian, when sheet erosion of the chalk was occurring in spring thaws over an underlying permafrost layer. Above these basal layers, the deposits contained molluscs of dry, bleak open habitats, such as would have existed under the conditions of the early Holocene epoch. Above these, in deposits richer in organic humus, molluscan species of forest-type were present, indicating woodland cover over Butser Hill and its slopes. The surface layers of the coombe-deposits, however, contain a representation of those molluscs that are characteristic of the chalk grasslands of Butser Hill and other similar areas today. What species of trees dominated the forest on these chalk areas in Hampshire at that time is not clear, but further east along the South Downs in West Sussex areas of ancient woodland, formerly enclosed and coppiced, survive in places on the escarpment, with *Tilia platyphyllos*, *Fraxinus excelsior*, *Ulmus glabra*, *Acer campestre*, *Sorbus aria* and *Corylus avellana*. These areas had clearly been enclosed in order to protect them from the general sheepwalk land-use of mediaeval times. Degraded sheepwalk-areas on the escarpment today are either secondary woodlands (of ash and/or sycamore) or planted beech-woods. The present abundance of beech on the chalk areas, particularly on the escarpments, seems nearly everywhere to be a relatively recent phenomenon, due in all probability to planting from mediaeval times onwards. Mediaeval records certainly indicate that some beech was present on parts of the east Hampshire Hangers, but the earliest detailed maps available show much of this escarpment either as open grassland, as arable (where less steep) or as coppice-woodland, presumably of hazel, ash and field maple, rather than beech.

The historical period

For information on the character of the former vegetation of Hampshire in the historical period, maps and documentation are available. It is clear, even from a relatively late document such as the first edition of the one-inch Ordnance Survey maps (1810–17), that a great part of the chalk uplands of central and mid-western Hampshire was open grassland, mostly sheepwalk or rabbit warrens. Some of this was certainly ploughed and cultivated during the emergency of the Napoleonic Wars when food imports were difficult, but much of what was cultivated seems to have reverted to grassland later, particularly after the repeal of the Corn Laws in 1846. These vast grasslands must have carried very species-rich vegetation – probably mostly chalk grassland, but with some areas on superficial noncalcareous drift carrying chalk-heath communities. The clearance of the original forest cover was certainly begun by the first arable farmers in Neolithic times but continued in the later prehistoric period.

P. J. Reynolds (pers.comm.) considers that arable cultivation on the chalk uplands reached its 'highwater mark' in the Iron Age but that it would also have extended to areas beyond them due to population pressure. These clearances would not only have destroyed the original forest cover and flora, but also have led to sheet erosion of the forest soils that had developed during mid-Holocene times. As seen above, there is some good evidence of this process in Rake Bottom on Butser Hill. Some areas escaped the general forest clearance, and now provide the few 'ancient woodlands' that still exist on the chalk uplands. These have not only rich floras of those woodland species that are now regarded as 'ancient woodland indicators' (including sometimes local epiphytic lichens, which are the best indicators of ancient woodland where there has been some continu-ity of mature trees, particularly oak, ash or field maple) but also deeper soils with a high acid-insoluble content and low calcium carbonate levels (Collins, 1982). Most of Collins' work was in West Sussex, but examples of such old woodlands occur in Hampshire at Crab Wood 437297, Hampage Wood 545308, Plash Wood, East Tisted 695325, Sutton Beech Wood 623333, and a few other sites. *Polygonatum multiflorum* is usually present, and sometimes *Geum rivale*, *Euphorbia amygdaloides* or *Paris quadrifolia*.

Other woods on the chalk plateau may have a poor ground-flora of species that colonize new sites readily. These woods are generally absent from earlier maps; they are usually dominated by beech, ash or sycamore, with much less hazel, and probably represent either old plantations or recolonization of abandoned sheepwalk or arable. Their soils are normally rendzinas – shallow, skeletal and on chalk.

In the last hundred years or so, most of these old sheepwalk-areas have been taken into arable farming, often into short-term ley pastures, and improved by fertilizers and/or reseeding, or simply abandoned to scrub-growth.

One can only speculate on the former flora of some of these areas, but Martin Down (which has survived to this day) and the Hampshire part of Porton Down (Isle of Wight Hill) do give us a probable picture of their past vegetation. Old records of species like *Antennaria dioica* (e.g. at Gander Down) and many former records of *Orchis ustulata* help to indicate too the former rich grassland floras that would have occurred.

The early OS maps also indicate that the sandy or gravelly areas of the Tertiary Beds of north-east Hampshire, the Lower Greensand of mid-to east Hampshire, and the Tertiary sands east of Southampton were, like those of the New Forest, largely open heathland, in many cases until the mid-19th century. Their former character survives in much of the old Royal Forest of Woolmer. However, the other old Royal Forests, notably the Forest of Bere, have changed greatly due to enclosure and cultivation.

CHAPTER IV

THE HABITATS AND VEGETATION OF PRESENT-DAY HAMPSHIRE

FRANCIS ROSE

(WITH CONTRIBUTIONS BY A. J. P. BRANSON, C. CHATTERS, C. R. HALL,
A. R. G. MUNDELL, N. A. SANDERSON AND P. J. WILSON)

The greater part of Hampshire is still extremely rural although there are extensive conurbations along the south coast, especially those sprawling around Bournemouth, Southampton and Portsmouth, and inland at Winchester, Andover, Basingstoke and in the Aldershot/Farnborough area (Fig.5).

The following accounts describe a range of habitats throughout Hampshire, for the most part outside these built-up areas. Many of the sites described are PRIVATE, where permission for visiting should always be sought. Other sites are owned or managed by various local and central government bodies. As with private land, access to these areas should be checked with the relevant agency; this is essential in the case of Ministry of Defence (MOD) land, where live firing may occur. A number of nature reserves are described in these accounts. Visiting arrangements for nature reserves are detailed in Chapter 6.

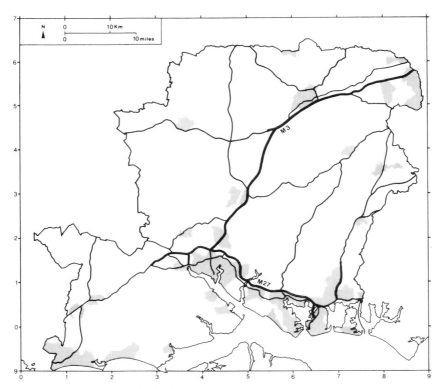

Fig. 5   The principal urbanized areas, shown in grey, are mainly along the coast, with only a few inland. Much of the remainder of the county, though traversed by a number of main roads, is still rural and quite thinly populated

14

1. The Coastal Habitats (Fig.6)

From west to east, **Hengistbury Head** (1790) is of Tertiary sands. South of Christchurch Harbour it has heathland, pine-wood and dry, sandy grassland and, at its north-east end, a long shingle-spit with some low dunes. It has a rich flora, including many annual species of *Trifolium*, such as *T. ornithopodioides*, *T. arvense*, *T. scabrum*, *T. glomeratum*, *T. suffocatum* and also *T. fragiferum* in damp grassland on the harbour side. Tidal salt-marsh is well developed on the north side. *Polygonum oxyspermum* occurs from time to time on the sandy beach to the north-east but the most notable plant is *Polygonum maritimum*, recently rediscovered here (see Systematic Account). Also here, on the cliff top, is *Spergularia rupicola*.

Christchurch Harbour (1890) contains good sandy and muddy salt-marshes, particularly at Stanpit Marsh, where occur *Eleocharis parvula*, *Althaea officinalis* and *Limosella aquatica* in upper zones, but it suffers from heavy 'visitor pressure' as it is a very popular yachting centre. However, on the south shore of the harbour are *Poa bulbosa* and *Crassula tillaea*. The shingle-spit has dunes to the north with *Jasione*, *Festuca arenaria*, *Vicia lathyroides*, and *Cakile maritima* and *Atriplex laciniata* on the strand.

The coast is now very built-up eastwards from Mudeford and Highcliffe to Barton. The undeveloped coast at **Hordle Cliff** (2692) consists of low, sandy or clay cliffs, but has few notable maritime species except *Spergularia rupicola*, *Parapholis incurva* and *Euphrasia tetraquetra*. East of this, the west Solent coastline is wonderfully free of major building development.

Hurst Castle Spit (3189), which protects the Solent from south-westerly storms, is, however, an interesting site. The great shingle-beach still has a few plants of *Lathyrus japonicus*, refound in 1993 after an absence of records for 30 years. *Crambe maritima* is rare here but *Silene uniflora*, *Geranium purpureum*, *Seriphidium maritimum* and *Glaucium flavum* are quite frequent, with much *Spergularia rupicola*, particularly on disturbed damp areas at the Milford on Sea end. *Inula crithmoides* occurs, with *Limonium vulgare*, etc, on the few patches of firm salt-marsh that remain on the landward side of the beach, but repeated breaches (and repairs) of the beach-line in storms have to some extent impoverished its vegetation over the last 50 years. The best salt-marsh is at the far end near the castle.

In the shelter of Hurst Spit to its north-east, lie extensive tidal mud-flats with much *Spartina anglica*, and at **Keyhaven Marshes** (3191) there is eroded but interesting salt-marsh with a good range of *Salicornia* species, including *S. dolichostachya*, *S. obscura*, *S. fragilis* and *S. nitens* on the lower muddy marsh. There is little consolidated upper marsh left now at Keyhaven, but prostrate red forms of *S. ramosissima* are common in the brackish marsh within the sea-wall. *Carex punctata* and *Eleocharis uniglumis* still occur here.

The next major coastal habitat for plants is the salt-marsh and shingle-beach complex of **Needs Ore Point** (4196 to 4297), west of the Beaulieu River estuary (part of the North Solent NNR (PERMIT ONLY) with no open access to public). Along the shoreline is a fine sandy beach with miniature dunes. Here *Elytrigia juncea*, and *Ammophila arenaria* occur with quite good populations of *Eryngium maritimum*, *Crambe maritima*, *Euphorbia paralias*, *Geranium purpureum* ssp. *forsteri* (not, however, seen very recently), *Polygonum oxyspermum*, *Honckenya peploides* and other strand-line plants. The older

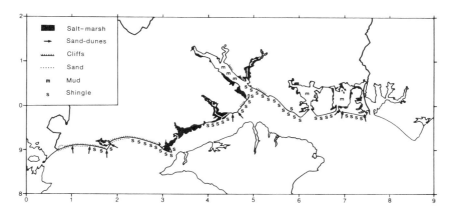

Fig. 6   The main types of coastal habitats in Hampshire are low-lying and there are no hard rock cliffs as found in the Isle of Wight and Dorset

shingle behind the beach-line, important as a breeding-site for several species of coastal birds, has areas of fixed shingle, with many *Trifolium* species including *T. subterraneum* and *T. ornithopodoides*, and rich communities of terricolous lichens, forming *Cladonia* heath, with such local species as *Cladonia foliacea* and *C. tenuis*. There are areas of *Festuca filiformis* turf, with various spring annuals including *Cerastium diffusum*, and areas of low scrub in which *Rosa pimpinellifolia* is locally abundant among *Ulex europaeus*. Other plants include the grasses *Bromus hordeaceus* ssp. *ferronii*, *Poa humilis* and *Catapodium marinum*. There are also *Armeria maritima*, *Digitalis purpurea*, *Rumex acetosella*, *Carex arenaria*, *Cynoglossum officinale*, and much else. Behind the shingle spit there is interesting salt-marsh, partly sandy, partly muddy, with *Puccinellia maritima*, *Limonium humile*, *L. vulgare* and the upper salt-marsh species *Sarcocornia perennis*, *Salicornia ramosissima*, *S. pusilla*, *S. europea*, *S. fragilis* (lower down) and *Suaeda maritima* and *Juncus maritimus*.

Inland from this salt-marsh creek there is a mosaic of dry and wet grassland and brackish hollows on clayey alluvium. Here *Bupleurum tenuissimum* occurs (pers.obs.) and *Genista tinctoria*, *Eleocharis uniglumis* and *Chamaemelum nobile* are locally frequent.

Higher up the **Beaulieu River** (4100 and elsewhere), there are fine, brackish reed-swamps fringing the river, in some of which *Sonchus palustris* is locally plentiful in this, its only Hampshire locality. Whether native or introduced is not known, but it appears like a native here in the same community as on the Medway in Kent and the East Anglian riversides, with *Althaea officinalis* and *Bolboschoenus maritimus*. *Salicornia pusilla* is in the upper marsh here and *Rubia peregrina* occurs along the wooded shore with *Iris foetidissima*.

East of the **Beaulieu River Estuary** (4298 to 4498), the scrub along the low cliffs has in places *Rubia peregrina* (a rare plant in Hampshire, but not at its eastern British limit, as it reaches Dover in Kent). The shingle beach from **Lepe** (4598), east past Stansore Point (OPEN ACCESS to here) to **Stanswood Bay** (4700) (access BY PERMISSION ONLY) is a fine little-disturbed natural coastal habitat. *Polygonum oxyspermum* occurs on the beach in a couple of places, and seems to tolerate the trampling of visitors well in one of these. *Ophrys sphegodes*, known here some years ago, does, however, seem to have gone at least for the present.

The beach has magnificent communities of *Crambe maritima* – among the finest in Hampshire – with also much *Geranium purpureum* ssp. *forsteri*, and to the east, the only population of *Euphorbia portlandica* on the Hampshire mainland. The rear of the beach has developed very interesting scrub communities, particularly of very stunted *Quercus robur*, beneath which there are good lichen communities on the shingle; *Armeria maritima*, *Glaucium flavum*, *Sedum anglicum*, *Tripleurospermum maritimum*, and *Prunus spinosa* (in a prostrate form) are also present.

At **Calshot Spit** (4801), *Geranium purpureum* also occurs, but the spit is disturbed and less interesting than the fine coastline to the west.

As one enters Southampton Water, there are still fine salt-marsh areas opposite **Fawley** Power Station, but much of the shoreline has been spoilt by reclamation and industrial developments, particularly north-west of Hythe. *Polypogon monspeliensis* and its hybrid X *Agropogon littoralis* are still plentiful here. Below **Eling**, however, **opposite Bury Farm** (377119), there is a very interesting salt-marsh. Here the front of the marsh carries a healthy sward of *Spartina alterniflora* in deeply-dissected marsh, with *S. anglica* intermixed. This is the only remaining population of *S. alterniflora*, deriving from the original accidental introduction of this species from N. America, as opposed to later, deliberate plantings. NOTE: This is a key site (of European importance) and deserves protection (see Systematic Accounts for further information).

The east side of Southampton Water has little salt-marsh or other communities of interest, but **Hamble Common** (4805), a public open space, has acidic, sandy, maritime grassland with *Agrostis curtisii* in one of its now few sites east of Southampton, in heath with *Molinia caerulea* and *Erica tetralix*, while the sandy shoreline has *Silene uniflora*, *Elytrigia atherica*, *Plantago coronopus* and *Allium vineale*.

The estuary of the R. Hamble has, however, some quite good muddy salt-marsh south of **Bursledon** (4808), with several *Salicornia* species (*S. pusilla*, *S. ramosissima*, *S. europaea*, *S. fragilis*, *S. dolichostachya*) and the general muddy salt-marsh species of the *Puccinellia maritima* community. This site is mentioned here because, though not very rich, it is the only good piece of salt-marsh left now between Southampton and Portsmouth Harbour. The now very local *Rumex pulcher* occurs on dry ground just above the salt-marsh.

Higher up the Hamble, there is a good fringe of salt-marsh on the muddy edge of the river below the oakwoods of Upper Hamble Country Park (see below) and besides most of the species recorded at Bursledon, *Althaea officinalis* is locally frequent.

The next estuary, that of the R. Meon at **Titchfield Haven** (5302), must once have had fine tidal marshes but an earlier Earl of Southampton dammed the estuary at its mouth, destroying both the saltings and Titchfield's prosperity as a port. The sandy beach here still has a little *Eryngium maritimum* and, a little inland on sandy ground, *Lotus angustissimus* occurs. The brackish meadows of the former estuary (5302), have a rich flora of considerable interest, including *Ranunculus sardous*. This is also a very good ornithological site.

East of Titchfield Haven the coast is built up past Hill Head and Lee-on-the-Solent, but at **Browndown** (5799), a very interesting wide expanse of apposition shingle-beach occurs. Parts of this have been disturbed by military use as a range and training ground, but considerable areas remain intact. On the undisturbed fixed shingle, *Calluna* heath, with much *Erica cinerea* occurs, together with *Digitalis purpurea*, *Silene nutans* ssp. *salmoniana*, *Pilosella officinarum*, *Lonicera periclymenum*, *Agrostis curtisii*, *Ulex minor*, *U. europaeus*, *Hypochaeris glabra* and *Rumex acetosella*. Terricolous lichens occur in plenty here: 16 species of *Cladonia* are present, including the usual heathland species and also the more local and coastal *C. foliacea* and *C. cervicornis*, also *Coelocaulon aculeatum* and *C. muricatum*. Areas of stunted oak scrub occur, both native *Quercus robur* and introduced *Q. ilex*. Epiphytic lichens are well developed on these trees in places. Heathland mosses like *Campylopus introflexus*, *C. paradoxus*, *Dicranum scoparium*, *Leucobryum glaucum* (very local) and *Polytrichum juniperinum* are common. There are damp hollows with *Salix cinerea*. More open areas, especially nearer the sea, have short turf of *Festuca filiformis*, with *Sedum anglicum*, *Plantago coronopus*, *Spergularia rubra*, and numerous small annuals like *Aira caryophyllea*, and *Cerastium* species. Along the shoreline, *Crambe maritima* and *Glaucium flavum* are common in places. The area is reminiscent of Dungeness Beach in Kent on a small scale, but that lacks *Calluna*. A fen by **Gomer Pond** (5899), north of Browndown, has *Cladium mariscus* and *Calamagrostis canescens*.

Gilkicker Point, south of Alverstoke (6097), is a further area of rather disturbed shingle with the commoner shoreline plants: it is most notable for the lagoon behind the Point, which is probably derived from a saline lagoon formed by a change in direction of alignment between successive storm-beaches. Here occur two Hampshire rarities, *Cladium mariscus* and *Carex punctata*. On the shingle occur *Linaria repens*, *Crithmum maritimum*, *Raphanus raphanistrum* ssp. *maritimus*, and *Bupleurum tenuissimum* in a grassy hollow.

The south-east corner of Hampshire contains the great harbours of **Portsmouth**, **Langstone** and **Chichester**, with **Portsea Island** and **Hayling Island** between these harbours. It is an extraordi-

nary fact that this is by far the richest part of the county for maritime vegetation of beaches, dunes, salt-marsh and brackish meadows – yet it is also the most densely-populated area of the county, with massive residential, industrial and MOD development. It must have been much richer still 150–200 years ago.

Portsmouth Harbour is now largely spoilt as regards plant habitats, but the neighbourhood of **Portchester Castle** (6204), is still interesting, and **Portchester Church** (within the castle area) has notable lichens, like *Roccella phycopsis*, whose main British habitats are on the sea-cliffs of Devon and Cornwall. **Horsea Island** (6304) and **Tipner peninsula** (6303) were interesting until recent years, but are now largely infilled and developed, though still good for interesting alien weeds. **Pewit Island** (6004) remains unspoilt.

Langstone Harbour, east of Portsea Island, is much less spoilt than Portsmouth Harbour. The shingle beach near **Eastney** (6798) in the south-east corner of Portsea Island still has a reasonable beach flora, including *Silene nutans*, but sadly *Petrorhagia nanteuillii* seems to have now gone due to severe disturbance; today this species probably survives in Britain only at Pagham in West Sussex, as the Kent site at Hythe has been bulldozed in recent years.

One of the richest coastal marshland sites is the Hampshire Wildlife Trust (HWT) nature reserve at **Farlington Marshes** (6803 to 6805). This fine area is known to have been tidal salt-marsh formerly, but was enclosed by a late 18th-century sea-wall to produce the cattle-fattening pastures which it still provides. It comprises dry neutral permanent pastures, brackish hollows on the site of former tidal creeks, and interesting dry, sometimes sandy areas along the sea wall; there is little extent of tidal salt-marsh. The flora is very rich with over 50 species of grass, including the rare *Polypogon monspeliensis*, which has been known in this general area since the 16th century. There also occurs the rare hybrid of this grass with *Agrostis stolonifera*. Other grasses include *Alopecurus bulbosus*, *Parapholis strigosa* and *Puccinellia maritima*, *P. distans*, *P. fasciculata* and *P. rupestris*. Both *Oenanthe pimpinelloides*, and *O. lachenalii* are locally plentiful in the meadow habitats. Formerly the earthen sea-walls of Farlington Marshes carried a rich flora of such scarce Mediterranean-Oceanic species as *Bupleurum tenuissimum* and *Trifolium squamosum*; the former has not been seen recently but the latter survives in quantity in brackish pasture land. Farlington is also of international importance ornithologically.

The **Binness Islands** (6903, 6904, 7003, 7004) east and south-east of Farlington Marshes are nei-

Plate 1   Formerly salt-marshes, enclosed in the 18th century, Farlington Marshes reserve is rich in plants, including the rare *Polypogon monspeliensis*. It is internationally important for its bird life. (*Photo*: P. R. Brough)

ther of easy access nor well surveyed, but they do have good salt-marsh, some shingle-beach with *Geranium purpureum*, and higher, dry areas with trees. *Inula crithmoides* is plentiful here, and the salt-marsh contains both *Limonium vulgare* and *L. humile*.

Hayling Island still has some of the best maritime habitats in Hampshire, in spite of much development. Good salt-marsh survives on the Langstone Harbour side of Hayling at (6999 to 7099), north of the hotel **North of Sinah Common** (PRIVATE), where there is still *Puccinellia maritima* marsh, with the rare *Spartina* x *townsendii* in shallow pools, *Limonium vulgare*, *Inula crithmoides*, and a good range of general salt-marsh plants including many *Salicornia* species and also *Bupleurum tenuissimum*.

Further north-east there is little tidal marsh now in Langstone Harbour, but excellent brackish meadows, formerly tidal marsh, exist east of the old railway embankment **North of North Hayling old Railway** (7103). Here occur, in *Agrostis stolonifera* grassland, and in the former tidal-creek beds and the drainage dykes, *Puccinellia fasciculata*, *Juncus maritimus*, *J. gerardii*, *Aster tripolium*, *Spergularia marina*, *S. media*, *Glaux maritima*, *Ranunculus sardous*, *Trifolium fragiferum*, *Suaeda maritima*, *Salicornia*

europaea, *Plantago maritima* and *Atriplex* species. On more elevated pasture here *Ononis spinosa* is abundant, with *Centaurium erythraea* and *C. pulchellum* in more open ground, with *Lotus corniculatus* and meadow grasses. The site still seems suitable, in its muddy saline depressions, for *Chenopodium chenopodioides*, formerly recorded here.

Passing round into Chichester Harbour east of Langstone Bridge, small areas of rich brackish meadows (with *Samolus valerandi* and *Juncus gerardii*) and salt-marsh can be found between **Langstone and Emsworth** (7205 and 7305) with *Limonium humile* and *Carex extensa*. More extensive tidal and brackish marsh occurs north and north-east of **Northney** (7304) on Hayling Island, with a good range of brackish meadow species, including *Ononis spinosa*, *Lotus glaber*, *Parapholis incurva* and *Bupleurum tenuissimum* on dry grassy banks, and still *Spartina maritima* in tidal marsh. However, much of the area (including the last Hampshire site for *Chenopodium chenopodioides*) has been destroyed to form the Northney marina basin.

The best remaining salt-marsh in Hampshire is on the **Gutner peninsula** (7301). This is now a RESTRICTED Hampshire County Council (HCC) nature reserve and has the full range of communities in three zones:

(i) at the top, dry grasslands on clayey alluvium, with *Oenanthe lachenalii*, *Petroselinum segetum* and *Bupleurum tenuissimum*, in an *Elytrigia atherica* and *Festuca rubra* community.

(ii) upper tidal-marsh, with *Puccinellia maritima*, *Parapholis strigosa*, *Inula crithmoides*, *Limonium vulgare*, *Armeria maritima*, *Seriphidium maritimum*, *Atriplex portulacoides* (sides of creeks), *Juncus gerardii*, *J. maritimus*, *Glaux maritima*, *Triglochin maritimum*, *Suaeda maritima*, etc. *Spartina maritima* occurs in some quantity in small pans.

(iii) more open mud-flats and creeks, with *Spartina anglica* and *Zostera angustifolia* in pools.

All the British *Salicornia* species occur at Gutner. *Sarcocornia perennis* is plentiful at the top of zone (ii), with *Salicornia pusilla* in more open areas. *S. ramosissima* and *S. europaea* occur widely in zone (ii) also; and on the open mud and creek-sides in zone (iii) there is much *S. fragilis*, *S. dolichostachya* and a little of *S. obscura* and *S. nitens*.

This site, (access by PERMIT ONLY through HCC Community and Countryside Department) is extremely important as, unlike several others, it has not been disturbed by severe erosion or excavation of clay for sea-wall repairs, as has happened at the next salt-marsh site east of Tourner Bury. However, in spite of this damage, **Tourner Bury Marsh** (7399 and 7300) (PRIVATE) still has *Spartina maritima*, but the clear zonation of communities seen at Gutner has gone. Good brackish meadows (with much *Ononis spinosa*, *Hordeum secalinum*, *Silaum silaus*, *Ranunculus sardous*, *Carex distans* and *Ruppia maritima* in the dykes) are still a feature of much of this eastern part of Hayling Island. The nearby Mengham Creek still has a sandy tidal zone with *Frankenia laevis*.

Finally, there is the beach and dune vegetation of the south coast of Hayling Island. Formerly this was a wilderness (and a naturalist's paradise) all the way from Ferry Point in the west to Eastoke Point in the east, but building development has largely destroyed the central part of the coast. Fortunately, however, the western part of this coast (Sinah Common) and the extreme eastern part (Sandy Point) remain (see below). One 150m stretch of undisturbed shingle also remains at **Mengham** (7198) in front of a built-up area where *Sagina subulata*, *Poa bulbosa*, *Moenchia erecta* and *Trifolium suffocatum* are still plentiful.

Sinah Common (6899 to 6998) is now in part a HWT nature reserve, partly public land and partly a PRIVATE golf-course. It has a rich flora of fixed-dune species, with a fine range of dune grasses including

Plate 2   Sinah Common, Hayling Island, is one of our finest shingle beaches with much *Crambe maritima* and *Geranium purpureum*; in the background can be seen the dunes of Gunner Point where *Eryngium maritimum* is locally plentiful and increasing. (*Photo*: A. R. G. Mundell)

Ammophila arenaria, Leymus arenarius, Vulpia bromoides, V. fasciculata, V. ciliata ssp. *ambigua, Bromus hordeaceus* ssp. *ferronii, Aira caryophyllea, Elytrigia juncea* (on fore-dunes), *Catapodium marinum, Poa humilis and Festuca filiformis. Lupinus arboreus* was spreading and dominating the south edge of the golf-course in the 1970s but has now become much reduced due to insect predation. To the north of the golf-course there are wet hollows with much *Carex punctata, Centaurium erythraea* var. *sublitorale* and *Juncus maritimus.*

South of the golf-course (6998) (OPEN ACCESS) there is a fine shingle-beach with *Sedum anglicum,* much *Crambe maritima, Raphanus raphanistrum* ssp.*maritimus, Glaucium flavum, Armeria maritima* and *Crithmum maritimum* while *Geranium purpureum* ssp. *forsteri* and *Erodium cicutarium* also occur. Behind the broad beach – which has undergone changes over time, first increasing and then more recently eroding severely at the western end – there are the largest sand-dunes in Hampshire, those of Gunner Point. Here, among *Ammophila arenaria* occur good, and now much increasing, populations of *Eryngium maritimum, Euphorbia paralias, Phleum arenarium* and *Calystegia soldanella,* all very local in Hampshire. *Polygonum oxyspermum* occurs on the beach to the west from time to time, but not constantly, and nearby are *Silene nutans, Hypochaeris glabra,* and *Geranium rotundifolium* on the golf-course.

East of the Golf-Course (7098), there is a fine, fixed-shingle beach behind the public car-park. This has good communities of spring annuals, including much *Teesdalia nudicaulis, Trifolium suffocatum, T. ornithopodioides, T. scabrum, T. striatum, T. subterraneum, Cerastium* species, *Vicia lathyroides* and also some *Poa bulbosa. Echium vulgare* is frequent and areas of leached acid turf with *Rumex acetosella, Jasione* and *Crassula tillaea* occur, with a little *Calluna vulgaris, Erica cinerea* and *Galium saxatile.* Altogether, this is one of Hampshire's richer beach and dune sites, but not as rich as **Sandy Point (Eastoke Point)** (7498). This area of low dunes, dune-slacks, sandy beach, and dune-heath is a veritable 'time-capsule' of what the vegetation of much of the south coast must have been before the major leisure-development of the 20th century. It survived protected for many years as the private grounds of a hospital, and very fortunately, when the hospital closed a few years ago, HCC bought it as a nature reserve. It is fenced off from the much-trampled public foreshore to protect its fragile vegetation, and access is by PERMIT ONLY.

Along the seaward edge within the fence are low *Ammophila arenaria, Elytrigia juncea* dunes with some *Leymus arenarius* and the finest populations of

Eryngium maritimum, Euphorbia paralias and *Calystegia soldanella* in the county. In more open patches, there occur on sandy shingle *Cakile maritima* and *Salsola kali* (fragile strand-line plants now very rare elsewhere in the county), also *Raphanus raphanistrum* ssp. *maritimus* and *Polygonum oxyspermum.* Along the open trackway behind the low dunes there are important populations of *Hypochaeris glabra, Vulpia ciliata* ssp.*ambigua* and *Sagina subulata,* with many annual clovers including *Trifolium suffocatum* and *T. ornithopodioides,* also *Ornithopus perpusillus* and *Cerastium diffusum.*

Areas of fixed shingle behind the dunes to the west have rich *Cladonia* lichen communities with much *C. foliacea, C. portentosa, C. uncialis, C. cervicornis* and *Coelocaulon aculeatum* interspersed with fine moss-carpets, mostly *Dicranum scoparium,* and *Tortula ruralis* ssp. *ruraliformis* on loose sand.

At one point, there are small but rich, brackish dune-slacks, among gorse scrub behind the main, low dune-line. Here the magnificent rush *Juncus acutus* occurs in some 15 clumps in its only locality now on the south coast between Sandwich in Kent and Somerset, associated with *J. maritimus, J. gerardii* and the finest population of *Carex punctata* in Hampshire, here at its eastern British limit. Other species of the short, drier, fixed-shingle turf include *Vulpia fasciculata, Teesdalia nudicaulis* and *Rumex acetosella.*

To the rear of the fixed-shingle and dune areas there is extensive acid heath on sand over shingle, with much *Calluna vulgaris, Erica cinerea, Polygala serpyllifolia, Carex pilulifera, Ulex europaeus,* and both *U. minor* and *U. gallii,* the last clearly distinct from *U. minor* in this, one of only two modern Hampshire sites. Grassy paths through the heath have *Galium verum, Spiranthes spiralis, Anacamptis pyramidalis,* a little *Orchis morio* and good patches of the very local *Viola lactea* and *V. canina.* Moist acidic depressions bring in *Erica tetralix, Scutellaria minor* and *Pedicularis sylvatica,* and in barer places *Radiola linoides, Centaurium erythraea* with its var. *sublitorale.* Salt-marsh formerly occurred in the lowest area behind the beach and dunes, but this is now sealed off and has largely dried out, with the loss of most salt-marsh plants except a little *Salicornia ramosissima* and *Bolboschoenus maritimus.*

It will be seen that Sandy Point is a site of exceptional importance; it is also excellent for invertebrates of this type of habitat. Outside the reserve fence, the national rarity *Polygonum maritimum* has been found by Paul Bowman in a hollow of the shingle in 1995; this is the second modern Hampshire site and the fifth locality in Britain in recent times.

The last site to consider on the coast is the small

sandy salt-marsh in the creek behind **Black Point** (7598), where the rare sea-heath, *Frankenia laevis* occurs in one of its only two remaining Hampshire sites; the other is at Mengham Creek, *c.*2km to the north-west.

2. The New Forest

The New Forest, on Tertiary sands and clays and overlying gravels, occupies much of SW Hampshire (see Fig.10, p.53). It consists of some 20,000ha of unenclosed forest, including 12,500ha of heathland and largely acid grassland; 2,900ha of wet heath and valley mires; 3,700ha of ancient, unenclosed woodlands open to grazing (the Ancient and Ornamental Woodlands); some 300ha of open 'lawns' of short turf; and about 8,400ha of Inclosures, largely either coniferous or broad-leaved plantations but including 'trapped' areas of ancient woodlands in a number of places within the Inclosure fences.

The New Forest is now unique internationally. It is no exaggeration to say that as a haven for wildlife it is foremost in lowland western Europe because

(a) it has the largest area of the 'Anglo-Norman' type of sub-Oceanic lowland dry heath (*Calluna vulgaris*, *Erica cinerea*, *Ulex minor*) left in Britain, or indeed in the world (see Fig.7, p.31);

(b) it has the largest and most numerous series of acid lowland *Sphagnum* mires (valley bogs) anywhere in Europe;

(c) it has the largest extent of little-managed primary woodlands in lowland western Europe, at least some of which (probably most) have been largely such since the early Holocene.

Apart from varying degrees of selective felling, the woodlands have not been altered by any extensive planting or by coppice-type management except in quite limited areas, and have remained as pasture-woodland, in most cases probably from their beginnings. The grazing in earlier epochs would have been entirely by large, wild herbivores, including red deer, wild cattle, and possibly wild horses. In the earlier historical period, starting in Saxon times, it became a Royal Hunting Ground and in or around the year 1079 William I decreed that it should become a Royal Forest, which it has remained to this day but now under Forestry Commission control.

At first, the red deer were the important animals of the chase, but the local commoners had the right to graze their cattle, ponies and sheep there, rights which still remain. The red deer were largely eliminated in the 19th century and an attempt was also made to eliminate the fallow deer, introduced in Norman times, but this was a failure in the long term and fallow as well as roe deer are still frequent, numbering above 1,000 in each case. There are still about 100 red deer and, in the south, some 200–300 sika deer. It is the ponies, however, which are the ubiquitous grazers and browsers. Though their stock has been improved by crossing with Arab strains, the origin of the ponies is lost in the mists of antiquity

Plate 3   The grazing of the ponies of the New Forest, which may be descended from native stock, is an essential factor in maintaining the character of the open forest. (*Photo*: C. R. Tubbs)

and it is possible that there is some native element in their gene complexes. Cattle are grazed in many more open areas, and pigs are still put to pannage in autumn, as they have been since at least Saxon times, to feed on acorns and beech-mast; nowhere else in England does this practice now survive in an organized way. Its management as pasture, or as pasture-woodland, is essential for the maintenance of the ecological character of the New Forest. For fuller details of the history of the Forest's economy and its fauna, see Tubbs (1986).

No other comparable area now survives anywhere in lowland Britain or indeed in the whole of lowland Western Europe: all other Royal Forests have been profoundly changed by massive enclosure and replanting, or else largely destroyed. By fortunate and complex accidents of history and politics, the New Forest survives as an almost intact mediaeval landscape.

It is not surprising to find that the Forest is of such botanical importance. If one considers only the vascular plants, **the woodlands** are not especially rich. Although some 50 indicator 'Ancient Woodland Vascular Plants' (AWVPs) (see Fig.11, p.54) still occur in the old woodlands, many of these are local or rare and of low biomass due to heavy grazing for centuries. Even so, some woodlands have a respectable number of ancient woodland indicators – Wood Crates (2608), for example, has 40 AWVPs, and the Bramshaw-Great Wood complex has 37; most others are much poorer.

Species common in most Hampshire woodlands in more basic sites, such as *Adoxa moschatellina*, *Mercurialis perennis*, *Orchis mascula*, *Epipactis helleborine*, *Allium ursinum*, *Melica uniflora*, *Viola reichenbachiana*, *Silene dioica*, *Ranunculus auricomus*, and even *Corylus avellana* and *Prunus avium* among the trees, are very rare and local in the open woodlands. On the other hand, *Anemone nemorosa*, *Sanicula europaea*, *Hyacinthoides non-scripta*, and *Oxalis acetosella* are frequent to common; whilst *Euphorbia amygdaloides* and *Ruscus aculeatus* are widespread and generally common; the spurge is no doubt protected from grazing by its acrid latex and the butcher's-broom by its tough, spiny cladodes. Ferns are generally plentiful: apart from *Pteridium aquilinum* which is general, *Blechnum spicant*, *Athyrium filix-femina* and *Oreopteris limbosperma* are extremely frequent, while *Dryopteris aemula* and *Phegopteris connectilis* have a few locations in sheltered ravines.

Among less common species, *Pulmonaria longifolia* and *Narcissus pseudonarcissus* occur in several places but they are more plentiful in enclosed woods where grazing, though not absent, is less severe. *Melittis melissophyllum* used to be in the open woodland, but

seems to survive now only in two Inclosures, **Brownhill/Wootton Coppice** (2399 to 2499) and **Holmsley** (2200).

The outstanding richness of the Forest in vascular plants, however, is to be found in its acid bogs, fen areas, and wet heaths, and in some of the wet lawns and pond-margins (see examples detailed below). *Gladiolus illyricus*, now confined in the British Isles to the Forest, is perhaps the most remarkable species present. It is still widespread in bracken communities in some 50 to 60 sites, associated with more enriched, better-drained, acid grassland brown soils, usually with open-woodland species such as *Anemone nemorosa*, *Hyacinthoides non-scripta*, *Serratula tinctoria*, *Lathyrus linifolius*, *Stachys officinalis*, *Carex montana*. In such sites, it is protected to some degree by the bracken from grazing and also from human predators, as it is largely concealed at flowering time.

Important species of the **valley bogs** that are now nationally rare include *Drosera anglica*, *Carex limosa*, *C. lasiocarpa*, *Utricularia intermedia*, *Hammarbya paludosa*, *Rhynchospora fusca*, *Eriophorum gracile*, *Dactylorhiza incarnata* ssp. *pulchella*, *Pinguicula lusitanica*.

Formerly *Spiranthes aestivalis* occurred but now seems extinct.

The **wet heath** areas of the Forest have some of the largest populations of *Lycopodiella inundata* left in Britain. *Eriophorum vaginatum* is locally abundant in some wet heath areas, but by no means general, occurring more in the north-west of the Forest.

Important species of **wet open ground**, often around ponds, include *Ludwigia palustris*, *Cicendia filiformis*, *Radiola linoides*, *Parentucellia viscosa*, *Deschampsia setacea*, *Baldellia ranunculoides*, *Sparganium natans*, *Wahlenbergia hederacea*, *Ranunculus omiophyllus*, *R.* x *novae-forestae*.

The calcareous bogs on the **Headon Beds** have fen species including especially *Epipactis palustris*, *Gymnadenia conopsea* ssp. *borealis*, *Eleocharis quinqueflora*, *Eriophorum latifolium*, *Schoenus nigricans*, *Pinguicula vulgaris* (one site only).

The **lawns** of the Forest, particularly the nutrient-enriched hollows inundated in winter, are the home of several species now largely extinct or very rare elsewhere in Britain. These include *Pulicaria vulgaris*, *Chamaemelum nobile*, *Mentha pulegium*, *Galium constrictum*, *Persicaria minor*. Grazing, which reduces competition from more palatable species, is essential for the survival of these species.

In the **dry heaths**, *Agrostis curtisii* is often abundant in open *Calluna* heath, while *Erica ciliaris* may be native in a few places. Lichens of the genus *Cladonia* are locally diverse and important here.

Though, as stated above, the open ancient woodlands of the Forest are not particularly rich generally in vascular plants (and even remarkably lacking in some, such as many *Rubus* microspecies), they are outstandingly important for their cryptogams, particularly the epiphytic lichens. Of these, 315 species are at present known, the largest number for any forest in Europe. These include many ancient woodland indicators.

The bryophyte flora of the Forest is also extremely rich, with some 320 taxa, over 60 of which are epiphytes.

Many of these bryophytes are extremely rare, or now absent (*) elsewhere in the southern counties. Notable species of oceanic, old woodland distributions include *Dicranodontium denudatum*, *Fissidens osmundoides**, *Hyocomium armoricum*, *Thuidium delicatulum*, *Zygodon forsteri* (Schedule 8 species, see p.68), *Frullania fragilifolia*, *Harpalejeunea ovata**, *Plagiochila killarniensis** and *Saccogyna viticulosa*.

Notable bryophytes of flushes and basic bogs include *Breutelia chrysocoma**, *Drepanocladus lycopodioides**, *D. vernicosus** (Schedule 8 species), *Scorpidium scorpioides** and *Preissia quadrata**.

The New Forest is probably the richest habitat for fungi of any British woodland. No comprehensive list has yet been produced, but there are certainly at least 2,600 species recorded. A definitive compilation of the numerous scattered records is in preparation by Gordon Dickson of Fareham (pers.comm.), and hopefully will be published before long.

Of the **ancient woodlands**, no two New Forest woods are identical in character, though most contain stands of beech (*Fagus sylvatica*) of great age and also stands of pedunculate oak (*Quercus robur*). There are some woods (probably those least selectively felled for naval timber) that have very little beech. Many of the older trees were pollarded in the past but new pollarding was not allowed after 1698. In some woods, particularly in the north and north-west of the Forest and Hollands Wood, sessile oak (*Quercus petraea*) largely replaces pedunculate oak. Holly (*Ilex aquifolium*) is generally abundant, often excessively so today, and, over a period of time, may well have replaced hazel (*Corylus avellana*), which is now very rare and local, due to its being very palatable as grazing. Ash (*Fraxinus excelsior*) is local, and confined to more base-rich alluvial areas near streams. Woods of alder (*Alnus glutinosa*), often coppiced in the past, dominate many wet valley-mires and flushes, often forming carr with rusty sallow (*Salix cinerea*). Wild service-tree (*Sorbus torminalis*) is very local, and common whitebeam (*S. aria*) is frequent only on the northern gravels. Field maple (*Acer campestre*), like ash, follows the richer soils. Yew (*Taxus baccata*) is occasional and only rarely plentiful, as in Sloden

Wood. Small-leaved lime (*Tilia cordata*) – much more frequent in earlier times, to judge from pollen data (and Lin- or Lynd- place names) – is now absent from the open Forest, as are elm (*Ulmus*) species. Hornbeam (*Carpinus betulus*) is very rare but does occur in a few sites, though may now be planted rather than relict: it was certainly present in prehistoric times. Wild cherry (*Prunus avium*) is remarkably rare; crab apple (*Malus sylvestris*) is common; all the hawthorns are *Crataegus monogyna*. Rowan (*Sorbus aucuparia*) is frequent throughout.

Examples of New Forest habitats are described more fully below.

(i) Woodlands

Wood Crates (2608). This splendid wood is mostly composed of very tall, high-canopy beech, developed particularly on superficial gravels, with, in places, a dense understorey. In a survey for the Crown of some of the New Forest Woods in 1566, John Taverner, the Queen's Surveyor, indicated that it then contained, as well as beech, some of the best oak in the Forest (*Book of Survey*). Old *Quercus robur* is still scattered in places, and much of the regeneration on former open lawns is of young *Q. robur*, which needs plenty of light to regenerate naturally. It is probable that in the 17th and 18th centuries much of the then mature oak was felled for naval ship-building. Like most old New Forest woods, Wood Crates is a mosaic of dense stands interspersed with open glades and lawns.

The dense stands of beech are on highly acidic soils, usually on gravel, with micropodsols formed just beneath the surface. The ground flora is limited: there are extensive carpets of *Leucobryum* moss (mostly *L. juniperoideum*) with locally abundant *Vaccinium myrtillus*, *Hyacinthoides non-scripta*, *Oxalis acetosella*, *Anemone nemorosa*, and *Teucrium scorodonia*. Many of the beeches are well clothed in lichens, particularly the beard lichen *Usnea ceratina*, also *U. cornuta* and *U. rubicunda*, and there are extensive epiphytic sheets of *Parmelia* species, including the New Forest specialities *P. horrescens* and *P. minarum* (the latter confined in the British Isles to the Forest and to two sites in Cornwall), and also much *P. reticulata* and *P. reddenda*. The lungwort lichen, *Lobaria pulmonaria* occurs occasionally, also the moss *Pterogonium gracile*. One of the moist glades has an abundance of *Wahlenbergia hederacea* among *Oreopteris limbosperma*. Along the streamsides in this wood a richer flora occurs with, locally, *Lamiastrum galeobdolon*, *Primula vulgaris*, *Sanicula europaea*, and fine stands of *Phegopteris connectilis* in 2708. *Fraxinus excelsior* and *Acer campestre* are locally frequent here (with the rare lichen *Wadeana dendro-grapha*). Alder carr in the valley bottoms has *Catabrosa aquatica* in one area, and the rare liverwort *Pallavicinia lyellii* on the alder bases in another. The moss *Fissidens osmundoides* has its only locality in lowland England on the banks of one stream. *Aquilegia vulgaris* occurs along this and other stream-banks in the old Forest woodlands.

West part of Busketts Wood (Little Stubby Hat) (3010). This is a remarkable wood, almost a pure ancient beech-wood, but with a dense holly understorey. John Taverner in 1566 described Little Stubby Hat as of '8 acres, set with beech'. It is still beech-dominated, but is larger now than then. Apart from some misconceived Forestry Commission attempts at thinning some 15 years ago, it may have been more or less undisturbed for at least 400 years, possibly far longer.

Its soils are acidic, with a limited *Leucobryum–Vaccinium* ground flora in general, as at Wood Crates, but the epiphytic lichens are so remarkable (183 species present in 0.5 sq.km, many very rare) that one is tempted to wonder whether this wood has been a beech-wood, largely intact, ever since *Fagus* first became locally important in the New Forest, about 500BC, as the increased wetness and coolness of climate possibly favoured beech rather than oak.

Stricknage Wood (2612). This again is largely ancient beech, but it differs from most Forest woods in lying in a deep, sheltered ravine. Again it is extremely lichen- and bryophyte-rich, with a profusion of the oceanic moss *Hyocomium armoricum* (very local in the Forest) along the main stream; while the liverwort *Harpalejeunea ovata* occurs here on at least one beech in its only locality outside the western and northern British uplands. The ground flora along the stream, particularly in flushed areas less accessible to grazing, is comparatively good, with a good range of ferns, *Hypericum pulchrum*, *H. androsaemum*, *Euphorbia amygdaloides*, *Hyacinthoides non-scripta*, a little *Corylus avellana*, *Lysimachia nemorum*, *Melampyrum pratense*, *Populus tremula*, *Anagallis tenella*, *Sanicula europaea*, *Stachys officinalis*, *Oreopteris limbosperma*, *Sorbus aria*, *Valeriana officinalis*, *Veronica montana*, *Viburnum opulus* and *Viola riviniana*.

A boring into peat in an ox-bow deposit well above present stream-level revealed beech pollen dominant throughout, so this may be another very early beech-wood (F. Rose & R. Scaife, unpublished data). 146 epiphytic lichens and 93 bryophytes are recorded for this quite small woodland. Open, flushed grassland to the east is the only locality of the moss *Breutelia chrysocoma* in lowland Britain.

Mark Ash Wood (2507). This extensive wood is included here because there is good direct evidence that much of it is real primary woodland (see above). Both beech and pedunculate oak of huge size are well represented; there is extensive holly understorey locally. An area of several hectares east of the central car-park was cleared in the 1960s to try to promote regeneration but, like many such efforts by the Forestry Commission at the time, it was a failure and the area is now heathy scrub. Parts of the centre of the wood suffered more damage in the 1987 and 1990 storms than any other ancient New Forest wood.

The epiphytic lichen flora is, in total, one of the richest in the Forest, with 186 species in *c*.1 sq.km. In the south of the wood there are two valley mires. The western one, **Church Moor** (2406), contains alder carr (with the rare lichen *Parmelia laevigata* in its only British site east of Dorset) and also a good open *Sphagnum* bog with *Drosera rotundifolia*, *Rhynchospora alba*, *Narthecium ossifragum*, and *Myrica gale*. This was the site of Clarke and Barber's peat investigations (see Chapter 3, p.11), and the vegetation seems to have changed little in this area for several millenia. To the east of the road is **Barrow Moor** (2507), with dense alder carr, formerly coppiced, in a deep valley. Here *Carex laevigata* and *Chrysosplenium oppositifolium* (strangely local in the Forest) are abundant on and below the spring-lines. Barrow Moor, according to Clarke and Barber (1987), is of much later origin than Church Moor. The vascular flora of Mark Ash Wood is poor (as in so many of the Ancient and Ornamental Woodlands), due probably to the heavy grazing and lack of more base-rich soils, but it contains spectacular areas of splendid, ancient forest. The lichen *Catillaria laureri*, confined to the New Forest in the British Isles, has one of its few sites here.

Turning to the more mixed, oak–beech woods of the New Forest, one comes first to the very extensive **Bramshaw Wood** (2516) in the north of the Forest which contains extensive areas of very tall beech forest to the north, and a most remarkable stand of tall *Quercus petraea* high forest in a wide area on the northern slopes of the escarpment. The vascular plant flora is limited in this wood, but local, rich patches produce a total of 39 AWVPs in the complex.

Beneath the dense, high canopy, probably up to 300 years old in places, and the holly understorey, little is to be found except *Euphorbia amygdaloides*, *Ruscus aculeatus*, *Oxalis acetosella*, *Vaccinium myrtillus*, and *Anemone nemorosa*, but *Hyacinthoides non-scripta*, *Primula vulgaris*, and *Viola riviniana* are locally frequent in less acid, better-lit patches. A total of 80 bryophytes is recorded, including carpets of *Dicranum majus*, *Leucobryum juniperoideum*, and

Rhytidiadelphus loreus – all ancient woodland species – while the rare, oceanic hepatic *Saccogyna viticulosa* occurs on moist slopes. The epiphytic lichens number 184 species, including *Lobaria pulmonaria*, *L. virens* and the best *L. amplissima* in the Forest high up on one old *Fagus sylvatica*.

The moss *Neckera crispa*, usually in chalk grassland, has its only Hampshire locality as an epiphyte also on two old *Quercus*. Interestingly glades, often with heath and patches of *Sphagnum* bog, diversify the wood, and there are two incised stream-valleys with *Alnus*, *Acer campestre* and *Fraxinus*, but soils are generally very acidic. Visually, Bramshaw and the adjacent Great Wood form one of the most beautiful and spectacular parts of the Forest, giving one the feeling that one has gone back in time several thousand years! No finer single, ancient high-forest area in Britain or indeed in lowland western Europe north of the Pyrenees is known to the author: parts of the Forêt de Compiègne, north-east of Paris, perhaps come nearest to it.

Another fine area that is comparatively little visited is the **Stubbs Wood–Frame Wood** complex (3503). This extensive woodland lies partly on plateau gravels, and partly on Tertiary sands and clays, and has several interesting boggy, open glades within it. It is composed largely of old, spreading trees of *Quercus robur*, *c.*250–300 years in age – there

Plate 4   Red Shoot Wood, one of the finest ancient sessile oak (*Quercus petraea*) woods in the New Forest and indeed in lowland England, is extremely rich in local lichens such as *Lobaria* ssp. (*Photo*: A. J. P. Branson)

25

are not many trees in the Forest much over this age, probably due to selective 17th-century felling for the Navy – and there are also large stands of somewhat younger *Fagus sylvatica*.

The ground flora, as elsewhere, contains much *Euphorbia amygdaloides*, *Anemone nemorosa*, *Ruscus aculeatus*, *Oxalis acetosella*, *Blechnum spicant*, *Vaccinium myrtillus*, and *Oreopteris limbosperma*; also *Ranunculus auricomus*, *Primula vulgaris*, *Hyacinthoides non-scripta*, *Sanicula europaea*, *Melampyrum pratense*, *Melica uniflora*, and *Lathyrus linifolius* locally, while *Malus sylvestris* and *Rosa arvensis* are common on the heavier soils. There are 25 AWVPs recorded here. As usual, the bryophytes (90 species, including the rare oceanic hepatic *Scapania gracilis* on rotting logs) and the epiphytic lichens (169 species, including many great rarities) are the main botanical interest: the lungwort species *Lobaria virens* is locally quite abundant, clothing some oaks in its green thallus.

A remote and beautiful area is **Red Shoot Wood** (1808), dominated largely by old *Quercus petraea*, of less height and of more spreading form generally than in Bramshaw Wood. *Fagus sylvatica* is less common, but *Malus sylvestris* is frequent and *Carpinus betulus* occurs as a few large specimens. The finest part of the wood is on a gentle south-facing slope in the north-west. This wood is not mentioned in early Crown reports of timber reserves and has the appearance of remaining undisturbed for many centuries, except for the occasional storm damage. Its bryophyte flora is not as rich as in some Forest woods (only 42 species recorded, probably an underestimate) but there are 25 AWVPs and 148 epiphytic lichen taxa in an area of only some 30ha of the wood, including some of the most luxuriant *Lobaria* sheets of the Forest, running 3–5m up some oaks. The nearby **Pinnick Wood** (1907) has a fine area of *Narcissus pseudonarcissus*.

South Ocknell Wood (2410) is a distinctive wood forming a narrow belt along the Highland Water, running south from the A31. Its northern part is of ancient, mostly pollard, oaks (mainly *Quercus robur*) on relatively-rich, valley alluvium. Further south, the ancient pollards of *Fraxinus* on very basic soil, in among *Prunus spinosa* scrub, are remarkable for their rich epiphyte flora of 150 lichens in a very small area (including the only site east of Devon for *Pannaria sampaiana*) and rare mosses such as *Leptodon smithii*.

Canterton Glen, east of the Rufus Stone (2712). This old beech-wood in a deep valley has remarkable bryophyte communities on the north-east-facing slopes; *Bazzania trilobata* and *Saccogyna viticulosa* occur in local abundance on *Leucobryum* carpets; *Plagiochila killarniensis* and *Zygodon forsteri* on *Fagus*. The hepatics are all species of strongly

western or oceanic distribution in Britain; the *Zygodon* is known in only three other sites in Britain. This wood is rich in unusual *Rubus* species.

There are many other very interesting open woodlands in the Forest, but the areas described above will have to serve as examples of the range of variation.

(ii) The Inclosures

The Inclosures are, as pointed out above, largely plantations, in some cases with relict areas of ancient woodland trapped within them. Many of the conifer plantations (e.g. **Slufters Inclosure** (2210)) represent plantings on former heathland. These, apart from occasional relics of heath vegetation along rides, etc., are of low botanical value generally. An exception is **Norleywood Inclosure** (3598) which contains unusual *Rubus* species (apparently because it has always been fenced).

The broad-leaved Inclosures (e.g. **Brockishill** (3011), **Amberwood** (2113), much of **Islands Thorns** (2114)) are more attractive. These are largely plantations of now mature oaks, sometimes mixed with beech, chestnut (*Castanea sativa*) or conifers, that were established in the late 18th to early 19th century to provide naval timber. The Navy changed to iron and steel as a construction material for their ships long before most of the trees were large enough to harvest. Some of these Inclosures were felled later and replanted with conifers, but many remain as broad-leaved woods, and the general policy of the Forestry Commission seems now to be to manage them for amenity and wildlife. This will involve creation of glades and group-fellings to bring about diversity and an uneven-aged, self-regenerating structure. Only the commonest lichens occur in these woods.

The ground flora in the enclosed woods was in the past sometimes richer than in the Ancient and Ornamental Woodlands, due to protection from grazing. However, the flora has deteriorated in the last 40–50 years or so, due to the fact that many Inclosures are now left open to stock. This has not only reduced the formerly diverse ride-side vegetation, but has also vastly reduced the Lepidoptera populations for which some of these woods were renowned. Incorrect ride-edge management has also adversely affected the Lepidoptera.

The oldest oak plantation of all, **South Bentley Inclosure** (2312), was planted *c*.1700, and regeneration since has created a more uneven-aged wood, although it is largely devoid of *Rubus* species. Probably because it is adjacent to the ancient Anses Wood, its epiphytic lichen flora has, over nearly 300 years, come to approach that of some Ancient and

Ornamental Woodlands in richness, with *Lobaria pulmonaria* and *Rinodina isidioides* among others. Those Inclosures with trapped ancient woodland (e.g. **Burley Old Inclosure** (2404), **Knightwood Inclosure** (2506), and **Highland Water Inclosure** (2509) are by far the most diverse and interesting. **Wick Wood** (2609), **Puckpits** (2509), and other old localities within Highland Water Inclosure are extremely lichen-and bryophyte-rich but such areas as, for example, Bolderwood Walk are more or less barren of *Rubus*.

(iii) The dry heaths

It is difficult to single out good areas of dry heath within such a vast tract but the area of **Black Common** (1809) near **Linwood**, through to **Black Barrow** (1810) is particularly interesting. Along the track, sandy grass-heath with *Moenchia erecta* and *Crassula tillaea* is well developed. The dry heath (*Calluna vulgaris, Erica cinerea, Ulex minor* association) to the north is extremely rich in lichens of the genus *Cladonia*, particularly *C. arbuscula, C. coccifera, C. crispata, C. gracilis, C. incrassata* (on a peaty bank, its only Forest site), *C. portentosa, C. squamosa, C. strepsilis* and *C. uncialis; Coelocaulon aculeatum* and *Pycnothelia papillaria* also occur. The lichens form extensive carpets here, and in humid heath the local mosses *Dicranum spurium, Hypnum imponens* and *Racomitrium lanuginosum* occur among commoner heathland mosses. Similar rich patches of lichen-and bryophyte-rich heath occur at **Shappen Hill** (2001), **Red Shoot Plain** (1808), **Handy Cross Plain** (2107), **Acres Down** (2708), **Fair Cross** (3009), **south of Ogdens** (1811), **East Beaulieu Heath** (4002), and (in VC8) **Plaitford Common** (2718).

After too-frequent fires, these lichen–bryophyte communities are slow to return, but hard grazing (by reducing heather competition?) seems to increase lichen-cover and diversity. Carefully controlled strip-burning of leggy heather, however, may sometimes be beneficial to the recolonization of lichens if carried out in late winter, but fire is not an ideal method of heath management generally. Hot summer fires are extremely destructive.

The pine-trees that occur on many heaths are considered to derive from 18th-century introductions.

(iv) Valley mires

There must be about one hundred of these, the finest series of this type of bog in Britain or western Europe. Their most distinguished plant, *Spiranthes aestivalis* has not been seen for over 30 years, though it may yet be refound: there are frequent rumours about its reappearance!

Here, it is possible to describe only a few examples. One of the finest is the great Avon Water mire, known as **Wilverley Bog** (2400 to 2599). This is a linear valley-mire along the north side of the Avon Water. The dry heathland on a podsol along its northern edge (with *Calluna, Erica cinerea, Agrostis curtisii* and *Cladonia* species) grades down the slope southwards through humid heath (with *Erica tetralix* mixed in with the *Calluna*, and the moss *Dicranum spurium*) into wet heath which has a high, winter water-table and lies on a peaty, stagno-gley substrate. Here *Erica tetralix* is dominant with frequent *Trichophorum cespitosum* and *Molinia caerulea*, and the ground is carpeted with the two wet-heath species of *Sphagnum, S.compactum* and *S. tenellum. Drosera rotundifolia* and *D. intermedia* are common and, on bare peat, *Lycopodiella inundata* is locally plentiful, with quantities of *Rhynchospora alba* on damper peat. Next comes a *Myrica* zone and then a *Sphagnum* bog on deeper peat; here the wine-red *S. magellanicum* is locally the dominant of the sward, with much ochre-coloured *S. papillosum* and hummocks of the deep-red *S. capillifolium; Eriophorum angustifolium* and *Narthecium ossifragum* occur in abundance.

In hollows, the tawny orange-yellow *Sphagnum recurvum* is dominant, with *S. cuspidatum* in pools. Numerous liverworts occur that are largely confined to growing on *Sphagnum*, (e.g. *Odontoschisma denudatum, Cephalozia macrostachya, Riccardia latifrons*), and on old animal dung one may find the interesting coprophilous (dung-loving) moss *Splachnum ampullaceum* (now nearly extinct in lowland Britain outside the New Forest, because there are usually now no animals on the heaths). So far, the plant communities are all very acidophilic; their water-supply comes off the leached plateau-gravels and the Eocene sands. As the main stream is approached, the influence of base-rich water from the Headon Beds becomes important, and rather less-acidic swamp communities with much *Phragmites australis, Pedicularis palustris*, and *Menyanthes trifoliata* occur. Along the runnels of water, the basiphile *Sphagnum teres* and *S. contortum* tend to replace *S. papillosum, S. recurvum* and *S. auriculatum*. Here there are rich pool-and flush-communities with *Carex limosa, C. lasiocarpa, Drosera anglica* (as well as the other two sundews on *Sphagnum* hummocks) *Pinguicula lusitanica, Dactylorhiza incarnata* ssp. *pulchella, Utricularia minor* and *Hammarbya paludosa* on pool-edges with more *Rhynchospora alba. H. paludosa* varies greatly in quantity from year to year, from over 100 inflorescences to none at all. *Osmunda regalis* occurs further west in carr.

Hincheslea Bog (2700 to 2800) is of very similar character but without *Carex lasiocarpa*, and Holmsley Bog (2300 to 2101), higher up the Avon Water, has a very similar assemblage of species with the addition of *Thelypteris palustris*. Small acid-flushes through these valleys may have much *Ranunculus omiophyllus* and *Isolepis cernua*.

Another very interesting valley-mire complex is that of Vales Moor (1904), running down to Cranes Moor (1902). Most of the Wilverley and Holmsley species occur here, but structurally the mire is different at Cranes Moor. It is on quite deep peat of great age, and appears to have developed into a raised bog in the past, between two diverging, base-rich *Schoenus nigricans* flushes. Unfortunately the upper peats have been cut away for fuel long ago, so much of the structure has gone. However, there is still an extensive area of flattish, acidic *Sphagnum* mire between the *Schoenus* flushes. This mire has given valuable data on the past history of the vegetation (both on site and in the region) but of course the sequence was broken by the peat-cutting phase. See Barber & Clarke (1987) where earlier work by Seagrief and by Newbould is also discussed.

North of Strodgemoor Bottom (1803) there is excellent wet heath with abundance of *Rhynchospora fusca*, as well as *R. alba*, and much *Lycopodiella inun-data*, *Drosera intermedia* and *D. rotundifolia*, grading down into a flushed *Schoenus nigricans* area below.

Many other New Forest valley mires show similar features, but usually on a smaller scale. Mention need only be made of Matley Bog (3307), on a wet, acid-flushed north slope with *Hammarbya paludosa*, and also *Rhynchospora alba* in abundance; and of the Denny Bog complex (3504), where *Utricularia intermedia* survives in one acidic peat-pool, while *Gentiana pneumonanthe* is plentiful in several border-ing wet heaths with *Molinia caerulea* and *Erica tetralix*.

Of acidic, dystrophic ponds and tarns, the oustand-ing example is at Hatchet Pond (3601) and, more especially, the smaller pond across the road to the south-east. Here *Ludwigia palustris* is abundant with *Baldellia ranunculoides*, *Sparganium emersum*, and on the winter-flooded, sandy turf around there is much *Cicendia filiformis*, *Anagallis minima* and *Radiola linoides*. In shallow water here *Pilularia globulifera*, *Littorella uniflora* and *Eleocharis acicularis* are locally common; *Elatine hexandra* is more restricted. *Galium constrictum*, a species quite widespread in the Forest, and *Illecebrum verticillatum* occur in wet hollows.

A rather calcareous lawn within heath on the Headon Beds at Marlpit Oak (2899) has a commu-nity in grassland among *Prunus* scrub and *Ulex*

Plate 5　East End Pond is one of the interesting acidic ponds of the southern New Forest with such species as *Ludwigia palustris*, *Mentha pulegium* and *Cicendia filiformis* (*Photo*: A. R. G. Mundell)

europaeus with *Carex montana*, *Viola lactea*, *Pulmonaria longifolia*, *Stachys officinalis*, and *Gymnadenia conopsea* ssp. *borealis*.

Open, heavily-grazed lawns of a more neutral pH occur in the area north of Cadnam. On **Cadnam Green** (2914) there are hollows, flooded in winter, with great quantities of *Pulicaria vulgaris* and with *Persicaria minor*, *Senecio aquaticus*, *Bidens tripartita*, *Chamaemelum nobile* and *Mentha pulegium* – a community maintained by pony-grazing. If grazing ceases, as in the former habitats for this community in Surrey and Sussex, the *Pulicaria* and *Mentha* disappear.

Finally, the highly calcareous mires on the **Headon Beds** must be mentioned. **Stony Moors** (2199) is perhaps the best of these. Here there is a short, grazed fen-sward with *Schoenus nigricans* (on hummocks), *Eriophorum latifolium*, *Eleocharis quinqueflora*, *Epipactis palustris*, *Gymnadenia conopsea* ssp. *borealis*, *Platanthera bifolia*, *Pedicularis palustris* and *Drosera anglica* (in wetter hollows); and the bryophytes *Drepanocladus revolvens*, *Cratoneuron commutatum* var. *falcatum*, *Philonotis calcarea*, *Campylium stellatum*, *Scorpidium scorpioides* and *Preissia quadrata*. This alkaline, rich-fen community on a spring-line is reminiscent of some spring-fens in Norfolk valleys.

More extensive calcareous mire with a similar flora occurs at **Boundway Hill** (2698), including much more of the *Epipactis* and *Gymnadenia*. This grades above into more acid-flushes, fed from plateau-gravels, with *Rhynchospora alba*, *Eleocharis multicaulis*, *Potamogeton polygonifolius*, and *Drosera intermedia* on *Sphagnum* lawns.

Similar calcareous marl-bogs occur at **Widden Bottom** (2899), with several of the same species as at Stony Moors, and also the Schedule 8 moss *Drepanocladus vernicosus*.

At **Acres Down** (2708) there is a rather similar flush on what seems to be the most northerly occurrence of the Headon Beds, outcropping at the top of a slope below plateau gravels. This is the only known New Forest site for *Pinguicula vulgaris*, at its south-eastern British limit at present. It is locally abundant with the more usual New Forest *Pinguicula lusitanica*, *Pedicularis palustris*, and carpets of rich-fen bryophytes. *Hammarbya paludosa* also occurs in the run-off from this flush down the slope.

Outside the New Forest boundary there are several areas (e.g. Poors Common, Barton Common) with heathland vegetation rather similar to that of the Forest but these, where ungrazed, are deteriorating.

Plate 6   Perhaps the finest of the calcareous valley mires fed by water from the Headon Beds in the New Forest, Stony Moors is rich in local bryophytes and fen species such as *Menyanthes trifoliata* and *Schoenus nigricans*. (*Photo*: B. M. & A. J. Rackham)

Plate 7 Boundway Hill, another fine calcareous valley mire, with much *Gymnadenia conopsea* ssp. *borealis* and *Epipactis palustris* below, while the upper areas (fed from acidic plateau gravels) have *Drosera* spp. and *Rhynchospora alba*. (*Photo*: B. M. & A. J. Rackham)

3. Other Tertiary Heathland

(i) The heathland north and east of Southampton

The first Ordnance Survey one-inch map of this area (Sheet 86: Winchester & The Solent (1810)) makes it clear that there were vast expanses of heathland north and east of Southampton earlier in the 19th century before most were taken into cultivation for market gardening (particularly of strawberries), or were later partly covered with new suburbs of Southampton (Fig.7).

Baddesley Common and Emer Bog (3921), a HWT reserve, is the last remaining area north of Southampton with good heath and bog vegetation. At the once aptly-named **Botany Bay** (4511), however, there was evidently at one time an extensive valley-mire on the large **Netley Heath** with much *Rhynchospora alba* and *Drosera intermedia* up to at least 1842, to judge from old records. Today only two patches of heath with valley-mire communities survive in this area, at **Netley Common** (4711) and **Netley Hill** (4811). Here there is still a surviving *Schoenus nigricans* community, with locally abundant *Narthecium ossifragum*, *Drosera rotundifolia*, *D. intermedia*, *Isolepis setacea*, *Eriophorum angustifolium* and *Molinia caerulea* in a carpet of *Sphagnum papillosum*.

The former basic flush that was evidently here is now less wet and is acidic; around it there is still wet heath with *Erica tetralix*, *Molinia*, *Calluna vulgaris* and *Ulex minor*.

East of the Hamble, **Titchfield Common**, formerly vast, has almost disappeared but provides the only Hampshire site for *Rubus imbricatus*. Beyond this to the east is the former Royal Forest of Bere, now wholly enclosed except for one fragment at **Shedfield Common** (5613). Here *Narthecium ossifragum*, *Drosera rotundifolia*, *Eriophorum angustifolium*, *Carex echinata*, *C. viridula* ssp. *oedocarpa*, *C. panicea*, *Juncus bulbosus*, *Dactylorhiza maculata* and *Eleocharis multicaulis* still survive in a *Sphagnum papillosum* carpet among wet heath vegetation of *Calluna vulgaris*, *Erica tetralix*, *Molinia caerulea*, with *Agrostis curtisii* and *Ulex minor* on drier heath above.

Wickham Common (5810) must have been similar heathland until fairly recently but is now overgrown with scrub or has been 'improved' – nevertheless *Calluna vulgaris*, *Erica tetralix*, *Narthecium ossifragum*, *Molinia caerulea*, *Agrostis curtisii* and a few other heathland plants still manage to survive, as well as the rare heath bramble *Rubus vigorosus*. The greater part of the Forest of Bere, however, is on London Clay with a few patches of

Bagshot Sands; what is left are some areas of oak woodland under Forestry Commission control (see p.55 below). **Purbrook Heath** (6607) still had *Pinguicula lusitanica* until some 25 or 30 years ago but this has now gone: formerly it was quite widespread on the heaths east of Southampton.

(ii) The Tertiary heaths of north-east Hampshire

Quite a few valuable relics remain of the former vast and almost continuous heaths on the Eocene sands and gravels in the north and north-east of Hampshire (see Fig.7). The more important of these are described below.

Tadley Common (6062) lies on the south slopes of the gravel plateau along the Berks border. It has valley bogs in the south-east part where springs occur over impervious strata. To the west there is still some rather overgrown, scrubby *Calluna* heath, and the valley bogs still have *Narthecium ossifragum, Drosera rotundifolia, D. intermedia, Eleocharis multicaulis* and *Eriophorum angustifolium* in *Sphagnum papillosum* and *S. recurvum* carpets. There is wet heath with *Erica tetralix* and *Trichophorum cespitosum* but Tadley Common was badly burnt in 1976; now *Polytrichum*

commune carpets have replaced much of the former wet heath and *Dicranum spurium* seems to be extinct.

Silchester Common (6162) is similar in topography and vegetation to Tadley Common, both having originally been part of one continuous heath. It is, however, in much better condition, is well managed and grazing is about to be recommenced. The *Sphagnum* bogs are quite rich in the valleys.

Hazeley Heath (7458 to 7657) is extensive, comprising an area about 3km long and 1km wide. It lies on the top and sides of a north-west–south-east gravel plateau and slopes down to the north-east. There are fine, diverse heath communities as well as extensive areas of scrub and birch-wood. There are also several very good valley-bogs on the slopes. The best area of bog has carpets of *Sphagnum magellanicum, S. papillosum, S. subnitens* (in flushes), *S. capillifolium, S. auriculatum* and *S. recurvum*, with good bog hepatics: *Mylia anomala, Odontoschisma sphagni, Kurzia pauciflora, Cephalozia macrostachya, C. connivens*. The vascular flora of the bog includes *Rhynchospora alba, Narthecium ossifragum, Anagallis tenella* (in flushes), *Eleocharis multicaulis, Hypericum elodes, Cirsium dissectum, Myrica gale* and *Scutellaria minor*.

There are also areas of wet heath with *Sphagnum*

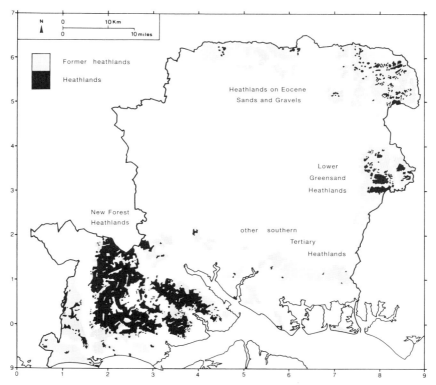

Fig. 7   Except in the New Forest, the formerly extensive heathlands have become very fragmented and are now concentrated on the north-east Tertiary strata west of Aldershot and on the Lower Greensand strata around Woolmer Forest

molle (a rare species), *Campylopus brevipilus*, *Serratula tinctoria* and *Salix repens*. On drier heath occur *Agrostis curtisii* and *Chamaemelum nobile* (grassy areas). This is certainly one of the richest heathlands in north-east Hampshire.

The wet heathland north-west of **Hawley Lake** (8357) has very good communities of *Lycopodiella inundata*, *Rhynchospora alba*, *Eleocharis multicaulis* and *Narthecium ossifragum* among *Erica tetralix* and *Molinia caerulea*. There are carpets of *Sphagnum papillosum*, *S. cuspidatum*, *S. tenellum* and *S. compactum*, with a good range of bog hepatics. *Pyrola minor* occurs in the woodland. This heathland, in common with much in north and east Hampshire, falls within a military training area.

Castle Bottom (7959) has another good valley-bog that had become rather overgrown but it is now being grazed very beneficially. The bog-and-wet-heath flora is similar to that at Hazeley (with *Rhynchospora alba* and *Myrica gale*) but is not quite so rich in species. To the east, on the old airfield, a grass-heath area (8059) has abundant *Botrychium lunaria*.

Nearby, parts of **Yateley Common** (8359) have good wet heath, and one valley bog that has suffered badly from fire. The area is particularly rich in local, dry-and wet-heath lichens, particularly *Cladonia strepsilis* (also at Castle Bottom) and *Pycnothelia papillaria*, besides commoner heathland species in plenty. One curiosity is the rare, otherwise upland moss *Tetraplodon mnioides* that grows on animal dung on moors in the north of Britain. Here it has colonized decayed dog excrement.

Bramshill Plantation (7462), was formerly heath, then largely planted with conifers. However, it includes extensive old gravel-pits containing shallow lakes which have important populations of *Pilularia globulifera*. A small colony of *Lycopodiella inundata* occurred by a stream (but may have been shaded-out by conifers).

Heath Warren (7659) has old gravel-pits like those at Bramshill Plantation, with a similar flora, but with the addition of *Lycopodium clavatum* in open, heathy scrub in what may be its only current Hampshire site. Moist, sandy tracks have *Radiola linoides*.

Eelmoor Marsh (8353), another military area, is a unique site (but there is currently NO PUBLIC ACCESS). Many years ago, the then War Department dug a series of deep ditches here to drain the wet heath (which used to have *Gentiana pneumonanthe*). These ditches bear, on their moist sides and floors, remarkable populations of *Pinguicula vulgaris* and *P. lusitanica*. Other plants of interest include *Narthecium ossifragum*, *Rhynchospora alba*, *Carex*

pulicaris, *Agrostis curtisii*, *Viola lactea*, *Salix repens*, *Serratula tinctoria*, *Anagallis tenella*, *Epipactis palustris* (in flushed area) and *Dactylorhiza incarnata* ssp. *pulchella*. This site is being carefully managed by removing pine and birch scrub, and maintaining water in the open ditches; the possibility of grazing is also currently being considered.

Caesar's Camp (8450) (MOD TRAINING AREA). Wet heaths here have good populations locally of *Lycopodiella inundata* and *Rhynchospora alba* on wet, rather bare, peaty rides. *Crassula tillaea* occurs nearby at Sunny Hill.

Bourley Bottom (8250) RESTRICTED ACCESS, MOD). There are areas of wet heath here, with *Narthecium ossifragum*, *Drosera intermedia* and *D. rotundifolia*. Along ditches feeding the reservoirs, *Wahlenbergia hederacea* occurs in quantity – the only site now known in north-east Hampshire, apart from a few plants near Fleet Pond beside the Gelvert Stream that flows from Bourley Bottom. The wet, sandy shore of the largest reservoir has *Carex viridula* ssp. *viridula*, *Littorella uniflora*, *Eleocharis acicularis* and *Elatine hexandra*, whilst the reservoir to the south in 8249 has *Viola lactea* and *V. palustris* beside it.

Bartley Heath (7253) is a HWT reserve. Much of this is now birch-wood or scrub, but the central area of wet heath has been kept open and extended. Here *Gentiana pneumonanthe* is plentiful in *Molinia caerulea*–*Erica tetralix* heath with *Succisa pratensis* and *Serratula tinctoria*.

Fleet Pond (8255) was once a famous botanical site but the aquatic plants have been seriously depleted by deteriorating water-quality. However, there are still some excellent marginal areas, with *Utricularia minor*, *U. australis*, *Potentilla palustris*, *Pedicularis palustris*, *Osmunda regalis*, *Ranunculus lingua*, *Carex vesicaria* and abundant *Carex curta* and *Eleogiton fluitans*. *Elatine hexandra* reappeared in a small pond dug for dragonflies.

4. The Wealden Heathland

(i) Lower Greensand heaths in east Hampshire

Most of the remaining heathland in this area (see Fig.7, p.31), largely on Folkestone Sands, formed part of the mediaeval Royal Forest of Woolmer, and most of what remains is still MOD property. The main block of **Woolmer Forest** (7829 to 8033) lies both north and south of the new A3 road between Greatham and Liphook, and covers about 1,400ha of which about 600ha is heathland. This is the largest continuous block of heath left on the Folkestone Sands in England. To the south of the A3 (apart from Longmoor Camp) most is open to the public at

Plate 8   The rich acidic mire of Eelmoor Marsh is dissected with drainage ditches cut long ago, where reasonable populations of both *Pinguicula vulgaris* and *P. lusitanica* occur in plenty close together on the oozing sides of the ditches. (*Photo*: A. R. G. Mundell)

Plate 9   Caesar's Camp, Aldershot, is typical acid heath on the Tertiary sands and gravels: areas of bare, wet peat have *Lycopodiella inundata*, *Rhynchospora alba*, *Drosera intermedia* and *D. rotundifolia* among *Erica tetralix*. (*Photo*: A. R. G. Mundell)

nearly all times. To the north of the A3, there are military firing ranges which are CLOSED to the public on most days until about 4 p.m., but are OPEN for various holiday periods including, usually, most of September. It is essential to check visiting arrangements before entering the site.

There is much good quality *Calluna vulgaris–Erica cinerea* heath, many areas of wet heath with *E. tetralix* and large stands of *Molinia caerulea*. Until recently, much of the southern half was heavily invaded by pine and birch, which had almost entirely colonized it since 1937. Before that, much of Woolmer was treeless, open heath just as Gilbert White described it 200 years ago. Most of the pine and birch to the west has now been cleared, and this work is to continue over the next few years.

Perhaps the main change since Gilbert White's time has been the drainage of the numerous valley bogs by the MOD, presumably to make infantry training easier. However there has been a change of policy, as it is now recognized that boggy areas are not only important for wildlife, but also that their presence is valuable in training troops to cope with boggy terrain. Accordingly, one drained valley-bog is being dammed to restore bog vegetation.

In such a large area, one can only select good examples of the vegetation to describe briefly, both on the main block of Woolmer Forest and on the outlying areas to the north-west, which are all part of the historic Forest and are currently all MOD property:

Longmoor Inclosure (7930) (MOD). Here there is an elevated ridge, capped like much of the higher ground in the Forest with plateau gravels. This bears fine heathland, and, on its southern slopes particularly, there are seepage lines over seams of impervious clay which produce wet heath of the *Erica tetralix–Sphagnum compactum* type with *Drosera rotundifolia*, *Trichophorum cespitosum* and good populations of *Eriophorum vaginatum* – a species locally common in Woolmer, which has not recently been seen on the north-eastern, Tertiary sand heaths. *Pyrola minor* occurs in birch–pine or sallow woodlands.

The cutting of the **old military railway** (especially at 7829) has interesting bryophyte communities on its moist, north-facing bank (with *Blasia pusilla*, *Nardia geoscyphus*, *Sphagnum palustre*, *Philonotis fontana*) with *Drosera rotundifolia* and, locally, much *Dactylorhiza praetermissa* and its hybrid with *D. maculata*.

Woolmer Pond (7832) was at one time the largest lake in Hampshire. Some ecologists consider that it is of natural origin, as other former meres in Woolmer Forest may have been. Until earlier this century, it had clear, weakly-acid water low in nutrients, and sandy shores with vegetation rather reminiscent of Hatchet Pond in the New Forest (*Littorella uniflora*, *Pilularia globulifera* and *Apium inundatum*). Probably largely as a consequence of the building of the military railway along its western side, sand and silt washed down into it, and gradually turned it into a *Sphagnum* swamp, with much *Molinia caerulea*, *Juncus* species, and some *Potentilla palustris*. As a result of this *Sphagnum* colonization, the pH of the water became very acid, the open water almost disappeared, and the natterjack toad, *Bufo calamita*, for which it had been an important site, became almost extinct. In recent years, there has been a large operation to clear the pond of the *Sphagnum* and other peat-forming vegetation and associated 'gunge': part of the former shelving, sandy shore has been recreated. The first result was the appearance of great quantities of *Persicaria minor* on the damp sand. The work was done just prior to a series of very dry years; the pond did not refill with water, though careful survey had shown that its natural impervious floor was intact. The very wet weather of late 1992, however, resulted in the pond refilling, and it is now most interesting to see the aquatic and shore-line vegetation that has redeveloped. As well as *P. minor*, in 1994, *Littorella uniflora* and *Hypericum elodes* were back in abundance after many years' absence, and *Callitriche brutia* (new to VC12) appeared on wet sand.

Heaths east of Woolmer Pond (7831 and 8032). Interesting bryophytes occur among the *Calluna* here, particularly (at the first site) *Lophozia herzogiana*, which is otherwise known only in New Zealand and may have been an introduction with troop movements during the 1939–45 war but which, sadly, seems to have disappeared recently under spoil from the pond clearance, and (at both sites) the local, humid-heath moss *Dicranum spurium*, in Hampshire now found otherwise only in the New Forest.

Cranmer Bottom Bog (7932). This is the only undamaged *Sphagnum*-dominated valley-mire now in the main area of Woolmer Forest. Its vegetation is rich, and includes the following plants. Among the bryophytes: *Sphagnum magellanicum*, *S. papillosum*, *S. capillifolium* (hummocks), *S. recurvum* (lawns), *S. cuspidatum* and *S. auriculatum* (wetter hollows), *S. compactum* and *S. tenellum* (wet, marginal heath), *Polytrichum commune*, *Aulacomnium palustre*, *Hypnum jutlandicum*, *Drepanocladus fluitans* (pools), *Cephalozia macrostachya*, *Cladopodiella fluitans* (pools), *Kurzia pauciflora*, *Odontoschisma sphagni* and *Mylia anomala*; and among the vascular plants: *Calluna vulgaris*, *Erica tetralix*, *Eriophorum angustifolium*, *E. vaginatum* (on drier marginal ridge), *Trichophorum cespitosum* (on drier marginal ridge),

Rhynchospora alba (in hollows), *Narthecium ossifragum*, *Vaccinium oxycoccos* (in centre on *Sphagnum*), *Drosera rotundifolia* (on *Sphagnum*), *D. intermedia* (hollows), *Potamogeton polygonifolius* (pools).

This bog probably represents a fine example of the valley mires which, according to Gilbert White, were scattered over the hollows of Woolmer in his day.

Small bog west of Queens Road (8131). This mire, surrounded by pine-and-birch-wood, is fed by seepage from the slopes of Weavers Down to the south. It is leased to the HWT as a reserve. It has many of the species present at Cranmer Bottom, including *Vaccinium oxycoccos*, and is the only known location in VC12 for the scarce *Sphagnum*-dwelling liverwort *Riccardia latifrons*.

Bog below Fern Hill (8033) between two linear earthworks. This mire – more of the nature of wet heath than true bog over deep peat – is notable for the great abundance of *Lycopodiella inundata* on rather bare, wet peat. In the period 1988–92 it was estimated that *c*.5,000 cones were produced by this population, which must be one of the largest remaining in Britain. *Rhynchospora alba* is very abundant, with the two *Drosera* species, *D. rotundifolia* and *D. intermedia*, *Narthecium ossifragum*, *Trichophorum cespitosum*, and *Carex panicea*, but no *Vaccinium oxycoccos*.

Bog south of Horsebush Hill developed similarly to that above, between two linear earthworks, south of 8032. It also has similar plants but *Lycopodiella inundata* is not quite so abundant. Here, and in several other places on Woolmer, the unique liverwort *Cryptothallus mirabilis* occurs under *Sphagnum* carpets in alder carr. This liverwort contains no chlorophyll and seems to be parasitic on a fungal mycelium.

Linchborough Park Lake (8032). An interesting floating *Sphagnum* bog occurs here, developed over a former lake. *Potentilla palustris* is abundant and sometimes *Utricularia australis*.

Bogs and wet-heath areas at the south end of **the Slab** (7834), and a little further south (7734) have *Lycopodiella inundata*, *Rhynchospora alba*, *Drosera* species, *Narthecium ossifragum* and *Vaccinium oxycoccos*.

Shortheath Common (7736). Here, there is an extensive floating *Sphagnum* bog, dominated largely by *Sphagnum recurvum* and *Polytrichum commune*, with what is probably the largest population of *Vaccinium oxycoccos* in the southern half of Britain. This area was probably originally a mere like Woolmer Pond; open water remains at the north-east corner at Shortheath Pond where *Utricularia australis* and *Hypericum elodes* occur.

A large part of Shortheath Common is now birch-wood with much bracken, but several areas of old *Calluna* remain where rabbits are active. These are very rich in heathland lichens, particularly the now very local *Cladonia arbuscula*, *Coelocaulon aculeatum*, *C. muricatum*; also *Cladonia gracilis* and *C. glauca*. The rare (in Hampshire) bryophytes *Ptilidium ciliare* and *Hypnum imponens* are here likewise very local but plentiful (as also on Kingsley Common). Shortheath has recently been purchased by HCC as a proposed LNR.

Kingsley Common 7938). This attractive, small MOD heathland (OPEN ACCESS) has a rich bryophyte and lichen flora like that at Shortheath, but there is little development of wet heath here and no real bog. On its south side at Fir Hill, a band of hard sandstone along the ridge has caused a steep, oak-wood scarp to develop.

Open, sandy grasslands on Woolmer are the last habitats to be considered on the Folkestone Sands. Along the northern side of Woolmer Road (7831) and north of the new A3 at 7931, there are areas of open, sandy turf, dominated partly by *Festuca filiformis*, of a character reminiscent of the Suffolk Breckland. Here occur *Vulpia ciliata* ssp. *ambigua*, *Teesdalia nudicaulis*, *Hypochaeris glabra*, *Crassula tillaea*, *Erodium cicutarium*, *Aira caryophyllea*, *A. praecox*, *Agrostis vinealis*, *Ornithopus perpusillus* and *Trifolium arvense*.

Arabis glabra occurs elsewhere in the Woolmer area on open, sandy ground. These localities are important as this species is in serious decline in Britain due to habitat loss.

It is useful here to summarize some floristic differences between the Folkestone Sands heath-and-bog-complexes and those of the other heath areas in Hampshire:

(a) *Vaccinium oxycoccos* is confined in Hampshire to the Folkestone Sands, extending on this formation to the bogs of south-west Surrey and west Sussex.

(b) *Eriophorum vaginatum* is much more general on Folkestone Sands wet-heath than on the New Forest heaths, whilst it may be extinct on the Tertiary heaths of north-east Hampshire.

(c) *Agrostis curtisii*, on the other hand, is not known on the dry heaths of the Folkestone Sands in Hampshire, although it is common in the New Forest, scattered on the south-east and north-east Tertiary soils, and also occurs at Ludshott Common (see below).

(d) *Myrica gale*, common in the New Forest bogs and occasional in the north-east, is not known on the Folkestone Sands.

Plate 10 The extensive Shortheath Pond, on Folkestone Sand heath in Woolmer Forest, has a rich aquatic and marginal flora with the alien *Sagittaria subulata*; also *Utricularia australis* and *Hypericum elodes*. (*Photo*: A. R. G. Mundell)

(ii) Heaths on the Hythe Beds of the Lower Greensand

One fine area of open heath remains at **Ludshott Common** (8535) (National Trust (NT)). As usual on Hythe Beds, there are no wet-heath (or bog) areas of any extent, but *Agrostis curtisii* has recently been found. **Bramshott Common** (8633) is of similar type but the vegetation is far more disturbed.

The **Sandgate Beds**. There is one very unusual site on the Lower Greensand at **Conford Moor**

(8133) (NT). Most of the common is on Folkestone Sands, but the Sandgate Beds and Bargate Beds beneath produce a calcareous spring-line with fen-type vegetation on the south-west slope. The north-west end of the fen is now the most interesting. Here among *Molinia caerulea* and *Erica tetralix*, or in the adjoining carr, occur such plants as *Epipactis palustris*, *Gymnadenia conopsea* ssp. *densiflora*, *Dactylorhiza praetermissa*, *Eriophorum latifolium*, *Valeriana dioica*, *Menyanthes trifoliata*, *Thelypteris palustris*, *Dryopteris* carthusiana, *Carex hostiana*, *C. viridula* ssp. *oedocarpa*, *C. panicea*, *C. nigra*, *C. pulicaris* and *Anagallis tenella*, with further calcifuge species appearing on the Folkestone Sands above. The site is becoming badly overgrown and is getting drier: it urgently needs restoration of the former grazing but so far political problems have prevented this.

5. Chalk Grassland

The former vast, open, sheep-grazed grasslands of the chalk plateau and scarp country of Hampshire, so clearly shown on the first edition of the Ordnance Survey one-inch maps (1810–17), as stated earlier, have largely disappeared. However, a limited number of fragments remain and it is these which now contain what is left of our chalk-grassland vegetation and flora. Some of the better examples will be considered from west to east: most are now nature reserves of some kind.

Martin Down and Tidpit Common Down (0319 to 0718) (NNR). This, the largest area of chalk grassland left in Hampshire, is also one of the largest left in the whole of England. It is essentially open, undulating, plateau grassland of the type that must once have been general, both on Salisbury Plain and in western and central Hampshire. The terrain is varied by the small escarpment on its eastern part (Tidpit Common Down) and by the ancient earthwork of the Bokerley Ditch. Much of the north-west part of Martin Down, south of the A354 road, was ploughed during the last war, and cultivation of part of it was not totally abandoned until *c*.1957. Further south and east, there is no recent history of cultivation. The flora of Martin Down is very rich; it comprises well over 200 species of vascular plants, and is also locally rich in bryophytes. Much of the vegetation is a *Festuca ovina* community, whilst much of the rest is dominated by *Bromopsis erecta*, but there is much diversity; some areas of *Crataegus monogyna* scrub occur, but *Juniperus communis* is very rare. *Brachypodium pinnatum* is more frequent here than on most other downs in Hampshire.

Noteworthy species to be seen include *Aceras anthropophorum*, *Asperula cynanchica*, *Campanula glomerata*, *Carex humilis*, *Coeloglossum viride*, *Gentianella amarella*, *G. anglica*, *Gymnadenia conopsea*, *Helictotrichon pratense*, *Hippocrepis comosa*, *Koeleria macrantha*, *Ophrys apifera*, *Orchis morio*, *O. ustulata* (locally very abundant in some years), *Phyteuma orbiculare*, *Polygala calcarea*, *Pulsatilla vulgaris* (only Hampshire locality), *Tephroseris integrifolia*, *Serratula tinctoria*, *Spiranthes spiralis*, *Stachys officinalis*, *Orobanche elatior* and *Euphrasia pseudokerneri*, besides most of the commoner calcicole species.

The greater part of the down is well managed by sheep grazing, and it is of particular interest that the strongest population of *Orchis ustulata* is in the north-west part that was cultivated till *c*.1957 but where sheep-grazing since has led to the redevelopment of excellent *Festuca* grassland. Good chalk-heath (with *Erica cinerea*, *Calluna vulgaris* and *Ulex minor*, *Galium saxatile* and *Carex pilulifera*, mixed with *Filipendula vulgaris* and *Carex humilis*) occurs on the summit of Tidpit Common Down.

The **Porton Down** area is MOD property with access by PERMIT ONLY. **Isle of Wight Hill** (2537), in Hampshire, is part of a much larger area of chalk grassland across the boundary in Wiltshire. There are a few notable vascular plants (e.g. *Galium pumilum* and *Iberis amara*, with *Helleborus foetidus* in open scrub-woodland), and the extensive areas of very open, stony grassland have particularly rich lichen- and bryophyte-communities, including fine stands of 16 *Cladonia* species and rare lichens such as *Toninia sedifolia*, *Psora decipiens* and *Rinodina aspersa*. In character, it is reminiscent of parts of the Breckland of East Anglia.

Shipton Bellinger East Down (2345) (MOD). This small area of chalk grassland on a west-facing slope is notable as one of the only two sites now known in Hampshire for the Continental-northern species *Astragalus danicus*, growing among more usual calcicoles like *Helianthemum nummularium* and *Hippocrepis comosa*. It is very precarious here at its southern limit in Britain but is still plentiful just over the Wiltshire border to the west.

Broughton Down (2932) (HWT reserve). This is an excellent area of escarpment grassland, facing north and north-east, with some good plateau grassland at the west end. *Asperula cynanchica*, *Coeloglossum viride*, *Hippocrepis comosa*, *Gymnadenia conopsea*, *Polygala calcarea*, *Tephroseris integrifolia* (abundant some years) and *Thesium humifusum* are all noteworthy here in *Festuca ovina–Bromopsis erecta* grassland, and *Juniperus communis* is locally plentiful. Parts of the down have become heavily invaded by scrub but the HWT is restoring the site to good grassland by its clearance work. Several rare mosses, such as *Weissia sterilis* and *W. tortilis*, occur here with local lichens in open turf.

Kimpton Down (2546) has a limited area of good chalk-grassland with *Polygala calcarea* and *Thesium*, but **Warren Hill** (2547) nearby, though looking promising from a distance, seems to have been treated with fertilizer or herbicides and the *Bromopsis erecta* grassland is very species-poor now.

Danebury Hill (3237) is a PUBLIC OPEN-SPACE and has excellent chalk-grassland on the eastern slopes and also south of the Iron Age hill-fort, with a good range of *Festuca ovina*-community species; also much *Coeloglossum viride*, *Gymnadenia conopsea*, *Helianthemum nummularium*, *Hippocrepis comosa*, *Polygala calcarea* (very fine) and *Thesium humifusum* in abundance. However, *Orchis ustulata*, locally frequent in the 1950s, is now very rare, being represented by only a few individuals and not visible every year. *Tephroseris integrifolia*, abundant in 1955, cannot now be found though the site (south of the hill-fort) seems unaltered.

Chilbolton West Down (3838), a Country Park area, has good, grassland flora with *Polygala calcarea*, *Tephroseris integrifolia*, *Serratula tinctoria*, *Campanula glomerata* (very fine on west slope), and *Saxifraga granulata* (on gravel drift).

Farley Mount (4029) is an extensive, well-managed Country Park with some fine areas of short turf. It is perhaps more notable for its lichens and bryophytes, however, than for any special vascular plants, but good communities occur with a diversity of calcicole species.

Magdalen Hill Down (5029) was once notable for its chalk-grassland plants and butterflies but became very overgrown with scrub. Today, however, it is managed by Butterfly Conservation (BC) (the British Butterfly Conservation Society), which has carried out an excellent scrub-clearance programme, and several of the more exacting species, including butterflies, are now beginning to reappear.

St Catherine's Hill and Twyford Down (4827 to 4927) has some excellent chalk-grassland, sadly cut through (in spite of much protest) by the new M3 route. However, it seems that much of the better grassland (with *Herminium monorchis* and *Serratula tinctoria*) will escape this mutilation.

Abbotstone Down (5836) is another good, though small, relic of plateau chalk-grassland, now managed as a Country Park. It has most of the commoner calcicoles, but is outstandingly rich in bryophytes, including the spectacular moss *Rhodobryum roseum*; also *Thuidium abietinum* ssp. *hystricosum*, *T. philibertii*, *Phascum curvicolle* and *Entodon concinnus*, all very local species now.

Beacon Hill, Warnford (6022) is a NNR and a quite outstanding site. It has both extensive *Bromopsis erecta* grassland (with much *Phyteuma orbiculare*, *Campanula glomerata* and *Scabiosa columbaria*) and also short *Festuca ovina* turf with locally abundant *Tephroseris integrifolia*, *Euphrasia pseudokerneri*, *Helianthemum nummularium* and *Hippocrepis comosa* populations. There is a fair range of orchids on Beacon Hill, including *Aceras anthropophorum*, *Coeloglossum viride*, *Spiranthes spiralis* and *Gymnadenia conopsea*. However, these seem to vary much from year to year. The grazing (by sheep) is

now satisfactory but the site has perhaps been overgrazed in the last few years. *Juniperus communis* is quite absent. The hill is interesting particularly because there are slopes of all aspects from south by east round to north, enabling marked variations in the vegetation to be studied. *Thesium humifusum* and *Polygala calcarea* are apparently absent. The variety of *Dactylorhiza fuchsii* with wholly purple labella and largely purple leaves occurs here.

Old Winchester Hill (6420) is a NNR, like Beacon Hill, and resembles it in several ways, particularly in having warm southern slopes and cool, damp northern coombes, the latter rich in bryophytes. *Phyteuma orbiculare* and *Hippocrepis comosa* are locally abundant here as on Beacon Hill but, unlike that site, it seems to have no *Helianthemum nummularium* in its turf. It does, however, have a fine population of *Juniperus communis* and a small colony of *Aceras anthropophorum*. *Tephroseris integrifolia*, however, appears not to have been seen recently.

Butser Hill and the adjacent **Oxenbourne Down**, (7020 to 7119), are found within the Queen Elizabeth Country Park and have a splendid range of chalk-grassland communities that cover all possible aspects of slope on or in its various coombes and ridges. The summit, at 270m the highest point on the South Downs escarpment in either Hampshire or Sussex, used to have good chalk heath in the 1950s, but it was later ploughed and cultivated, and now carries monotonous 'improved' grassland on the acid Clay-with-flints capping. However, the Country Park management plan to recreate some chalk heath here; calcifuge species such as *Calluna vulgaris*, *Rumex acetosella* and *Digitalis purpurea* still survive locally.

The vascular plant flora of Butser Hill is interesting with much *Phyteuma orbiculare*, *Campanula glomerata* and *Euphrasia pseudokerneri* locally, and *Hippocrepis comosa* and *Helianthemum nummularium* locally common on a south-westerly-aspect spur. Perhaps the main botanical interest of the hill lies in its bryophyte and lichen floras, the richest of any Hampshire chalk-grassland. Indeed, Butser has probably the richest, terricolous lichen flora of any single site on the English chalk.

The spectacular coombe of **Rake Bottom** has very steep north-east-facing slopes with bryophyte communities more characteristic of the limestone gorges of the Mendips and the Pennines. Here occur *Scapania aspera*, *Porella arboris-vitae*, *Frullania tamarisci*, *Neckera crispa* and *Bryum pallens*, in among carpets of *Rhytidiadelphus* species and *Hylocomium splendens*.

In complete contrast, the warm south-facing

Plate 11   North-facing chalk scarp of Broughton Down SSSI where much of the invading scrub is now being cleared to improve this fine chalk grassland Reserve; *Tephroseris integrifolia*, *Thesium humifusum* and *Polygala calcarea* are in abundance. (*Photo*: R. B. Gibbons)

Plate 12   Old Winchester Hill, a NNR on chalk with fine grasslands: *Juniperus* and *Aceras anthropophorum* occur here. (*Photo*: A. R. G. Mundell)

slopes have a thermophilous bryophyte flora which includes the largely Mediterranean *Pleurochaete squarrosa* in its only Hampshire locality, with other warmth-loving species such as the mosses *Weissia tortilis*, *Entodon concinnus*, *Phascum curvicolle* and *Thuidium abietinum* ssp. *hystricosum*, and the lichens *Cladonia convoluta* (its only Hampshire site), *C. foliacea* and *C. pocillum* among others.

The enclosed coombes of the south face have the remarkable moss *Rhodobryum roseum* (like small, green, many-petalled flowers) on the ant-hills. The turf in between, grazed only by rabbits, has the very local *Tortella tortuosa* and a profusion of small lichens on bare soil and on chalk pebbles and flints.

Butser Hill has some 125 bryophytes recorded (86 of these on the ground) and 82 lichens in the chalk grassland or on stones. These totals have not been reached in any other English site so far. Butser Hill lacks, however, many of the more local vascular plants of chalk grassland such as *Tephroseris integrifolia*, *Thesium humifusum*, *Polygala calcarea*, *Filipendula vulgaris*, and many orchid species.

Buriton chalk pit (7319) is a small site with *Bromopsis–Festuca* turf above and east of a quarry. This turf has *Herminium monorchis* and *Ophrys insectifera* in quantity – species not yet found on Butser Hill.

Ports Down (6306 to 6706) is a PUBLIC OPEN SPACE. This narrow ridge of chalk, isolated from the main chalk area to the north by a belt of Eocene strata some 6km wide, bears chalk grassland on its south-facing slope. Though Portsmouth suburbs adjoin the whole of its south side, and though it is put under much pressure by walkers, it retains some areas of surprisingly high-quality grassland. *Centaurea calcitrapa* and *Phyteuma orbiculare* have not been seen recently, but short, open *Festuca* turf (kept short partly by the passage of feet) still has much *Thesium humifusum*, *Euphrasia pseudokerneri* and *Spiranthes spiralis* with *Cirsium acaule* and *Helictotrichon pratense*.

Very local lichens of open calcareous ground, such as *Catapyrenium squamulosum*, *Cladonia pocillum*, *Leptogium schraderi* and *Toninia sedifolia*, occur here still.

Elsewhere on Ports Down, *Campanula glomerata*, *Hippocrepis comosa*, *Gentianella amarella* and *Ophrys insectifera* are still to be found. Much of the Down, however, is now coarse grass or scrub with many alien or ruderal species present.

Coulters Dean (7419) (PRIVATE, access by application to HWT only) is just south of the brow of the South Downs escarpment. There are old accounts of it early this century in Tansley (1939), writing on the chalk, when it was clearly recognized as a former arable site. Today it is a fine piece of chalk grassland with much *Phyteuma orbiculare* and *Campanula glomerata*, as well as a good variety of butterflies.

Catherington Down (6914), a small HWT reserve on the west-facing slope of a dry valley on the chalk, has a flora similar to that of Coulters Dean.

Passing further north, one comes to the generally east-facing escarpment of the Hampshire Hangers north of Petersfield. From old maps it is clear that much of this scarp was formerly open downland; much remained in this condition until *c.*1920, as is clear from the writings of the poet, Edward Thomas. Today, only fragments of grassland remain on the scarp, as at **Shoulder of Mutton Hill** (7328) and **Wheatham Hill** (7427), with a fair range of more widespread chalk grassland species, including *Juniperus communis*. These areas are under HCC control and, at Wheatham Hill particularly, strenuous efforts are being made to maintain the grassland and the *Juniperus* by selective removal of scrub, yew, and some of the beech inadvisedly planted here so extensively some 25–30 years ago. *Helianthemum nummularium*, *Asperula cynanchica*, *Centaurium pulchellum* and the local moss *Thuidium abietinum* ssp. *hystricosum* are among the species present. There are few orchids apart from *Dactylorhiza fuchsii* and *Platanthera chlorantha* in the grassland. *Polygala calcarea* and *Hippocrepis comosa* seem to be absent.

Further north, **Noar Hill**, or more strictly **High Common**, (7431 and into the adjoining 1km squares 7331 and 7432) is of different character. This site is a series of ancient chalk-workings with ridges and banks in between them. It has a remarkable orchid flora, including *Herminium monorchis* (more than 10,000 inflorescences in good years), *Coeloglossum viride*, *Gymnadenia conopsea* ssp. *conopsea*, *Dactylorhiza fuchsii*, *Anacamptis pyramidalis*, *Ophrys apifera*, *O. insectifera*, *Listera ovata* and *Spiranthes spiralis*. Other interesting species in the short *Festuca* turf include *Carex pulicaris* (at the foot of a bank where presumably there is some sub-surface water-seepage), *Gentianella anglica* (on scree) and *Campanula glomerata*. *Helianthemum nummularium* is quite rare, and *Hippocrepis comosa*, *Asperula cynanchica*, and *Polygala calcarea* are absent, but *Juniperus communis* is locally common. *Orobanche elatior* occurs here on *Centaurea scabiosa* in what is a very isolated site in east Hampshire.

Finally, there are several important chalk-grassland sites in the far north. **Beacon Hill, south of Burghclere**, (4557) is a fine hill with an interesting flora, including much *Juniperus communis*, all the usual chalk grasses, *Filipendula vulgaris*, *Coeloglossum viride*, *Hippocrepis comosa*, *Helianthemum nummularium*, *Ophrys apifera*, *Serratula tinctoria*, *Dactylorhiza*

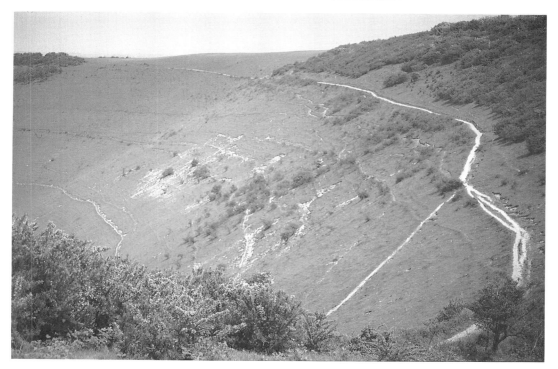

Plate 13   Rake Bottom, Butser Hill – one of the longest and deepest coombes on the English chalk. Its north-east-facing slope (foreground) is extremely rich in local, chalk-grassland bryophytes. (*Photo*: A. R. G. Mundell)

Plate 14   View from Noar Hill, south-west of Selborne. This fine chalk-grassland site is notable for its rich flora including many orchids (such as *Herminium monorchis* in plenty) and for its Junipers. (*Photo*: W. & C. Wain)

41

praetermissa var. *junialis*, and the very local (in Hampshire) *Cirsium eriophorum*. *Phyteuma orbiculare* and *Campanula glomerata* do not seem to be present, but *Polygala calcarea* is found here. The best area is on the earthworks of the hill-fort.

Downland at **Ashmansworth** (4158) has one of the few Hampshire populations of *Gentianella germanica* and its hybrid with *G. amarella*.

A very interesting site 2km to the east is **Ladle Hill** (4857) (PRIVATE), where the richest grassland is on the south bank of the Iron Age hill-fort. Here, in short *Festuca ovina* turf, *Hippocrepis comosa*, *Helianthemum nummularium*, *Tephroseris integrifolia*, and *Polygala calcarea* are plentiful in early June. In late July, *Orchis ustulata* (the late-flowering form) may be in some numbers, together with *Anacamptis pyramidalis* and (more locally) the very rare *Galium pumilum*. *Herminium monorchis* was noted on the downland to the west some years ago, but has not been seen more recently.

Similar-looking downland occurs eastward on Watership Down (4957) and especially west of **White Hill** (5156), but so far these areas have proved less productive.

The Harrow Way, north of Overton (5050), is a surviving stretch of an ancient drove-way with a rich, chalk-grassland flora, including *Coeloglossum viride*, *Gentianella amarella*, *Helianthemum nummularium*, *Hippocrepis comosa*, *Koeleria macrantha*, *Polygala calcarea* and *Euphrasia pseudokerneri* in a sward of *Bromopsis erecta*. It is not grazed by stock but rabbits still seem to maintain the short, species-rich turf.

Micheldever Spoil Heaps (5143, through 5144 and western edge of 5244), a HWT reserve, access by PERMIT ONLY, is another site of artificial origin, formed where chalk was dumped during the digging of a railway tunnel. It is notable for the abundance of *Teucrium botrys* (one of our rarest British plants) and locally of *Vulpia unilateralis* and *Potentilla neumanniana* (mainly a species of the Mendips and further north). The open nature of the sward has resulted in a rich bryophyte flora.

Plate 15   The Micheldever Spoil Heaps, created from chalk when the London–Southampton railway was cut, have a notable flora including the national rarity *Teucrium botrys* and much else. (*Photo*: A. R. G. Mundell)

6. Fens, Fen-Meadows and neutral-to-acid Grassland (Fig.8)

(i) Calcareous Fens and Fen-meadows

Apart from the calcareous mires of the New Forest (already described above), Hampshire is still remarkably rich in small valley-fens, compared with other southern counties. Some of these have survived because they have been (or still are) common land. Some are in the major river-valleys; others are associated with calcareous spring areas. In Sussex and Surrey nearly all such sites have been 'improved' or destroyed. Similar ones, however, survive about Cothill in Oxfordshire (formerly in north Berkshire) and more widely in Norfolk and N Suffolk.

The richest site of all in terms of quality of vegetation is probably **Stockbridge North Fen** (3535) (PRIVATE). This is an area of ancient peat-cuttings in the valley of the R. Test, immediately north of Stockbridge. It is a flood-plain type of fen rather than a spring-fed one, though it is likely that some of its water is derived from the spring-line along the edge of the Test Valley. Such sites were no doubt once far more extensive and continuous along the valleys of Hampshire's calcareous rivers.

The fen contains a series of more or less rectangular, very wet depressions, with higher strips or 'baulks' between them, no doubt where peat was left uncut to allow access to the turbary areas. The vegetation is essentially sedge-dominated, with much *Juncus subnodulosus* and *Phragmites australis*. Twelve species of *Carex* occur here, most notably (in abundance) the rare *Carex diandra* (which now has only three sites in the whole of south-east England, all of which are in Hampshire), together with *Carex acutiformis, C. distans, C. disticha, C. flacca, C. hostiana, C. viridula* ssp. *brachyrrhyncha, C. nigra, C. ovalis, C. panicea, C. paniculata, C. riparia* and *C. rostrata*. Also here among the Cyperaceae are *Eleocharis palustris, Eriophorum angustifolium* and the rare calcicole *E. latifolium*.

Other vascular plants of significance include *Anagallis tenella, Briza media, Centaurea nigra* (radiate form of old fen-meadows), *Epipactis palustris* (thousands of inflorescences), *Galium uliginosum, Geum rivale, Gymnadenia conopsea* ssp. *densiflora* (in some numbers on baulks), *Juncus subnodulosus, Menyanthes trifoliata, Dactylorhiza fuchsii, D. incarnata* ssp. *incarnata, D. praetermissa, D. praetermissa* var. *junialis, Pedicularis palustris, Ranunculus lingua,*

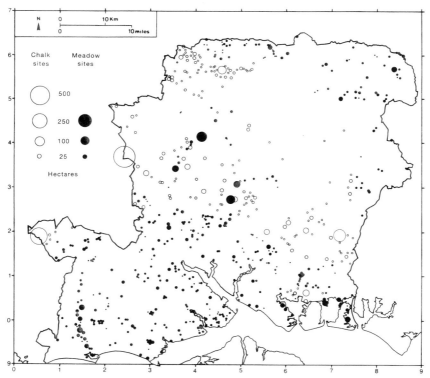

Fig. 8 Chalk grasslands, which formerly covered wide areas of the chalk plateaux and escarpments in the county, are now mainly reduced to small 'unimproved' fragments. Likewise, most old meadows are now mere fragments in the river valleys. This map is based on material supplied by Hampshire County Council

Plate 16   Stockbridge North Fen is one of the finest calcareous valley fens in S. England, with an abundance of local or rare *Carex* spp. and orchids such as *Epipactis palustris* and *Gymnadenia conopsea* ssp. *densiflora*. (*Photo*: B. M. & A. J. Rackham)

Thalictrum flavum, Triglochin palustre and *Valeriana dioica*.

Notable fen bryophytes include *Drepanocladus revolvens, Campylium elodes, C. stellatum, Calliergon giganteum* and *Plagiomnium elatum*.

Chilbolton meadows (3840) is another Test Valley fen-meadow complex, but of wet meadows rather than fen. It is quite rich, but much less so than Stockbridge North Fen, lacking *Epipactis palustris, Gymnadenia conopsea, Carex diandra, C. viridula* ssp. *brachyrrhyncha* and *Ranunculus lingua*. Unlike Stockbridge North Fen, however, it has *Eleocharis uniglumis* and *Blysmus compressus*.

Bransbury Common (4141) (PRIVATE) is, in contrast, a very large site with an extraordinary range of plant communities. In total some 230 species are recorded here. The western part consists of rough, cattle-grazed, alluvial meadows along the north side of the R. Dever, a tributary of the R. Test, extending over to the Test banks themselves to the north-west, where the meadows are rather drier. North-eastwards, the meadows become wetter and more fen-like with numerous *Carex* spp., and much *Juncus articulatus* and *J. subnodulosus*. Here there are wet, open, flushed areas with *Anagallis tenella, Eleocharis*

quinqueflora and the largest population of *Gymnadenia conopsea* ssp. *densiflora* known in the county. On drier but calcareous banks on its west side, *G. conopsea* ssp. *conopsea* occurs along with several hybrids between the two subspecies.

Among the sedges in the wetter area there occur *Carex diandra, C. viridula* ssp. *brachyrrhyncha, C. hostiana, C. distans, C. pulicaris* and one of the two Hampshire populations of *C. dioica*, which is locally abundant. Further east, closer to the R. Dever, there is a lower-lying area of very wet, peaty, mossy fen, with much *Juncus subnodulosus, Epipactis palustris, Pedicularis palustris, Menyanthes trifoliata, Phragmites australis*, and more *Gymnadenia conopsea* ssp. *densiflora*, as well as *Thalictrum flavum*. A less wet meadow to the south has *Blysmus compressus*.

North of the wet fen, there are a number of low, sinuous ridges of chalk (possibly the remains of pingo formation in periglacial conditions) where quite rich chalk-grassland occurs. Here are *Asperula cynanchica, Carlina vulgaris, Cirsium acaule, Festuca ovina, Gentianella amarella, Helianthemum nummularium, Hippocrepis comosa, Koeleria macrantha, Sanguisorba minor* ssp. *minor* and *Thesium humifusum*. Other ridges nearby are of leached, sandy material with *Calluna vulgaris*, *Carex pilulifera*, *Genista anglica*, *Pedicularis sylvatica*, and *Potentilla erecta*. Still further north, there are areas of old oak–holly–birch woodland with some beech.

It will be apparent that Bransbury Common is of very unusual character. There are similar places in central Norfolk where fen and calcareous Breckland communities occur intermixed in a mosaic on periglacially patterned terrain.

The Itchen Valley seems (from old records) to have had communities rather similar to the Test fen-meadow complexes in the past, but today it is much altered. The richest remaining fen-meadow areas are some of the former water-meadows – north of Winchester (**Winnall Moors** (4930), with *Carex elata* and *Sagina nodosa*), south of Winchester (**below Otterbourne** (4723)), and also above **Ovington** (5631) where such plants as *Blysmus compressus*, *Dactylorhiza praetermissa*, and *Geum rivale* are abundant, but the more exacting orchids and *Carex* species seem now not to occur.

In the north-east of the county there are still excellent small valley-fen areas associated with the chalk springs that feed the R. Loddon and the Whitewater. These were more extensive until the construction of the M3 motorway destroyed much of them by drainage and dumping of chalk spoil.

Mapledurwell Fen (6752), though now minute in area, is still extremely rich and well managed by HWT (access by PERMIT ONLY). Rough meadow with *Geum rivale* and *Juncus subnodulosus* grades down into a spring-fed area to the north-west. The Trust now has this well grazed and/or mown, which has led to the reappearance of several species apparently lost for some time.

The flora here includes *Anagallis tenella*, *Blysmus compressus*, *Carex dioica*, *C. disticha*, *C. hostiana*, *C. nigra*, *C. panicea*, *C. paniculata*, *C. pulicaris*, *Dactylorhiza praetermissa*, *D. traunsteineri* (plentiful in May 1992), *Epipactis palustris*, *Gymnadenia conopsea* ssp. *densiflora*, *Hydrocotyle vulgaris*, *Menyanthes trifoliata*, *Molinia caerulea*, *Pinguicula vulgaris*, *Primula veris*, *Succisa pratensis*, *Triglochin palustre* and *Valeriana dioica*. The *Epipactis* and *Gymnadenia* occur outside the reserve in another flush not far away, but further nearby fens (though extensive) are now exceedingly overgrown with *Epilobium hirsutum* and *Carex acutiformis* due to lack of grazing. Fen bryophytes such as *Campylium stellatum*, *Climacium dendroides* and *Plagiomnium elatum* are still plentiful at Mapledurwell.

Greywell Moors (7150 through to 7251) is a more extensive valley-fen at the head of the R. Whitewater. Over the years this site deteriorated from open, rich, *Juncus subnodulosus*-dominated fen to an extensive area of alder–sallow woodland with dense stands of *Carex acutiformis* in the remaining open areas. Fortunately two small areas remained rich and diverse, one because of its wetness, the other because it continued to be grazed by cattle. The HWT is now undertaking extensive clearance of the carr woodland, including mowing of the *Carex acutiformis* stands, and is reintroducing grazing wherever feasible. Many of the fen bryophytes have declined, but the rich areas still contain such vascular plant species as *Anagallis tenella*, *Briza media*, *Carex diandra*, *C. disticha*, *C. echinata*, *C. flava* x *viridula*, *C. hostiana*, *C. nigra*, *C. panicea*, *C. pulicaris*, *C. rostrata*, *C. viridula* ssp. *brachyrrhyncha*, *Dactylorhiza praetermissa* (and hybrids with the now-lost *D. traunsteineri*), *Danthonia decumbens*, *Epipactis palustris*, *Eriophorum angustifolium*, *E. latifolium*, *Galium uliginosum*, *Geum rivale*, *Gymnadenia conopsea* ssp. *densiflora*, *Juncus subnodulosus*, *Menyanthes trifoliata*, *Pedicularis palustris*, *Rhinanthus minor*, *Stachys officinalis*, *Succisa pratensis*, *Triglochin palustre*, *Thelypteris palustris* and *Valeriana dioica*.

Greywell Moors is now known as the Ted Wallace Reserve, in memory of the eminent botanist, the late E. C. Wallace, who did much work here and loved the place. It is hoped that, over the years, the management work now in hand will lead to restoration of the former fen-communities over much of the former fen area. *Eriophorum gracile* and *Cladium mariscus* have not been seen for a number of years, but creation of peat-pits could well lead to the reappearance of at least the former.

To the north of Greywell Moors, the grounds of the **Pumping Station** (723514) (PRIVATE) have a number of the Greywell Moors' species in quantity, particularly the orchids, and north of that there are further, fine fen-meadows with much *Eriophorum latifolium* and *Epipactis palustris*.

The HWT reserve at **North Warnborough Common (Warnborough Greens)** (7352) comprises a fine series of quite wet, calcareous fen-meadows and is almost as species-rich as Greywell Moors. A long history of common grazing has resulted in a more grassy sward without *Juncus subnodulosus*, *Phragmites australis* and *Pedicularis palustris*. However, it does have *Blysmus compressus*, the Hampshire rarity *Juncus compressus*, *Eleocharis uniglumis* and quantities of fine *Dactylorhiza incarnata* ssp. *incarnata*, as well as many of the sedges of less swampy ground present at Greywell. After a period of neglect and coarse-herb invasion it is now well managed by the HWT. The interesting, radiate form of *Centaurea nigra* is again a feature, as it is in all the old, Hampshire calcareous meadows, along with *Achillea ptarmica*, *Festuca pratensis* and *Stachys officinalis*.

Plate 17 Greywell Moors, a HWT Reserve, is still very rich in local fen species despite having become very overgrown. Intensive management work is now gradually restoring its former glory. (*Photo*: A. J. P. Branson)

Tichborne Common (5731), east of the R. Itchen, has a small fen-meadow area fed by chalk springs and grazed by cattle, which is still quite a rich site. Fen species include *Anagallis tenella, Caltha palustris, Carex viridula* ssp. *oedocarpa, C. disticha, C. flacca, C. hostiana, C. nigra, C. panicea, C. viridula* ssp. *brachyrrhyncha, Dactylorhiza incarnata, Epipactis palustris, Equisetum telmateia, Festuca pratensis, Galium uliginosum, Geranium pratense, Geum rivale, Hydrocotyle vulgaris, Iris pseudacorus, Juncus subnodulosus, Leontodon hispidus, Lychnis floscuculi, Menyanthes trifoliata, Pinguicula vulgaris, Rhinanthus minor, Senecio aquaticus, Silaum silaus, Triglochin palustre* and *Valeriana dioica*.

South of the main chalk outcrop is **The Moors, Bishop's Waltham** (5616) (HCC LNR, parts of which have restricted access by PERMIT ONLY). This is a complex of alder carr, spring-fen, and old meadows of varied lime content. It is a site of outstanding importance.

A number of springs arise from the chalk (or chalky head) which produce a series of small streams that join up to flow into the Mill Pond. This central area of The Moors is covered with peat, of a sedge type, that is up to 1.75m deep and is very wet. It carries alder woodland that is much more extensive now than early last century, and contains the bryophytes *Hookeria lucens* and *Trichocolea tomentella*, both rare

46

in Hampshire outside the New Forest, and such ancient woodland species as *Polygonatum multiflorum*, *Galium odoratum*, *Ruscus aculeatus* and *Sanicula europea* in the better-drained parts.

To the east, there is a remarkable area dominated by tussocky *Molinia caerulea* with *Erica tetralix*, *Genista tinctoria* and *Sphagnum palustre* on the hummocks. Between the hummocks occur *Epipactis palustris*, *Gymnadenia conopsea* ssp. *densiflora*, *Dactylorhiza maculata*, *D. fuchsii*, *D. praetermissa*, *Stachys officinalis* and *Valeriana dioica*. Further to the east, there are strong calcareous springs which have the tufa-forming moss *Cratoneuron commutatum* var. *commutatum*, very rare in Hampshire, and a fine range of *Carex* species including *C. hostiana*, *C. viridula* ssp. *brachyrrhyncha*, *C. pulicaris* and *C. rostrata*.

Stretching east and north of these interesting springs, there is extensive fen-meadow with *Blysmus compressus*, *Carex acutiformis*, *Cirsium dissectum*, *Eleocharis uniglumis*, and other fen species. This grades into drier meadows with *Achillea ptarmica*, *Festuca arundinacea*, *F. pratensis*, *Genista tinctoria*, *Oenanthe pimpinelloides*, *Senecio aquaticus*, *Silaum silaus*, *Sison amomum* and *Stachys officinalis*.

To the north and east, there is a very fine series of drier, old hay-meadows, the more acid of which have *Oenanthe pimpinelloides* in vast abundance, with much *Vicia cracca*. One has much *Orchis morio*; other, more calcareous meadows (where chalky head is close to the surface) have such plants as *Briza media*, *Bromus commutatus*, *Cirsium acaule*, *Festuca rubra*, *Helictotrichon pubescens*, *Knautia arvensis*, *Leontodon hispidus*, *Linum catharticum*, *Pimpinella saxifraga*, *Primula veris*, *Succisa pratensis* and *Trisetum flavescens* as well as many butterflies. This is only an outline of a remarkable site with a total of 283 recorded species of vascular plants and many, very local, fen bryophytes.

Lye Heath, east of Southwick (6408) (PRIVATE), lies wholly on Tertiary deposits, but is clearly more or less calcareous in some of the flushes where *Briza media*, *Epipactis palustris*, *Juncus subnodulosus*, *Anagallis tenella* and *Pedicularis palustris* occur, while *Oenanthe pimpinelloides* and *Genista tinctoria* are locally abundant in less-flushed areas of meadow.

(ii) Old, more-acidic Meadows

There are still many areas of ancient meadow on less peaty, or non-peaty, more-acidic soils in Hampshire, particularly in comparison with other surrounding counties. The finest series of all, considered of prime

Plate 18   At Bishop's Waltham Moors, another fine calcareous spring-fen fed by chalk springs, *Hippuris vulgaris* can be seen in the pond; ancient meadows occur to the rear. (*Photo*: A. R. G. Mundell)

Plate 19   Ashford Hill Meadows is probably the finest meadow-complex in terms of flora and range of vegetation-types in southern Britain with over 320 species of vascular plants, including *Genista tinctoria* (seen here). (*Photo*: P. R. Brough)

national importance, is the **Ashford Hill Meadows** NNR (5662). The total number of vascular plants recorded in this site is 321. There is a great range of old, meadow-communities here, ranging from quite dry grassland on loam or sand to quite waterlogged areas on heavy clay, and from moderately-acidic areas to quite calcareous, flushed areas.

It is possible to mention only a selection of the more interesting species present which include *Achillea ptarmica, Anagallis tenella, Berula erecta, Briza media, Bromus racemosus, Carex disticha, C. echinata, C. ovalis, C. panicea, C. pulicaris, Cirsium dissectum, Conopodium majus, Dactylorhiza maculata* ssp. *ericetorum, Elymus caninus, Eriophorum angusti-folium, Epipactis palustris, Euphrasia anglica, Galium saxatile, G. uliginosum, G. verum, Geum rivale, Hordeum secalinum, Hottonia palustris, Hydrocotyle vulgaris, Isolepis setacea, Lathyrus linifolius, Leontodon hispidus, Molinia caerulea, Nardus stricta, Orobanche rapum-genistae, Pedicularis palustris, P. sylvatica, Primula veris, Pulicaria vulgaris, Rhinanthus minor, Sanguisorba minor* ssp. *minor, S. officinalis, Serratula tinctoria, Silaum silaus, Stellaria palustris, Stachys officinalis, Thymus pulegioides, Triglochin palustre, Valeriana dioica* and *Viola palustris.*

It will be obvious that Ashford Hill contains a remarkable range of meadow communities, perhaps the most diverse of any one complex in England. Of those 60 species regarded as indicative of ancient unimproved grasslands on the Tertiary soils of Hampshire, 47 occur at Ashford Hill.

Other old, acidic meadows with some of the 'ancient meadow' species that are present at Ashford Hill occur near **Bentley** Railway Station (7942); north of **Greatham** church (7631); **Ron Ward's Meadow** (6060); **east of the Mount, Highclere** (4361); **Hall's Farm, Bramshill** (7462); and **Minley** (8157).

On the Berkshire border, north of **Stratfield Saye** (PRIVATE), occurs our only remaining population of *Fritillaria meleagris*; there is a far richer fritillary meadow in the adjacent field in Berkshire.

(iii) Grasslands fringing the New Forest

Within the farmlands scattered discretely around the New Forest is a remarkable collection of unimproved grasslands. Together with similar vegetation within the open Forest, these amount to a nationally impor-tant area of acid-to-neutral grasslands which have little in common with the typical unimproved grass-lands of lowland England. They do, however, have strong links with similar vegetation in the south-west of England and Wales.

These grasslands are strongly associated with the younger strata of the Hampshire Basin, particularly those between the Bracklesham Beds and the Headon Beds. Smaller concentrations of similar grasslands occur on these beds elsewhere in Hampshire. The major features are the mixture of sand and clay bands found in these strata. These produce frequent spring-lines which hinder agricultural improvement as well as producing very varied soil conditions. The natural infertility of soils developed in these strata, and the associated superficial gravels and head deposits, also mitigate against agricultural improvement.

The core vegetation communities of these grass-lands are herb-rich, permanent pastures on the drier brown earths and stagno-gleys, and a complex range of wet acid-grasslands on gleys and peats. The former is *Cynosurus cristatus–Centaurea nigra* grassland – *Danthonia decumbens* sub-community. These are usually dominated by *Agrostis capillaris* and *Festuca*

rubra but with a high cover of associated herbs. Typical species of well-developed stands include *Briza media, Carex pallescens, Danthonia decumbens, Genista tinctoria, Lathyrus linifolius, Orchis morio, Pedicularis sylvatica, Polygala serpyllifolia, Senecio erucifolius, Serratula tinctoria, Silaum silaus, Stachys officinalis* and *Succisa pratensis.* Species found more rarely include *Ophioglossum vulgatum, Polygala vulgaris, Primula veris* and *Thymus pulegiöides. Oenanthe pimpinelloides* is often found but is usually more abundant in partially-improved pastures.

The character of the wet grassland is more complex. Moderately-grazed, rush-dominated stands are mostly *Juncus effusus/acutiflorus–Galium palustre* rush pasture – *J. acutiflorus* sub-community, with the richest stands usually lacking *J. effusus.* Lightly-grazed grassland dominated by *Molinia caerulea* is especially variable, with both *Molinia–Cirsium dissectum* fen meadow – *Juncus acutiflorus–Erica tetralix* sub-community and *Molinia–Potentilla erecta* mire – *Anthoxanthum odoratum* sub-community usually present. Pony-grazed grasslands lack any tall dominants and consist of a species-rich mixture of *Agrostis canina* and *Carex* species. This latter vegetation is the

Plate 20 Ancient Breamore Marsh, still grazed by cattle and geese, is noted for the quantities of the rarity *Cyperus fuscus* that appear on the cracked mud around the ponds as water-levels fall in late summer. (*Photo*: R. B. Gibbons)

main community of the winter-wet Forest lawns and appears to be an acid equivalent of the base-rich flood-pasture described as *Cynosurus cristatus–Caltha palustris* grassland.

Characteristic species of these wet grasslands include *Achillea ptarmica*, *Anagallis tenella*, *Carex echinata*, *C. hostiana*, *C. nigra*, *C. panicea*, *C. pulicaris*, *C. viridula* ssp. *oedocarpa*, *Cirsium dissectum*, *Dactylorhiza maculata*, *D. praetermissa*, *Hydrocotyle vulgaris*, *Nardus stricta* and *Pedicularis sylvatica*. Less frequent species include *Carex montana* which occurs in the drier parts of a few *Molinia caerulea* grasslands.

Within these frequently found communities, types of vegetation occurring more rarely are of even greater diversity. Very dry soils support parched acid-grassland, mainly *Festuca ovina–Agrostis capillaris–Rumex acetosella* grassland – *Hypochaeris radicata* sub-community, which provide a habitat for spring annuals such as *Trifolium subterraneum*. In the **Avon Valley** the more extensive, dry grasslands include *Carex arenaria*, *Crassula tillaea* and *Trifolium* species.

In contrast, the wettest parts of spring-lines often support mire communities. Acid waters support *Sphagnum* mires, mainly *Narthecium ossifragum–Sphagnum papillosum* – *Rhynchospora alba–Sphagnum auriculatum* sub-community, in nutrient-poor situations and *Carex echinata–Sphagnum recurvum* mire – *Juncus acutiflorus* sub-community, in more fertile acid springs. The former includes species such as *Drosera rotundifolia*, *Eleocharis multicaulis*, *Myrica gale*, *Schoenus nigricans* and *Rhynchospora fusca*, and the latter *Viola palustris* and occasionally *Carex curta* and *C. rostrata*.

Much rarer are base-rich flushes, but an extraordinary series of base-rich mires occurs in the **Cadland** area (4599 to 4501). Here base-rich fen-meadow – mainly *Juncus subnodulosus–Cirsium palustre* fen-meadow with species such as *Carex disticha* – occurs in close juxtaposition with acid communities such as *Juncus–Galium* rush-pasture, *Carex–Sphagnum* mire and *Narthecium–Sphagnum* mire.

An interesting example occurs in species-rich heathy *Molinia caerulea–Cirsium dissectum* fen-meadow on **Upper Pennington Common** (2995) where small, marshy flushes have species such as *Eleocharis quinqueflora*, *Eriophorum latifolium* and *Pinguicula lusitanica* in brown moss-mats composed of species such as *Campylium stellatum*, *Drepanocladus revolvens* and *Scorpidium scorpioides*. Identical flushes are also found in the south of the Forest itself.

In some sites, the grassland grades into heath which underlines the close links such communities have with the vegetation of parts of the New Forest.

7. Aquatic Vegetation of Waterways

Being a coastal county, Hampshire contains a number of rivers which both rise and enter the sea entirely within the county (Fig.9, p.52). The largest of these are the chalk rivers, notably the Test, the Itchen and the Meon, together with smaller clay rivers of the Hampshire Basin, particularly in the New Forest. The north and east of the county have the headwaters of the Thames tributaries and the R. Rother respectively, and in the west of the county is the great flood-plain of the lower R. Avon. In addition to these natural rivers, Hampshire shares the man-made Basingstoke Canal with Surrey.

The **chalk rivers** of Hampshire are renowned for the quality and clarity of their water. They are typified by *Ranunculus penicillatus* ssp. *pseudofluitans*, *Hippuris vulgaris*, *Oenanthe fluviatilis* and *Rorippa nasturtium-aquaticum*, with the bryophyte *Fontinalis antipyretica* particularly where hard substrates are present. Chalk rivers have escaped the worst excesses of land-drainage engineering, but have become progressively modified to meet the needs of fisheries, most notably by mechanical weed-cutting, the systematic narrowing of channels by chalk-infill, and by the excavation of salmon-holding pools.

The **New Forest rivers** rise in seepages and wetlands of Forest mires, the upper watercourses often being indistinguishable from the general wetlands. These watercourses are very diverse but include a variety of species including *Eleogiton fluitans*, *Myriophyllum alterniflorum*, *Apium inundatum* and *Potamogeton polygonifolius*. Where these small streams gather, they may form distinct rivers within narrow, grassy flood-plains. The rare, marginal grass *Leersia oryzoides* was formerly found beside the swampy margins of the tributaries of the Lymington River. This grass was considered extinct in the wild and attempts have recently been made to reintroduce it from local material held in cultivation. Typical aquatics from these rivers include *Callitriche hamulata*, *C. obtusangula* (more locally) and *Ranunculus peltatus*.

Where rivers run through riparian woodlands, debris dams may support populations of *Ludwigia palustris*. The Beaulieu River has an isolated population of *Potamogeton alpinus*. The lower stretches of the river enjoy a brackish influence with a notable population of *Eleocharis parvula*. The estuarine woods of the New Forest and the bare, poached ground of Forest wetlands, including river margins, are described elsewhere in the accounts of the coast and New Forest. Collectively, the New Forest rivers are probably the least-modified lowland river-systems within western Europe.

Plate 21a,b   Eelmoor Flash, Basingstoke Canal, before dredging (above) and after dredging (below). Although necessary to maintain open water, dredging has at times been overdone, and motorized boats are also damaging the aquatic vegetation in which the Canal is so rich. (*Photo*: D. P. Dimmock)

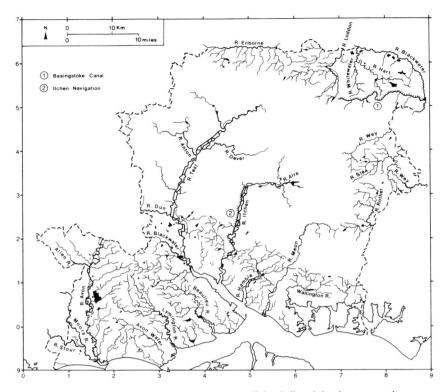

Fig. 9   The complex network of streams in areas off the chalk and the almost streamless, porous, chalk plateau, with the few major rivers that flow through it, are well shown in this map. The two main canals are indicated by numbers

The Thames tributaries include the **R. Loddon** with its populations of *Potamogeton pectinatus* and *Sagittaria sagittifolia*. It is doubtful if *Potamogeton nodosus* survives as a native in Hampshire, but it is certainly present a few metres over the boundary in Berkshire and has recently been reintroduced in the Hampshire parts of the Loddon, Whitewater and Blackwater rivers.

The flood-plain associated with the Hampshire length of the **R. Avon** contains many features associated with major river-systems. The valley contains extensive meanders, ox-bow lakes, side-channels and backwaters, as well as pools and small lakes occasionally linked with the river during extensive flooding. This complex of riparian habitats supports 66 species of aquatic and wetland plants, including notable populations of *Limosella aquatica*, *Butomus umbellatus*, *Juncus compressus*, *Cyperus fuscus* and in the tidal reaches *Eleocharis parvula*. The R. Avon shows a great range of habitat diversity, and a more varied flora than any other chalk river in Britain.

The **Basingstoke Canal** has been recognized by English Nature as Britain's richest waterway for aquatic plants, 101 species having been recorded

since 1984 in official but unpublished reports. During that time, 34 submerged or floating species have been found in the Hampshire part of the canal, but many have suffered due to the increasing use of the canal by motor-boats. *Sagittaria sagittifolia* remains plentiful; *Potamogeton alpinus*, *P. perfoliatus*, *Hippuris vulgaris* and *Utricularia australis* are among the fine range of aquatics to be seen, whilst the margins support such scarce species as *Butomus umbellatus*, *Hottonia palustris* and *Eleocharis acicularis*.

8. The Woodlands (excluding the New Forest)

Hampshire is indeed fortunate in the extent and diversity of its woodlands. About 16 per cent of the landscape is covered with woodlands compared with the average for Britain of *c*.7 per cent (Fig.10). Only Sussex, Kent and Surrey are close to this figure among lowland counties. This figure comprises some 70,000ha: much of it consists of conifer plantations and other recent woodlands, but about 30,000ha seem (from maps and other evidence) to be woodlands of ancient origin. Much of this total is contributed by the unique woodlands of the New Forest

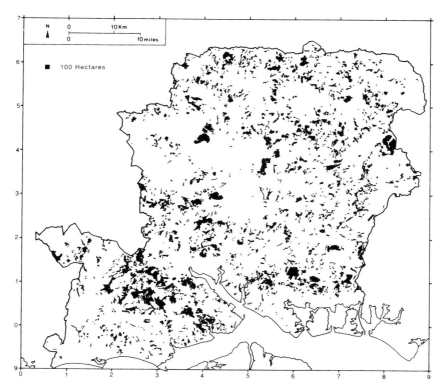

Fig. 10   Of the ancient woodlands identified by the HCC survey team from early maps, most are old coppice-woods. Some have been felled and replanted but in the open New Forest many are ancient pasture woodland. Note absence of ancient woodland from much of the central chalk plateau around Winchester

(see above), but ancient woodlands of very diverse size are found throughout the county, except in parts of the chalk plateau where old woodlands are often very sparse, especially north and north-west of Winchester.

The ancient woodlands of Hampshire, apart from the New Forest already described, fall into several categories based on their soil and topographic situations:

(a) the woodlands of the Tertiary strata of the Hampshire Basin;

(b) those of the Tertiary strata of the north and north-east;

(c) the woodlands of the chalk plateau, where most old woodlands are on superficial drift soils such as Clay-with-flints;

(d) the woodlands of the chalk scarps and hangers, mostly on shallow highly calcareous soils;

(e) the almost unique woodlands of the Malmstone on the Upper Greensand escarpment;

(f) the woodlands of the Gault clay;

(g) the old, riverside woodlands on non-calcareous soils, in very limited areas on the Lower Greensand, especially by the R. Rother and the R. Wey;

(h) small areas of woodland on the dry uplands of the Lower Greensand; and finally

(i) the open pasture-woodlands of mediaeval deer-parks.

With such a diversity, it is impossible in this account to do more than select a few examples to describe. Before doing this, however, it should be pointed out that the NCC (now English Nature) produced a table of the 100 vascular plant species that in the NCC South Region (which included Hampshire) were found to be most strongly associated with woodland of ancient origin. These 100 species are known as the AWVPs (Ancient Woodland Vascular Plants) (Fig.11, p.54) and form part of a continuum from those commoner species found in both ancient and some secondary woodlands through to those (often much rarer) species that seem to be strictly confined to known ancient woodlands. This somewhat arbitrary figure of 100 was chosen as it is con-

SITE		NO	Grid Ref	OS Sheet	County
Locality		HA	Recorder/s		Date/s

SOUTH REGION

ANCIENT WOODLAND VASCULAR PLANTS - The 100 species which in NCC's South Region are most strongly associated with ancient woodland and are typical components of botanically rich ancient woodland communities.

	A	B		A	B		A	B
Acer campestre*			Festuca gigantea			Polygonatum multiflorum		
Adoxa moschatellina			Frangula alnus			Polypodium vulgare (s. lato)		
Agropyron caninum [1]			Galium odoratum			Polystichum aculeatum		
Allium ursinum			Geum rivale			Polystichum setiferum		
Anemone nemorosa			Helleborus viridis			Populus tremula		
Aquilegia vulgaris*			Holcus mollis			Potentilla sterilis		
Blechnum spicant			Hordelymus europaeus			Primula vulgaris*		
Bromus ramosus [2]			Hyacinthoides non-scripta			Prunus avium		
Calamagrostis epigejos			Hypericum androsaemum			Pulmonaria longifolia		
Campanula trachelium			Hypericum pulchrum			Quercus petraea*		
Cardamine amara			Ilex aquifolium			Ranunculus auricomus		
Carex laevigata			Iris foetidissima			Ribes nigrum*		
Carex pallescens			Lamiastrum galeobdolon			Ribes sylvestre*		
Carex pendula*			Lathraea squamaria			Rosa arvensis		
Carex remota			Lathyrus montanus [4]			Ruscus aculeatus		
Carex strigosa			Lathyrus sylvestris			Sanicula europaea		
Carex sylvatica			Luzula forsteri			Scirpus sylvaticus		
Carpinus betulus*			Luzula pilosa			Sedum telephium		
Cephalanthera longifolia			Luzula sylvatica			Serratula tinctoria		
Chrysosplenium oppositifolium			Lysimachia nemorum			Solidago virgaurea		
Colchicum autumnale			Malus sylvestris*			Sorbus torminalis		
Conopodium majus			Melampyrum pratense			Stachys officinalis		
Convallaria majalis*			Melica uniflora			Tamus communis		
Corydalis claviculata [3]			Milium effusum			Thelypteris oreopteris [5]		
Crataegus laevigata			Moehringia trinervia			Tilia cordata*		
Daphne laureola			Narcissus pseudonarcissus*			Ulmus glabra		
Dipsacus pilosus			Neottia nidus-avis			Vaccinium myrtillus		
Dryopteris affinis			Orchis mascula			Veronica montana		
Dryopteris carthusiana			Oxalis acetosella			Viburnum opulus*		
Epipactis helleborine			Paris quadrifolia			Vicia sepium		
Epipactis leptochila			Phyllitis scolopendrium*			Vicia sylvatica		
Epipactis purpurata			Platanthera chlorantha			Viola palustris		
Equisetum sylvaticum			Poa nemoralis			Viola reichenbachiana		
Euphorbia amygdaloides								

Column A: current records
Column B: old records

*Only tick these species if they occur well within the wood and do not appear to have been planted.

[1] *Elymus caninus*   [4] *Lathyrus linifolius*   [5] *Oreopteris limbosperma*

[2] *Bromopsis ramosa*

[3] *Ceratocapnos claviculata*

Fig. 11   This table, issued in November 1984 in the form of a record card, gives the 100 indicator species of ancient woodland vascular plants (AWVPs) selected by the former South Region of NCC (now English Nature) covering Hampshire. Changes in nomenclature since that date are given below.

venient for arithmetical comparison of sites, but it seems to work quite well. It must be remembered first that many of these may also occur beside sunken lanes (see p.61) and in ancient hedgebanks, which are often effectively linear relics of ancient woodlands, and secondly that there are also other far rarer species of ancient woodland too scarce to use in any practical table of comparison, such as *Gagea lutea* and *Cephalanthera rubra*.

Bryophytes can also be used as 'indicators' of ancient woodland, but in Hampshire (outside the New Forest) it has proved difficult to construct any effective table or index using them. Epiphytic lichens, on the other hand, have proved even more valuable than the vascular plants in distinguishing ancient woodlands, but they can be used effectively in woodlands (usually old pasture woodlands) only where there are individual trees (or stands of trees) of considerable age and there is continuity with the past. In coppiced woodlands, therefore, except where there are many old standard-trees, lichens cannot be used satisfactorily for this purpose. They are, however, very useful indicators in woodlands derived from former mediaeval deer-parks or old forests.

(i) Old woodlands of the Hampshire Basin

The outstanding woodland to consider here is **Roydon Woods** (3000 to 3299), just outside the New Forest. This HWT nature reserve comprises about 300ha of very varied woodland. Some 370 vascular plants are recorded and the AWVP total is 73, the highest for Hampshire and one of the highest in England. 122 bryophytes and 146 epiphytic lichens are recorded here. On the lichen Revised Index of Ecological Continuity (RIEC) (Rose, 1976), Roydon scores 100 per cent with 20 indicator species, a total exceeded elsewhere in Hampshire only in some of the richest New Forest Ancient and Ornamental Woodlands.

The northern part of the complex (Bakers Copse) was once part of the former Brockenhurst Park old deer-park and has many ancient oaks and ashes rich in rare bryophytes and lichens, including New Forest specialities such as *Lobaria pulmonaria*, *Sticta limbata*, *Degelia plumbea*, *Zamenhofia coralloidea*, *Z. hibernica*, *Thelopsis rubella*, *Parmelia crinita*, and *Wadeana dendrographa*. There are also rare bryophytes such as *Pterogonium gracile*, *Hookeria lucens*, *Frullania fragilifolia*, *Zygodon baumgartneri* and *Porella cordaeana*. *Carex strigosa* has its only south-west Hampshire population in a flushed, streamside woodland adjacent to an area of (doubtfully native) *Carpinus betulus* woodland.

The woodland along the flood-plain of the Lymington River here is exceptionally rich in old trees with rare epiphytes. The rest of the Roydon Woods complex is largely ancient hazel-coppice with oak standards. Interesting species present include much *Ruscus aculeatus*, *Euphorbia amygdaloides*, *Geum rivale* (in flushed areas), *Sorbus torminalis*, *Pulmonaria longifolia* (plentiful), *Carex montana*, *Narcissus pseudonarcissus*, *Elymus caninus*, *Cardamine amara* and the rare 'Lusitanian' fern *Dryopteris aemula* in a ravine. However, some old woodland species frequent in much of central and eastern Hampshire, such as *Polygonatum multiflorum* and *Paris quadrifolia*, are absent from Roydon (and south-west Hampshire).

The soils are mostly rather acidic, brown forest-soils on Tertiary clays and loams, and on plateau gravels, but flushes from the Oligocene Headon Beds are calcareous in places and add much variety to the vegetation.

Upper Hamble Country Park (4911 to 5012) is a fine oak–hazel woodland, with much *Sorbus torminalis*, *Tilia cordata* and *Fraxinus excelsior* locally, on the plateau and along the valley of the R. Hamble. Here one can see the phenomenon, rare now, of stunted, ancient oak-woodland in direct contact with tidal salt-marsh. The AWVP total is 64, a very high figure, and some 143 strictly woodland vascular plants have been recorded so far. The lichens and bryophytes are interesting, but not exceptional – possibly due to some slight effects of pollution from the Southampton Water industrial zone.

The **Forest of Bere** was an extensive Royal Forest until it was largely enclosed early last century. It lay for the most part on London Clay, with areas of Bagshot Sands on the higher ground, and it seems from old maps to have been a mosaic of pasture woodlands, scrub areas, and open, damp, grazed grasslands. Today it has nearly all been enclosed and much is now farmland, but some large blocks remain as Forestry Commission woodland, notably those at **West Walk** (5913), **Boarhunt** (6012), **Creech Walk** (6411), and **The Queen's Inclosure** (6910).

The greater part of these four blocks consists of commercial conifer (or recent hardwood) plantations of little interest to the botanist, but each of the four areas contains extensive stands of oak (largely *Quercus petraea*), planted early last century to provide naval timber, much of which survives and is of particular lichenological interest. A number of lichens indicative of some long degree of ecological continuity occur in each of the blocks. The reason for this may be that the original woodland cover was by no means completely cleared before the 19th-century planting. In the valley of the stream south of Woodend, and particularly at Boarhunt, there are a number of quite old pollards and maiden trees of oak and beech, and it is in these areas that the most interesting epiphytic lichens and bryophytes occur. They include the lichens *Arthonia vinosa*, *Bacidia biatorina*, *Catillaria atropurpurea*, *Chaenotheca hispidula*, *Lecanactis premnea*, *Loxospora elatina*, *Micarea pycnidiophora*, *Pachyphiale carneola*, *Schismatomma quercicola*, and the bryophytes *Hookeria lucens* and *Frullania tamarisci*.

As is often the case on London Clay, the vascular plant flora is limited. However, in some of the easternmost copses of the former Forest of Bere, and also just beyond its former boundary east of Southwick, there remain some extensive areas of good, semi-natural oak–hazel coppice-with-standards with a good flora including much *Carex strigosa* in places and, where the soil is sandier, there are some of the most interesting *Rubus* populations in Hampshire.

Botley Wood (5410 and adjacent grid squares) (not legally part of the old Bere Forest) is an extensive woodland largely on London Clay which is also quite diverse in its flora, including *Rubus* species, and is very good for Lepidoptera and Hymenoptera. *Tilia cordata* occurs in several places here, as does *Sorbus torminalis*.

Other interesting woods in the Hampshire Basin are the PRIVATE **Cranbury Park Woods** (4422) and **Ampfield Wood** (4123), also PRIVATE.

(ii) Woodlands of the north and north-east Tertiary Region

This region has comparatively few good, old woodlands to the east, where heathy country prevails; further west there are many, some of which have still not been well surveyed. The outstanding one in this area is **Pamber Forest** (LNR, OPEN ACCESS) (6160 to 6161), a large wood which was originally part of a Royal Forest but has been managed in the last century or so as coppice, or partly as even-aged, high forest. This woodland lies on acidic clays and sands, ranging from brown forest-soils in the lower areas to podsols on the edge of Silchester Common. The predominant trees are oaks and ashes with much hazel-coppice; areas of alder carr occur by some streams. The number of AWVPs recorded is at least 53, a high number, and includes most of the typical old woodland plants of less base-rich soils such as *Anemone nemorosa*, *Blechnum spicant*, *Convallaria majalis*, *Lathyrus linifolius*, *Malus sylvestris*, *Melampyrum pratense*, *Milium effusum*, *Oreopteris limbosperma* (on the acidic northern edge), *Polygonatum multiflorum*, and *Vaccinium myrtillus*. On more base-rich areas occur *Adoxa moschatellina*, *Orchis mascula*,

Platanthera chlorantha, *Ranunculus auricomus*, *Sanicula europaea* and *Sorbus torminalis*, and one alder carr to the north has *Equisetum sylvaticum* and the moss (rare in North Hampshire) *Hookeria lucens*. The bryophyte flora is not exceptional (about 40 species) and there are only 58 recorded lichens; these relatively poor totals reflect the lack of ancient trees, most of which have been removed in the past, and the relatively limited micro-habitats for bryophytes. Nevertheless Pamber Forest is a very fine woodland, which is now benefiting from careful management planned to increase its habitat diversity. This management is helping to restore its once famous insect fauna.

The old woodlands around the fine meadow complex of **Ashford Hill** (5662) (described above) are also rich in plants and invertebrates. **Maggotty Moor Copse** (5359) (PRIVATE), north-east of Kingsclere, is another old woodland area on Tertiary clays and sands with alder carr rich in such bryophytes as *Hookeria lucens* and *Trichocolea tomentella* (in 5360); it has at least 32 AWVPs in its varied terrain.

West of Ecchinswell (4960) lie some fine oak–ash–hazel-woods on Tertiary Beds influenced by the adjacent chalk; there is a rich flora including *Paris quadrifolia*. **Highclere Park** (4459) is one of the best of Hampshire's few remaining old parklands. It has interesting old, non-calcareous grassland (with *Gentianella campestris* (in 4560)) as well as woodland with ancient oaks around **Milford Lake** (4560), with good epiphytic lichens and bryophytes of ancient-woodland type.

There are a number of interesting ancient woods in the Odiham area. Of particular interest is **Butter Wood** (7151 and 7152) (PRIVATE) which is largely wood-pasture with adjoining areas of coppice. It straddles Upper Chalk through Reading Beds to London Clay, and this varied geology is reflected in a high AWVP count of 68 species, including *Allium ursinum*, 14 species of *Carex* including locally abundant *C. strigosa* and *C. pallescens*, *Chrysosplenium oppositifolium*, *Daphne laureola* (and formerly *D. mezereum*), *Epipactis purpurata*, *Ruscus aculeatus*, *Scutellaria minor* and *Sorbus torminalis*. A good glade and ride flora includes such species as *Blackstonia perfoliata*, *Centaurium pulchellum*, *Lythrum portula*, *Ophioglossum vulgatum*, *Serratula tinctoria* and *Succisa pratensis*.

Odiham Common (7552 and 7553) is also a large area of former wood-pasture with coppiced areas. It is still grazed along its southern edge where there are some interesting grassland-communities. To the north of the wood it becomes more heathy with species such as *Anagallis tenella*, *Hydrocotyle*

Plate 22   Pamber Forest, one of our ancient woodlands on Tertiary clays and sands, now has few ancient trees due to past fellings, but still has one of the richest assemblages of 'ancient woodland indicator' species in the county, including *Narcissus pseudonarcissus* (seen here). (*Photo:* P. R. Brough)

vulgaris, Radiola linoides, and *Genista anglica* along some of the wider rides. Sadly, both Butter Wood and Odiham Common have very few old pollards so the epiphytic flora is rather poor.

(iii) The woodlands of the Chalk plateau

As explained above, the general deforestation of the chalk uplands led to much erosion of the superficial, largely non-calcareous, soils which formerly covered the plateau. A few remarkable ancient woods do, however, remain on the chalk plateau on the superficial deposits, where historical factors have contributed to their continued existence.

One of the finest examples is **Crab Wood** (4329), (much with OPEN ACCESS, HCC) south of Sparsholt. This is largely ancient hazel-coppice with oak and ash standards but it still contains many old oaks with interesting ancient woodland lichens and bryophytes. Crab Wood has a total of 47 AWVPs on its largely rather base-rich but in some parts more acid soils. These include *Adoxa moschatellina, Campanula trachelium, Conopodium majus, Convallaria majalis, Dryopteris affinis, Euphorbia amygdaloides, Galium odoratum, Geum rivale, Lamiastrum galeobdolon, Luzula sylvatica, Melampyrum pratense, Neottia nidus-avis, Orchis mascula, Polygonatum multiflorum, Stachys officinalis* and *Ulmus glabra.*

Hampage Wood (5329, 5430, 5431) (PRIVATE) is known to be ancient and must once have resembled Crab Wood, but it has lost much of its interest due to extensive felling and conifer planting. However, *Geum rivale* and *Polygonatum multiflorum* are both abundant on the basic clay soil of the Clay-with-flints.

Other ancient, chalk-plateau woods (all PRIVATE) are **Hedgemoor Copse** (2631), which has a good stand of apparently native *Tilia cordata*, *Epipactis leptochila* and had, formerly at least, *Vicia sylvatica*; **Cheriton Wood** (6029), now largely coppice; **Bramdean Common** (6329), an area of former pasture-woodland; **Sutton Beech Wood** (6233), a delightfully varied wood, partly on shallow soils over chalk; **Stony Brow Wood** (6730, 6830), which has *Epipactis purpurata* and *Platanthera bifolia*, and the extensive woods in **Herriard Park** (6646), where *Cephalanthera longifolia* occurs in the calcareous areas, but much of the woodland is clearly ancient oak–hazel-coppice on Clay-with-flints.

Many present-day woods on the chalk plateau, however, are of secondary origin, either due to planting (usually of beech) or to natural colonization of former sheepwalk or rabbit warren. Most of these woods, even if not now coniferized, are usually rather limited in their floras, but a few do have great interest. East of West Meon, **Chappetts Copse** (6523) (HWT reserve) is almost certainly largely secondary in origin, to judge from old maps, but it contains what is probably the largest population of *Cephalanthera longifolia* in Britain, as well as *Ophrys insectifera*, *Neottia nidus-avis* and other chalk-woodland species. **Boulsbury Wood** (0715) (in VC8 but now in Hampshire) is an ancient wood with 57 AWVP species, with good stands of *Tilia cordata* and such plants as *Convallaria majalis* and *Vicia sylvatica*.

Another clearly secondary wood on former chalk downland is **Galley Down Wood** (5718 and 5719) (PRIVATE except for PUBLIC PATH). This is largely a beech-plantation, and contains the largest populations of *Neottia nidus-avis* and *Cephalanthera damasonium* known in Hampshire. There are glades within the wood with typical chalk-scrub species (*Euonymus europaeus*, *Viburnum lanata*) and grassland species (*Sanguisorba minor*, *Polygala vulgaris*). There is also some *Cephalanthera longifolia* in an older part of the wood to the south, and at the north end a patch of Clay-with-flints has some ancient pollard beeches with *Ruscus aculeatus* and *Ophrys insectifera*. This northern end may well be ancient woodland, as it contains a range of typical AWVPs. It seems probable that many of the orchids associated with present-day calcareous beech-woods were formerly confined to such calcareous borders of ancient woods on Clay-with-flints as then existed, and may even have undergone some increase in populations with the beech-plantations of the 18th and 19th centuries: they cannot all be regarded in Hampshire as true ancient woodland species.

(iv) The Chalk Hangers

The Chalk Hangers extend from west of Petersfield to near Selborne. It is clear from old maps (especially the very accurate tithe maps) that ancient woodland along this escarpment was very limited until well into the 19th century. Some areas of (probably ancient) coppice are shown on the maps – much of the rest was open sheep-walk. Nevertheless, a very fine series of woodlands occurs along the hangers today. In the area from north of Petersfield along to Selborne Hanger, there is a total AWVP count of 64. It seems as if this rich flora has spread out from the small areas of ancient woodland to colonize much of the rest of the escarpment.

Selborne Hanger (7333) (NT) and the northern part of **High Wood Hanger** (7432) do seem from their structure to be ancient beech-woods; Selborne Hanger was certainly well established in Gilbert White's time (*c*.1785) and High Wood Hanger has ancient beech-pollards. Elsewhere, the areas of known ancient woodland show an interesting zonation, from wych elm, field maple, ash and hazel on the deeper soils at the scarp foot, to beech, yew and whitebeam woodland on the shallow soils higher up.

The hangers as a whole are notable for the number of colonies of *Cephalanthera longifolia* present – more than in any other area of similar size in Great Britain. Other notable species that are widespread in parts of the hangers are *Arum italicum* ssp. *neglectum* (along the moist, chalk debris at the base of most of the hangers), *Atropa belladonna*, *Carex strigosa* (on the moister, basal areas), *Myosotis sylvatica*, *Paris quadrifolia*, *Polygonatum multiflorum*, ferns such as *Polystichum setiferum* and *Phyllitis scolopendrium* and, high up in a few, open beech-wood sites on rubbly chalk soil, *Helleborus foetidus* in quantity.

The bryophyte flora is rich, with one special rarity on tree-bases in the area north of Steep: *Isothecium striatulum*, a very southern species with no other Hampshire locations.

One of the richest areas for old woodland species is the little coombe of **Lutcombe Bottom** (7326) (OPEN ACCESS, HCC) around and by the stream below a strong spring. Though this wood was clearly very small in the past, it has a high proportion of the ancient woodland species of the hangers. **Oakshott Hanger** (7327) (PRIVATE) is particularly rich in orchids of calcareous woodland and scrub, as is **The Warren** (7228) (mostly OPEN ACCESS).

Plate 23 This photo shows the great diversity of vegetation on the Wealden Edge Hangers on the South Downs near Petersfield. Although there are now extensive stands of Beech and Yew on the drier upper slopes, while Ash, Maple and Wych Elm prevail below, in earlier times much was open grassland (as foreground) and management is aimed at restoring more of it. (*Photo:* R. B. Gibbons)

(v) The Upper Greensand Hangers

Much of the scarp of the Upper Greensand is very steep due to the hard beds of Malmstone which is a weakly calcareous sandstone. This scarp is largely occupied by narrow, linear woodland, most of which is probably primary, though modified over the centuries into coppice-with-standards. Two of the richest areas are described below. The Upper Greensand scarp extends west from the Sussex border to the south of Petersfield, west again to Langrish, then north-east through Steep and Hawkley to below Selborne, then north to north of Binsted.

In the **Long Copse – Milking Hanger** valley (7434 and 7435), the Malmstone scarp occupies both sides of a narrow valley, with the intervening valley-floor (partly on gault clay) wooded as well. The woodland is composed of ash–hazel coppice, with standards of *Quercus robur, Fraxinus excelsior, Acer campestre* and both coppice and some standards of *Ulmus glabra, Prunus avium* and *Ilex aquifolium*. It has an AWVP count of 44; with adjacent woods, the total is 53. The plants present here include *Adoxa moschatellina, Allium ursinum, Anemone nemorosa, Blechnum spicant, Carex strigosa, C. sylvatica, Chrysosplenium oppositifolium* (by the stream),

Digitalis purpurea, Euphorbia amygdaloides, Galium odoratum, Hyacinthoides non-scripta, Lamiastrum galeobdolon, Luzula pilosa, Melica uniflora, Mercurialis perennis, Milium effusum, Orchis mascula, Oxalis acetosella, Paris quadrifolia, Polygonatum multiflorum, Polystichum aculeatum, P. setiferum, Primula vulgaris, Sanicula europaea, Viburnum opulus, Viola reichenbachiana and *V. riviniana*.

The bryophytes that occur on small boulders of Malmstone are remarkable; in the whole of Hampshire, *Brachydontium trichodes* and *Jungermannia pumila* are, it seems, confined to this one wood, while *Campylostelium saxicola, Seligeria recurvata* and *Rhynchostegiella curviseta* are more widespread but are confined to the Malmstone boulders along this escarpment. Other very local mosses not wholly confined to the Malmstone include *Dichodontium pellucidum, Fissidens pusillus* var. *tenuifolius, Mnium stellare* and *Taxiphyllum wissgrillii*.

Wick Hill Hanger (7533) has a similar flora to that of the last wood but the escarpment is much steeper, carrying on the cliff a fine population of *Tilia cordata* including some inaccessible maiden trees; the rare liverwort *Porella arboris-vitae* occurs here as an epiphyte on *Fraxinus*.

The lichens of the Malmstone hangers are not of

particular interest as there are few, very old trees and the tree-boles are generally too shaded to have rich epiphytic floras.

(vi) Woodlands of the Gault

The county has a fine series of woodlands on the base-rich stagno-gley soils on Gault outcrop. The largest example is the **Alice Holt Forest** (8241) (Forestry Commission), an old Royal Forest. Much of it is now conifer plantations but large areas of oak, replanted in the early 19th century, occur in the south-west part at **Goose Green Inclosure** (8040). There is a good flora typical of heavy, base-rich, clay woodland, with much *Carex strigosa*. *Crataegus laevigata*, in Hampshire, is almost confined to this area on the Surrey border, though common in old woodlands to the east. The lichen flora of the mature oaks is remarkably rich in old forest species, and there has clearly been some habitat continuity here for epiphytes over a long time.

Other interesting woodlands on the Gault include the ancient pasture woodland of **Bins Wood** (7637) (Woodland Trust (WT)), which is still grazed, and the PRIVATE woods east of Selborne such as **Wick Wood** (7534) and **Combe Wood** (7534). These are of old hazel–ash–maple coppice with standards of *Quercus robur*, and have *Carex pendula*, *C. strigosa*, *Orchis mascula*, *Paris quadrifolia*, *Platanthera chlorantha* and *Sanicula europaea*. They become very waterlogged in winter.

(vii) The riverain woodlands of the Lower Greensand

These woodlands are unlike any others in Hampshire. They are fed by springs from the Lower Greensand, including those from the calcium-and iron-rich strata of the Bargate Beds, and so have a richer flora than other wet woods along rivers elsewhere in the county. They have mostly developed on the flood-plains of the R. Rother and the R. Wey, and are largely of alder, often with extensive peatbeds. Much of the year they are extremely waterlogged.

A good example of these is the Rother woodland from **Adhurst St Mary** (7625), north-east of Sheet (PRIVATE), downstream to below **Sheet Mill** (7624). *Alnus glutinosa* is generally dominant, with *Salix cinerea* ssp. *oteifolia*, and with some *Quercus* and *Fraxinus* on the better-drained environment of the river-banks. Areas of *Mercurialis perennis* occupy drier terrain under *Corylus*, whilst the swampy woodlands or the river banks have *Caltha palustris*, *Cardamine amara*, *C. pratensis*, *Carex paniculata*, *C. remota*, *Chrysosplenium alternifolium*, *C. oppositi-*

folium, *Deschampsia cespitosa*, *Dryopteris carthusiana*, *Iris pseudacorus*, *Lysimachia vulgaris*, *Myosotis sylvatica* and *Stellaria neglecta*.

(viii) Drier woodlands of the Lower Greensand

Some areas of ancient woodland survive in Woolmer Forest around the northern and eastern edges of the heathland that comprises most of its area. These are essentially relics of pasture-woodland with old *Quercus robur*, *Fagus sylvatica* (some ancient pollards present), *Betula pubescens*, *Ilex aquifolium*, *Corylus avellana*, *Sorbus aucuparia* and usually much *Pteridium aquilinum*. Good examples are on the south side of **Passfield Common** (8133) (NT) and at the **Holly Hills** (8232) (MOD). At both sites the woodland is on the coarse, free-draining Folkestone Sands which produces light, acid soils, but both woodlands show a transition below to alder carr, fed by springs from the calcareous Bargate Beds, and have here, as in the riverain woods described previously, communities of *Caltha palustris* and of both species of *Chrysosplenium*; *Valeriana dioica* also occurs in the flushes.

The outcrop of **Hythe Beds** in Hampshire is limited to a small area along the Surrey and Sussex borders and, due to management changes, contains little woodland of interest. Two sites, however, need mention.

Waggoners Wells (8534) (NT) is a deep valley with a chain of ponds, containing some good relic woodlands of *Quercus robur* and *Q. petraea*, *Fagus sylvatica*, *Betula pendula* and *Sorbus aucuparia*, with a *Vaccinium myrtillus* understorey. The vascular plants are limited, as is usual on such podsolic soils, but there are interesting, very local, lichen epiphytes, mainly on old *Quercus*, such as *Arthonia vinosa*, *Catillaria atropurpurea*, *Cladonia incrassata* (on *Betula* roots), *Lecanactis premnea*, *Lecanora pallida*, *Pachyphiale carneola*, *Pertusaria pupillaris*, *Stenocybe septata* (on *Ilex*), *Thelopsis rubella* and *Thelotrema lepadinum* (especially on *Ilex*). The bryophytes include the very local mosses *Dicranum majus* and *Plagiothecium undulatum*, and the epiphytic liverwort *Frullania tamarisci*. The vegetation is reminiscent of the New Forest, and it is an exceptional site for cryptogams in east Hampshire, with 88 lichens recorded. Old records, however, indicate that formerly most of the area was heathland, but probably a fringe of old woodland has always occurred in places along the stream.

Whitmoor Vale (8635) is a woodland of *Quercus petraea*, *Betula pendula* and *Sorbus aucuparia*, also with *Vaccinium myrtillus*, on a steep, north-east slope rich in calcifuge bryophytes of upland character.

Similar woodlands of greater extent occur in adjacent parts of Sussex and Surrey.

(ix) Old deer-parks

Mediaeval deer-parks are an important habitat for epiphytic lichens and, as such sites now scarcely occur in western, continental Europe, many are of international importance in terms of conservation. Today, Hampshire has very few of these. Apart from Highclere Park, described above (p.56), by far the best example of this type of open pasture-woodland with ancient, pollard trees is **Hurstbourne Park** (4447) (PRIVATE). Here the ancient oaks have such relic epiphytic species of the 'Wildwood', the term used by Rackham (1980), as the lichens *Caloplaca herbidella*, *Chaenotheca trichialis*, *Lecanactis lyncea*, *L. premnea*, *Lecanora quercicola*, *L. sublivescens*, *Thelopsis rubella* and the bryophytes *Frullania tamarisci*, *Pterogonium gracile* and *Zygodon baumgartneri*. As is usual in former deer-parks, the vascular plants are limited but acid grassland with *Agrostis capillaris* and *Galium saxatile* is a feature. The western bramble *Rubus leyanus* also has a small outlying colony here.

9. Other Habitats

(i) Arable land

Despite the effects of agricultural intensification since the 1940s, Hampshire possesses what is probably the richest and most diverse arable flora of any county in Britain. It has perhaps been spared some of the worst excesses of prairie-farming, and many of the more sensitive species can still be found at the corners and edges of fields. The relatively mild climate may be one of the main reasons for the persistence of several species of predominantly southern distribution in Europe, and the varied geology permits the occurrence of species with very different soil preferences within a small area.

On the preponderantly freely-draining, **acidic substrata of the south of the county**, *Chrysanthemum segetum* and *Misopates orontium* may sometimes be found in considerable quantity, chiefly in spring cereals or root-crops. *M. orontium* may also be found in gardens around the south of the New Forest. The rare grass *Briza minor* sometimes occurs, and in one place near Lymington the very rare *Gastridium ventricosum* grows in at least one field. *Fumaria densiflora*, *Legousia hybrida* and *Kickxia* species may also be found but are much more frequent on calcareous soils to the north. The diminutive and probably under-recorded *Myosurus minimus* occurs in a few seasonally-flooded spots.

The **loamy chalk soils between Winchester, Basingstoke and Andover** are home to some of Britain's rarest arable annuals. *Papaver argemone*, *P. hybridum*, *Fumaria densiflora* and *Valerianella dentata*, as well as the more common *Sherardia arvensis*, *Lamium amplexicaule*, *Anthemis cotula*, *Kickxia* species, *Legousia hybrida* and *Euphorbia exigua*, are all fairly widespread, whilst of more local occurrence are *Silene noctiflora*, *Petroselinum segetum* and *Lithospermum arvense*. The most outstanding species of this area may all be found together at the edge of one field near Longparish which has *Adonis annua*, *Torilis arvensis*, *Fumaria parviflora*, *Galeopsis angustifolia* and *Scandix pecten-veneris*. *Adonis annua* may still be found in small numbers at a few other sites, although it has not been seen for some years at the famous locality near Alresford. *Galeopsis angustifolia* appears to be more abundant in this area than anywhere else in Britain, whilst one of only three other recent, known sites in Hampshire for *Torilis arvensis* is near Botley. *Legousia speculum-veneris* occurs in quantity at Wootton St Lawrence.

The **Allen Valley** (9906 to 0001), in the south-west border-area, also has chalky soils, and most of the more widespread species mentioned above occur here. *Adonis annua*, *Galeopsis angustifolia* and *Euphorbia platyphyllos* have been recorded in several places.

A group of plants associated with disturbed ground but which cannot be strictly regarded as arable species include the very rare *Filago lutescens*, *Teucrium botrys* and *Ajuga chamaepitys*. Characteristically, these are all generally found in those parts of arable fields which are cultivated only occasionally and which are highly susceptible to damage by rabbits, i.e. between the regularly-cultivated area and the permanent vegetation of the field boundary. However, *F. lutescens* is now to be found regularly only on one sandy roadside verge in north-east Hampshire, whereas the other two species may each be found in two sites. Most of the British population of *T. botrys* occurs on the chalk of **Micheldever Spoil Heaps** (see p.42), and *A. chamaepitys* may be found nearby. Both species occur together in one field-corner near Andover.

It is not possible to include all the numerous aliens from seeds in foreign shoddy or wool-combings used for mulching arable land, few of which survive frost and therefore do not become established. The hardy ones, whose seeds have been found to germinate through many years and which now constitute the habitual weeds of a field, are included. Lists of wool aliens found in Hampshire have been published (Lousley, 1961; Ryves, 1975, 1976, 1977).

(ii) Sunken Lanes

Ancient, deeply-cut lanes, formed by the erosive

effect of the traffic of horses and pedestrians over hundreds if not thousands of years, are a notable feature, particularly of the Wealden region of Hampshire, extending east into Sussex and north-east into Surrey. They do occur elsewhere in the county, but are especially well developed on the Upper Greensand from Langrish and Weston to the south-west of Petersfield, north and north-east past Steep, Buriton, Hawkley, Selborne and the Worldhams to north of Binsted.

The steep sides of these lanes often support a very rich woodland flora and can be regarded, in effect, as ancient linear woodlands; their flora may well have first colonized them when such woodland, now sometimes cleared, bordered these lanes. The best of them may display both dry woodland communities above and flushed below. Ferns such as *Polystichum setiferum*, *P. aculeatum* and *Phyllitis scolopendrium* are often abundant, with local or scarce plants such as *Paris quadrifolia* and *Orchis mascula*. The best of these lanes may have AWVP totals similar to many ancient woodlands, especially about Hawkley, and there is often also a rich bryophyte flora, particularly on rock-faces or loose boulders of Malmstone.

Sunken lanes also occur on the Lower Greensand, both on the Bargate Beds and the Hythe Beds, particularly south and east of Liss and about Bramshott and Headley. Here the flora tends to be more calcifuge and richer in local bryophytes, as well as some quite rare species, such as the mosses *Eurhynchium schleicheri*, *E. pumilum*, *Rhynchostegium megapolitanum*, *Schistostega pennata*, *Bartramia pomiformis*, and the liverworts *Targionia hypophylla* and *Reboulia hemisphaerica*. Sunken lanes occur, too, where lanes descend the chalk escarpment on the Hangers, and there are also a few on the Tertiaries of North Hampshire and South Hampshire. Similar habitats are well known in the West Country, but the Hampshire (and Sussex) ones appear to be as rich or richer in interesting plants. The main threat to them is road-widening and heavy lorry traffic which may erode the sides of the narrow lanes.

Hampshire is so rich in these lanes that special efforts should be (and indeed are being) made for their conservation. Francis Rose has been specially commissioned to study the sunken lanes of the East Hampshire District Council area, and the results will be published as a separate report, probably at about the same time as this Flora appears.

(iii) Waste Land

The waste ground associated with both derelict and currently-active industrial, port and military sites, especially along the coastline and estuaries of Hampshire, is rich in alien and adventive plants. These, however, do not normally form distinct communities in the phytosociological sense, and their distribution should be investigated with the help of the systematic text in this Flora.

(iv) Churchyards

A final word is needed on the nearly three-hundred ancient Hampshire churchyards. These are often havens for many interesting plants, especially ferns, mosses and many rare lichens on the varied stonework and memorials present. Particularly interesting and noteworthy churchyards are those at **Portchester** (626045), **South Hayling** (722001), **Headley** (822363), **Hambledon** (646152), **Bishop's Waltham** (556176), **Droxford** (608182); with over 110 lichen species), **Headbourne Worthy** (487320), **St Cross** (476277), **Barton Stacey** (435412), **Selborne** (742338), **Boldre** (324993), **Easton** (509323) and **Brockenhurst** (305018). **Winchester Cathedral** itself (483293) is also exceptionally rich in lichens and mosses, on both the Norman and mediaeval stone-walls of the Cathedral, and on monuments in the Close and on old brick-walls: over 110 lichen species were recorded here in 1994.

Plate 24　The more ancient of Hampshire's numerous old churchyards are very rich in lichens; Ashford Hill, though more recent, incorporates former ancient meadow with such rare plants as *Sanguisorba officinalis*. (*Photo:* P. R. Brough)

CHAPTER V

A COMPARISON OF HAMPSHIRE'S FLORA WITH THOSE OF SOME OTHER SOUTHERN COUNTIES

FRANCIS ROSE

1. Hampshire

Hampshire, with an area of about 3,800 square kilometres is botanically the richest county in the British Isles. Excluding the critical genera, it has over 1,400 species of established vascular plants; it is, however, very difficult to define the precise number because of uncertainty of the status of many species. Nonetheless, in terms of species of natural or semi-natural habitats, it is certainly the richest county. Some northern and western British counties have a far greater extent of semi-natural uncultivated terrain, but far fewer species are present in these areas.

Why is Hampshire so rich? Several factors appear to be responsible for this:

(i) Its southern coastal situation, providing relatively high summer temperatures, very high sunshine hours per year, and quite mild winters (particularly in the southern half of the county). It shares these features with other south coast-counties; not quite as sunny as the Sussex coast, it is considerably more so than south-west England.

(ii) Although it lacks coastal cliffs of relatively hard, erosion-resistant rocks such as are present to the west, and of chalk as are present to the east and south in Sussex, Kent and the Isle of Wight, and although there is almost no hard rock anywhere in the county, except very locally for the Malmstone scarp, there is a great variety of topography and soils. Both extensive calcareous and acidic terrains are present, and extensive freshwater, brackish and saline habitats too, as compared with counties to the west.

(iii) Glacial drifts (which impose a certain monotony of potential habitat over much of East Anglia and the Midlands) are absent in Hampshire, because it was never glaciated. The lack of glaciation has also meant that Hampshire is much hillier and less planed-down than much of central and eastern England.

(iv) The remarkable number and extent of relatively little-modified and varied wetlands, meadows and chalk scarps that have survived. This is partly due to factor (iii) but still more to complex historical and economic factors concerned with land management, including the far greater survival of unenclosed or unimproved common-land as compared even with Sussex and still more with Kent, where – though the structure and geology is similar – unenclosed land is confined to only a very few small areas.

(v) Some 28,000ha of ancient semi-natural woodland (about ten per cent of the British total).

(vi) Above all, the presence in south-west Hampshire of that extensive and now internationally unique complex of habitats which make up the New Forest.

As a result of these factors, Hampshire is rich in a diversity of phytogeographical elements: Oceanic-southern species like *Cicendia filiformis, Wahlenbergia hederacea, Pinguicula lusitanica, Dryopteris aemula*; Continental-southern species like *Hippocrepis comosa, Asperula cynanchica* and many orchids; Mediterranean species like *Frankenia laevis, Rubia peregrina, Juncus acutus*; and even some Continental-northern species of bogs like *Carex limosa, C. lasiocarpa, Drosera anglica* and *Hammarbya paludosa*. These last have remarkably disjunct occurrences in Hampshire (and Dorset), being today known nowhere else within 240km to the north or north-east. Matthews (1937) has provided a full account of phytogeographical elements in Britain.

Valuable comparisons can be made with adjacent counties where enough information is available. Some comparative lists are given below and, whilst it is difficult to be precise because of the uncertain status of a few species, these lists indicate that there are about 65 species of vascular plants in this county no longer known in Sussex. Kent is even poorer by comparison: there, 87 extant Hampshire species are either unrecorded or extinct. Conversely, Sussex and Kent each have about 43 species that are not now known in this county.

Hampshire is particularly rich in members of the Cyperaceae; there are 73 species and subspecies of this family present, including 47 species and sub-species of *Carex*. Furthermore, it now has 35 species and subspecies of Orchidaceae, another four being extinct. No other county has so many. The corre-sponding figures for Kent are 32 and four extinct.

In these comparative lists, the following symbols and abbreviations are used:

*   – quite frequent on the mainland, at least locally, in suitable habitats.

†   – not native in Hampshire, but native in Sussex

HE – formerly in Hampshire, now extinct

KE – formerly in Kent, now extinct

K   – still in Kent

K? – one old (dubious) Kent record

NF – New Forest and adjacent area only

SE – formerly in Sussex, now extinct

SX – still in Sussex

2. The Isle of Wight

(i) Some Hampshire species surprisingly absent from the Isle of Wight

There are of course many species in Hampshire that have not been recorded in the Isle of Wight. This is not surprising considering its much greater area and wider range of habitats, so there seems little point in listing them all. However, there are a number of species that are either quite common or locally fre-quent in Hampshire, and indeed elsewhere in south-ern England, whose apparent absence from the island does seem noteworthy. The more striking of these are: *Alisma lanceolatum, Blysmus compressus, Brachypodium pinnatum, Cardamine amara, Carex viridula* ssp. *brachyrrhyncha, C. vesicaria, Cepha-lanthera longifolia, Chrysosplenium alternifolium, Convallaria majalis, Dipsacus pilosus, Drosera interme-dia*, Elymus caninus*, Eriophorum vaginatum*, Gentiana pneumonanthe, Geum rivale*, Gnaphalium sylvaticum, Herminium monorchis, Hydrocharis mor-sus-ranae, Hypericum maculatum, Lycopodiella inun-data*, Melittis melissophyllum, Myosotis sylvatica, Ononis spinosa*, Paris quadrifolia*, Petasites hybridus*, Phyteuma orbiculare*, Polygala calcarea*, Poly-gonatum multiflorum*, Polystichum aculeatum*, Pota-mogeton lucens, Potentilla argentea, Ranunculus* penicillatus*, R. circinatus, Rubus ciss'huriensis*, R. glareosus*, R. asperidens*, Sagittaria sagittifolia*, Saxifraga granulata, Schoenoplectus lacustris*.

(ii) Native in the Isle of Wight, absent from Hampshire

With one exception, the following Isle of Wight species have never been correctly reported as natives in Hampshire (although *Matthiola incana* is an estab-lished garden-escape and *Melampyrum arvense* a rare former casual): *Asplenium marinum, Centaurium tenuiflorum* HE?, *Clinopodium menthifolium, Fumaria reuteri* ssp. *martinii, F. purpurea, Matthiola incana, Melampyrum arvense, Oenanthe silaifolia, Orobanche artemisiae-campestris, Pilosella peleteriana, Pyrola rotundifolia, Rubus aequalidens, R. angusticuspis, R. cornubiensis, R. dumnoniensis, R. effrenatus, R. salteri* and *Scilla autumnalis.* Also *Ophrys sphegodes*, now probably extinct in Hampshire but refound, 1992, in the Isle of Wight. In addition, some species are far commoner on the island than on the mainland, e.g. *Gentianella anglica* and *Geranium rotundifolium.*

3. Sussex

(i) Native in Hampshire, absent from Sussex (presence in Kent is also shown)

Arabis glabra SE K, *Astragalus danicus, Carex diandra* KE, *C. dioica* SE, *C. humilis, C. lasiocarpa* NF, *C. limosa* NF, *C. punctata, Carum verticillatum* NF, *Cephalanthera rubra* K?, *Cirsium eriophorum* K, *Cladium mariscus* K, *Colchicum autumnale, Cyperus fuscus, C. longus* (?native) K, *Dactylorhiza traun-steineri, Deschampsia setacea, Drosera anglica* NF SE, *Eleocharis parvula, E. quinqueflora* SE, *Equisetum hyemale* SE, *Erica ciliaris* NF (probably native), *Eriophorum gracile* NF, *E. latifolium, Euphorbia port-landica* SE, *Euphrasia micrantha* SE K, *Fritillaria meleagris* SE, *Gagea lutea, Galium constrictum* NF, *Gastridium ventricosum, Gentianella germanica, Glad-iolus illyricus* NF, *Hammarbya paludosa* NF SE, *Hordelymus europaeus* K, *Hypericum montanum* SE K, *Illecebrum verticillatum* NF K, *Isolepis cernua, Juncus acutus* SE K, *Leucojum aestivum* (?native), *Lotus angustissimus* SE K, *L. subbiflorus, Oenanthe fluviatilis* K, *Ophioglossum azoricum* NF, *Pedicularis palustris* SE, *Pinguicula lusitanica, P. vulgaris* SE, *Poly-gonatum odoratum, Potentilla neumanniana, Pulicaria vulgaris* SE, *Pulmonaria longifolia, Pulsatilla vulgaris* (probably native, in VC8 only), *Ranun-culus* x *novae-forestae* NF SE K, *Rhynchospora fusca* NF, *Sagina subulata* SE, *Sanguisorba officinalis, Schoenus nigricans, Sonchus palustris* (probably native) K, *Sparganium angustifolium* NF, *S. natans* NF,

Spergularia rupicola, Teucrium botrys K, *Ulex gallii* SE K, *Utricularia intermedia* NF, *U. minor* SE? KE, *Vicia sylvatica* K.

(ii) Native in Sussex, absent from Hampshire

Bupleurum baldense, Cardamine bulbifera[†]*, Carex vulpina, Centaurea calcitrapa* HE?, *Ceratophyllum submersum, Chenopodium chenopodioides* HE, *Cicuta virosa, Clinopodium calamintha* HE, *Erodium maritimum* HE, *Festuca altissima, Filago pyramidata* HE, *Genista pilosa, Gymnocarpium robertianum* HE, *Hippophae rhamnoides*[†]*, Huperzia selago* HE (recorded in Sussex until at least 1966, ?still present), *Hymenophyllum tunbrigense, Lactuca saligna, Leersia oryzoides* HE (reintroduced into Hampshire, but no longer native), *Limonium binervosum* HE, *Lonicera xylosteum, Lythrum hyssopifolia* HE[†]*, Medicago minima, Oenanthe aquatica* HE?, *O. silaifolia, Ophrys sphegodes* HE, *Orchis purpurea* (?now extinct) *Ornithogalum pyrenaicum, Petrorhagia nanteuilii* HE, *Peucedanum palustre, Phyteuma spicatum, Pimpinella major, Potamogeton acutifolius* HE, *P. friesii* HE, *Pyrola rotundifolia, Scrophularia umbrosa, Seseli libanotis, Sibthorpia europaea, Silene conica, Sium latifolium* HE, *Teucrium chamaedrys* HE[†]*, Verbascum lychnitis*[†]*, Vicia lutea* HE[†]*, Wolffia arrhiza*.

These comparative lists for Sussex and Hampshire reveal several interesting points:

(a) Unlike Hampshire, Sussex has lost many species due to land-use changes, particularly loss of wetlands of various kinds.

(b) The New Forest, with its uniqueness, alone accounts for many of Hampshire's survivals.

(c) A few species are at their eastern or southern limit in Hampshire, a county more oceanic than Sussex but also with a more 'Continental' element to its flora.

(d) The list of species still in Sussex but never found in Hampshire includes:

    (1) a few species confined to the Wealden Sand rocks in the south-eastern part of England, e.g. *Hymenophyllum tunbrigense, Festuca altissima* and *Sibthorpia europaea* for which there are no suitable habitats in Hampshire;

    (2) some chalk-cliff species; and

    (3) others, like *Teucrium chamaedrys, Cardamine bulbifera, Seseli libanotis, Phyteuma spicatum, Clinopodium calamintha*, which are strongly Continental species that do not extend as far west as Hampshire, possibly for climatic reasons

or equally possibly because of historic land-use.

4. Kent

(i) Native in Hampshire, absent from Kent (presence in Sussex is also shown)

Agrostis curtisii SX, *Astragalus danicus, Arum italicum* ssp. *neglectum* SX, *Botrychium lunaria* KE SX, *Campanula patula* KE SX, *Carex diandra* KE, *C. dioica, C. hostiana* SX, *C. humilis, C. lasiocarpa* NF, *C. limosa* NF, *C. montana* NF SX, *C. punctata, C. viridula* ssp. *viridula* KE, *Carum verticillatum* NF, *Cephalanthera rubra* K?, *Cicendia filiformis* NF SX, *Colchicum autumnale* KE, *Crassula tillaea* KE?, *Cyperus fuscus* NF, *Dactylorhiza traunsteineri, Deschampsia setacea* NF, *Drosera intermedia* SX, *D. anglica* NF, *Eleocharis parvula, E. quinqueflora* KE, *Equisetum hyemale, Erica ciliaris* (?native), *Eriophorum gracile* NF, *E. latifolium* KE, *E. vaginatum* KE SX, *Euphorbia portlandica, Fritillaria meleagris* KE, *Gagea lutea* KE?, *Galium constrictum* NF, *Gastridium ventricosum* KE, *Gentiana pneumonanthe* KE SX, *Gentianella anglica* KE? SX, *G. campestris, G. germanica, Geranium purpureum* SX, *Geum rivale* SX, *Gladiolus illyricus* NF, *Gymnadenia conopsea* ssp. *borealis* SX, *G. conopsea* ssp. *densiflora* KE SX, *Hammarbya paludosa* NF, *Isolepis cernua, Leersia oryzoides* NF (reintroduced) SX, *Leucojum aestivum* (?native) KE, *Limonium humile* SX, *Limosella aquatica* SX, *Littorella uniflora* KE SX, *Lobelia urens* NF KE? SX, *Lotus subbiflorus, Ludwigia palustris* NF, *Lycopodiella inundata* KE SX, *Melittis melissophyllum* SX, *Mentha pulegium* NF KE, *Myrica gale* KE SX, *Ophioglossum azoricum* NF, *Pedicularis palustris* KE, *Phegopteris connectilis* NF SX, *Phyteuma orbiculare* KE SX, *Pilularia globulifera* SX, *Pinguicula lusitanica, P. vulgaris, Polygonatum odoratum* NF, *Polygonum maritimum* SX, *Potentilla neumanniana, Pulicaria vulgaris* KE, *Pulmonaria longifolia* NF, *Pulsatilla vulgaris* (?native), *Ranunculus omiophyllus* KE, *Raphanus raphanistrum* ssp. *maritimus* SX, *Rhynchospora alba* KE SX, *R. fusca* NF, *Sagina subulata, Sanguisorba officinalis, Schoenus nigricans, Sparganium angustifolium* NF, *Spergularia rupicola, Thesium humifusum* KE SX, *Trichophorum cespitosum* KE SX, *Utricularia intermedia* NF, *U. minor* KE, *Vaccinium oxycoccus* SX, *Viola lactea* KE SX.

(ii) Native in Kent, absent from Hampshire

Asplenium septentrionale (till 1983, ?extinct), *Callitriche truncata, Cardamine bulbifera, Carex vulpina, Centaurea calcitrapa* HE?, *Ceratophyllum* submersum, *Chenopodium chenopodioides* HE, *C. vulvaria* HE, *Clinopodium calamintha* HE, *Corydalis solida*, *Crepis foetida* (at least until recently), *Cyperus longus* HE?, *Dryopteris cristata* (until at least *c.*1960), *Eryngium campestre* HE, *Filago pyramidata* HE, *Gymnocarpium dryopteris*, *Hippophae rhamnoides*, *Lactuca saligna* (but not seen recently), *Limonium binervosum* HE, *Medicago minima*, *Oenanthe silaifolia*, *Ophrys fuciflora*, *O. sphegodes* HE, *Orchis purpurea*, *O. simia*, *Orobanche caryophyllacea*, *O. artemisiae-campestris*, *O. minor* var. *maritima*, *Peucedanum officinale*, *Pimpinella major*, *Polygala amarella*, *Potamogeton acutifolius*, *P. coloratus*, *Pyrola rotundifolia*, *Salvia pratensis*, *Schoenoplectus triqueter*, *Silene italica*, *S. nutans* var. *smithiana*, *Sium latifolium* HE, *Verbascum lychnitis*, *Vicia bithynica* HE, *V. lutea*, *Wolffia arrhiza*.

The Kent-Hampshire comparative lists are similarly revealing, except that the differences are more accentuated:

(a) Kent has more Continental-southern species (including *Polygala amarella*, *Orobanche caryophyllacea*, *Salvia pratensis* and some orchids) that do not at present extend further west in Britain.

(b) Many species have become extinct in Kent due to the drainage of wetlands and, more recently, to the serious reduction in numbers of acid valley-mires to just two or three.

5. Other adjacent counties

Hampshire is so much richer in plants than the remaining adjacent counties of Dorset, Wiltshire, Berkshire and Surrey – partly because the latter three have no coastlines – that it seems sufficient merely to list the relatively few species these other counties have that are not known in Hampshire.

(i) Native in Dorset, absent from Hampshire

Asplenium marinum, *Atriplex longipes*, *Callitriche*
truncata, *Centaurium tenuiflorum* HE, *Cirsium tuberosum* (found, 1992), *Erodium maritimum* HE, *Gnaphalium luteoalbum*, *Isoetes echinospora*, *Leucojum vernum* (?native), *Leersia oryzoides* HE, *Limonium recurvum*, *Lythrum hyssopifolia* HE, *Mibora minima* (found, 1992; ?native), *Ophrys sphegodes* HE, *Pilosella peleteriana* ssp. *peleteriana*, *Polycarpon tetraphyllum*, *Potamogeton acutifolius* HE, *Scorzonera humilis*, *Sibthorpia europaea* (found, 1992), *Suaeda vera* HE, *Vicia bithynica* HE.

(ii) Native in Wiltshire, absent from Hampshire

Asarum europaeum HE, *Campanula latifolia*, *Carex digitata*, *C. filiformis*, *Cirsium tuberosum*, *Gentianella ciliata* (?extinct), *Ophrys sphegodes* HE (refound, 1988), *Ornithogalum pyrenaicum*, *Pimpinella major* and *Scrophularia umbrosa*.

(iii) Native in Berkshire, absent from Hampshire

Clinopodium calamintha HE (north Berkshire only), *Oenanthe aquatica* HE?, *O. silaifolia*, *Ornithogalum pyrenaicum*, *Parnassia palustris*, *Pimpinella major*, *Potamogeton coloratus*, *P. compressus*, *P. nodosus* HE (but reintroduced), *P. praelongus*, *Silene conica* and *Sium latifolium* HE.

Orchis militaris and *O. simia*, formerly native in Berkshire but with no confirmed sightings since the 19th century, have never been recorded for Hampshire.

(iv) Native in Surrey, absent from Hampshire

Carex depauperata (refound, 1992), *C. filiformis*, *C. vulpina*, *Cynoglossum germanicum*, *Dryopteris cristata*, *Oenanthe silaifolia*, *Pimpinella major*, *Rhinanthus angustifolius* HE, *Scilla autumnalis*.

Orchis purpurea, now extinct in Surrey, has never been recorded for Hampshire.

CHAPTER VI

CONSERVATION OF THE FLORA

PETER BROUGH AND PAUL BOWMAN

1. The Growth of Botanical Conservation in Hampshire

Organized conservation of the Hampshire flora at a practical level has unfortunately lagged behind the accelerating loss of habitats over the past 150 years, and is a relatively recent phenomenon.

Until the 1950s, recording of the flora was not generally accompanied by steps to conserve the rarer species. Consequently, loss or major changes of habitats led to apparent extinction of species such as *Damasonium alisma*, *Ophrys sphegodes* and *Ranunculus ophioglossifolius*, all of which were recorded by Townsend as having been present in Hampshire in the last century. In a few cases it was over-collecting by botanists which contributed to the demise of species and which, from some accounts, must have been a factor in the loss of *Spiranthes aestivalis* from the New Forest whence hundreds of specimens were dug up and removed.

However, it is important to emphasize that the major cause of habitat loss during the past hundred years has been the revolution in agricultural practices brought about first by mechanization and secondly by the widespread use of herbicides and inorganic fertilizers. Vast areas of unimproved chalk-downland and meadows have been lost, to the extent that only isolated fragments remain in most areas. Surveys begun in 1966 (Blackwood & Tubbs, 1970) showed that the already-reduced areas of chalk grassland were still shrinking at the rate of about one per cent each year as a result of ploughing, planting, scrub-encroachment or road construction. Figures for heathland loss are similarly depressing. Since 1810, well over 50 per cent of heathland in Hampshire has been lost, most of the remainder being in the New Forest. Outside this specially protected area, losses have been severe, with well over 90 per cent destroyed. It needs to be said that loss of heathland and chalk grassland in Hampshire since

*c.*1950 has largely been due to neglect of traditional grazing (leading to the spread of bracken, scrub or secondary woodland) rather than to positive destruction by ploughing up or development by housing or industry.

Elsewhere in the county over the same period, urbanization has been a major cause of loss of habitat. London overspill has brought large-scale development into Hampshire (mainly in the south and north-east of the county) despite the undoubted sensitivity and biological richness of its countryside. Often the policy of avoiding major development of this kind in Areas of Outstanding Natural Beauty (AONBs) does not help conservation because the designation of such Areas takes no special account of biological diversity. Outside these Areas, major building projects are frequently 'slotted in' between Sites of Special Scientific Interest (SSSIs) or other rich sites, with immeasurably damaging effects. Secondary effects of population growth can be just as damaging, as for example the proliferation of major road-building schemes such as the routing of the M3 motorway through Twyford Down with its profoundly harmful effects on habitats and landscape. Even lesser road-widening operations often lead to the loss of important roadside-verge sites.

Against this background, a number of organizations have been stimulated to work to halt the decline in the quality and quantity of wildlife habitats with its consequent damage to the county's rich flora and fauna. At a county level, the Hampshire and Isle of Wight Wildlife Trust (formed in 1960 as the Hampshire and Isle of Wight Naturalists' Trust), has grown steadily both in terms of its membership and its ability to promote nature conservation in the county. The Trust now owns or leases and manages over 50 nature reserves, mainly in Hampshire, covering an area of around 2,088ha. As previously shown, this is only a small fraction of the county's total area and so an equally and perhaps even more important role for the Trust is the promotion of wildlife conservation throughout the whole of the rest of the county, including its urban environment.

This work includes liaising with landowners over management of important wildlife sites; involvement at Structure Plan and Local Plan inquiries; commenting on planning applications; and, not least, an educational role in stimulating interest in wildlife conservation at all levels. Roadside verges are important in the county as refuges for plants, often representing the last vestiges of a habitat destroyed in the areas immediately adjacent to them. The Hampshire County Council has co-operated in the production of a roadside-verge policy to conserve and protect such areas.

The County Council has played and continues to play a major part in helping to conserve the county's flora, not least through its innovative Countryside Heritage Policy, designed to encourage the conservation of habitats which do not quite reach SSSI standard and which, without that protection, would be particularly vulnerable to potential damage. The Council has an active policy to conserve important wildlife habitats, and is a major landowner of such local nature reserves (LNRs). It also provides advice to landowners on sensitive land-management, an important example being the Council's involvement in woodland-felling applications.

The Nature Conservancy Council (in England, now reconstituted as English Nature) was founded in 1949 as a government agency to promote the designation and management of SSSIs, of which there are currently some 43,390ha in Hampshire. It is also a significant landowner in the county, with such areas as Old Winchester Hill and Beacon Hill, Warnford.

Despite the financial constraints on its work, English Nature plays a major role in conserving the county's flora through its application of the Wildlife and Countryside Act, 1981. Part of this Act encompasses habitat protection, including the designation of SSSIs. A specific aspect of the Act in relation to plants makes it an offence for anyone intentionally to pick, uproot or destroy any wild plant listed in Schedule 8, which is reviewed quinquennially; it also makes it unlawful for any unauthorized person to uproot any other wild plant. In addition to protecting the rarer species, it may increasingly deter those people who dig up plants for their gardens such as primroses and cowslips, which have decreased in frequency.

Vascular plants listed in Schedule 8 (as amended, March 1995) which have been recorded in Hampshire (vice-counties 11 and 12) are:

Ajuga chamaepitys	‡*Luronium natans*
Altheaea hirsuta	†*Lythrum hyssopifolia*
**Carex depauperata*	†*Melampyrum arvense*
†*Centaurium tenuiflorum*	*Mentha pulegium*
Cephalanthera rubra	*Ononis reclinata
†*Chenopodium vulvaria*	†*Ophrys sphegodes*
Cyperus fuscus	†*Petrorhagia nanteulii*
†*Damasonium alisma*	*Polygonum maritimum*
Eriophorum gracile	*Pulicaria vulgaris*
†*Eryngium campestre*	†*Ranunculus*
Filago lutescens	*ophioglossifolius*
†*F. pyramidata*	†*Rhinanthus angustifolius*
Gentianella anglica	(as *R. serotinus*)
(endemic to Britain)	*Salvia pratensis*
Gladiolus illyricus	†*Stachys germanica*
**Gnaphalium luteoalbum*	*Teucrium botrys*
Himantoglossum	†*Thlaspi perfoliatum*
hircinum	†*Veronica spicata*

as well as the bryophytes:

Drepanocladus vernicosus *Zygodon forsteri*

and the lichens:

†*Caloplaca luteoalba*	†*Physcia tribacioides*
Catillaria laureri	†*Teloschistes flavicans*
Parmelia minarum	

* probably or certainly erroneous
† probably or certainly extinct
‡ probably deliberately introduced

Another national body with local interests is the National Trust which has acquired some important wildlife sites in Hampshire such as Ludshott Common, Stockbridge Down, and Bramshaw Commons and Manorial Wastes. Its remit is to manage such owned sites and it does not have wider responsibilities for the surrounding countryside. However, under the National Trust Act of 1907, it is empowered to declare its land inalienable, and subsequent legislation has given it the right to appeal to Parliament against compulsory purchase orders.

The Woodland Trust too has acquired and manages a number of botanically valuable woodland sites such as Binswood, and is looking for others to purchase.

In addition, a number of local authorities and organizations collectively play a significant part in helping to conserve our flora – District Councils, field clubs, natural history societies and many more.

Nor must the vital role played by individual botanical recorders in discovering additional sites of threatened species, or even species new to the county, be forgotten. For species under threat, *The British Red Data Book* (RDB) has been valuable in recording a wider range of endangered (E) and vulnerable (V) species than those cited above under Schedule 8 of the Wildlife and Countryside Act. The greatest number of such species, listed according to habitat, occur in lowland pasture or open grassland, followed by those of wetland habitats, and then those of woodland and scrub. British RDB species in categories 'E' or 'V' recorded in Hampshire are all in Schedule 8 (listed above) and cited (as Sched. 8) after the frequency category of the relevant species in the systematic accounts. Useful though the national RDB list is, a county list compiled on similar lines would be even more valuable in highlighting species threatened at a local level in Hampshire; conservation measures might then prevent such species reaching the national list. It is hoped that a county RDB list will be produced in the near future.

PETER BROUGH

2. List of Nature Reserves

The following abbreviations are used in the tables below:

(i) Organizations managing reserves:

BC – Butterfly Conservation (The British Butterfly Conservation Society)

BDBC – Basingstoke & Deane Borough Council
EN – English Nature
GBC – Gosport Borough Council
HCC – Hampshire County Council
HDC – Hart District Council
HWT – Hampshire Wildlife Trust
SCC – Southampton City Council
WT – The Woodland Trust

(ii) Conditions of access:

F – Access along Footpaths
F/P – Access along Footpaths; Permit elsewhere
F/R – Access along Footpaths; no access to Restricted areas
O – Open Access
O/P – Open Access to certain areas; Permit elsewhere
O/R – Open Access except to Restricted areas
O/r – Open Access except to small restricted areas
P – Permit required

Table 1 National Nature Reserves (NNR)   (See Postscript on p.74)

Reserve	Map Ref.	Managed by	Habitat	Date declared	Area (to nearest ha)	Access
ASHFORD HILL	561620	EN	neutral-acid meadows	1986	20	F/P
BEACON HILL, WARNFORD	603226	EN	chalk grass/scrub/wood	1986	39	F/P
MARTIN DOWN:		EN/HCC				
S of A354	046193	"	chalk grass/chalk heath	1978	251	O/r
Tidpit Down	059180	"	chalk grass/chalk heath	1982	13	O/r
N of A354	038204	"	chalk grass/Roman Road	1983	37	O/r
Kitt's Grave	032205	"	chalk grass/scrub/wood	1986	33	O/r
NORTH SOLENT:						
Beaulieu Estate	380037-420969	EN	coastal shingle & sand/ salt-marsh/wetland/	1980	660	P
Cadland Estate	454014-458990	EN	heath/mixed wood	1982	103	F/P
OLD WINCHESTER HILL:	643208	EN	chalk grass/scrub/ mixed wood	1951	62	F/P

Small extension added   1971

Table 2 Local Nature Reserves (LNR)   (See Postscript on p.74)

Reserve	Map Ref.	Managed by	Habitat	Date declared	Area (to nearest ha)	Access
ASHFORD HANGERS (& THE WARREN)	738268 / 728283	HCC/HWT	beech, ash, elm, maple, & yew wood	1979	142	O/R
BROXHEAD COMMON	806374	HCC	dry heath/wood	1979	46	O
CALSHOT MARSHES	484021	HCC	salt-marsh/tidal mud	1979	49	F/R
CASTLE BOTTOM	795597	HCC	heath/valley bog/wood	1991	29	O
CATHERINGTON DOWN	690143	HCC/HWT	chalk grass/fringe wood	1979	12	O
CHESSEL BAY	441128	SCC	mud-flat/shingle/salt-marsh	1989	14	O
CRAB WOOD	438298	HCC/HWT	oak–ash/hazel coppice	1979	39	O
FARLINGTON MARSHES	685043	HWT[1]	coastal grass/reeds/lagoon	1974	120	O/P
FLEET POND	823552	HDC	lake/reeds/carr/heath	1977	55	O
GUTNER POINT	735015	HCC	salt-marsh/tidal mud	1991	66	P
HOOK-WITH-WARSASH		HCC		1988	227	F
Hook Valley, Hook Links	493045		coastal wetland/wood/shingle			
Bunny Meadows	488071		tidal mud/reeds/meadow			
MERCURY MARSHES, HAMBLE	484078	HCC	salt-marsh/reeds/scrub	1988	7	O
THE KENCH, HAYLING ISLAND	692998	HCC	salt-marsh/tidal mud	1991	6	O
LYMINGTON-KEYHAVEN MARSHES	325925	HCC	coastal grass/marsh/lagoon	1990	184	O/R
OXENBOURNE DOWN	715190	HCC/HWT	chalk grass/scrub/yew wood	1979	84	P
PAMBER FOREST	615610	BDBC	mixed broad-leaved wood	1980	193	O
SANDY POINT	748992	HCC	coastal dune/heath/grass	1991	15	P
SHORTHEATH COMMON	775365	HCC	heath/bog	1994	60	O
THE MOORS, BISHOPS WALTHAM	561168	HCC	wet meadows/fen/carr	1991	14	F/P
THE WILD GROUNDS	580009	GBC	coastal marsh/carr/oakwood	1981	27	P
TITCHFIELD HAVEN	535025	HCC	reeds/lagoons/meadow	1973	103	F/P
Upper Titchfield Haven	542039	HCC[2]	wet meadows	1993	13	P

[1] owned by Portsmouth City Council
[2] owned by Hampshire Wildlife Trust

Table 3 Hampshire Wildlife Trust Nature Reserves

Some reserves are managed jointly, as indicated. A few sensitive sites, and those on the Isle of Wight, have been omitted from the list. In some cases (e.g. Keyhaven) there has been a series of leases, progressively increasing the reserve area. In such cases, the date of initial acquisition and the current area of the reserve are given.

Reserve	Map Ref.	Managed by	Habitat	Date declared	Area (to nearest ha)	Access
ANCELLS FARM	824558	HWT	wet heath/pond	1984	2	O
BARTLEY HEATH & WARNBOROUGH GREENS	730527	HWT	wet heath/pools/birch–oak	1986	91	O
	729521	HWT	chalk–river meadows			O
BASINGSTOKE CANAL FLASHES	842528	HWT	open water	1978	2	O/P
BLACKDAM	654516	HWT	marsh/scrub/ponds	1973	4	O
BROUGHTON DOWN	294327	HWT	chalk grass/beech wood	1978	26	O
CATHERINGTON DOWN	690143	HWT/HCC	chalk grass/fringe wood	1963	12	O
CHAPPETTS COPSE	653232	HWT	beechwood on chalk	1981	13	P
THE CHASE	444627	HWT	mixed wood/carr/lake	1968	48	O
COULTERS DEAN	747193	HWT	chalk grass/scrub	1972	1	P
CRAB WOOD	438298	HWT/HCC	oak–ash/hazel coppice	1969	39	O
CURBRIDGE	528118	HWT	coppice wood/salt-marsh	1968	10	O
EMER BOG	397215	HWT	heath/bog/carr/mixed wood	1982	49	F
FARLINGTON MARSHES	685043	HWT	coastal grass/reeds/lagoon	1962	120	O/P
FLETCHWOOD MEADOWS	340113	HWT	neutral-acid meadow	1984	5	P
FLEXFORD:						
Upper	424220	HWT	alder carr/meadow	1982	10	O
Lower	424214	HWT	meadow/wood	1988	9	O
GREYWELL MOORS	720510	HWT	fen/carr	1989	11	O
HEADLEY GRAVEL-PIT	513627	HWT	disused gravel-works	1990	7	F
HOE ROAD MEADOW	565174	HWT	hay meadow	1992	3	O
HOLMSLEY GRAVEL-PIT	206990	HWT	open water/disused pit	1978	3	P
HOOKHEATH MEADOWS	646080	HWT	wet meadows/wood/scrub	1991	14	P
HYTHE SPARTINA MARSH	433073	HWT	salt-marsh	1974	9	O
KEYHAVEN & PENNINGTON MARSHES (& Hurst Spit)	310910	HWT	salt-marsh/tidal mud/ shingle spit	1962	797	F
LONG ALDERMOOR	273097	HWT	alder-willow carr/grass	1964	3	P
LOWER TEST	364150	HWT	salt-marsh/reeds/meadows	1977	120	F/P
LYMINGTON RIVER REEDS	308917	HWT	reeds/river	1993	32	F
MAPLEDURWELL FEN	678520	HWT	fen	1986	1	P

Table 3 (cont.)

Reserve	Map Ref.	Managed by	Habitat	Date declared	Area (to nearest ha)	Access
MICHELDEVER SPOIL HEAPS	520445	HWT	chalk spoil/scrub	1979	8	P
NOAR HILL	740320	HWT	chalk grass/scrub	1972	12	O
OLD BURGHCLERE LIME QUARRY	473573	HWT	disused chalk quarry	1968	3	P
OXENBOURNE DOWN	715190	HWT/HCC	chalk grass/yew wood	1966	85	P
RON WARD'S MEADOW	601606	HWT	hay meadow	1992	14	P
ROYDON WOODS	310003	HWT	mixed wood/heath/meadows	1978	300	F/P
SHUTTS COPSE	638264	HWT	oak–hazel wood	1975	4	P
SINAH COMMON	693995	HWT	sand-dune slack	1962	5	P
ST CATHERINE'S HILL	485275	HWT	chalk grass/scrub	1973	30	O
SWANWICK	505097	HWT	disused clay-pits	1991	28	O
THE WARREN	728283	HWT/HCC	ash–hazel–beech–yew wood	1968	23	O
WARREN BOTTOM COPSE	550540	HWT	oak–hazel wood	1981	3	P
WEAVERS DOWN BOG	811340	HWT	wet heath/bog	1987	2	P
WHITEHOUSE MEADOW	840564	HWT	wet acid grass/wood	1991	1	O
WINNALL MOORS:						
Upper	492310	HWT	wet meadows	1981	25	P
Lower	487300	HWT	fen/reeds	1981	15	O

NOTE. Upper Titchfield Haven Reserve, owned by HWT but managed by HCC, is included in Table 2.

Table 4 Butterfly Conservation Reserves

Reserve	Map Ref.	Managed by	Habitat	Date declared	Area (to nearest ha)	Access
BENTLEY STATION MEADOW	794429	BC	meadow/wooded stream	1992	4	O
MAGDALEN HILL DOWN	502293	BC	unimproved chalk grass	1989	9	O
YEW HILL (Compton Down)	456265	BC	unimproved chalk grass	1989	3	O

Table 5 Woodland Trust Properties

Reserve	Map Ref.	Managed by	Habitat	Date declared	Area	Access
BINSWOOD	764370	WT	ancient wood pasture	1985	62	O
HOME FARM	653415	WT	newly-planted wood/open space	1990	137	O
JONATHANS WOOD	373499	WT	woodland	1987	0.2	O
OTTERBOURNE PARK WOOD	458223	WT	woodland	1986	24	O
PARK WOOD	685104	WT	woodland	1991	3	O
ROE SPINNEY	207024	WT	newly-planted wood	1987	0.4	O
RUNNYDOWN COPSE	570182	WT	woodland	1988	4	O
UPPER BARN & CROWDHILL COPSE	485203 485197	WT	woodland	1990	31	O
VALLEY PARK WOODS	424210	WT	woodland	1988	28	O

Postscript

On 28 November 1995, EN and HCC declared four new NNRs. These are Ashford Hangers, Castle Bottom, Lymington–Keyhaven Marshes, and the whole of Titchfield Haven, all listed as LNRs in *Table 2* on p.70. At the same time, two new LNRs – Hacketts Marsh, 487090, 21ha, and Herbert Plantation, 475623, 25ha – were declared, and the enlargement of two other reserves was announced – Martin Down NNR (*Table 1*, p.69) to 339ha and Crab Wood LNR (*Table 2*, p.70) to 73ha.

HWT has also taken over management of three new reserves (announced too late to be included in the Tables) at Blashford Lakes, Ringwood; Anton Lakes, Andover; and Baddesley Common, adjoining Emer Bog.

Addresses for further information:

National Nature Reserves (in Hampshire):
English Nature, 1 Southampton Road, Lyndhurst, Hants SO43 7BU.
Tel.(01703) 283944.

Local Nature Reserves (HCC owned):
Hampshire County Council, Countryside and Community Dept., Mottisfont Court, High Street, Winchester, Hants SO23 8ZF.
Tel.(01962) 846002.

(For information on other Local Nature Reserves apply to the appropriate local council which owns/manages the reserve).

Hampshire Wildlife Trust Nature Reserves:
Hampshire Wildlife Trust, 8 Romsey Road, Eastleigh, Hants SO50 9AL.
Tel. (01703) 613636/613737.

Butterfly Conservation:
Head Office, P.O. Box 222, Dedham, Colchester, Essex CO7 6EY.
Tel.(01206) 322342.

The Woodland Trust:
Autumn Park, Dysart Road, Grantham, Lincs. NG31 6LL.
Tel. (01476) 74297.

PAUL BOWMAN

CHAPTER VII

SOME EARLIER WORKERS ON THE HAMPSHIRE FLORA

DAVID E. ALLEN

Blest with probably the richest flora of any county in Britain, and with the further good fortune to lie in that part of the kingdom in which searchers after plants have always been most numerous, Hampshire has predictably had a long and crowded history of botanical investigation. Down through the years the number who have made lists for their neighbourhood or contributed at least a record or two must total many hundreds. Most of the earlier ones find mention in the relevant section of Townsend's Flora, though there were some whose work was as yet unknown or insufficiently appreciated at that period – in particular, the full scale of the pioneering achievement of JOHN GOODYER (1592–1664), a manorial steward in early 17th-century Petersfield and district, the first true amateur naturalist in Britain of any stature (for virtually everyone else up to then had a pecuniary motive for interesting themselves in herbs). Most appropriately, we now know, the family with which Gilbert White was multiply connected by marriage was directly descended from Goodyer's sister. That corner of Hampshire, it turns out, has good claim to be regarded as the cradleland of English natural history.

There is space in these pages, alas, to recall only the leading figures: those who compiled the major published accounts which have served as the focus for fieldwork at successive periods or else who, while not rising to that height, strove no less hard to co-ordinate the efforts of their contemporaries with a similar end in view. Strikingly, four of these belonged to that narrow social layer known to the Victorians as the 'squarsonry' – clerical families who doubled as landed gentry – while two others came to Hampshire botany from years spent in India, also a background highly characteristic of the era.

Book-length monographs describing a county's flora (most often just its flowering plants and ferns) have been a proud tradition of British botany since John Ray's Cambridge catalogue of 1660, though the genre did not attain its classic form and dimensions till two hundred years later. Hampshire was an obvious early candidate for one of these productions, but perhaps because of its very size and floristic richness there were to be three abortive attempts, of greater or lesser magnitude, before that goal was eventually reached.

The first of those attempts, easily the most substantial of the three, was by WILLIAM ARNOLD BROMFIELD (1801–1851). Born and brought up in Boldre (where the vicar at the time of his baptism was the celebrated writer, the Revd William Gilpin), Bromfield came of a family with deep Hampshire roots. An ancestor had been a New Forest verderer and Bow-bearer to King Charles II, while his father, by being able to prove that he was 'Founder's Kin', had the privilege of a Winchester College education at a preferential rate. For some reason the only son did not follow in the father's footsteps, either in that respect or in going up to Oxford and subsequently entering the Church; instead, he opted to study medicine and went for that purpose to Glasgow University. Through an accident of legislation it had just then become obligatory for anyone who wished to practise medicine in England or Wales to go on to obtain the licence of the Society of Apothecaries, candidates for which were traditionally examined, *inter alia*, on their knowledge of wild herbs and their medicinal uses. Most of the universities had hurriedly appointed professors of botany in response to this, and they in their turn instituted classes in the field. Glasgow's new professor, W. J. Hooker, particularly shone at that novel form of teaching and awoke a lifelong enthusiasm for field botany among quite a number of his students. One of those was Bromfield. For him the prospect of a career in medicine lost such appeal as it may have had, and on leaving university he decided instead to travel, having come into wealth on the early death of his father. Returning to England after four years, he then set up

74

home with his sister, living in turn in Hastings, Clifton and Southampton before finally settling in the Isle of Wight in 1836. The rest of his life was henceforward to be almost completely given over to compiling a Flora of that island and mainland Hampshire (the two at that time still a single administrative entity), a work conceived on the heedlessly expansive scale such as only someone of ample means and leisure could contemplate and notable, in due course, for the enviable elaborateness with which locality details are cited. Interrupted by further lengthy spells of foreign travel, however, the book was still unpublished when a bout of typhus contracted in Syria resulted in his early death. Fortunately he had published shortly before, in 1848–50, a preliminary version of the intended section on Hampshire, under the title *Flora Hantoniensis*, in the form of a lengthy paper serialized in *The Phytologist*, the main journal of the day devoted to British botany. An interleaved copy of this, with many corrections and additions by him, was found after his death and is now in the library at Kew. The Isle of Wight section, in a more advanced state, and with the advantage that none of it had been publicly released, was subsequently seen into print as *Flora Vectensis*. When, fifteen years later, Townsend appeared on the scene and resumed the work on the joint county that this energetic predecessor of his had begun, his task was considerably lightened by inheriting these very solid foundations on which to build.

They were not the only foundations. ROBERT SOUTHEY HILL (1817–1872) was another who would appear to have taken up the challenge of that now-gaping lacuna in the literature and gone much of the way towards publishing a Hampshire Flora. In his case, however, the manuscript was lost: all that survived for Townsend (and for us) was his local herbarium of some 1,500 sheets, which was purchased on his death for a hoped-for county museum and eventually, when those hopes proved ill-founded at that time, donated to the British Museum (Natural History). Like Bromfield's, Hill's Hampshire roots went deep: his mother had been a friend of Jane Austen. As with Bromfield, too, his keenness for botany dated from his days as a medical student – though for him those days began more humbly, with an apprenticeship in Basingstoke, and were followed perforce by practice in that town for the rest of his life. According to his obituary, he was 'probably better acquainted than any one living with the general natural history of North Hants', but on account of 'an insuperable aversion to publishing his opinions or observations, he not as widely known in the scientific world as his varied attainments merited.'

FREDERIC ISAAC WARNER (1841–1896) did not suffer from such inhibitions. In partnership with his brother as a solicitor and insurance agent in Winchester, he at once emerged as the leading botanical light when, in 1869, a scientific and literary society was founded there, publishing frequently and at length in its early annual reports (including on fungi and bryophytes), and creating a separate botanical section, which organised its own programme of field and indoor meetings. In 1872 these gave rise to a printed list of vascular plants recently found in the Winchester district, totalling 404 species in all. That this was seen by Warner as merely the prelude to a Flora of the county as a whole is evident from Townsend's later words, but with his health failing and recognizing that a publication worthy of that name could be but a distant prospect, he magnanimously stepped aside and passed over all his data to the newcomer and likelier author. All trace of his 'very good and complete' herbarium of Hampshire plants has unfortunately now been lost; and although the society was to continue in being for seventy years more, its botanical activity effectively ceased for good as soon as he stepped down as its Honorary Secretary in 1876.

By that time FREDERICK TOWNSEND (1822–1905) had been living in the county for eleven years. He had visited it at least once earlier, in 1844, when the records show that he added horned pondweed to the Hampshire list and botanized around Wickham with Bromfield. 'My first lessons in botany were learnt on Hampshire ground', he was later to recall, though a fondness for the subject was actually a family tradition: his sister Elizabeth was also sufficiently keen to form a herbarium, which reputedly incorporated specimens inherited from their ancestors, and a cousin, Albert John Hambrough (1820–1861), was a well-known Isle of Wight botanist. Two others who were to contribute notably to the eventual Flora, Miss Charlotte Ellen Palmer (1830–1914) and her nephew Bolton King (1860–1937), were also either relations or close family friends, the former later acquiring Elizabeth Townsend's collection. The Palmers were long-standing neighbours of the Townsends in the far south of Warwickshire, whither Frederick's clergyman father had come to take up a family-owned living.

Frederick, the second son, early showed talent as an artist, and after leaving Harrow School went to Italy for a time with the thought of making painting his profession. Deciding against that, he then went up to Trinity College, Cambridge, at a later age than usual, and quickly gained the friendship there of the Revd W. W. Newbould (who was later to render him extensive assistance in tracing early Hampshire records) and, more important, of C. C. Babington, the country's foremost critical botanist, whose views were to remain a lifelong influence. Around the same time he also joined the two national botanical societies and began contributing specimens to their respective annual exchanges.

It was thus a well-prepared mind that he brought to the county when, in 1865, two years after his marriage, he settled at Shedfield, in a large, attractive house which still stands today just outside the village. Possessed of independent means, he could have chosen to live anywhere in Britain or abroad, and it may be that he selected Hampshire because of the scope that he was aware it offered botanically. He lost little time, at any rate, in starting to accumulate records, though from his own account it would appear that the idea of writing a Flora did not take shape till 1872 at the earliest. Initially he had in mind restricting this to mainland Hampshire only, in view of the very full coverage of Wight in Bromfield's *Flora Vectensis*. The rarity and high cost of that work, however, caused him to change plan, a decision which we cannot now but regret, for the time and effort that he consequently put into working the Island was necessarily at the expense of a more thorough exploration of the mainland. Indeed, considering the poor transport at that period and the problems this posed in penetrating remoter areas, the period allowed for fieldwork was unduly truncated, for internal evidence suggests that the last records admitted were those of 1879. By then the first pages may even have been in type, for the discovery by Henry Groves of the adder's-tongue spearwort near Hythe had to go into an appendix, even though it had been 'found last year', which the British Museum sheet shows to have been 1878. At that point Townsend fell seriously ill and two more years elapsed before he was fit to return to the editing. As a result it was not until 1884 that *Flora of Hampshire* was finally published – a year later in fact than asserted on the title-page (as shown by the dates of some records on a last-minute addendum inserted just before the index). Deservedly, it appeared to high acclaim, for thin though the spatial coverage was by present-day standards the taxonomy was up-to-the-minute and even broke new ground in some respects.

Long before then, though, Townsend had ceased to reside in the county, having succeeded in 1874 to the ownership of the family seat, a 17th-century hall near Shipston-on-Stour. Here he lived the life of an ideal country squire, greatly improving the house and its garden, riding to hounds and pursuing with all his characteristic proficiency his favourite recreations of archery and photography – to which he was to add

cycling when around 74. Election to the House of Commons, two years after the Flora came out, removed him from Hampshire botany even further.

Nevertheless, he never lost touch. Patiently logging the numerous additions that came in, at the end of 20 years (having put behind him a monograph of the eyebrights) he eventually decided that he owed it to the county to provide it with his Flora in an enlarged and updated edition. For a man by then going on for 80 the amount of work this involved must have been taxing in the extreme (the lengthy section on the brambles had to be totally rewritten, for a start), but he was fortunate to have the assistance of an outstanding younger field botanist, the Revd E. S. Marshall. Even so, his personal expertise was well in evidence in the finished text, notably in a special, six-page account of the perplexing genus *Salicornia*.

The new work – for that is effectively what it was – is said to have issued from the press towards the end of 1904, though again there is cause to treat the date with some suspicion (for a record is included seemingly based on a specimen labelled as collected in August of the following year). The important thing, however, is that it came out in time, for his death was to take place within just a matter of months. Modest to the last, he would have wished for no finer memorial – unless it was the cord-grass of Southampton Water, which Henry and James Groves, the two young brothers who had been his earliest and most prolific Hampshire co-workers, had named in his honour a quarter of a century before.

Absentee though he had been for so many years, Townsend's continuing presence in the background had had a sustaining effect on botanical activity in the county. With his death, and the appearance almost simultaneously of a newly definitive Flora, it would not have been surprising if interest had waned for a period. That that did not happen was due in part to the recent arrival in the county (albeit on its very edge) of another of Britain's foremost critical botanists – as though as a heaven-sent replacement for Townsend. This was EDWARD FRANCIS LINTON (1848–1928), one of a pair of clergymen brothers who were equally prominent in national botanical circles throughout that generation. Linton's background was remarkably similar to Townsend's but, unlike him, he did not have the luck in later life to inherit grandeur. After ten years as a vicar in Norfolk ill health had forced him into temporary retirement in a more amenable climate, bringing him to Bournemouth in 1888. Here he launched into intensive study of three of the largest and most challenging critical groups, the hawkweeds, the brambles and the willows, for all three of which he was chiefly responsible for the issue of authoritative national sets, for the encouragement and guidance of fellow specialists. At the same time he explored the surrounding countryside on foot, work which culminated in 1900 in his publishing a *Flora of Bournemouth*. Within the space of four years Hampshire thus had the benefit of two book-length monographs, both of the highest quality. One year later, long days in the field having fully restored his health, Linton felt able to return to parish work and moved to Edmondsham, just across the Dorset border, as rector. Two decades here led to innumerable further records, with the result that in 1919, one year before his final retirement, he reissued the Flora with a lengthy appendix listing the more interesting additions. His last ten years were spent in Southbourne, but were rendered unproductive by frailty. Concealing much kindness and good humour behind a deceptively stern and pompous exterior, Linton was a most exact and painstaking observer, with a range of expertise that eventually exceeded even Townsend's. Though he established a botanical society during his earlier years in Bournemouth, he was nevertheless all along too marginally located to be able to assume the leading role in the county's botany that Townsend had for so long filled.

Instead, that role fell at first to Canon Vaughan, a botanical lightweight by comparison. JOHN VAUGHAN (1855–1922) had come to Hampshire in 1881, shortly after ordination, initially as a curate in Alton. Here he had married the daughter of his vicar and discovered a flair for public speaking in lecturing on natural history at the town's Curtis Museum. When, in 1885, the Hampshire Field Club was formed, he joined it almost immediately and was invited to act as local secretary for the Alton district. After a series of livings in other parts of the county he was appointed a residentiary canon of Winchester Cathedral in 1909, a post he was to hold till his death. This brought him into the centre of things; and when the Field Club a few years later adopted a system of subject secretaries, he was by then the natural choice to serve in that capacity for his favourite field of botany. Around that time he contemplated bringing out a supplement to Townsend's Flora, in conjunction with the Revd John Edward Kelsall (1864–1924), co-author of the then standard work on the county's birds, who had explored the Milton area over many years. Nothing came of that, however, and instead, from 1919 onwards, he contented himself with annual botanical reports to the *Proceedings* of the Club. But it was as a lecturer and writer that he was chiefly influential, with a happy knack of communicating his enthusiasm and an enviable fluency with the pen. Botany was only one of those enthusiasms but it was well to the fore in the essays he contributed to numerous magazines, three collections of which were subsequently issued as books.

It was to JOHN FREDERICK RAYNER (1854–1947) that the task of producing the by then much-needed supplement to Townsend's Flora accordingly fell. In business as a florist at Swaythling most of his life, Rayner took full advantage of his location to work the New Forest and the Isle of Wight particularly intensively. A botanical 'all-rounder', he was equally at home with bryophytes and fungi as with flowering plants and ferns. Like Canon Vaughan, he was also an energetic popularizer of the subject and ever-ready to assist the local natural history societies, in most of which he held office at one time or another. Though active for many years previously, it was during the First World War that he emerged to prominence, notably through annual reports on fungi he then began contributing to the Field Club's *Proceedings*, and the publication of two substantial papers on the alien flora of Hampshire and Wight in 1924 and 1925. In 1923 the Club asked him to fill the gap left by Canon Vaughan's death and revive the plan for *A Supplement to Frederick Townsend's Flora of Hampshire and the Isle of Wight* – to give it the rather ponderous title it bore when it eventually appeared six years later under the auspices of the Club. The announcement that this was in hand served to raise a fresh flurry of activity in the county in the intervening years, to which the Club's annual botany reports, now contributed by Rayner, bear ample witness. He for his part went to special pains to collect material of hitherto underworked critical groups, sending this to national and international specialists (with a dispiriting lack of success in the case of the dandelions, an outcome which only deepened his scepticism of the hair-splitting of 'garret-botanists'). For him personally the book fittingly crowned his many years work on local botany, for soon afterwards he retired to live in Kent. It was in Hampshire, however, that his heart always remained, and on his death, in his ninety-third year, his ashes were scattered in accordance with his wishes in his beloved New Forest, in a heathy spot not far from Picket Post.

By good fortune, no sooner had the Field Club lost Rayner than two further capable workers materialized who effectively filled his place.

One of these was HENRY PUREFOY FITZGERALD (1867–1948), a one-time science master at Wellington College who, after a period market-gardening in Kent, had settled at Chandler's Ford during the 1920s. Already the author of books on plants and the founder of a long-lived Botanical Essay Society, he had in fact been a Hampshire botanist many years earlier, contributing a list of records additional to Townsend's Flora to the Field Club's initial *Proceedings*, back in 1887. Many of these finds were from the district around Preston Candover, where his family had been the lords of the manor for generations (the village inn is still called the 'Purefoy Arms') and where he grew up. In a small copse near there, at the early age of twelve, he made the only Hampshire find of coralroot in a possibly native site, a record communicated to Townsend – along with yellow star-of-Bethlehem, an addition to the county list – just as the first edition of the Flora was passing through the press. 'A complete herbarium illustrative of the flora of Candover Valley', mentioned as in his possession in 1890, unfortunately cannot now be traced. On returning to Hampshire he immersed himself in local affairs but found time between duties as a magistrate and the secretaryship of Winchester Croquet Club to lead many of the botanical excursions of the Field Club during the 1930s.

The weightier botanical figure locally during that decade, however, was PATRICK MARTIN HALL (1894–1941), a chartered surveyor and land agent in Fareham. A keen naturalist in boyhood, he first made his mark while a Scholar at Winchester College, submitting many critical violets to the then British authority on the group and co-authoring a paper on orchids. He was to specialize in both of these, and latterly also in bladderworts, on returning to the subject around 1927. His organizing ability was soon recognized and the Field Club invited him to take over as botany recorder, a capacity in which he performed with such drive and accuracy that the Botanical Society and Exchange Club of the British Isles increasingly began to call on his talents, in 1936 inviting him to serve as its first editor. As broad in his interests as Townsend and Purefoy Fitzgerald, he extended his taxonomic abilities to the study of old glass as well as playing cricket for the county and serving as long-time secretary of the Hampshire Hogs. Tragically, when war broke out, his administrative gifts led to his being overburdened, his health gave way and he died, very suddenly, while still in his forties. His main, very extensive herbarium he bequeathed to the British Museum (Natural History), but with the stipulation that a subsidiary collection of Hampshire and Isle of Wight voucher specimens that he had formed should be returned to the county when Winchester acquired the new natural history museum that was at that time envisaged.

It was friendship with Hall that was mainly responsible for luring into Hampshire in the 1930s a man who has been credibly described as 'one of the greatest British amateur botanists of this century'. This was EDWARD CHARLES WALLACE (1909–1986). A bachelor whose entire career was spent with W. H.

Smith's, the booksellers and newsagents, Wallace lived at Sutton in Surrey and over the years built up immense field knowledge and experience, which he was always delighted to share with others. Though primarily a bryologist (and secretary of the British Bryological Society for 22 years), he also had a special interest in sedges and willows, making many excellent finds in the county in those pre-war years. Subsequently he filled the vacuum in Hampshire critical botany left by Hall's death, monitoring all the records sent in for the northern half of the county. In tribute to his work, Hampshire Wildlife Trust has named after him its new reserve at Greywell Moors, a hunting-ground to which he was especially attached.

Yet another major figure to emerge at that period, albeit a solitary one, was GEORGE ANNESLEY ROSS WATTS (1873–1949). A retired Indian Cavalry colonel who had earned his botanical spurs helping with the new *Flora of Devon*, Watts did a great deal of quiet fieldwork in the north-east of the county after moving to Fleet around 1933. Precise and methodical, he wrote up each day's work in a series of diaries and described in detail every new species that he came across in a further set of notebooks. Bequeathed to the British Museum (Natural History), these have since proved a prolific source of records for that corner of Hampshire.

Hall's premature death in 1941, by robbing the county of its pivotal figure, might well have resulted in a prolonged stagnation, continuing long after the end of the Second World War. Once again, however, providence intervened and ensured that the succession was broken only temporarily. For in 1950, following a career as a research chemist, ALICK WILLIAM WESTRUP (1910–1964) came to Portsmouth to teach at what was then its Municipal Technical College (now the University). An all-round naturalist with a particular leaning towards botany, he was already a keen member of the Botanical Society of the British Isles when, soon after his arrival, that body launched the national mapping scheme that was eventually to find embodiment in the *Atlas of the British Flora* in 1962. Westrup volunteered to co-ordinate the recording for the 10km grid-squares covering south-east Hampshire and the Isle of Wight, undertaking the greater part of the huge amount of work that this involved himself. Out of that grew the idea of producing an entirely new Flora of the two counties, employing the 'tetrad' (2 x 2km grid-square) as the new and smaller mapping unit, an approach just then coming into fashion. This ensured a very much completer coverage than previously, promising the much more detailed picture of plant distribution in the county that the growing emphasis on conservation was making an increasingly urgent matter. With his customary boundless energy, Westrup had made an excellent start to this end when his death abruptly took place – again, like Hall's, at a prematurely early age. It was a grievous loss in several ways: to Hampshire botany as a whole, of course; to Portsmouth and District Natural History Society, of which he was a former president (and which today has a special lecture dedicated to his memory); and, not least, to the botanical scene more generally – for he was a colourful figure, with his invariable beret, his foghorn voice and what must have been one of the last motor-cycles in Britain with a sidecar (which he found handy for his field equipment).

In his will Westrup left everything he had accumulated towards the Flora to the recently-formed Hampshire and Isle of Wight Naturalists' Trust (as the Wildlife Trust was then known). This laid an onus on that body to find someone who would continue to co-ordinate the work and so save it from lapsing indefinitely. With some reluctance, MARGARET PHOEBE YULE (1892–1981) gallantly consented to assume this role. Brought up in Bedfordshire in a botanical family, she was the widow of a colonel, with whom she had retired to Fleet after a final, brief time in India. After his death she moved in 1958 to Bournemouth, where she became active in its Natural Science Society and took up botany again, pursuing it with the same degree of commitment that she brought to her varied other interests: millinery and fine needlework, book-binding and, more surprisingly, Egyptology (the celebrated authority on that, Dr Margaret Murray, was her aunt). Subsequently she made her home at Godshill with a friend who shared her botanical enthusiasm, Miss E. Sylvia Haines. Unfortunately, the fieldwork for the new Flora had only got into full swing by the time of Westrup's death and the volume of records that this was producing had grown to tidal-wave proportions. The task of entering these, let alone the accompanying correspondence, was a formidable one indeed for someone in her eighties and, eventually, her health weakened; after two accidents she found it necessary to hand over and Lady Anne Brewis was appointed by the Trust in her place.

From that point on, the team who have eventually seen the enterprise through to its conclusion gradually came into being – and the past merged into the present.

CHAPTER VIII

BOTANICAL RECORDING AND THE VICE-COUNTY SYSTEM

PAUL BOWMAN

1. The Vice-County Divisions

A practical method of recording the geographical distribution of the British flora and fauna was first devised by H. C. Watson and effectively dates from 1852, when, in the third volume of his *Cybele Britannica* (pp.524–528), he gave a list of the 112 vice-counties into which he proposed to divide the country. The object of the vice-county system was to provide recording areas more equal in size than the counties by dividing the larger counties into two or more vice-counties and merging the smallest counties with adjoining larger ones.

The maps originally used by Watson for his county boundaries were those of England and Scotland published by the Society for the Diffusion of Useful Knowledge in an atlas dated 1844. Thus his county boundaries were those in existence prior to 1844. Beyond that we have no precise information, but certainly changes made after 1844 have to be taken into account.

Watson divided Hampshire into three vice-counties: Isle of Wight (VC 10) (then part of the County of Hampshire, but now a separate Administrative County), South Hants (VC11) and North Hants (VC12). As originally defined, the latter 'are separated by a line traced along the high roads from Winchester westward to Stockbridge, eastward to Petersfield; and continued thence to the borders of Wilts and Sussex.' This was interpreted more precisely in 1969 by J. E. Dandy in *Watsonian Vice-Counties of Great Britain*, which included two 1:625,000 maps.

This line runs along the present A30 road from the Wiltshire boundary east of Lopcombe Corner (261352), eastward to Stockbridge (359350) and the A272 from that point to Winchester (475299) and via St Paul's Hill, Upper High Street, High Street, The Broadway and Bridge Street (486292), then southward along Chesil Street (487289), eastward along

the old B3406 via East Hill and Petersfield Road to the former junction with the A31 (497291 – but now truncated on the west side of the M3 motorway and the junction replaced by a roundabout), eastward along the A31 Petersfield Road to the A272 junction (517289), along the A272 to Petersfield and through the town centre via Winchester Road and Station Road to the junction with the old A3 road (748236), then along the old A3 via Ramshill and London Road north-eastward to Sheet roundabout (756249), then via the A272 to its junction with the old A3, now B2070 (766245), and then south-eastward along the A272 to the Sussex boundary near Maidenmarsh (774240).

Frederick Townsend, in his *Flora of Hampshire, including the Isle of Wight*, employed the three vice-counties for recording purposes, but further divided the county into Districts based on water-catchment areas, with watersheds defining their boundaries – the larger districts being subdivided into Sub-districts so that the recording areas were of a manageable size. J. F. Rayner also used these divisions in his *Supplement to the Flora of Hampshire*.

Towards the end of the 19th century, legislation in the form of Local Government Acts saw substantial exchanges of territory between neighbouring counties. Further changes to the boundaries have been made this century, the most recent large-scale revision being the major re-organization of county boundaries in 1974. Much later, comparatively minor but widespread transfers embodied in 'the Dorset, Hampshire, West Sussex and Wiltshire (County Boundaries) Order 1991' took effect in 1992. As Dandy (1969) remarked, 'the Vice-county System cannot be worked on a basis of changing boundaries' and stability is essential if the great accumulation of records built up under it is to have permanent value. Consequently, this Flora includes records not only from land currently in Hampshire but also from areas that were formerly in the county when the Watsonian vice-counties were originally defined, but are so no longer. The value of the vice-county system for biological recording is that it is, by definition, unchangeable. Subsequent boundary changes are detailed below.

2. Schedule of County Boundary Changes

Key letter relating to map of boundary changes (Fig. 12) is given after the date.

1879 (I) – From Berkshire to Hampshire
SU6363, VC22, 887ha: Mortimer West End tithing (once in Stratfield Mortimer civil parish, Berks); constituted a civil parish in 1894.

1895 (D) – From Wiltshire to Hampshire
SU0717, VC8, 4008ha: Martin and South Damerham (now Damerham) civil parishes.

1895 (E) – From Wiltshire to Hampshire
SU1220, VC8, 738ha: Area of Whitsbury civil parish.

1895 (F) – From Wiltshire to Hampshire
SU2818, VC8, 1965ha: Area of Bramshaw civil

parish, to become Bramshaw East (now part of Bramshaw, Hants); West Wellow (now part of Wellow civil parish); Melchet Park and Plaitford civil parishes which, with the detached No. 2 part of Whiteparish, now form Melchet Park and Plaitford civil parish, Hants.

1895 (H) – From Hampshire to Berkshire
SU3760, VC12, 896ha: Combe civil parish.

1895 (J) – From Hampshire to Surrey
SU8240, VC12, 234ha: Dockenfield civil parish.

1895 (K) – From Sussex to Hampshire
SU8231, VC13, 128ha: Part of Bramshott parish that was formerly in Sussex (including Griggs Green added to the parish in 1844); now part of Bramshott civil parish, Hants.

1931 (C) – From Dorset to Hampshire; 1974 – back to Dorset
SZ0695, VC9, 1121ha: Kinson civil parish comprising Bearwood, Kinson, Ensbury, Northbourne, West Howe and Ensbury Park transferred to Hants in 1931 when

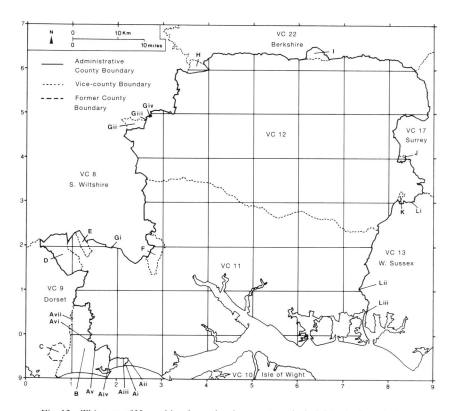

Fig. 12   This map of Hampshire shows the vice-county and administrative boundaries, the changes to the latter described in the text, and the 10 × 10km squares of the National Grid covering the county

Bournemouth County Borough was extended; transferred back when the Borough became part of Dorset in 1974.

1974 (B) – From Hampshire to Dorset
SZ1395, VC11, 11052ha: Bournemouth District, Christchurch District, including civil parish of Hurn and parts of Christchurch East and Sopley civil parishes; St Leonards and St Ives civil parish (now in Wimborne District).

1974 – see also 1931 (C)

1992 (G) – From Hampshire to Wiltshire: 940ha; from Wiltshire to Hampshire: 1ha

(i) SU194197–201193: VC8, Redlynch civil parish, Wilts; VC11, Hale civil parish, Hants: adjustments along curtilages of residential properties and B3080 Forest Road.
(ii) SU2347, VC12: South Tedworth civil parish (except for small adjustment along its boundary with Shipton Bellinger and Kimpton civil parishes) transferred to Kennet District, Wilts.
(iii) SU262482–266490, VC8: North Tidworth civil parish, Wilts; VC12, Kimpton civil parish, Hants: narrow adjustments along fences and 9ha woodland loop at 265489.
(iv) SU278504, VC12, 7ha: Faberstown in Kimpton civil parish, Hants: transferred to Ludgershall civil parish, Kennet District, Wilts.

1992 (A) – From Dorset to Hampshire: 27ha; from Hampshire to Dorset: 19ha

(i) SZ218931–220936, VC11, Borough of Christchurch in Dorset; New Milton civil parish, Hants; realignment to centre of Walkford Brook in Chewton Bunny, culverted in its lower section.
(ii) SZ216947–225947, VC11: 7ha of Borough of Christchurch, Dorset, to New Milton civil parish, Hants; irregular strip north of railway.
(iii) SZ203948–216947, VC11: 11ha of Bransgore civil parish, Hants, to Borough of Christchurch, Dorset; triangular areas south of railway.
(iv) SZ181941–186943, VC11: 3ha of Bransgore civil parish, Hants, to Borough of Christchurch, Dorset; narrow wedge south of railway.
(v) (a) SZ154962–154964, VC11: 2ha of Sopley civil parish, Hants, to Borough of Christchurch, Dorset; realignment to centre of R. Avon on east bank.
    (b) SZ158965–163968, VC11: 15ha of Burton civil parish, Dorset, to Sopley civil parish; rectangular area at Sopley Park College.
    (c) SZ163970, VC11: 1ha of Sopley civil parish to Borough of Christchurch; land east of Harpway Lane.

(vi) SZ139998–SU139004, VC11: 10ha of St Leonards and St Ives civil parish, Dorset, to Sopley civil parish, Hants; realignment to centre of R. Avon on east bank.
(vii) SU107078–107082, VC11: Ellingham, Harbridge and Ibsley civil parish, Hants, to Verwood civil parish, Dorset; realignment to centre of Ebblake Stream.

1992 (L) – From Hampshire to West Sussex: 39ha; from W. Sussex to Hampshire: 10ha.

(i) SU844300–853313, VC12: 34ha of Bramshott and Liphook civil parish, Hants, to Linchmere civil parish, Chichester District, W. Sussex.
(ii) SU736104–740125, VC11: 5ha of Rowlands Castle civil parish, Hants, to Stoughton civil parish, W. Sussex; VC13: 10ha of Stoughton civil parish, to Rowlands Castle civil parish; parkland, residential properties and open land along Woodberry Lane and Finchdean Road.
(iii) SU752053–752058, VC13: 2ha of Southbourne civil parish, W. Sussex, to Borough of Havant, Hants; residential and open land fringing west side of Mill Pond, Emsworth.

3. Disputed Sections of Vice-County Boundary

In addition to changes to the county boundaries, there are cases where it is not clear precisely where the vice-county boundaries lie (e.g. because roads were re-routed during the period between Watson's original specifications and Dandy's map, prepared about a century later). Examples of this (listed below) occur where Dandy's map differs from county boundaries shown on the first edition of the one-inch Ordnance Survey maps (1810–17), now available in facsimile, or from the map given in Townsend's *Flora of Hampshire*. These are not indicated on Figure 12.

1. South Wiltshire (VC8) / South Hampshire (VC11)

(a) Redlynch civil parish (VC8) and Hale, Fordingbridge and Bramshaw civil parishes (VC11) from Windyeats Farm 211181 to Lord's Oak 260176.

Comparison of Dandy's map with the facsimile of the one-inch OS map of 1811 (Sheet 85: Salisbury & New Forest) shows discrepancies of up to 470 metres.

(b) Bramshaw civil parish (formerly Bramshaw East) (VC8) and Copythorne civil parish (VC11) from Stagbury Hill 287160 to Wittensford 285137.

Again, comparison of Dandy's map with the one-inch OS map shows discrepancies of up to 1.2km.

2. South Wiltshire (VC8)/North Hampshire (VC12)

(a)   An area of Tangley civil parish between Redhouse and Roundaway Farms at 3250.

Grose (1957) showed this as VC12 incorporated in Wiltshire, which he estimated at approximately one quarter of a square mile, or about 65ha. He did not, however, give the date when this transfer took place. Dandy (pers.comm.) said he followed Grose as his authority for claiming the area as part of VC12. Recent research has provided no evidence to support this and the conclusion is that any change took place before 1839, and thus before the vice-counties were defined. We therefore assume that this land has always been within VC8.

(b)   Triangular area east of Dunch Hill Plantation in South Tedworth civil parish at 2148.

Grose (1957) showed this as VC8 and claimed the boundary alteration had been made since 1852, but did not give supporting evidence. He estimated the area at about half a square mile, or some 129ha. Comparison of the South Tedworth Tithe Map, surveyed 1840, with the first edition six-inch OS map of 1873 shows that the configuration of the county boundary is in agreement on both, and also with that of successive editions up to the current maps at 1:50,000 and 1:25,000 scales. The recent facsimile of the one-inch OS map of 1817 (Sheet 77: Devizes) shows, however, that the area (estimated at about 30ha) was in Wiltshire at that date. If the 1840 Tithe Map is correct, any change must have taken place before the vice-counties were constituted and the area therefore remains part of VC12.

3. South Hampshire (VC11)/North Hampshire (VC12)

(a)   A272 St Paul's Hill and B3044 Stockbridge Road junction, Winchester 475299 to Hockley House, junction of course of old road with A272, 570271.

The Dandy boundary follows the modern route and not the former high road and track shown on Townsend's map (and as intended by Watson), so that, for example, Cheesefoot Head which Townsend assigned to VC11 is now in VC12.

(b)   Harnham Hill 584274 to The Dean, Bramdean 638265.

The vice-county boundary on Townsend's map diverges southward by up to 1.6km from the Dandy line (the A272), so that records for Hinton Ampner, Brockwood and Inwood Copse which Townsend assigned to VC12 are now in VC11. Until late in the 19th century, the main Petersfield–Winchester road

ran considerably south of the present A272.

4. Berkshire (VC22)/North Hampshire (VC12)

Mortimer West End (VC22) 616625 to 661625. Dandy puts this area in VC22. Mortimer West End was once a tithing of Stratfield Mortimer parish in Berks but, according to Ordnance Survey boundary records, was transferred to Hants in 1879. A local historian, however, asserts that it has always been in Hampshire, at least since Domesday, and this is supported by evidence from several sources including 19th-century and earlier maps, and Domesday Book for Hampshire (Munby, 1982: cap.29, sect.16).

The Hampshire Flora Committee has decided however that, until such time as a wide-ranging review of the Watsonian vice-counties in Britain is undertaken, the Dandy interpretation is to be accepted in all these disputed cases.

4. The National Grid and Tetrad Recording

From 1945, Ordnance Survey maps incorporating the present National Grid were available for the whole of Great Britain. Their preparation had started before the Second World War, following the recommendations in the Final Report of the Davidson Committee in 1938. On the OS map which adopted the metric grid, the country was divided into 100km squares, each of which was originally given a numerical reference and, subsequently, prefix letters were added. These 100km squares are subdivided into one hundred 10km squares (centrads) which are, in turn, subdivided again into one hundred 1km squares.

It should be noted that confusion can arise if reference is made to earlier OS maps with different grids, such as that based on the Cassini projection which was used in World War I, or the one-inch Fifth (Relief) Edition of 1932, on sale until 1937 (Seymour, 1980).

The 10km-square grid system was used for the first detailed distribution atlas of vascular plants in the British Isles (Perring & Walters, 1962). In order to survey the flora of a large county the size of Hampshire as uniformly as possible, however, it was decided to adopt the tetrad system of recording, as has been used in many other counties – a refinement of the national scheme, there being 25 tetrads to one 10km square. The Flora Committee thus set out to achieve a far more detailed record of all native and naturalized plants growing within each 2 x 2km square (four small grid squares on the 1:50,000 OS map, defined by the even-numbered grid figures). Some other county floras have given letter designations to the tetrads; this approach has been rejected for Hampshire as it is considered far more prone to error than the four-figure tetrad grid reference.

Conveniently, the whole of Hampshire falls neatly into two 100km squares of the National Grid, designated by the prefix letters (with numerical equivalents in brackets) SZ(40) covering the south coast, and SU(41) the remainder of the county. In this work, these prefix letters have been omitted as four-figure grid references within Hampshire are unambiguous.

The four-figure tetrad grid-references are arrived at by reading the even-numbered grid lines first eastward from the SW corner of a 10km square (the eastings) and then northward (the northings) from the same point, as shown in the example (Fig. 13).

In boundary tetrads, only records obtained from within and up to the county- or former county-boundary have been included and not those for the whole tetrad. As originally devised by A. W. Westrup, who initiated the Hampshire flora recording scheme in the 1950s, many of the irregularly-shaped areas within tetrads along the county and vice-county boundaries and along the coast were amalgamated with the squares adjacent to them for economy of effort in recording. It became apparent that this method distorted the mapped distribution of a plant to the extent that a coastal species was

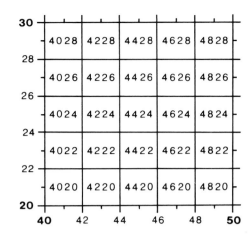

Fig. 13   This diagram illustrates the numbering system of the 'tetrads' or 2 × 2km squares (25 to one 10km square) used for recording and mapping plant distributions on the species maps in the Systematic Account of the Vascular Flora

being incorrectly plotted in a square lacking any suitable habitat. We have sought to ensure, so far as possible, that individual species' records along the boundaries and the coast have been assigned to the correct square.

Plate I - *Lycopodiella inundata* (L.) Holub. Marsh Clubmoss (p.91)   A species of bare, moist peat on wet-heaths. Much declined in Britain, Hampshire's New Forest and Woolmer Forest are now its main British strongholds. (*Photo*: R. P. Bowman)

Plate II - *Pilularia globulifera* L. Pillwort (p.94)   Found on mud or gravel in and around acid ponds. The New Forest now has the largest concentration of this species in Europe. (*Photo*: R. P. Bowman)

Plate III - *Illecebrum verticillatum* L. Coral-necklace (p.118) This species is frequent and even increasing on bare, moist ground in the New Forest but is very rare elsewhere in Britain. (*Photo*: A. R. G. Mundell)

Plate IV - *Ludwigia palustris* (L.) Elliott. Hampshire-purslane (p.180) In the New Forest, this prostrate plant is found in shallow, peaty ponds and hollows but is no longer a permanent member of the flora elsewhere in Britain. (*Photo*: P. R. Brough)

Plate V - *Cicendia filiformis* (L.)
Delarbre. Yellow Centaury (p.195)
An inconspicuous but pretty little plant
which, in some years, is still locally
frequent on bare, moist ground in the
New Forest although now very rare
elsewhere in Britain.
(*Photo*: P. R. Brough)

Plate VI - *Gentiana pneumonanthe* L.
Marsh Gentian (p.197)   This beautiful
gentian is still locally plentiful in wet
heathland, particularly in the south-west
of the New Forest but very rare elsewhere
in Britain.
(*Photo*: P. Sterry, Nature Photographers Ltd.)

Plate VII - *Pulmonaria longifolia* (Bastard) Boreau. Narrow-leaved Lungwort (p.201) This attractive plant, with pale spots on its leaves, is confined in Britain to woodlands and rough grassland on either side of the Solent, in south-west Hampshire, eastern Dorset and the northern Isle of Wight. (*Photo*: R. B. Gibbons)

Plate VIII - *Teucrium botrys* L. Cut-leaved Germander (p.206) A few remaining sites in Hampshire now support the great bulk of the British population of this plant of bare, chalky ground or scree. (*Photo*: P. Sterry, Nature Photographers Ltd.)

Plate IX - *Filago lutescens* Jord. Red-tipped Cudweed. (p.240) A rare plant of open, sandy ground, now almost confined to single sites in Hampshire, Surrey and Sussex. (*Photo*: A. R. G. Mundell)

Plate X - *Pulicaria vulgaris* Gaertn. Small Fleabane (p.241) Dependent on grazed grasslands for its survival (as animals usually refuse to eat it), this plant still has several strong populations in the New Forest but is now extinct over most of Britain and western Europe. (*Photo*: P. R. Brough)

Plate XI - *Cyperus fuscus* L. Brown Galingale
(p.263)   Now restricted elsewhere in Britain
to only four or five sites, this plant occurs on
mud, normally enriched by goose-droppings,
round a few ponds in south-west Hampshire.
(*Photo*: P. R. Brough)

Plate XII - *Carex limosa* L. Bog Sedge (with
Erica tetralix and *Narthecium ossifragum*)
(p. 271)   In southern England, this sedge is
now confined to a few acidic valley-mires in
the New Forest and east Dorset.
(*Photo*: P. R. Brough)

Plate XIII - *Cephalanthera rubra* (L.) Rich. Red Helleborine (p.296)   In Britain today, this fine orchid is known only in three open, calcareous beech-woods, one of which is in Hampshire. It is, however, still frequent in central and southern Europe. (*Photo*: A. J. P. Branson)

Plate XIV - *Hammarbya paludosa* (L.) Kuntze. Bog Orchid (p.299)   This tiny, inconspicuous orchid of wet, flushed bogs has now one of its few major European strongholds in the New Forest. (*Photo*: P. R. Brough)

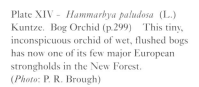

Plate XV - *Gymnadenia conopsea* ssp. *borealis*
(Druce) F. Rose. Northern Fragrant Orchid
(p.300)   Although this carnation-scented orchid is
of largely northern and western distribution in the
British Isles, it is frequent in wet, calcareous mires
in parts of the New Forest.
(*Photo*: A. R. G. Mundell)

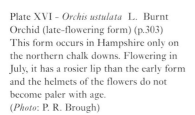

Plate XVI - *Orchis ustulata* L. Burnt
Orchid (late-flowering form) (p.303)
This form occurs in Hampshire only on
the northern chalk downs. Flowering in
July, it has a rosier lip than the early form
and the helmets of the flowers do not
become paler with age.
(*Photo*: P. R. Brough)

CHAPTER IX

RECORDING THE VASCULAR FLORA

PAUL BOWMAN

The records of the Hampshire flora principally cover the period 1950–1992, with a relatively small number dating back to 1930. Continuity with the second edition of Townsend's *Flora of Hampshire*, which covered the earliest period of recording up to 1904, and with Rayner's *Supplement* for the subsequent period up to 1929, has thus been ensured. Some earlier records which Townsend had overlooked, or which had not then been published, have been extracted from the botanical literature; other early records have come to light as a result of examination of specimens in the national herbaria, and these have all been incorporated. Additionally, a number of records to mid 1995 have been included wherever it was practicable to do so.

Plan of the Systematic Account

(i) Format of headings, text and records

Sequence and nomenclature. With a very few (generally minor) exceptions, these are based on D. H. Kent's *List of Vascular Plants of the British Isles* (1992), which follows closely the order and names in C. A. Stace's *New Flora of the British Isles* (1991). One important exception concerns the treatment of *Silene nutans*, where we accept the views of F. N. Hepper rather than those of Kent and Stace. Another is the reversion of *Drosera longifolia* to its former name of *D. anglica*, the first name now being treated as a synonym on the recent advice of D. H. Kent. A few other taxa not listed in these works are also included. The abbreviations for authors of scientific names follow Brummitt & Powell's *Authors of Plant Names* (1992), with two exceptions: 'fil.' (the son of) is preferred to 'f.', e.g. Hook. fil.; and the contraction 'Michx' is preferred to 'Michx.'.

Synonyms. Where the taxonomic name has changed since J. E. Dandy's *List of British Vascular Plants* (1958) or, in a very few instances, since

Clapham, Tutin & Moore's *Flora of the British Isles*, edn 3 (1987), the name therein has been included as a synonym, enclosed in parentheses (round brackets). Similarly, certain names used in Townsend's *Flora* and Rayner's *Supplement* have been quoted to facilitate reference to them.

English Names. These are based on Dony, Jury & Perring's *English Names of Wild Flowers*, edn 2, (1986). A very few in that list which are considered unsuitable have been replaced by longer-established and more familiar English names but, in a few cases, well-known, alternative English names are also given. For more-recently-established alien species and some hybrids, the names given in the *New Flora* are used or, in their absence, those used in Clement & Foster's *Alien Plants of the British Isles* (1994).

Status Categories. These are in accordance with the classification used in *Flora of the Isle of Man* (D. E. Allen *et al.*, 1986). The four categories are indicated by the following letters:

N Native: indigenous to Hampshire (includes more-recent appearances due to factors other than man, e.g. spread by salt- or fresh-water, wind, birds or other animals).

C Colonist: an invader which arrived in the county unintentionally as a result of human activity (typically as a weed of cultivation) and now normally present only in open and artificial habitats.

D Denizen: now growing wild spontaneously but suspected or known to have been introduced originally as a crop or herb.

H Hortal: an ornamental, either deliberately planted and now spreading spontaneously, or an escape into the wild from gardens.

A species in the categories **C, D** and **H** may be native elsewhere in the British Isles.

Many species are of dual or even multiple status, so more than one letter has been used to indicate this. For example, *Anagallis arvensis* is described as **N,C** since on open, coastal sand it is native but on bare, arable and disturbed ground it is a colonist.

Frequency. This is a brief statement of the overall distribution and frequency in the county as a whole. The main categories used, in descending order, are:

Abundant, Very common, Common, Locally common, Frequent, Locally frequent, Occasional, Local, Very local, Rare, Very rare.

In order to describe some individual distribution patterns more accurately, other variations of these terms have been used, e.g. 'Locally very common' or 'Very locally frequent'. Certain species show a bimodal type of distribution: more frequent in restricted areas but thinly scattered elsewhere. These are described in such terms as 'Locally frequent and occasional' or 'Very local and rare'. Where the distribution of some species is incompletely known, then 'Under-recorded' or 'Overlooked' have been used.

Species described as 'Extinct' are those which are presumed or known to be extinct in the county, either as a result of destruction or alteration of the habitat, or because they have not been refound for many years despite repeated searching. The whole entry is enclosed in angle brackets, i.e. < >.

Those species cited under Schedule 8 of the Wildlife and Countryside Act 1981 which have occurred in Hampshire at some time are listed in Chapter VI, p.68, and are indicated after the frequency category by '(Sched. 8)'.

First record (or first evidence) of occurrence in the county, *not* previously published in Townsend's *Flora*, is formally given in the following order: name of recorder or finder, and year; locality, with four-figure grid reference (1km), if known; vice-county; herbarium location, if a specimen exists; initials of determiner, if any; literature source.

First records are also given where those previously published related to the Isle of Wight, in which case the first-known records for the Hampshire mainland are cited. Some first records which appeared in Townsend under 'Excluded Species' have likewise been cited formally as '*Fl. Hants*, excl.sp.'. Certain of the very earliest published first records, such as those by John Goodyer and Gilbert White, are repeated for their intrinsic historical interest.

Habitat. This summarizes the usual habitats in which the plant occurs in Hampshire (not necessarily the same as in other counties), its frequency in those habitats, and its geographical range and occurrence on particular geological strata or soil types. Remarks on conservation and population-size and origin, where appropriate, are also included.

Records. With the exception of rarities, for which all or most records are given (particularly for the unmapped species), only a *selection* of records has been chosen for each vice-county. Whenever possible, examples are given of where the plant is in quantity in a typical habitat, where it has been seen in fairly recent years in preference to older records, or where it is very scarce or inaccessible. In many cases, however, efforts to relocate a plant in a particular site may result in disappointment due to the extended period of recording, widespread alteration to or loss of habitat, and the impossibility of monitoring each and every site. Moreover some species, such as ephemeral colonists of disturbed ground, are very prone to disappear soon after discovery though sometimes they may reappear in later years if the ground is disturbed, allowing dormant seeds to germinate.

The records are usually presented in the following order: locality (identifiable, with certain exceptions, on the current OS maps, scale 1:50,000 or 1:25,000), 1km grid reference, or the approximate one; details of habitat and quantity, if appropriate; initials of recorder (or alternatively the recorder's herbarium abbreviation); year of record; abbreviation of herbarium where specimen held, if any; initials of determiner, where relevant; and, in parentheses, literature source, if any. For some localities the grid reference may at first sight be confused with the year of record, e.g. 'Christchurch 1894' under *Oxalis lasiandra* (p.186), but as the date always follows the recorder, and the grid reference the locality there should be no confusion. Exceptionally, when the exact locality is unknown, the 10km reference is given instead e.g. SU45.

For unmapped taxa of relatively restricted range, an attempt has been made to indicate the distribution either by enumerating (after the habitat statement) the total of recorded tetrads for each vice-county since 1930, e.g. *Oxalis corniculata* (p.186) – VC11: 30 □; VC12: 21 □, or by appending a list of other recorded tetrads (not 1km squares) following the records for each vice-county, e.g. as under *Impatiens parviflora* (p.189).

Excluded species. Published records which are now considered to be probable or certain errors of recording or of identity, and those of plants known to have been deliberately planted in a wild situation are shown enclosed in square brackets, i.e. [ ].

Appendixes. A comprehensive alphabetical 'List of Recorders and Referees', showing the standardized abbreviations used in the text for both (a) Individuals, and (b) Corporate Bodies, is given in Appendix I; 'Abbreviations for Herbaria' are listed in Appendix II; a list of standard 'General Abbreviations, Terms and Symbols' used in the text appears in Appendix III; and Appendix IV gives the abbreviations used for

'Books, Periodicals, and Unpublished Manuscripts', cited in the text of the Systematic Accounts for Vascular Plants, Lichens, and Bryophytes.

Bibliography and References. A complete list of works referred to in the text, and some others consulted in the preparation of this Flora but not specifically referred to, follows the Appendixes.

(ii) The Maps

The total of 576 maps of vascular plants includes 10 special maps of Hampshire and the Isle of Wight combined. There are also two of lichens and one of mosses. Records are defined by the following symbols:

- ■ Tetrad record 1930 onwards, presumed extant
- ◩ Tetrad record 1930 onwards, presumed non-extant
- □ Tetrad record before 1930, presumed non-extant

The distribution maps were as accurate as possible at the time they were prepared. However, as they were compiled over a number of years, a few species with tetrad records showing them as extant have since become extinct in them and a few have since been more widely recorded than is shown on the map. Their present status is as given in the text, and there are inevitably some discrepancies between text and maps.

The original species' data for Watsonian Vice-counties 11 and 12 were held by the vice-county recorders on record cards and on manually-produced and updated maps. To computerize these maps, the Hampshire Wildlife Trust provided a BBC Master computer, and a 'home-grown' program was written allowing entry to a screen-displayed county map on a tetrad basis. Initially all species' data held were entered in this format and updated as necessary.

To provide the map data in the IBM format required by the publisher, all the data were transferred to an IBM PS/1 computer using a combination of software and hardware. The map-data files were then modified to be compatible with Alan Morton's DMAP program which was used to make the final corrections and to add a late batch of species' records. The final maps were produced in Encapsulated Postscript (EPS) format enabling them to be incorporated with the text using modern technology.

SYSTEMATIC ACCOUNTS
OF THE HAMPSHIRE FLORA

CHAPTER X

THE VASCULAR FLORA

ANNE BREWIS, PAUL BOWMAN AND FRANCIS ROSE

Lycopodiopsida

LYCOPODIACEAE

<**Huperzia selago** (L.) BERNH. ex
SCHRANK & C. MART. (*Lycopodium
selago* L.)   Fir Clubmoss.   **N**   Extinct

First record, R. Pulteney 1783, 'near
Ringwood', VC11, Hb.BM (*Fl.Hants*,
p.531).

Formerly on wet heaths. *Fl.Hants*
gave four sites in the New Forest, and
three in VC12 on the Bagshot Sands.

VC11: Near Lyndhurst, *HG & JGr*
1877, Hb.BM; last seen at Backley
Bottom, New Forest, *JFR* 1906,
(*Suppl.Fl.Hants*, p.128), possibly in
Pulteney's site. **VC12**: Haseley [Haze-
ley] Heath, *RSH* 1863; heaths near
Aldershot, especially near the canal
drawing a line NNW from Caesar's
Camp, *WON in litt.* (*Phytologist* **4**: 21);
several places near Eversley, *RK c.*1870
(*Proc.Hants Fld Club* **8**: 132, 1918).>

Lycopodiella inundata (L.) HOLUB
(*Lycopodium inundatum* L.)   Marsh
Clubmoss.   **N**   Very local   Map 1
Plate I

Acid, wet heath and the fringes of
bogs, on bare peaty soil, where liable to

flooding in winter. Frequent in the
New Forest, rare on Avon Valley
heaths, very local in Woolmer Forest
and the NE tertiary heaths.

VC8: Plaitford Common, 2717,
2718, *FR* 1985–91. By an oversight,
listed as 'not refound during the Wiltshire Flora Mapping Project' (*Wilts
Fl.*, App. IV, p.370). **VC11**: Town
Common 1495, *RPB* 1956, *CEP* 1974;
Sopley Common 1397, *RMW* 1987;
Broad Bottom, Vales Moor 1904, *RPB*
1960, 1990; rare in ditch, Baddesley
Common 3821, *RPB* 1958, since overgrown. **VC12**: Some former sites
destroyed in Woolmer Forest, but still
very abundant there locally, persisting
in several abandoned, damp rides, that
from Fern Hill to Horsebush Hill 8033
being now perhaps the best Hants site,
PLeB 1984, 1994; the Slab, Bordon
7834, *FR* 1989; Hawley Common
8358, *RAB* 1956, *CRH* 1983–90; Long
Bottom, near Aldershot 8450, large
colony, *CRH* 1983, much reduced by
1991; Heath Warren 7659, *CRH*
1985–91; Bramshill Common 7562,
CRH 1986–89; Yateley Heath Wood
8057, *CRH* 1987, since destroyed;
Hazeley Heath *c.*7458, *EH & JHo*
1963, not seen since.

Lycopodium clavatum L.   Stag's-
horn Clubmoss.   **N**   Very rare
Map 2

Dry heathland, on bare sand or gravel,
old sand-pits and especially along
newly-made plantation rides. Several
new records during 1970–80, mostly
followed by disappearance of the plants
which may have become overgrown or
have declined due to climatic change.
Perhaps now persisting in only one or
two sites. Field experience indicates
that in lowland England this species
does not persist indefinitely in known
sites, but becomes overgrown by grass

swards, etc. It seems to depend on
phases of soil disturbance for its reappearance.

VC11: Hen Wood 6622, small pit at
ride junction (on Clay-with-flints), *JF*
1978, Hb.AB, *RPB* 1981, one dead
plant only, *RCS* 1990; SE of Newlands
Plantation 1708, by roadside; outside
SW entrance to Sloden Inclosure 2012
and Noyce's Hill [Nices Hill] *c.*2011,
GHMS 1910 (*Book of Gorley*, p.95),
last seen at Nices Hill, *JHL* 1958, not
refound *AWW* 1963; Cadman's Pool
2212, *AG* 1974–75; A333 [now B2177]
Staple Cross 6109, bare sandy S road-
bank E of crossroads, *JCD* 1974, *RPB*
1975–81, since shaded out by scrub;
Havant Thicket 7111, *JRW* 1975.
VC12: Chawton Park Wood 6736, *Atk*
1948, *AAB* 1971, Hb.HCMS
(*Watsonia* **11**: 391); above old sand-pit
on road from Eversley vicarage to
Bramshill Park *c.*7659 and Hartfordbridge Flats *c.*8058, *RK c.*1870
(*Proc.Hants Fld Club* **8**: 129); Heath
Warren 7659, *CRH* 1985–95, Hb.AB
(*Watsonia* **17**: 183), this could be very
close to *RK*'s site; Woolmer Forest
8033, on a ride, seen by *ECW* since
1931, not refound, probably destroyed
by mowing, *FR & ECW c.*1975.

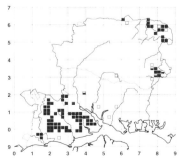

Map 1 Lycopodiella inundata

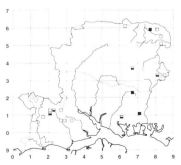

Map 2 Lycopodium clavatum

<Diphasiastrum complanatum
(L.) HOLUB ssp. **issleri** (ROUY) JERMY
Issler's Clubmoss. **N** Extinct

First British record, J. Lloyd 1866,
'Lower Wagner's Wells', Bramshott,
VC12, Hb.BM, Hb.CGE (as *Lycopodium complanatum* L.) (*Gdnrs'Chron.*
11 Aug. 1866, pp.753–754; 3 Aug.
1867, pp.808–809).

  A. C. Jermy (*Fern Gaz.* **13**: 257–265)
considers that there are two ecotypes in
Britain: a lowland one formerly in S
and W England (VCs 12, 34, 37), and a
low-mountain one, associated with
ancient pine-forest, in Scotland.
Waggoners Wells (modern corruption
of former spelling) is a series of three
old hammer-ponds near Grayshott
8534–8634. In 1866 Lloyd collected
specimens from this locality where he
regarded it as undoubtedly wild. 'It
was found by a woman named Sarah
Young while occupied cutting heath
for broom-making.' In the next year's
communication he stated that the spot
was on 'a sandy peat, the elevation not
more than 600 or 700 feet, the situation
sheltered, and growing near the roots
of Heath, about 18 inches high, by
which it appears to be almost smothered'. The material was sterile. If his
estimate of the altitude is reasonably
correct, the site may have been on the
heights of the Bramshott Common
open-heath plateau, and not in what is
now the wooded valley below it. There
was formerly a broom-making industry
at Grayshott.>

SELAGINELLACEAE

Selaginella kraussiana (KUNZE) A.
BRAUN Krauss's Clubmoss. **H**
Very rare

First record, C. D. Drake 1967,
spreading on lawns at Highcliffe Castle
2093, VC11, Hb.RPB, Hb.AB
(*Rep.S'ton N.H.S.*, p.12).

Equisetopsida

EQUISETACEAE

Equisetum hyemale L. Rough
Horsetail. **N** Very rare

First record, G. M. A. Hewett 1887,
Lord's Wood, VC11, Hb.OXF.
  VC11: Locally abundant on a
spring-line on clay in Lord's Wood,
Southampton 3915, *RPB* 1953–92
(now within a housing estate, but still
growing in a small, specially-

designated reserve). Experimental
transplants to Appleslade 1809, and
Long Aldermoor 2709, did not survive.
A record for 10km square SU61 (*Fern
Atlas*, p.14) must be an error as no
record-source or specimen can be
traced. **VC12**: In ancient woodland on
a spring-line over a clay seam, Fishpond Copse, NE of Bentley 8045, just
inside Hants, *CRH & RBG* 1985,
Hb.AB, det. *FR* (*Watsonia* **17**: 183),
still present, *CRH* 1992.

E. variegatum SCHLEICH. Variegated Horsetail. **N** Very rare or
extinct

First record, R. P. Bowman 1961,
forming a dense mat 2 x 5m on the
moist floor of an old sand-pit at Hoe,
Rownhams 3819, VC11, Hb.RPB
(*Rep.S'ton N.H.S.*, p.1). This pit is
now filled, and transplants moved
earlier to sandbanks at this site have
been obliterated. A few plants were
moved by *ASC* to Otterbourne 4522,
but have not been refound.

E. fluviatile L. Water Horsetail.
N Locally frequent

In still water, wet bogs or swamps,
both acid and basic.

E. x litorale KÜHLEW. ex RUPR. (*E.
fluviatile* x *E. arvense*) Shore Horsetail. **N** Very local and occasional

First record, A. H. G. Alston & N. Y.
Sandwith 1937, between North Warn-
borough and Odiham, VC12 (*Rep.
B.E.C.* for 1937, p.522).
  Usually on marshy ground. With or
without parents. Probably overlooked.
  VC11: Holmsley Inclosure 2200,
Hb.RPB 1987, det. *CNP*; Crockford
Bridge 3498, *ASC* 1962; Fletchwood
Meadows 3411, Hb.RPB 1986, det.
CNP; Brambridge 4621, plentiful,
ASC 1962. Also 3098, 3816, 5208.
VC12: Conford 8133, Hb.AB 1969,
det. *PGT*; Yateley 8260, wet, marshy
meadow, *ARGM* 1987; Hammer
Bottom 8632, *AB* 1968, det. *PGT*;
Aldershot 8853, flooded gravel-pit, in
plenty, *AB* 1979; Walldown, near R.
Deadwater 8034, *AB* 1985. Also 7250,
8052, 8232, 8254, 8432.

E. arvense L. Field Horsetail. **N**
Locally very common

On waste ground, dry pastures, roadsides, and neglected farmland. A
rampant colonizer of bare sand. Less
common on chalk.

E. sylvaticum L. Wood Horsetail.
N Very local Map 3

In boggy, acidic woodland, especially
around springs.
  VC11: Chiefly around Southamp-
ton. Lord's Wood 3916, *RPB* 1953;
Cramp Moor 3822, *FR & PB* 1981;
Hale 1818, *JO* 1982; The Glen, Lower
Swanwick 5009, *RMV* 1988. **VC12**:
Silchester Common 6262, *FR & ECW*
1975; Ewshot 8150, *CRH* 1984; Beacon
Hill, Ewshot 8250, *VL* 1960,
Hb.HCMS, *ARGM* 1982, declining
CRH 1987–92; Blackwater Copse 6258,
large patch throughout alder stand,
probably spreading into three tetrads,
ILR 1991; Great Danmoor Copse
7360, abundant, *CRH* 1985–91.

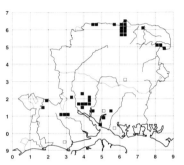

Map 3 Equisetum sylvaticum

E. x bowmanii C. PAGE (*E. sylvaticum*
x *E. telmateia*) **N** Very rare

First British record, R. P. Bowman
1986, near A337, Minstead Road,
Minstead 2910, VC11, road-banks on
wet clay, Hb.E (holotype), det. *CNP*.
This new hybrid, a British endemic, is
described in *Watsonia* **17**: 273–277.
  VC11: A337 Shave Wood 2912,
dominant over 225m along W roadside
verge and ditch, *AJB* 1989, Hb.RPB;
A337 Brockis Hill 2911 and Frenches
Bushes 2912, *RPB* 1989.

E. palustre L. Marsh Horsetail. **N**
Locally common Map 4

In fens, wet meadows, and less acid
parts of bogs.

E. x font-queri ROTH. (*E. palustre* x
E. telmateia) **N** Very rare

First record, M. W. Rowe 1991, South
Baddesley, Boldre 3496, 3596, VC11,
roadside for over 400m, Hb.RPB, det.
CNP (*Watsonia* **19**: 279).

E. telmateia EHRH. Great Horsetail.
N Locally common Map 5

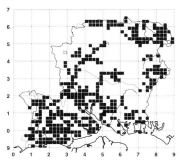

Map 4 Equisetum palustre

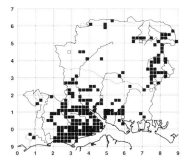

Map 5 Equisetum telmateia

In woodland or fields, on roadside- and railway-banks, on wet clay or Malm-stone, nearly always on spring-lines at the junction of pervious strata with underlying clay.

Pteropsida

OPHIOGLOSSACEAE

Ophioglossum vulgatum L. Adder's-tongue. **N** Locally frequent Map 6

In old, damp grassland, amongst bracken on heaths, in moist woodland, old marl-pits, fens, and under scrub.

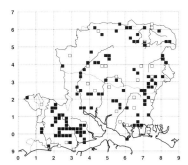

Map 6 Ophioglossum vulgatum

On gravel, fen peat, clay or Malm-stone. Decreased on chalk, but has colonized various new sites.

VC11: Widley 6706, waste land, Hb.AWW 1951; Beaulieu old airfield 3500, *RPB* 1981; Farlington 6804, *MB* 1984. **VC12**: Noar Hill 7431, Hb.AB 1982–90; Bramley Training Area 6657, *CRH* 1989; pasture in Wolverton 5558, *PB* 1983; Tower Hill 2438, *MRe* 1991.

O. azoricum C. PRESL (*O. vulgatum* ssp. *ambiguum* (Coss. & Germ.) E. F. Warb.) Small Adder's-tongue. **N** Very rare

First record, A. J. & Mrs B. Rackham 1984, Warwick Slade 2706, VC11, in small flood-hollows, Hb.BM, det. *ACJ & AMP* 1989 (*Watsonia* **18**: 215).

The newly-discovered New Forest sites are the first recorded inland occurrences in Britain. Otherwise restricted to moist, short turf in scat-tered sites along the western coasts of Britain and Ireland and offshore islands north to the Shetlands.

VC11: Beaulieu old airfield 3500, in stony flood-hollows on the bed of a former hard-standing, with *Littorella uniflora*, *RPB* 1987, det. *ACJ & AMP* 1989, where increasing and spreading to a runway bed at 3400, *SNHS* 1990. Similar plants have been found N of Ocknell Pond 2312, in hollow on bed of old airfield; near Fletchers Thorns 2704, in damp perimeter-strip in two places; and NW of Crockford Bridge 3498, reseeded pasture, *RPB* 1992. In each locality they are associated with *O. vulgatum* and possible intermediates are present, but these mixed colonies need further study to determine their relationship. A chromosome count may help to solve this. A large population at Avon Forest Park 1201,1202, *FAW* 1985, probably this species, awaits final confirmation; here it grows in dry turf on sand beneath bracken, occasionally under heather clumps, where the plants are remarkably tall and slender.

Botrychium lunaria (L.) Sw. Moonwort. **N** Rare Map 7

First record, J. Goodyer 1618, 'Drox-ford in a wood by Strugnells in the Thetcher', VC11 (*Early Brit.Bots*, p.110).

In short, open turf on sand or loam, occasionally on chalk. Much decreased, but there is some indication of recent spread to some New Forest sites in grassy perimeter-strips around the new inclosures, on old airfields where heather invades and by hilly roadsides

where grit is swept on to verges; also on grass-heaths under bracken.

VC11: Beaulieu old airfield 3400, *CDD* 1966, *c*.1000 fronds, *RPB* 1972; Badminston Common 4501, acid grass-land with concrete rubble, *NAS* c.1985; Marchwood Inclosure 3807, grassy strip, *RPB* 1988. **VC12**: Micheldever Spoil Heaps 5144, *RPB* 1964, increasing since scrub clearance, *MT & BT* 1984; Farnborough Airfield 8553, 50 fronds, *ARGM* 1986, 1994; Blackbushe Airfield 8059, 1700 fronds, *CRH* 1989, much declined, *CRH* 1994.

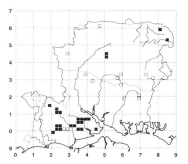

Map 7 Botrychium lunaria

OSMUNDACEAE

Osmunda regalis L. Royal Fern. **N** Very local Map 8

First record, R. Turner 1664, 'ditch near the Well in Holshot Lane in Hampshire', VC12 (*Turn.Bot.*, p.100).

In wet moss, fen carr, heathland ditches and around ponds. Fairly frequent in the New Forest and SW; rare elsewhere. There is evidence of recent spread to new sites. In some places it may be an old garden relic; where known, these are not mapped.

VC11: Bournemouth cliffs 0890, on wet patches (spores carried across from Studland?) *RPB* 1978; R. Avon near

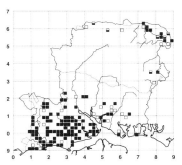

Map 8 Osmunda regalis

Leybrook Common 1302, frequent in carr, *RPB* 1985; Newlands Copse, Roydon Woods 3200, *IB* 1978; Mopley Pond 4502, Hb.AWW 1962, *RPB* 1988; Tantany Wood 3604, fine stand in alder carr, *FR* 1989. **VC12:** Knowl Hill, Kingsclere 5359, Sperling 1943 (*Proc.Hants Fld Club* **16**: 62); Eelmoor Marsh 8453, *ARGM* 1976–94; Bordon 8034, two plants in dry ditch, *CWa* 1982; Blackwater Valley 8757, *RT* 1985, destroyed 1991; Wellington Country Park 7363, *MN* 1985; Blackmoor golf-course 7734, *SP* 1986, destroyed by 1990.

ADIANTACEAE

Adiantum capillus-veneris L. Maidenhair Fern.   **H**   Very rare

Never more than a garden escape in Hants.

VC11: Shirley 3913, *WFB* 1972, since lost; All Saints' Church, Awbridge 3223, basement stairway, *RPB* 1988; St Peter's Church, Curdridge 5213, brick wall of basement stairway, *RPB* 1990.

MARSILEACEAE

Pilularia globulifera L.   Pillwort. **N**   Very local   Map 9   Plate II

First British record, C. Merrett 1666, near Petersfield, VC11/12, probably citing a record by J. Goodyer (*Merr.Pin.*, p.57).

On mud, fine gravel or wet clay, in or around shallow ponds on heaths; in old gravel-pits; open-bog zones and acid swamps. Locally in ditches and muddy ruts in inclosure rides. Sometimes forming an extensive sward. Fairly common in the New Forest, where A. C. Jermy (pers.comm.) considers there is probably the largest concentration of sites in Europe. Very local elsewhere.

VC11: Near Burley 1901, swampy track of disused railway, abundant, *JO* 1985; Greenmoor 3399, marl-pit pond, *MR* 1976; Fish Pond, Rownhams 3816, *RPB* 1951, lost when bog drained for housing estate in 1970s. **VC12:** Heath Warren 7659, extensive over wet, gravelly area, *PB* 1983; Bramshill Plantation 7563, abundant in ponds and ditches, *CRH & ARGM* 1986; flooded gravel-pit near Ramillies Park 8853, *ARGM* 1985; lake near Aldershot 8852, Hb.AB 1979 (*Watsonia* **13**: 327), *AJB* 1989; several places in Wellington Country Park 7262, 7263, 7363, *ARGM* 1985. Formerly present, but

not recently found, at Fleet Pond 8254, on Blackmoor golf-course 7834, and S of B2131 Longmoor Road 8131, bog infilled with refuse 1973.

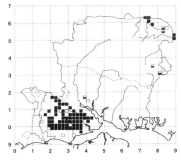

Map 9 Pilularia globulifera

POLYPODIACEAE

Polypodium vulgare L. *sensu lato* Polypody.   **N**   Locally very common Map 10

First record, Gilbert White 1765, 'in the hollow lane', Norton, Selborne 7334, VC12 (*White's Jnls* **1**: 167).

Sheltered banks in woods and lanes; an epiphyte on trees, especially old oaks; old walls. Not on chalk. *P. vulgare* L. *sensu stricto* and *P. interjectum* Shivas, Intermediate Polypody, have not been mapped separately, as there are many intermediates. It appears that, whereas *P. interjectum* is the commonest in SW Hants and in the basic Weald escarpment, *P. vulgare* is the commonest on the Lower Greensand.

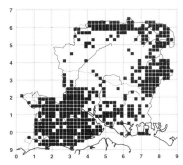

Map 10 Polypodium vulgare agg.

P. x mantoniae ROTHM. & U. SCHNEID. (*P. interjectum* x *P. vulgare*) **N**   Under-recorded

Probably sporadic with the parents, but seldom recorded. Expertly determined records for VC11: 1402, 2414, 3014, 6018.

P. cambricum L.   Southern Polypody.   **N**   Very rare

First record, G. F. Peterken 1966, Denny Wood 3305 or 3306, VC11, two plants epiphytic on oak, det. in laboratory *GFP* (*Atlas Brit.Fl.Crit.Suppl.*, p.3). The normal habitat in W Britain is limestone walls or rocks.

VC11: Lyndhurst Hill, Emery Down 2808, epiphytic on small oak, *DCW* 1989, comm. *AEB*, Hb.RPB, det. *RHR* 1990 (*Watsonia* **18**: 420); near Christchurch Priory 1592, roadside brick wall, *PS* 1989, Hb.RPB, det. *RHR* 1991; Beaulieu Abbey 3802, low stone wall of ruins of fulling mill, *WFS* 1992, Hb.RPB, conf. *RHR*; Tithe Barn, St Leonard's Farm 4096, *AEB* 1993, Hb.RPB, conf. *RPB*; Netley Abbey 4509, *PS* 1993, Hb.RPB.

DENNSTAEDTIACEAE

Pteridium aquilinum (L.) KUHN Bracken.   **N**   Very common

Often dominant in dry acidic woodland and heathland. Owing to its deep roots, it frequently succeeds heather after a heath fire or if grazing has long ceased. Bracken invading *Calluna* heath forms a grave threat to much of our interesting heathland vegetation but can be suppressed by fern-specific herbicides, or by adequate grazing.

THELYPTERIDACEAE

Thelypteris palustris SCHOTT (*T. thelypteroides* (Michx) Holub ssp. *glabra* Holub)   Marsh Fern.   **N** Rare   Map 11

First British record, J. Goodyer 1633, 'in a very wet moore or bog...called Whitrow Moore, where Peate is now digged, a mile from Peters-field in Hampshire', VC11, known for 'many yeares' (*Ger.em.Johns.*, p.1136). This marsh still exists, but fern not refound, *FR*.

In wet, acid alder–carr, often rooted in sphagnum, rarely also in fen carr. Three of its six New Forest sites are on the Headon Beds; 'Whitrow Moor' and Conford are on the Sandgate Beds, and Greywell and Itchel on chalk.

VC11: Dibden Bottom 3906, *RPB* 1951–92; Holmsley Bog 2300, still abundant, *JHL* 1985; Nightingale Wood 3717, *RPB* 1952–92. **VC12:** Greywell Moors 7251, Hb.AWW 1960, abundant, *ARGM* 1985–94; Conford, *GMA* 1939, refound at 8233, abundant,

FR 1986–94; Itchel Mill Springs 7849, *CRH* 1991; Hazeley Heath *c.*7458, *EH* 1957; Fleet Pond 8154, *CRH* 1994.

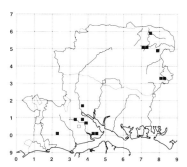

Map 11 Thelypteris palustris

Phegopteris connectilis (MICHX) WATT (*Thelypteris phegopteris* (L.) Sloss.) Beech Fern. **N** Very rare

VC11: In two boggy alder-woods in the New Forest. Near Wood Crates, where described in 1884 (*Fl.Hants*, p.527) as 'abundant for about a mile up the stream'. Still abundant there from just N of Cole Bridge 2708, and a small colony just S of it, 2707, in damp cushions of bryophytes around bases of alders and on mossy stream-banks, the dominant fern species, *RPB* 1956, now more restricted in abundance to the upper 300m of the valley and apparently, southward, shaded out in places by dense hollies, *RPB* 1992; very locally in Highland Water Inclosure 2408, *FR* 1974.

Oreopteris limbosperma (BELLARDI ex ALL.) HOLUB (*Thelypteris oreopteris* (Ehrh.) Sloss.) Lemon-scented Fern. **N** Very locally frequent Map 12

In damp, acid woodland, particularly in moist rides, and in boggy ditches or flushes. Still abundant in most old New Forest woodlands, and often in plantations, but apparently extinct on the Lower Greensand and rare on the northern Tertiaries.

VC11: Bursledon old brickworks 5009, one plant in wooded gully, *RPB* 1990; West Walk 6012, *JRw* 1985, 75+ plants, *RPB* 1990. **VC12**: Highclere Park 4560, *FR* 1974; Silchester Common 6161, *FR* 1984; Turner's Wood, Fleet 8055, *CRH* 1990; Hazeley Heath 7558, *CRH* 1987; Sandford Wood East 5551, *ILR* 1991. The record in *Watsonia* **10**: 420 for Waggoners Wells 8634, AB 1970, is withdrawn, the site being just inside Surrey, VC17.

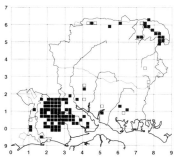

Map 12 Oreopteris limbosperma

ASPLENIACEAE

Phyllitis scolopendrium (L.) NEWMAN Hart's-tongue. **N** Frequent

Woodland and hedgebanks; most abundant in moist, calcareous sites, especially chalk and Malmstone scarps, and absent only where very acid. Also on damp walls, and inside drain-holes.

Asplenium adiantum-nigrum L. Black Spleenwort. **N** Frequent Map 13

On walls, especially damp ones, and shady hedgebanks. Occurs throughout the county, but commonest in the SW and on the Bargate Stone lanesides.

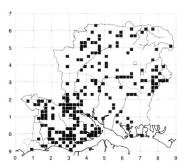

Map 13 Asplenium adiantum-nigrum

<**A. fontanum** (L.) BERNH. Smooth Rock-spleenwort. **H** Extinct

Formerly on a kitchen-garden brick wall, Ashford House 7426, VC12, Hb.BM *c.*1852 (*Fl.Hants*, excl.sp., p.530).>

A. trichomanes L. ssp. **quadrivalens** D. MEYER Maidenhair Spleenwort. **N** Local and occasional

'Mr Goodyer saith that in January,

1624, he saw enough to lade an horse growing on the bancks in a lane, as he rode between Rake and Headly in Hampshire neere Wollmer Forest', VC12 (*Ger.em.Johns.*, p.1146). This shows that, at one time, the habitat existed for *A. trichomanes* to grow in lanes, as in SW England; indeed *Fl.Hants* (p.520) contains other records of it in lanes. However, it is now very scattered, and generally on old walls or railways.

VC11: Beckley Moor Copse 2296, epiphyte on mossy oak by stream, *ILR* 1994; well at Bishop's Palace, Bishop's Waltham 5517, *AB* 1975; East Tytherley churchyard wall 2929, *RMB* 1969. **VC12**: Alleyway, Whitchurch 4647, *PB* 1984; railway arch, Soldridge 6534, *AB* 1982.

A. ruta-muraria L. Wall-rue. **N** Locally frequent

On old walls and railway arches, though some of these sites are being destroyed.

Ceterach officinarum WILLD. Rustyback. **N** Very local and occasional Map 14

On old walls, especially of mortared flint, and railway masonry.

VC8: Damerham 1016, *JO* 1991. **VC11**: Old railway, St Cross 4726, *RPB* 1970; Dibden churchyard 3908, *RPB* 1984; High Street, Bursledon 4809, *PAB* 1988 (*Rep.S'ton N.H.S.*, p.22). **VC12**: More frequent, e.g.: Railway bridge over A31 at Alresford 5732, *AH* 1976; Whitchurch 4647, alleyway and on wall, *PB* 1984; Silchester ruins 6362, *WGH* 1984; Nether Wallop 2936, *GDF* 1987; Leckford 3738, 3737, two bridges on disused railway, *RMV* 1984; Blackmoor churchyard wall 7833, *AB* 1993; garden wall, Western Road, Liss 7727, *FR c.* 1970–94.

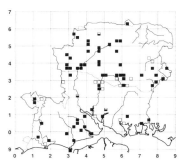

Map 14 Ceterach officinarum

WOODSIACEAE

Onoclea sensibilis L. Sensitive Fern. **H** Very rare

First record, R. P. Bowman 1970, swampy wood along a stream, Newtown Common 4763, VC12.

VC12: In alder carr, E bank of R. Rother at Liss Forest 7728, *JOc* 1990 (*Watsonia* 18: 419).

Athyrium filix-femina (L.) ROTH Lady-fern. **N** Locally common Map 15

Damp woodland, both acidic and basic, wooded lanes, stream- and ditch-banks. Common on sand; rare on Clay-with-flints capping chalk, and in damp sites at the bases of chalk and Malmstone hangers. Extremely common in the New Forest, less so elsewhere.

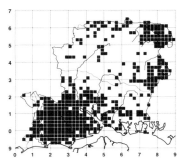

Map 15 Athyrium filix-femina

[**Gymnocarpium dryopteris** (L.) NEWMAN (*Thelypteris dryopteris* (L.) Sloss.) Oak Fern.

A fern from 'a bottome called Rogers Deane in yᵉ parish of Faringdon [VC12] in Hampshire about a mile and a half from yᵉ church...about a mile north east from Dogford Wood', shaded by great ancient beeches, many of which were cut down in 1654; J. Goodyer record (in How's annotated copy of *Phyt.Brit.*, p.35, in Magdalen College Library, Oxford, so before 1656, the year of his death). Attributed by Gunther (*Early Brit.Bots*, p.189) to *G. dryopteris*, but that is most improbable as it is a fern of predominantly acid soils and the Farringdon locality is on chalk; it may in fact have been the following species.]

<G. robertianum (HOFFM.) NEWMAN (*Thelypteris robertiana* (Hoffm.) Sloss.) Limestone Fern. **N?** Extinct

One old record may refer to a native locality: a large patch, for several years up to 1883, in the hanger above Hawkley, VC12, C. W. Greenwood *in litt.* (*Fl.Hants*, excl.sp., p.530). It still occurs in a coombe in W Sussex on similar terrain – chalk scree in an ash-wood. Searched for unsuccessfully at Hawkley by *PMH* and *ECW* in 1941, and by *FR* in 1974 and 1985.>

<Cystopteris fragilis (L.) BERNH. Brittle Bladder-fern. **H?** Extinct

Formerly on a wall, Weston (Southampton), VC11, *FHCP* 1929 (*Suppl.Fl.Hants*, p.126). Also found at Four Marks Station 6635, VC12, railway platform, *AB* 1972 (*Watsonia* 10: 420), but gone by 1984.>

DRYOPTERIDACEAE

Polystichum setiferum (FORSSK.) T. MOORE ex WOYN. Soft Shield-fern. **N** Locally common Map 16

The first British record is attributed to J. Goodyer, 1633, in *Druce Com.Fl.*, p.382. It is doubtful however if Goodyer's '*Filix mas non ramosa pinnulis latis auriculatis spinosis*', which he described from 'the shadowie moist rockes by Maple-durham neere Petersfield', VC11 (*Ger.em.Johns.*, p.1130) sufficiently distinguishes this species from *P. aculeatum*, which is equally likely to have occurred in the locality. Gunther, in *Early Brit.Bots*, p.183, is uncertain to which species the description applies.

In sheltered woodland and lanebanks. Uncommon on the chalk plateau and on very acid soil. Common elsewhere, especially on the Wealden Edge Hangers, and in lanes of the Malmstone escarpment.

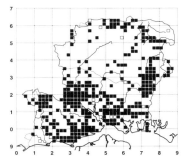

Map 16 Polystichum setiferum

P. x bicknellii (CHRIST) HAHNE (*P. setiferum* x *P. aculeatum*) **N** Very rare

First record, J. E. Winterbottom *c*.1838–42, East Woodhay, VC12, Hb.BM, det. *ASl c*.1980.

VC11: Lane at Shedfield, *CP* n.d., Hb.OXF, det. *ASl c*.1980. **VC12**: Lane between Froxfield and Privett 6927, *JF* 1989, det. *ACJ*.

P. aculeatum (L.) ROTH Hard Shield-fern. **N** Very locally frequent Map 17

First record, Gilbert White 1766, Selborne, VC12 (*White's Jnls* 1: 194).

Banks in dry woodland and shady stream-gullies, mainly on basic soil. Far less common than *P. setiferum*, and somewhat reduced in some lanes of the Malmstone (where still fairly frequent) by mechanical scraping of lane-sides. Rare in the SW and NW.

VC11: East Wellow 3020, stream-bank, *RPB* 1959; Bakers Copse, Roydon Woods 3101, stream-bank, *FR & RJT* 1983; Curbridge 5211, wooded gully, *MR* 1976. **VC12**: Hawkley 7430, lane, *AB* 1985; East End 4060, *NFC* 1982; Ashford Hill 5562, meadows, *PB* 1983; Nashes Green 6745, *CRH* 1986; The Withys 8148, *CRH* 1985.

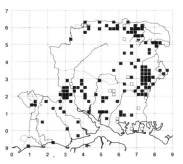

Map 17 Polystichum aculeatum

Cyrtomium falcatum (L. fil.) C. PRESL House Holly-fern. **H** Very rare

First record, Mrs D. E. Bulloch 1992, Portsmouth Naval Base 6200, established on wall of dock, Hb.RPB, det. *EJC* (*Watsonia* 20: 286).

A stiff-textured, evergreen fern grown in conservatories, and probably spreading from wind-blown spores; half-hardy in western coastal parts of British Isles, native of S Africa and E Asia.

Dryopteris filix-mas (L.) SCHOTT Male-fern. **N** Very common

In woodlands and hedgebanks.

D. x complexa FRASER-JENK. nothossp. **complexa** (*D.* x *tavelii* auct., non Rothm.; *D. filix-mas* x *D. affinis* ssp. *affinis*)   **N**   Very rare or overlooked

First record, R. M. Veall 1989, Spearywell Wood 3127, VC11, Hb.RMV, det. *CF-J* (*Watsonia* 18: 419).

D. affinis (LOWE) FRASER-JENK. Scaly Male-fern.   **N**   Locally frequent   Map 18

In acid woodland, particularly in sheltered places. Common in the New Forest and on Malmstone. Also locally on acid drifts over chalk. An oceanic species in Britain. The map combines both subspecies.

ssp. **affinis** (*D. pseudomas* (Woll.) Holub & Pouzar)

VC8: Martin Down 0321, deciduous wood, *RMV* 1990. **VC11**: Ampfield 3822, RMV 1989, det. *CF-J*. Also recorded in at least 29 other tetrads.

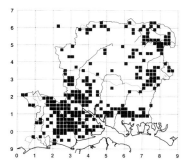

Map 18 Dryopteris affinis

ssp. **borreri** (NEWMAN) FRASER-JENK. (*D. borreri* (Newman) Newman ex Oberh. & Tavel)

VC11: Spearywell Wood 3127, *RMV* 1989, det. *CF-J*. Also recorded in at least 41 other tetrads.

D. aemula (AITON) KUNTZE   Hay-scented Buckler-fern.   **N**   Very rare

First record, Mrs A. E. Bolton 1987, Wilverley Inclosure 2401, VC11, conf. *FR*, Hb.RPB (*Watsonia* 17: 183).

Damp mossy stream- and ditch-banks in woodland on acid soil in the New Forest.

VC11: Howe Copse, Roydon Woods 3299, *AEB* 1990, Hb.RPB (*Watsonia* 18: 419); Avon Water, Sheepwash Lawn, E of Wootton Bridge 2599, boggy willow-carr, *AEB* 1991; King's Hat Inclosure 3805, *AEB* 1994.

Its recent discovery in Hants means that it is now known in all the counties along the south coast of England, and in S Wilts too.

D. carthusiana (VILL.) H. P. FUCHS (*D. lanceolatocristata* (Hoffm.) Alston)   Narrow Buckler-fern.   **N**   Locally frequent   Map 19

In acid, boggy woods and carr, and less-acid, open bogland. Locally frequent on sandy soils, especially in the New Forest. Rarely, on chalk in damp places, e.g. Chattis Hill 3236, VC12, in moss layer amongst bramble, *RPB* 1967.

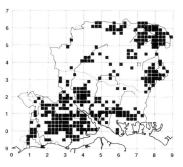

Map 19 Dryopteris carthusiana

D. x deweveri (J. JANSEN) WACHT. (*D. carthusiana* x *D. dilatata*)

Recorded for VC11 and VC12 in *Hybr.Fl.Brit.Is.*, p.117.

D. dilatata (HOFFM.) A. GRAY   Broad Buckler-fern.   **N**   Common

First British record, J. Goodyer, 1633, 'on the moist shadowie rockes by Maple-durham in Hampshire, neere Peters-field', VC11 (*Ger.em.Johns.*, p.1129).

Wet or dry woodland, most luxuriant on sand, in boggy wooded valleys; avoids open chalk country.

BLECHNACEAE

Blechnum spicant (L.) ROTH   Hard-fern.   **N**   Locally common   Map 20

Acid woodland, generally damp, often on ditch-banks. Also on sheltered, well-drained valley-slopes. Strongly calcifuge; in woods, common on the sands, but very rare on humus over chalk, e.g. The Warren 7328, *FR* 1990.

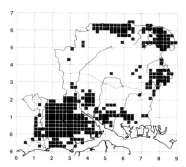

Map 20 Blechnum spicant

AZOLLACEAE

Azolla filiculoides LAM.   Water Fern.   **H**   Very local

First record, Mrs E. Rothwell *c*.1920, in a pond just outside Christchurch, VC11 (*Suppl.Fl.Hants*, p.128).

In ditches and slow-flowing or still water. Locally abundant, but sporadic and diminished by hard winters. Periodic records from the whole R. Avon, and the Basingstoke Canal, though in the latter it has been rare since dredging in 1975–90. VC11: 28☐; VC12: 13☐.

VC11: Holbury Manor 4203, small roadside ponds, *RPB* 1966; Beaulieu Heath 4004, *RPB* 1982, since gone; Marshcourt River 3534, *KC* 1982; Hackett's Marsh 4809, slow streams and pond, *SNHS* 1989. **VC12**: Princes Marsh, Liss 7726, small pond, *FF* 1984; pond at North Warnborough 7251, *CRH* 1988; Vann Farm, Hawkley 7430, small pond, *AB* 1989; pond at Town Mill, Whitchurch 4647, and down the R. Test at least as far as Longparish, *VAJ* 1989.

Pinopsida

PINACEAE

Pinus sylvestris L.   Scots Pine.   **D**   Locally abundant

Not native within historical times, but extensively planted since 1756, and fully naturalized on sandy and gravelly heathland. Subfossil remains in peat in the New Forest indicate that it was once native there. The pollen analyst, R. Scaife considers there is good evidence that some of the pine in the New Forest bogs and wet heaths may be of native, relict origin, but most workers do not at present accept this view.

P. nigra ARNOLD ssp. **nigra**
Austrian Pine.   **H**

Widely planted, but rarely self-sown.

ssp. **laricio** MAIRE   Corsican Pine.
D,H

Also planted commercially and occasionally self-sown, e.g. near Aldershot 8450, *ARGM* 1985.

P. pinaster AITON   Maritime Pine.
H   Very local

First record, W. A. Bromfield 1850, naturalized about Bournemouth, VC11 (*Phytologist* 3: 261. 888).

   Planted and occasionally self-sown on heathland, e.g. near Bournemouth, in the Avon Valley, the New Forest, and on heaths E of Fleet. VC9: 2 □; VC11: 22 □; VC12: 2 □.

CUPRESSACEAE

Juniperus communis L. ssp.
communis   Juniper.   **N**   Local
Map 21

Forming scrub in chalk grassland, usually on slopes. Still very locally plentiful, especially in W and NW, though much decreased in the last century. Very rare on New Forest heathland as scattered relics of what must once have been a larger population. Fires on heaths (and chalk grasslands) may have led to its great reduction.

   VC11: W of Markway Bridge 2403, one old bush bordering wooded, old course of stream, *DVW* 1990, comm. *AEB* (evidently the site recorded by Townsend in *Fl.Hants* 1904 (p.306), so the bush may be around 100 years old); Ashley Hole 2015, one bush, cut off low, *DVW c.*1989; Fritham Plain 2213, a deer-frayed bush on edge of heath, *CRT c.*1990; Ringwood Ford Bottom 2610, 2611, two isolated bushes amongst pines on valley side, *LM*, comm. *AEB* 1990; Beaulieu old airfield 3400, edge of former runway, *NAS* 1990; Peel Common 5702, one old bush on neutral, gravelly soil, *FR* 1976; track to Broughton Down 2833, *RPB* 1965; Old Winchester Hill 6420, *RPB* 1952. **VC12**: Noar Hill, *AB* 1982; Beacon Hill, Old Burghclere 4556, abundant, *RPB* 1969.

   Recently there has been some planting of *Juniperus* on roadside verges, using propagations from wild Hampshire stock, as at: **VC11**: By A3, E of Butser Hill 7219; by M27, Ports Down

6006. **VC12**: By A34, Litchfield 4653; by A339, NW of Basingstoke 5854.

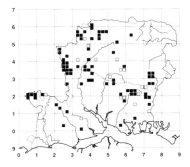

Map 21 Juniperus communis ssp. communis

TAXACEAE

Taxus baccata L.   Yew.   **N,H**
Common

Native and abundant over much of the chalk, especially in the Wealden Edge Hangers and coombes of the E South Downs. Forms pure woods as about Butser Hill and The Warren, Hawkley. Frequent, too, in mixed woods on well-drained, acid soil in the New Forest, on the Upper and Lower Greensand, and in the S Hants Basin. Much planted in shrubberies and church-yards; widely dispersed by thrushes and other birds which eat the fruits of both native and planted trees.

   John Evelyn recorded that 'besides the use of the wood for bows...(for which the close and more deeply dyed is best) the...artists in Box, Cabinet-makers, and Inlayers (particularly for Parquetè-floors) most gladly employ it...also for the cogs of mills, posts to be set in moist grounds, and everlasting axle-trees, there is none to be compared with it; likewise for the bodies of lutes, theorboes, bowls, wheels and pins for pulleys; yea, and for tankards to drink out of...' (*Silva*, p.379).

Magnoliopsida

MAGNOLIIDAE
(DICOTYLEDONS)

ARISTOLOCHIACEAE

<**Asarum europaeum** L.
Asarabacca.   **H**   Extinct

Formerly naturalized at Thruxton,

VC12, J. Hussey, who sent specimens to *FT* (*Fl.Hants*, excl.sp., p.364).>

<**Aristolochia clematitis** L.   Birth-wort.   **D**   Extinct

A herbal relic, formerly on old walls or hedgerows. *Fl.Hants* (excl.sp., p.364) gives two localities; St Cross, Winton, VC11, and Bordon Lodge, Woolmer Forest, VC12, but it no longer occurs in either.>

NYMPHAEACEAE

Nymphaea alba L. ssp. **alba**   White Water-lily.   **N,H**   Local

In ponds, especially old clay- and gravel-pits in SW, and in slow-flowing waters. Native, but also increasingly planted in ponds – as are *N.* x *marliacea* Latour-Marl., and other cultivars derived from *N. odorata* Aiton x *N. alba*. Absent as a native from NW and much of E.

   VC11: Allbrook 4520, sluggish stream, *RPB 1974*. **VC12**: Basingstoke Canal, Greywell 7251, *RPB* 1973; Linchborough Pond, Woolmer Forest 8132, relic, possibly native, *AB* 1984.

Nuphar lutea (L.) SM.   Yellow Water-lily.   **N**   Locally frequent
Map 22

In ponds, slow-flowing rivers, New Forest streams, and the Basingstoke Canal.

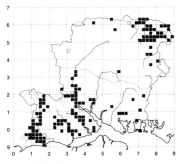

Map 22 Nuphar lutea

Cabomba caroliniana A. GRAY
Carolina Water-shield.   **H**   Very rare

First record, C. R. Hall 1990, in several places from Colt Hill Bridge and E towards Broad Oak 7451, 7551, VC12, det. *EJC*. Increased 1991–92, then declining, but still persists, *CRH* 1995.

   An aquarists' weed, so far established in one region of the Basingstoke

Canal. Native of south-eastern N America.

CERATOPHYLLACEAE

Ceratophyllum demersum L. Rigid Hornwort. **N,H** Locally frequent and occasional Map 23

In ponds and slow-flowing waters. Considerably extended since *Fl.Hants*, but its spread may be partly due to introductions by aquarists from garden ponds.

VC11: Old reservoir, Mansbridge, Southampton 4415, in plenty, *RPB* 1975. **VC12**: R. Whitewater, Dipley 7457, *AB* 1976.

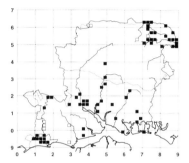

Map 23 Ceratophyllum demersum

RANUNCULACEAE

Caltha palustris L. Marsh-marigold. **N** Locally common

In wet meadows, marshes, fens, alder carr and ditches, but not in very acid bogs.

Helleborus foetidus L. Stinking Hellebore. **N** Rare

First record, Gilbert White 1765, 'Selborne-wood' 7333, VC12 (*White's Jnls* 1: 164).

In steep, open, beech-woods on chalk, or on bare or disturbed chalky ground. In an isolated site near Nether Wallop, and in a few other localities, mainly on the eastern chalk. Sometimes a hard winter produces many seedlings, but new colonies tend to be smothered if rank vegetation invades.

VC11: Only a few plants survive: Peak Copse, Upham 5420, *RPB* 1985. Formerly in adjacent Grasted Copse, *PMH* 1935, *RPB* 1977, since destroyed; Morestead 5125, *WMB & RHJ* 1965, not seen *RPB* 1979; Stakes Lane, Upham 5319, chalk-pit, *RPB* 1955, not seen 1978; M27 Wallington 5906, N

bank below houses, probably an escape, *RBa* 1993. **VC12**: Isle of Wight Hill 2537, doubtfully native, *RPB* 1967, *PJW* 1991; Greywell 7150, chalk dell, *TC* 1941, Hb.HCMS (*Rep.B.E.C.* for 1941–42, p.478), *FDG* 1950, later destroyed; Soldridge *c*.6534, railway embankment, *MB* 1963, *JH* 1972; Old Park Wood, Bishops Sutton 6130, *AB* 1970, and 6229, *RPB* 1981; Selborne Hill 7333, *AB* 1984, abundant, *FR* 1994; Ashford Hill 7326, *JHe* 1971, *DBa* 1989; edge of Bradley Wood 4652, on old railway, *AB* 1965. In constructing the Litchfield bypass over this railway, chalk was scooped out to make an artificial bank on the E side of the road, on which a patch of *H. foetidus* appeared, *GVD* 1978. Plants also re-emerged on the W side, up a cliff at the edge of the wood, *AB* 1978, seen on both sides of the road, *EAP* 1986. The residue of the chalk from the bypass appears to have been used for landscaping, for *H. foetidus* has appeared on artificial banks elsewhere, viz., Basingstoke Station 6352, *WGH* 1980; outside a sand-pit on the B3004, Kingsley 7737, *AB c.*1988, still flourishing 1991; edge of River Wey Estate, Andover 3746, one plant by railway, *MFW* 1991.

H. viridis L. ssp. **occidentalis** (REUT.) SCHIFFN. Green Hellebore. **N** Rare Map 24

First record, Gilbert White 1766, 'in the stony lane towards Alton', Selborne 7334, VC12 (*White's Jnls* 1: 195).

In oak, hazel, or ash coppice, usually on deep calcareous loam; very sparse, except in the Petersfield–Selborne region. Recently destroyed at some sites by copse clearance.

VC8: Ashridge Copse, Damerham 1014, *DJD* 1989. **VC11**: Still at Gambledown, Lockerley 2824, *RPB* to 1993; Upham 5421, *SS* 1965; The Miscombe, Buriton 7519, *FR & MB* 1977, *RPB* 1991. **VC12**: Malshanger

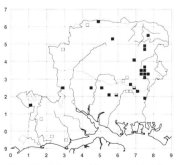

Map 24 Helleborus viridis ssp. occidentalis

5652, *AB* 1978; still in one of Gilbert White's two sites, Dorton, Selborne 7434, *AB* 1985, *FR* 1994.

Eranthis hyemalis (L.) SALISB. Winter Aconite. **H** Very rare

First record, J. Vaughan 1886, near Alton, VC12 (*Suppl.Fl.Hants* p.5).

Naturalized in a few woods and grassy places, on chalk or Malmstone. **VC11**: Kilmeston 5925, hedge bottom, *RPB* 1975. Also 4022, 6222. **VC12**: Froyle 7442, under trees along road, *AB* 1973. Also 3636, 3638, 7638.

Aconitum napellus L. ssp. **napellus** (*A. anglicum* Stapf) Monk's-hood. **H** Rare

Well naturalized in a few shady places, as by streams.

VC8: Whitsbury Castle ditches 1219, Hb.RPB 1976. **VC12**: R. Test, Gavelacre, Bransbury 4142, Hb.RPB 1965; near Kingslere, by stream in copse, about half a mile N of Sydmonton, *ABJ* 1911, Hb.BM; Ecchinswell 4959, *WGH* 1990; Plastow Green 5261, *PB & WGH* 1982.

Recorded (*sensu lato*) **VC11**: 1404, 3418, 3420, 3624, 5622. **VC12**: 3650, 4238, 5456.

Anemone nemorosa L. Wood Anemone. **N** Locally very common

In deciduous woodland, especially oak, ash or hazel, also under bracken on grass-heaths in the New Forest, on loam or sand; avoids very chalky or very acid soil.

A. apennina L. Blue Anemone. **H** Very rare

First record, P. M. Hall 1928, spinney near Breach Farm, Bighton 6235, VC12, Hb.BM.

VC11: St Cross 4727, shady streamside, long established, *KC* 1972, *RPB* 1989.

Pulsatilla vulgaris MILL. Pasqueflower. Status uncertain Very rare

First record, P. E. Toynton 1983, Martin Down 0518, VC8, one plant in ancient chalk turf, which has flowered intermittently for several years up to 1994. A remarkable occurrence, far S of the nearest recorded native locality in Berks. Although this is suspected of having been introduced by some unknown agency, the possibility cannot be ruled out that it may be a native relic, especially as one or two other plants have been seen not far away on the Dorset side of the county boundary. It was however noted by *JDG* in the far north of Wilts (now Glos), VC7 (*Fl.Wilts*, p.82, as *Anemone pulsatilla*).

Clematis vitalba L.   Traveller's-joy, Old Man's Beard.   **N**   Locally very common

First record, ?W. Bayley *c*.1570–72, 'White vyne. In every hedge about Winchester', VC11/12 (ms note, thought to be by Dr Walter Bayley, under *Clematis altera Dioscorides* on p.442 of a copy of Du Pinet's *Historia Plantarum* 1561, Botany Library, BM(NH) (See *Early Brit.Bots*, pp.235–236)).

Woods, scrub and hedges, abundant on chalk and Malmstone. Local elsewhere, on basic soils, such as made-up roadsides and alluvial deposits in river valleys. Its feathery seeds carry it to occasional outposts on acid soil.

C. flammula L.   Virgin's-bower.   **H**   Very rare

First record, G. H. Forster & J. L. S. Lansley 1985, South Hayling 7099, VC11, a fine plant on fixed shingle, straggling over brambles for *c*.6m, *GHF* 1992, Hb.RPB, still present 1994 (*BSBI News* **68**: 37).

Ranunculus acris L.   Meadow Buttercup.   **N**   Very common

Meadows and roadside verges; abundant except on dry or very acid soil, but considerably reduced in total quantity by general 'improvement' of old meadows.

R. repens L.   Creeping Buttercup.   **N,C**   Very common

Abundant in meadows, damp woods, waste ground, and in gardens as a weed; except where very dry or acid.

R. bulbosus L.   Bulbous Buttercup.   **N**   Common

Abundant in chalk grassland; frequent in other dry grassland, especially on roadside verges, but far less prevalent than formerly now that so many old meadows have been lost.

R. sardous CRANTZ   Hairy Buttercup.   **N,C**   Locally frequent   Map 25

First record, Gilbert White 1766, 'Field-crow-foot with a very small flower, *Ranunculus hirsutus annuus flore*

minimo' (var. *parvulus*) Selborne, VC12 (*White's Jnls* **1**: 201).

Frequent in damp, permanent pasture or occasionally fallow fields near the coast; locally frequent in the New Forest in grassy flood-hollows, pond-margins and wet verges. Rare and sporadic on sand or chalk in the E.

VC11: Southwick Park 6209, *JRw* 1991; Soake 6711, pasture in old pits, *RPB* 1991. **VC12**: Near Dora's Green 8148, *VL* 1959; Warren Corner 8149, *BPD* 1975; Dockenfield *c*.8240, *AMM* 1962; Kingsley sand-pit 7737, 7637, *SP & AB* 1979; Selborne 7432, Hb.AB 1970 (*Watsonia* **10**: 421), later identified as var. *parvulus* (*q.v.*).

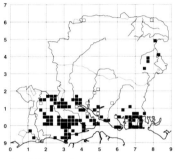

Map 25 Ranunculus sardous

var. **parvulus** L.

Abundant in places on the verge of the widened road B3006 from Selborne 7432 to Empshott 7532, Hb.AB, 1970–73.

R. parviflorus L.   Small-flowered Buttercup.   **N,C**   Rare

In short turf and disturbed open sandy or chalky ground, almost always near the coast. Formerly much more frequent, now rare and sporadic.

VC11: Mockbeggar *c*.1609, *ESH* 1964; Milford on Sea 2792, old sand-pit, *RPB* 1988; Hurst Castle 3189, *PS* 1989; Hatchet Pond 3601, *AB* 1971, *RPB* 1990; Sowley shore 3895, *RPB* 1957, 1978; Inchmery quay 4398, *RPB* 1952; Stansore Point 4698, 4699, *RPB* 1975, *RFG* 1990; B3056, Matley Wood 3307, *RPB* 1991; East End 3697, edge of heath, along hedge, *GHF* 1991; Gravelly Marsh 4197, *RPB* 1993; West Common, Exbury 4300, derelict arable over gas pipeline, *c*.70 plants, *RPB* 1991; near Mount Pleasant, Lymington 3097, on levelled tip, *RPB* 1991. Formerly in newly-laid garden lawn, Highcliffe 2094, *CDD* 1965; near

B3054, Beaulieu Heath 3599, *AEB* 1979; Stone Point 4598, on shingle, *HMS* 1931, *RPB* 1949; roadside at Hill Head 5402, *PMH* 1933, Hb.BM; Catherington *c*.6914, frequent as a weed, *NEGC* 1938, Hb.HCMS. **VC12**: Basingstoke Common 6552 or 6652, small but flourishing colony on chalky bank, *GWW* 1943, comm. *NEGC* (*Rep. B.E.C.* for 1943–44, p.699), since built on.

R. arvensis L.   Corn Buttercup.   **C**   Rare   Map 26

First record, Gilbert White 1766, Selborne, VC12 (*White's Jnls* **1**: 213).

Sandy and chalky cornfields; formerly common, especially in the E, but modern agricultural practices have made it rare. Now found mostly in disturbed ground on calcareous soils.

VC11: Hursley 4325, *RPB* 1975. **VC12**: Selborne 7532, abundant on widened road through cornfields, *AB* 1969, reappeared in cornfield 1976 and 1986, *AB*; Popley 6354, *BRB* 1991; near Chawton Park Wood 6635, edge of football field, *AAB* 1981; Fair Oak 5561, in field of chamomile, over 200 plants, *PB* 1987; Rooks Farm, Rotherwick 7056, *AJPB* 1991.

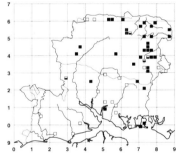

Map 26 Ranunculus arvensis

R. auricomus L.   Goldilocks Buttercup.   **N**   Locally frequent   Map 27

In old deciduous woodland, on chalk, Malmstone, base-rich clay, or loam; more frequent in E Hants, from Fareham northwards.

VC11: Ivy Wood, Brockenhurst 3102, *RPB* 1957, *AEB* 1983; Stubbs Wood 3603, *RPB* 1959; Dummer's Copse, West End 4615, *WP* 1968. **VC12**: East Tisted churchyard 7032, *AB* 1975; Thornycombe Wood, Vernham Dean 3355, *APNH* 1980; Fishpond Copse, NE of Bentley 8045, *FR* 1985; Winnells Copse, Rotherwick 7056, *AJPB* 1991.

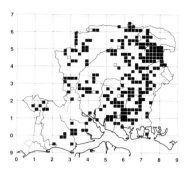

Map 27 Ranunculus auricomus

R. sceleratus L.   Celery-leaved Buttercup.   **N**   Locally frequent   Map 28

In marshes, both freshwater and saline, open mud in pastures, around ponds, and in ditches. Frequent near the coast, in estuaries, on the R. Avon, and in the NE.

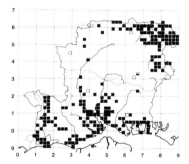

Map 28 Ranunculus sceleratus

R. lingua L.   Greater Spearwort. **N,H**   Rare

Fens, swamps, ponds, streamsides, marl-pit pools; persistent in some old natural fen sites, but often planted in roadside ponds, whence sometimes spread by ducks.
   VC11: Moors River 0900, *PMH* 1939, Hb.BM, also 1199, 1298, 1297, *RPB & CDD* 1954–61, no confirmed record since; Upper Pennington Common 3095, *RPB* 1961–83; Crockford Bridge 3499, *NDS* 1927, *RPB* 1950–92; Sowley Pond 3796, *NDS* 1927, *RPB* 1952; Pitts Deep 3795, *RPB* 1953–92; Kimbridge 3225, gravel-pit, *RPB* 1963; Deborah Copse, Bossington 3230, small fenny pond, *ILR* 1992; near Mopley Pond 4501, small pond, *RPB* 1988; Farlington 6806, bomb crater, Hb.AWW 1951, transplanted by *MB*, 1965, to

Titchfield Haven *c.*5302 and Farlington Marshes 6805, still flourishing at the latter in two ponds, 1990; Marshcourt River, S of Stockbridge 3534, *RPB* 1960. **VC12**: Stockbridge North Fen 3535, *FR* 1985, 1990; Alresford Pond 5833, *RPB* 1969; Fleet Pond 8255, *CRH* 1984, 8254, *CRH* 1990; Headley Park 8138, *GGG* 1968.

R. flammula L. ssp. **flammula** Lesser Spearwort.   **N**   Locally very common

Wet meadows, marshes, ponds, streamsides, boggy New Forest lawns, and swampy open woods. Absent from the chalk, except for a few ponds on Clay-with-flints.

<R. ophioglossifolius VILL. Adder's-tongue Spearwort.   **N** Extinct (Sched. 8)

Formerly in a wet ditch W of Hythe, *HG* 1878, Hb.BM (*Fl.Hants*, p.9). The ditch was drained some years later. Now known only in Gloucestershire.>

R. ficaria L. ssp. **ficaria**   Lesser Celandine.   **N**   Very common

Woodlands, hedgebanks, streamsides and wet meadows, on loamy or clay soils; abundant throughout the county, except where very dry or acid. Diploid and fertile.

ssp. **bulbilifer** LAMBINON   **N or D** Under-recorded

First record, P. M. Hall 1935, Whitedell Farm, Fareham 5808 or 5908, VC11.
   In shady places, generally near houses. Tetraploid and largely sterile. The bulbils may have been introduced with earth or for their special medicinal use for treating piles.
   VC8: Wooded road to Knoll Farm, Damerham 0917, *RPB* 1992. **VC11**: Allington Manor 4616, *BRB* 1964. Also 1496, 5624, 7222, 7420. **VC12**: Odiham and Greywell churchyards, *MMcC-W* 1978. Also 4838, 5262, 5460, 5842, 5856, 6262, 7028, 7232, 7238, 7428, 7450, 7856, 8430.

R. hederaceus L.   Ivy-leaved Crowfoot.   **N**   Locally frequent   Map 29

First record, Gilbert White 1766, Selborne, VC12 (*White's Jnls* 1: 195).
   On bare, muddy ground, or in still, shallow water, especially in rather acid conditions. Almost confined to the SW, where common, and to the NE, where now very local.

VC11: Hookheath Meadows 6408, *FR* 1983. **VC12**: Bransbury Common 4141, *RPB* 1988.

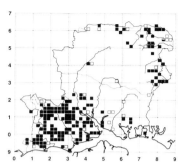

Map 29 Ranunculus hederaceus

R. omiophyllus TEN. (*R. lenormandii* F. W. Schultz)   Round-leaved Crowfoot.   **N**   Locally frequent   Map 30

On bare, muddy peaty soil, often where flushed; also in ditches and on pond-margins. Common in much of the New Forest, very local near Southampton and frequent on the NE sands.
   VC8: Lopshill Common 0913, stream-bank, *RPB* 1989; Plaitford Common 2718, *FR* 1991. **VC11**: North Ripley 1799, *NAS* 1989; SW of Braishfield 3624, *NAS* 1988. **VC12**: Ashford Hill meadows 5662, *PB* 1982; Bramshill Common 7561, 7562, in ditches, *CRH* 1986.

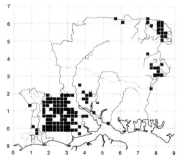

Map 30 Ranunculus omiophyllus

R. x novae-forestae S. D. WEBSTER (*R. x lutarius* auct., non (Revel) Bouvet; *R. omiophyllus* x *R. tripartitus*) New Forest Crowfoot.   **N**   Very local Map 31

In or around small, shallow pools and occasionally larger bodies of water, beside small streams, drainage-channels, flushes, flood-hollows and poached mud at cattle-crossings, most frequently on clay, including the calcareous Headon Beds, in less acid water generally than *R. omiophyllus*. Virtually confined to the New Forest and frequent in the southern part. It is apparently unknown elsewhere in Britain, although there are several old records of *R. lutarius* for VC14 (*Fl.Sussex*, p.8). In 1977, after widespread flooding, it was particularly plentiful.

After examination of specimens from a wide selection of sites in Hb.RPB and of older ones dating back to 1876 in Hb.BM, Hb.CGE, Hb.E and Hb.RNG, S. D. Webster and C. D. K. Cook confirm that almost all are the hybrid. It can be quite variable and some populations, which may be back-crosses, are highly fertile, with small flowers.

VC11: Gravel pits, Setley near Brockenhurst, *HG & JGr* 1877 (as *R. lutarius*), Hb.BM (holotype), Setley Marl Pit 3099, in shallow muddy ponds, Hb.RPB 1980, det. *SDW & CDKC*; Howen Bottom 2315, flush near stream, Hb.RPB 1977, det. *SDW & CDKC*; Balmer Lawn 3003, pond margin, Hb.RPB 1976, det. *SDW & CDKC*; Hatchet Pond 3601, *CDKC* 1966, Hb.BM, *RFG* 1990. Elsewhere recorded only at Browndown 5898, *HJMB* 1953, but no specimen seen and not reported there since.

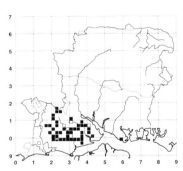

Map 31 Ranunculus x novae-forestae

R. omiophyllus x R. peltatus N Very rare

VC11: Holmsley Bog 2201, *SDW* 1982, Hb.RNG, Hb.RPB. This is sterile but it resembles fertile plants found in 1896 by T. Hilton at Copthorne Common, E Sussex, and described as *R. x hiltonii* Groves & J. Groves, which persisted there until at least 1926 (*Watsonia* **16**: 25–27).

R. tripartitus DC. Three-lobed Crowfoot. **N** Very rare or extinct

Because of the difficulty in separating back-crossed hybrids from pure *R. tripartitus*, it is not certain if any of the latter still exists in the New Forest and there are no confirmed recent records. However, specimens which are extremely close to it have been found in a roadside pond N of Crockford Bridge 3599, VC11, *AEB & RPB* 1988, Hb.RPB, det. *SDW*.

A specimen labelled 'Aldershot, Surrey, 1886', in Hb.LIV, det. *CDKC* 1963, was apparently collected on the VC17 side of Aldershot.

R. baudotii GODR. Brackish Water-crowfoot. **N** Very local Map 32

Ponds, ditches and wet hollows, in alluvial, brackish but non-tidal marshes, in the estuarine and reclaimed coastal regions. Very rare elsewhere.

VC11: Inland at Lee near Romsey 3517, pool in disused gravel-pit, *RPB* 1975, conf. *FR*; Kimbridge Junction 3225, stagnant ditch, *WCNHS* 1927–31. Coastal sites: Stanpit Marsh 1691, 1692, *RPB* 1986; Pennington Marshes 3292, *RMV* 1986; Farlington Marshes 6803, 6804, 6805, *MB* 1990.

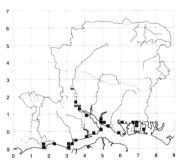

Map 32 Ranunculus baudotii

R. trichophyllus CHAIX Thread-leaved Water-crowfoot. **N** Rare Map 33

In ponds, ditches and slow streams with high mineral content. Scattered through the lowlands and river valleys, but very rare in ponds on the chalk uplands. Can be persistent at some sites, but often transient.

VC11: Busketts Lawn 3111, small clay-pit pond, Hb.RPB 1990, det. *SDW*; Breamore Marsh pond 1518, *AWW* 1954, Hb.RPB 1990; Hildon House 3131, *GDF* 1972; pond at Lower Upham 5319, *RPB* 1975; Sinah Common lagoon *c*.6999, *LNHL* 1976. **VC12**: Duns Mere, Highclere 4560, *AB* 1976; dewpond on Ladle Hill 4756,

AB 1976; Wellington Country Park 7263, *ARGM* 1985; Hartley Wintney *c*.7658, *UR* 1966.

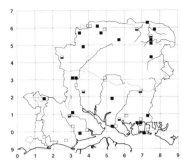

Map 33 Ranunculus trichophyllus

R. aquatilis L. Common Water-crowfoot. **N** Very local Map 34

In ponds, ditches and slow streams. Very local in the SW near the coast and in the S New Forest, rare in the N and NE.

VC11: Pennington Marshes 3292, 1986; St Leonards Grange, Beaulieu 4098, roadside pond, 1986; Setley Marl Pit 3099, 1977; all Hb.RPB det. *SDW*. **VC12**: Sherfield on Loddon 6858, *IMcD* 1971; pond in Alice Holt Forest 7942, *AB* 1977; R. Enborne *c*.5063, 5463, R. Hart 7658, and R. Whitewater 7363, *PDG* 1977.

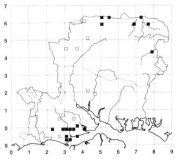

Map 34 Ranunculus aquatilis

R. peltatus SCHRANK (*R. aquatilis* ssp. *peltatus* (Schrank) Syme) Pond Water-crowfoot. **N** Locally common Map 35

Ponds, ditches and slow streams, in both shallow and deep water. Very variable, becoming attenuated in deep streams, sometimes without any floating leaves. The commonest water-crowfoot in the New Forest and in still waters elsewhere.

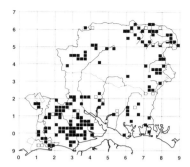

Map 35 Ranunculus peltatus

R. penicillatus (DUMORT.) BAB.
Stream Water-crowfoot.

ssp. **pseudofluitans** (SYME) S. D.
WEBSTER (*R. aquatilis* ssp. *pseudoflui-
tans* (Syme) A. R. Clapham)   **N**
Locally common   Map 36

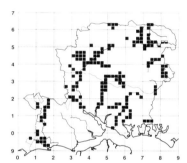

Map 36 Ranunculus penicillatus ssp.
pseudofluitans (incl. vars pseudofluitans
& vertumnus)

var. **pseudofluitans**

The commonest Water-crowfoot in
fast-flowing, usually but not always
highly-calcareous, water. It is
extremely plastic, the leaves getting
longer with the swiftness of the
current, giving rise to reports of *R.
fluitans*. This is especially true in the R.
Avon, specimens from which had to be
cytologically determined.

var. **vertumnus** C. D. K. COOK (incl.
R. sphaerospermus auct., non BOISS. ET
BLANCHE)   Rare or under-recorded
Map 37

Broadly characterized by having
double the number of leaf-segments,
bunched into 'balls', and typically
inhabiting the upper reaches of clear
streams, in very sluggish water.
According to S. D. Webster, not all

specimens labelled '*R. sphaerospermus*'
are necessarily var. *vertumnus*. The first
record of '*R. sphaerospermus*' for Hants
was F. Stratton 1871, running streams,
Winchester, VC11, Hb.OXF. The
earliest specimen, however, is that of
R. S. Hill 1839, 'streams about
Basingstoke', VC12, Hb.BM. In the
1960s it was recorded at scattered
localities along the Basingstoke Canal E
to Pondtail, but it disappeared as the
canal silted up, except at Greywell
where it remained plentiful. After the
canal was dredged, it had recolonized
from the undredged Greywell refuge
eastwards to Broad Oak by 1986, but
has since contracted westwards again,
coinciding with increased boating. The
type locality is the Basingstoke Canal at
Greywell, *CDKC* 1958, Hb.CGE.
Elsewhere it has been recorded
recently as follows:

VC11: Upper R. Itchen, New
Cheriton 5827 and The Moors,
Bishop's Waltham 5616, Hb.RPB
1986; Mill Stream, Bedhampton 7006,
HB.RPB 1990, all det. *SDW*. **VC12**:
Near the Wallop Brook 2938, *RMV*
1988; R. Alre 5833, 5932, *ARGM*
1988; stream through Passfield 8234,
AB 1979; Bourne Rivulet, R. Lyde and
R. Rother, *PDG* 1978, all det. *SDW*; R.
Whitewater, Greywell 7251, *SDW*
1982; Candover Stream 5634 and R.
Alre 5732, *AB* 1991.

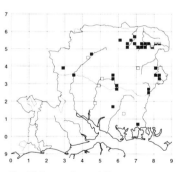

Map 37 Ranunculus penicillatus ssp. pseudofluitans var. vertumnus

[**R. fluitans** LAM.   River Water-
crowfoot.

This species was recorded in error in
Fl.Hants (p.4) and in the early years
of the present recording scheme. It
does not exist in Hants, according to
N. T. H. Holmes, referee for
Ranunculus subgenus *Batrachium*.]

R. circinatus SIBTH.   Fan-leaved
Water-crowfoot.   **N,H** Very rare

In still or slow-flowing waters with
relatively high mineral content.
Fl.Hants, p.4, shows it to have been
common in the Avon, the Test, the
Anton and the Itchen. N. D. Simpson's site at Bickton, on the Avon,
1956, has not been refound. Presumably pollution or canalization have
resulted in only two sites remaining on
the Avon and one on the Test. It is
often introduced into fishing lakes, as
at Sinah Common lagoon, later to
disappear, and also reaches waters
uncongenial to it, e.g. Basingstoke
Canal and Fleet Pond, through the
agency of aquarists, but in these places
it has not been seen to flower.

VC11: R. Avon, Knapp Mill 1593,
1594, Hb.RPB 1976, det. *FR*; Fishlake
Meadows, Romsey 3522, *RPB* 1975.
VC12: Dogmersfield Lake 7551, *CRH*
1987.

Adonis annua L.   Pheasant's-eye.
C   Rare   Map 38

First record, Gilbert White 1768,
Selborne, VC12 (*White's Jnls* 1: 245).
   In chalky, arable fields, formerly
common in the N and W, now rare.
   There are 25 records since 1930, of
which the most recent are: **VC8**: Knoll
Farm, Damerham 0917, *JO* 1986–89.
VC11: North Charford Down Farm
1520, *CS* 1991; Nine Mile Water Farm
3034, *RPB* 1968; Broughton Down
Farm 2934, *GDF* 1972. **VC12**: South
Side Farm, Longparish 4343, *WMB*
1962, *JSn* 1986, comm. *AJB*; Brown
Candover, N of Robey's Farm 5740,
EAB 1965; Borough Down Farm 5037,
ARL 1965; Lower Wield 6340, *EH*
1968; Fob Down Farm, Alresford
5733, *JLSL* 1978; Battledown Farm,
Basingstoke 5949, *RJH* 1984; Augurs
Hill Copse 3842, *DMa* 1987; S of
Overton 5148, and Hundred Acres
field, near Spring Pond Farm, Laver-

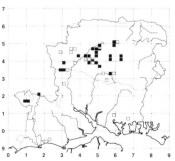

Map 38 Adonis annua

stoke Estate 4847, both *GC* 1986; Upper Norton Farm 4842, *SF* 1991.

Myosurus minimus L.   Mousetail.
N?,C   Rare   Map 39

On open, disturbed, sandy, gravelly or clayey ground, often arable, where subject to winter flooding. Once sporadic near the coast, it is now rare and often impermanent, although several recent records have extended its range.

VC11: Berry Hill near Throop 1096, by sewage works, *FAW* 1983; Water-ditch 1895, *FAW* 1987; Shelley Farm, Ower 3217, trampled patch in pasture, *RMV* 1990, Hb.RPB; Keyhaven Road, Keyhaven 3091, field track and foot-path *MEY & GY* 1988; W of Brown-wich Pond 5103, cornfield border, *RFG* 1989; Little Park Farm, Swan-wick 5208, *PMH* 1934; Brooker's Farm, Rowner, very abundant on clay, *PMH* 1939; Beaulieu Road Station 3406, abundant in pony-pens 1953–69, only about 40 plants in 1989, *AJSh*; S of Titchfield 5403, common on track leading to reserve until churned up by cattle, *MB* 1970; Mayflower Park, Southampton 4111, tipped soil along old railway, *EJC & RPB* 1991. VC12: Near Round Wood, Froyle 7442, *CL* 1959; Greatham 7730, new nursery-garden on site of cornfield, *JMe* 1978–89; Church Crookham, *HMS* 1928 (*Suppl.Fl.Hants*, p.1); Church Crookham 8152, temporary garden weed, *ARGM* 1982–83; Farnborough 8757, *SBa* 1995.

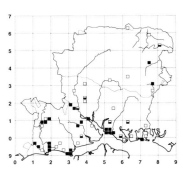

Map 39 Myosurus minimus

Aquilegia vulgaris L.   Columbine.
N,H   Local   Map 40

In open, chalk woodland, especially in glades and scrub; by streamsides and on rides in New Forest woodland, particularly on the Headon Beds.

Widespread but sparse, and records outside the New Forest away from ancient woodland, or off the chalk, are probably garden escapes. The map attempts to show native distribution only.

VC8: Kitt's Grave, Martin Down 0320, *RPB* 1988; Boulsbury Wood 0814, *AB & JO* 1984. VC11: Bratley Water 2309, *SNG* 1985; Lower Granville Copse, Hambledon 6316, Hb.AWW 1957; Coulters Dean 7419, *FR* 1972; Bottom Copse, Exton 5820, *HCA-H* 1975. VC12: Cheriton Wood 6129, *RPB* 1969; Micheldever Wood 5337, *DEF* 1975; Old Park Wood, Bramdean, *PMH* 1930; Great Park, Weston Common 7044, *JBM* 1942; Sheephouse Copse 7545, *FDG* 1966, *CRH* 1989; Roundhills Hanger, Hawk-ley 7328, *AB* 1966, reappeared after clearance, *DBa* 1989; Vernham Row 3257, *GDF* 1981; Harewood Forest 4045, *DEA* 1976, 3842, *MFW* 1991; Pamber Forest 6161, *HJMB* 1984.

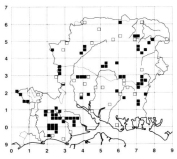

Map 40 Aquilegia vulgaris

Thalictrum flavum L.   Common Meadow-rue.   **N**   Very locally frequent   Map 41

On river-, stream- and ditch-banks, and alluvial marshes or open carr, on

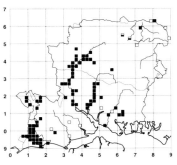

Map 41 Thalictrum flavum

base-rich soil. Mainly by the Stour, the Moors River, the Avon, the Test and the Itchen, where it is sometimes plentiful.

VC11: Avon Water, Wootton Bridge 2499, *AEB* 1990; Old Canal, Fishlake, Romsey 3622, *RMV* 1987. VC12: Danebury 3337, 50 plants along corn-field fence and roadside verge, where recently disturbed, *RPB* 1985; Anton Lakes 3646, *MFW* 1991; R. Blackwater 8162, *JA & WSm* 1986.

T. minus L.   Lesser Meadow-rue.
H   Very rare

VC11: Avon Common 1298, a few plants, presumably introduced, persist-ing on sand under bracken at edge of heath near roadside, *RPB* 1983.

BERBERIDACEAE

Berberis vulgaris L.   Barberry.
D,N?   Rare   Map 42

Often bird-sown from gardens having been grown formerly as a herbal cure for jaundice; doubtfully native.

VC11: Ober Water, Rhinefield 2503, *RPB* 1956–90; Marwell 5121, roadside hedge, (probably *GWP*'s site, *Suppl.Fl.Hants*, p.6), *RPB* 1983. VC12: Abbotstone 5634, *RPB* 1965; A339, Basingstoke 6450, hedge, *AB* 1976; Home Farm, Hackwood Park 6450, roadside hedge, *GHF* 1977; SE of Laverstoke 5145, one bush in ancient boundary-hedge, *DEA* 1977; Saxon Drove 5534, *DEA* 1984; Butter Wood 7252, *AJPB* 1986; near Cowdown, Harewood, *HFC* 1942 (*Proc.Hants Fld Club* 15: 306).

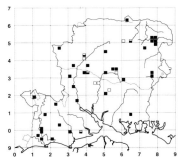

Map 42 Berberis vulgaris

B. aggregata C. Schneid.   Clus-tered Barberry.   **H**   Very rare

VC12: Ridge Hanger, Steep 7325, Hb.JF 1985, det. *JMM* (*Watsonia* 18: 215).

B. buxifolia LAM. Box-leaved Barberry. **H** Very rare

VC11: Ober Water, Rhinefield 2503, in scrub beside stream, *RPB* 1956–92.

Mahonia aquifolium (PURSH) NUTT. Oregon-grape. **H** Occasional

Widely planted and often bird-sown from gardens and shrubberies, most often in the NW. VC11: 14 □; VC12: 25 □.

PAPAVERACEAE

Papaver atlanticum (BALL) COSS. Atlas Poppy. **H** Very rare

Rather persistent on waste ground.
VC11: Shirley 3913, 3914, 4014, 4112, *WFB* 1963–65; A33 Compton 4625, *RPB* 1975; NW Hayling Island 7103, old railway, *RPB* 1990. Also 4008, 6604.

P. somniferum L. ssp. **somniferum** Opium Poppy. **H** Frequent

A frequent garden escape, on rubbish-dumps and tipped soil. VC8: 1 □; VC11: 35 □; VC12: 49 □.

P. rhoeas L. Common Poppy. **C** Frequent

Previously common and generally distributed (*Fl.Hants*, p.20), but now sadly depleted by modern agriculture. Still common on disturbed ground (except in cornfields) including verges of newly-widened roads. Thinly scattered around unsprayed headlands in cornfields and on other arable land.

P. dubium L. ssp. **dubium** Long-headed Poppy. **C** Locally common

Open arable and disturbed ground, on sand, gravel and chalk. Less frequent in SW.

ssp. **lecoqii** (LAMOTTE) SYME (*P. le-coqii* Lamotte) Yellow-juiced Poppy. **C** Rare Map 43

On bare calcareous soil.
VC11: West Meon 6424, backyard of a house, on building-soil, *LEW* 1960; Beaulieu 3802, at foot of old walls, *RPB* 1985; Boldre 3198, garden weed, *AEB* 1985; South Hayling 7098, bank behind beach, *RFG* 1990. VC12: Repeatedly around Selborne, *AB* 1964–90; A3057 verge, Wherwell 3741, *RPB* 1977; Hill Brow 7826, garden, on

Sandgate Beds, *AB* 1982; Alton 7139, *GHF* 1977.

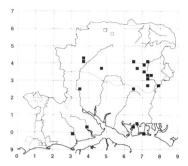
Map 43 Papaver dubium ssp. lecoqii

P. hybridum L. Rough Poppy. **C** Locally frequent Map 44

A quite frequent arable weed on the NW and central chalk; its abundance depends upon the degree of crop-spraying.
VC8: Knoll Farm, Damerham 0919, *JO* 1987. VC11: Chalton Down 7314, *EAP* 1979; on dredgings from the R. Avon, Hale 1718, *JO* 1983; North Charford Down Farm 1520, *CS* 1991, conf. *JO*; Clarendon Way, Houghton 3231, *SNHS* 1992. VC12: Wallers Ash 4936, *AB* 1967, despite spraying, still occasionally found, *OMS* 1989; Middle Wallop 3139, *GDF* 1984; cornfield by Wield Wood 6138, *ANHS* 1986; Steventon Warren Farm 5444, *PJW* 1991; Kempshott 5949, corner of cornfield, *DPD* 1993.

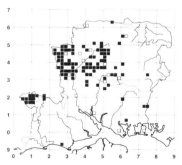
Map 44 Papaver hybridum

P. argemone L. Prickly Poppy. **C** Local Map 45

In cornfields on chalk or sand. 'Somewhat common' in *Fl.Hants* (p.21) but now rare, except in arable and disturbed waste ground in the N.

VC8: Toyd Farm, Martin 0820, *JO* 1982; Tidpit Common Down 0617, 0618, *RPB & JO* 1986. **VC11**: Ashley Heath 1104, disused railway, *RPB* 1991; Breamore Down 1420, *RPB* 1977; Newtown, Sherfield English 3023, *RMV* 1986. **VC12**: Haw Bridge 7441, gateway, *AB* 1977–80; Wield Wood 6138, *ANHS* 1986; Blackmoor 7733, *AB* 1985; Cove 8355, railway embankment, *TD* 1991; Rooks Farm, Rotherwick 7056, *AJPB* 1991.

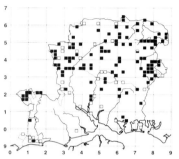
Map 45 Papaver argemone

Meconopsis cambrica (L.) VIG. Welsh Poppy. **H** Very rare

VC11: Ringwood Forest near Ebblake 1007, pine-plantations in two remote areas, *RPB* 1987–89; Buriton 7319, shady roadside near tip, *DPJS & JMC* 1989. VC12: New Stoner Hill 7226, naturalized in hanger, *CWG* 1882 (*Fl.Hants*, excl.sp., p.24), last seen *FR* 1978.

Glaucium flavum CRANTZ Yellow Horned-poppy. **N** Local

On marine shingle-beaches. Scattered, and locally plentiful, from Hayling Island to Hurst Castle. Decreased around Christchurch, but one plant on Hengistbury new dunes 1790, *RMW* 1989. VC11: 24 □.

Chelidonium majus L. Greater Celandine. **D** Frequent

First record, Gilbert White 1765, 'on a bank at Faringdon', VC12 (*White's Jnls* 1: 167–168).
An ancient introduction, now widespread on hedgebanks and old walls, and in shady, waste places, chiefly near dwellings. Used to this day for treating warts.

Eschscholzia californica CHAM. Californian Poppy. **H** Rare or under-recorded

First record, J. H. Lavender 1960, Stanpit 1692, VC11.

VC11: Established on Bournemouth cliffs 0890, *AB* 1977; and on slipped clay at Barton on Sea 2392, *RPB* 1977; Melville Road, Eastney 6799, established on waste ground, *RBa* 1992. **VC12**: Stoke 4050, competing successfully above old chalk-pit, *GDF* 1984 (*Watsonia* 17: 184).

FUMARIACEAE

Pseudofumaria lutea (L.) BORKH. (*Corydalis lutea* (L.) DC.) Yellow Corydalis. **H** Occasional

Naturalized on old walls, mainly in N and C Hants. VC11: 19 ☐; VC12: 35 ☐.

Ceratocapnos claviculata (L.) LIDÉN (*Corydalis claviculata* (L.) DC.) Climbing Corydalis. **N** Locally frequent Map 46

First record, J. Goodyer 1621, 'At Southsea Castle in flower' 6493, VC11 (*Early Brit.Bots*, p.151).

In open woodland, generally on sand or gravel, disappearing as woods darken but reappearing on scrub clearance; along ancient hedged field-boundaries and in scrubby parts of heaths and unimproved grassland, often amongst bracken; fixed shingle-beaches. Very local, except in SW.

VC11: Still at Toothill 3818, as in *Fl.Hants* (p.24), *RPB* 1992; Black Water, Needs Ore Point 4197, spreading after reed-cutting, *RPB* 1984–92; Bigg's Copse, Shedfield 5513, *DEA* 1979; Browndown Common 5899, Hb.AWW 1963. **VC12**: The Old Moor, Blackmoor 7731, *AB* 1967; wood opposite Headley Park 8138, *AMM* 1959, *AB* 1979; Rushmoor Flash 8552, *ARGM* 1978.

Fumaria capreolata L. White Ramping-fumitory. **C, N?** Very rare

First record, Miss C. E. Palmer 1899, garden of The Yews, Odiham, VC12 (*Fl.Hants*, p.24 as *F. pallidiflora* Jord.).

On waste ground. Essentially a S European species at the northern limit of its range in the British Isles where (except in the Channel Islands) it is represented by ssp. *babingtonii* (Pugsley) P. D. Sell, stated in *New Fl.* (p.133) to be an endemic. Hants specimens have not been determined at subspecific level; probably only a casual in the county.

VC11: Ringwood, *FKM* 1937, det. *NYS*; Southern Lane, New Milton 2394, *JLeR* 1989, Hb.RPB, det. *MGD* (*Watsonia* 18: 420).

F. bastardii BOREAU Tall Ramping-fumitory. **C** Very rare

On disturbed open soil and arable land. Greatly decreased since *Fl.Hants*.

VC11: Station Road, Sway 2798, hotel flower-border, *EAP* 1983, Hb.RPB 1991, det. *MGD*; Waterford, Lymington 3394, sea-wall, Hb.RPB 1989, det. *MGD*; Hollybrook Recreation Ground, Southampton 3914, *RMV* 1990, Hb.RPB, det. *MGD*; Portchester, *PMH* 1934, det. HWP; W of A2030, Great Salterns 6702, DPJS 1991, Hb.RPB, det. *MGD*; Christchurch, in allotments, *NDS* 1944, det. *HWP*. **VC12**: Odiham, *CP* 1903, Hb.BM, Hb.HWB.

F. muralis SONDER ex KOCH ssp. **boraei** (JORD.) PUGSLEY Common Ramping-fumitory. **C** Locally frequent Map 47

Hedges, field- and wood-borders, arable and disturbed ground, shingle and bushes on the coast. Townsend considered it rare (*Fl.Hants*, p.25). It is

not so now, but is commonest in the SW nearer the coast and very local farther inland.

[ssp. **muralis**

The records in *Fl.Hants* (p.25) and *Suppl.Fl.Hants* (p.8) are dubious; there have been none since.]

F. officinalis L. ssp. **officinalis** Common Fumitory. **C** Common

On arable and disturbed waste-ground.

ssp. **wirtgenii** (KOCH) ARCANG. **C** Under-recorded

Probably widespread, especially on chalk.

VC11: St Cross cricket-ground 4728 or 4828, *PMH* 1934, det. *HWP*; Casbrook Common refuse-tip 3425, *WFB* 1969, det. *MGD*. **VC12**: Fob Down Farm, Alresford 5733, *AB* 1985, det. *MGD*.

F. densiflora DC. (*F. micrantha* Lag.) Dense-flowered Fumitory. **C** Locally common Map 48

Formerly rare (*Fl.Hants*, p.26), but it has increased and is now a frequent arable weed on chalk; occasional on other soils.

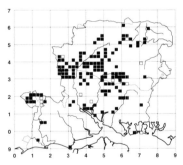

Map 48 Fumaria densiflora

F. parviflora LAM. Fine-leaved Fumitory. **C** Rare Map 49

On cultivated ground on chalk; still rare as in *Fl.Hants* (p.26).

VC11: Broughton Down 2932, Hb.RPB 1965; S of Broughton Down 2832, Hb.RPB 1987; Buckholt 2733, *JO & VW* 1987. **VC12**: Andover Down 3945, Hb.AWW 1962; Alresford 5831, in quantity on building site, *AB* 1977; Southside Farm, Longparish 4443, *PHC & AJB* 1986.

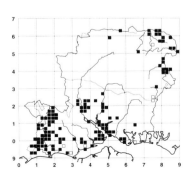

Map 46 Ceratocapnos claviculata

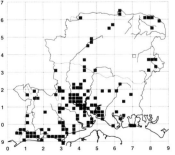

Map 47 Fumaria muralis ssp. boraei

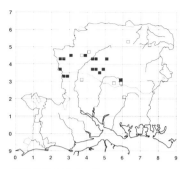

Map 49 Fumaria parviflora

F. vaillantii LOISEL.   Few-flowered Fumitory.   **C**   Very rare

On cultivated ground on chalk.

VC12: Chilbolton Down 4137, *FR* 1955; N of Ashe 5351, *WEW* 1958, det. *FR*; Herriard Park 6747, cornfield, *FR & AB* 1976; Warren Farm, Micheldever Station 5042, cornfield, *AB* 1976, det. *FR*; The Down, Roundwood Farm 5144, *GC* 1986.

ULMACEAE

Ulmus is an extremely difficult genus, treated in widely different ways by past and present specialists in the British elms. R. Melville determined almost all the Hampshire specimens, the majority of which were collected before the onset of Dutch elm disease which killed off nearly all the mature elms in the county. Under the current nomenclature some names used by Melville have become obsolete. These have been retained in the following account, pending publication of a radically new taxonomic approach at present under way.

Ulmus glabra HUDS.   Wych Elm. **N,D,H**   Locally frequent

First record, J. Goodyer 1633, 'This prospereth and naturally groweth in any soile moist or dry, on high hills, and in low vallies in good plenty in most places in Hampshire, wher it is commonly called VVitch Hasell' (*Ger.em.Johns.*, p.1481).

Native in old woodland, mainly on chalk and Malmstone; a minor constituent of ash-woods, often with maple, whitebeam, hazel and, rarely, small-leaved lime, on rock or scree of steep escarpments. Also in oak-ash-woods, usually on basic clayey soil. Widely planted in hedges, tree-belts and parkland, involving perhaps several cultivars. Particularly fine on the Wealden Edge Hangers, from Langrish to Selborne. Most larger trees and suckers died of disease in the 1970s, but some trees, especially younger ones, survived, and coppice regrowth is generally healthy. Currently, in the hangers of the chalk and Malmstone, there are many moderate-sized maiden trees up to 15m tall still free from disease. Some very large trees have also survived the disease, notably one in Wick Hill Hanger 7535, VC12, *FR* 1990.

U. glabra x U. procera?

VC12: Berryfield Hanger 7326, above Ashford, a large tree (*c*.24m tall and with bole *c*.60cm in diameter) found by *FR* survived, free from any elm disease, until overturned by the October 1987 hurricane. This tree was used by HCC to supply hundreds of cuttings in the hope that these would be disease-free. The root-plate was replaced, after removing the fallen bole, and had healthy stems growing from it up to 1994. It may be possible to re-populate those parts of the Hangers that have lost their elms with these offspring. It is quite likely that this hybrid has acquired immunity from the elm disease. It has features of both putative parents, and is situated on the Hanger high above some *U. procera*. It is probably a natural hybrid, but further research is required (F.R.).

U. x vegeta (LOUDON) A. LEY (*U. glabra* x *U. minor*)   Huntingdon Elm. **H**   Very rare

VC11: Portmore, Boldre 3497, Hb.RPB 1959; Nursling Mill 3515, Hb.RPB 1983; Mopley 4501, Hb.RPB 1976; A3057, Timsbury 3425, Hb.RPB 1983; all det. *RM*; Westcliff, Hythe 4108, a form with strongly arcuate-flexuous branches, Hb.RPB 1983, det. *RM* (as *U. glabra* x *U. angustifolia*, with possible introgression from some other taxon).

U. x hollandica MILL. (*U. glabra* x *U. minor* x *U. plotii*)   Dutch Elm.   **D** Locally frequent

In hedges, on roadsides and stream-banks; invades scrub and woodland borders, suckering into small thickets, but is often self-seeding. On fertile farmland, widespread and locally common. Its distribution is incompletely known owing to past confusion with *U. procera* and *U. glabra*. Although introduced into Britain in the 1680s, its date of introduction into Hampshire is unknown but it has been extensively planted. VC11: 63 ☐; VC12: 67 ☐.

Dr A. Hunter (1776) had a poor opinion of the Dutch Elm, which he said was 'brought from Holland at the beginning of King William's reign, and was for some time a fashionable tree...' but the wood was 'good for nothing, so it is almost banished this country' (*Silva*. Notes, p.120).

VC11: Halterworth, Romsey 3721, *RPB* 1983, det. *RM*; Titchfield 5405, A27 roundabout, *KGM* 1991. **VC12**: Lutcombe Bottom 7326, by stream, *KGM* 1991; Avington 5232, *KGM* 1991.

U. procera SALISB.   English Elm. **N,D**   Common

In hedgerows, where frequently dominant, and on roadsides. In scrub, margins of woods and neglected grasslands, forming spinneys by vigorous suckering; also on low, gravelly sea-cliffs. Especially frequent on deep rich soil in river valleys and on lane-sides on the Lower Greensand. In some districts, e.g. the New Forest, it is mainly in the vicinity of farmsteads, which may indicate ancient planting, but it is generally considered native. Since about 1971, nearly all mature trees, many over 130 years old, have died of disease. By 1983 healthy regrowth of suckers was general. The status of this species in Britain is still obscure. By some it is thought to be an ancient hybrid introduction, but is apparently endemic to England. Townsend considered it to be planted in Hampshire (*Fl.Hants*, p.371).

The leaves, having been stored like hay, used to be fed to cattle in the winter. According to Evelyn, 'Elm is a timber of most singular use, especially where it may lie continually dry or wet, in extreams; therefore proper for water-works, mills....and some that have been found buried in bogs have turned like the most polished and hardest ebony.' (*Silva*, pp.132–133).

U. procera x U. minor ssp. **angustifolia   N**   Rare

An increasingly recorded hybrid. The destruction of all mature elms seems to have provided the stimulus for this increase by opening up hedgerows. The pinhead gall, caused by the mite *Eriophyes campestricola* Frauenfeld, is very common on the leaves of *U.*

procera and its hybrid with *U. minor* but almost never on other elms, so its presence is a valuable identification guide.

VC11: Rockford 1607, Hb.RPB 1976; North Hinton 2197, Hb.RPB 1983; A35 Holmsley 2298, Hb.RPB 1983; Poles Lane, Lymington 3294, Hb.RPB 1983; Langstone Harbour, Warblington 7205, Hb.RPB 1982; all det. *RM*. Also 0696, 0896, 1094, 1096, 1402, 1608, 2894.

U. minor MILL. ssp. **angustifolia** (WESTON) STACE (*U. angustifolia* (Weston) Weston)   Goodyer's Elm. **N**   Very locally frequent   Map 50

First British record, J. Goodyer 1624, 'This kinde I have seene growing but once, and that in the hedges by the high way as I rode betweene Christ Church and Limmington in the New Forrest in Hampshire', VC11 (*Ger.em.Johns.*, p.1478).

Hedgerows, roadsides, wood borders, scrub, streamsides and river terraces. On river and marine gravels and clay, in a broad belt in which it is frequent over the coastal plain between East End 3696 and the R. Stour, Muscliffe 0996 (Dorset), and the Avon Valley north to Rockford 1608, VC11. Outliers at Canterton 2713, *RPB* 1969, Testwood 3514, *RPB* 1986 and Ashfield, Romsey 3619, Hb.RPB 1983, det. *RM*.

Goodyer's Elm, the type of *U. angustifolia*, as it was previously known, is a medium-sized tree, with sinuous branches, widely ascending from well below the middle, forming a broad fan-topped crown (see frontispiece) – very different in habit from Cornish Elm (ssp. *minor* var. *cornubiensis* (Weston) Richens). It may be endemic to S Hants, and before the outbreak of the disease was a characteristic tree of the SW coastal plain.

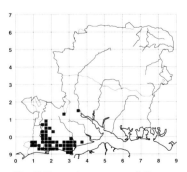

Map 50 Ulmus minor ssp. angustifolia

Almost all mature trees have died, but regeneration from suckers is now good. A felled mature tree at Rockford Green 1507 was about 150 years old.

ssp. minor

The following two taxa, recognized by Melville and now referable to *U. minor* ssp. *minor*, are the progeny of comparatively modern plantings:

1. **U. coritana** MELVILLE var. **coritana H**

VC11: Near Ashurst Bridge 3412, cleared wood, Hb.RPB 1961, det. *RM*.

2. **U. carpinifolia** GLED. **H** Occasional

Hedges and tree-belts, usually plantings. Records, some of which are unverified, include continental forms. VC11: *c*.15 □; VC12: 13 □.

U. minor MILL. ssp. **sarniensis** (C. K. SCHNEID.) STACE (*U. sarniensis* (C. K. Schneid.) H. H. Bancr.)   Jersey Elm. **H**   Rare

Frequently planted in avenues by roads and in parkland, but can spread locally by suckers. VC11: *c*.10 □.

VC11: Salterns Road, Hill Head 5401, Hb.RPB 1976, det. *RM* (as nothomorph of *U. x sarniensis* (Loudon) H. H. Bancr.).

U. plotii DRUCE   Plot's Elm. **H** Very rare

VC12: Cooper's in the Wood Farm 4551, wooded lane-hedge, a few young trees, Hb.RPB 1969, det. *RM*.

CANNABACEAE

Humulus lupulus L.   Hop.   **N,D** Frequent and locally common

Moist, open woods, fen carr, and hedges, often climbing wire stays of telegraph-poles. Locally common and native; also an escape in hedges in the present, or former, hop-growing areas in E and NE Hants.

URTICACEAE

Urtica dioica L.   Common Nettle. **N,C**   Abundant

Woods, fens, roadsides, hedges, waste ground; abundant everywhere and probably even commoner now than in the past due to the use of agricultural

fertilizers. It is stimulated by high phosphate levels.

U. urens L.   Small Nettle.   **N,C** Locally common

On arable and open waste-ground, and in garden beds; chiefly on light soil. Frequent to locally common. Also a shoddy weed.

Parietaria judaica L. (*P. diffusa* Mert. & Koch)   Pellitory-of-the-wall. **N,D**   Local

Generally a relic of herbalism, on old walls, particularly in churchyards and about ruins; rarely on tipped rubble. Concentrated in the older built-up areas; elsewhere uncommon and scattered. Native in coastal habitats. VC8: 1 □; VC11: 49 □; VC12: 16 □.

VC11: R. Test, Testwood 3614, on steel piling, *RPB* 1980; Horsea Island 6304, 6404, general on S and W sides, *CMcL* 1979. **VC12**: Roman walls, Silchester 6362, *PB* 1982; Abbotts Ann 3343, old wall, *MFW* 1991.

Soleirolia soleirolii (REQ.) DANDY (*Helxine soleirolii* Req.)   Mind-your-own-business. **H**   Occasional

First record, J. F. Rayner 1923, Bassett, Southampton *c*.4216, VC11, at foot of wayside wall (*Proc.IoW N.H.S.* 1: 267).

On damp masonry along watercourses, moist paths, and soil in gardens and greenhouses with a preference for the coast. Originally a garden escape. VC9: 1 □; VC11: 23 □; VC12: 15 □.

VC11: Hambledon *c*.6414, *AWW* 1951; Hockley Mill 4825, walls of mill-leat, *RPB* 1979. **VC12**: R. Test, Whitchurch 4647, on wall, *PB* 1984.

MYRICACEAE

Myrica gale L.   Bog-myrtle.   **N** Locally common   Map 51

Bogs, wet heath, and acid carr; abundant throughout the New Forest, frequent on the N and NE Bagshot Beds; absent from the Lower Greensand heath areas, and now very rare on the SE Tertiaries.

VC11: Gomer Pond 5899, Hb.AWW 1952; Breach Hill 5214, *JRw* 1990. **VC12**: Pen Wood 4561, *VF* 1981.

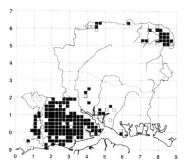

Map 51 Myrica gale

M. cerifera L. (*M. caroliniensis* sensu Wangenh., non Mill.)   Bayberry.   **H** Very rare

First record, H. H. Haines 1934, Scrape Bottom, Wilverley 2301, VC11, *RPB* 1986.

A bird-sown garden escape.
VC12: 'Wood near the fish pond, between Fleet and Crookham' *c*.7953, group of several plants, *GARW* 1937 (*Watts MSS*), seen *HJMB* 1963, but now built on.

FAGACEAE

Fagus sylvatica L.   Beech.   **N,D,H** Very common

First record, J. Goodyer *c*.1650–1656, 'in ye parish of Faringdon [VC12] ....Great antient beeches' (ms. note in How's copy of *Phyt.Brit.* p.35).

Often dominant on the chalk, in woodlands, although many of these are planted. Certainly native on the sands and gravels of the New Forest, where pollen studies indicate that it was in Mark Ash Wood as early as 450BC; moreover a characteristic lichen epiphyte flora is associated with it (including two species known nowhere else in Britain). On acid soils it grows better, and to a greater age, than on chalk. Probably native in the chalk hangers N of Petersfield, where documentary records indicate its presence in the early Middle Ages.

Castanea sativa MILL.   Sweet Chestnut.   **D**   Locally common

Planted as a crop on the drier and mostly acid ground, freely self-sowing, and dispersed by squirrels and birds such as corvids, usually not far from parent trees.

Quercus cerris L.   Turkey Oak. **H**   Locally common

First record, B. King 1899, Holidays Hill, VC11 (*Fl.Hants*, excl.sp., p.385).

Has spread widely, usually as occasional trees and saplings, into most natural woods on acid soil throughout Hants. The secondary host of the crown or knopper gall which seriously affects *Q. robur* (*q.v.*). VC11: 107 □; VC12: 82 □.

Q. ilex L.   Evergreen Oak.   **H** Occasional

First record, Miss H. Butler and G. C. Druce 1915, seedlings in shingle, Hayling Island, VC11 (*Suppl.Fl.Hants*, p.96).

Planted in parkland, ornamental woods, and as a shelter-belt, especially by the sea, where it seeds freely on the shingle. VC8: 1 □; VC11: 32 □; VC12: 4 □.

VC11: Highcliffe 1992, in one sampled quadrat a 60 per cent frequency was recorded, demonstrating its potential threat to the native vegetation at some coastal sites, *KPa* 1990; Fawley Power Station 4702, on foreshore, *RMV* 1988; Cadland 4699, shingle beach, *RPB* 1984; Browndown 5898, Hb.AWW 1952.

Q. petraea (MATT.) LIEBL.   Sessile Oak.   **N,D**   Locally frequent   Map 52

First record, J. Goodyer before 1664, '*Quercus serotina, procerior foliis fructorq; minoribus*, Dor-Oak, plentiful on Linwood hill in Bramshaw Parish, Wilts. Ex Mssts, Mr. Goodyer.' *c*.2414, VC11 (*Merr.Pin.*, p.100).

In ancient woodland on acid sandy or gravelly soil. Locally common and dominant in parts of the New Forest, e.g. Bramshaw Wood, Great Wood, Hollands Wood. Less common on the Hythe Beds near Liss, Bordon and Headley. Also in some large woods on the Tertiaries E of Southampton, in

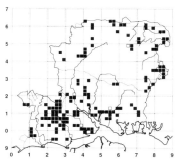

Map 52 Quercus petraea

Harewood Forest and NE Hants. Occasionally planted.
VC11: Dock Copse 5011 and Mushes Copse 5509, *APNH* 1980; at Lodge Hill, West Walk 6012, there is a huge, old, hollow pollard of this species – 'Lady Daley's Oak', *JRw & RPB* 1990. **VC12**: Barley Pound Copse 7946, *GHF* 1978; Walldown, Bordon 8034, *MDo* 1984; Pamber Forest 6161, *HJMB* 1984.

Q. x rosacea BECHST. (*Q. petraea* x *Q. robur*)   **N,D**   Under-recorded

There are scattered records in VC11 and VC12, but, as some forms of the hybrid closely resemble *Q. robur*, it is probably more frequent than the records suggest.

Q. robur L.   Pedunculate Oak. **N,D**   Abundant

In woods, hedges and old parklands. Dominant in many woods, especially in the New Forest, and on heavy clay soils elsewhere; also much planted in the past. Some trees of great size and age occur, e.g. in the New Forest, and in Highclere and Hurstbourne Parks. Many dwarf oaks with decumbent branches and often no visible trunk grow on barren shingle at Sinah Common, Hayling Island, and at Cadland Beach. At Castle Malwood near Rufus Stone 2712, VC11, in the New Forest is an ancient tree which produces new leaves in December and a second crop in spring. The seventeenth-century botanist, Dr William How recorded it on fol.2 of his annotated copy of *Phyt.Brit.* between 1650 and 1656: '*Quercus natalitis Dni virens*, ye Christmas greene oake,....neere y[e] Castle of Malwood, Hampshire, Kg. J. went to visit and caused it to be paled about.' (*Early Brit.Bots*, p.283). At about the same time, John Aubrey also recorded it (*Aubrey N.H.Wilts*, p.53). Another 'Christmas greene oake' grows at Long Valley, Aldershot 8452, VC12, *CRH* 1984–91.

Q. robur is the primary host of the crown or knopper gall, caused by the gall wasp *Andricus quercuscalicis* (Burgsd.), which reached Britain from the Continent in the early 1960s, and which attacks and damages the acorns. The secondary host is *Q. cerris*, so elimination of this alien tree would lead to the elimination of the knopper gall.

BETULACEAE

Betula pendula ROTH   Silver Birch. **N,H**   Frequent and locally abundant

In open woodland, mainly on dry acid soil, especially on fringes and in clearings; as scrub, colonizing dry heathland and chalk downs. Also planted.

B. x aurata BORKH. (*B. pendula* x *B. pubescens*) **N** Under-recorded

This is probably frequent with both parents present.

VC11: Near Durley Mill 5214, Hb.RPB 1975, det. *GAM*. Also 1016, 6622. VC12: 3238, 3642, 3834, 6830, 8030.

B. pubescens EHRH. ssp. **pubescens**. Downy Birch. **N** Frequent and locally abundant

Mainly in damp, open woodland, scrub, wet heath and carr. Rather less frequent, both generally and on chalk, than *B. pendula*, but more tolerant of boggy conditions. The two species often grow intermixed. Severe heath fires provide ideal conditions for explosive spread of both birches, through seedlings growing in the layer of nutrient-rich ashes. Many pure birch woods have formed in this way on heathland, especially since the decline of rabbits.

Alnus glutinosa (L.) GAERTN. Alder. **N** Locally very common
Map 53

In boggy woods, especially along spring-lines, and in marshy valleys; along riversides and often dominant in carr.

'Its timber is very valuable for works intended to lie constantly under water, where it will harden, and last for ages...(*Silva*, Notes, p.242). 'The bark, macerated in water, with a little rust of iron, makes a black dye, which may also be used for ink' (*Silva*, p.244).

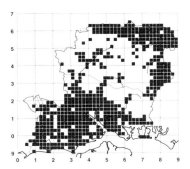

Map 53 Alnus glutinosa

A. incana (L.) MOENCH Grey Alder.
H Rare, under-recorded

First record, Lady Anne Brewis 1969, Longmoor 8131, VC12, in a hedge, det. *BM*.

Planted, and increasingly bird-sown.
VC11: Buriton 7319, old chalk-pit, *AB* 1981. VC12: Farnborough Airfield 8453, in wood, *WRBH* 1978, conf. *AB* 1980 (*Watsonia* 13: 334), seedlings plentiful *ARGM* 1987–91.

Carpinus betulus L. Hornbeam.
N?,D,H Frequent

Commonly planted, it can also occur in old woodland and in hedges. Sidley Wood, Ashmansworth 4055, VC12, a hill-top wood, contains the largest population in Hants. It may be native there, at Roydon Woods 3000, VC11, and about Liss and Bordon, VC12, but its status is uncertain, though it is surely native in SW Surrey and W Sussex. Long ago it may have been planted as a source of charcoal, or of hardwood for the moving parts of mill machinery. According to palynological evidence (see p.12), it was certainly native in prehistoric times.

'Of all the foresters, the Horn-beam preserves itself best from the brutting of deer, and therefore to be kindly entertained in parks.' (*Silva*, p.148)).

Corylus avellana L. Hazel. **N**
Very common

In woods, hedges and scrub. Unusual in the unenclosed New Forest. Pollen studies indicate that it was common there in prehistoric times, but intensive grazing has largely eliminated it, as it is eagerly browsed by deer and ponies. Only a small percentage of the total area in Hants is now effectively managed as coppice; the remainder has either become sadly neglected or been cleared for conifers.

AIZOACEAE

Carpobrotus edulis (L.) N. E. BR. Hottentot-fig. **H** Very rare

First record, J. F. Rayner 1924, Bournemouth cliffs, VC11 (*Proc.IoW N.H.S.* 1:248).

VC11: Established abundantly on sandy cliffs at Bournemouth, tetrads 0890, 1090, 1290, 1490.

CHENOPODIACEAE

The genus *Chenopodium* is mainly distributed across SE England. With the exception of *C. bonus-henricus* and

C. chenopodioides, all species occupy the same ecological niche, and are often dispersed by passing through horses. It is fascinating to note the fluctuations in their populations between the time of Townsend and the present. In *Fl.Hants* (pp.345–348), he lists all but *C. album* as rare or very rare. Of these, *C. ficifolium*, *C. polyspermum* and *C. rubrum* have all become relatively frequent. *C. glaucum*, though still extremely rare, has increased from four pre- to nine post-1930 records. *C. murale* has remained about the same (27 pre- and 23 post-1930 records); while records for *C. vulvaria* have been reduced from 11 to 3, and for *C. urbicum* from 14 to 3. These last two species, as well as *C. chenopodioides*, may now be extinct.

Chenopodium bonus-henricus L. Good-King-Henry. **D** Very local
Map 54

First record, Gilbert White 1766, Selborne, VC12 (*White's Jnls* 1: 198).

An old pot-herb; established on roadsides and grassy waste-ground near villages, therefore liable to be destroyed.

VC11: Common Marsh, Stockbridge 3534, *SS* 1964, *RPB* 1992; Horsebridge 3430, Hb.AWW 1963. VC12: Bransbury Common 4142, *RPB* 1965; Egbury 4352, *RPB* 1969; Sopers Bottom, Appleshaw 3149, on dumped farm-waste, *MFW* 1991; Woodmancott 5642, in lane, *RPB* 1969.

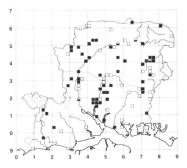

Map 54 Chenopodium bonus-henricus

C. glaucum L. Oak-leaved Goosefoot. **N?,C** Very rare

First record, T. J. Foggitt 1921, Redbridge 3613, VC11, Hb.BM. Enriched waste-ground.

VC11: Sowley Pond, Eastleigh, and Winchester, Hb.EST 1921–25; Romsey, *RMz* 1930, Hb.BM; New

Forest, *GF* 1938, Hb.LIV; Milford on Sea, *ESH* 1971. **VC12**: Aldershot *c*.8453, manure heap at W edge of Laffan's Plain, *GARW* 1932 (*Watts MSS*), *FEWV* 1953; drained bed of Fleet Pond, *PMH & ECW* 1941; widened A325, Farnborough 8652, two plants, *TD c*.1973; Itchen Stoke 5532, Hb.RPB 1968 (*Watsonia* **10**: 422).

C. rubrum L.   Red Goosefoot. Locally frequent   **N,C**   Map 55

Fl.Hants (p.347) states 'very rare on mainland'. It is now widespread and locally frequent, especially on manure heaps and in dried-up ponds.

    VC11: Upham 5319, dry pond bed, *RPB* 1984. **VC12**: Hartley Mauditt 7436, covering dried-up pond, *CL* 1949, *AB* 1976.

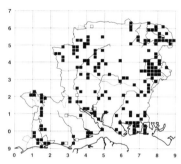

Map 55 Chenopodium rubrum

var. **pseudobotryodes** H. C. WATSON

On salt-marshes, resembling *C. chenopodioides*.

    VC11: North Hayling 7203, *AB & FR* 1975.

C. chenopodioides (L.) AELLEN (*C. botryodes* Sm.)   Saltmarsh Goosefoot. **N**   Very rare or extinct

First record, E. S. Marshall 1900, N coast of Hayling Island, VC11 (*Fl.Hants*, p.348)

    On saline mud, in ditches or creeks of drained salt-marshes.

    VC11: Specimens in Hb.BM: N side of Hayling Island, *ES* 1900; near North Hayling Station *c*.7103, *TJF* 1922; Northney, North Hayling *c*.7204, *PMH* 1934. Much ground has since been lost to a marina and it has not been refound here nor at Mrs M. L. Wedgwood's site at Bursledon Bridge 4909, Hb.OXF (*Suppl.Fl.Hants*, p.89). It could, however, survive in brackish hollows in the NW part of Hayling

Island, where suitable terrain for it remains. It is still frequent in similar habitats in Kent and S Essex, and locally in E Sussex.

C. polyspermum L.   Many-seeded Goosefoot.   **C,N**   Locally frequent

First record, Gilbert White 1766, Selborne, VC12 (*White's Jnls* **1**: 219).

    Cultivated and waste ground, especially when well manured; dry pond-beds. Widespread, but scarce on chalk.

C. vulvaria L.   Stinking Goosefoot. **C,N**   Very rare or extinct (Sched. 8)

Formerly a native of open, dry sandy ground and shingle near the coast.

    VC11: Last native record at Hayling Island, *MTH* 1920. Colonist at Southampton Docks, *JEL* 1958; Chandler's Ford *c*.4220, *MMcK* 1964; SE of Rockbourne 1216, *ESH* 1967.

C. hybridum L.   Maple-leaved Goosefoot.   **C**   Very rare

Enriched waste-ground. Most records are from the Winchester or Andover areas.

    VC11: Nursling gravel-pit 3515, surviving a few years, *RPB* 1964; Winchester College art-school 4828, garden weed, *AB* 1979; Winchester, waste ground by river, *AB* 1970. **VC12**: Over Wallop church car-park 2838, *GDF* 1982; Winnall Down Farm 5029, *AB* 1984; Nether Wallop car-park 3036, *RPB* 1984; Quarley *c*.2642, *MPY* 1966.

C. urbicum L.   Upright Goosefoot. **C**   Very rare or extinct

Waste ground, manure heaps. Even rarer now than in *Fl.Hants*, with only three records.

    VC11: Hurn 1296, *JCDa* 1944; Winkton, near Christchurch 1696, *BNSS* 1950–54; Holbury *c*.4203, *MJC* 1955, Hb.SPN (*Watsonia* **5**: 120).

C. murale L.   Nettle-leaved Goosefoot.   **C**   Very local and rare   Map 56

Sandy arable fields and waste ground near the coast; rare inland. Occurs irregularly at most sites.

    VC11: Firgrove Farm, Hurn 1000, *CDD* 1969; field S of Burton Common 1994, Hb.RPB 1985; New Lane, Keyhaven 2990, edge of beet-crop, plentiful, *RPB* 1991; Victoria Park, Portsmouth 6300, *PAB* 1987; Guildhall, Portsmouth 6400, Hb.AWW 1951. **VC12**: Wonston 4739, manure

heaps, *AB* 1969, 1984; Amery Farm, Alton 7139, *JLSL* 1977.

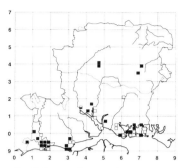

Map 56 Chenopodium murale

C. ficifolium SM.   Fig-leaved Goosefoot.   **C**   Frequent   Map 57

First record, E. F. Linton 1893, Portchester Station 6105, VC11, with other casuals (*Rep.B.E.C.* for 1893, p.403).

    Cultivated fields, especially with root crops; common on manure heaps and formerly in shoddy. In Surrey it was first noticed in 1832, but the Surrey records for it are sparser than in Hants, where it is increasingly common.

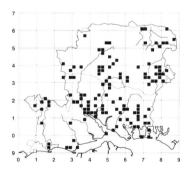

Map 57 Chenopodium ficifolium

C. berlandieri MOQ. (*C. zschackei* Murr)   Pitseed Goosefoot.   **C** Very rare

VC11: North Stoneham *c*.4317, *MJC* 1955, Hb.SPN.

C. opulifolium SCHRAD. ex KOCH & ZIZ   Grey Goosefoot.   **C**   Very rare

First record, J. F. Rayner 1928, South Stoneham *c*.4415, VC11 (*Suppl.Fl. Hants*, p.88).

    On disturbed soil.

    VC11: Southampton 4211, waste ground, *WFB* 1962; Southampton,

MJC 1955, Hb.SPN, det. *PA*. **VC12**: Grayshott dump 8336, *AB* 1965.

C. album L.   Fat-hen.   **N,C** Very common

On cultivated and waste ground, especially where manured.

C. x variabile Aellen (*C. album* x *C. berlandieri*)   **C**   Very rare

VC11: Romsey *c.*3521, *MJC* 1954, Hb.SPN.

Atriplex prostrata BOUCHER ex DC. (*A. hastata* sensu L. (1754), non L. (1753))   Spear-leaved Orache.   **N,C** Frequent and locally common

On waste ground, beaches and upper salt-marsh areas. Also a common weed of cultivated ground, often taken for *A. patula* and consequently overlooked.

A. glabriuscula EDMONDSTON Babington's Orache.   **N**   Very local

First record, J. J. Dillenius *c.*1724 'near Portsmouth on the right hand of the roade half a mile before you come to the Town' VC11, Hb.OXF, det. *GCD* as *A. babingtonii* Woods (*Dill.Herb.*, p.142).

Sandy and shingle beaches, waste ground near the sea. Frequent along the coast and estuaries, but never inland. VC11: 25 □.

A. littoralis L.   Grass-leaved Orache. **N**   Locally common   Map 58

First record, M. de Lobel before 1616, Portsmouth, VC11 (*Lobel Stirp.Illus.*, pp.86–87).

Sea-walls and beaches. Common on the coast and in estuaries. An inland record, on the A3 verge at 6909, *AB* 1986, may be the result of road-salting.

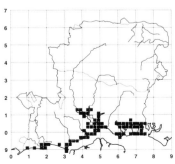
Map 58 Atriplex littoralis

A. patula L.   Common Orache. **N,C**   Common

On sea-walls, waste ground and banks by the coast. Inland on manured fields, waste and cultivated ground, disturbed roadside verges.

A. laciniata L.   Frosted Orache.   **N** Rare   Map 59

On sandy, rarely shingly, sea-beaches, especially on the drift-line. Decreasing due to sustained trampling of habitat.

VC11: Hengistbury sand-spit 1891, *CEP* 1967; *RPB* 1985–92; Sowley Shore 3795, one plant, *RPB* 1985; Park Shore, Beaulieu 4096, *RPB* 1963, 45 plants, 1992; Sinah Common dunes 6998, and Sandy Point, Hayling Island 7498, *FR* 1980, 7598, *RPB* 1989.

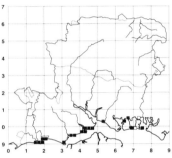
Map 59 Atriplex laciniata

A. halimus L.   Shrubby Orache.   **H**

First record, J. F. Rayner 1923, rough grassy ground, Hengistbury, VC11 (*Proc.IoW N.H.S.* **1**: 265).
VC11: Planted by the seaside. Recorded from tetrads 1090, 1892, 3090, 7298.

A. portulacoides L. (*Halimione portulacoides* (L.) Aellen)   Sea-purslane. **N**   Locally common

First record, D. C. Macreight 1834, Portsmouth Harbour, VC11, Hb.BM.
On salt-marshes, well-drained creek-banks, edges of eroded pans, and at the upper edge of tidal marshes; rarer behind sea-walls, and sometimes on clay and shingle at the foot of cliffs. On the New Forest coast, occasionally grazed by ponies during severe winters.

Beta vulgaris L. ssp. **maritima** (L.) ARCANG.   Sea Beet.   **N**   Locally common   Map 60

Sea-walls, upper parts of salt-marshes, shingly and sandy shores. Common all

along the coast and estuaries. One inland record: A3 Horndean Down 7015, VC11, on bare chalk in new verge, *AB* 1983.

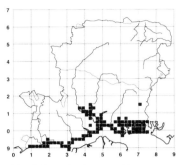
Map 60 Beta vulgaris ssp. maritima

The Glassworts (*Sarcocornia*, *Salicornia* spp.)

These plants grow in coastal salt-marshes; collectively, under the name of marsh samphire, they are agreeably edible. Their Hampshire stronghold is in the creeks of Hayling Island. In 1957, P. W. Ball defined a number of species, the type locality of which was at Northney, North Hayling 7204. Unfortunately, this site, like many along the Hampshire coast, is now a marina. The glassworts present formidable taxonomic difficulties; the formula now devised by J. M. Géhu, the French authority, and *FR*, and accepted by C. A. Stace, is as follows:

Sarcocornia perennis (MILL.) A. J. SCOTT (*Salicornia perennis* Miller) Perennial Glasswort.   **N**   Locally frequent   Map 61

First record, J Woods 1850, Hayling Island, VC11, (as *S. lignosa* Woods) (*Fl.Hants*, p.344).

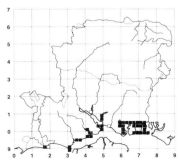
Map 61 Sarcocornia perennis

In upper, more consolidated zones of salt-marshes, both on mud and sand. All other glassworts are annual.

Salicornia pusilla WOODS   One-flowered Glasswort.   **N**   Very local
Map 62

First record, J. Woods 1850, Hayling Island, VC11 (*Fl.Hants*, p.343).

Upper zones of salt-marshes, on firm mud or nearby sand. Records show it to have been most frequent around Chichester, Langstone and Portsmouth harbours, though rare in the W Solent; but since the 1960s much has probably been lost to reclamation.

VC11: Beaulieu River, Gilbury Hard 4100, *RPB* 1978, det. *DHD*; Needs Ore Point 4297, *RPB* 1984; Titchfield Haven 5302, *AWW c.*1960; Fareham Creek 5804, *AWW c.*1960; Horsea Island 6304, *CMcL c.*1962; Tourner Bury Marsh, Hayling Island 7399, *FR* 1984.

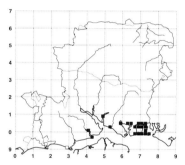

Map 62 Salicornia pusilla

S. pusilla x S. ramosissima   N
Very rare or overlooked

Plants considered to be this hybrid have been seen with both parents at Needs Ore Point 4297, Northney, North Hayling 7204, Black Point, Hayling Island 7598, *RPB* 1984; Tourner Bury, Hayling Island 7300, *AB, RPB & FR* 1984; Gutner Peninsula, Hayling Island 7301, *FR* 1986.

S. ramosissima WOODS   Purple Glasswort.   **N**   Locally common

First record, J. Woods 1847, Hayling Island, VC11 (*Fl.Hants*, p.343).

Middle and upper parts of consolidated salt-marshes, in the same zone as *Puccinellia maritima*, where it is often reddish and semi-prostrate. Such experimental work as has been done

suggests that these very different-looking plants are only habitat forms.

S. europaea L.   Common Glasswort.   **N**   Rare or under-recorded

First record, J. Woods 1850, Havant, VC11 (as *S. stricta* Dumort) (*Fl.Hants*, p.343).

In the lower zones of salt-marshes, often with *S. ramosissima*, but on more open mud. There are only a few reliable records of this segregate, mainly in the SE, probably due to confusion with forms of the very variable *S. ramosissima*, so the distribution is imperfectly known.

VC11: Bursledon 4808, *FR* 1976; Fareham Creek 5804, *AWW* 1957; North Hayling station 7103, in brackish meadow, *FR* 1989. Also 6898, 7098, 7200, 7298.

S. obscura P. W. BALL & TUTIN   Glaucous Glasswort.   **N**   Very rare

First record and type locality, P. W. Ball 1957, Northney, North Hayling 7204, VC11, pan in upper part of salt-marsh, Hb.BM (*Watsonia* 4: 204); now a marina.

This plant prefers the sloping sides of upper salt-marsh creeks.

VC11: Keyhaven 3191, *JMG* 1981; Gutner Peninsula, Hayling Island 7301, *FR* 1986.

S. nitens P. W. BALL & TUTIN (*S. ? emerici* Duval-Jouve)   Shiny Glasswort.   **N**   Very rare

First record and type locality, P. W. Ball 1957, Northney, North Hayling 7204, VC11, bare mud in upper part of salt-marsh, Hb.BM (*Watsonia* 4: 204); now a marina.

In possibly the only two extant localities for this glasswort, it is always in the wettest part of the salt-marsh (pers.obs.).

VC11: Paulsgrove *c.*6305, salt-marsh, *AWW* 1961, det. *PWB*, probably lost to reclamation; Keyhaven Marshes 3191, bare mud inside sea-wall, *JMG* 1981; Gutner Peninsula, Hayling Island 7301, *FR* 1986 (*AWW* also found it somewhere in same tetrad).

S. fragilis P. W. BALL & TUTIN (*S. lutescens* P. W. Ball & Tutin)   Yellow Glasswort.   **N**   Very local

This is probably only a modified habitat-form of *S. dolichostachya*. On firm, open mud or muddy sand, in the lower marsh-zones. Commonest round Hayling Island; rare elsewhere.

VC11: Keyhaven 3191, Hb.NDS n.d., det. *PWB, JMG* 1981; by R. Hamble, Bursledon 4808, *FR* 1976; Langstone 7206, *AWW c.*1960; Gutner Peninsula, Hayling Island 7301, *FR* 1986. Also 6898, 7204.

S. dolichostachya MOSS   Long-spiked Glasswort.   **N**   Locally frequent

First record, G. C. Druce 1929, Hayling Island, VC11 (*Suppl.Fl.Hants*, p.90). Frequent in the lower zones of muddy salt-marshes.

<**Suaeda vera** FORSSK. ex J. F. GMELIN (*S. fruticosa* auct., non Forssk.)   Shrubby Sea-blite.   **N** Extinct

The only location was 'near the spot where the Ry. viaduct crosses the lines of Portsea Island', 6604, R. A. Pryor *c.*1874 (*Fl.Hants*, p.341). As it is still plentiful at Brands Bay, Poole Harbour, and on Chesil Beach, Dorset, it may recolonize.>

S. maritima (L.) DUMORT.   Annual Sea-blite.   **N**   Locally common

Salt-marshes, plentiful both on mud and in more consolidated tidal marshes, also in brackish areas behind sea-walls, and as a colonist of dredged shingle.

Salsola kali L. ssp. **kali**   Prickly Saltwort.   **N**   Very rare

Sandy shores, especially about the drift-line. Now lost or impersistent in many of the recorded sites due to heavy trampling of the very few undeveloped sandy beaches remaining, and endangered in Hants.

VC11: Needs Ore 4297, *FR* 1978, not refound *RPB* 1984; Stansore Point, Lepe 4698, single plant, *RPB* 1975; Hengistbury sand-spit 1891, *SRD & AEB* 1979; not seen again for a number of years but reappeared at S end of spit 1890, and on New Dunes 1790, *c.* 60 plants, *RPB* 1993; Sandy Point, Hayling Island 7498, 7598, *FR* 1980, plentiful over 250m on drift-line, *RPB* 1989. The most recent record is Park Shore 4096, eight plants, *RPB* 1994. Also 1892, 2092, 3090, 6698, 7098.

AMARANTHACEAE

Amaranthus retroflexus L. Common Amaranth.   **C**   Rare but under-recorded

First confirmed record, J. R. Moon 1990, Abbotts Ann 3243, VC12, on disturbed ground near the entrance to a rough field, seven or eight plants 1990–91, det. *EJC*.

A casual of disturbed and waste ground, confused in the past with *A. hybridus*.

VC11: W of Turmer Hill 1209, abundant in old maize-crop, Hb.RPB 1992; North Charford Down 1619, corner of arable field, *RMV* 1992, Hb.RPB, both det. *EJC*. There are several other unverified records for VC11 and VC12.

A. hybridus L.   Green Amaranth. **C**   Rare

A shoddy weed and a bird-seed casual, sometimes established for a year or two. Many other species of *Amaranthus* have occurred as casuals, especially in shoddy fields.

PORTULACACEAE

Claytonia perfoliata DON ex WILLD. (*Montia perfoliata* (Donn ex Willd.) Howell) Springbeauty.   **C**   Locally frequent   Map 63

First record, J. Hussey 1849, Bure Lane, Mudeford 1892, VC11 (*Phytologist.N.S.* 1: 389).

On open, sandy disturbed ground, and as a garden weed on sandy soil. Local, but increasing on the coast; frequent about Blackmoor and Whitehill, and in the Aldershot area.

VC11: Hengistbury 1790, *MR* 1976; Lepe shore 4398, *RPB* 1984; Love Lane, Petersfield 7523, *MS-W* 1976; Sinah Common dunes 6899, spreading, *RPB* 1975. **VC12**: Silver Birches Inn, Greatham 7831, *AB* 1984; Whitehill Police Station 7934, *AB* 1984; Rowledge churchyard 8243, *RCS* 1986; Farnborough Green cemetery 8656,

CRH 1991; Amport House 2944, *AO* 1991.

C. sibirica L. (*M. sibirica* (L.) Howell) Pink Purslane.   **H**   Very local

First record, F. Browning 1924, Tilmore, Petersfield *c*.7424, VC12, ditch-side in damp lane (*Proc.IoW N.H.S.* 1: 238).

Naturalized in damp woodlands, where it can become invasive. It is now by far the commonest flowering plant at Waggoners Wells. It often gets washed down streams.

VC11: Dockens Water, Linwood 1810, *ESH* 1978; Millersford Bottom 1816, *JO* 1982; Danes Stream, Milford on Sea 2892, *RPB* 1980. Also 1000, 1294, 1408, 1608, 1614, 1808, 2692, 3822, 4408, 7622. **VC12**: Blackmoor 7833, *PMH* 1933, Hb.BM, lost to roadworks 1984, but later reappeared in quantity nearby, *AB*; Newtown Gully 4763, *CL* 1961–63; Tilmore Road, Petersfield 7424, good colony on stream bank, *RBa* 1992; Waggoners Wells 8534, recently introduced and spreading, *GARW & PMH* 1935 (*Proc.Hants Fld Club* 15: 65). Also 7430, 7828, 8432, 8634.

Montia fontana L.   Blinks.   **N,C** Locally common   Map 64

In short turf on sand or gravel, on moist sandy banks or in flood-hollows, especially where water stands in winter; around springs and in densely vegetated watercourses, often where polluted by sewage effluent; covering old bonfire sites on wet ground; ill-drained lawns. Common on damp, acid soils, especially in the New Forest, but almost absent from the SE. The distribution of the different subspecies is very incompletely known at present, but ssp. *fontana* is not found in southern England.

ssp. **variabilis** WALTERS

First records, A. W. Westrup 1962, Holmsley Station 2300, VC11, Hb.AWW, det. *SMW* and Blackmoor 7733, VC12, Hb.AWW, det. *SMW*; often searched for since but not refound.

ssp. **amporitana** SENNEN (ssp. *intermedia* (Beeby) Walters)

First record, W. R. Linton 1889, Boldre, Hb.GL.

Usually in the wettest places, or fully aquatic.

VC11: Denny Bog, New Forest, *FHP* 1963, Hb.BM; Godshill 1715, *WFB* 1974, det. *SMW*, Hb.RPB; Bransgore 1898, *RMV* 1990, conf. *RPB*. Also 2810, 3602. **VC12**: Heckfield Heath 7261, *AWW* 1963, det. *SMW* as intermediate with previous subspecies.

ssp. **chondrosperma** (FENZL) WALTERS (ssp. *minor* Hayward)

First record, E. S. Marshall 1888, Hythe, VC11, cornfield, Hb.CGE.

The commonest subspecies, with numerous records.

VC11: Wootton 2298, *AEB* 1980; Pennington Marshes 3292, Hb.RPB 1977, det. *SMW*; Farlington Marshes 6804, along foot of old bank, comm. *RABi*, det. *RPB*. **VC12**: Blackmoor Park 7832, *AWW* 1960; Padworth Common 6264, *PB* 1984.

CARYOPHYLLACEAE

Arenaria serpyllifolia L. ssp. **serpyllifolia**   Thyme-leaved Sandwort.   **N,C**   Frequent and locally common

On dry, open ground at edges of arable fields and chalk grassland, especially on ant-hills, and on banks.

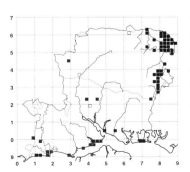

Map 63 Claytonia perfoliata

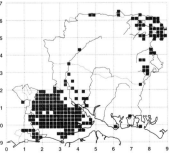

Map 64 Montia fontana

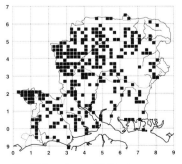

Map 65 Arenaria serpyllifolia ssp. leptoclados

ssp. **leptoclados** (RCHB.) NYMAN (*A. leptoclados* (Rchb.) Guss.) Slender Sandwort. **N,C** Frequent and locally abundant Map 65

In similar places to the last, but less common in the E, while sometimes abundant on the chalk arable of the N and W. Like the last, it occurs on the sands, and is the more frequent on acid soils in the SW.

A. balearica L. Mossy Sandwort. **H** Very rare

Naturalized on walls.

VC11: Ridding Meads' wall, Winchester College 4828, *WMB & PMPH* 1960, not seen recently.

Moehringia trinervia (L.) CLAIRV. Three-nerved Sandwort. **N** Common

In woodland and shady hedgebanks, both dry and damp, on the more base-rich soils; rather scarce in the New Forest.

Honckenya peploides (L.) EHRH. Sea Sandwort. **N** Very locally frequent

On sand and shingle beaches on the coast. It seems to be more resistant to trampling than some other beach species.

Minuartia hybrida (VILL.) SCHIS-CHK. Fine-leaved Sandwort. **N** Rare Map 66

On banks, tracks, field-borders, railway tracks and wall-tops, almost always on the chalk. Once common on bare chalk, but now very scarce.

VC11: Owslebury *c.*5123, roadside, *PMH* 1930, Hb.BM (*Proc.Hants Fld Club* 10: 297); Kent's Wood, Broughton 2734, edge of arable field,

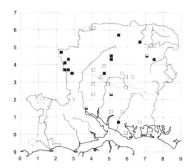
Map 66 Minuartia hybrida

RPB 1966; Titchfield Abbey 5416, old brick-wall, *RPB* 1988. **VC12**: Froyle Place 7542, old brick-wall, *CL* 1937, Hb.HCMS, *ANHS* 1991; South Wonston 4735, old railway, *MS-W* 1972; Shipton Bellinger downs 2346, edge of cornfield, *MEY & DWF* 1970, conf. *JEL*; Old Basing 6652, on wall, *MMcC-W* 1919, *GARW 1933*, Hb.BM, *PB* 1986; Micheldever Spoil Heaps 5244, *HFG* 1991, conf. *AJB*.

Stellaria media (L.) VILL. Common Chickweed. **N,C** Very common

On arable, waste and bare ground. Almost ubiquitous.

S. pallida (DUMORT.) CRÉP. Lesser Chickweed. **N,C** Very local Map 67

On open, sandy or stony beaches and dunes. More rarely inland, on sandy ground.

VC11: Jockstrill Common, Sopley 1597, Hb.RPB 1988; Black Common, Linwood 1809, *FR & NAS* 1990; Sowley shore 3795, *RPB* 1971; Browndown 5899, Hb.AWW 1952. **VC12**: Bramley Ordnance Depot 6656, on cinder-track, *FR* 1980; Winslade Lane, Ellisfield 6446, *ANHS* 1985; Puckridge 8452, roadside verge, *ARGM* 1991, det. *FR*.

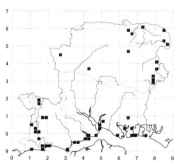
Map 67 Stellaria pallida

S. neglecta WEIHE Greater Chickweed. **N** Rare Map 68

In moist woodland, roadsides and river-banks on sandy soil, and almost exclusively in the valleys of the Rivers Wey, Avon, Rother, Blackwater and Enborne.

VC11: Marl Lane, Fordingbridge 1414, *MPY* 1972, 1415, *ESH* 1976; Ibsley 1510, roadside verge, *MPY* 1972; Sheet 7624, *FR & AB* 1976,

RPB 1990. **VC12**: Butlers Land Copse 6662, *ILR* 1991; Jouldings Ford, Bramshill 7563, *CRH* 1991; Sydmonton Common 4962, *NFC* 1978; Ashford Hill meadows 5661, *PB* 1983; Kingsley 7838, streamside by wooded path, *JCh* 1991; by R. Rother above Liss 7727, 7728, 7828, *FR* 1990.

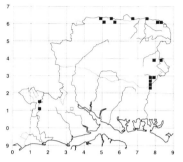
Map 68 Stellaria neglecta

S. holostea L. Greater Stitchwort. **N** Very common

In hedgerows, verges and woodland, on most soils except the very acid; sparse in the New Forest.

S. palustris RETZ. Marsh Stitchwort. **N** Rare Map 69

In marshy meadows and ditches, rare and decreased. In several sites by the R. Avon and the Moors River, and very sparsely on the Rivers Wey, the Blackwater, the Whitewater and the Enborne.

VC11: Moors River 1298, *CDD* 1961; R. Avon, Hurn 1496, *RPB* 1956, 1984; Coward's Marsh 1594, *RPB* 1976; Kingston North Common 1403, *RPB* 1986; Ringwood 1404, extensive in fen, *HCC* 1986; Marlborough Deep 2298, one plant, *NAS* 1987–88. **VC12**:

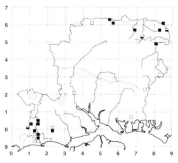
Map 69 Stellaria palustris

Ashford Hill meadows 5562, *BRB* 1962, *PB* 1982; Dora's Green 8148, *AduSB* 1960, not refound, *AB* 1975, but site then too shaded – could be the 'bogs on the borders of Hants towards Farnham' of *Fl.Hants* (p.65); Foxlease meadows 8356, *CRH* 1985–94; Hartley Wespall 6956, *CRH* 1986; Blackwater Meadows 8460, *JA & SW* 1986.

S. graminea L.   Lesser Stitchwort. **N**   Common

In open, acid grassland, grass-heaths and scrub; avoids chalk.

S. uliginosa MURRAY (*S. alsine* Grimm)   Bog Stitchwort.   **N** Locally common

In swampy woodland, marshes, ditches and mildly-acid bogs. On all acid soils, and locally in chalk wetlands.

Cerastium arvense L.   Field Mouse-ear.   **N**   Locally frequent Map 70

On banks, trackside verges, open field-borders, and in short turf on chalk, more rarely on sand. Fairly well re-presented on the western and central chalk plateau, but much has been ploughed up.
    VC8: Martin Down 0519, field-border, *RMV* 1984, *FR* 1994. **VC11**: Stoney Cross, old airfield 2511, *RPB* 1981; Sinah Common dunes 6999, Hb.AWW 1950; Butser Hill 7120, *AB* 1979; Black Common, Linwood 1809, 2m patch on sand, *RPB* 1991. **VC12**: Worthy Down 4535, *RPB* 1969; Ashley Warren 4956, *PB* 1982; Dunch Hill 2148, *RPB* 1988; Blackmoor Park 7832, *AB* 1986, probably now extinguished by agricultural improvement.

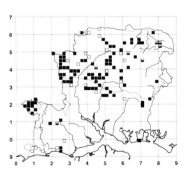
Map 70 Cerastium arvense

C. tomentosum L.   Snow-in-summer.   **H**   Very local

Established on sandy ground or verges and on banks outside gardens, e.g. Sinah Common dunes 6999, VC11, Hb.AWW 1952. VC8: 2 ☐; VC11: 14 ☐; VC12: 18 ☐.

C. fontanum BAUMG. (*C. holosteoides* Fries)   Common Mouse-ear.   **N** Very common

In short grassland, roadsides and waste ground; and, in a dwarf state, in bare sandy places on heathland. All plants examined critically are ssp. *vulgare* (Hartman) Greuter & Burdet, but ssp. *holosteoides* (Fries) Salman, van Ommering & de Voogd may also occur.

C. glomeratum THUILL.   Sticky Mouse-ear.   **N,C**   Common

In dry, short turf or open ground on light soils, and as an agricultural weed.

C. diffusum PERS. (*C. atrovirens* Bab.) Sea Mouse-ear.   **N,C**   Locally common   Map 71

Common in coastal turf, on sand-dunes, cliff-tops and beaches. Rare inland along old railways, but frequent on verges in the New Forest where it has spread rapidly on recently made, sandy car-barriers and road-banks, *RPB* 1977.
    VC11: A27 near Locks Heath 5207, abundant, *RPB* 1991; Common Marsh, Stockbridge 3534, in old pits, *RPB* 1976. **VC12**: Bramley Ordnance Depot 6656, 6657, on cinder-track, *FR* 1980, Hb.AB (*Watsonia* 13: 329); Aldershot 8751, on roadside verge, *CRH & ARGM* 1991, det. *FR* (*Watsonia* 19: 143); near Fleet Pond 8255, *CRH* 1993.

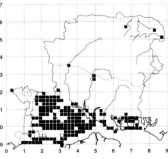
Map 71 Cerastium diffusum

C. pumilum CURTIS   Dwarf Mouse-ear.   **N**   Very rare

First record, A. W. Westrup 1951, Paulsgrove chalk-pit, Ports Down

6306, VC11, Hb.AWW. Not refound, *RPB* 1984.
    On chalk downs or on bare chalk.
VC12: Micheldever Spoil Heaps 5144, 5244, *SS* 1957, *BSBI* 1965, comm. *RAB & ECW*, *BAG* 1984, *HFG* 1991, conf. *AJB*; Beacon Hill, Old Burghclere 4557, *CL* 1960, det. *AWW*.

C. semidecandrum L.   Little Mouse-ear.   **N**   Locally common Map 72

In open, sandy and gravelly places, and in short turf; sporadic along the coast, commoner in sandy places inland in the Avon Valley, the New Forest, Woolmer Forest and the Aldershot area; rarely on bare chalk.
    VC8: Martin Down 0418, *JHL* 1965. **VC11**: Otterbourne Hill Common 4522, *RPB* 1991. **VC12**: Micheldever Spoil Heaps 5244, *GHF* 1982.

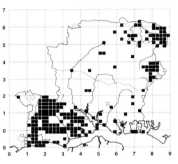
Map 72 Cerastium semidecandrum

Myosoton aquaticum (L.) MOENCH Water Chickweed.   **N**   Locally frequent   Map 73

In the mud of streamsides, and in wet woodland. Locally common, but absent from the upper reaches of the chalk rivers. It has increased since Townsend's day, who recorded 'wet places; rare' (*Fl.Hants*, p.64).

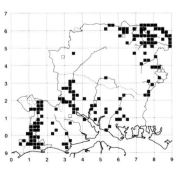
Map 73 Myosoton aquaticum

VC11: R. Avon, Ibsley 1409, on shingle, *RPB* 1984; Fishlake Meadows, Romsey 3522, *RMV* 1987; Matley Passage 3307, *RPB* 1953; Rother meadows, Penns Place 7623, *FR* 1991. **VC12**: Ashford Hill meadows 5562, *PB* 1983; all along the R. Blackwater, *CRH* 1992.

Moenchia erecta (L.) P. GAERTN., B. MEY. & SCHERB.   Upright Chickweed. **N**   Very locally frequent Map 74

On dry, open, sandy or gravelly turf, especially on banks or mounds. Occasional on the coast, more often in the New Forest, rare on other sandy soils.

VC11: Hengistbury 1790, *MR* 1976; Black Common, Linwood 1809, *FR & NAS* 1990; Beaulieu Road Station 3406, *RMB* 1969; East Boldre 3700, short turf near road, *RPB* 1986; Farlington Marshes 6804, old bank, *RPB* 1990; Mengham Beach, Hayling Island 7198, *FR* 1993. **VC12**: Newtown Common 4662, main road, *CL* 1964; Hazeley Heath 7657, grassy verge, *DEB* 1962–67; Silchester Common 6262, on track, *WGH* 1990–91; Fleet Cricket Ground 8053, *Watts MSS* 1944, *CRH* 1991; Blackbushe 8159, *VK* 1986; Farnborough Airfield 8553, 8653, abundant in several sites, some since destroyed, *ARGM* 1978, surviving in 8553, 8554, 8653, 8654, *CRH* 1994.

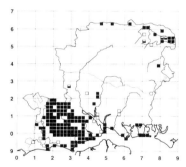

Map 74 Moenchia erecta

Sagina nodosa (L.) FENZL   Knotted Pearlwort. **N**   Very local   Map 75

On wet-clay turf and basic flushes on sandy, gravelly or alluvial soils. Very much decreased since *Fl.Hants*. Occasional in the SW, very rare elsewhere.

VC11: Marlborough Deep 2298, Hb.AWW 1963, *RPB* 1987; Crockford Bridge 3598, *JOM* 1970; Greenmoor 3399, *AEB* 1979; Common Marsh, Stockbridge 3534, *RPB* 1960; High

Wood, Upham 5423, Hb.AWW 1963. **VC12**: Micheldever Spoil Heaps 5244, *SP* 1982, *ARGM* 1992; Odiham *c.*7450, *AJSt & WEW* 1969; Winnall Moors 4931, *MSC* team 1986; Isle of Wight Hill 2437, 2438, 2537, 2538, *MRe & PJW*.

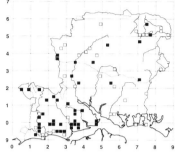

Map 75 Sagina nodosa

S. subulata (Sw.) C. PRESL.   Heath Pearlwort. **N**   Very locally frequent Map 76

On open, gravelly or sandy ground, on heaths, local in the New Forest, and very rare elsewhere. Decreased since *Fl.Hants*.

VC11: Matcham's View 1302, *CDD* 1967; Goatspen Plain gravel-pits 2201, *RPB* 1981;   Setley 3099, levelled gravel-pit, *AEB* 1982; W of Hatchet Pond 3601, *FR* 1973; Sandy Point, Hayling Island 7598, *FR* 1980; Mengham Beach, Hayling Island 7198, plentiful on fixed shingle, *FR* 1993. **VC12**: Stratfield Saye *c.*7060, *AWW* 1963. Formerly in several heathland sites in the NE and perhaps now extinct in N Hants.

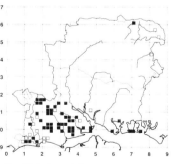

Map 76 Sagina subulata

S. procumbens L.   Procumbent Pearlwort. **N**   Very common

On moist waste-ground, paths, walls, lawns, etc.

S. apetala ARD. ssp. **apetala** (*S. ciliata* Fr.)   Fringed Pearlwort.   **N** Locally common, but under-recorded

On dry, sandy and gravelly, open ground, railway tracks and masonry. Probably in artificial habitats only, on the chalk.

ssp. **erecta** F. HERM. (*S. apetala* auct., non Ard.)   Annual Pearlwort.   **N** Common

On open ground, wall-tops, etc.

S. maritima G. DON   Sea Pearlwort. **N**   Very locally frequent

On open ground, and in short turf in the drier parts of salt-marshes; near the sea and in estuaries only.

Scleranthus annuus L. ssp. **annuus** Annual Knawel. **N,C** Local Map 77

First record, J. Goodyer 1618, 'In a barren rye feild belowe Tichfield Bay', VC11 (*Early Brit.Bots*, p.110).
   On dry, arable and disturbed soil, on sand, gravel and Malmstone; infrequent on the chalk. Diminished of late.

VC11: Bransgore 1997, in sandy arable field, *QK* 1963; A31 Ashley, Ringwood 1304, chippings at roundabout, *RPB* 1988; mouth of R. Hamble 4805, *RPB* 1984; Otterbourne Hill reservoir 4522, *RPB* 1991. **VC12**: Chawton Park Farm 6937, *AB* 1976; Broomhurst Farm 8156, roadside on disturbed soil, *CRH* 1987–92; Bramshill Common 7562, tipped soil, *CRH* 1987.

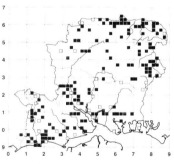

Map 77 Scleranthus annuus ssp. annuus

<**Herniaria glabra** L.   Smooth Rupturewort. **N**   Extinct

Formerly on sandy shores near Portsmouth, J. Hill 1746 (*Fl.Hants*, p.73). No record since.>

<**H. hirsuta** L.   Hairy Rupturewort. **C**   Extinct

THE FLORA OF HAMPSHIRE

Formerly on sandy waste-ground near Christchurch 1492, where first seen 1879 (*Fl. Hants*, p.73). Last record *JEL* 1924, Hb.LANC. Destroyed by tipping.>

Illecebrum verticillatum L. Coral-necklace. **N,C** Very local Map 78 Plate III

First record, Miss M. T. Hillard 1920, Titchfield Haven 5302 (*Suppl.Fl.Hants*, p.87).

On bare, wet gravelly soil around ponds, flood-hollows, drainage-channels and track-ruts but not persisting in a closed sward; now frequent in the New Forest. In Wilverley Inclosure, *HJW* 1925 (*Suppl.Fl.Hants*, p.87) – perhaps introduced with imported conifers. The spread to new sites has continued steadily for some 50 years; seeds are probably dispersed on the feet of free-ranging cattle and ponies, and also on the wheels of forestry vehicles. The strong Hants population is in marked contrast to that in Cornwall, where it has declined over the past 50 years.

VC11: Hatchet Pond 3601, *RPB* 1952–92; Pilley Pond 3398, *AEB* 1978; refound in Wilverley Inclosure 2401, dry puddle in ride, *AEB & JO* 1987. One isolated site in Southleigh Forest 7308, Hb.AWW 1957, was refound by *EAP & FR* 1981, but extensive tipping has now obliterated the gravelly ditches in which it was last seen in 1982.

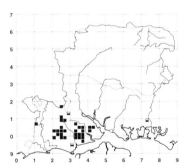

Map 78 Illecebrum verticillatum

Polycarpon tetraphyllum (L.) L. Four-leaved Allseed. **C** Very rare

VC12: As a weed in a garden in Aldershot 8749 for more than 20 years, *DNT* 1982.

Spergula arvensis L. Corn Spurrey. **C** Common Map 79

First record, Gilbert White 1765, 'in a ploughed field', Selborne, VC12 (*White's Jnls* 1: 167).

On sandy arable fields and waste ground; avoids pure chalk.

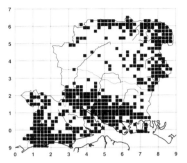

Map 79 Spergula arvensis

Spergularia rupicola LEBEL ex LE JOL. Rock Sea-spurrey. **N** Rare Map 80

Sandy and gravelly sea-cliffs and bare ground on cliff-tops and on sea-walls of the W Solent. Not refound in the Beaulieu estuary, Shirley Brook, Hamble estuary, or at Hill Head, where recorded in *Fl.Hants* (p.72).

VC11: Still frequent in the Lymington watershed on masonry and stiff clay of the sea-wall between Keyhaven Marshes 3191, *RPB* 1987 and Lymington 3394, *DEA* 1964, although reduced, at least temporarily, by recent reconstruction of the wall at Pennington Marshes, Normandy Marsh and the Salterns. Colonization of natural habitat at Rook Cliff, Milford on Sea 2791, 2891, and Hengistbury–Southbourne 1691, 1591, was noticed by *RPB* 1989–90 and by *SRD* several years earlier. It is possible that these populations originated from wind-dispersed seeds from the Isle of Wight where the species is particularly frequent on the W coast. One recently-found colony near Portchester Castle 6204, on new sea-wall, *RBa* 1992, conf. *RPB*.

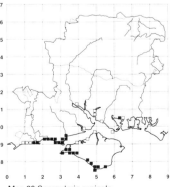

Map 80 Spergularia rupicola

S. media (L.) C. PRESL (*S. marginata* Kitt.) Greater Sea-spurrey. **N** Locally frequent

In salt-marshes and occasionally on low cliffs, as on slipped clay at Barton on Sea.

S. marina (L.) GRISEB. Lesser Sea-spurrey. **N** Locally common Map 81

In salt-marshes or on slipped clay; also on bare, reclaimed land on the coast. Rather more widespread than *S. media*, perhaps due to a greater adaptability in colonizing open ground.

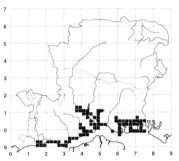

Map 81 Spergularia marina

S. rubra (L.) J. PRESL & C. PRESL Sand Spurrey. **N** Locally common Map 82

On bare sand or gravel, on paths, on heaths, and in pits; on dunes and fixed shingle near the sea.

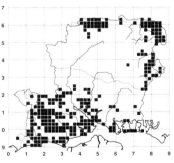

Map 82 Spergularia rubra

Lychnis coronaria (L.) MURRAY Rose Campion. **H** Rare

First record, J. F. Rayner 1924, on cliff between Mudeford and Highcliffe 1992, VC11 (*Proc.IoW N.H.S.* 1: 238).

A garden escape, under-recorded but sometimes persistent.

VC11: Established at Gunner Point,

118

Hayling Island 6999, on sand-dunes, *RPB* 1985–86.

L. flos-cuculi L. Ragged-Robin. N Locally very common Map 83

In damp meadows, marshes, ditches, streamsides, open, wet woodlands and rides; common in all suitable habitats.

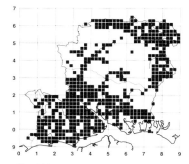

Map 83 Lychnis flos-cuculi

<Agrostemma githago L. Corn-cockle. C Extinct

First record, Gilbert White 1766, Selborne, VC12 (*White's Jnls* 1: 213).

Once a cornfield weed of the chalk, in *Fl.Hants* it was 'local but pretty generally distributed'. Recent records are of plants from seeds deliberately sown by roads, or transient garden-escapes.

VC11: Chidden 6517, edge of wheat field, *PJR* 1974, who collected seed for his Butser Ancient Farm 7118 (now moved to Bascomb Copse, Chalton 7116). VC12: Deane railway 5450, in corn stubble, *WEW* 1958; Froyle *c.*7442, in cornfield, *CL* 1958.>

Silene nutans L. var. **salmoniana** F. N. HEPPER Nottingham Catchfly. N Very rare

On coastal fixed shingle or sand-dunes. VC11: Still abundant at Browndown 5799, 5898, 5899, *RPB, EJC & EAP* 1989; a once-large population at East-ney 6798, 6799, 6899, has been severely reduced by a caravan-site and other developments, *EAP & RPB* 1988, 6799, *RBa* 1992; on the positive side, it has spread to Sinah Common golf-links and dunes 6998, 6999, *RPB* 1975, *DB* 1980; also near Fort Monkton 6198, *RFG* 1990. Until 1975 it was in two places at Barnes Lane, Milford on Sea 2892, *HBr* 1929; an unconfirmed report in 1989 indicates it may still survive there. Ports Down SU60, *JPo* 1975.

NOTE. Field experience in Kent and elsewhere has convinced the author that C. A. Stace (*New Fl.*, p.216) and D. H. Kent (*Vascular Pl.Brit.Is.*, p.51) are incorrect in sinking the two varieties described in 1951 by F. N. Hepper (*Watsonia* 2: 80–90). The plant of shingle beaches and sandy soils in Hants is very distinct from the plant of the Dover chalk cliffs in Kent, var. *smithiana* Moss. Var. *salmoniana* is surely the correct name of the Hants plants (F.R.).

S. vulgaris GARCKE ssp. **vulgaris** Bladder Campion. N Locally very common

Rank grassland, field-borders, roadside verges, hedgebanks, scrub and in open ground; very common on the chalk, occasionally on clay or gravel.

S. vulgaris x S. uniflora N

VC11: Hurst Castle 3189, in turf over stabilized shingle N of castle, several plants of obviously hybrid origin with one large plant of *S. vulgaris*, *EMM-J & WBT* 1927–28 (*Bladder Camp.*, p.178).

S. uniflora ROTH (*S. maritima* With.) Sea Campion. N Locally frequent

On coastal sand and shingle; on fixed shingle (e.g. Browndown 5799, VC11), and occasionally on low sea-cliffs.

S. noctiflora L. Night-flowering Catchfly. C Very local Map 84

This is now a fairly frequent but sparse arable weed of chalk (subject to crop-spraying) all around the Martin–Breamore, Winchester, Andover, and Odiham–Crondall areas. It shows an increase on *Fl.Hants* (pp.59–60), which cited only four mainland records, one of which, 'Browndown

in Stokes Bay' is probably an error for *S. nutans*.

VC8: Knoll Farm, Damerham 0918, barley headland, *JO* 1987. VC11: W of Duck's Nest, Rockbourne 1020, edge of arable field, *JO* 1987; Roman Road, Chilcomb 4927, edge of field, *EAP* 1984; Longwood Warren 5227, *RPB* 1984. VC12: Lane near Swanthorpe House 7846, *AduSB* 1959, *AB* 1968, 1976 (*Watsonia* 11: 393); near Micheldever Station 5143, *MBJ* 1984; Worthy Down oil-boring 4535, *PS* 1986; Lower Wootton 5753, arable, *WGH* 1976–90; near Wallers Ash tunnel 4936, stubble field, *AB* 1967 (*Watsonia* 10: 422).

S. latifolia POIRET ssp. **alba** (MILL.) GREUTER & BURDET (*S. alba* (Mill.) E. H. L. Krause, non Muhl. ex Britton) White Campion. N Common

On arable, waste ground and hedge-banks; especially on light soils; less common in the New Forest.

S. x hampeana MEUSEL & K. WERNER (*S. latifolia* x *S. dioica*) N Occasional

Waysides, field-borders and waste ground, usually in areas where both parents occur, but doubtless under-recorded.

S. dioica (L.) CLAIRV. Red Campion. N Frequent and locally very common

Common in hedges and woodland, on all types of soil except the most acid. On chalk it is commonest where there are superficial drifts of clay or loam.

S. gallica L. Small-flowered Catch-fly. C Rare Map 85

An arable weed on sand or gravel, much declined since *Fl.Hants*.

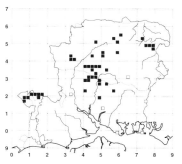

Map 84 Silene noctiflora

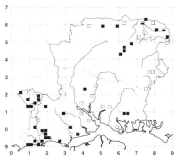

Map 85 Silene gallica

119

VC8: Damerham 0913, arable field, *RPB* 1965. **VC11**: Southbourne 1491, bank in car-park and on cliff-top, plentiful, *RPB* 1988–90; Sowley 3696, cornfield, *AEB* 1978. **VC12**: Hall's Farm, near Bramshill Common *c*.7563, *AMS* 1960, *PH* 1968; Farnborough Airfield 8653, *ARGM* 1981; Broomhurst Farm, Fleet 8156, on roadside, *AB* 1980, not since.

Saponaria officinalis L.   Soapwort. **D,H**   Local

First record, Gilbert White 1766, Selborne, VC12 (*White's Jnls* 1: 192).

A handsome garden-plant, formerly grown for its property of restoring old fabrics. Pieces of persistent stolon establish themselves from garden rubbish; in hedgebanks on roadsides, on waste ground, and sand-dunes. Especially common on the sand. VC11: 31 □; VC12: 36 □.

<Petrorhagia nanteuilii (BURNAT) P. W. BALL & HEYWOOD (*Kohlrauschia prolifera* auct., non (L.) Kunth)   Childing Pink.   **N**   Extinct (Sched. 8)

Formerly on fixed shingle in thin turf, and abundant on the W end of Sinah Common, Hayling Island 6899; most was destroyed in 1924 by the ferry buildings, though *LNHL* saw it in 1928 before the site became a car-park. A small population at Fort Cumberland 6899, *GARW* 1930, shingle behind sea-wall, Hb.AWW 1957, was last seen in 1968, *MPY*.>

Dianthus plumarius L.   Wild Pink. **H**   Very rare

VC11: Long established on the walls of Beaulieu Abbey 3802, and on a chalk-bank at Compton 4625, *RPB* 1949.

D. deltoides L.   Maiden Pink. **H,N?**   Very rare

First record, H. M. Wilkinson 1880, in a wood one mile from Ringwood, VC11; specimens, gathered several years before, sent to *FT* (*Fl.Hants*, excl.sp., p.72).

In grassland on sand or gravel. Possibly formerly native, now only introduced.

VC11: Only recent record: Avon Forest Park, St Leonard's 1201, dry, grassy heath under bracken – a dense patch 8 x 7m, *NS* 1983, Hb.RPB 1986, det. *SSH* (*Watsonia* 17: 185); field at New Milton, *AJM* 1943, Hb.BM; Hinton Admiral 2094, *KG* 1949.

VC12: Field at Pardown, Oakley, *DHS* 1914 (*Suppl.Fl.Hants*, p.20); Newtown 4662, gravel-pit, *HWh*, comm. *AJW* (*Rep.B.E.C* for 1941–42, p.483).

D. armeria L.   Deptford Pink.   **N** Very rare

On open, sandy or gravelly grassland and banks. There are many old records, but only one or two sites have survived.

VC11: Avon Forest Park 1201, in acid grassland on sand, *FAW* 1986 (*Watsonia* 17: 185), and few plants in grassy heath, under bracken, *GFLeP* 1987, *RPB* 1988–90; Dunshill Lane, Breamore *c*.1517, *CRM c*.1840 (*May Ptgs Cat*: 101), not refound, *JO* 1992; pathway near Breamore Wood, *NDS* 1933, Hb.BM; sea-wall near Portchester, *HG & JGr* 1881, Hb.BM, *PMH* 1929, *WJLP* 1934, has gone like many other old sea-walls; Sinah Common 6899, quite common near ferry, *LNHL* 1928, now a car-park; Sinah Common golf-links 6999, *DWF* 1958, *LNHL* 1975, was reported in 1981 to be overgrown by rank herbage or *Lupinus arboreus*. **VC12**: Over Wallop 2838, *AVNHS* 1961, was not seen in 1980; Woolmer Forest 7933, firebreak, *CMo* 1984 (*Watsonia* 15: 393), might be native, but is very close to Whitehill built-up area and gardens.

POLYGONACEAE

Persicaria campanulata (HOOK. fil.) RONSE DECR. (*Polygonum campanulatum* Hook. fil.)   Lesser Knotweed. **H**   Very rare

First record, R. P. Bowman 1957, Boldre 3297, VC11, lane near river, Hb.RPB.

A garden escape, not known to be spreading.

VC11: Near Christchurch, *KG* n.d.; Sandleheath 1215, in bracken by path, *RPB* 1991; Bassett Wood 4216, *BL* 1975; Lower Ratley, near Awbridge 3223, *AB* 1979, *RMV* 1986. **VC12**: Basingstoke Canal, Pondtail 8253, near gardens, *CRH* 1986, det. *ARGM*, still present, *CRH* 1995.

P. wallichii GREUTER & BURDET (*Polygonum polystachyum* Wall. ex C. F. W. Meissn.)   Himalayan Knotweed.   **H**   Rare

First record, G. A. R. Watts 1932 or 1933, between Fleet and Crookham, VC12 (*Proc.Hants Fld Club* 12: 296).

Naturalized in wooded places, roadsides, stream-banks, etc., but usually close to habitations.

VC11: Upper Pennington Common 2995, *RPB* 1986, det. *JRA*; Burley Outer Rails 2305, *JO* 1987; St Cross meadows 4727, by stream, *KC* 1981. Also 2600, 2800, 4214, 4412. **VC12**: On A3, emerging from Adhurst St Mary 7624, *AB* 1982. Also 6042, 6250, 6640, 6842, 7428, 7828, 8436.

P. bistorta (L.) SAMP. (*Polygonum bistorta* L.)   Common Bistort.   **N,D** Very local   Map 86

First record, Gilbert White 1766, Selborne, VC12 (*White's Jnls* 1: 193).

In damp, unimproved meadows and, rarely, in moist open woods; an old pot-herb, also found near villages as a garden throw-out. Uncommon in VC12, rare and decreasing with changing meadow management, in VC11.

VC8: Foxes Lane, West Wellow 2920, *RMV* 1986. **VC11**: Stanpit Marsh 1692, *RPB* 1961–91; Bishop's Waltham 5516, last record *RPB* 1974. **VC12**: Nether Wallop 3036, *RPB* 1984; meadow by Short Lythe, Selborne 7433, *FR* 1983; Cheesecombe Copse, Hawkley 7428, *FR* 1982; Plastow Green 5261, *WGH* 1982; near Ewshot 8150, several colonies, *CRH* 1984; Inhurst 5661, in wet meadow, *PB* 1987; Oakhanger stream, Chapel Farm 7635, and R. Slea, S of Dockenfield 8239, *NRCB* 1986.

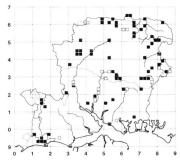

Map 86 Persicaria bistorta

P. amplexicaulis (D. DON) RONSE DECR. (*Polygonum amplexicaule* D. Don)   Red Bistort.   **H**   Very rare

First record, Miss M. MacKeith 1967, Hursley 4426, VC11, near dumped gravel, det. *BM* (*Rep.S'ton N.H.S.*, p.13).

A garden outcast, not yet well established.

VC11: Furzey Lodge 3602, *CDD* 1969, det. *RPB*. Also 1404, 4022. **VC12**: 3652.

P. amphibia (L.) GRAY (*Polygonum amphibium* L.) Amphibious Bistort. N Locally common Map 87

Floating in still or slow-moving fresh water; terrestrial on mud, or even drier open ground and arable fields near water.

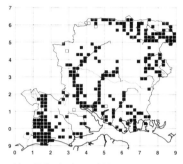

Map 87 Persicaria amphibia

P. maculosa GRAY (*Polygonum persicaria* L.) Redshank. **N,C** Common

Arable and waste ground, pond-borders, woodland rides, usually where wet in winter.

P. x lenticularis (HY) SOJÁK (*Polygonum* x *lenticulare* Hy; *P. maculosa* x *P. lapathifolia*) N Very rare

VC11: Recorded in *Hybr.Fl.Brit.Is.* (p.274).

P. x condensata (F. W. SCHULTZ) SOJÁK (*P. maculosa* x *P. mitis*) N Very rare

VC11: Lower Test, Testwood 3614, swampy marsh-pasture, in brackish zone, *RPB* 1986, det. *JRA*; Jockstrill Common, Sopley 1596, a few plants with parents, *AJB & RPB* 1987.

P. x brauniana (F. W. SCHULTZ) SOJÁK (*P. maculosa* x *P. minor*) N Very rare

VC11: Lower Test, Testwood 3614, *RPB* 1986, det. *JRA*. **VC12**: Recorded in *Hybr.Fl.Brit.Is.* (p.275).

P. lapathifolia (L.) GRAY (*Polygonum lapathifolium* L., incl. *P. nodosum* Pers.) Pale Persicaria. **N,C** Frequent to locally common

Arable and waste ground, wet, disturbed ground around ponds, etc.

P. hydropiper (L.) SPACH (*Polygonum hydropiper* L.) Water-pepper. N Locally very common

Ditches, streamsides, marshy pastures, pond-margins, woodland rides that are wet in winter. Very common, except on the chalk.

P. mitis (SCHRANK) OPIZ ex ASSENOV (*Polygonum mite* Schrank; *Persicaria laxiflora* (Weihe) Opiz) Tasteless Water-pepper. N Rare

Marshy places and drains in alluvial pasture. Probably declined since *Fl.Hants*, with most of the records in one area.

VC11: Stour Valley *c.*1096, *MPY* 1960–63, det. *AWW*; Hurn Airport 1198, *BE* 1991; R. Stour, Jumpers Common 1394, Hb.RPB 1976; Christchurch meadows *c.*1492, *JRP* 1965; Avon Causeway Bridge 1497, *MPY* 1960, Hb.AWW; R. Avon, Hale 1718, Hb.RPB 1976; Lower Test 3614, Hb.RPB 1975, *MSC* 1986; Moortown Farm, Ringwood 1403, mill-stream, *RPB* 1986; Jockstrill Common, Sopley 1596, 1597, several patches, *RPB* 1987. **VC12**: Heckfield Heath 7261, *DMRB* 1985, Hb.RNG; Fleet Pond *c.*8254, *Watts MSS* 1932, not since. The record for Bramshill Common 7462, *CRH* 1980 (*Watsonia* 17: 190, as *P. mite*) is an error resulting from confusion with a record of *P. minor* for this locality, *CRH*, pers.comm. 1995.

P. minor (HUDS.) OPIZ (*Polygonum minus* Huds.) Small Water-pepper. N Local Map 88

Gravelly, open marshy pastures, muddy borders and beds of ponds and streams, where much trodden at cattle-crossings; meadow-drains, wet pits and muddy track-ruts. In the New Forest, often with *Pulicaria vulgaris* and always in places inundated in winter. The New Forest is now perhaps the major British stronghold for this declining species. Frequent there, local in the Avon Valley, but very rare elsewhere.

VC11: Lower Test, Nursling 3614, *RPB* 1976; Ipley Bridge 3806, Hb.RPB 1975; Common Marsh, Stockbridge 3534, Hb.RPB 1975. **VC12**: Old sand-pit on the Slab, Bordon 7835, *MS-W* 1978, det. *FR*; Stony Heath, Baughurst 5758, dried-up shallow pond, *WEW* 1957, conf. *ECW*; Bramshill Plantation 7462, thinly scattered on shore of largest lake, *AJB* 1987; Woolmer Pond

7831, 7832, all round sandy shore restored by dredging, *FR* 1990, Hb.AB.

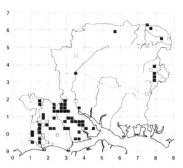

Map 88 Persicaria minor

Polygonum maritimum L. Sea Knotgrass. N Very rare (Sched. 8)

First published British record, W. Borrer 1836, 'Christchurch Head on the sandy shore towards Muddiford', VC11, Hb.BM (*Trans.Linn.Soc.* 17: 458).

Sandy sea-beaches just above the strand-line, loosely associated with *Cakile maritima* and *Atriplex glabriuscula*.

VC11: Refound on Hengistbury sand-spit 1891, one strong plant which produced numerous flowers and seeds, *TWa* 1990, conf. *AJB, DAP & RMW* (*Watsonia* 18: 427), increasing in 1992 to 49 plants, and in 1993 to over 140 plants over a 222m extent at S end of spit 1890, 1891, *RPB*; Avon Beach, Mudeford 1891, 10+ plants, *RPB* 1995 (none seen 1992); Sandy Point, Hayling Island 7598, 15 plants, *RPB* 1995.

Since its first discovery, seen by several botanists on both sides of the harbour-mouth up to 1902, when *WMR* collected it at Mudeford, Hb.LANC. It was feared lost through increasing erosion by the sea, but somehow survived. The building of a harbour-mouth wall on the Mudeford side destroyed almost all suitable habitat there, so the plant was presumed extinct. The miraculous rediscovery in 1990, after an apparent absence of 88 years, followed the severe gales and coastal flooding of the previous winter, when much sand must have been displaced, evidently uncovering some long-buried seed.

A Mediterranean species, found elsewhere in the British Isles only in Cornwall, where plants coincidentally appeared at two sites in 1990, in Sussex, 1992, the Isle of Wight, 1995, and on Herm.

P. oxyspermum C. A. MEY. &
BUNGE ex LEDEB. ssp. **raii** (BAB.)
D. A. WEBB & CHATER (*P. raii* Bab.)
Ray's Knotgrass.   N   Rare   Map 89

On sea-beaches of sand or shingle,
usually just above the strand-line.
Rare, but persistent, as it resists
moderate trampling.

VC11: Hengistbury 1891, sand-spit,
CEP 1967, three plants refound, *RPB
& TWa* 1989, increasing to more than
100 plants, *RPB* 1993; new dunes
1790, 12 plants, *TWa* 1989; High Cliff
2193, five plants on limestone chippings beside undercliff road, *RPB*
1989; Sowley Shore 3795, *RPB*
1973–89; Park Shore 4096, 118 plants,
RPB 1992; Stansore Point 4698,
FEWV 1963, *FR* 1991; Sandy Point,
Hayling Island 7498, *AB, EAP & FR*
1980.

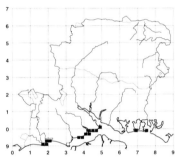

Map 89 Polygonum oxyspermum ssp. raii

P. arenastrum BOREAU (*P. aequale*
Lindm.)   Equal-leaved Knotgrass.
N,C   Very frequent, under-recorded

Open waste-, arable or heavily-trodden
ground, even on asphalt; occasionally
on beaches.

P. aviculare L.   Knotgrass.   **N,C**
Common

Roadsides, open waste- and arable
ground, paths in woods, beaches etc.
Abundant throughout the county.

P. rurivagum JORD. ex BOREAU
Cornfield Knotgrass.   **N,C**   Local

Open waste- or arable ground, usually
on chalk; occasionally on strand-lines
of beaches. VC8: 2 □; VC11: 47 □;
VC12: 80 □.

Fallopia japonica (HOUTT.) RONSE
DECR. (*Reynoutria japonica* Houtt.;
Polygonum cuspidatum Siebold & Zucc.)
Japanese Knotweed.   **H**   Locally
frequent

First record, G. A. R. Watts 1932, W
side of Aldershot 8551, VC12, plentiful
(*Watts MSS*). Also noted earlier as an
escape in waste places, but unlocalized,
JFR (*Proc. IoW N.H.S.* 1: 170).

Planted as ground-cover, and, on the
army ranges, to consolidate the butts; a
garden outcast that is well-nigh indestructible. It has spread vegetatively,
forming dense thickets on tips, waste
ground, railways, stream-banks, etc.,
and is now widespread and still
increasing.

F. x bohemica (CHRTEK & CHRTKOV)
J. P. BAILEY (*Reynoutria* x *bohemica*
Chrtek & Chrtkov; *F. japonica* x *F.
sachalinensis*)   **H**   Very rare

First record, R. M. Veall 1988, Sarisbury 5007, VC11, outside cemetery,
conf. *JPB* (*Watsonia* 18: 220).

VC11: Old Shirley, Southampton
3914, edge of pleasure-ground, *RMV*
1989.

F. sachalinensis (F. SCHMIDT ex
MAXIM.) RONSE DECR. (*Polygonum
sachalinense* F. Schmidt ex Maxim.;
Reynoutria sachalinensis (F. Schmidt ex
Maxim.) Nakai)   Giant Knotweed.
H   Rare

First record, G. A. R. Watts 1933, lane
near Fleet Cemetery 8053, VC12
(*Watts MSS*).

Planted and naturalized, generally
near water.

VC11: Milford on Sea, *NDS* 1935
(*Proc. Hants Fld Club* 15: 70); Exbury
refuse-tip 4200, *RPB* 1962–84. Also
1214, 1492, 2092, 2296, 2896, 3816,
4414. **VC12**: Also 4638, 7240, 8452,
8852.

F. baldschuanica (REGEL) HOLUB
(*F. aubertii* (L. Henry) Holub; *Polygonum baldschuanicum* Regel)   Russian-
vine.   **H**   Occasional

First record, A. H. G. Alston 1947,
seashore at Mudeford, VC11, patch
about two yards square, Hb.BM.

Planted as a creeper, and spreading
rampantly over hedges and bushes,
usually near dwellings.

VC11: Also 1292, 1490, 1892, 2092,
2892, 3694, 3812, 4010, 4212, 4410,
4402, 4698, 4602, 6498, 6404. **VC12**:
Anton Lakes 3647, *MFW* 1992; Yateley 8260, escaped across a garden fence
and clambering 6m up a pine, *ARGM*
1987. Also 6634, 7240.

F. convolvulus (L.) A. LÖVE (*Polygonum convolvulus* L.)   Black-
bindweed.   **N,C**   Common

Arable and waste ground, hedges and
wood-borders, especially on light
soils.

F. dumetorum (L.) HOLUB (*Polygonum dumetorum* L.)   Copse-
bindweed.   **N**   Very rare   Map 90

Open woods, copses and shady
hedgerows. Always on sandy soil, of
intermittent appearance but likely to
reappear following coppicing. Almost
confined to the SW border areas.

VC8: Whitsbury Wood 1318, *IMG*
1956 (*Suppl. Fl. Wilts*, p.49); near
Manor Farm, Plaitford 2720, *JO* 1984.
VC11: Ivy Lane, Blashford 1507, once
abundant, now scarce, *ESH* 1971,
Hb.AWW, *RPB* 1988–92; Gorley
c.1610, *VM* 1968; Godshill 1613, 1614,
MPY & ESH c.1970, but overgrown
before 1976; Hipley Copse 6110, one
year only, *ILR c*.1986. **VC12**: Heckfield 7360, *WEW* 1957, *PB & WGH*
1992.

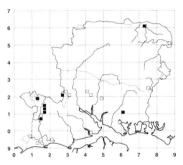

Map 90 Fallopia dumetorum

Rumex acetosella L. ssp. **acetosella**
(*R. tenuifolius* (Wallr.) A. Löve)
Sheep's Sorrel.   **N**   Locally very
common

Open grass-heaths, sand-dunes, fixed
shingle, old pastures, disused pits and
arable land, on dry, acid soils; in chalk
grassland, confined to ant-hills or to
acid superficials. Often dominant
around rabbit-burrows.

var. **tenuifolius** WALLR.

Heaths or acid grassland, sand-pits,
shingle beaches; always on very dry,
acid soil. Rare, except on the Lower
Greensand and the NE Bagshot sands;
strangely absent from the New Forest.

VC8: Abundant on gravel in Boulsbury Wood 0715, *AB & JO* 1984.
VC11: Sherfield English 2822, sand-
pit, Hb.RPB 1963, conf. *JEL*. **VC12**:
Bramley Ammunition Depot 6657, on
cinders, *AB* 1979.

ssp. **pyrenaicus** (POURR.) AKEROYD (ssp. *angiocarpus* auct., non (Murb.) Murb.) **N,C** Under-recorded

First record, E. F. Linton 1892, Bournemouth, VC11, Hb.BM, det. *WCB*.

VC11: Titchfield 5306, roadside verge, *RMV* 1988, Hb.RPB.

R. acetosa L. ssp. **acetosa** Common Sorrel. **N** Very common

Old grassland and meadows, roadsides, woodland glades; found least often on shallow, purely chalk soil.

R. hydrolapathum HUDS. Water Dock. **N** Locally common Map 91

Ditches, riversides, swamps, fens, pond-borders; mainly along the principal river valleys.

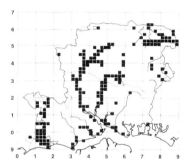

Map 91 Rumex hydrolapathum

R. x schreberi HAUSSKN. (*R. hydrolapathum* x *R. crispus*) **N** Very rare

VC11: Swamp just N of St Leonards Grange, Beaulieu 4098, *FEWV* 1958, det *JEL*.

R. x lingulatus JUNGNER (*R. x weberi* Fisch.-Benz.; *R. hydrolapathum* x *R. obtusifolius*) **N** Very rare

There are two old records for VC11 and one for VC12 in *Fl.Hants* (p.355), and one more VC12 record, listed under *R. maximus* Schreber, in *Suppl. Fl.Hants* (p.93).

VC11: Lower Test, Nursling 3614, marsh by tidal river, *LL* 1986, Hb.RPB, det. *JRA*.

R. cristatus DC. Greek Dock. **H?** Very rare

First record, Mrs D. L. Brookman 1993, Heckfield 7360, VC12, five stems beside B3011 evidently spread from the Reading (VC22) site, Hb.AB.

R. patientia L. Patience Dock. **C** Very rare

First record, A. C. Leslie 1983, Aldershot Station 8650, VC12, well established, Hb.AB.

R. crispus L. Curled Dock. **N** Very common

Rank grassland, arable waste-ground, roadsides, sandy and shingly beaches. The common plant is ssp. *crispus*, but ssp. *littoreus* (J. Hardy) Akeroyd and possibly ssp. *uliginosus* (Le Gall) Akeroyd are likely to occur in coastal habitats, but have not yet been recorded.

R. x schulzei HAUSSKN. (*R. crispus* x *R. conglomeratus*) **N** Very rare or overlooked

VC11: Beaulieu River near Bailey's Hard 3901, Hb.RPB 1985, det. *JRA* (*Watsonia* 16: 444).

R. x sagorskii HAUSSKN. (*R. crispus* x *R. sanguineus*) **N** Very rare or overlooked

VC11: Otterbourne Hill Common 4522, in scrub, Hb.RPB 1978, det. *JRA* (*Watsonia* 16: 445).

R. x pseudopulcher HAUSSKN. (*R. crispus* x *R. pulcher*) **N** Very rare

VC12: Chilbolton Common 3940, *JF* 1988, Hb.AB, det. *JRA* (*Watsonia* 18: 221), *AJB* 1989.

R. x pratensis MERT. & KOCH (*R. crispus* x *R. obtusifolius*) **N** Under-recorded

Fl.Hants (pp.354–355) describes it as 'rather uncommon', yet lists many localities.

VC11: Lyndhurst allotments 2909, *AJB & JO* 1987, det. *AJB*; Shelley Farm, Ower 3217, potato-field, *GC* 1987; Aldermoor, Southampton 3915, *RMV* 1989. VC12: Wonston *c*.4638, *AWW* 1962.

R. conglomeratus MURRAY Clustered Dock. **N** Frequent and locally common

Wet pastures, marshes and watersides, open waste-ground and roadsides. In woodland it gives way to *R. sanguineus*.

R. x muretii HAUSSKN. (*R. conglomeratus* x *R. pulcher*) **N** Very rare or overlooked

VC11: Gorley *c*.1511, near small pond, *ESH* 1968, det. *JEL*; Common Marsh, Stockbridge 3534, *JF & PS* 1989; Beaulieu 3902, Hb.RPB 1983, det. *JRA*. VC12: Chilbolton Common 3940, *JF* 1988, Hb.AB, det. *JRA* (*Watsonia* 18: 221).

[**R. x abortivus** RUHMER (*R. conglomeratus* x *R. obtusifolius*)

VC11: Hambledon, *GCD* 1929 (*Suppl.Fl.Hants*, p.93). Record unconfirmed and not given in *Hybr.Fl.Brit. Is.*, p.287, or in *BSBI Hdbk* No. 3, p.177, where this hybrid is discussed.]

R. sanguineus L. var. **viridis** (SIBTH.) KOCH Wood Dock. **N,C** Common

In woodland, garden shrubberies and in waste- or grassy places near woods. Extremely shade-tolerant; scarcer in woods on the most acid soil.

var. **sanguineus** **H,C** Very rare

VC11: S of The Kennels, Minstead 2910, roadside verge, *SNHS* 1990, Hb.RPB 1993. VC12: Basing 6652, 50 plants along hedgerow, *AJB* 1990.

R. pulcher L. Fiddle Dock. **N** Local Map 92

In short turf of old, dry open grassland where grazed or trampled; mainly on sea- or river-gravel, or on sand. Frequent along the Avon Valley, widespread but local along the coast. Increasingly rare northwards, and generally in river valleys.

VC11: By R. Avon at Fordingbridge 1514, *AB* 1976; Common Marsh, Stockbridge 3534, *TWO & BAO* 1976; Hambledon churchyard 6415, *FR* 1975. VC12: Headley 5262, gravel-pit, *CL* 1962.

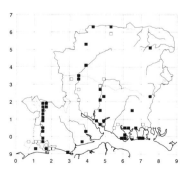

Map 92 Rumex pulcher

R. x ogulinensis Borbás (*R. pulcher* x *R. obtusifolius*)   **N**   Very rare

VC12: Chilbolton Common 3940, *JF* 1988, det. *JRA*, Hb.AB (*Watsonia* **18**: 221).

R. obtusifolius L.   Broad-leaved Dock. **N,C**   Very common

Waste ground, roadsides, meadows, field-borders, and disturbed rank grassland.

<R. palustris Sm.   Marsh Dock.   **N** Extinct

VC11: 'Ditches and wet places...in the neighbourhood of Gosport, 1848...probably extinct' (*Fl.Hants*, p.353). 'Near mill, Lockerley, 1928' *HMS* (as *R. limosus* Thuill.), in *Suppl.Fl.Hants* (p.93), was likely to have been an alien.>

<R. maritimus L.   Golden Dock. **N**   Extinct

Several old records for the Great Salterns, Portsea Island, VC11 (long ago turned into playing fields) or their neighbourhood: 'marshes at the Salterns', Portsea Island, 1846, (*Maj.Smith MS Cat.*). Also 'Near Great Salterns, 1919; Hayling, 1920; Havant, 1922', *MTH* (*Suppl.Fl.Hants*, p.93). 'Alresford: Druce' in *Suppl.Fl. Hants* is not supported by a specimen in Hb.OXF, nor was it included for VC12 in *Druce Com.Fl.*>

PLUMBAGINACEAE

Limonium vulgare Mill. Common Sea-lavender.   **N**   Locally common   Map 93

First record, Miss C. R. May 1840, sea wall, Tipner *c.*6303, VC11 (*May Ptgs Cat.*: 681).

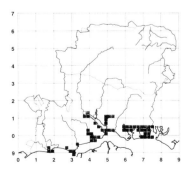

Map 93 Limonium vulgare

Coastal and estuarine tidal salt-marshes, on mud in the upper and middle zones, usually with *Puccinellia maritima*.

L. x neumanii C. E. Salmon (*L. vulgare* x *L. humile*)   **N**   Very rare

VC11: Needs Ore Point 4297, *RPB* 1984, *HJD* 1986; North Hayling, *JEL* 1935, Hb.RNG, det. *PMH*. Wicor, Portchester 5905, *JEL & PMH* 1929, Hb.RNG, now gone.

L. humile Mill.   Lax-flowered Sea-lavender.   **N**   Rare   Map 94

Coastal tidal salt-marshes, on mud or sand, mainly in the upper zone. Very rare, except around Langstone and Chichester Harbours, and at Hayling Island.

VC11: Needs Ore Point 4297, *RPB* 1964–92; Elson, Gosport 6002, 6003, *RPB* 1988; Pewit Island 6003, *RPB & JO* 1988; Langstone Mill 7204, Hb.RPB 1982, *FR* 1985; SW of Emsworth 7305, plentiful, *FR* 1986. After field survey in 1989, records for Stanpit Marsh 1792, Hengistbury 1790 and Hurst Castle 3090 are all considered to be errors. Wicor, Portchester 5905, *PMH* 1929, Hb.BM, now gone, the habitat having been filled in.

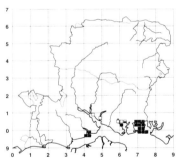

Map 94 Limonium humile

<L. binervosum (G. E. Sm.) C. E. Salmon   Rock Sea-lavender.   **N** Extinct

Between Christchurch Harbour and the sea *c.*1891, VC11, *BK* 1888 (*Fl.Hants*, p.338, as *Statice occidentalis* Lloyd), and Hayling Island, VC11, 1919–20 (*Suppl.Fl.Hants*, p.68). No subsequent record at either site.>

Armeria maritima (Mill.) Willd. ssp. **maritima**   Thrift.   **N** Locally common   Map 95

Coastal and estuarine upper salt-marshes, sandy and shingly beaches and in the turf behind them, gravelly and sandy sea-cliffs; common. Very rare inland.

VC11: B3056 verge, near Stephill Bottom 3505, *RPB* 1981. VC12: Micheldever Spoil Heaps 5244, two plants in chalk turf, *RPB* 1968 (*Watsonia* **10**: 426); A31 Chawton 6937, eastbound verge, *GM* 1992; centre of A325 dual carriageway, Aldershot 8652, *TD* 1985.

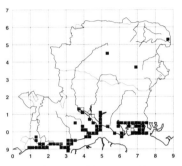

Map 95 Armeria maritima ssp. maritima

<A. pseudarmeria (Murray) Mansf.   Estoril Thrift.   **H**   Extinct

Naturalized on cliff at Lee-on-the-Solent 5600, VC11, *JEL* 1957 (*Suppl. Wild Fl.Guide*, p.24). This site was destroyed later for the hydrofoil service.>

C. A. Stace and E. J. Clement state that a broad-leaved *Armeria*, naturalized in abundance in about 200m of cliff-top turf at East Cliff, Boscombe 1091, *RCS* 1981, Hb.RPB 1990, is not *A. pseudarmeria*; they are unable to name it but suggest it may be one of the garden cultivars (pers.comm.).

ELATINACEAE

Elatine hexandra (Lapierre) DC. Six-stamened Waterwort.   **N**   Rare Map 96

In nutrient-poor, peaty water, on shallow beds or muddy edges of lakes. It flowers even when submerged. There are 18 sites extant, some revealed by drought or temporary draining. Recently, many new sites have been discovered in the NE.

VC11: Sowley Pond 3796, *LWF* 1969; Hatchet Pond 3601, *JCDa* 1936, *RPB* 1983; Ellingham 1407, 1408, bed of gravel-pit lakes, Hb.RPB 1987. VC12: Frensham Great Pond 8340,

AB 1976 (*Watsonia* 11: 392); Fleet Pond 8254, *AB* 1964, destroyed by washed-down sand by 1970, reappeared 1989 in newly-dug dragonfly pond 8255, *CRH*; ponds all over Bramshill Common 7560, 7562, *AJB & CRH* 1989. In numerous flooded gravel-pits along the R. Blackwater, from Moulsham Lakes 8062 to Spring Lakes, Aldershot 8851, containing in the aggregate a vast population which has colonized new lakes within two years or so, *CRH* 1992; Yateley 8261, flooded gravel-pits, Hb.AB 1976 (*loc.cit*).

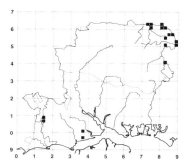

Map 96 Elatine hexandra

[**E. hydropiper** L. Eight-stamened Waterwort.

Claimed for Hants by Townsend in *Fl.Hants* (p.75) on the basis that it occurred in Frensham [Great] Pond 8440, almost all of which, except for about 2ha on the SW shore, lies in Surrey. There is no proof that this species has ever been found in the small portion of the pond lying in Hants, VC12. Lousley, in *Fl.Surrey* (p.140), considered it probably extinct in the pond and in Surrey.]

CLUSIACEAE

Hypericum calycinum L. Rose-of-Sharon. **H** Occasional

Often planted as ground-cover, sometimes escaping into woodland. VC11: 21 ☐; VC12: 4 ☐.

VC11: Honeycomb, Broughton 3131, *RPB* 1977; Hedgemoor Copse 2630, *FR & AB* 1980.

H. androsaemum L. Tutsan. **N** Locally frequent Map 97

Associated with old woodland, shady stream- and hedgebanks; mostly, but not always, on acid soil. Commonest in the New Forest. On Malmstone and Gault clay in the E.

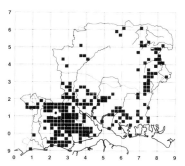

Map 97 Hypericum androsaemum

H. x inodorum MILL. (*H. x elatum* Aiton; *H. androsaemum* x *H. hircinum*) Tall Tutsan. **H** Very rare

First record, Mrs J. Goater 1966, large bush by track, Denny Wood 3306, VC11, *AB* 1980, Hb.RPB.

H. hircinum L. ssp. **majus** (AITON) N. ROBSON Stinking Tutsan. **H** Very rare

First record, E. B. Bishop 1920, Highcliffe, VC11 (*Rep.B.E.C.* for 1920, p.116).
VC11: Lane at Fritham, *RCA* 1938, and hedge near Lymore, *JCDa & RCPh* 1938 (*Proc.Hants Fld Club* 15: 65); Lymore Lane, Lymington, *NDS* 1940, Hb.BM; Christchurch, old wall by Marsh Lane 1692, and Mudeford Road 1792, *JP* 1965; Burton Common refuse-tip 1995, Hb.RPB 1985, det. *ALG*.

H. perforatum L. Perforate St John's-wort. **N** Very common

Scrub, hedgebanks, roadsides, wood-borders, chalk grassland; especially on light soils.

H. x desetangsii LAMOTTE (*H. perforatum* x *H. maculatum*) **N** Very rare

First records, R. M. Veall 1990, Michelmersh 3425, roadside verge, and Ampfield 4023, VC11, hedge between arable fields, Hb.RPB, det. *NKBR* (*Watsonia* 18: 421).
VC8: 1222. **VC11:** Also 0820, 1220, 3426, 3626.

H. maculatum CRANTZ ssp. **obtusiusculum** (TOURLET) HAYEK Imperforate St John's-wort. **N** Locally frequent Map 98

Widespread though sparse on edges of pastures and grass verges, in open scrub, wood-borders and hedgebanks; prefers heavier soils.

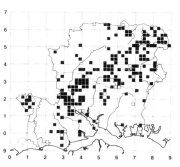

Map 98 Hypericum maculatum ssp. obtusiusculum

H. tetrapterum FR. Square-stalked St John's-wort. **N** Locally common

Stream-banks, ditches, marshes, damp meadows and carr; on all except very acid soils.

H. humifusum L. Trailing St John's-wort. **N** Locally common Map 99

In heathy grassland, verges and woodland rides; mostly on acidic sands or gravels, but quite widespread on chalk.

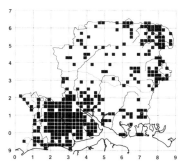

Map 99 Hypericum humifusum

H. pulchrum L. Slender St John's-wort. **N** Frequent and locally common

Open woods, heaths etc; mostly on drier, more acid soils but sometimes in open scrub and rank grassland on chalk. Commonest in the New Forest.

H. hirsutum L. Hairy St John's-wort. **N** Locally common

First record, Miss C. R. May 1837, hedgerow in Breamore, VC11 (*May Ptgs Cat.*: 151).

In open woodland, scrub and hedges; on chalk and heavy clay. Almost absent from the SW, apart from a few sites on the Headon Beds. In the SE, unknown S of Ports Down.

H. montanum L. Pale St John's-wort. **N** Very rare

On hedgebanks, wood-borders, and in coppice, on chalk soils where some sandy drift is admixed. It can reappear after a long absence when old wood-land sites are coppiced.

VC8: Whitsbury Wood 1318, *JDG* 1960, Hb.JDG (*Suppl.Fl.Wilts*, p.14). VC11: Old Winchester Hill, *CWMB* 1951 (*Watsonia* **2**: 338), conf. *ECW*. VC12: Marnel Dell 6354, *EH* 1959, later destroyed; Highnam Copse 7445, *CL* 1959, *CRH* 1990–95; Lee Wood 7847, *ADuSB* 1959; Gravelly Wood 7746, *FR* 1973, abundant, *AB* 1976, only a few in 1990; Burghclere old rail-way 4758, *VF* 1975, not seen 1981.

H. elodes L. Marsh St John's-wort. **N** Very locally common Map 100

Open, acid bogs, especially in pools. Very common in the New Forest but becoming rare elsewhere.

VC11: Browndown 5899, *HCC* 1984; Upper Lake, Rowland's Castle 7110, *HCC* 1985. VC12: Foxlease, Hawley 8256, *ARGM* 1978, *CRH* 1991; Wyndhams Pool, Yateley 8259, *CRH* 1985; Woolmer Pond 7831, greatly increased after restoration of the open shore of much of the pond, *FR* 1994.

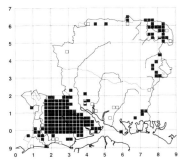

Map 100 Hypericum elodes

TILIACEAE

Tilia platyphyllos SCOP. Large-leaved Lime. **N** Very rare

First record, R. P. Bowman 1991, three old pollards in mature beech-wood on N-facing chalk scarp NW of hairpin bend on the Ditcham road, The Miscombe, Buriton 7619, VC11,

Hb.RPB, conf. *CDP*. (In 1990, *RCS* reported one large mature tree on the county-boundary bank *c*.20m to the SSE, and also eight huge coppice stools, but these have been identified by *CDP* as the hybrid, although from their position they could be natural hybrids – see below).

T. platyphyllos seems to reach the western limit of its native distribution on the South Downs at The Miscombe, just inside Hampshire. It is now known at some 15 sites in ancient coppice-woodland along the scarp of the South Downs in West Sussex, never in the secondary (often quite mature) woodland that occupies much of the former sheepwalks of the escarp-ment. From the huge size of many of the formerly-coppiced stools and the associated ground-flora, it seems almost certain that these South Downs populations are native relics. All 15 are of the native form of *T. platyphyllos* (though some hybrids are also present). It may well be that *T. platyphyllos–Ulmus glabra–Acer campestre* forest was the pre-Neolithic climax vegetation on the South Downs escarpment.

T. x vulgaris HAYNE (*T. platyphyllos* x *T. cordata*) Lime. **D,N?** Frequent

Commonly planted.

VC11: Possibly native at The Miscombe, Buriton 7619, *RCS* 1990, det. *CDP*, close to the *T. platyphyllos* trees and in Rakefield Hanger 7121, *DBa & FR* 1991. Lime wood is a well-known favourite of carvers for its easy working and was exclusively used by the great craftsman, Grinling Gibbons. In detailing its various uses, John Evelyn took conspicuous pride in having been the first to recommend Gibbons to King Charles II (*Silva*, p.205).

T. cordata MILL. Small-leaved Lime. **N,H** Very local and rare Map 101

In ancient woodland, on basic or on acid soil; now mostly reduced to groups of trees here and there. Its one-time presence in the New Forest is betrayed by place-names such as Lynd-hurst and Linford. The systematic surveys of the HCC Planning Depart-ment and the HWT have recently discovered many new sites in the Hamble and Meon valleys, near Lymington, NW of Southampton and on the Malmstone hangers, where, in coppice, it is locally abundant. Where it occurs as a native, it seems to be good evidence of primary woodland that has never been totally cleared and

replanted. It is also planted in parks but less often than *T. x vulgaris* despite forming a finer tree with a cleaner bole free of bosses. In pre-Neolithic times it appears from palynological evidence to have been abundant in the forests of England. The map excludes planted records, as far as is known.

VC8: Boulsbury Wood 0714 (neutral soil), *FR* 1976. VC11: Hedgemoor Copse 2631, *c*.50 old and young trees (chalk), *FR* 1980; Webb's Copse, Linwood 1909 (acid), *HCC* 1985; Ampfield Wood 4124, *HCC* 1986; Upper Hamble Country Park 4910, *HCC* 1984; Hookgate Coppice, Titchfield 5205, *FR* 1990; Little Holywell, Huntage and Great Lion Copses, Swanmore 5914 (acid), *APNH* 1979; Ramsdean Down 7121 (chalk), *CRC* 1986; Nursted Copse 7521 (Malmstone), *MO* 1987. VC12: Bordean Hill 7023 (chalk), *FR* 1973; Little Hanger, Bradshott 7631 (Malm-stone), *HCC* 1985 (*Watsonia* **17**: 467); Wyck Hill Hanger 7434 (Malmstone), *HCC* 1986, on cliff in plenty, *FR* 1988. VC22: Benyon's Inclosure 6263, *WGH* 1992.

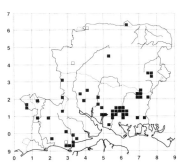

Map 101 Tilia cordata

MALVACEAE

Malva moschata L. Musk Mallow. **N** Common

First record, J. Goodyer 1618, 'At Mapledurham' *c*.7321, VC11 (*Early Brit.Bots*, p.111).

In dry pastures and scrub, on road-sides and hedgebanks, especially on sand, chalk and gravel. Less common on the coast.

M. sylvestris L. Common Mallow. **N,C** Common

On hedgebanks, roadsides, field-borders and waste ground, especially on dry, rather basic soil; not on chalk grassland.

M. parviflora L.   Least Mallow.   **C**
Very rare

First record, Miss E. S. Todd 1921, Christchurch, VC11 (*Rep.B.E.C.* for 1921, p.376).

A former casual of shoddy-fields and near mills; rarely established.

VC11: New Milton *c.*2294, roadside, *GY* 1968, det. *JEL*; Vincent Street, Shirley 4013, *WFB* 1966.

M. pusilla SM.   Small Mallow.   **C**
Very rare

First record, D. H. Scott 1923, Church Oakley [Oakley 5650], VC12, farmyard (*Proc.IoW N.H.S.* **1**: 239).

Casual only.

VC11: Lower Toothill 3718, foot of farmyard-wall, *RPB* 1954; Portsmouth *c.*6400, *AWW c.*1951. **VC12:** Basingstoke Canal near Eelmoor Bridge 8452, *GARW* 1932 (*Watts MSS*).

M. neglecta WALLR.   Dwarf Mallow.
N,C   Locally frequent   Map 102

First record, Gilbert White 1766, Selborne, VC12 (*White's Jnls* **1**: 205).

On dry banks, roadsides and waste ground. Widespread and frequent, especially on sandy, disturbed, non-acid soil.

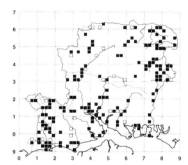

Map 102 Malva neglecta

Lavatera arborea L.   Tree-mallow.
H   Very local

Joint first British record, J. Parkinson 1640, 'Neere Hurst Castle', VC11 (*Theatrum Bot.*, p.306).

Of garden origin, but naturalized along the coast (native in W England).

VC11: Hengistbury Head 1690, on cliff, *MHug & JHug* 1969; West Lane, Hayling 7102, *JRW* 1975. Also 0890, 1090, 1290, 1490, 1890, 2694, 3292, 4610, 5604, 5804, 6004, 6098, 6404, 6498, 7098, 7298, 7498.

Althaea officinalis L.   Marsh-mallow.   **N**   Very local

Along the drift-line, and in upper tidal marshes; rarely in brackish pastures. Still plentiful in the Hamble and lower Beaulieu estuaries, persisting at Stanpit Marsh and Titchfield Haven, but no longer at the Mudeford, Hayling and Emsworth sites.

VC11: Curbridge 5211, *RPB* 1968; Cadland beach 4699, *MR* 1976. Also 1690, 1692, 4098, 4000, 4298, 4808, 4810, 5008, 5010, 5202.

A. hirsuta L.   Rough Marsh-mallow.
N?   Very rare (Sched. 8)

First record, Mrs C. I. Sandwith 1916, field near Itchen Stoke, VC12 (*Rep. B.E.C.* for 1916, p.477).

Doubtfully native. According to *EJC* it was a rare cornfield weed. Accepted as native in Kent and Somerset, and also in France, where it persists on bare, crumbling chalky ground (F.R.). In recent years the seed has been included in wildflower packets.

VC8: A36 Plaitford 2819, three plants in N roadside verge, *MC-B* 1990, conf. *RPB*. **VC11:** Hedgemoor Copse 2631, disturbed ground by old chalk-pit in arable field, two or three plants, *VW* 1987 (pit later filled in). Some records, e.g. 'waste places by mill, Swaythling', *JFR* 1918 (*Suppl. Fl.Hants*, p.24), are obviously casual, but one site may have been native: **VC12:** New edge of cornfield, where ploughed into old chalk-pit, Hannington Down 5554, six or seven plants, *ARF & EAB* 1966 (field since enlarged still further).

The 1991 record for North Harbour, Cosham, VC11, (*Watsonia* **19**: 144) cannot be accepted, as it is now known that wildflower seed had been sown there.

SARRACENIACEAE

[**Sarracenia flava** L.   Trumpets.   **H**

An alien pitcher plant, apparently planted in a valley bog in the New Forest near Burley 1903. Reported by *DJH* 1983; subsequent research into its identity, origin and occurrence amongst native bog-species in 1984–85 is described by *REDa & AJCr* (*Watsonia* **16**: 173), two plants, *GHF* 1992. Two plants of *S. purpurea* L., Pitcherplant, at Holmsley Bog 2201, *MNo & AEB* 1987, were also obviously introduced.]

DROSERACEAE

Drosera rotundifolia L.   Round-leaved Sundew.   **N**   Locally common
Map 103

First record, R. Turner 1664, 'in moist boggy woods, as in lower Danemoor in Holshot [Danmoor, Holdshott 7360, VC12] and in a boggy piece of ground...adjoining to the same wood called the Grove which will scarce bear anything else but this plant' (*Turn. Bot.*, p.274).

Still widespread on wet heaths and in valley bogs, frequently on sphagnum, on the Folkestone Sands and on the NE Tertiaries; very common in the New Forest, very rare in the Forest of Bere.

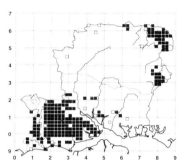

Map 103 Drosera rotundifolia

D. x obovata MERT. & KOCH (*D. rotundifolia* x *D. anglica*)   **N**   Very rare

VC11: Holmsley Bog *c.*2201, *PMH* 1931, Hb.BM; Vales Moor 1903, *RPB* 1961.

D. x beleziana E. G. CAMUS (*D. rotundifolia* x *D. intermedia*)   **N**

VC11: New Forest, *DAW* (*Hybr.Fl.Brit.Is.*, p. 244).

D. anglica HUDS. (*D. longifolia* L. *pro parte*)   Great Sundew.   **N**   Rare
Map 104

In nutrient-enriched flushed valley bogs, with surface-water and some water-movement, on deep peat, over the Barton and Headon Beds, with one isolated site in the Avon Valley over the Bracklesham Beds.

VC11: Town Common 1496, *LW* 1981, this site is close to, or perhaps identical with, 'Ramsdown near Heron Court, Christchurch, J. Curtis' (*Fl. Hants*, p.54). Otherwise, only in the southern New Forest: the upper Avon Water watershed 2199, 2100, 2104, 2201, 2400, 2499; Vales Moor 1903 and Hincheslea Bog 2700, 2800. Long extinct in the Forest of Bere. The VC12 record for Ewshot in *Suppl. Fl.Hants* (p.46) is an error for *D. intermedia*.

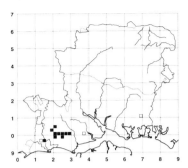

Map 104 Drosera anglica

D. intermedia HAYNE Oblong-leaved Sundew. **N** Locally common Map 105

First record, Gilbert White 1766, '*Ros solis....folio oblongo*', Selborne, VC12 (*White's Jnls* 1: 213).

Wet heaths and valley bogs, often on bare, wet peat or in pools. Common in the New Forest, more local on the NE Tertiaries, and rather local on the Folkestone Sands.

VC11: Netley Hill 4811; Shedfield Common 5613, *FR* 1986. **VC12**: Heath N of Blackbushe Farm 8057, *CRH* 1987; still locally frequent in wet rides and wet heaths in Woolmer Forest, e.g. Fern Hill to Horsebush Hill 8033, *PLeB* 1985, *FR* 1991.

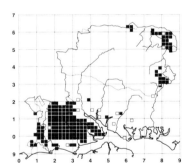

Map 105 Drosera intermedia

CISTACEAE

Helianthemum nummularium (L.) MILL. (*H. chamaecistus* Mill.) Common Rock-rose. **N** Locally common Map 106

First record, Gilbert White 1766, Selborne, VC12 (*White's Jnls* 1: 201).

In chalk grassland and open scrub, though much reduced by ploughing; in SW rarely, on basic soil.

VC11: New Milton 2596, grassy top of railway cutting, *RPB* 1961; Bad-

minston Common 4501, on concrete rubble in grassland, *NAS c.*1986, 1990.

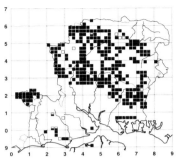

Map 106 Helianthemum nummularium

VIOLACEAE

Viola odorata L. Sweet Violet. **N,H** Locally very common

On chalk and Malmstone, occasionally on marl and valley gravels; especially common in shady places, e.g. hedge-banks and scrub. Sometimes a garden escape. The violet and the white forms are equally common.

V. x scabra F. BRAUN (*V. x permixta* Jord.; *V. odorata* x *V. hirta*) **N** Rare

There is one old record for VC11 and six for VC12 (*Fl.Hants*, p.49, and *Suppl.Fl.Hants*, p.17), and 20 more recent ones for VC12, e.g. roadside verge outside Blackmoor Park 7832, *AB* 1980, 1991; Monkwood 6731, *GHF* 1982.

V. hirta L. Hairy Violet. **N** Locally common

First record, R. S. Hill 1835, near Worting, VC12 (*Fl.Hants*, p.49).

In chalk grassland and open scrub. Rare off the chalk; near the SW coast it is mainly on Headon marls.

V. riviniana RCHB. Common Dog-violet. **N** Very common

Abundant in all broad-leaved woods, hedgerows, and on heathland except the most acid.

V. riviniana x V. lactea N Rare Occurs on heathland where both parents are found, but sometimes it has replaced *V. lactea*.

VC11: Pennington Common 3095, *RPB* 1986; Wickham Common 5810, *PMH* 1935, Hb.BM. **VC12**: Fleet Pond 8155, *CP* 1880, Hb.OXF, det. *ESG*; Eelmoor Marsh 8353, several,

ARGM 1981; Farnborough Airfield 8553, two widely separated patches, *CRH* 1994.

V. x bavarica SCHRANK (*V. x intermedia* Rchb., non Krock.; *V. riviniana* x *V. reichenbachiana*) **N** Very rare or overlooked

VC12: Monkwood 6730, *AB* 1969; Inadown Farm 7133, roadside, *AB* 1970; Dorton, Selborne 7434, *GHF* 1982.

V. reichenbachiana JORD. ex BOREAU Early Dog-violet. **N** Locally very common

Common in calcareous woodland, especially in beech-woods on chalk and by lanes on Malmstone and Bargate Beds; locally in woods on neutral soils; rare on the Headon Beds in the New Forest.

V. canina L. ssp. **canina** Heath Dog-violet. **N** Local Map 107

Rare, except in the New Forest where it is locally frequent in short turf on heathland. Scattered elsewhere, in acid grassland and on chalk superficials. Often on grassy ant-hills.

VC11: Sandy Point, Hayling Island 7498, *FR, AB & EAP* 1980; Common Marsh, Stockbridge 3534, *RPB* 1984. **VC12**: West Down, Chilbolton 3838, *AB* 1972; Yateley Common 8158, *CRH & ARGM* 1985; Silchester Common 6262, *PB* 1980; Fleet Cemetery 8053, *CRH* 1990.

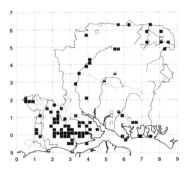

Map 107 Viola canina ssp. canina

[**V. canina x V. odorata x V. hirta**

Recorded (as *V. canina* x *V. sepincola* Jord.) for Odiham, VC12, *CP* 1917 (*Rep. B.E.C.* for 1917, p.98), but D. H. Valentine in *Hybr.Fl.Brit.Is.* (p.155) says 'the existence of such a hybrid is very unlikely'.]

V. carina x V. lactea N Very rare or overlooked

VC11: Dead Man's Hill 2116, *AAB* 1980; Middle Common Road, Upper Pennington 3095, *MEY c.*1980; Hatchet Pond 3601, *WAP* 1930 (*Proc.Hants Fld Club* **10**: 296); Wickham Common 5810, *PMH* 1935; Gravelly Marsh 4196, *AB* 1976, det. *FR*; Sandy Point, Hayling Island 7498, *FR*, *AB & EAP* 1980.

V. lactea SM. Pale Dog-violet. N Very local Map 108

Dry grassy heathland, often amongst gorse. Very rare except in the New Forest where widespread and locally frequent. It hybridizes freely with *V. riviniana*, and occasionally with *V. canina*.

VC11: Barton Common 2593, *RPB* 1988; King's Garden 2109, *RMV* 1986; near Pilley Bailey 3398, *RPB* 1980; Thorney Hill 2000, *RPB* 1976; Copythorne Common, 3115, *FR* 1994; Sandy Point, Hayling Island 7498, *FR & EAP* 1980. **VC12**: Eelmoor Marsh 8453, *ARGM* 1975–91; Bartley Heath 7253, Hb.AB 1972, *CRH* 1986; Pyestock Common 8253, *TAS* 1984, re-invigorated by two fires, *CRH* 1990.

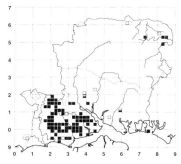

Map 108 *Viola lactea*

[**V. persicifolia** SCHREB. (*V. stagnina* Kit.) Fen Violet.

Reportedly found in a small clay hollow N of Holmsley Station, VC11, by B. King in 1882 and again 1885; thought by *EFL* to be *V. canina* and treated by Townsend as an excluded species in *Fl.Hants* (p.52).]

V. palustris L. ssp. **palustris** Marsh Violet. N Local Map 109

Frequent in the New Forest, very local elsewhere, amongst sphagnum, in alder and willow carrs; less frequent in open mildly acid bogs.

VC11: Shedfield 5512, Hb.AWW 1956; Ober Water, Aldridgehill 2803, *RPB* 1987; Sherfield English 2921, *RBG* 1984. **VC12**: Sparse in Woolmer Forest, Highclere Park, Silchester Common and the NE; Newtown Common 4763, *NFC* 1977, 1981; Greatham Moor 7830, *JR* 1976.

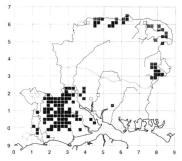

Map 109 *Viola palustris* ssp. *palustris*

V. tricolor L. ssp. **tricolor** Wild Pansy. N,C,H Rare

As a native, very rare but status often uncertain. Arable fields or bare ground on light, usually acid soils.

VC11: S of Crab Wood 4429, in ditch by Roman road, *SS* 1962, Hb.RPB, det. *CCT*; Horndean 7012, *PMH* 1932. **VC12**: Hazeley Heath *c.*7558, *EH & JHo* 1960; Farnborough Airfield 8554, *ARGM* 1976. Also 7046, 7448, 7644, 7650, 7852, 8048.

V. x contempta JORD. (*V. tricolor* x *V. arvensis*) C Very rare

VC11: Recorded in *Hybr.Fl.Brit.Is.*, p.162. **VC12**: Headley gravel-pit 5162, *WMK* 1975, Hb.AB, det. *RDM*; Wellington Country Park 7363, *AB* 1977, det. *FR*.

V. arvensis MURRAY Field Pansy. N,C Common

First record, Gilbert White 1765, 'in a wheat stubble in great abundance', Selborne, VC12 (*White's Jnls* **1**: 167).

An arable weed of chalk and sandy soils.

TAMARICACEAE

Tamarix gallica L. (*T. anglica* Webb) Tamarisk. H Local

Planted on the coast as a wind-break, and occasionally naturalized. VC11: 22 □.

FRANKENIACEAE

Frankenia laevis L. Sea-heath. N Very rare Map 110

First British records, J. Goodyer 1621, 'on the sea shoare in the west parte of the Iland of Haylinge...and in other places by sea likewise' (*Early Brit.Bots*, p.148) and 'on the diches bancks at Burseldon Ferrey' 4909, VC11 (*Ger.em.Johns.*, p.567).

In sandy upper salt-marshes; now an endangered species, confined to small populations at Black Point 7598, Hb.AWW 1960, *RPB* 1972–95, and Tourner Bury, Hayling Island 7399, edge of creek bordering wood, *AB* 1984 (*Watsonia* **16**: 185). A record for Lepe, *BWhi* 1949 (*Wild Fl.Mag.* **1950**, p.293) is most probably an error.

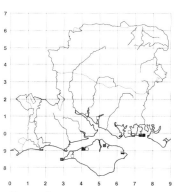

Map 110 *Frankenia laevis*

CUCURBITACEAE

Bryonia dioica JACQ. White Bryony. N Locally very common

Hedges, borders of woods and scrub. Abundant on the chalk, common elsewhere on lighter soils, but rare on heavy clay, as in the Forest of Bere, and almost absent from the New Forest.

SALICACEAE

Populus alba L. White Poplar H Local

Always planted, but spread by suckers. Commoner by the sea. This appears to have been over-recorded and some are suspected of being *P. x canescens*.

P. x canescens (AITON) SM. (*P. alba* x *P. tremula*) Grey Poplar. H Locally frequent

Often planted, especially in damp places, it can sucker into extensive clones which look wild. However, they are generally all male, the female being much rarer.

VC11: Three small trees among hollies on a heathy slope W of A35, Markway Hill 2403, *RPB* 1959–88; Sandy Point, Hayling Island 7498, scrub in marsh, *AB* 1980. **VC12**: Along *c*.0.5km of R. Rother, E of Kippences Farm 7728, many male trees, some large, *FR* 1980–94.

P. tremula L.   Aspen.   **N**   Locally common   Map 111

In woods, scrub on damp heathland and, rarely, in fen carr; readily colonizing open sites. Mainly on the heavier non-calcareous soils. Sparse on chalk, and there usually on superficial clays and loams. Aspen is often used for making match-sticks because of the non-spit quality of its burning (A. F. Mitchell, pers. comm.).

VC11: Michelmersh 3425, colonizing chalk-spoil in pit, *RPB* 1983; Drove Copse, Mottisfont 3126, grove of twelve large old trees, *RPB* 1984.

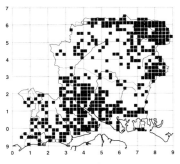

Map 111 Populus tremula

P. nigra L. ssp. **betulifolia** (PURSH) W. WETTST.   Black Poplar.   **N?,H** Very rare

First confirmed record, J. E. Little & L. Beeching Hall 1927, Christchurch Priory 1692, VC11, by millstream, Hb.K, conf. *EM-R* 1976.

Almost certainly native of banks of rivers and streams. Existing river-bank trees are probably relics of old colonies, propagated vegetatively. Others have been planted, some very likely from cuttings from wild riverside trees, others from trade stock of unknown origin. All reliable records are given; others are probably cultivars of *P. x canadensis*, with which it is much confused.

VC11: Christchurch Priory 1692, a pollard, *EM-R* 1976 (*Nat.Wld.* No. 10, p.27), not there in 1984; Waterford Lane, Lymington 3295, a male tree, planted; and Hazeley, Twyford 5025, several of both sexes planted on World War I camp-site by Hillier Nurseries, both comm. *EM-R* 1994; R. Test, Broadlands 3520, two old trees 33m and 34m high, *AFM* 1976; near Portsmouth Cathedral 6399, mature tree of *c*.150 years, *ERo* 1993, conf. *EM-R* 1994. **VC12**: King's Pond, Alton 7239, several young trees growing from the hollow stump of an immense felled tree, *AB* 1976; R. Loddon below, Pyotts Hill, Basing 6653, *AB* 1976; Warnborough Greens 7352, two large trees, *AJPB* 1987; Greywell Mill 7150, one tree, *AJPB* 1986; R. Lyde at Lyde Mill 6954, female, *JOp* 1984; Blackwater Meadows 8460, a pollard and one or two trees on field-boundary, *NAS & HCC* 1987, and in 8559, a male tree, *JES* 1994.

'Italica' (*P. nigra* var. *italica* Münchh.)   Lombardy Poplar.   **H**

This cultivar, derived from a fastigiate mutant, is much planted along roads.

P. x canadensis MOENCH   Hybrid Black Poplar.   **D,H**   Occasional

Includes the numerous crosses between *P. nigra* and the American *P. deltoides* Marshall. Extensively planted as a timber tree in wet sites, especially 'Serotina' (var. *serotina* (Hartig) Rehder), the subject of most erroneous records of *P. nigra* in Hants. It is used in the manufacture of match-boxes (A. F. Mitchell, pers.comm.)

P. candicans AITON (*P. gileadensis* Rouleau)   Balsam Poplar, Balm-of-Gilead.   **H**   Very rare

First record, J. F. Rayner 1915, Mill-brook Station 3912, VC11 (*Proc.Hants Fld Club* 10: 116, as *P. balsamifera* L.).

Not often planted now, but persists by moist roadsides or stream-banks.

VC11: 4098, 4000. **VC12**: Appleshaw and Alton, *GCD* 1929 (*Suppl.Fl.Hants*, p.98). 7032, 7256, 7430, 8036.

[**Salix pentandra** L.   Bay-leaved Willow.   **H**   Rare

There are two records for VC11 in *Suppl.Fl.Hants* (p.97) and three more recent ones; two for VC12 in *Fl.Hants* (p.379) and a further five recent

records. All were doubtless of planted origin.]

S. fragilis L.   Crack Willow.   **N?,D** Locally very common

Along rivers, streams and in wet places; a rapid colonist of flooded gravel-pits. Frequently planted. Rare along the New Forest streams. In Nursling gravel-pit 3515, 3516, VC11, large stands of trees about 65 years old are heavily festooned with ivy. Regarded by R. D. Meikle as completely linked by a series of intermediates to *S. alba*.

S. x rubens SCHRANK   (*S. fragilis* x *S. alba*)   **N?**

VC11: By R. Avon near Burton *c*.1594, between Christchurch and Winkton, *EFL* 1900 (*Fl.Bmth*, p.199).

S. alba L.   White Willow.   **N or H** Locally common

Common along the large rivers where it is extensively planted – both as an amenity tree and to stabilize the banks – thus obscuring the native distribution. Rare in E Hants.

S. triandra. L   Almond Willow. **N?,D**   Local   Map 112

A shrub of marshland along streams and river-banks. Fairly frequent along the river valleys. Occasionally spreads in wet gravel-pits. Planted as an osier and doubtfully native.

VC11: R. Avon, S of Ibsley Bridge 1409, *RPB & JO* 1984. **VC12**: R. Wey near Neatham, Alton 7340, *AB* 1970, det. *RDM*.

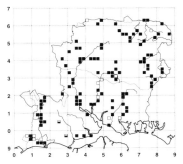

Map 112 Salix triandra

S. x mollissima HOFFM. ex ELWERT (*S. triandra* x *S. viminalis*)   Sharp-stipuled Willow.   **D**   Under-recorded

VC11: Breamore Mill 1617, *RPB* 1978, det. *RDM* (nv. *undulata* (Ehrh.) Wimmer). **VC12**: Ramsdell 5856, *EAB* 1968.

S. purpurea L.   Purple Willow. **N,D**   Locally frequent   Map 113

In wetlands of the major river valleys; on mudbanks of streams, and in meadow-drains; in marshy holts, often dominant. Fairly common, becoming more frequent in the lower reaches, and extending into the upper tidal zone. Rare in E Hants. Planted as an osier.
   VC11: Lower Test, Nursling 3614, *RPB* 1953. **VC12**: R. Wey at Holly-water 8033, *AB* 1982.

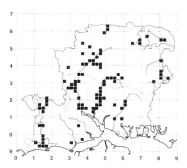

Map 113 Salix purpurea

S. x rubra HUDS. (*S. purpurea* x *S. viminalis*)   Rose Willow.   **N,D** Under-recorded

VC11: Nursling water-meadows 3614, one bush by the bridge, apparently spontaneous, *RPB* 1976, det. *RDM*.

S. x forbyana SM. (*S. purpurea* x *S. viminalis* x *S. cinerea*)   Fine Osier.   **D** Under-recorded

R. D. Meikle (*BSBI Hdbk 4*, p.80) considers this to be 'either cultivated or a relic of cultivation'.
   VC11: R. Test, Mottisfont Station 3326, Hb.RPB 1975; R. Test, Houghton 3431, *RPB* 1977; R. Test, Nursling 3615, *RPB* 1979. **VC12**: Bullington 4541, Hb.RPB 1975; Fleet Pond 8254, *VL* 1959, *CRH* 1992, Hb.AB. All det. *RDM*.

S. viminalis L.   Osier.   **N,D** Locally common

In nearly all the rivers and wetlands, often growing in the water. Planted as an osier and also wild.

S. x sericans TAUSCH ex A. KERN. (*S. x laurina* auct., non Sm.; *S. viminalis* x

S. caprea)   Broad-leaved Osier.   **D** Under-recorded

VC12: Longmoor, near Queens Road 8030, probably planted as osiers, *AB* 1966, det. *RDM*; Sunny Hill Road 8450, near Aldershot, *ARGM* 1991, det. *RDM*.

S. x smithiana WILLD. (*S. viminalis* x *S. cinerea*)   Silky-leaved Osier.   **N,D** Rare

Planted as osiers, but also wild.
   VC11: Titchfield Haven 5302, Hb.RPB 1987, det. *RDM*. Also 1214, 1692, 3414, 3416, 7022. **VC12**: Warren Corner *c*.8048, *AB* 1970, det. *RDM*. Also 3036, 4242, 6054, 6642, 6852, 7628, 7656, 7852, 8654, 8852.

S. caprea L. ssp. **caprea**   Goat Willow, Great Sallow.   **N**   Common

A common shrub in woodland rides, hedgerows and scrub, especially on basic soil.

S. x reichardtii A. KERN. (*S. caprea* x *S. cinerea*)   **N**   Under-recorded

This hybrid is likely to occur wherever the two parents are present together. It can resemble either parent or produce a series of intermediates.

S. cinerea L. ssp. **oleifolia** MACREIGHT (*S. atrocinerea* Brot.) Rusty Willow, Rusty Sallow.   **N** Frequent and locally abundant

As common as *S. caprea*, but tends to be in more acid situations, and more often in wet places. Often dominant in valley-bog carr in the New Forest.
   On its value for charcoal, Evelyn wrote that 'Sallow-coal is the soonest consumed, but of all others the most easy and accommodate for painters scriblets to design their work and first sketches on paper with, & as being fine, and apt to slit into pencils.' (*Silva*, p.254).

S. x multinervis DOELL (*S. cinerea* x *S. aurita*)   **N**   Rare or under-recorded

VC11: 8 □; VC12: 3 □.
   VC11: Widden Bottom, Sway 2899, Hb.RPB 1987, det. *RDM*; Baddesley Common 3921, Hb.RPB 1984, det. *RDM*. **VC12**: Greywell 7251, fen meadows, *FR* 1983; sphagnum-pool near Weavers Down 8029, *AB* 1976, det. *RDM* (*Watsonia* 20: 288).

S. x subsericea DOELL (*S. cinerea* x *S. repens*)   **N**   Very rare

First record, G. H. Forster 1993, Whitten Bottom 2000, VC11, one shrub about 1m high, Hb.RPB, det. *RDM* (*Watsonia* 20: 288).

S. aurita L.   Eared Willow, Eared Sallow.   **N**   Locally frequent   Map 114

A low shrub on wet heathland, especially in valley bogs fringing carr, and in boggy acid woods. Locally common in the New Forest, but very rare in N Hants. This species tends to merge into *S. x multinervis*.
   VC8: Lopshill Common 0913, (*Fl. Wilts*, p.514), conf. *RPB* 1983. **VC11**: Roydon Woods 3100, Hb.RPB 1976, det. *RDM*; Emer Bog 3921, group of low bushes, *RPB* 1992. **VC12**: Conford 8233, *AB* 1969, det. *RDM*; Hazeley Heath 7558, *FR & ECW* 1975; Bourley Bottom 8250, *FR & ARGM* 1978.

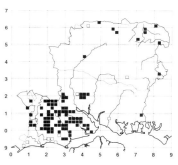

Map 114 Salix aurita

S. x ambigua EHRH. (*S. aurita* x *S. repens*)   **N**   Very rare

VC12: Bramshill, *GCD* (*Fl.Hants*, p.383).

S. repens L.   Creeping Willow.   **N** Locally common   Map 115

Very common in the New Forest, and fairly common on most other surviving

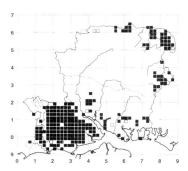

Map 115 Salix repens

heathland. Much rarer than formerly on the Folkestone Sands heaths.

VC8: Lopshill Common 0913, *RPB* 1989. **VC11**: Sinah Common golf-links 6999, Hb.AWW *c*.1950, *EAP* 1985. **VC12**: Conford Moor 8233, both sexes still plentiful, *FR* 1992; Greywell waterworks 7251, *FR* 1992.

BRASSICACEAE

<Sisymbrium irio L. London-rocket. **C** Extinct

VC11: Shoot gravel-pit, *MTH* 1919; Holmsley, waste ground near railway, *ER* 1924 (both *Proc.IoW N.H.S.* **1**: 233). **VC12**: Odiham, garden weed, *EFL* 1902, Hb.BM.>

S. loeselii L. False London-rocket. **C** Very rare or extinct

First record, Miss W. F. Buckle 1981, Regents Park Road, Shirley 3913, VC11, established on a wall, Hb.AB, det. *EJC* (*Rep.S'ton N.H.S.*, p.[12]).

S. altissimum L. Tall Rocket. **C** Very local Map 116

First record, N. D. Simpson 1924, Knapp Mill, Christchurch 1593, VC11, Hb.BM.

On derelict or sandy ground, and an invader from the ports.

VC11: Western Docks, Southampton 4111, *WFB* 1962; Gunner Point, Hayling Island 6999, *RPB* 1985. **VC12**: Puckridge 8552, *TD* 1980; Aldershot 8751, *TD* 1983; roadworks on M3, Winchester 4930, *AB* 1985.

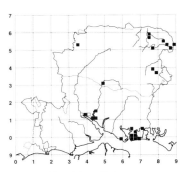

Map 116 Sisymbrium altissimum

S. orientale L. Eastern Rocket. **C** Very local

First record, F. Buckell 1888, Romsey, VC11, Hb.BM.

Similar distribution and habitat to that of *S. altissimum*, but extends to

SW Hants and is more frequent around Portsmouth.

VC11: Tipner 6303, *FR* 1981. Also 0890, 1090, 1290, 1292, 1490, 2692, 3026, 3812, 4008, 4012, 4210, 4414, 4606, 4624, 6000, 6004, 6400, 6402, 6404, 6498, 6600, 6602, 6698, 6898, 7098, 7002. **VC12**: Basingstoke 6452, *AWW* 1962. Also 3644, 6652, 7038, 7238, 7432, 7442, 7632, 7836, 8458, 8650, 8852.

S. officinale (L.) SCOP. Hedge Mustard. **N,C** Very common

In hedgerows, on roadsides, and on waste and arable ground.

Descurainia sophia (L.) WEBB ex PRANTL Flixweed. **C** Very rare

First record, J. F. Rayner 1922, South Stoneham House 4415, VC11, weed in garden (*Proc.IoW N.H.S.* **1**: 232, as *Sisymbrium sophia* L.).

Casual on waste ground, roadsides, rubbish-tips and sometimes in grassland, where it may be a fodder-casual, or arrive as an impurity in grass-seed.

VC11: Farley Mount 4028, *GDF* 1972; IBM North Harbour, Cosham 6404, *Gr* 1974 (*IBM List*, p.5, 1991); Eastern Road, Portsmouth 6703, *DPJS* 1991, Hb.RPB. Also 7004. **VC12**: Danebury 3236, *AO* 1975 (*Watsonia* **11**: 392); Fleet Dump 8253, *VL* 1960.

Alliaria petiolata (M. BIEB.) CAVARA & GRANDE Garlic Mustard. **N** Very common

First record, J. Goodyer 1618, 'At Droxford', VC11 (*Early Brit.Bots*, p.111).

In hedgerows, roadside verges and moist woodland.

Arabidopsis thaliana (L.) HEYNH. Thale Cress. **N,C** Frequent and locally common Map 117

In open, sandy and gravelly ground, especially near the coast and on heathland, in short turf on roadsides and banks, and on walls. 'Common but rather local' in *Fl.Hants* (p.32 as *Sisymbrium thalianum* J. Gay). Probably then overlooked; now truly abundant in places.

<Isatis tinctoria L. Woad. **D** Extinct

VC11: Disused brickfield near mouth of R. Meon 5302, *MTH* 1919. **VC12**: Chalk-pit N of Bedales, Steep *c*.7425, *FBr* 1925. Both in *Suppl.Fl.Hants*, (p.16).>

Bunias orientalis L. Warty-cabbage. **C** Very rare

First record, J. F. Rayner 1917, Millbrook *c*.3912, VC11 (*Suppl.Fl.Hants*, p.16), *AB* 1970.

Waste ground and roadsides, sometimes persistent.

VC11: Western Docks, Southampton *c*.4012, *WFB* 1966 (*Rep.S'ton N.H.S.*, p.10); roadside by housing estate N of Horndean 7014, Hb.AWW 1963, det. *EJC* 1974; Ratlake 4123, *EL* 1960. **VC12**: Woolmer Forest, *DrD* 1917, Hb.RDG (*Watsonia* **16**: 184); Ropley *c*.6430, Hb.AWW *c*.1963; Crondall 7848, roadside, *CL* 1955, 7848–7948, *ADuSB* 1960.

Erysimum cheiranthoides L. Treacle Mustard. **C** Locally frequent Map 118

On arable and disturbed ground. 'Very rare' in *Fl.Hants* (p.33); it has invaded from the London area and is increasingly common in E Hants, while still infrequent in the SW and quite absent in the NW.

VC11: Shelley Farm, Ower 3219, *RMV & RPB* 1986; Sutton Park, West Meon 6325, cabbage field, *DEA* 1983.

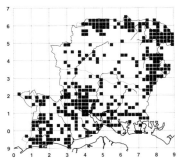

Map 117 Arabidopsis thaliana

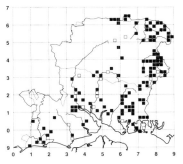

Map 118 Erysimum cheiranthoides

VC12: Osborne Farm, Sleaford 8038, *AB* 1984; King's Pond, Alton 7239, *JLSL* 1976.

E. cheiri (L.) CRANTZ (*Cheiranthus cheiri* L.) Wallflower. **H** Rare

Naturalized on old walls.
　VC11: Still at *Fl.Hants* sites: Christchurch 1692, Beaulieu 3802, Southampton 4111, Netley 4508, Winchester 4828, Bishop's Waltham 5517 and Portchester Castle 6204; also at Ashley 3830 and Petersfield 7423. **VC12**: Basing 6652 and Odiham 7350.

Hesperis matronalis L. Dame's-violet. **H** Locally frequent and occasional

First record, Gilbert White 1766, Selborne, VC12 (*White's Jnls* 1: 202). *Fl.Hants* (p.33) records this, in brackets, as 'scarcely naturalised'. Now well established near some rivers, notably the Wey and the Rother, which flow from the hills around Selborne, where it is also quite at home, spreading on hedgebanks and verges. VC8: 1 □; VC11: 25 □; VC12: 56 □.
　VC8: Martin Down 0518, near clearing through scrub, *RPB* 1988. **VC11**: A32 Warnford 6323, N roadside hedge, *RPB* 1974. **VC12**: Banks of R. Rother, Liss 7727, 7728, *FR* 1992; R. Slea, Kingsley 7938, Hb.AWW 1963, *AB* 1991.

Matthiola incana (L.) R. BR. Hoary Stock. **H** Very rare

First record, Mrs M. P. Yule 1960, Bournemouth cliffs, VC11.
　VC11: Barton on Sea 2392, on ruined building near cliff-top, *RPB* 1985. Also well established in 0890, 1090, 1290, 1490.

Barbarea vulgaris R. BR. Winter-cress. **N,C** Common

On open, loamy river-banks, and on open waste-ground.

B. intermedia BOREAU Medium-flowered Winter-cress. **C** Locally frequent Map 119

First record, E. F. Linton 1895, Milford on Sea, VC11, Hb.BM.
　Disturbed or bare ground, new roadside verges and ley grassland; rapidly increasing.
　VC11: Ringwood 1604, disused railway, *RPB* 1981. **VC12**: Hawkley parish hall 7429, *AB* 1978.

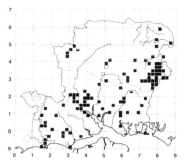

Map 119 Barbarea intermedia

B. verna (MILL.) ASCH. American Winter-cress. **D** Very local

Chiefly around Fareham, Southampton and Christchurch. Grown as a salad-crop during World War II. VC11: 36 □; VC12: 2 □.
　VC11: Hurst Castle 3190, Hb.RPB 1975; Hordle 2795, *GH* 1981, Hb.LANC; Sinah Common dunes 6998, *RPB* 1988. **VC12**: Waste ground by Fleet Station 8155, *GARW* 1932 (*Watts MSS*).

Rorippa nasturtium-aquaticum (L.) HAYEK (*Nasturtium officinale* R. Br.) Water-cress. **N** Locally common

On streamsides, marshes, swamps and pond-margins, especially on base-rich substrata.

R. x sterilis AIRY SHAW (*R. nasturtium-aquaticum* x *R. microphylla*) Hybrid Water-cress. **N,D** Occasional, but under-recorded

Widely cultivated. Serious loss of species-rich fen-meadows has been caused by conversion into water-cress beds, especially in the Meon and Itchen Valleys.

R. microphylla (BOENN.) HYL. ex A. LÖVE & D. LÖVE (*Nasturtium microphyllum* (Boenn.) Rchb.) Narrow-fruited Water-cress. **N** Local, but under-recorded Map 120

First record, Gilbert White 1766, Selborne, VC12 (*White's Jnls* 1: 197).
　In similar situations to *R. nasturtium-aquaticum*.
　VC11: Cadnam Green 2914, *RMV* 1986; Crockford Bridge 3598, *RPB* 1975, conf. *FR*; R. Meon 6821, *HJMB* 1957. **VC12**: Yateley 8260, small pond, *ARGM* 1987; Eversley 7762, ditches near river, *CRH* 1989; Itchel Mill Springs 7849, *AB* 1991, conf. *FR*.

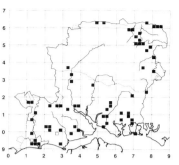

Map 120 Rorippa microphylla

R. palustris (L.) BESSER (*R. islandica* auct., non (Oeder ex Murray) Borbás) Marsh Yellow-cress. **N** Locally frequent

Open marshes and edges of open water in the swamp-zone. 'Not common' in *Fl.Hants* (p.38, as *Nasturtium palustre*), but now well dispersed.
　VC11: Upper Kingston 1603, dry pond-bed, *RPB* 1984; South Charford 1619, roadside pond, *RPB & JO* 1990; Lower Test, Nursling 3615, meadow-drain, *JWCP & RPB* 1990. **VC12**: Ashford Hill meadows 5662, *PB* 1982; Andover 3346, dried-up pond, *MFW* 1991.

var. **microcarpa** (BOENN.) BECK

VC12: Rare on R. Blackwater and Basingstoke Canal; Farnborough Green 8757, flooded gravel-pit, Hb.AB 1976, det. *RDM*.

R. x erythrocaulis BORBÁS (*R. palustris* x *R. amphibia*) Thames Yellow-cress. **N** Very rare

VC12: Yateley 8261, flooded gravel-pits, Hb.AB 1976, det. *BEJ* 1980.

R. sylvestris (L.) BESSER Creeping Yellow-cress. **N,C** Locally frequent Map 121 (overleaf)

Native on rather bare river-banks and shingle, but now also a weed of open ground on light soils. First recorded 1883, with only two later records, *Fl.Hants* (p.38, as *Nasturtium sylvestre* R. Br.) considered it a great rarity. Now common along some river valleys: Avon, Test, Itchen and Blackwater.
　VC11: Ibsley 1409, *RPB* 1984; Cadnam Green 2914, ditch on W edge, *RMV* 1986. **VC12**: Wallop Brook, Garlogs 3035, *GDF* 1981; Blackmoor 7733, agricultural weed, *AB* 1988–91; R. Anton 3544, *MFW* 1991.

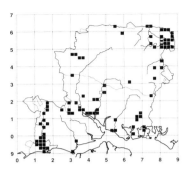

Map 121 Rorippa sylvestris

R. amphibia (L.) BESSER Great Yellow-cress. N Very local Map 122

In swamps, by rivers and in marshes, on silty soils. Given as 'very rare' in *Fl.Hants* (p.39, as *Nasturtium amphibium* R. Br.), it has increased in Townsend's locations for R. Itchen, R. Blackwater and the Basingstoke Canal, and occurs in a few other isolated sites.

VC11: Lymington River 3296 or 3396, *MPY c.*1960; Beaulieu River, Fulliford 3208, *RPB* 1951; Itchen Navigation, Compton Lock to Tumbling Bay, 4725, 4726, Hb.RPB 1979. **VC12**: Overton 5049 or 5149; *EAB* 1961; Foundry Brook *c.*6060, *BRB* 1963; Sherfield on Loddon *c.*6656, *BRB* 1965; widespread in Basingstoke Canal, Crookham eastwards, *CRH* 1990.

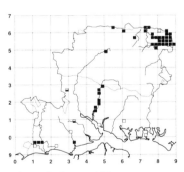

Map 122 Rorippa amphibia

R. austriaca (CRANTZ) BESSER Austrian Yellow-cress. C Very rare

First record, R. P. Bowman 1988, Fleetend, Warsash 5005, VC11, disused gravel-pit, Hb.RPB, det. *TCGR*. Also Chilling 5004, disused gravel-pit, Hb.RPB 1988 (*Watsonia* 17: 466).

Armoracia rusticana P. GAERTN., B. MEY. & SCHERB. Horse-radish. H Common

An indestructible garden relic, either near houses or on tips.

<Cardamine bulbifera (L.) CRANTZ Coralroot. N? Extinct

VC12: Small copse near Preston Candover, *HPF* 1879 (*Fl.Hants*, p.34, as *Dentaria bulbifera* L.). This is the only record that could have been native but its geographical isolation from the areas where it is accepted as such (i.e. in the Weald of Sussex, Surrey and Kent) makes this status unlikely.>

C. amara L. Large Bitter-cress. N Locally frequent Map 123

In alder carr and marshes along streams, especially where the water-supply is relatively base-rich or iron-rich. Probably rather overlooked in *Fl.Hants* (p.34) which states 'very rare'.

VC11: Lymington River 3102, *RPB* 1957; Titchfield Haven 5302, *RPB* 1962–92; R. Rother, Sheet Mill 7624 to Whitrow Moor 7623, *FR* 1992. **VC12**: Ashford Hill meadows 5662, *PB* 1983; Conford 8232, *AB* 1983; Marsh Lane, Eversley 7961, *VK* 1983.

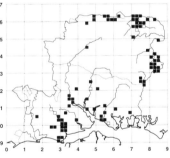

Map 123 Cardamine amara

C. pratensis L. Cuckooflower. N Common

Damp meadows, ditches, and in damp clearings in woods. The double form occurs occasionally, as in Ellingham churchyard 1408, VC11. Several chromosome races occur but have, as yet, been inadequately studied. The common plant of meadows and ditches is a heptaploid (2n = 56), but in woodland this is replaced by a tetraploid (2n = 30) with broader, flat leaflets, 'C. *dentata* Schult.'.

DEA has determined the latter from: **VC11**: Lovedean, near Portsmouth, Hb.AWW 1957; *DEA* has collected it himself from Matley Bridge 3307.

VC12: Alresford Pond, *JV* 1886, Hb.OXF; Liss, *JSG* 1902, Hb.K; Alice Holt, Hb.AWW 1957.

On the SW edge of the New Forest, apparent hybrids occur of the tetraploid with the delicate, white-flowered 'C. *fragilis* Boreau' – a putative hexaploid. This third race has been determined by *DEA* from: **VC11**: Milford on Sea, *JWW* 1935, Hb.K. **VC12**: Selborne Common, *BLB et al.* 1938, Hb.K; field near End Mill, Stratfield Saye, *AHGA* 1953, Hb.BM.

A fourth representative in Hants is the dwarf northern race of bogs, 'C. *nymani* Gand.': **VC11**: Hinton Admiral, *NDS* 1921, Hb.BM. In Holmsley Bog apparent hybrids occur between this last and the tetraploid.

C. impatiens L. Narrow-leaved Bittercress. N Very rare

First record, W. E. Warren 1937, Long Copse, Selborne 7435, VC12, near the stream, not refound by *AB & FR* 1971 as the wood was too dark, but it may reappear if the wood is cleared.

Woods on open calcareous ground and on Malmstone-derived soils with a good moisture-supply.

VC12: Catham Copse, Bentley 7842, *WEW* 1938 (*Rep.B.E.C.* for 1939–40, p.267), *PMH* 1939, Hb.BM, now encroached by conifers, but seen *AB* 1974, *JPAJ* 1977. The records for VC11 in *Suppl.Fl.Hants* (p.10): 'Chark, 1919; S. Hayling, 1920; N. Hayling, 1921–22' are inadmissible as no voucher specimens are known. They were omitted from *Atlas Brit.Fl.* (p.44).

C. flexuosa WITH. Wavy Bitter-cress. N Locally very common

In moist woodlands, by shady streams and ditches, and in bare places in marshland, where soil is moderately base-rich.

C. hirsuta L. Hairy Bitter-cress. N Common

A weed on damp paths, walls, gardens, etc., especially on coast and inland on sandy or gravelly ground.

Arabis glabra (L.) BERNH. (*Turritis glabra* L.) Tower Mustard. N Very rare

In hedgebanks or in open woodland, on dry sandy soils. It disappears when shaded out and can reappear if disturbance or scrub-cutting admits light.

VC12: One road-bank on the B3004

from East Worldham to Sleaford has provided five sites, from W. A. Bromfield's first record in 1850, at 8038, to the present time, at 7737; moreover, plants reappeared temporarily at Bromfield's original site when the road was re-routed for a new bridge, *AB* 1985; Eversley, *CP c.*1894 (*Suppl.Fl. Hants*, p.10), reappeared abundantly on hedgebank near Eversley church 7761, *JO* 1950 (*Watsonia* 2: 192), and in the widened verge of A327, 7861, *EH* 1968–84, where now destroyed; Green Lane, Rotherwick 7156, *EAB* 1968, not seen *c.*1974 *FR & AB*; Woolmer Forest 8133, still amongst bracken by an old track, *JH* 1977, *CWa* 1988, *FR* 1994; S of Frensham Great Pond 8439, *DPY* 1947, Hb.BM.

A. hirsuta (L.) Scop.   Hairy Rockcress.   **N**   Local   Map 124

In chalk grassland, on banks and in old chalk-pits, amongst short open vegetation; decreasing. Rarely, on walls or banks off the chalk.

VC11: R. Test, Nursling Mill 3515, *RPB* 1978–79; Butser Hill 7119, *FR* 1991; Ports Down 6206, 6306, frequent, *MB* 1975. VC12: E of Tichborne 5930, *ARGM* 1988; Isle of Wight Hill 2437, *GDF* 1988; East Tisted old railway 6931, *DPJS* 1987–89; Micheldever Spoil Heaps 5244, *HFG* 1991, conf. *AJB*; Noar Hill 7331, *AB* 1994.

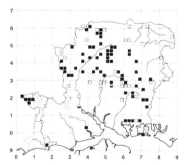

Map 124 Arabis hirsuta

Aubrieta deltoidea (L.) DC. Aubretia.   **H**   Very rare

First record, R. P. Bowman 1984, Manor Farm, Rockbourne 1118, VC11, on inaccessible roof-buttresses. Now established on a few old walls.
VC11: Also 4098.

Lunaria annua L.   Honesty.   **H** Occasional

First record, G. D. Field 1982, bridle-

road to Kimpton Down Farm 2646, VC12.

This common, annual garden-escape occasionally persists on roadside verges and woodland margins, etc. VC8: 1 ☐; VC11: 9 ☐; VC12: 6 ☐.

VC11: Rockbourne churchyard 1118, *RPB* 1984; Crow, Ringwood 1604, E side gravel-pit lake, *RPB* 1991. VC12: Common in the NW, especially down the Pillhill Brook and R. Anton, from Amport to the Clatfords, *MFW* 1991.

Berteroa incana (L.) DC.   Hoary Alison.   **C**   Very rare

First record, F. Buckell 1892, Lyndhurst Station railway bank 3310, VC11, Hb.BM.

A bird-seed alien and colonist.
VC11: Beaulieu Abbey 3802, *AJCB* 1982; Sinah Common golf-links 6999, *DWF* 1958, 6899, *EAP* 1980–88. VC12: Bordon Station 7836, abundant, *AB* 1960, still surviving in industrial estate, 1986; old Bordon railway, Blacknest Crossing 7941, *PEH* 1972; military railway, Longmoor 7931, *MNe* 1972, conf. *AB*.

Lobularia maritima (L.) Desv. Sweet Alison.   **H**   Very local

Banks and waste ground near the sea, and on rubbish-tips. Perhaps best naturalized on the Bournemouth cliffs. VC11: 12 ☐.

Draba muralis L.   Wall Whitlowgrass.   **C**   Very rare

First record, Miss W. G. Beddington 1937, shrubbery of Longstock Park 3638, VC12 (*Proc.Hants Fld Club* 15: 64), introduced from Hillier Nurseries, Winchester, VC11, *GCD* 1923 (*Proc. IoW N.H.S.* 1: 232), where it thrived for at least 40 years (*Biol.Fl.* No. 75, in *J.Ecol.* 48: 737).

Probably brought in on transported stone.
VC11: Station Road/Crookhorn Lane, Soberton 6117, on wall as a garden weed, *RBa* 1992, Hb.EJC, conf. *EJC*. VC12: Ashford Chace 7426, old wall, *JF* 1988, Hb.AB (*Watsonia* 17: 466).

Erophila majuscula Jord.   Hairy Whitlowgrass.   **N**   Very rare

First record, J. Cryer 1924, Ringwood, VC11, Hb.E, det. *TTE & SAF* 1982.

E. verna (L.) DC.   Common Whitlowgrass.   **N**   Frequent and locally common

On walls, verges, paths, and in dry places on bare soil, especially ant-hills. Although var. *verna* is probably the common plant everywhere, very few specimens have been expertly determined.

var. **praecox** (Steven) Diklic   Probably under-recorded

VC11: Hayling Island sandhills, *WCB* 1928, Hb.BM; Fort Cumberland, Portsmouth 6899, sandy turf, *PMH* 1933, Hb.BM; South Hayling 7198, car-park on beach, Hb.AWW 1959; Sinah Common dunes 6999, Hb.AWW 1960. VC12: Wall near Winchester, *ABJ* 1897, Hb.BM; Bransbury Common 4141, Hb.AWW 1962. All det. *TTE*.

E. glabrescens Jord.   Glabrous Whitlowgrass.   **N**   Rare, but under-recorded

First record, W. A. Pearce 1896, Ashley, VC11, Hb.BM.
VC11: Oliver's Battery near Winchester, *ABJ* 1897, Hb.BM; wall near St Cross, Winchester, *ABJ* 1897, Hb.BM; Bere Farm, Wickham 5909, sandy arable field, *PMH* 1933, Hb.BM; The Holt, Rowland's Castle 7211, Hb.AWW 1960; A31, Pauncefoot Hill, Romsey 3420, Hb.RPB 1985; near Black Hill, Wellow 2917, *RMV* 1989; near B3056, Matley Passage 3307, *RMV* 1989; B3054, SW of Beaulieu 3801, *RMV* 1989; A27 Locks Heath 5207, *RPB* 1991. Also 2400, 3600. VC12: Longmoor Inclosure 7829, *FR* 1992; N of Woolmer Road, E of Greatham 7831, *FR* 1992. All det. *TTE*.

Cochlearia anglica L.   English Scurvygrass.   **N**   Locally frequent Map 125

First record, J. Gerard 1597, Portsmouth, VC11 (*Ger.Herb.*, fig.2, p.324).

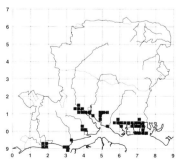

Map 125 Cochlearia anglica

In muddy, tidal salt-marshes, usually in the lower zones and on tidal river-banks.

VC11: Long Island, Langstone Harbour 7104, Hb.AWW 1956; Hurst Castle spit 3189, on both mud and shingle, *RPB* 1966.

[**C. officinalis** L. Common Scurvy-grass.

All mainland records in *Fl.Hants* (p.39) are considered to be erroneous, no specimens having been seen.]

C. danica L. Danish Scurvygrass. **N,C** Locally common Map 126

First record, H. C. Watson *c*.1830, stony beach at Portsmouth, VC11 (*New Bot.Guide* 1: 46).

Sparse turf on sea-walls, shingle or sandy beaches, and dunes near the sea. Inland, along roadside verges, especially in the bare, gritted parts of central reservations of the newer dual carriageways. It is thought that the continual passage of road vehicles is primarily responsible for rapid seed-dispersal along roads from the coast, whilst the modern practice of salting icy roads has provided a congenial habitat.

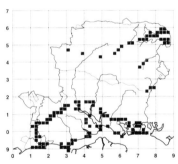

Map 126 Cochlearia danica

VC11: It is abundant at frequent intervals from Holdenhurst 1395 to Ashley 1304 on the A337, *RMW* 1986, RPB 1987–88; in every tetrad on the A31 between St Leonards 1002 and Copythorne 3014, *RPB* 1991 and frequent on the M27 between Hill-street 3416 and Cosham 6404, *RPB* 1991, *DPJS* 1992. **VC12**: On the A31 at Cuckoo's Corner 7441 and E to the roundabout at Farnham 8245 in Surrey at its junction with the A325, *GM* 1991, along the Hants stretch of which from 8551–8653 it is now found, *CRH* 1989, and at Aldershot 8652, *TD* 1985 (*Watsonia* 17: 184), *CRH* 1989; Miles

Hill 8353, *ARGM* 1985, 1993. It is along the M3 from 7453–7855, *AJPB* 1988; the A323 near Elvetham 7855, *CRH* 1991; the A30 between Murrell Green 7455 and Blackwater 8459, *CRH* 1992 and the A3 NE of Peters-field from 7624–7825, *EAP* 1992.

Capsella bursa-pastoris (L.) MEDIK. Shepherd's-purse. **C** Abundant

A weed of cultivation and other disturbed soils.

Teesdalia nudicaulis (L.) R. BR. Shepherd's Cress. **N** Very local Map 127

On sand-dunes or shingle beaches by the sea; in open sandy ground and on bare banks inland.

VC11: Avon Causeway 1397, *JO & PS* 1988; Rockford Common 1608, *MPY* & *ESH c*.1970, *RPB* 1976–92; Keyhaven 3192, *LWF* 1971; by Sinah Common car park 6999, *EAP* 1979. **VC12**: Many places in Woolmer Forest, but vulnerable to encroaching scrub, *AB* 1984; opposite Longmoor Camp 7931, *FR* 1994; Fleet Pond 8255, heath beside railway, *CRH* 1983; Church Crookham 8051, churchyard, *ARGM* 1985; Farnborough cemetery 8655, abundant, *CRH* 1991.

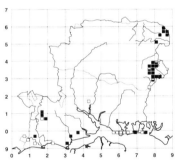

Map 127 Teesdalia nudicaulis

Thlaspi arvense L. Field Penny-cress. **C** Locally common

In cultivated ground, especially on light soils. 'Not common' (*Fl.Hants*, p.41). Now locally common, especially in the E. It seems slightly resistant to spraying. *Atlas Brit.Fl.* (p.39) shows it has a distribution pattern similar to that of *Diplotaxis muralis*, *Coronopus squamatus*, *Lepidium draba*, *Erysimum cheiranthoides*, *Sisymbrium orientale* and *S. altissimum*, i.e. mainly in the warmer, drier, more cultivated parts of S and E Britain.

<**T. perfoliatum** L. Perfoliate Penny-cress. **C** Extinct (Sched. 8)

VC12: Railway bank, Steventon 5448, where probably introduced with ballast, *ESH* 1965, det. *AM* (*Watsonia* 10: 421), *JEL* 1974, Hb.RNG. Not seen 1987.>

Iberis amara L. Wild Candytuft. **N or C** Very rare

Disturbed soil on chalk.

VC11: Stock's Bottom, Meonstoke *c*.6319, on land ploughed in 1939 after being uncultivated since 1914–18 war, also on rabbit-holes in adjoining down-land, *PMH* 1940 (*Proc.Hants Fld Club* **15**: 65)). **VC12**: Oakley 5650, *WAP* 1932 or 1933 (*Proc.Hants Fld Club* **12**: 293); old Alton–Basingstoke railway line 6940, *KAC* 1943; Isle of Wight Hill (Porton Ranges) 2437, bare chalk of rabbit-scrapings, *DG* 1988 (*Watsonia* **18**: 216); Beacon Hill, Old Burghclere 4557, *EFW* 1956.

Lepidium campestre (L.) R. BR. Field Pepperwort. **N** Local and occasional Map 128

First record, R. S. Hill 1840, 'Sher-borne, St John's', 6255, VC12 (*Fl.Hants*, p.43).

In bare hedgebanks, field-borders and freshly-cut woodlands, usually on sand or loam, sometimes on chalky arable. 'Common' in *Fl.Hants* but now decreased.

VC11: North Poulner 1507, 1606, gravel-pit lake, Hb.RPB 1990; White-ley 5209, ditch-bank, Hb.RPB 1987; Beckford Farm, Hipley 6211, abun-dant, Hb.AWW 1957; Buckholt 2532, roadside verge, *RMV* 1987. **VC12**: Weyhill *c*.3046, *GDF* 1984; Hen Wood, Herriard 6647, when recently cleared, *FR* 1976; High Cross *c*.7026, *AB* 1970; Riseley Ford 7463, *WEW* 1957.

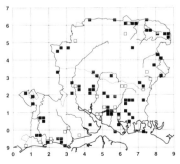

Map 128 Lepidium campestre

L. heterophyllum BENTH.   Smith's Pepperwort.   **N**   Locally frequent   Map 129

In similar places to *L. campestre*, but more often in short turf and open ground near the coast, where fairly common.

VC11: Keyhaven Marshes 3192, side of gravel-road, *RMV* 1986; Stone Point 4598, *RPB* 1975; by Sinah Common lagoon 6999, *EAP* 1980. **VC12**: Herriard Common 6544, *CL* 1955; railway bank near Fleet Station 8255, *NCC* railway survey 1978.

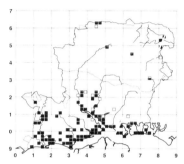

Map 129 Lepidium heterophyllum

L. ruderale L.   Narrow-leaved Pepperwort.   **N?,C**   Very locally frequent

Characteristic of earthen banks and bare waste land near the sea, where probably native. Now common about Portsmouth and, locally, at the head of Southampton Water. Rare in the NE and in a few other scattered sites inland. VC11: 33 □; VC12: 4 □.

VC11: Dibden Bay 4108, abundant, *RPB* 1953; Hythe Marina 4208, *AB* 1988; Town Quay, Southampton 4311, *PS* 1991. **VC12**: Spreading through W. Surrey into Aldershot area, *VL* 1959; Dockenfield 8240, *AMM* 1959.

<**L. latifolium** L.   Dittander.   **N?,D**   Extinct

Formerly on open waste-ground on the coast. Whether or not once native in Hants is unknown, but probably at one time planted commercially. In N Kent it occurs as a native along tidal rivers and near the coast, and in Sussex rarely as far W as Fishbourne, where there is a large population about 9 km from the Hants boundary.

VC11: Bournemouth *c*.1093, border of park, *MPY*, lost *c*.1962 due to land-scaping. Also gone from Bitterne and Lymington, where recorded in 1921 (*Suppl.Fl.Hants*, p.14). A casual near

Southampton University 4215, *WP* 1972.>

L. draba L. ssp. **draba** (*Cardaria draba* (L.) Desv.)   Hoary Cress.   **C** Locally common and increasing   Map 130

First record, F. I. Warner 1842, 'towards...Eastney barracks' 6698, VC11 (*Fl.Hants*, p.44).

In waste places. 'Rare but increasing' in *Fl.Hants*, now further increased, spreading along the coast and locally inland.

VC11: North Park, Avon Forest Park 1202, *FAW* 1984–85; Millbrook shore 3812, *CDD* 1958; ubiquitous at Portsmouth, *AB*; Petersfield 7423, car-park, *JF* 1986. **VC12** Bishops Sutton 6031, *ANHS* 1982; Andover, common, *MFW* 1991; A30 Hartfordbridge 7757, central reservation, *CRH* 1990.

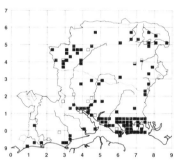

Map 130 Lepidium draba ssp. draba

Coronopus squamatus (FORSSK.) ASCH.   Swine-cress.   **N**   Frequent and locally common   Map 131

Banks and open ground, especially in pastures where puddled by cattle. Most common in SE.

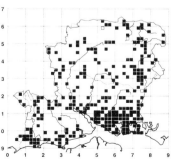

Map 131 Coronopus squamatus

C. didymus (L.) SM.   Lesser Swine-cress.   **C**   Locally common   Map 132

First record, J. Woods 1805, Lymington (*Phytologist* 3: 260).
Invasive on open waste- and disturbed ground, including roadsides, especially near the sea. *Fl. Hants* (p.44) states that it is 'local' but 'abundant about Andover'. It is now widespread and increasingly common in the S and locally around Andover and the NE conurbations, but very scattered elsewhere. Apparently originally from America (*Top.Bot.*, p.28).

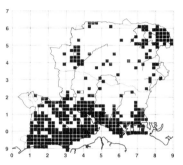

Map 132 Coronopus didymus

Diplotaxis tenuifolia (L.) DC. Perennial Wall-rocket.   **C,N?**   Local

A persistent colonist, possibly native, but likely to have arrived through the ports. On old walls, railways and waste ground. Commoner on walls and more coastally concentrated than *D. muralis*. One of the earliest sites was in South-ampton 'old walls, particularly near steamboat landing', VC11, *WAB* 1848 (*Fl.Hants*, p.31). Today it is common in Southampton but slightly less so in Portsmouth, where it arrived only in 1920.

VC11: Bishopstoke 4619, pavement, *DEA* 1985. **VC12**: Farnborough 8655, on disturbed roadside soil, *CRH* 1990.

D. muralis (L.) DC.   Annual Wall-rocket.   **C,D**   Local and occasional   Map 133

First record, H. Trimen 1862 or 1863, Bournemouth, VC11 (*Fl.Hants*, p.32). On walls, waste ground, shingle and bare chalk. 'Rare' in *Fl.Hants*, but now established especially on the coast, particularly around Portsmouth. Sometimes ploughed in as 'green manure'.

VC11: St Catherine's Hill, Winchester 4827, on paths, S slope, *RMV* 1988; Ports Down, plentiful, *JV* 1891–93 (*Fl.Hants*), refound on bare places on track along ridge of Ports Down, *PMH* 1935, Hb.BM, 6406, *RPB* 1986. **VC12**: Aldershot 8550, disturbed sandy soil, *TD & ARGM* 1990; with *Erucastrum gallicum*, tank-track above Shipton Bellinger 2346, *MFW* 1989.

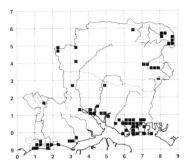

Map 133 *Diplotaxis muralis*

Brassica oleracea L. var. **oleracea**
Wild Cabbage.   **N or D**   Very rare

First record, F. Rose 1978, Paulsgrove 6306, VC11, many plants on upper face of chalk-pit, with every appearance of wildness.

The native habitat is chalk or lime-stone sea-cliffs, which is why it has hitherto been found on the Isle of Wight rather than Hants.

VC11: Rook Cliff, Milford on Sea 2791, several large plants, origin uncertain, *RPB* 1988; Hengistbury Head *c.*1790, one plant, *FAW* 1993, conf. *HJMB*.

B. napus L.   Rape.   **D**   Occasional, but under-recorded

Common on roadsides and along tracks, spreading from crops of the oil-bearing seed. Two subspecies may occur but no segregated records are known.

B. rapa L.   Wild Turnip.   **D**
Frequent, but under-recorded

Escapes from cultivation to disturbed verges and waste ground. Three subspecies have been distinguished, but they have not been studied in Hants.

B. nigra (L.) W. D. J. KOCH   Black Mustard.   **N,C**   Rare

Open waste-ground, slightly more frequent near the coast rather than along rivers in Hants.

VC11: Frogmore Lane, Southampton 3715, casual, Hb.RPB 1976, det.

FR; Hengistbury Head 1691, *JOM* 1970; Ports Creek, Hilsea 6504, over 300m along hedgebank, Hb.RPB 1990, det. *TCGR*. Also 2492, 2824, 6298, 6600. **VC12**: Headley Mill 8135, *AB* 1980 (*Watsonia* 13: 328); North Warnborough *c.*7250, *MMcC-W* 1978; Aldershot *c.*8650, *DNT* 1969; Bordon Station 7836, *AB* 1961.

Sinapis arvensis L.   Charlock.   **C**
Very common

A weed of arable and disturbed ground.

S. alba L.   White Mustard.   **D**
Locally frequent

Grown as a crop or for ploughing in as 'green manure', and often escaping.

Erucastrum gallicum (WILLD.) O. E. SCHULZ   Hairy Rocket.   **C**   Rare

First record, Miss S. G. Rooke 1923, Christchurch, VC11 (*Proc.IoW N.H.S.* 1: 234).

A recurring casual in waste places, mostly on bare chalk, and sometimes grown to bind and stabilize steep, chalk road-cuttings. In the NW, probably dispersed by army vehicles.

VC11: Fort Cumberland 6798, Hb.AWW 1950; Ports Creek, Hilsea 6604, bare chalk over pipeline, Hb.RPB 1990; A3 Gravel Hill 7118, transient on chalk cutting, *AB* 1976. Also 6898. **VC12**: Shipton Bellinger 2144, 2346, *RPB* 1970; Warren Hill 2647, verge of military road, *GDF* 1982; Perham Down ranges *c.*2448, on bare chalk of tank-tracks, *MFW* 1989. Also 2244, 3246, 6248, 8452.

Coincya monensis (L.) GREUTER & BURDET ssp. **recurvata** (ALL.) LEAD-LAY (*Rhynchosinapis cheiranthos* (Vill.) Dandy)   Wallflower Cabbage.   **C**
Very rare

VC11: Persists in the Fawley area, where first recorded by J. Groves 1879–95 (*Fl.Hants*, p.31), increasing in roadside hedges and bare gravelly ground 4402, 4403, 4502, *RPB* 1972–91; Tanner's Brook, Millbrook 3913, Hb.RPB 1975, det. *EJC*, still there *RPB & AEWy* 1992; Peartree Green, Itchen 4312, *PAB* 1989.

Hirschfeldia incana (L.) LAGR.-FOSS.   Hoary Mustard.   **C**   Local and occasional   Map 134

First record, A. W. Westrup 1958,

Southampton Docks 3912, VC11, Hb.AWW.

A casual on shingle, roadsides, and waste places, spreading from the ports and now well established; has also occurred as a wool-alien.

VC11: Calshot 4702, dredged shingle, Hb.RPB 1973, det. *EJC*, still there, *RPB* 1990; Wicor 6005, abundant, *EAP* 1981; Portsmouth 6798, 6700, *RPB* 1978, det. *EJC*. **VC12**: Alton 7239, abundant on building site, *AB* 1976.

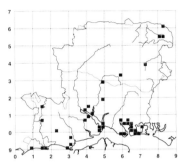

Map 134 *Hirschfeldia incana*

Cakile maritima SCOP.   Sea Rocket.
N   Very local

On and above the strand-line, on sand or shingle on dunes or beaches. Like its associated species, *Eryngium maritimum*, *Atriplex laciniata* and *Salsola kali*, it has been lost or severely reduced at many sites due to heavy trampling and erosion. Lately often as single transient plants, except at Southbourne, Hengistbury, Mudeford and Sandy Point, which hold small populations. More recently a partial recovery has been noted at some beaches.

VC11: Park Shore 4096, *c.*40 plants, *RPB* 1992; Titchfield Haven 5202, *EAP* 1986; Hayling Ferry Inn 6899, ten plants, *EAP* 1986. Also 0890, 1090, 1290, 1490, 1690, 1890, 1892, 2092, 3090, 3694, 4298, 4498, 4698, 4804, 5400, 5898, 7498.

Rapistrum rugosum (L.) J. P. BERGERET   Bastard Cabbage.   **C**   Rare

First record, Miss E. K. Gorringe 1951, Hayling Island, VC11, Hb.AB.

A casual, mostly on tips about Southampton. Hants specimens have not been determined at subspecies level.

VC11: Western Docks 4010, *WFB* 1966; St Denys 4313, *PS* 1991;

Pennington tip 3292, Hb.RPB 1975, det. *EJC*. Also 3614, 4012, 4812, 4818, 6604, 6610. **VC12**: Aldershot 8852, Hb.AB 1979, det. *DMcC* (*Watsonia* **13**: 328), 8550, *TD & ARGM* 1990, Hb.AB.

Crambe maritima L.   Sea-kale.
N   Local   Map 135

On unconsolidated shingle-beaches, often with *Glaucium flavum*. Earlier this century it had decreased in range and quantity, but very recently a large local increase and a westward dispersal to several new sites has been noted, where isolated plants have become established.

VC11: Southbourne 1590, *RPB* 1990; new dunes, Hengistbury Head 1790, three small plants, *LW* 1987; Hordle Cliff beach 2692, *RPB* 1989. Formerly in 'immense quantity' on the beach at Calshot Spit 4802 (*Fl.Hants*, p.28), later reduced, probably by the former sea-plane base, but 840 plants were counted over 600m in 1985, and it is now abundant at Stanswood Bay 4699, 4799. At Needs Ore Point 4297, a thriving population of mainly young plants, *RPB* 1984, indicates a recent spread, since none were seen during 1951–66.

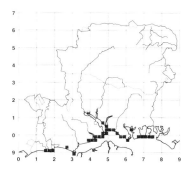

Map 135 Crambe maritima

Raphanus raphanistrum L. ssp. **raphanistrum**   Wild Radish.   **C**
Common

A weed of cultivation, especially on sand and gravel.

ssp. **maritimus** (SM.) THELL.. (*R. maritimus* Sm.)   Sea Radish.   **N,C**
Very local   Map 136

On and above the strand-line on sandy or shingle-beaches, cliff-tops and banks along the coast. The only record in *Fl.Hants* (p.29) was for Mudeford. It is now frequent between Bournemouth

and Hengistbury, about Portsmouth and in South Hayling.

VC11: Barton Cliff 2392, *RPB* 1989; Warren Shore 4196, *AB* 1976; Needs Ore Point 4297, one plant, *RPB* 1992; Hill Head 5401, *RPB* 1989; Fort Gilkicker 6097 and Browndown 5898, *RPB* 1985; Gunner Point, Hayling Island 6899, 6999, with both yellow and white flowers, *AB* 1980. Last recorded at Mudeford 1892, *JEL* 1934. One inland record on A3 Clanfield Down 7116, in widened verge, *AB* 1986.

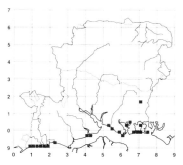

Map 136 Raphanus raphanistrum ssp. maritimus

RESEDACEAE

Reseda luteola L.   Weld.   **N,C**
Locally common

Mainly on chalk, especially bare ground. Scattered sites on gravel and near coast. Rare in SW.

R. alba L.   White Mignonette.   **C**
Very rare

First record, W. Stevens Bayton 1831, Stokes Bay near Gosport *c*.5898, VC11 (*Eng.Bot.Suppl.* **1**: 2628).

A casual on waste ground.

VC11: Waste ground next to the Royal Hotel, South Hayling 7198, for at least 14 years until built on, *AB* *c*.1966; High Street, Southampton 4111, on rubble, *WFB* 1965; West Cliff, Hythe 4108, bare gravelly bank of new footpath over drain, three plants, *APHo* 1990 (*Watsonia* **18**: 421), not since.

R. lutea L.   Wild Mignonette.   **N**
Locally very common

On chalk, in open grassland and on disturbed ground; occasional else-where, as along railways and on waste land. Rare in SW.

ERICACEAE

Rhododendron ponticum L.
Rhododendron.   **H,D**   Locally abundant

First records, J. F. Rayner 1924, North Stoneham *c*.4317 and Hinton Admiral *c*.2094, VC11 (*Proc.IoW N.H.S.* **1**: 257).

Commonly planted on acid soils, the rhododendron is thoroughly natural-ized. In many places it is invasive, especially in acid woodland, where it can dominate the shrub layer, and on ungrazed heathland, e.g. in the Avon Valley. Fortunately it remains rather rare in the New Forest.

R. luteum SWEET   Yellow Azalea.
H   Very rare

First record, R. P. Bowman 1954, E of Rhinefield Sandys Inclosure 2604, VC11, banks by road and in open pine-wood.

VC11: Bakers Copse, Roydon Woods 3101, large bush in ancient woodland near stream, *RPB* 1990; N of Hartford Heath, Beaulieu 3904, on wet heath, *RPB* 1976. Also 4016. **VC12**: 8254, 8434, 8458.

<**Kalmia angustifolia** L.   Sheep-laurel.   **H**   Extinct

First record, G. A. R. Watts 1943, three large dense clumps in woods near Monk's Pool, Fleet 7953 or 8053, VC12 (*Watts MSS*), *JEL* 1960, not seen *AB* 1965, now built on.>

Gaultheria shallon PURSH   Shallon, Salal.   **H,D**   Local

First record, J. F. Rayner 1919, Rhine-field *c*.2603, VC11, among gorse (*Proc.IoW N.H.S.* **1**: 257).

Introduced from western N Amer-ica; often planted on acid soil as food and cover for pheasants, spreading locally, and in some places overwhelm-ing the indigenous heathland veget-ation. Attempts to control its spread on Hengistbury Head 1790, VC11, have been only partly successful, as it regenerates rapidly after clearance. Extensive on Pinecrest Hill, Hawley 8458, VC12, *CRH* 1986. VC11: 20 □; VC12: 8 □.

G. shallon x G. mucronata   H
Very rare

VC11: Recorded in 1981 (*New Fl.*, p.350).

G. mucronata (L. fil.) HOOK. & ARN. (*Pernettya mucronata* (L. fil.) Gaudich. ex Spreng.) Prickly Heath. **H** Very rare

First record, Miss T. White 1962, Hengistbury Head 1790, VC11. Rarely established on heathland.

VC11: Water Slade Bottom 1707, two large bushes in bog, *RPB* 1990. Also 1802, 2000, 2408, 2410, 4216, 4218. **VC12**: Headley Down 8335, bird-sown in several places, *AB* 1988.

Arbutus unedo L. Strawberry-tree. **H** Very rare

First record, C. D. Drake 1975, cliffs of Highcliffe 2193, VC11, several trees, well established and fruiting, but not seen since extensive cliff-defence works.

Elsewhere this native of W Ireland and the Mediterranean Basin is obviously planted.

Calluna vulgaris (L.) HULL Heather. **N** Locally abundant Map 137

Dry and moist heaths, open heathy woods; abundant and usually dominant. Frequent on Clay-with-flints capping and in other acid spots on the chalk downs. Rarely on earthen seawalls.

VC11: Mengham Salterns, Hayling Island 7399, RPB 1976.

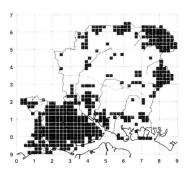

Map 137 Calluna vulgaris

Erica ciliaris L. Dorset Heath. **N?,H** Very rare

There are five or six instances of a single plant or patch of this species being found in the New Forest, generally near a path, with one near Burley village. The locations are 2002, 2301, 2302 and 3307 (where it covers a square metre). Specimens from the last two sites are in Hb.RPB. At the other site 2209, it is known to have been

planted in *c*.1965. An undated annotated map record on heath W of Slufters Inclosure 2209 or 2210, *JEL* may have been from the previous site, or from an additional one. It has not so far been refound. The habitats are similar to those in Dorset where it is still locally common and apparently spreading eastwards (*Watsonia* **20**: 89–95). It must be remembered that, before the growth of Bournemouth, the Dorset heaths were continuous (apart from river valleys) with the New Forest heathland. It is quite possible that some of the New Forest sites are native, but there must always be a suspicion that they were planted. *FR* is now convinced that it is a relatively recent native of the New Forest, having spread from Dorset; *RPB* is doubtful of this.

E. tetralix L. Cross-leaved Heath. **N** Locally abundant Map 138

In wet heaths and on drier hummocks in bogs. Abundant on the major heathlands; scattered and very local in relict sites and a few acid marshes.

VC11: Normandy Marsh 3394, *RPB* 1973; Sandy Point, Hayling Island 7498, *AB*, *EAP & FR* 1980. **VC12**: Foot of West Down, Chilbolton 3938, *SB* 1950.

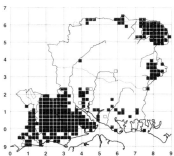

Map 138 Erica tetralix

E. cinerea L. Bell Heather. **N** Locally abundant Map 139

Dry heaths and open heathy woods, usually on sand or gravel, but occasionally on chalk superficials.

E. lusitanica RUDOLPHI Portuguese Heath. **H** Very rare

First record, R. P. Bowman 1988, Avon Forest Park 1201, VC11, one bush on sandy heathland, Hb.RPB, det. *DMcC*.

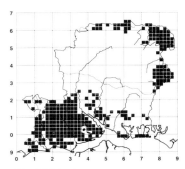

Map 139 Erica cinerea

Vaccinium oxycoccus L. Cranberry. **N** Very rare

First record, Gilbert White 1765, 'on the bogs of Bean's-pond in Wullmere forest', VC12 (*White's Jnls* 1: 162–163).

Only in sphagnum bogs of the Lower Greensand in Woolmer Forest, where several fine populations are known, some of them recent new records, or rediscoveries. At one or two sites, however, it has suffered from the collecting of sphagnum for the florists' trade, as the cranberry plants get pulled up with the sphagnum. At another the bog was drained for a golf-course. Extinct in VC11, with no record since *Fl.Hants* (p.247) for Droxford Forest.

VC12: Shortheath Bog 7736 has by far the best remaining population in S England. Cranmer Bottom 7933, *EJ* 1968, *AB*, *FR & PLeB* 1985; Cranmer Bog 7932, plentiful, *JRC & FR* 1988–93; along Slab stream 7735, *AB* 1976, *SP* 1989, but being destroyed here by MOD use; Weavers Down Bog 8131, *AB* 1983; Greatham Moor 7830, abundant, *PHC* 1982, *FR* 1994; Langley 8029, in small bog, *FF* 1976, *FR* 1987; Blackmoor golf-course and the Slab 7734, 7834, abundant in bog, *FR* 1989; near old Bordon station 7934, *SP* 1988.

V. macrocarpon AITON American Cranberry. **D,H** Very rare

First record, R. Melville 1927, near Lyndhurst, VC11, Hb.K (*Rep.B.E.C.* for 1936, p.266).

Sphagnum bogs and wet heaths, presumably bird-sown from nurseries.

VC11: Two Bridges Bottom 3499, *RPB* 1958, spread to a nearby site, 1984; Ashley Heath 1004, *JRW* 1979; S edge of Matley Wood 3307, *AEB* 1988. **VC12**: Kingsley Common 7938, *EJ* 1968 (*Watsonia* 10: 426), *AB* 1985, not seen recently.

V. myrtillus L.   Bilberry.   **N**
Locally abundant   Map 140

First record, Gilbert White 1766,
Selborne, VC12 (*White's Jnls* **1**: 213).

In open heathy woods of beech,
oak–birch or pine, and dry heaths, on
highly-acid soil. Locally abundant on
the elevated plateau-gravels of the New
Forest, the higher ground on Lower
Greensands in Woolmer Forest and SE
of Liss, also W of Aldershot; elsewhere
very local.

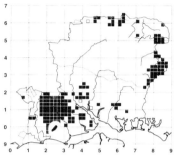

Map 140 Vaccinium myrtillus

V. corymbosum L.   Blueberry.
D,H   Very rare

First British record, R. P. Bowman
1980, Ashley Heath 1004, VC11, 40 to
50 bushes amongst pines and birches,
Hb.RPB, det. *EJC* (*BSBI News* **37**:
20–21).

Cultivars are grown in a nursery
8km away and, as the berries are
known to be eaten by thrushes, this
may be the source.

PYROLACEAE

Pyrola minor L.   Common Winter-
green.   **N**   Rare   Map 141

In damp woods of pine, birch or beech
with plenty of leaf-litter. Generally on
acid soil, but exceptionally on London
Clay at Warren Wood 8149, VC12,
BPD 1975, and formerly, apparently,
on or over chalk at: Basing Park (*Fl.
Hants*, p.249); Thedden, Alton, *JV*
1883, Hb.BM; and Gunners Plantation, Alton 7141, *KAC* 1949. All
other sites are on the Tertiaries, or on
the Lower Greensand, often near a
stream. Two stations in Woolmer
Forest have been lost, probably
through becoming too dry.

VC11: Formerly at Chandler's Ford
4321, 4322, in oakwood, *JG* 1928, lost
to building by 1956. Kimbridge Wood
3225, *HMS* 1936 (*Proc.Hants Fld.Club*

13: 266). **VC12:** Beacon Hill 8250, *VL*
1962 (*Proc.B.S.B.I.* **4**: 426), very few
CRH 1987; Hawley Common 8457,
8458, 793 plants counted, *CRH* 1987;
Bourley Hill 8350, *ARGM* 1980, 28
plants *CRH* 1992; Crookham 8252,
estimated 800 plants, *ARGM & CRH*
1986–91; Longmoor airstrip 8131, *AB*
1988; Woolmer Forest 7933, abundant
in small pine- and birch-copse, and
under sallows at 7832, *AB* 1981; damp
copse on the Slab 7835, *L-Lo* 1983;
The Wylds, Liss 7929, *JMe* 1976;
Headley 8335, *JBe* 1988. Plants transplanted in 1979 because of road works
from 8131 to 7830 at Longmoor are
flourishing in the new site.

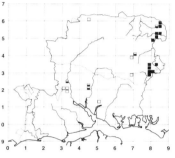

Map 141 Pyrola minor

MONOTROPACEAE

Monotropa hypopitys L. (incl. *M.
hypophegea* Wallr.)   Yellow Bird's-
nest.   **N**   Local   Map 142

First British record, J. Goodyer 1620,
'in a hedgerowe in a ground belonging
to Droxford farme, neare y^c foot path
that leadeth from Droxford to
Waltham' *c*.5818, VC11 (ms note on
back of fol.249 of Bannister's *Herbarium Siccum* (Herb. Sloane) in Botanical
Dept. of BM(NH). *Early Brit.Bots*,
p.122).

Saprophytic on leaf-mould, chiefly
under beeches on chalk, but in
Woolmer Forest under pine and birch.
Widespread but scattered and much
decreased.

VC11: Hocombe Road, Chandler's
Ford 4422, *MAG* 1977; Broughton
Down 2932, *RPB* 1987; Queen Elizabeth Country Park, *c*.7320, quite
common, *DBa* 1989; Ludgersham
Copse, Buriton 7319, abundant in pine
plantation, *DPJS & JMC* 1988. **VC12:**
Crawley Forest 4236, *AAB* 1972; Isle
of Wight Hill 2437, *GDF* 1988;
Woolmer Forest 7932, sporadic, *AB*
1980; Longmoor airstrip 8131, *AB*
1982–88; The Warren, Hawkley 7328,

FR 1986; Bramshott Common 8532,
on sand, *CD* 1992.

M. hypopitys and *M. hypophegea*,
previously regarded as distinct species,
are treated in *New Fl.* (p.359) as ssp.
hypopitys and ssp. *hypophegea* (Wallr.)
Holmboe.

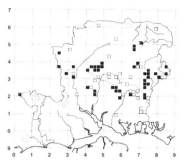

Map 142 Monotropa hypopitys

PRIMULACEAE

Primula vulgaris HUDS.   Primrose.
N   Common

In coppiced woodland, scrub, hedgebanks, sunken lanes and railway banks,
on all but the most acid soil. The dark
state of most remaining deciduous
woodland, and the neglect of hedges,
has led to a great reduction in primroses, though they reappear on coppicing. Widespread, but very scanty in the
grazed woods of the New Forest.

P. x polyantha MILL. (*P. x tommasini*
Gren. & Godron; *P. vulgaris* x *P. veris*)
False Oxlip.   **N,H**   Occasional

Copses and open scrub, widespread
and occasional, usually as isolated
plants. VC11: 10 ☐; VC12: 30 ☐.

P. veris L.   Cowslip.   **N**   Locally
common   Map 143

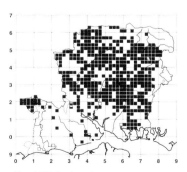

Map 143 Primula veris

In damper chalk grassland, old meadows on clay or alluvium, and open beechwood or scrub on chalk. Since 1950 it has declined seriously, as nearly all old meadows have been 'improved' or ploughed. It is also much less abundant on some chalk grasslands through lack of grazing. Rare in the SW.

Hottonia palustris L.   Water-violet.   **N**   Very rare   Map 144

First record, W. O. Newnham 1849, 'abundant in a pool called The Lake, in a green lane at Aldershot, close to the west side of a stream called the Blackwater', VC12 (W. A. Bromfield, *Phytologist* **3**: 697).

Shallow pond-margins, slow streams, canals and ditches, usually in shade. With the exception of one site in VC11, it is practically confined to the NE corner of VC12, where it was much reduced by dredging of the Fleet–Aldershot section of the Basingstoke Canal in 1978, and at Fleet Pond and ditches near it by recent deterioration in the water quality.

VC11: Setley Marl Pit 3099, *RPB* 1956–93. **VC12**: Fleet Pond 8155, and in woods 8154, *CWa & ARGM* 1980, both later lost, but transplants thriving (*ARGM* 1988) at several places around the pond, 8255, etc. until lost in 1990 drought. Transplants from the Canal by *ARGM* in 1978 still flourish in Rushmoor and Claycart Flashes 8552, *CRH* 1992; Eelmoor Flash 8452, large native colony, *CRH* 1992; Foxlease 8256, abundant in several widespread places in stream, *ARGM & JK* 1978, still in ditches, *CRH* 1991; fishing lake near R. Blackwater, Farnborough 8853, *AB* 1980, *CRH* 1991; pool in Ashford Hill meadows 5662, *PB* 1987.

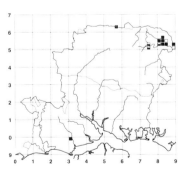
Map 144 Hottonia palustris

Lysimachia nemorum L.   Yellow Pimpernel.   **N**   Locally common

In dry to moist woods, especially where

well lit. Less common on very shallow chalky soils, and absent on the very acid ones.

L. nummularia L.   Creeping-Jenny.   **N,H**   Locally common   Map 145

First record, Gilbert White 1768, Fyfield, VC12 (*White's Jnls* **1**: 247).

Pond-margins, ditches in wet meadows, streamsides and marshy, open woods. Widespread and fairly common, but rather sparse in chalk wetlands, except by the upper R. Itchen. Sometimes also a garden escape; the map attempts to show the native range only.

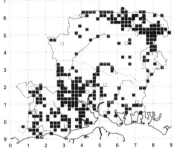
Map 145 Lysimachia nummularia

L. vulgaris L.   Yellow Loosestrife.   **N**   Locally common   Map 146

First record, Gilbert & Thomas White 1767, 'in the bogs of Bean's-pond' VC12 (*White's Jnls* **1**: 222).

Streamsides, marshes, fens, wet open woods, and in carr; common in the SW, the Test Valley, and the Thames Basin in the NE, less so along the R. Itchen and in Woolmer Forest; rare or absent elsewhere.

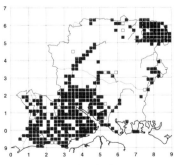
Map 146 Lysimachia vulgaris

L. punctata L.   Dotted Loosestrife.   **H**   Local

First record, G. A. R. Watts 1938, roadside, Hitches Lane, Fleet 7954, VC12 (*Watts MSS*).

An increasing garden escape, becoming established on waste ground, grassy scrub and damp, shady waysides, usually near gardens.

VC11: Upper Pennington Common 2995, *RPB* 1989; Aldermoor, Southampton 3915, *RMV* 1986. Also 1406, 2092, 2098, 2496, 3218, 3612, 3816, 4098, 4016, 4018, 4606, 4612, 4808, 5216, 5418, 5616, 5898, 5822, 6824. **VC12**: Near Four Marks 6534, *GHF* 1977; Norris Hill, Fleet 8353, *TD* 1987. Also 4060, 6436, 7428, 7456, 7656, 7854, 8052, 8054, 8056, 8060, 8254, 8256, 8852.

L. thyrsiflora L.   Tufted Loosestrife.   **H**   Very rare

First record, R. P. Bowman 1956, Burley Manor Pond 2103, VC11.

VC11: Ober Water, Rhinefield 2603, *RPB* 1984. This population is completely naturalized. The plants rarely produce flowers, but did so in 1984.

Trientalis borealis RAF.   Starflower.   **C**   Very rare

First British record, C. R. Lancaster 1964, Hillier Nurseries near Romsey, VC11, an increasing colony, originating from seed on roots of imported azaleas. Native of eastern N America.

Anagallis tenella (L.) L.   Bog Pimpernel.   **N**   Locally common   Map 147

Flushed bogs, fens, peaty ditch-sides, wet meadows and wet rides in heathy woods. Very common in the New Forest, local on other acid soils and in chalk wetlands. With cessation of grazing, it tends to decline and disappear, as in much of Woolmer Forest.

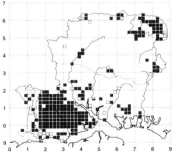
Map 147 Anagallis tenella

VC11: Common Marsh, Stockbridge 3534, *RPB* 1963; Bed Well, Lord's Wood 3816, *RMV* 1989. **VC12**: Chilbolton Common 3840, *RBG* 1979, *CRH* 1992; Conford 8233, on wet track, *AB* 1981, *FR* 1993; Ancells Farm 8255, *CRH* 1983; Bourley 8249, 8250, abundant on ditch-sides, *ARGM* 1985; water meadows near Ashford Hill 5662, *PB* 1982; Stockbridge North Fen 3535, *FR* 1986.

A. arvensis L. ssp. **arvensis**   Scarlet Pimpernel.   **N,C**   Very common

Native on sand-dunes, and on sandy or shingly beaches; colonist on arable soil, and on disturbed and waste ground.

forma **azurea** HYL.   Very rare

VC11: Very abundant in field, Finchdean 7212, *AB* 1975. Also 4226, 7098. **VC12**: 7658, 7832.

ssp. **foemina** (MILL.) SCHINZ & THELL.   Blue Pimpernel.   **C**   Very rare

A weed of cultivation, but may also be introduced in bird-seed.
   VC11: South Hayling 7199, site of Royal Hotel, Hb.AWW 1963; Shirley 3914, garden weed, *WFB* 1966 det. *DMcC*; Breamore *c*.1418, *MPY* 1970. **VC12**: Alice Holt Forest *c*.8042, *GGG* 1968.

A. minima (L.) E. H. L. KRAUSE   Chaffweed.   **N**   Very locally frequent   Map 148

First record, W. A. Bromfield 1848, Shortheath, VC12 (*Fl.Hants*, p.335, as *Centunculus minimus* L.).
   Bare wet clay, sandy mud, fine gravel or peat on heaths, bare places and trodden short turf along tracks, in ditches, around ponds, and in wood-rides. Locally frequent in the New

Forest, very rare, on acid soil, every-where else.
   VC8: Martin Wood 0616, *RPB* 1967. **VC11**: Pilley Pond 3398, *GHF* 1977, 1991; Parnholt Wood 3728, *RPB* 1968. **VC12**: Great Pen Wood 4562, *VF* 1968; SE end of Fleet Pond 8254, *GARW* 1938 (*Watts MSS*), not found since; Shortheath Pond 7736, known many years, not seen recently, *AB*; Heath Warren 7759 *RCS* 1986; Woolmer Forest 7932, with *Radiola linoides*, *CRH* 1991.

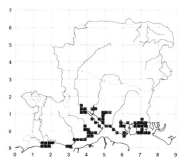

Map 149 Glaux maritima

Glaux maritima L.   Sea-milkwort.   **N**   Locally frequent   Map 149

First record, Miss C. R. May 1841, seashore, Tipner *c*.6303, VC11 (*May Ptgs Cat.*: 532).
   Coastal and estuarine salt-marshes, in compact turf, on bare mud or sand, and on the seashore just above high-water mark.

Samolus valerandi L.   Brookweed.   **N**   Very local   Map 150

First British record, J. Goodyer 1618, 'By a mill at Emsworth' *c*.7505, VC11 (*Early Brit.Bots*, p.111).
   Creeks and drains in estuarine and coastal brackish marshes; inland in the

New Forest around pools in old marl-pits, and on marshy stream-banks.
   VC11: The Furlongs, Redbridge 3613, *RPB* 1952, 1992; Crockford Bridge 3598, *RPB* 1950, 1992; Conigar Point, Warblington 7305, *MB* 1982; Yew Tree Heath 3607, *RPB* 1987; Lisle Court 3495, brackish marsh, *AEB* 1986. **VC12**: Longmoor Camp, Bordon 8031, shallow pond on disturbed heathland, *NAS* 1994.

HYDRANGEACEAE

Deutzia scabra THUNB.   'Plena'   **H**

VC12: Bramshott Common 8532, fully naturalized in the surrounding scrub, from an avenue presumably planted by the Canadian forces during World War II, *AB & CD* 1992.

GROSSULARIACEAE

Ribes rubrum L. (*R. sylvestre* (Lam.) Mert. & Koch)   Red Currant.   **N,D**   Frequent and locally common

In alder and willow carr, oak–ash-woods along streams, and often in dryer hazel coppice. Occasional in wet hedgerows as a woodland relic. Common and native but many bird-sown plants from gardens also occur. Occasionally white currants occur as in a copse near Alton 7037, VC12, *AB* 1983.

R. nigrum L.   Black Currant.   **N,D**   Locally frequent   Map 151

In alder and willow carr and other wet woodland, along streams. The map shows the probable native range; other records are of garden origin.
   VC11: Mill Stream, Ringwood 1504, wet willow-holt, *RPB* 1985; Bidden-field 5512, alder carr, *RPB* 1974.

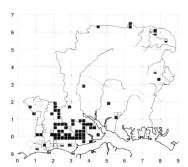

Map 148 Anagallis minima

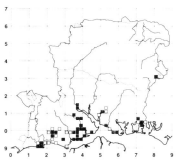

Map 150 Samolus valerandi

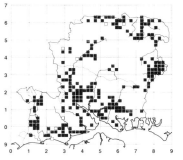

Map 151 Ribes nigrum

VC12: Newtown Gully 4763, *NFC* 1977; Goodworth Clatford *c*.3542, in quantity along river-bank, *GDF* 1983; Fishpond Copse, NE of Bentley 8045, *AB* 1985.

R. sanguineum PURSH Flowering Currant. **H** Occasional

First record, J. F. Rayner 1924, Christchurch, VC11, waste place (*Proc. IoW N.H.S.* **1**: 246).

Naturalized in scrub, waste ground and old pits, usually as single bird-sown bushes. VC11: 15 □; VC12: 4 □.

VC11: Sinah Common 6999, one large bush in sand-dunes, *AB* 1975; East End 3697, willow thicket in old marl-pit 3697, *RPB* 1954. **VC12**: Puckridge 8552, scrub beside canal-towpath; and hedgerow near Malta Barracks 8652, *ARGM c*.1985.

R. uva-crispa L. Gooseberry. **N,D** Frequent and locally common

In woods, hedges, by streams, and in shady road-cuttings. Most commonly naturalized, but probably native at least on the E chalk hangers and Malmstone, where it is frequent, and perhaps in moist alder-woods.

VC11: Nursted 7521, rocky wooded road-cutting, *RPB* 1974; Buriton 7319, Hb.AWW 1952. **VC12**: Noar Hill, S side 7431, *FR* 1980; Fishpond Copse, NE of Bentley 8045, *AB* 1985.

CRASSULACEAE

Crassula tillaea LEST.-GARL. Mossy Stonecrop. **N** Very local Map 152

Heathland, along paths and in open sandy or gravelly turf where moist in winter but drying out in early summer. Recorded all over the New Forest, the Avon Valley and on Shedfield Common in *Fl.Hants* (pp.163–164). Still locally frequent in the western part of this range including the coastal area, and very locally so in Woolmer Forest and on the coast of Hayling Island. Often spread on the wheels of vehicles. Found in W. Sussex in 1993 but very rare in SE England. The Hampshire sites resemble those of the E. Anglian heaths.

VC11: Bournemouth 0991 to Mudeford 1891, *RPB* 1988–90; Kingston North Common 1403, *JO* 1984; N of Heath Pond, Petersfield 7523, on path, *MS-W* 1975, *FR* 1994; Crow Hill Top 1803, *MEY* 1990; South Hayling 7098, behind beach, *RPB* 1989–94; Ashley

Trailway 1305, on disused railway, *RPB* 1991; Plumley Farm, Harbridge 1209, ruts by farmyard, *RPB* 1992; Sway 2799, heath over gas-pipeline, *RPB* 1991. **VC12**: Drive and farm-tracks on Blackmoor Estate 7733, 7832 (now gone from the last) *AB* 1926–91; E of Sunny Hill, Aldershot 8450, *ARGM* 1991; Woolmer Forest 7931, sandy ground along line of former railway, *FR* 1990–94 (*Watsonia* **18**: 426).

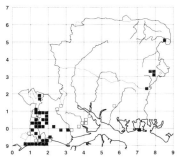

Map 152 Crassula tillaea

C. helmsii (KIRK) COCKAYNE New Zealand Pigmyweed. **H,C** Very locally abundant

First record, Miss M. McCallum-Webster 1962, Vine Cottage, Ewshot 8149, VC12, in newly cleaned-out pond, Hb.BM. Previously recorded 1956 at the Glen Eyre (artificial) pond, the University, Southampton, VC11, but planted.

On mud, in and around ponds. A native of Australasia, available from aquarists since 1927. A rampant colonist, soon smothering other aquatics. Distributed on footwear and by waterfowl and grazing ponies. Increasing rapidly. VC11: 23 □; VC12: 10 □.

VC11: Pond by Royal Oak, North Gorley 1611, *RPB* 1976; wet hollow near Hatchet Pond 3601, *FR & SRD* 1978. **VC12**: Shallow ponds in Woolmer Forest 7832, *CWa & ARGM* 1986; Basingstoke Canal, at Rushmoor Flash and Claycart Bridge 8552, *CRH* 1986; from Fleet 8253 to Aldershot 8851, *CRH* 1992.

Umbilicus rupestris (SALISB.) DANDY Navelwort. **N,H?** Very local and rare Map 153

Dry or moist shady hedgebanks, often at the base of oaks; twice only on old walls; on somewhat acid soils. Locally plentiful in the SW, rare on Lower Greensand, etc., in NE. Perhaps an

introduction at a few sites outside gardens.

VC11: Nursling 3716, *RPB* 1948–87; Dragon Lane, Bisterne 1501, *MPY* 1969, *RPB* to 1993; Brockenhurst churchyard 3001, on oaks, *FR* 1981. **VC12**: Wishanger Lane 8438, steep road bank, *ANHS* 1987; Barford 8538, shady lane S of stream, *RPB* 1972; Chiltley Lane, Liphook 8431, *FF* 1968, *AB* 1986; Silchester ruins 6262, *WGH* 1984.

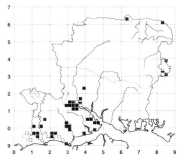

Map 153 Umbilicus rupestris

<Sempervivum tectorum L. House-leek. **H,D** Extinct

Once planted on cottage roofs for medicinal purposes, it disappeared as they were pulled down. F. I. Warner's plant, recorded on a roof in Selborne, VC12 (*Fl.Hants*, p.167) was seen by *AB* as a child, but in the 1920s the house was demolished to widen the road.>

Sedum telephium L. Orpine. **N,H** Locally frequent Map 154

First record, Gilbert White 1766, 'it abounds in the sandy fields near the forest' (Woolmer Forest) VC12 (*White's Jnls* **1**: 197).

Hedge- and railway-banks; old open woods on sand, gravel, Malmstone and clay.

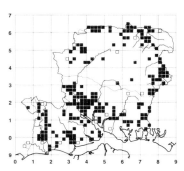

Map 154 Sedum telephium

VC11: Lymington River, Roydon Woods 3100, *RPB* 1990; Ampfield 3922, railway bank, *KC* 1980; West Walk 5813, roadside verge, *HWT* 1978. **VC12:** Woolmer Forest 8033, bank near old railway, *AB* 1984; Bilgrove Copse, Enham Alamein 3649, *MFW* 1991; Great Nightingales Copse, Hook 7154, *CRH* 1986.

S. spurium M. BIEB.   Caucasian Stonecrop.   **H**   Very rare

First record, J. F. Rayner 1920, waste place, Lordswood *c*.4015, VC11 (*Proc. IoW N.H.S.* **1**: 247).

VC11: Beaulieu old airfield 3500, on concrete hard-standing, abundant, *RPB* 1981; near Romsey Station 3521, on S-facing bank, *PAB* 1987; Hilsea Lines 6504, *PAB* 1989. **VC12:** Hazeley Heath gravel-pit 7657, two well-established plants, *MMcC-W* 1978.

S. rupestre L. (*S. reflexum* L.) Reflexed Stonecrop.   **H**   Occasional

An escape from cottage gardens, and sometimes well established on sandy banks in woodland, e.g. at Bordon 8034, VC12, *AB* 1985–91. VC11: 17 □; VC12: 15 □.

VC11: Hordle cliff car-park 2891, *RPB* 1977; Fort Cumberland 6899, *EAP* 1981. **VC12:** Towards Riseley Mill *c*.7462, 'yards of it, some distance from house.', *WEW* (pers.comm.) 1957; old railway, Ropley 6232, *JLSL* 1979.

S. acre L.   Biting Stonecrop.   **N,H** Locally frequent

Dry open sand, shingle or chalk, both coastal and inland; also on old walls, roofs, crumbling tarmac and concrete rubble, especially on old airfields, where probably of garden origin. Locally common near the sea but rarer inland since myxomatosis reduced rabbit populations with consequent losses of suitable habitat.

S. album L.   White Stonecrop.   **H** Very local

First record, R. Turner 1664, 'On the church at Heckfield in Hampshire useth to grow abundance of it.', 7260, VC12 (*Turn.Bot*, p.321).

Old walls, crumbling concrete, and sometimes on well-drained soil, often on old airfields. Widespread and locally plentiful; increasing. VC11: 25 □; VC12: 21 □.

VC11: Beaulieu old airfield 3400, *JO* 1983; Stoney Cross old airfield 2312,

RPB 1981; Sinah Common golf-links 6999, *EAP* 1985. **VC12:** Longmoor airstrip 8031, *AB* 1980; roof of Blackmoor War Memorial 7633, *AB* 1980–86; Thruxton aerodrome 2846, concrete trackway, *MFW* 1989.

S. anglicum HUDS.   English Stonecrop.   **N,C**   Very locally common   Map 155

On fixed shingle, stony and sandy seashores, and in maritime heath. In VC12, introduction.

VC11: Pennington Marshes 3293, on banks, *MR* 1976; Sinah Common 6999, *RPB* 1985. **VC12:** Old railway, Burghclere–Highclere 4757, *NFC* 1975.

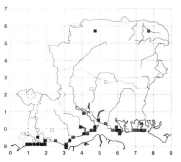

Map 155 Sedum anglicum

S. dasyphyllum L.   Thick-leaved Stonecrop.   **H**   Very rare

First records, J. F. Rayner 1924, on stone walls, Portchester Castle 6204, VC11, and Liphook *c*.8331, VC12 (*Proc. IoW N.H.S.* **1**: 246).

On old walls.

VC11: Still at Portchester Castle, *AWW* 1950, *JO & RPB* 1988, *FR* 1993, plentiful; extreme W end of Horsea Island 6304, *CMcL*, not seen since 1976.

SAXIFRAGACEAE

Saxifraga granulata L.   Meadow Saxifrage.   **N**   Local and rare   Map 156

Dry grassland on gravelly superficial soils over the chalk; old meadows on valley gravel deposits. Most frequent over the NW and central chalk; virtually absent now in the S and E. Since the 1960s, widespread losses have occurred as old meadows were systematically 'improved'. Its strongholds are now the N and W downs, and a few verges and churchyards. It is quite

absent as a native in Sussex, but reappears further E on the sandy or gravelly soils in Kent.

VC11: S side A272, Bramdean 6128, *FR* 1978; meadow beside A338, Ibsley 1510, *ESH c*.1926–76, *RPB* 1977–93; Rockbourne 1118 and Harbridge 1410 churchyards, *RPB* 1984; verge of drive, St Ives House, Ashley Heath Road 1204, *JO* 1984. **VC12:** Netherton Bottom 3756, *FR & SRD* 1975; Coombe churchyard 3660, *FR* 1984; Ladle Hill 4757, *ARGM* 1977; Newtown churchyard 4663, *NFC* 1981; Vernham Row 3257, *GDF* 1981; Greywell Moors 7150 and South Warnborough churchyard 7247, *AJPB* 1990.

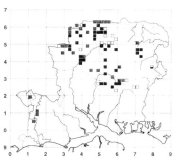

Map156 Saxifraga granulata

S. tridactylites L.   Rue-leaved Saxifrage.   **N**   Very local and occasional   Map 157

First record, Gilbert White 1766, Selborne, VC12 (*White's Jnls* **1**: 196).

'Roofs, wall tops and dry places; probably common' (*Fl.Hants*, p.167), but many of its habitats are now destroyed and it is very uncommon.

VC8: Kitt's Grave, Martin Down 0320, on bare chalk, *PET* 1990. **VC11:** Southwick churchyard 6208, Hb.AWW 1951; Colebrook Street, Winchester 4729, *JLSL* 1977; Port-

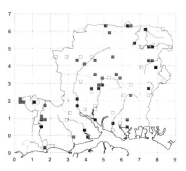

Map 157 Saxifraga tridactylites

chester Castle 6204, *EAP* 1981; *FR* 1993; Ringwood churchyard 1405, shingle path, *RPB* 1989. **VC12:** Bullington 4542, ballast on old railway, *SNHS* 1968; wall by The Bury, Odiham 7451, *AJPB* 1991; Headley 5063, *NFC* 1977; Alresford church, *PB* 1984; Silchester church, *WGH* 1984.

Tolmiea menziesii (PURSH) TORR. & A. GRAY   Pick-a-back-plant.   **H** Very rare

First record, W. Pulfrey 1975, Swaythling *c*.4414, VC11 (*Rep.S'ton N.H.S.*, p.11).

Tellima grandiflora (PURSH) DOUGLAS ex LINDL.   Fringe-cups. **H**   Very rare

First record, Miss D. W. Fawdry 1958, Southleigh Park 7307, VC11. **VC8:** North End, Damerham 1016, *JO* 1991. **VC9:** Kinson Common, Bournemouth 0695, *MAS* 1991. **VC11:** West Wood, Southampton 4409, *IW & MS* 1995, det. *RPB*; Locks Heath 5006, stream-bank, *FJPW* 1983. **VC12:** Earlestone Common 4761, in hedgerow, *CL* 1965, *CRH* 1987; near Fleet Pond 8254, *CRH* 1985; W of Wheatham Hill 7426, well naturalized in hanger woodland, *FR* 1992.

Chrysosplenium oppositifolium L. Opposite-leaved Golden-saxifrage.   **N** Locally common   Map 158

First record, J. Goodyer, before 1633, 'on the shadowie moist rockes by Mapledurham' *c*.7321, VC11 (*Ger.em.Johns.*, p.842).

In swampy woods on spring-lines, and along streams, often where alder is dominant. Also along moist, steep and shaded road-cuttings and ravines, and at the foot of hangers. Locally common on the Tertiaries and on the Malm-stone and Lower Greensand. Not

restricted to base-rich situations, but rather uncommon in the New Forest carrs, perhaps due to heavy grazing.

VC11: Ditch S of Ladycross Lodge 3302, *MR* 1976; Barrow Moor, Mark Ash Wood 2507, *FR* 1980; Purbrook 6908, Hb.AWW 1955; Dean's Farm, Weston 7222, *RPB* 1984 and Copyhold Barn, S of Weston 7321, in rocky ravine, *RPB* 1993 (probably where Goodyer saw it). **VC12:** Whitchurch *c*.4448, *CL* 1965; Blake's Pond, Yateley Green 8160, *VK* 1986.

C. alternifolium L.   Alternate-leaved Golden-saxifrage.   **N**   Rare Map 159

First British record, W. Browne 1650 to 1656, '*in paludoso nemori non procul ab aedibus D. Fanteleroii in pago vulgo Hedley vocato Comitati Hamptonis*' [in a marshy wood not far from the house of Dr Fauntleroy known locally as Headley in the County of Hampshire] VC12, (How's ms note in his copy of *Phyt.Brit.*, Magdalen College Library, Oxford (*Early Brit.Bots*, p.302)).

It requires alkaline water, rich in other nutrients besides calcium and now appears almost confined to alder carrs developed on spring-lines fed from the Bargate Beds, along the Rother from Whitrow Moor 7723, VC11, up to Stodham 7626, VC12, *AB & FR* to 1994; also the Wey and its branches from Conford to Headley, 8133, 8138, 8232, 8233, 8237, *FR* 1960–94. One isolated site by a chalk spring, above Ashford Chace 7326, *NDS* 1919, *FR* 1994. Formerly on the Eocene beds at Crammoor, Ampfield 3922, VC11, *HTW* 1935 (*Proc.Hants Fld Club* 15: 66), in alder carr, *FR* 1960, destroyed by 1981. A pre-1930 record for Chewton Glen *c*.2293, in *Atlas Brit.Fl* (p.139) has not been confirmed and is thought to be an error for *C. oppositifolium*.

<Parnassia palustris L.   Grass-of-Parnassus.   N   Extinct

No record for VC11 or VC12 since those cited at length in *Fl.Hants* (pp.169–170), but for which no known herbarium specimens exist. Gilbert White recorded planting a specimen in full bloom, brought to him from Rutland by Mr. S. Barker, into a bog at the bottom of Sparrow's hanger 7433, on 8 September 1785 (*White's Jnls* 3: 103). Not now found S of Cothill in N Berkshire.>

ROSACEAE

Spiraea x pseudosalicifolia SILVER-SIDE (*S.* x *billardii* auct., non Hérincq; *S. salicifolia* x *S. douglasii*))   Confused Brideworth.   **H**   Occasional

According to A. C. Leslie (*Suppl.Fl. Surrey*, p.105), this is the commonest of the escaped spiraeas which have been taken for *S. salicifolia* or *S. douglasii* and to which nearly all the Hants aggregate records probably belong. VC11: 11 ☐; VC12: 6 ☐.

VC11: Wootton Bridge 2500, *WMK* 1982, det. *AB*. **VC12:** Yateley 8261, margin of flooded gravel-pit, *ARGM* 1987, det. *ACL*.

Filipendula vulgaris MOENCH Dropwort.   **N**   Local   Map 160

First record, Gilbert White 1766, Fyfield, VC12, 'on yᵉ downs' (*White's Jnls* 1: 206).

On dry chalk grassland, occasionally on chalk superficials. Locally frequent and competing successfully in rank grass, as at Martin Down 0518, VC8. Almost absent from the eastern chalk. Very rare in the New Forest.

VC11: B3078 Deadman Hill 2016, small patch in S verge, *RPB* 1991; Burley Beacon 2003, a few plants under gorse, on marl, *RPB* 1986–88;

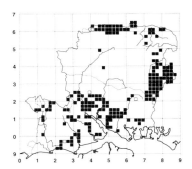

Map 158 Chrysosplenium oppositifolium

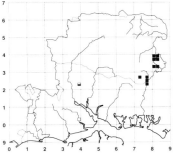

Map 159 Chrysosplenium alternifolium

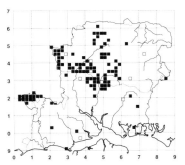

Map 160 Filipendula vulgaris

Catherington Down 6914, Hb.AWW 1958. **VC12**: Worthy Park 5032, *AH* 1976; on natural, low chalk banks, Bransbury Common 4141, *FR* 1978.

F. ulmaria (L.) MAXIM. Meadow-sweet. **N** Locally very common

Common in nearly all marshy places, fens, wet woodland, old meadows, and ditches, but rare on the chalk where found only where water is near the surface or by springs.

Rubus idaeus L. Raspberry. **N,D** Common

In open woods, scrub, waysides and in fen carr. Fairly common, especially on gravel. Sometimes spreading from cultivation.

R. cockburnianus HEMSL. White-stemmed Bramble. **H** Very rare

First record, Lady Anne Brewis 1976, amongst other brambles near Sinah Warren, Hayling Island 6999, VC11, Hb.AB, det. *EJC*. A garden escape.

R. fruticosus L. agg. Bramble. **N,C,D** Very common

Woodland margins and clearings, hedges, scrubby heathland, waste ground; mainly on gravel or sand but extending (in the case of certain forms) to clay and chalk.

This difficult group – made up of a great number of mostly asexual microspecies many of which, even so, can and do hybridize, a few quite frequently – has been studied intensively in the county since 1972 by D. E. Allen, who has contributed the account that follows. Based mainly on material of his own collecting (of which vouchers for all vice-county records (det. or conf. *AN*) have been or will be deposited in Hb.BM or Hb.HCMS) and supplemented by observation in the field, it also draws on older records in so far as it has proved possible to confirm these or trace and redetermine specimens.

Two-thirds of Hampshire is geologically favourable to the group, while geographically it lies where Britain's richest *Rubus* assemblage, that of SE England, overlaps that of the SW. As a result it holds probably more named forms than any other county. Compared with 103 and 101 reliably on record for Surrey and Devon respectively, Hampshire has (or had till recently) 137 of those on the current British Isles list (43 per cent of the total), 117 in VC11 and 113 in VC12. In addition, there are at least another 50–60 forms occurring over a wide area or in quantity in one locality that have so far defied matching with any named entity. The more salient of these are included in the list below, with serial numbers standing in for names. Every part of Europe with reasonable *Rubus* diversity has a comparable proportion of unnamed forms, their numbers being so legion that it is now the convention to describe only those with a distribution that can be characterized as 'regional'.

Few forms have noticeably individual habitat requirements: subtle differences in atmospheric moisture, rather, seem the main determinant of ranges. This makes the group uniquely valuable for inter-district floristic comparisons, for its repertoire of range-patterns shows up contrasts and affinities on a helpfully smaller scale than the rest of the plant world can offer. Thus, despite a separating stretch of sea nowhere wider than 8km, Hampshire and the Isle of Wight prove to have sharply different *Rubus* florulas. Three of the most generally distributed and common Hampshire species, *R. cissburiensis*, *R. glareosus* and *R. asperidens*, are completely missing from Wight and a fourth, *R. moylei*, is probably a recent arrival in its solitary locality. Also absent inexplicably are such other widespread Hampshire brambles as *R. bertramii*, *R. euryanthemus*, *R. platyacanthus* and *R. rubritinctus*. The last of these is a western species frequent around Southampton Water and across the southern New Forest and thus particularly to be expected, the more so as the non-Hampshire element in Wight is mainly western in its affinities too: *R. aequalidens* A. Newton, *R. angusticuspis* Sudre, *R. cornubiensis* (W. M. Rogers ex Ridd.) Rilstone, *R. dumnoniensis* Bab. and *R. effrenatus* A. Newton. Chance, rather than climate, probably explains the absence from Hampshire of some of these five, as Wight in turn lacks *R. durotrigum* and *R. hastiformis*, which similarly seem to be mere fortuitous gifts to Hampshire of berry-eating birds on west-to-east passage. To that same agency, too, is perhaps to be attributed the presence in both counties of the mainly Cornish *R. rilstonei*. Accompanying that in Hampshire however, are the almost equally strongly western *R. longithyrsiger* and *R. questieri*, which along with such species as *R. altiarcuatus*, *R. briggs-ianus*, *R. hylocharis*, *R. incurvatus* and *R. tamarensis* give evidence of constituting a more solidly established 'Atlantic' ingredient in the county's *Rubus* flora. Though naturally concentrated in the New Forest and its vicinity, this western group has members, most notably *R. adscitus*, *R. dentatifolius*, *R. leyanus* and *R. prolongatus*, which occur here and there far to the north and east in the county as well.

But it is not only the west that produces Hampshire's surprises. *R. confertiflorus*, *R. integribasis*, *R. leucostachys* and *R. surrejanus* are species of SE England which differ from others with that range in penetrating way beyond the county's eastern edge, in most cases as far as the New Forest and in some even farther. There is, too, a northern element, represented by *R. calvatus*, *R. echinatoides*, *R. lindebergii*, *R. scissus* and, more remarkably, *R. lentiginosus*, a species mainly of N Wales, and *R. leptothyrsos* and *R. septentrionalis*, which are almost exclusively Scottish. There is a group of rarities which the county shares with the central Welsh Marches: *R. angloserpens*, *R. babingtonii* and *R. informifolius*. And there is even a trans-Channel group, represented by *R. boulayi*, *R. caesarius*, *R. campaniensis*, *R. oxyanchus*, *R. thyrsigeriformis* and *R. transmarinus*.

Study of these microspecies has value for historical ecology too. Not obviously-ancient woods may betray their antiquity in their richness in *Rubus* species, especially rare ones. Only from its bramble flora could one guess today that insignificant, otherwise dull Hampage Wood 5430 once supplied all the beams for Winchester Cathedral roof. Younger woods, poor in specialized niches, as in the Micheldever group 5236, characteristically have three or four species in joint abundance but disproportionately few others. To display such helpful clues, however, woods must be free from overgrazing – unlike most New Forest ones which, away from the more frequented parts, have been largely stripped of brambles, presumably by roe deer (of the diet of which they constitute the major portion).

sect. **Rubus**

subsect. **Rubus** (sect. *Suberecti* P. J. Müll.)

R. arrheniiformis W. C. R. WATSON Very rare **VC11**

A widely- but very thinly-distributed near-endemic of England and Wales confined in Hants to the New Forest: Long Aldermoor, Minstead 2709, in quantity, accompanying the only known Hants population of *Carum verticillatum*, *AB* 1983; Hightown Common 1805, one patch; about Linford 1707, 1807, in three places.

R. bertramii G. BRAUN   Locally common   **VC11,12**

Dry heathy scrub. Mainly confined to the New Forest and E Hants.

R. briggsianus (W. M. ROGERS) W. M. ROGERS   Very rare   **VC11,<12>**

A strongly-western British Isles endemic, confined now in Hants to the SW: old marshland drainage-ditch S of Fordingbridge 1413; gorse scrub at S tip of Beaulieu Heath 3698; one bush, Broom Hill, East End 3698; and Fox Hill 2511. Specimens, apparently correctly det. *WMR*, are also in several herbaria from a most unlikely locality for this peat-lover, deep in the chalk belt: rough open ground on the Andover road near the fourth mile-stone from Winchester 4535, *WLWE* 1900 (*Rep.B.E.C.* for 1906, p.217). Presumably a freak occurrence, it cannot now be found there.

An apparent hybrid of this species with *R. ulmifolius*, **H545**, occurs on Setley Plain 2900, 2999, and locally in plenty at the S end of Beaulieu Heath 3497–3698. An identical plant of this putative parentage was collected just across in VC9 by Focke and Briggs in 1899, Hb.BM.

R. divaricatus P. J. MÜLL.   Local **VC11,12**

Frequent in the New Forest and on some of the commons round Southampton, reappearing in the NW but replaced in E Hants by *R. bertramii*.

R. fissus LINDL.   Very local **VC11,12**

Frequent along the N edge of the New Forest, occurring in places near the E edge as well. Once also found in far NW Hants: damp copse, Newtown Common, *ABJ* 1906, Hb.BM, det. *WMR* – a stray from populations just across in Berkshire.

R. glanduliger W. C. R. WATSON Very local   **VC11,12**

Virtually endemic to Hants and W Sussex, its main populations in the latter continue into Woolmer Forest and its environs, where it is wide-spread. A patch found in Buckland Wood, near Lymington 3197 in 1990 represents a major extension to its range.

R. integribasis P. J. MÜLL. ex BOULAY   Rare   **VC11,12**

Strays across from its British head-quarters in Surrey to Bramshott Common 8533, 8633, where it is plentiful along the N side of the A3 for nearly 1km. Since its discovery there (*BAM* 1965, Hb.CGE) this supposedly SE England species has been found scattered right across S Hants: Mallards Moor and Badnam Copse, Bursledon 4709, 4808, in plenty, and nearby Priors Hill Copse 4609; Hamble Common 4806; one bush outside Home Copse, Chilworth 3918; Blackwell Common 4301; and Redhill Park, Bournemouth 0995, one bush. The flower-colour ranges from white to bright pink (Home Copse) or deep mauve (Badnam Copse).

R. nessensis HALL   Local   **VC11,12**

Frequent in wet woodland and on dry commons in the gravel district centred on Southampton, but unaccountably all but absent from the New Forest (as first noted by J. G. Baker in 1879), even on its fringes almost confined to the Totton and Fordingbridge neigh-bourhoods. Reappears in the far N, but scarce there except on Yateley Common 8259, 8260. Otherwise just a single E Hants record: old railway, Longmoor 8031, *AB* 1981.

R. nitidiformis SUDRE   Very rare **VC11**

A dwarf form of this SE England species has been known since 1974 on Southampton Common on the N side of The Lake 4114 and on Chilworth Common 4117. Watson cites it for VC11 on unknown evidence (*Rubi Hdbk*, p.64, as *R. nitidoides* W. C. R. Watson).

R. nobilissimus (W. C. R. WATSON) PEARSALL   Rare   **VC11,12**

A near-endemic of S England, this formerly occurred in several parts of Hants but apart from Hawley Lake 8457 all recent records are from the 'greater' New Forest: Chilworth Common 4017; Calveslease Copse,

North Baddesley 3919; outside Manor Wood, Minstead 2710; A31 by Malwood 2712; Godshill gravel-pits 1716; Kingston North Common 1402; gorsy 'lawns' on outskirts of Brocken-hurst 2801 (where collected, unwit-tingly, *TRAB* 1886, Hb.BM, det. *WMR*), 2902, 2903, 3003; Pig Bush 3605; Culverley 3604; Hill Top to N edge of King's Copse Inclosure 4202; Foxhunting Inclosure 3804. In the last four sites and one of the Brockenhurst ones the flowers are all pure white instead of the normal lilac or pink.

R. plicatus WEIHE & NEES Occasional   **VC11,12**

Usually on dry heathland (though seldom plentifully), rarely on alluvium – as by West Horton Farm, Bishop-stoke 4718 and Sandy Balls 1614 – a habitat it favours much more in Wight.

R. scissus W. C. R. WATSON   Rare **VC11,12**

A predominantly northern species long known in the SW corner of the New Forest, on open heath and in open woodland. Outliers occur at Culverley 3604, Deerleap Inclosure 3309, King's Copse Inclosure 4202 and Appleslade Inclosure 1809. Also in NW Hants in Sandford Wood, Kingsclere 5459, 5559, locally plentiful on afforested former heathland.

R. sulcatus VEST   Very rare **VC11,12**

Ultra-dependent on dispersal by birds, this species occurs erratically through-out its European range, often as single bushes – as in Stoke Park Wood 4719, Queen Elizabeth Park, Farnborough 8656 and on Yateley Common 8159. On Shedfield Common 5613, however, and beside the A326 outside Staple-wood 3710 it occurs in colony strength. The sole old record is: Sway *c*.2798, *WRL*, Hb.LIV.

R. vigorosus P. J. MÜLL. & WIRTG. Very rare   **VC11**

Until early this century extended from its strong VC9 populations to several sites in Bournemouth and on the New Forest edges, but (as in Wight) now much decreased. Apart from a patch among bracken on Wickham Common 5810 and single bushes on a roadside by Woodington, East Wellow 3120, among eroded gorse by Hill Top, Beaulieu 4003 and on Chark Common 5701, it survives today in any quantity only on Browndown Common, Gosport 5898.

H410. Very local. **VC11.** Tall and suberect, with erect panicle branches, long-clawed lilac petals and hairy anthers, evidently the product of a cross between *R. nobilissimus* and one of the *Sylvatici*. Widespread, in places common, from Romsey to the New Forest margins, reappearing at Hythe.

subsect. **Hiemales** E. H. L. KRAUSE

ser. **Sylvatici** (P. J. MÜLL.) FOCKE

<**R. semicarpinifolius** SUDRE (*R. adspersus* Weihe ex H. E. Weber) Extinct <**VC12**>
Tadley Common 6062, *FAR* 1894, Hb.K, det. *AN*. Repeated attempts to refind this 'Continental' (mainly Norfolk) species there have proved in vain.>

R. albionis W. C. R. WATSON Occasional **VC11,12**
In quantity only in Hum Hole, Bitterne 4413, an ancient clay-pit with a moist microclimate suited to this western species, and, anomalously, Moon's Copse, Brockwood Park 6326 (whence it spills across to Bramdean Common 6329). Otherwise widely and very thinly scattered across SW Hants, with a slight clustering of sites in the woods along the S margin of the New Forest. A long-known, outlying Berks population extends into birch-wood at Mount Pleasant, Tadley 6061.

R. boulayi (SUDRE) W. C. R. WATSON Very local **VC11,12**
Abundant in shady places in the coastal belt between Bournemouth and Lymington, spilling into the S New Forest. Largely absent from the rest of the Forest, it reappears far to the NE on Southampton Common 4113, 4114, in a copse SW of Chilworth 3918 and Ampfield Wood 3823, 3924. An outlying population just in VC12 at Durngate, Winchester 4829, is on riverbanks, unusually. This trans-Channel species is otherwise known in Britain only on the VC9 side of Bournemouth and in Parkhurst Forest in Wight.

R. calvatus LEES ex A. BLOXAM Rare **VC11,12**
A northern endemic with big fruits attractive to birds and with a disjunct

range accordingly. Spills over from its large W Surrey populations to three sites on the NE edge of Aldershot 8752, 8852, 8853, Frensham Pond 8439, Liss Forest ex-railway 7829, *AB*, and War Down 7218, *ESE*, Hb.NMW, det. *DEA*. All other records are on the SW fringe (whence they continue into VC9): Hightown Common 1705 and a bush in the Forest boundary hedge, Shobley 1806; moor by chine, Bournemouth West 0790, *WMR* 1888, Hb.OXF.

R. confertiflorus W. C. R. WATSON Very local **VC11,12**
An endemic of SE England confined to heathy scrub or open woodland in just four areas: plentiful on Cadnam Common 2915, one bush on Copythorne Common 3115 and continuing very sparsely along the N edge of the New Forest; around Ringwood and Burley, locally in abundance; Woolmer Forest and environs; Wildgrounds, Rowner 5701 and Browndown Common 5899.

R. crudelis W. C. R. WATSON Very rare **VC12**
A species almost endemic to the Surrey heaths which spills across the border: corner of Queens Road and Longmoor Road 8131, *AB* 1972, det. *AN*; ex-railway, Longmoor 8031, *AB* 1981, det. *AN*; Ludshott Common 8535, *ESE* 1968, Hb.NMW, det. *DEA*; Passfield Common 8133; wood by Frensham Pond Hotel 8439. The Longmoor sites must surely be in the area of the 'common near Liphook' on which *FAR* and *WMR* found it on their walk along the S margin of Woolmer Forest in 1900, Hb.BM, Hb.K.

R. errabundus W. C. R. WATSON Very local **VC11,12**
Predominantly a species of N Britain which reappears on heaths from Devon to W Sussex. Generally distributed, even locally common throughout the 'greater' New Forest but exclusively as a micromorph (genetic dwarf) which at present lacks a name. The typical plant is very rare: Liss Forest ex-railway 7829; Priors Hill Copse, Butlocks Heath 4709; track towards Plumley Farm, Turmer Hill 1309.

R. imbricatus HORT Very rare **VC11**
A patch among gorse fringing a birch-wood ('Bowling Green') once forming

the E edge of now-vanished Titchfield Common 5307. A solitary bush at the NW corner of the New Forest in Millersford Bottom 1916 is probably a micromorph of this species but too underdeveloped for certainty.

R. laciniatus WILLD. Occasional **VC11,12**
A widely-scattered escape, a relic on commons and heaths of inter-war picnics. Now largely replaced in cultivation by *R. armeniacus*.

R. lentiginosus LEES Very rare **VC12**
Collected by Townsend in 1873 at Fleet Pond 8255 (*Fl.Hants*, p.130), where it was refound in 1984 thinly scattered through the alder carr fringing the E side, spilling over into dry birch-scrub. This population is an outlier of others across the Berks border, the combined area being the only one in which this species is known outside the Irish Sea region.

R. leptothyrsos G. BRAUN Rare **VC12**
Plentiful over much of Hawley Common 8357, 8457, 8458; Queen Elizabeth Park, Farnborough 8656. A Scottish species with only isolated English sites and none closer than East Anglia, this may originally owe its presence in Hants to introduction with conifers (its suspected origin on the Sandringham estate in Norfolk too).

R. leucandriformis EDEES & A. NEWTON Occasional **VC11,12**
Widely but very thinly distributed across the southern two-thirds of Hants, though almost absent from the New Forest except on its edges and largely replaced round Bournemouth by *R. pullifolius* (with which it was first confused). Though mainly in dry, open scrub, on acid heathland and chalk alike, it occurs in greatest quantity on estuarine clay, which may be the original habitat of this mainly Wessex endemic.

R. lindleianus LEES Frequent **VC11,12**
Widely but patchily distributed, mainly off the clay and chalk. Equally at home in dry gorse-scrub and (Fleet Pond 8255, Conford Moor 8133, West Horton copse, Bishopstoke 4718) alder carr.

R. macrophyllus WEIHE & NEES
Very local   **VC11,12**

Mainly in woods and heathy scrub N
and W of Basingstoke (plentiful on
Silchester Common 6262; locally abun-
dant in Ewhurst Park 5757, 5857) and
in the woods semicircling Fording-
bridge on the W. Isolated sites are
Otterbourne Common 4522, Green
Drove, Upper Enham 3650, 'Bowling
Green' wood, Titchfield Common
5206 and Weston Common 6943, 6944,
with single clumps only in Set Thorns
Inclosure 2699 and Roper's Copse,
Shalden 7143 and on Casbrook
Common 3524.

R. mollissimus W. M. ROGERS
Very local   **VC11,12**   Map 161

A mainly Wessex endemic of highly-
acid ground with a sharply bipolar
range in Hants: heaths and woods on
the NE Bagshot Beds; and scattered
towards the S edge of the New Forest
from E of Brockenhurst to W of Holmsley, including in *Myrica* bog. Also in
two sites E of Southampton: Botley
Wood 5410 and Green Lane, Old
Netley, 4710.

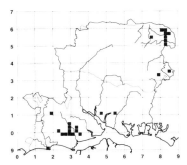

Map 161 Rubus mollissimus

R. oxyanchus SUDRE   Local   **VC11**

Frequent and locally abundant in
shady places to the W, S and E of the
New Forest (but virtually absent from
the Forest itself), spilling across
Southampton Water and with a distant
outlying colony on the S Hants Ridgeway outside Hyden Wood 6919. A
dwarf (genetic?) form grows beside the
Hill Top to Exbury road near Moon-
hills Gate 4002. SW Hants is the
British headquarters of this trans-
Channel species.

R. platyacanthus P. J. MÜLL. &
LEFÈVRE   Local   **VC11,12**

On heath-margins mostly along the
Berks and Surrey borders and, plentifully, in the NE quarter of the New
Forest. Absent, however, from the
Bournemouth area, as from SW
England generally: *EFL*'s 1893 gathering from near Hengistbury Head,
distributed in the classic set of British
Rubi and long accepted as this species,
is a mixture of *R. nemoralis* and *R.
pullifolius*.

R. pullifolius W. C. R. WATSON
Very local   **VC11**

An essentially Bournemouth-area
endemic, locally plentiful there on
scrubby heath-margins, continuing
very thinly along the edges of the New
Forest N to Millersford 1916 and E to
Shirley Holms 3098 and Pennington
Common 3095. Also distant outlying
occurrences on Southampton Common
(the type locality) and vicinity 4014,
and in Nightingale Wood, Rownhams
3818.

R. purbeckensis W. C. BARTON &
RIDD.   Very local   **VC11**

Plentiful on Hengistbury Head 1690,
1790, once continuing W to Southbourne (*HJR* 1929, Hb.BM) and
formerly abundant round Milford on
Sea (*WMR* 1895, Hb.BM), now otherwise only very thinly and interruptedly
along the central stretch of the New
Forest S margin to just beyond East
End, reappearing on the NE edge near
Ironshill Lodge 3209 and in Bramshaw
Wood and adjoining Woodside Bottom
2517. Long supposed endemic to the
Wessex coastal belt, this species has
recently been found along the E coast
of Ireland.

R. pyramidalis KALTENB.   Local
VC11,12

Virtually confined to the New Forest
(where it is patchy but locally plentiful), the commons N and E of
Southampton and the Berks and
Surrey border-belts, typically on dry,
open heathland. Surprisingly absent
from the Bournemouth area except for
a single bush on Hengistbury Head
1790. The micromorph, var. *parvi-
folius* Frid. & Gelert, is almost equally
widespread and even replaces the type
in the Woolmer Forest area and on the
W edge of the New Forest round
Linford.

R. questieri LEFÈVRE & P. J. MÜLL.
Very local   **VC11**

A strongly-western species, abundant in
copses on the S side of Hythe, trickling
thence to the Solent. Also on the New
Forest margins at widely-separated
points: Bramshaw Wood and adjoining
Woodside Bottom 2517; Hyde
Common 1712 and Gorley Hill 1611;
Setley Plain 2999, in a gorse-thicket.

R. sciocharis (SUDRE) W. C. R.
WATSON   Very rare   **VC11**

A large colony on Shedfield Common
5613 and a patch beside road parallel
with A338 S of Ashley crossroads
1303, among birches in both cases.
Also a patch beside the B3055 in
Brockenhurst 2902.

R. silvaticus WEIHE & NEES   Rare
VC12

Heaths and woods near the Berks
border: copses W of Highclere 4260;
Sydmonton Common 4962; Sandford
Wood 5459; Tadley Common 6061;
Silchester Common 6262; Heckfield
Heath 7261, in some quantity. Older
records are probably erroneous. A
'Continental' species, scarce and scat-
tered across England and Wales.

R. subintegribasis DRUCE   Local
VC11

Endemic to Dorset, S Wilts and S
Hants, this variable species of heath-
margins is common in Redhill Park,
Bournemouth 0895 and in parts of the
New Forest, spills across Southampton
Water and extends N to the Romsey
district. Watson cites it (*Rubi Hdbk*,
p. 62) for VC12 on the basis of a
Woolmer Forest record of Rogers, but
the latter's specimen (Hb.BM) is not
this species.

H190.   'Forest of Bere *salteri*'.
VC11. Common in almost all the frag-
ments of this forest, even down to
Gosport. Well known to Townsend.
The Shedfield Common '*R. hirtifolius*'
of Watson (*Rubi Hdbk*, p. 79).

H383.   'Hampshire-Surrey *monensis*'.
Rare. **VC11,12.** Plentiful on Copythorne Common 3014, 3115 and a bush
or two in three New Forest sites, reappearing in the NE corner in carr fringing Fleet Pond 8255 and over in Surrey
on Chobham Ridges and Chobham
Common (*BAM* 1963–64, Hb.CGE).

H677.   Very rare. **VC12.** With broad
white petals and a partly parallel-sided
terminal leaflet. A large patch in an

alder-wood clearing on SE side of Fleet Pond 8254. In Hb.BM from St Leonards Forest, VC13, and round Tunbridge Wells, VC14 and VC16, variously labelled '*R. hirtifolius*' and '*R. consobrinus*'.

H1081. Very local. **VC12.** Lightly armed, with a lax, flat-topped panicle, a large, roundish uppermost panicle leaflet and a glabrous purple stem. Plentiful on wood-margins on Hook Common 7253 and occurs elsewhere in NE Hants and on Royal Common, Elstead in Surrey (*LCu* 1908, Hb.OXF; *HJR* 1922, Hb.BM). There is also a Berks specimen from Sandhurst in Hb.OXF (*GCD* 1895) misdetermined as *R. questieri* and *R. egregius* Focke.

ser. **Rhamnifolii** (BAB.) FOCKE

R. altiarcuatus W. C. BARTON & RIDD. Rare **VC11**

A strongly-western species distributed at intervals along the NW margin of the New Forest for 4km, from Godshill Ridge 1815 to Gorley Hill 1611 – an oddly restricted range, especially as it is quite widespread in Wight.

R. amplificatus LEES Rare **VC11,12**

Dotted across S Hants, often as single bushes, with a clustering along the W side of Southampton Water and the lower Beaulieu River (where Baker recorded it in 1879), favouring, as in Wight, birch-wood fringing tidal creeks. It reappears in far NW Hants on the Clay-with-flints, more in keeping with its calcicolous tendency elsewhere in Britain and Ireland: frequent in Combe Wood 3559 and a bush in Wilster Copse 3656. Marrelsmoor Coppice, Purbrook 6708, in far SE Hants, holds the only other woodland population of any size.

R. boudiccae A. L. BULL & EDEES Very local **VC11,12**

A recently-described East Anglian species which has since proved widespread in Hants, Wight, the Arden district of Warwickshire and the N half of Ireland. Widely dotted about as single bushes or patches, it has been found in quantity only on Hengistbury Head 1790, around Godshill 1614, 1715 and below Walbury 3660. More tolerant of basic soils than the closely-

related *R. cardiophyllus*, it is characteristic of wood-borders and dry heathland reverting to scrub.

R. cardiophyllus LEFÈVRE & P. J. MÜLL. Locally common **VC11,12**

Shuns clay and chalk, so absent from large areas. Rarely, in non-acid reedswamp, as at Winnall Moors, Winchester 4829.

R. cissburiensis W. C. BARTON & RIDD. Locally common **VC11,12**

An aggressive SE England endemic with the appearance of a recent colonist, still rare in SW Hants (and absent from Wight). Largely indifferent to geology, it is abundant in many chalk beech-woods as well as characteristic of the margins of heathy commons.

R. curvispinosus EDEES & A. NEWTON Very local **VC11**

Endemic to Wessex except for some bushes on Hampstead Heath, VC21, this mainly Bournemouth-area species has a similar Hants range to *R. oxyanchus*, extending to the New Forest round Ringwood and along the coastal belt and the S and E Forest margins, but with outlying clumps on and beyond its N margin as well.

[**R. dumnoniensis** BAB.

Cited for VC11 by Edees & Newton (*Brambles Brit.Is.*, p. 91) on the strength of specimens in Hb.NMW collected by *ESE* on Barton Common and Hengistbury Head, which have, however, proved to be *R. curvispinosus* and *R. boudiccae* respectively. This western species is nevertheless a likely Hants species and may indeed be represented by two bushes on the New Forest W margin above Shobley Bottom 1806, unfortunately too atypical for certainty.]

R. elegantispinosus (A. SCHUMACH.) H. E. WEBER Rare **VC11,12**

A garden escape scattered over much of Winchester, also in Andover 3645 and Lymington 3295, but missing from the rest of Hants except for one bush on Chark Common golf-links 5702. Apart from Bath, these are the most western sites of this mainly E Britain species.

[**R. furnarius** W. C. BARTON & RIDD.

The New Forest plants ascribed to this

in *Watsonia* **18**: 81 have proved to be *R. septentrionalis*.]

R. incurvatus BAB. Very rare **VC11**

A western, mainly Welsh species largely absent from S England. Kent Hill wood, Harbridge 1310, in quantity; Hengistbury Head 1790; Brockenhurst, *CBu* 1917, Hb.BRISTM, det. *AN*.

R. lasiodermis SUDRE Rare **VC11**

A regional endemic with Bournemouth as its focus, this heath-margin species is not well understood and liable to be confused with a common and variable New Forest plant which appears a hybrid derivative of it. The true plant is known for sure only from Redhill Park 0895; Hyde Common and old gravel-pits, Abbots Well 1712; Stoke Park Wood 4719; Chark Common 5701 (one bush); Minstead *c.*2811, *JGB* 1879, Hb.BM.

<**R. lindebergii** P. J. MÜLL. Extinct <**VC12**>

North Camp, Aldershot 8853, *GCD* n.d., Hb.OXF, det. *AN*. Much the most southerly English locality of this widespread northern species, which elsewhere tends to be calcicolous.>

R. londinensis (W. M. ROGERS) W. C. R. WATSON Very rare **VC12**

This Thames Valley endemic has an outlying western population on Hazeley Heath 7458, over which it is thinly scattered.

R. milfordensis EDEES Very local **VC11,12**

A regional near-endemic continuing into NE Hants – in places abundantly – from its headquarters on the Surrey commons, with one outlying site (Allwood Copse, Ellisfield 6447) as much as 16km inside the county. Also one stray bush outside Dunwood, near Romsey 3023, far to the west.

R. nemoralis P. J. MÜLL. Locally common **VC11,12**

Widespread and locally abundant in SW Hants (in the New Forest the most characteristic bramble, ceasing abruptly at its boundaries), but thinning out rapidly northwards and eastwards. Though plentiful on Hamble Common 4806, absent from Southampton Common 4114 and

Chark Common 5701 and indeed most of the rest of Hants except the NE, where it again attains abundance on Silchester Common 6262. The micromorph, var. *microphyllus* (Lindeb.) W. C. R. Watson (*R. pistoris* W. C. Barton & Ridd.), otherwise almost wholly a northern taxon, is common in the northern third of the New Forest, virtually replacing the type.

R. pampinosus LEES   Rare
VC11,12

A western British endemic with substantial populations in VC9 which spill across to the New Forest, where it occurs mostly singly, sometimes under tall gorse: Blackwell Common and Gatewood Hill 4401; Wootton Coppice Inclosure 2399; boundary hedge, Sway 2799; The Ridge, Lyndhurst 3107; Castle Malwood Park 2711. It reappears in quantity in the SE in Havant Forest, extending very sparingly across to The Holt 7111; and has also been collected in the NE on Hawley Common 8357.

R. polyanthemus LINDEB.   Local
VC11,12

Characteristic of dry woodland clearings and margins, tolerating clay, but often unaccountably absent, including from much of the New Forest and most of SE Hants. Especially abundant in Sandford Wood 5459.

R. prolongatus BOULAY & LETENDRE
Local   **VC11,12**

Abundant in woods, hedges and heath-scrub in the district astride the SW corner of the New Forest, generally with the equally western *R. rubritinctus*. Thinly scattered elsewhere in the Forest and across Southampton Water, it reappears in quantity in the wooded district SW of Alton with an outlier to the NE on the one-time Isnage Heath 7645. Anomalously, also in profusion in two woods between Winchester and Stockbridge – Great Up Somborne Wood 4031; Long Copse 4034 – where gravel outcrops through the chalk.

R. rhombifolius WEIHE ex BOENN.
Very local   **VC11,12**

On heath-margins here and there along the N, W, and S edges of the New Forest; rarely also on some of the N Hants commons and in the Woolmer Forest area (Oakhanger 7534, *TBS* 1844, Hb.CGE, Hb.K; ex-railway, Liss Forest 7729).

R. rubritinctus W. C. R. WATSON
Local   **VC11,12**

A strongly bird-dependent species scattered across the SW coastal belt and the S New Forest (where it tends to cluster round streams) and all round Southampton Water, petering out eastwards at Wickham Common 5910. Reappears on the NW edges of the Forest around Godshill and strays as far N as the M3 embankment by Butter Wood 7152 and as far E as Rowland's Castle 7310. Clearly intrusive in places (e.g. on roadsides at Holmsley but not in adjacent woods) and anomalously absent from Wight, it has seemingly colonized Hants from the W at a relatively recent period.

R. septentrionalis W. C. R. WATSON
Very rare   **VC11**

A mainly Scottish species long known just over in VC9 in Branksome Park, Bournemouth. Since 1986 a usually white-flowered micromorph of it has been detected in heathy scrub in the SW New Forest: Brockenhurst 2801, Hb.RDR 1991; near Burley Lodge 2305; N of Goatspen Plain 2202; Rockford Common 1708.

R. subinermoides DRUCE   Locally
common   **VC11,12**

Widely distributed, in places abundant, in open woodland on clay or moderately acid gravel. Rare round Southampton, however, and largely absent from SW Hants away from the W side of Southampton Water and round Beaulieu, in plenty there only on a small clay outcrop by Black Bush Plain 2415.

H993.   Rare. **VC11**. With a long cylinder of bright pink flowers, long stamens, large buds and abruptly acuminate leaflets white-felted beneath. Restricted to the Swanwick–Fareham–Gosport district (particularly plentiful on Chark Common 5702) and an area near Plymouth, VC3 (plentiful about Kingston, *ESM* 1894, Hb.BM).

ser. **Sprengeliani** FOCKE

R. sprengelii WEIHE   Locally
common   **VC11,12**

Mainly in the New Forest, both sides of Southampton Water, the district E and SE of Romsey and along the Berks border. Oddly, all but absent from the

Forest of Bere and the Bournemouth area.

ser. **Discolores** (P. J. MULL.) FOCKE

R. armeniacus FOCKE (*R. procerus* auct. brit., non P. J. Müll. ex Boulay) 'Himalayan Giant'   Frequent
VC11,12

An aggressive and fast-increasing escape, still mainly in built-up areas but already commoner than *R. ulmifolius* in Winchester. It appears indifferent to geology.

R. armipotens W. C. BARTON ex A. NEWTON   Locally common
VC11,12

An endemic of SE England which has plentifully colonized the eastern third of Hants, peters out in the centre and reappears along the Wilts border as East Dean 2627 and round Highclere 4360. Clearly adventive in Romsey 3521 and in a scatter of S Hants localities (as on a wartime site at Furze Hill 3301). Tolerant of clay and chalk and at home in alder carr at Fleet Pond 8255. The commonest bramble round Alton.

R. hylophilus RIP. ex GENEV.   Very
local   **VC11,12**

Spills across on to heaths and wood-margins in NE Hants, as far as Hook Common 7253, from its British headquarters in Surrey, occurring especially plentifully on the W side of Hawley Lake 8357. Distant outlying patches on Hamble Common 4805, among youngish gorse, and along the roadside margin of Priors Hill Copse, Butlocks Heath 4608, are seemingly recent arrivals.

[**R. lamburnensis** RILSTONE

A very variable bramble of dry heathy areas frequent and locally common in SW Hants (and Wight) has been identified with this Cornubian species, but whether correctly needs fuller study.]

R. neomalacus SUDRE   Very rare
VC12

A stray from its Surrey populations on Bramshott Common 8533, *AB & AN* 1974 (since destroyed by A3 widening). Also a single bush in Itchen Wood 5235, 1986.

R. rossensis A. NEWTON   Very local
VC11

Frequent in three areas, especially on wood-margins: Southampton and a 15km radius to the E (where Townsend knew it as 'R. argentatus'); W of the Beaulieu River; and N and NW of Romsey. Mainly a species of the S Welsh Marches but also in Devon and W Dorset.

R. stenopetalus LEFÈVRE & P. J. MÜLL. Very local VC11,12 Map 162

A species of basic soils frequent on wood-margins in the Micheldever area (where it was widely collected c.1900 by WLWE, Hb.BM, Hb.HME), trickling W to complete its British range in Wilts via Long Copse, Crawley 3934, Michelmersh Wood 3527, Tytherley Common 2728, Harewood Forest 4144, ESE 1968, Hb.NMW, copses round Clatford Oakcuts 3339, 3439, and Wilster Copse, Upton 3656. Otherwise known only in the Paris Basin and Belgium.

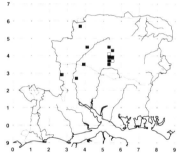

Map 162 Rubus stenopetalus

R. ulmifolius SCHOTT Very common VC11,12

At home on calcareous no less than moderately-acid soils and in full sun. Markedly less plentiful in the NW corner (Fl.Hants, p.130, as R. rusticanus Merc.). Particularly prone to cross.

R. winteri P. J. MÜLL. ex FOCKE Very local VC11,12

Common on the chalk, in hedges and woods, N and W of Winchester at least as far as Stockbridge and Longstock and again by the Wilts border round South Tidworth 2346 and Shipton Bellinger 2345. Elsewhere in Britain mainly a Midlands species.

H557. Very local. VC11. Close to the Continental R. amiantinus (Focke)

Foerster, with white flowers, reddish styles and cuneate leaflets biserrate above. Common in hedges in the southern parts of the Forest of Bere, as about Swanwick and Purbrook. Tolerant of clay.

ser. Vestiti (FOCKE) FOCKE

R. adscitus GENEV. Very local VC11,12

Apparently a recent colonist from SW England, unrecorded till 1936. Abundant in three districts especially favoured by western brambles: the woods semicircling the NW tip of the New Forest, those alongside the SW side of Southampton Water, and Havant Forest; also, more surprisingly, in those between Michelmersh and King's Somborne (spilling across to Parnholt Wood 3728). Smaller populations in Dock Lane, Beaulieu 3902; Hen Wood 6522; woods around Hurstbourne Priors 4146, 4348, 4447; Allwood and Fryingdown Copses, Ellisfield 6446. An aggressive species, tending to be in profusion where it occurs. Tolerant of chalk and clay, moreover.

R. boraeanus GENEV. Very rare VC12

Except for a patch near Winchester at Avington crossroads 5329, known only on or near the central stretch of the Berks border: Silchester, locally abundant, FT 1873 (Fl.Hants, p.133); two clumps by car-park, Birchen Copse 7262, AB 1977, DEA & AOC 1982; one bush till 1989 beside B3011, Hazeley 7459; one bush at a cross-paths, Sandford Wood 5459.

R. caesarius D. E. ALLEN Very rare VC11

A patch on hedgebanks along Segensworth Road, Park Gate 5207, at the N tip of the one-time Titchfield Common, is the only locality so far known for this recently-described species outside Jersey, where it is locally abundant.

R. conspersus W. C. R. WATSON Locally common VC11,12

An endemic of SE England abundant in the Woolmer Forest area and in places near the Sussex border.

R. criniger (E. F. LINTON) W. M. ROGERS Very local VC11,12

An endemic mainly of the N Midlands and East Anglia, apparently in the process of colonizing Hants. Plentiful round Aldershot and Farnborough (where Townsend collected it in 1873) and on the gravel belt abutting on the London Clay from Mottisfont to Otterbourne with an outlying colony at West Wood 4229. Solitary bushes or clumps occur widely elsewhere, S to Hayling Island and Lymington and W to South Tidworth, but at Turkey Island, Shedfield 5613, it rises to colony strength.

R. leucostachys SCHLEICH. ex SM. Very local VC11,12

An endemic of SE England (and the Channel Islands) mainly restricted to E Hants and especially plentiful W of Alton. A large population in Long Wood, Littleton 4432 forms a stepping-stone to the district by the Wilts border round East Tytherley 2729 and West Dean 2527, where it again becomes frequent. Sometimes on heath-margins, as on bare New Forest roadsides by Franchises Wood 2316.

R. surrejanus W. C. BARTON & RIDD. Very local VC11,12 Map 163

An endemic of SE England which crosses the length of the Surrey border in profusion, only to thin out westwards very rapidly. Unexpectedly, it has a secondary area of abundance round Shootash (the dominant bramble in Dunwood 3123), several colonies between there and the New Forest and further, isolated ones S of Ringwood, in two areas of Winchester 4629, 4829 and on margin of Newtown Common 4762. Its recent discovery on the Wilts-Somerset border supports the impression of a westward spread still in progress.

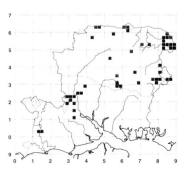

Map 163 Rubus surrejanus

R. vestitus WEIHE   Locally abundant
VC11,12

A clay-loving species largely absent
from the New Forest and some of the
gravel districts. The red-flowered form
is the less widespread and especially
common in woods between Winchester
and the Meon Valley.

H73.   Very local. **VC12**. A derivative
of *R. subinermoides* with dark green
leaves and a long narrow panicle bearing smallish white flowers with narrow,
deeply-notched petals. Common in
Micheldever Wood and its satellites,
trickling N towards Overton and NE to
reappear in plenty in woods and on
roadsides round Ellisfield; also in
Round Copse, Basing 6853. Well
known to Eyre, it was misdetermined
for him as (*inter alios*) *R. silvaticus* and
R. questieri, Hb.BM, Hb.HME.

H107.   Very local. **VC11**. Super-
ficially resembles *R. radulicaulis*
Sudre, with red flowers and obovate
leaflets. Plentiful in parts of the New
Forest and in open woodland in the
Southampton–Ampfield–Otterbourne
triangle, reappearing by the Sussex
border in the Havant area woods. Also
in SE Wight. Possibly *R. grypoacanthus*
Lefèvre & P. J. Müll. of the Paris area.

H511.   Very local. **VC11**. With neat,
white *R. adscitus*-like flowers on a
broad, lax pyramid. Abundant in
Radnall Wood, Fordingbridge 1317
and occurring at intervals down the
Avon Valley almost to Christchurch. A
solitary bush on the margin of Manor
Wood, Minstead 2709 has probably
come in with recently-planted trees.

H683.   Rare. **VC11**. With large
yellowish stem leaves with an obovate-
cuneate terminal leaflet, broad white
petals and bright green styles. Widespread round Holmsley 2201, 2300 and
in some quantity also on Hengistbury
Head 1790.

ser. **Mucronati** (FOCKE) H. E. WEBER

R. mucronatiformis (SUDRE)
W. C. R. WATSON   Local   **VC11,12**

Of all the regional endemics the most
precise delimiter of the 'greater' New
Forest, extending to the limit of the
gravel belt near Romsey and Winchester, then round by way of Upperbarn
Copse, Fair Oak 4820 to Winnard's
Copse, Sarisbury 5007. Outlying

colonies occur in Parnholt Wood 3728;
Spearywell Wood, Mottisfont 3127;
Hampage Wood 5329; Marylane Plantation, Four Marks 6933; and almost in
Sussex in The Holt, Rowland's Castle
7211. An aggressive species, usually
abundant where it occurs. Deceptively
dwarf (a micromorph?) in parts of the
New Forest.

H494.   Very local. **VC11**. High-arch-
ing, with long lower inflorescence
branches, cuneate leaflets and scattered
long glands and acicles. Locally
frequent in the westernmost fragments
of the Forest of Bere, ceasing abruptly
at the R. Hamble (but just crossing it at
Catland Copse 5010). Matches a bramble widespread in the W half of
Belgium, misidentified there with *R.
spinulifer* P.J. Müll. & Lefèvre.

ser. **Micantes** SUDRE ex BOUVET

R. decussatus W. C. BARTON ex A.
NEWTON   Rare   **VC11,12**

A variable endemic of wood-margins
abundant in copses by the Surrey
border E of Bentley 7945, 8045 and
very thinly sprinkled across S Hants
from its Sussex High Weald headquarters – but, surprisingly, reappearing in
quantity in far NW Hants.

R. diversus W. C. R. WATSON   Very
rare   **VC12**

Cited by Watson (*Rubi Hdbk*, p.174)
for VC12, but two Townsend gatherings thence in Hb.SLBI so determined
by him are *R. glareosus*. The true plant
was found in 1993 in quantity in Fox
Plantation, Tangley 3352, apparently a
planted-over old common.

R. erythrops EDEES & A. NEWTON
Rare   **VC11,12**

An endemic of wood- and heath-
margins in the SE, found mainly along
the central stretch of the E half of the
county: Thorny Down Wood 5539,
WLWE 1910, Hb.BM, Hb.HME (still
plentiful there); Blackmoor Wood 7732
and Benhams Lane 7832, *AB & AN*
1972; Broxhead Common 8037, *AB &
AN* 1972; Shalden Green copse 6943,
abundant; Thedden Copse 6839; Red
Wood, West Meon 6625; Dodsley
Wood 5338; Gabriel's Copse, Twyford
4923. Also a patch on Southampton
Common, NE corner 4215 and in
quantity in Morgaston Wood, SE
corner 6256. Several populations have

pure white flowers instead of the
normal pink. Tolerant of chalk.

R. glareosus W. M. ROGERS
Common   **VC11,12**

Except in SW Hants (from which it is
virtually absent) and on the chalk and
heaviest clays, in almost every wood,
usually in profusion, which makes its
absence from Wight most remarkable.

R. hantonensis D. E. ALLEN   Local
VC11,12   Map 164

Described in 1985 and named after the
county, to which it is almost endemic
(three localities are known in Wight),
this very distinct species is occasional
to abundant in dry, oak–holly-woods in
Southampton and the districts to the N
and E, continuing thinly across the E
half of the Forest of Bere and the New
Forest. In the latter, exceptionally, it
has abundantly colonized rides in the
coniferized W end of Brownhill Inclosure 2300, and is common also in Pig
Bush 3604 and Gatewood 4300. More
distant localities are Squabb Wood,
Romsey 3221, Preston Oak Hills 6344,
and – by the Surrey border –
Bramshott Common 8533, 8633. For a
detailed historical account see *Watsonia*
15: 387–388.

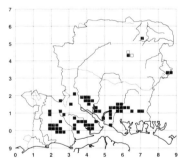

Map 164 Rubus hantonensis

R. hastiformis W. C. R. WATSON
Very rare   **VC11,12**

A large patch in a hazel-thicket
annexed to a garden SW of Bursledon
station 4809, and single bushes in
Bushy Leaze Wood 6838 and the hedge
on the corner of an old lane, Froxfield
7227. A species with large fruits
especially attractive to birds, this is
endemic to Devon, Cornwall and SW
Wales apart from several similarly stray
occurrences in Sussex.

R. leightonii LEES ex LEIGHT.
Local **VC11,12**

Common round Bournemouth and to
the W and NE of the New Forest, but
absent from much of the Forest itself
and widely but very thinly scattered
over the rest of Hants. Noticeably a
colonist of garden shrubberies and
waste ground, it has the look of a once
rather scarce species helped by human
activity to become much more widespread.

R. melanodermis FOCKE   Very local
VC11,12

One of the species characteristic of the
Wessex coastal belt, frequent and
locally in plenty round Bournemouth
and Ringwood and E to Chewton
Common 2194, with outlying populations in Dawkins Bottom, Setley 3000
and in a birch-wood near Buckland
Rings 3097, but scarce in the New
Forest and often only singly there. A
large patch on Browndown Common
5899, a roadside clump at Park Gate
5108 and a clump on the margin of
Preshaw Wood 5822 mark a weak
trickle E of Southampton Water. A
bush on Yateley Common 8259, in the
far NE, is presumably a bird-sown waif.

R. micans GODR.   Local   **VC11,12**

Though preponderantly south-western
in its English distribution this species
has an adventive appearance almost
throughout its Hants range, confined
to roadsides or waste ground and especially associated with the railways – in
particular dotted along the line of the
one-time track from Brockenhurst to
Ringwood. Suggestively, Rogers knew
it only at Milton 2495, yet it is
common today round Brockenhurst
and Hordle and scattered through the
district W of Southampton (though in a
distant outpost in VC12 near Ellisfield 6343 it is as scarce still as when
Eyre found it there in 1903). Only in
Long Wood, Littleton 4432, 'Ravens-
court' copse, Buckland 3196 and
Gundymoor Wood, Havant 6907 – the
latter two near the coast – does it have
the indigenous look that it has in clay
copses in Wight.

R. moylei W. C. BARTON & RIDD.
Very common   **VC11,12**

Though largely missing from Wilts,
Wight, NW and SW Hants (presumably for climatic reasons), one of the
county's most characteristic brambles,
around Winchfield, VC12, exceeding

even *R. ulmifolius* in abundance. It
occurs on acid and basic soils alike.

R. norvicensis A. L. BULL & EDEES
Very local   **VC11,12**

This recently-described East Anglian
species has proved identical with an
abundant bramble of hedges, woods
and waste ground within a 10km radius
of Romsey, where it was collected as
far back as 1914 by R. S. Standen,
Hb.BM. It trickles thence NE to
Winchester and S to Southampton and
the edge of the New Forest at Cobblers
Corner 3099, reappearing in SE Hants
in Beechen Copse, Dundridge 5717,
5818, in copses on Hayling Island and
on the S Hants Ridgeway outside
Hyden Wood 6818. A patch outside a
garden at Silchester 6262 suggests
dispersal sometimes with nursery
plants – as does its presence in plantations in Guernsey. Often ruderal, it
has a recent look in Hants and may still
be spreading.

R. raduloides (W. M. ROGERS)
SUDRE   Very rare   **VC12**

A common Cotswolds species which
trickles across Wilts to just inside the
NW tip of VC12 at Combe Wood
3559, where a colony occurs in open
birch-wood on the basic soil it prefers.

R. trichodes W. C. R. WATSON
Rare   **VC12**

Woods in the N: roundabout by
Government House, Aldershot 8653;
Shapley Heath, Winchfield 7554,
including abundantly in copse; Shapley
Lake copse 7555; Harewood Forest
4043, in cleared area of S section.

[**R. wedgwoodiae** W. C. BARTON &
RIDD.

When originally described, in 1933,
cited for VC11, but the specimen in
question (near Bishopstoke, *JGr* 1878,
Hb.BM) proves to have been so determined by Riddelsdell in error.]

ser. **Anisacanthi** H. E. WEBER

R. adamsii Sudre   Rare   **VC12**

Apart from one huge bush among
rhododendrons in Queen Elizabeth
Park, Farnborough 8656, confined to
the district W and S of Alton: Wield
Wood 6138 (one bush 1974); Chawton
Park Wood 6736; Weathermore Copse
6835, locally plentiful along margin.

R. ahenifolius W. C. R. WATSON
Very local   **VC12**

A heath-edge endemic mainly confined
to Surrey. Along the one-time southern boundary of the Forest of Pamber
from West Heath 5958 to Bramley
Frith Wood 6460, locally in plenty on
roadsides and in copses, with a distant
clump on margin of Basing Forest
6455. Also on Silchester Common 6262
and the Mount Pleasant section of
Tadley Common 6061.

R. campaniensis VAN WINKEL in
sched.   Rare   **VC11**

A bramble known for some years in
quantity on Emsworth Common 7408,
extending to parts of Havant Forest
7111, was confirmed by H. Vannerom
in 1992 as identical with this yet-to-be-
described species abundant on the
coastal plain round Antwerp. Also
known on a common in Kent, its trans-
Channel range is unexpectedly
disjunct.

R. cinerosus W. M. ROGERS   Very
local   **VC12**

Heath-and wood-margins mainly near
the Berks border: Silchester Common
6262 (the type locality); Tadley
Common 6061; along hedge of B3051
by Dairy House Farm, Kingsclere
5460; Ashford Hill 5662, one bush;
margin of Newtown Common 4762,
one bush; Thorny Down Wood 5539;
Bramley Frith Wood 6459, 6460, abundant; Hartley Wood Common 6958.

R. dentatifolius (BRIGGS) W. C. R.
WATSON   Local   **VC11,12**

A western species of open, heathy
woodland with an oddly patchy distribution: common in the SW New Forest
round Burley and on its N margins by
Turf Hill Inclosure 2017, 2117 and in
the N half of Bramshaw Wood 2516,
2517, but shunning the coastal region
as far as Gosport, where it reappears at
Browndown Common 5899 and all
over Chark Common 5702. It is again
common in the SE corner, all over
Emsworth Common 7408 and Southleigh Forest 7308, extending to Havant
Thicket 7109. That the SW coastal belt
is too dry for it is suggested by its sole
Southampton area locality being the
moist bottom of an old clay-pit in
Bassett Wood 4216. Other outlying
populations are at West Walk entrance
5912, Park Hills Wood, Fair Oak 5019
and, far off in VC12, Preston Oak Hills
6343.

R. formidabilis LEFÈVRE & P. J. MÜLL.   Very rare   **VC11**

Locally common on rides at the W end of Parnholt Wood 3728 and one bush in nearby Humbers Wood 3628. A French species otherwise known in Britain only on Surrey commons and one wood in E Sussex.

[**R. infestus** WEIHE ex BOENN.

Cited for VC11 and VC12 by Watson (*Rubi Hdbk*, p.129), in the former case presumably based on three Rogers records, one of which has proved a misdetermination. A northern species which penetrates to Berks, it could well occur.]

R. leyanus W. M. ROGERS   Rare   **VC11,12**

A near-endemic of SW Britain with a puzzlingly disjunct Hants distribution: Barton Common 2593, still in the abundance in which L. Cumming first found it in 1917 (*Rep.B.E.C.* for 1917, p. 219); between Bransgore and Hinton Admiral, *MAR* 1917, Hb.BM; sprinkled in woods and hedges within a 4km radius of Wickham, with an outlying bush in Creech Walk 6411; plentiful in an ancient woodland fragment in Hurstbourne Park 4447; one huge clump on bridleway to Combe Wood, below Walbury 3660. A pink-flowered, lightly glandular bramble locally frequent in Breamore Wood 1419, which Watson, Hb.BM, Hb.CGE, referred to *R. mucronatoides* Ley ex W. M. Rogers, as also is another pinkish form with unusually short stamens in Grove Croft Copse, Monk Sherborne 6057.

H218.   Very local. **VC12**. With long, suberect lower inflorescence branches, sometimes many strong yellow rachis prickles, large white narrow petals and prickly, very long-pointed sepals. Scattered over the clay district W and S of Four Marks and widely dotted across NE Hants. Specimens collected round Ellisfield by *WLWE* in 1905–09, Hb.BM, Hb.HME, were det. *WMR* as *R. bloxamianus*, *R. dentatifolius* and *R. phaeocarpus*. Another from Ditton Common, Surrey, Hb.CGE, was det. *WCRW* as '*R. spinulifer*'. An apparent derivative of this and *R. vestitus*, **H179**, is common in woods and hedges in the Ellisfield district.

H220.   Very local. **VC11**. Robust, aggressive, with largish white flowers and large incised leaves with a very broadly ovate-cordate, long-acuminate terminal leaflet. Abundant, in places dominant on the W fringes of the Forest of Bere and especially in the wooded bournes on the E side of Southampton Water, with outlying patches on the W side as far as Matley Wood 3307 and Keeping Copse, Bucklers Hard 4000. Resembles *R. morganwgensis* var. *sabrinae* W. C. Barton & Ridd. of S Wales.

H911.   Rare. **VC11**. An early-fruiting bramble with vinous prickles, small ternate leaves, largish white flowers, long stamens, red-based styles and ultimately clasping sepals. Abundant throughout Norley Inclosure 3598 and occurring up to 1km around, with a distant patch outside Perrywood Ivy Inclosure, Brockenhurst 3102.

H1052.   Rare. **VC12**. With many broad-based patent stem prickles, whitish-felted leaflets and a long narrow inflorescence, congested above, bearing deep rose petals and long-pointed sepals ultimately erect. In a wide semicircle of woods on the Berks side of Basingstoke: Ewhurst Park, plentiful in copse E of lake 5756; frequent in E part of Morgaston Wood 6256 and S end of nearby Basing Forest 6455; Butlers Land Copse 6662; Shapley Lake copse, Murrell Green 7555. Apparently identical with Watson's '*R. badius*' (in part) and '*R. scutulifolius*' of Springpark Wood, near Addington in NE Surrey, HB.CGE, Hb.SLBI.

ser. **Radulae** (FOCKE) FOCKE

R. bloxamii (BAB.) LEES   Locally common   **VC11,12**

Unaccountably patchy. In greatest quantity round Bournemouth (one of its two British centres), along the W edge of the New Forest, W and N of Romsey, round the N edges of Southampton Water and between Alresford and the Meon Valley; but absent from much of the New Forest and its environs and most of N Hants. On chalk on Danebury Hill 3237, in some quantity.

R. cantianus (W. C. R. WATSON) EDEES & A. NEWTON   Rare   **VC11,12**

A clay-loving species which spills across from local abundance in Wilts to the central part of W Hants: Doles Wood 3752, *ESE* 1968; copses and hedges round Appleshaw 2948, 3148; Harewood Forest 4045, one clump; Squabb Wood 3321, one bush; Fox Plantation, Tangley 3352; Green Drove, Upper Enham 3650; Rowbury Copse, near Longstock 3439. Also a patch on Upper Pennington Common 3095. Otherwise endemic to Kent and the Chilterns.

R. echinatoides (W. M. ROGERS) Dallman   Very local   **VC12**

Spills across on to wood-margins and, more rarely, hedgebanks in the NE quarter of Hants (as far as Dogford Wood, Four Marks 6732) from its large populations on the adjacent Berks and Surrey commons. Especially widespread in the district N of Winchfield. Also in the NW corner in and by Combe Wood 3660.

R. echinatus LINDL.   Frequent   **VC11,12**

Characteristic of wood-margins and woodland-relic hedges. Tolerant of, perhaps preferring, clay and chalk, so very rare in SW Hants. Seldom in quantity and in genuine abundance only in Sutton Beech Wood 6232, under a high larch-canopy. Particularly plentiful in the district W of Alton.

R. euryanthemus W. C. R. WATSON   Locally common   **VC11,12**

Plentiful, often abundant in woods in the Romsey–Southampton–Brockenhurst triangle, yet almost absent from the W half of the New Forest and all the rest of Hants except for Woolmer Forest, where it again occurs in some plenty. Strongly calcifuge and characteristic of birch–holly woodland.

R. flexuosus P. J. MÜLL. & LEFÈVRE   Locally common   **VC11,12**

Frequent, in places abundant on the sands and gravels except round Bournemouth and in the N half of the New Forest; also sometimes in quantity on clay, as in Pamber Forest 6160. In particular profusion round Havant, and in Upper Hamble Country Park 4911 and Wendleholme Copse, Warsash 4907. Less often out of woodland than in Wight, but conspicuously so on Hengistbury Head 1790.

R. fuscicaulis EDEES   Very local
VC11,12

A species mainly of the S Welsh Marches, largely confined in Hants to the northern clay: abundant over most of Harewood Forest (where Townsend collected it in 1873); Great Pen Wood 4461; Freefolk Wood 4944, locally abundant; Hang Wood, Up Nately 7052, locally abundant; Hook Common 7153; Hampage Wood 5430; Floud Wood, Froxfield 7125; Coombe Wood and adjoining hedge-bank 6718.

R. informifolius EDEES   Very rare
VC12

Chawton Park Wood 6736, a clump and an isolated bush in SW corner, and widespread in next-door Bushy Leaze Wood. Otherwise endemic to the central Welsh Marches and more especially Wyre Forest.

R. insectifolius LEFÈVRE & P. J. MÜLL.   Locally abundant   **VC11,12**

In great profusion along the W half of the S margin of the New Forest (its British headquarters) and again in the centre of the Forest, but virtually absent from its N and E sides. Unaccountably patchy, similarly, in the rest of Hants: scarcely at all round Southampton or in Woolmer Forest or in the SE, yet abundant in various woods between Four Marks and Basingstoke, in the S part of Basing Forest 6454, in part of West Walk 5912, in Hen Wood 6622, in Whitmoor Hanger, Grayshott 8536 and by the Wilts border on Tytherley Common 2628. Tolerant of clay, it is typically in quantity where it occurs.

[**R. largificus** W. C. R. WATSON

An unnamed bramble, **H454**, has erroneously passed in Hants for this mainly Wealden species, from which it differs in having pink petals and pale styles. It is plentiful in woods and on roadsides in and around Southampton, scattered NW to Shootash 3122 and SE to Chark Common 5701, with a stray New Forest patch on the margin of Appleslade Inclosure 1809. Partly ruderal, it may have colonized the county comparatively recently.]

R. longithyrsiger LEES ex FOCKE
Very local   **VC11,12**

In great abundance in woods along the SW side of Southampton Water and W along the S margin of the New Forest

as far as Norley Inclosure 3598 and N to Foxhunting Inclosure 3805. Though collected as early as 1879 (Beaulieu, *JGr*, Hb.CGE), its aggressiveness and continuous distribution in part through recent conifer plantations suggest a late immigration from SW England. Occurrences in further, distant parts of Hants – Nightingale Wood 3817 (a roost casual); Michelmersh Wood 3526; N end of Hipley Copse 6111, in profusion; Bramley Frith Wood 6460 – may represent a secondary spread.

R. pallidus WEIHE   Rare   **VC11,12**

An indicator of ancient woodland. In strength at the N end of Humbers Wood 3629, in the N part of Botley Wood 5410 and in its satellite Brook Wood 5512, a relic oakwood fragment at Betty Mundy's Bottom, Preshaw 5822 and Frobury Park Copse, Ecchinswell 5059. Single patches or bushes have also been noted in Sheepwash Coppice, Purbrook 6609 and Tytherley Common 2629. Most if not all old records relate to *R. euryanthemus* or *R. glareosus.*

R. percrispus D. E. ALLEN & R. D. RANDALL   Rare   **VC11**

A newly-described species otherwise known mainly round Colchester and Bristol. Thinly scattered across the south of the county, mostly near the coast: roadside, Wick 1593, *RDR*; in a holly on B3055, Brockenhurst 2901; wooded roadside, South Baddesley 3596; green lane, Little Arnewood House, near Hordle 2797; Southampton Common 4113, one bush 1984.

R. radula WEIHE ex BOENN.   Very local   **VC11,12**

Abundant in Micheldever Wood and its satellites, rippling thinly outwards for 1km or more in most directions, E as far as Medstead and NE to the Bradley–Ellisfield district (where Eyre collected it *c.*1900, Hb.HME). There is a second focus round Andover, and isolated bushes occur on wood-margins elsewhere. Perhaps wholly a recent incomer into the county from the north (its British headquarters is SE Scotland).

R. rudis WEIHE   Local   **VC11,12**

Common, sometimes abundant in open woods in the W half of the chalk-belt, scarcely penetrating S of Winchester or E of a line from Alton to Silchester

(but, exceptionally, common in Moulsham Copse, Yateley 8161). A form with flowers twice the normal size occupies Grotto Copse, Ashmansworth 4357.

R. rufescens LEFÈVRE & P. J. MÜLL.   Local   **VC11,12**

Though really abundant only in Boathouse Copse, Ewhurst Park, near Kingsclere 5857, plentiful in several places in the NE and well clustered round Havant, on the SE side of Southampton and in the clay woods round Fordingbridge. Otherwise widely dotted around and with a tendency southwards to occur in shrubberies in towns, as in Bournemouth, Lyndhurst and Winchester, giving it the look there of a recent colonist – though if this is the plant collected by Townsend at Chewton (where both the Glen 2193 and the Common 2194 hold it today) and determined by Babington as 'a rare form' of *R. hystrix* (*Fl.Hants*, p.138), it has been in the south for over a century. So late a south-westward spread is surprising, for the general absence there of the infertility so characteristic of this species suggests that part of Hants is more congenial to it.

H120.   Rare. **VC12**. Allied to *R. pallidus*, with a broad, lax inflorescence with very long lower branches bearing small, neat, white flowers with green styles and purple, prickly sepals. Abundant in Faccombe Wood 3955 and the N half of Hampage Wood 5430, frequent in Doles Wood 3752 and widespread on Hook Common 7253.

H183.   Very rare. **VC12**. A tall bramble with reddish flowers conspicuous on the E margin of Upper Common, Ellisfield 6345 is identical with the well-known plant of High Beach, Epping Forest, VC18, successively referred by Watson to *R. cruentatus* P. J. Müll. and *R. gravetii* (Boulay ex Sudre) W. C. R. Watson. It is certainly close to some Continental specimens determined as the former.

H277.   Very local. **VC11**. Similar to 'Wolford *fuscus*' of the E Cotswolds. Abundant throughout Squabb Wood, Romsey and in neighbouring copses and hedgerows, with a distant population to the NE in Great Up Somborne Wood 4031.

ser. **Hystrices** FOCKE

R. atrebatum A. NEWTON   Very local   **VC12**

A British near-endemic mainly, as its name implies, in the stretch of country once inhabited by the Atrebates. Widespread and locally abundant in the NE woods and heaths, extending W as far as the Kingsclere area (Wolverton Wood 5658; Boathouse Copse, Ewhurst Park 5857). A colony in Stonybrow Wood, Ropley 6730 constitutes a distant outlier.

R. babingtonii T. B. SALTER   Very rare   **VC12**

Repeated searches have failed to turn this up in the type locality near Selborne, a hedge between Wick Hill Hanger and Oakhanger 7535, *TBS* 1844, Hb.BM, Hb.E; but it was rediscovered in 1974 in Wield Wood 6038, where Eyre collected it in 1899, Hb.BM, Hb.HME (two other old records, however, have proved to be misdeterminations by Rogers). A second locality on the central chalk, Hampage Wood 5430, has yielded several further bushes and another was found in 1992 growing up through a young spruce in Allwood Copse, Ellisfield 6447, but no other Hants bramble has such an orchid-like elusiveness. Like *R. angloserpens* and *R. informifolius*, it is otherwise endemic to the Welsh Marches (except for one site in Middlesex), so the local population stands little chance of replenishment.

R. bercheriensis (DRUCE ex W. M. ROGERS) W. M. ROGERS   Occasional   **VC11,12**

Widely scattered over all but the SW, occurring in quantity mainly in alder carr (as at Bohunt Manor lake, Liphook 8330; Shedfield Common 5612; West Horton copse, Bishopstoke 4718; N edge of Browndown Common 5800), of which it is characteristic.

R. dasyphyllus (W. M. ROGERS) E. S. MARSHALL   Locally common   **VC11,12**

Mainly in N and C Hants but here and there in the SE too. Patently a recent colonizer, spreading southwards, it has just reached the New Forest at its NE tip. Particularly well established in the chalk copses, where competition from pre-existing bramble species is minimal.

<R. durotrigum R. P. MURRAY   Extinct   **<VC11>**

One small bush of this almost exclusively E Dorset endemic was found in 1979 in an ancient bridleway-hedge by Roydon Manor, Brockenhurst 3100. It had gone by 1988.>

R. hylocharis W. C. R. WATSON   Rare   **VC11,12**

A widespread, mainly western-British Isles endemic at the SE of its main range in the woods of NW Hants: Sydmonton Common 4962, one bush; Sandford and Wolverton Woods 5459, 5559, 5658; Boathouse Copse, Ewhurst Park 5857; Well Close Copse, Kingsclere 5460, one bush. A patch in Johnston's Coppice, Purbrook 6807, is presumably part of an outlying population which is centred in W Sussex.

R. infestior EDEES   Rare   **VC11,12**

An endemic of SE England extending from its Surrey headquarters to a wide scatter of E Hants sites: Bramshott Common 8533 (first found, locally abundant, *WMR* 1900, Hb.BM); Yateley Common 8159, 8459; ancient hedgerows by Coombe Wood 6718, 6719; margins of relic fragment of ancient woodland at Betty Mundy's Bottom, Preshaw 5822.

R. marshallii FOCKE & W. M. ROGERS   Rare   **VC12**

An endemic of SE England abundant round Haslemere, Surrey, which spills very thinly just across the border: Bramshott Common 8633, one clump; Holm Hills 8232; Alice Holt Forest 8042, one clump; Liss, in two places, *JSG* 1918, Hb.K. The only population, however, is 14.5km inside the county, on Bramdean Common 6329.

R. asperidens SUDRE ex BOUVET (*R. milesii* A. Newton)   Locally common   **VC11,12**

In Britain a species mainly of central S England, this has its headquarters in Hants, of which it is one of the characteristic brambles, though very local in the SW and absent from much of the N. Preferring dry oak-woods, it is tolerant of clay and chalk.

R. murrayi SUDRE   Very local   **VC11,12**

A heath-and wood-margin species almost restricted to three areas of the

'greater' New Forest: Ganger Common 3823 and parts of adjoining Ampfield Wood; E and S of Brockenhurst (abundant on Setley Common 3099); and around Burley. Otherwise only in Hampage Wood, Winchester 5430 and Radnall Wood, Fordingbridge 1317.

R. naldretti (J. W. WHITE) W. C. R. WATSON   Very rare   **VC11,12**

An endemic of W Sussex which spills across to Petersfield: copse on E side of Heath Pond 7522. A specimen collected on Southampton Common, *BAM* 1964, Hb.CGE, det. *DEA & AN*, may have been an ephemeral stray.

R. newbridgensis W. C. BARTON & RIDD.   Rare   **VC12**

Abundant in Micheldever Wood and its satellites, but tightly confined to them. Endemic mainly to the High Weald, this must be a relatively-recent immigrant, for these woods are not ancient. It was already widespread, however, when Eyre collected it there in 1900, Hb.HME (though Rogers, unaccountably, misdetermined the specimen as *R. marshallii*, of which it long stood as the sole Hants record).

R. phaeocarpus W. C. R. WATSON   Locally common   **VC11,12**

Abundant in many parts of the far N (as also on the Berks side of the border), but more and more local southwards and largely absent from the SW. Away from the N it has the look of a recent intruder, as also suggested by its restriction in many woods there just to an outermost corner or tip. Its tolerance of clay seems to have given it an adaptive advantage.

R. rilstonei W. C. BARTON & RIDD.   Rare   **VC11**

Thinly scattered in woods and heath scrub in several places at the SE tip of the New Forest around Blackfield. Also a stray, ephemeral bush in Allen's Copse, Shootash 3121, *CRL* 1988, det. *DEA*. Apart from one locality in Wight, otherwise confined to extreme SW Britain and Brittany.

[R. scabripes GENEV.

Cited for VC11 by Watson (*Rubi Hdbk*, p.189), possibly repeating a Breamore Wood record, *AHE & NDS* 1933, Hb.BM (*Rep.B.E.C.* for 1935, p.28), which he himself had later corrected to *R. bloxamii*. Bushes in the far NW corner, in a hedge at Woolton Hill 4262 and a small holly-copse at High-clere 4360, resemble it but do not tally satisfactorily and may be hybrids of it only.]

R. tamarensis A. NEWTON   Rare
VC11,12

W of Chilworth roundabout 4117, a once-large population much reduced by building of the M27; Southampton Common 4215, colony on N edge; Harewood Forest 4044, 4043, 3842, straddling the A303. First collected in 1974 but identified 15 years later as this species. Otherwise endemic to SW England, especially the higher parts of Devon.

R. thyrsigeriformis (SUDRE) D. E. ALLEN   Very local   **VC11**

Plentiful in several woods in the W half of the Forest of Bere and abundant on Southampton Common and in the district NW of the city, but quickly thinning out, though dotted as far as the New Forest (round Stoney Cross 2412, 2511) and almost to King's Somborne, Winchester and Gosport. Otherwise known only round Cherbourg and in two places in Somerset, it seems a relatively-recent cross-Channel immigrant still engaged in primary spread. For a fuller account see *Watsonia* 17: 435.

H438.   Rare. **VC12.** With orange prickles, narrow apiculate leaflets and a long narrow inflorescence bearing flowers with narrow pink petals. Locally plentiful along the clay rides of now-coniferized Sydmonton Common 4962, 4963, a patch on nearby Newtown Common 4762 and across in Berks on Greenham Common (various collectors 1931–36, Hb.BM as *R. infestus*, *R. furvicolor* Focke and '*R. melanoxylon*').

H552.   Rare. **VC11,12.** Deceptively variable, with a lax, flat-topped inflorescence bearing early, starry pink flowers with long white stamens and usually reflexed sepals developing long leafy points. Dotted over NE Hants on wooded heath margins, extending into Berks and Sussex. A specimen from Burley Old Inclosure 2504 is the basis of an erroneous record of *R. tumulorum* Rilstone in *Watsonia* 16: 228 (repeated in *Brambles Brit.Is.*, p.245). Merits describing if more than the one population (Shapley Hill, Winchfield 7654) can be discovered.

H568.   Very local. **VC11,12.** Variable, robust, late-flowering, with very unequal curved stem prickles, long-acuminate biserrate leaflets and a long nodding inflorescence of pale pink petals, red or green styles, long-pointed sepals and large delicious fruits. Locally abundant in Alice Holt Forest and dotted across E Hants, resurfacing in some strength on the M3 bank at Beggar's Bush, Shapley Heath 7554 and in copses round Rockbourne 1217, 1317. Represented in herbaria from many sites in Sussex, a few in Surrey and one or two in Kent, this is Watson's '*R. indusiatus*' in the main.

H576.   Very local. **VC11,12.** Aggressive, with a large inflorescence, narrow white petals, leafy-pointed and ultimately clasping sepals, falcate to geniculate prickles and the uppermost panicle leaf oblong. Local to abundant in copses at the E end of the Forest of Bere and in most of the woods from Southampton to Winchester, extending W to Parnholt Wood 3728 and N to Cobley Wood, Micheldever 5244.

H742.   Very local. **VC11.** With long ascending lower inflorescence branches and smallish creamy-pink flowers with long stamens. Common in hedges and woods round Hordle and Sway, spilling into the adjoining parts of the New Forest. A 1908 gathering from Milford on Sea (*LCu*, Hb.OXF) was misreported as *R. glareosus* (*Rep.B.E.C.* for 1930, p.350).

ser. **Glandulosi** (WIMM. & GRAB.) FOCKE

R. angloserpens EDEES & A. NEWTON   Rare   **VC11**

In ancient woodland in the Forest of Bere: Place Wood 6309, *ESE* 1968, locally abundant; Sawyer's Wood, Southwick 6408; Landingplace Copse, Curbridge 5212; copse by Netley station 4608. Otherwise endemic to the Severn Valley and Herts.

[**R. hylonomus** LEFÈVRE & P. J. MÜLL.

Cited for VC11 by Watson (*Rubi Hdbk*, p.206) on unknown evidence. Widespread in the Weald and on record just across the Surrey border, this could well be a Hants species.]

R. pedemontanus PINKW.   Rare
VC11,12

Entirely carpets Breamore Wood 1419, its British *locus classicus*, where it was discovered by Townsend (*Fl.Hants*, p.139, as *R. bellardii* Weihe & Nees) and whence E. F. Linton distributed it in 1893 for the historic 'Set of British Rubi'; Great Pen Wood 4461, *WHM* 1939, Hb.CGE, and The Chase 4462; Grotto Copse, Ashmansworth 4357, abundant under firs; Ampfield Wood 3924, one patch under bracken, 1976. A record by Rogers from Highfield Copse, Southampton 4214 has to be treated with reserve in the absence of a specimen, the more so as *R. scaber*, with which it was formerly much confused, is known from nearby Hut Wood – and all the other records but one are from the W edge of the county.

R. scaber WEIHE   Very local
VC11,12

Mainly in four widely-separated districts: Bramdean Common 6329 to Warnford Park 6222 and abundant in several copses in between; the Forest of Bere fragments, especially West Walk 5912; Sandford and Wolverton Woods, Kingsclere 5459–5658; and Harewood Forest (locally abundant in S section 3742–3943). Also in Ampfield Wood 3924; Stoke Park Wood 4719; Chawton Park 6736 and Bushy Leaze Woods, Alton 6838; Great Pen Wood 4462; Fox Plantation, Tangley 3352; Ashen Wood, Bucklers Hard 3999; and – in far SW Hants – abundantly in a copse at Bransgore 1897. Some of these are *Fl.Hants* localities for '*R. glandulosus*', but that name was applied broadly and other records therein for it are errors or doubtful. Hut Wood 4218, *JFR* 1906, Hb.BM, is the only additional old locality authenticated by a specimen.

H710.   Rare. **VC11.** Low, with a nodding inflorescence with erect-ascending branches, very wavy rachis, narrow white pointed petals and very long, bright green sepals. Entirely carpets Spearywell Wood, Mottisfont 3128.

sect. **Corylifolii** LINDL.

The product of Dewberry x Bramble crosses, the innumerable forms in this section in Britain almost all have such very restricted ranges that they are now considered best disregarded taxonomically. Of the handful widespread enough to be treated as exceptions, there occur in Hants:-

R. britannicus W. M. ROGERS   Very rare   **VC11,12**

A species of SE England represented just by a large patch in the centre of Gundymoor Wood, Havant 6907, and by another in a clay copse by Clanville Lodge, Penton Grafton 3248.

R. conjungens (BAB.) W. M. ROGERS   Very local   **VC11,12**

Frequent in hedges in the district N of Fordingbridge and plentiful along the Lunway at South Wonston 4635, but otherwise scarce and very scattered.

R. nemorosus HAYNE & WILLD.   Very local   **VC11,12**

Thinly scattered in heathy hedges and open, especially damp woodland round the W, S and NE margins of the New Forest and across to the Southampton district. Very rare elsewhere: Round Copse, Basing 6853; Goose Green Inclosure 8040, *AB & AN*; Sydmonton 4857, *GCD* (*Suppl.Fl.Hants*, p.39, as *R. balfourianus* Bloxam ex Bab.).

R. pruinosus ARRH.   Locally frequent   **VC11,12**

Hedges and woods in the central part of the chalk belt, especially common in the Micheldever area; plentiful also in alder-willow carr in West Horton copse, Bishopstoke 4718 and in regenerating scrub on Baddesley Common 3921. Otherwise scattered widely but very thinly.

R. transmarinus D. E. ALLEN   Local   **VC11,12**

Widely scattered, but especially plentiful between Southampton and Romsey. A trans-Channel species, also in the Channel Islands and near Cherbourg.

R. tuberculatus BAB.   Locally common   **VC11,12**

Plentiful in the coastal districts, extending up the Itchen Valley to Winchester and reappearing in some quantity in the area W of Andover. Elsewhere scarce. Characteristic of wood-margins and tolerant of chalk.

sect. **Caesii** LEJ. & COURTOIS

R. caesius L.   Dewberry.   **N** Locally common.

In hedges, scrub, and open woodland; chiefly on basic soils. Very common on the chalk. Some records may be in error for *R. fruticosus* sect. *Corylifolii*.

Potentilla palustris (L.) SCOP. Marsh Cinquefoil.   N   Local   Map 165

First record, Gilbert & Thomas White 1767, 'in the bogs of Bean's-pond', VC12 (*White's Jnls* 1: 222).

In mildly-acid flushed bogs, pools and grassy marshes. Very local, except in parts of the New Forest, Woolmer and Bere Forests.

VC11: Emer Bog 3921, abundant, *RPB* 1957, 1992; Hookheath Farm, Southwick 6408, *MB* 1970. **VC12**: Woolmer Pond 7831, *AB* 1978, *FR* 1994; Milking Bridge Field, Woolton Hill 4361, *NFC* 1971, *MEd* 1984; Shortheath Common 7736, abundant in swamps, *FR* 1994.

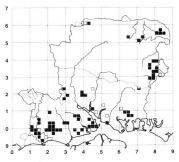

Map 165 Potentilla palustris

P. anserina L.   Silverweed.   **N** Very common

Moist grassy places and bare ground in all open habitats, including turfy salt-marshes, dune-slacks, and above the strand-line on seashores. Universal.

P. argentea L.   Hoary Cinquefoil. **N**   Rare   Map 166

On bare sand or in sparse turf on heathy commons, in sand-pits and by roadsides. Of spasmodic appearance; local around Woolmer Forest, very rare elsewhere.

VC11: Woodington sand-pit, East Wellow 3120, Hb.RPB 1963, pit since infilled; Hurn Airport 1298, *BE* 1991; N of Fort Cumberland 6899, 24 plants in old field, *DEG* 1994. **VC12**: Harewood Forest 3943, *RMV* 1985; Hazeley Heath 7657, *HJMB* 1986; Woolmer Forest ranges 7933, *AB* 1986; Shortheath 7636, *FR* 1994.

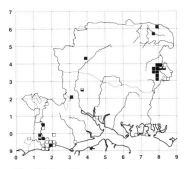

Map 166 Potentilla argentea

P. recta L.   Sulphur Cinquefoil. **H,C**   Rare

First record, Miss D. W. Fawdry 1959, Sinah Common golf-links 6999, VC11.

Bare sandy or gravelly waste-ground, roadsides, and old railways. Often transient, but established on Hayling Island, and on the Kingsley roadsides, 7837, 7838, VC12, having spread from the now-demolished railway.

VC8: Tetrad 0420. **VC11**: Avon Forest Park 1201, *FAW* 1986; Calshot 4701, *AEWy & RPB* 1987. Also 1492, 3292, 4214, 4400, 6404, 7098. **VC12**: Itchenstoke Down 5530, roadside, *RSm* 1991. Also 6456, 7258.

P. intermedia L.   Russian Cinquefoil.   **C**   Very rare

First record, J. F. Rayner 1924, Christchurch, VC11 (*Proc.IoW N.H.S.* 1: 245).

In similar situations to *P. recta*.

VC11: Near Langhorn Road, Southampton 4315, waste ground, *MBa & PE* 1962 (*Rep.S'ton N.H.S.*, p.8); West Meon Station 6423, abundant, *BWh* 1968, Hb.AB, *SNHS* 1986; Ashlett Green, Fawley 4603, *JOM, AJG & RPB* 1987. **VC12**: Bordon 7836, 7835, old railway, Hb.AB 1969, (*Watsonia* 10: 424), *AB* 1968–78.

P. norvegica L.   Ternate-leaved Cinquefoil.   **H**   Rare

First record, J. F. Rayner 1915, Millbrook Station 3912, VC11, reclaimed land (*Proc.Hants Fld Club* 10: 110).

In similar situations to *P. recta*, but later records are confined to the NE and E, and to VC12.

VC12: Farnborough 8453, 8654, *ARGM* 1980, since lost (*RAE Survey*); Bordon 7836, old military railway, *L-Lo* 1983; Warren Heath 7759, *RCS*

1986; Woolmer Forest 7933, *AB* 1993. Also 7830, 7834, 7838, 8030, 8052, 8252, 8254, 8432.

P. neumanniana RCHB. (*P. tabernae-montani* Asch.) Spring Cinquefoil. **N?,C** Very rare

First record, G. A. R. Watts 1933, 'railway bank at Micheldever Station' 5143, VC12 (*Watts MSS*), specimen *PMH* 1933 in Hb.BM.

Bare chalk on railway spoil-heaps, in sparse turf and open scrub. Otherwise absent in SE England, so the Hants sites may be fairly recent in origin. It appeared on the chalk spoil-heaps and cuttings on the Southampton–London railway, whether from disturbance of buried seed or as a colonist is not known.

VC8: N of Whitsbury Down, between Great Yews and Round Clump 1122, *BW* 1941 (*Rep.B.E.C.* for 1941–42, p. 486, as *P. verna* L.), not refound. **VC12**: N of Micheldever Station, reduced after 1963 by conversion of part of its area to improved pasture. Still quite plentiful over a wide area of Micheldever Spoil Heaps, and in roadside turf in 5143, 5144, 5244, also at the Elf Oil fuel-storage depot 5143, on layer of chalk over tanks, *ILR* 1992.

P. erecta (L.) RAEUSCH. ssp. **erecta** Tormentil. **N** Frequent and locally very common

Heaths, acidic grassland and open woodland; also a feature of chalk heaths, where acid soil overlies the chalk and in a few old alluvial meadows on neutral soil.

P. x suberecta ZIMMETER (*P. erecta* x *P. anglica*) **N** Occasional

Occasional with one or both parents. **VC11**: Wootton Farm, Holmsley 2298, *GH* 1952, Hb.LANC.

P. anglica LAICHARD. Trailing Tormentil. **N** Very local and occasional

First record, T. Yalden *c.*1770, 'Forest of Bere, opposite Ashlands' *c.*6010, VC11 (*Ray Syn.MS*, p.256).

Heathy grassland, gravelly ground and banks, rides in open woods. Widespread but scattered. Much confused with the hybrids, but fertile. VC11: 8 □; VC12: 13 □.

VC11: Hordle cliff 2791, abundant in grassland, *GH* 1976, Hb.LANC; Hamer gravel-pit 1210, Hb.RPB 1964,

det. *FR*; Sinah Common golf-links 6999, Hb.AWW 1950; Matley Passage 3307, Hb.AWW 1959; Tourner Bury, Hayling Island 7300, *FR* 1980. **VC12**: Herriard Park 6646, *FR* 1976; Woolmer Pond, old railway 7831, Hb.AWW 1951, Hb.AB 1970, det. *JDG*; Eelmoor Marsh 8353, *AB* 1975, conf. *FR*.

P. x mixta NOLTE ex RCHB. (*P. anglica* x *P. reptans*)

P. x italica Lehm. (*P. erecta* x *P. reptans*) **N** Occasional

In similar habitats to the parent species. These two hybrids are said to be indistinguishable individually (*Hybr. Fl.Brit.Is.*, pp.208–209). Recorded in the aggregate form from many sites, and probably often mistaken for *P. anglica*.

VC11: Wellow 3018, *RMV* 1985, det. *BHa*; Sandy Point, Hayling Island 7498, *AB, FR & EAP* 1980. **VC12**: Holt Pound 8142, *PJ* 1970, det. *JDG*.

P. reptans L. Creeping Cinquefoil. **N** Very common

Grassland, bare ground, roadsides and waste land. Universal.

P. sterilis (L.) GARCKE Barren Strawberry. **N** Common

Old woodlands and their borders, hedgebanks, shady streamsides, and sometimes on old masonry. Generally common, especially on basic soil, but rare on shallow chalky soils.

Fragaria vesca L. Wild Strawberry. **N,C** Common

In woods and scrub, in hedges and on banks. Also colonizing bare gravel, chalk downs and walls. It avoids the more acid soils except in such places as roadsides where introduced lime is present.

F. moschata (DUCHESNE) DUCHESNE (*F. muricata* sensu D. H. Kent, non L. nec Mill.; *F. vesca* L. taxon *moschata* Duchesne) Hautbois Strawberry. **D** Very rare

No longer cultivated, and now a very rare, established alien.

VC11: Lordswood 4016, hedgerow near cottages, Hb.RPB 1953, site built upon in 1970s. **VC12**: Bramshott 8433, wall of old rectory and in grounds, *AB* 1967, weeded out a few years later; and Waggoners Wells 8534, two patches of

the female form on banks of lake, Hb.AB 1973, det. *ACL* 1976 (both *Watsonia* **10**: 424), still present, *AB* 1994.

F. ananassa (DUCHESNE) DUCHESNE (*F. vesca* L. taxon *ananassa* Duchesne) Garden Strawberry. **D** Very local

First record, E. C. Wallace 1937, Whitehill, Bordon 7834, VC12, Hb.BM.

Rubbish-tips, clearings, hedgerows and especially railway banks. A frequent escape from cultivation. In E Hants it can run along hedgerows, as at South Hay 7740, *AB* 1969. VC11: 18 □; VC12: 25 □.

VC11: Boorley Green, Botley 5014, Hb.AWW 1956. **VC12**: Weyhill *c.*3046, cutting in chalk along main road, abundant, *GDF* 1984.

Duchesnea indica (ANDREWS) FOCKE Yellow-flowered Strawberry. **H** Very rare

First record, A. W. Westrup 1951, Stent's Glove Factory, Brockhampton 7106, VC11, Hb.AWW.

Dispersed from gardens on to waste ground by birds.

VC11: Battenbury Avenue, Portsmouth 6503, Hb.AWW 1951; Ridding Meads, Winchester College 4828, foot of wall, *KC* 1989, Hb.RPB.

Geum rivale L. Water Avens. **N** Locally common Map 167

In damp places on basic soil, whether along rivers, in damp woodland, wet meadows, or in fenland. Rarely in drier woods on chalk. In the SW, virtually restricted to the Avon Valley and Lymington River. Reaches its eastern limit in Hants at Reedy Copse 8230, VC12, *APNH* 1980, on the Sandgate Beds, with only one native site in Sussex, near the Hants boundary.

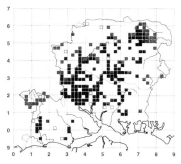

Map 167 *Geum rivale*

VC8: Park Water, Plaitford 2621, *RMV* 1986. **VC11**: Heywood Mill 3199, *RPB* 1954; Denny Lodge 3305, in ditch, *MR* 1976; Ratlake 4123, *RMV* 1987; Southwick 6208, *RPB* 1985. **VC12**: Hampshire Gate 3354, *GDF* 1981; Winslade Lane, Ellisfield 6446, *ANHS* 1985; Odiham Common 7551, *CRH* 1991; Jacks Meadow, Wheatham 7427, *DBa* 1989–1994; Hampage Wood 5430, on Clay-with-flints on the chalk plateau, *FR* 1984; Greywell Moors 7050, abundant, *FR* 1994.

G. x intermedium EHRH. (*G. rivale* x *G. urbanum*)   **N**   Local and occasional

Widely scattered where the parents occur together. VC8: 4 □; VC11: 28 □; VC12: 29 □.

G. urbanum L.   Herb-Bennet, Wood Avens.   **N**   Very common

Woods, scrub, hedgerows, waysides. Very common except on acid soil.

Agrimonia eupatoria L.   Agrimony.   **N**   Very common

Wood- and field-borders, scrub, hedgerows, verges, banks, and rank grassland on the downs. Very common, especially on basic soils.

A. procera WALLR. (*A. odorata* auct., non (L.) Mill.)   Fragrant Agrimony. **N**   Locally frequent   Map 168

Wood-borders and rides, shady lanes, thickets, overgrown pits, occasionally on road-banks. Widespread, but usually on much more acid soils than the last, occasionally on chalk superficials.

VC11: Stansore Point, Lepe 4699, bushy area on shingle, *RPB* 1963; Otterbourne Hill 4522, road-bank, *RPB* 1978; edge of Tourner Bury Wood, Hayling Island 7399, abundant,

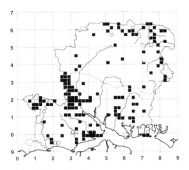

Map 168 Agrimonia procera

AB 1984. **VC12**: Nothing Hill, Kingsclere 5158, roadside, Hb.RPB 1979; Longmoor Road 8231, *FF* 1966, *AB* 1987, Blackbushe Airfield 8059, *AB* 1983.

Sanguisorba officinalis L.   Great Burnet.   **N**   Rare   Map 169

In marshy meadows on alluvium or peat, and on damp grass-heaths on the calcareous Headon Beds, usually on slightly flushed slopes, in heather tussocks which offer protection from grazing. Rare and very local, confined to the SW New Forest, and the R. Enborne, R. Loddon and R. Blackwater basins in the NE.

VC11: Dur Hill Down 1900, *AEB* 1986; Whitten Bottom 2000, *RPB* 1987; Holmsley Walk 2001, *AEB* 1986; 2101 *GDF* 1986; Burley Beacon 2002, 2003, *AEB* 1986; Stony Moors 2199, *SRD* 1981; Holmsley Inclosure, in damp rides, 2100, 2200, *RPB* 1956–87; 2299, Miss Jenkins 1975. **VC12**: Bramshill, meadow by R. Blackwater, between the two fords 7562, *PMH & ECW* 1937, *NCC* Flood Plain Survey 1986; Ashford Hill 5462, churchyard, *PB* 1982; Darby Green 8360, and Blackwater 8460, unimproved meadows, *ARGM* 1987–88; R. Loddon 6858, unimproved pasture, *MEd* 1984. **VC22**: Mortimer West End 6363, frequent in wet meadow, *BRB* 1965, *PB* 1982.

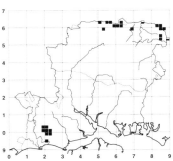

Map 169 Sanguisorba officinalis

S. minor SCOP. ssp. **minor** (*Poterium sanguisorba* L.)   Salad Burnet.   **N** Locally common   Map 170

First record, Gilbert White 1765, 'Downs between Alresford & Andover [VC12] are full of Burnet: so full in many places that it is almost the only herb that covers the Ground: & is eaten down very close by sheep, who are fond of it' (*White's Jnls* **1**: 154).

Very common in short chalk-grassland; local in other basic grassland, especially near the coast, grass-heaths on the Headon marls in the S New Forest, on imported soil along railways, and in turf in some churchyards.

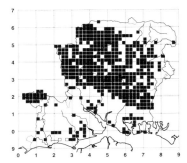

Map 170 Sanguisorba minor ssp. minor

ssp. **muricata** (GREMLI) BRIQ. (*Poterium polygamum* Waldst.& Kit.) Fodder Burnet.   **D**   Occasional

Near arable land on roadsides, banks and waste land; mainly on chalk. VC11: 13 □; VC12: 18 □.

VC11: Monument Road, Portchester 6106, Hb.AWW 1950. **VC12**: Farringdon *c.*7034, *MOC* 1982; canal embankment beside Tundry Pond 7752, *ARGM* 1988.

Acaena novae-zelandiae KIRK (*A. anserinifolia* auct., non (J. R. Forst. & G. Forst.) Druce)   Pirri-pirri-bur. **C**   Very rare

First record, R. P. Bowman 1981, Beaulieu old airfield 3500, VC11, a few plants on bare gravel and rubble, Hb.RPB. There is also an unconfirmed modern record for tetrad 3496.

<**Alchemilla xanthochlora** ROTHM. **C**   Extinct

VC12: Privett 6727, verge of old drive N of church, Hb.AWW 1962. Probably introduced with grass-seed mixture. Recently ploughed.>

A. filicaulis BUSER ssp. **vestita** (BUSER) M. E. BRADSHAW (*A. vestita* (Buser) Raunk.)   Lady's-mantle.   **N** Very rare

First record, J. Gerard 1597, 'in the towne pastures by Andover', VC12 (*Ger.Herb.*, p.802).

In old pastures, verges and rides, on basic soil. Some of the earlier stations have definitely been destroyed by 'improvement', and others, which have not been checked, have probably also been lost, so there is now only one recent record.

VC11: Near West Wellow (possibly VC8), *PMH* 1933, Hb.BM; East Parley 1098, sand-pit, *MPY c.*1960, Hb.AWW. **VC12**: Between Linkenholt and Faccombe Wood *c.*3756, *ECW* 1979, Hb.RNG; Cow Down Copse 5850, grassy ride, *WEW* 1958, conf. *MEB, GM* found rides gone 1986; Mattingley, in two places – roadside edge of wood 7258, and in field 7358, *PH* 1965, none seen *CRH* 1990; Hound Green 7359, *BRB* 1965 (*Rep.S'ton N.H.S.*, p.12), *CRH* 1988–90; Selborne, field in Coombe Wood 7534, *AB* 1961, Hb.AWW, and between Long Lythe and Long Copse 7434, *KAC c.*1920, Hb.HCMS, meadow below Milking Hanger, Hb.AB 1970, since 'improved'.

A. mollis (BUSER) ROTHM.   **H**   Rare

First record, R. P. Bowman 1972, Goatspen Plain gravel-pits 2201, VC11.

A common garden plant, increasingly becoming established in the wild.

VC11: Holmsley old airfield, in short turf 2299, *RPB* 1985, conf. *SMW* (*Watsonia* 17: 188); Turf Hill 2017, verge of gravel-track on heath, *RPB* 1987. Also 1600, 1608, 2692, 2802, 3816. **VC12**: Yateley 8261, margin of flooded gravel-pit, *ARGM* 1987; Weston Common 6944, self-sown in clearing planted with conifers, *ETu* 1986. Also 7050, 8250, 8252.

Aphanes arvensis L.   Parsley-piert. **N,C**   Common

A weed of arable and waste places or bare ground, especially on basic soil.

A. inexspectata LIPPERT (*A. microcarpa* auct., non (Boiss. & Reut.) Rothm.)   Slender Parsley-piert. **N,C**   Locally common   Map 171

A common weed of sandy arable fields; also on anthills, in old pits, and on heathland verges. Usually on acid soil.

Rosa arvensis HUDS.   Field-rose. **N**   Common

First record, Miss C. R. May 1832, chalk-pit, Breamore, VC11 (*May Ptgs Cat.*: 285).

In hedges, scrub and woods, and around the edges of heaths. Common, especially on heavy clay and on chalk.

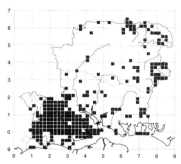

Map 171 Aphanes inexspectata

R. pimpinellifolia L.   Burnet Rose. **N,H**   Very local   Map 172

Open grass-heaths, mostly on the Headon Beds, old gravel- and marl-pits of the New Forest. Also in maritime turf, on shingle and amongst gorse on the seashore.

VC11: Fort Cumberland, Eastney 6899, *PMH* 1929; 6798, *RPB* 1988, *FR* 1994; Lower Crockford Bottom 3599, in low gorse, *RPB* 1965; Browndown Ranges 5799, Hb.AWW 1952, *TCGR* 1983. Five inland records are probably of garden escapes. A double-flowered form is naturalized in Hook-with-Warsash churchyard 5005.

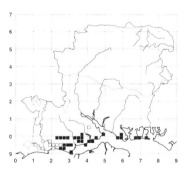

Map 172 Rosa pimpinellifolia

R. rugosa THUNB. ex MURRAY Japanese Rose.   **H**   Occasional

First record, Lady Anne Brewis 1963, Hogmoor 7835, VC12, well established on sandy ground by road.

A naturalized garden escape, generally on the sand. VC8: 1 □; VC9: 1 □; VC11: 13 □; VC12: 10 □. Some records may refer to *R. 'Hollandica'*, a cultivar hybrid between *R. rugosa* and either *R. majalis* J. Herm. (*R. cinnamomea* L.) or the closely related *R. marrietii* Lév.

VC11: Hamble 4706, shingle-beach

RPB 1985. **VC12**: Stokehill Farm 3951, in lane, *GDF* 1983.

R. 'Hollandica' hort.   Dutch Rose. **H**   Very rare

VC11: N of Widden Bottom 2999, N road bank, *RPB* 1985–91.

R. filipes REHDER & E. H. WILSON **H**   Very rare

First record, G. H. Forster 1989, Janesmoor Plain near North Bentley Inclosure 2413, VC11, one extensive bush climbing high over a holly, probably bird-sown, Hb.RPB, det. *RHS*, Wisley (*Alien Pl.Brit.Is.*, p.141).

R. carolina L.   Pasture Rose.   **H** Very rare

First record, Lady Anne Brewis 1963, Hogmoor 7834, VC12, Hb.EJC, det. *EJC* 1989. Garden throw-out from old cottage since demolished, established in a roadside thicket, 1963–87 (*Alien Pl.Brit.Is.*, p.140).

R. gallica L.   Provence Rose.   **H** Very rare

First record, R. P. Bowman 1985, Dibden 4009, VC11, side of track amongst reeds beside brackish drain, Hb.RPB, det. *ALG* (*Alien Pl.Brit.Is.*, p.141).

R. stylosa DESV.   Short-styled Field-rose.   **N**   Frequent

In woods, scrub and hedges, on chalk and sand, often in shadier places. Less common than *R. canina*, but often overlooked for this rose.

VC11: A35, Holmsley Station 2300, Hb.RPB 1975, det. *RM*; near Droxford 5918, *JF* 1988, conf. *ALP*. **VC12**: Ashford Chace 7326, Hb.AWW 1963; Harewood Peak 4046, *AB & JF* 1988, conf. *ALP*.

R. x andegavensis BASTARD (*R. stylosa* x *R. canina*)   **N**   Very rare or overlooked

VC11: East End, Lymington 3697, *RPB* 1975, det. *RM*.

R. canina L.   Common Dog-rose. **N**   Very common

Woods, thickets, hedges, heaths; a vigorous colonizer of ungrazed chalk-grassland. Universal.

R. x dumalis BECHST. (*R. canina* x *R. caesia*)   **H?**   Very rare

First record, Mrs J. Fryer 1988,
Winnall Moors 4929, VC12, Hb.AB,
det. *ALP* (*Watsonia* **18**: 425). As *R.
caesia* Sm. is a northern plant, this may
be bird-sown from a garden.

R. x dumetorum THUILL. (*R. x
concinnoides* Wolley-Dod; *R. canina* x
R. obtusifolia)   N   Under-recorded

VC11: Titchfield Haven 5302,
Hb.RPB 1975, det. *RM*.

R. x scabriuscula SM. (*R. x curvispina*
Wolley-Dod; *R. x aberrans* Wolley-
Dod; *R. canina* x *R. tomentosa*)   N
Very rare

First record, R. P. Bowman 1976,
roadside near Deadman Hill 1916,
VC11, det. *RM*.
   VC11: Hatchet Pond 3601, *AB*
1979, det. *RM*.

R. x toddiae WOLLEY-DOD (*R. canina*
x *R. micrantha*)   N   Very rare

First record, R. P. Bowman 1990,
Ports Creek, Hilsea 6504, VC11,
Hb.RPB, det. *ALP* (*Watsonia* **18**: 425).

R. obtusifolia DESV.   Round-leaved
Dog-rose.   N   Locally frequent
Map 173

In thickets, hedges, verges, streamsides, heath-borders, gravel-pits and
waste land. Generally on gravel or clay,
avoiding the chalk. Rather frequent in
the SW, but doubtless often overlooked elsewhere.
   VC11: Crockford Bridge 3598,
Hb.RPB 1975, det. *RM*; Holmsley
Station 2300, *EB-Br & ENo* 1975, det.
FR; Wallington River 6009, *AB* 1978
det. *FR*; R. Hamble near Durley Mill
5114, *AB* 1978, det. *FR*. VC12: Mare-
lands, near Bentley Station 7943, *AB*
1975, det. *FR*; Grooms Farm,
Frithend 8138, *AB* 1985, *ANHS* 1988.

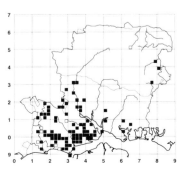

Map 173 Rosa obtusifolia

R. tomentosa SM.   Harsh Downy-
rose.   N   Rare   Map 174

In scrub, wood-borders, roadside
verges on heaths, and on chalk downland. Rare and very local in the New
Forest, and on the chalk downs.
   VC11: Dibden Bottom 3806, 3807,
several scattered bushes on roadside
verges, streamside and heath, *RPB*
1975–92; North Gate 3804, *RPB* 1976;
Standing Hat, Balmer Lawn 3103,
RPB 1977, all Hb.RPB and det. *RM*;
Hincheslea Moor 2601, roadside, *RMB*
1979, *RPB* 1989; West Wood,
Sparsholt 4129, Hb.RPB 1982, *RMV*
1988. VC12: A31, Matterley Farm
5429, *AB* 1979, det. *RM*; B3400 Harewood Peak 4046, in hedge, *AB* 1978,
det. *RM*; tree-belt N of A303, 5043,
AB 1978, det. *RM*; Noar Hill 7431,
chalk-pit, *AB* 1978, det. *RM*.

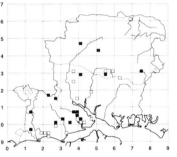

Map 174 Rosa tomentosa

forma **foetida** (R. Melville considered
this almost certainly to be *R. tomentosa*
x *R. micrantha*).

VC11: Brune's Purlieu 1714, *AB* 1979.
VC12: Noar Hill 7431, in two places,
AB 1968; Button's Brow, Goleigh
7330, *AB* 1967; Chilbolton Down
4136, *AB* 1969; all det. *RM*.

R. x avrayensis ROUY (*R. tomentosa* x
R. rubiginosa)   N   Very rare

VC12: Recorded by *RM* in *Hybr.Fl.
Brit.Is.* (p.226).

R. sherardii DAVIES   Sherard's
Downy-rose.   N   Very rare

First record, J. F. Rayner 1923, Red
Hill, Bournemouth, VC11, det. *AHW-
D* (*Suppl.Fl.Hants*, p.43). Not refound
since and the locality is now largely
built-up.
   As presently known, restricted to
heathland scrub on the Headon Beds in
the New Forest.

VC11: Goatspen Plain 2301, few
bushes along E roadside, and Burley
Beacon 2002, two clumps on edge of
scrub, Hb.RPB 1990, both det. *ALP*
(*Watsonia* **18**: 426); Durns Town, Sway
2898, hedge around allotments, *VS*
1993, Hb.RPB.

[**R. mollis** SM. (*R. villosa* auct., non
L.)   Soft Downy-rose.

There are single old records in
Fl.Hants (p.144) and *Suppl.Fl.Hants*
(p.43). These must be considered
either errors of identity or introductions.]

R. rubiginosa L.   Sweet-briar.
N,H   Occasional   Map 175

Chalk grassland and scrub; rather local.
In a few scattered sites on other soils,
in some of which it may be of garden
origin.
   VC8: Martin Down 0319, *RPB*
1981. VC11: Whitten Bottom, near
Thorney Hill Holms 2000, single bush,
RPB 1979; Broughton Down 2833,
Hb.RPB 1975, det. *RM*; B3078,
Godshill Ridge 1815, *c.* seven small
bushes apparently native, *RPB* 1985;
Chalton Down 7315, plentiful, *AB*
1984. VC12: Bridge over R. Test, Test-
combe 3838, *AB* 1977; bridge over M3
near Winchfield 7755, *AB* 1980, det.
RM; Rookery Dell, Monk Sherborne
6056, *PB* 1982; East Woodhay 4060,
woodland above chalk-pit, *NFC* 1977.

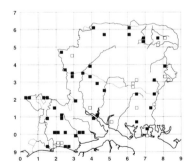

Map 175 Rosa rubiginosa

R. micrantha BORRER ex SM.
Small-flowered Sweet-briar.   N
Locally common   Map 176

In chalk grassland and scrub, bushy
heathland, roadside verges, hedges and
on the seashore. On the downs it often
occurs with the previous species, but is
more widespread and frequent.
Common throughout the New Forest.

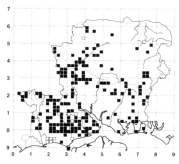

Map 176 Rosa micrantha

R. x bishopii WOLLEY-DOD (*R. micrantha* x *R. agrestis*)   **N**   Very rare

VC11: South Charford Drove, Breamore Down 1320, VC11, *RPB* 1991, det. *ALP* (*Watsonia* **19**: 146).

R. agrestis SAVI   Small-leaved Sweet-briar.   **N**   Very rare

First record, E. F. Linton 1891 (as *R. sepium* Thuill.), thicket on Breamore Down, VC11, rather plentiful (*J.Bot.* **29**: 344).

VC11: Still at Linton's site, Breamore Down 1320, 1420, 30 bushes at edge of scrub, Hb.RPB 1991, det. *ALP* (*Watsonia* **19**: 146); Gallows Hill 1321, one bush, *PS* 1994, Hb.RPB. VC12: Noar Hill 7431, Hb.AB 1978; N of A303, 5043, in tree-belt with *R. tomentosa*, Hb.AB 1978, both det. *RM* (*Watsonia* **13**: 333).

Prunus cerasifera EHRH.   Cherry Plum.   **D**   Frequent

First record, R. P. Bowman 1948, Test Lane, Redbridge 3614, VC11.

Field- and roadside hedges, treebelts. Widespread and locally frequent, but under-recorded, perhaps due to early flowering. Barely naturalized, mostly originating from plantings. VC8: 2 □; VC11: 35 □; VC12: 31 □.

VC11: Coombe Lane, Sway *c.*2798, *CWh* 1963, Hb.BM; Three Oaks, Curdridge 5416, near disused railway and stream, *RPB* 1975. VC12: Honey Lane, Selborne 7634, *AB* 1963–78; W of Upton Grey 6848, edge of copse, several fruiting trees, *AB* 1980; Pies Farm 6834, *AAB* 1982; junction of A327 with Love Lane, Yateley 8061, *ARGM* 1987.

P. spinosa L.   Blackthorn.   **N** Very common

Open woods, clearings, hedges, streamsides and neglected downland.

Often forms dense thickets excluding other shrubs. Universal.

P. x fruticans WEIHE (*P. spinosa* x *P. domestica* sensu lato)   **D**   Very rare or under-recorded

VC11: Crow, Ringwood 1604, old railway, *RPB* 1977, det. *RM*; Hamble 4708, roadside thicket opposite airfield, *RPB* 1977. VC12: Near Liphook 8330, *AB* 1976, det. *CAS*.

P. domestica L. ssp. **domestica** Wild Plum.   **D**   Frequent

Hedges and thickets, probably often bird-sown from orchards and gardens. Widespread, and rather frequent.

VC11: Forest Lake, Crow 1604, *RPB* 1977, det. *RM*. VC12: Old Burghclere Lime Quarry 4757, *RPB* 1979; Honey Lane, Selborne 7534, *AB* 1985.

ssp. **insititia** (L.) BONNIER & LAYENS Bullace.   **D**   Occasional

In similar habitats to the above but origins obscure. Widespread but infrequent.

VC11: Setley 3000, wooded track, *RPB* 1978, det. *RM*; Barton Common 2493, old hedge, *KK & AB* 1977; Redbridge Lane, Nursling 3715, Hb.RPB 1977, det. *RM*. Also 1602, 1806, 1896, 3022, 3090, 3422, 4416, 4814, 5408, 5412, 5416, 6806, 6820, 6822, 7200, 7206. VC12: Mill Green 5262, at bridge, *AB* 1976; Wonston 4739, road to Stoke Charity, *AB* 1970 (*Watsonia* **10**: 424); lane to Ladle Hill 4857, *AB & FR* 1975. Also 4652, 4834, 5062, 6050, 6452, 6846, 7224, 8252.

ssp. **italica** (BORKH.) GAMS ex HEGI (*P. italica* Borkh.)   Greengage.   **D** Very rare

First record, Miss V. M. Leather 1959, lane from Crondall 8149, VC12, Hb.AB.

P. avium (L.) L.   Wild Cherry.   **N** Frequent and locally common

Woods, copses, ancient untrimmed hedges. Common on a wide range of soils, except markedly-acid ones. Very scarce in the New Forest. Most typical of old oak- and mixed deciduous woodland on Clay-with-flints, or on chalk scarps, or on the Malmstone. In the south of England ripe fruits are scarce, e.g. in The Warren, Hawkley 7328, VC12. The wood is a high quality timber with a reddish colour, used in panelling and cabinet-making. The

heartwood darkens so much on exposure that it can be used to repair mahogany. A local Hampshire name for it is the 'Merry Tree' (A. F. Mitchell, pers.comm.).

VC11: Great Copyhold Copse, West Meon 6725, many mature trees in almost pure stands, *RPB* 1975.

P. cerasus L.   Morello Cherry, Dwarf Cherry.   **H**   Very rare

An escape from cultivation, forming thickets.

VC11: No confirmed modern record. VC12: 'Roadside hedge 2 miles SE of Crondall', 8046, *Watts M.SS* 1935; White Hill, Kingsclere 5156, roadside, Hb.RPB 1975 (*Watsonia* **11**: 394); Boar Knoll, Palestine 2540, trackside, *RPB* 1968–85; Dean Heath Copse, North Waltham 5747, edge of copse, *RPB* 1969; Georgia Farm 2941, a thicket at site of long-destroyed cottage, *GDF* 1982.

P. padus L.   Bird Cherry.   **H**   Very rare

Not native in Hants.

VC11: Bordean Hanger, Langrish 7023, half-way up the hill, *JF* 1985. VC12: Old Basing 6552, single tree by R. Loddon, *ARGM* 1980; Bordon Camp 8036, running down to R. Wey, *AB* 1982; Alice Holt Forest 8142, abundantly seeding, *RCS* 1986.

P. serotina EHRH.   Rum Cherry.   **H** Very rare

First record, R. P. Bowman 1975, West Walk, Wickham 5812, VC11, plantation rides and stream-banks, regenerating freely, Hb.RPB.

VC11: Bottom Copse, Corhampton Down 5820, small mature tree, *RPB* 1979. Also 3814, 6012.

P. lusitanica L.   Portugal Laurel. **H**   Rare

Often planted in shrubberies and spreading spontaneously in a few places. VC11: 11 □; VC12: 11 □.

P. laurocerasus L.   Cherry Laurel. **H**   Frequent

Woods and shrubberies, commonly planted, but often spreading rampantly from seed, and tending to obliterate the native herb-flora in some woods on acid soil.

Pyrus pyraster (L.) BURGSD. (or **P. communis** L.)   Wild Pear.   **D** Rare

Doubtfully wild, but may appear wherever a core is dropped. Also planted in hedges. VC11: 26 □; VC12: 10 □.

VC11: Sowley Copse 3696, three isolated trees, looking native, *RPB* 1957, reduced to one by 1988; Lower Exbury 4298, field near shore, *RPB* 1972; stable-block, Queen Elizabeth Country Park 7118, *DBa* 1989. VC12: Ashford Chace 7326, one tall tree, *AB*, *JF & BAG* 1986; Eversley Copse 7961, huge tree, *CRH* 1986.

Malus sylvestris (L.) MILL. Crab Apple. **N** Locally frequent Map 177

A sign of ancient woodland and heathland. Widespread, and locally frequent, on heavy acid soil, particularly in the New Forest, where it is a familiar tree of dry bracken-clad heathland, and the open glades of ancient woods. Also frequent in the old woods on the Gault, Upper Greensand, and London Clay in the NE. It has been much confused with *M. domestica* and puzzling intermediates which may be hybrids. Doubtful records have not been included on the map.

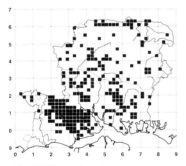

Map 177 Malus sylvestris

M. domestica BORKH. (*M. sylvestris* ssp. *mitis* (Wallr.) Mansf.) Apple. **D** Frequent

In hedges, thickets and waste land. Descended from the cultivated apple. Includes the great majority of 'crab apples' outside ancient woodland.

M. x purpurea (BARBIER) REHDER (*M. niedzwetskyana* Dieck x *M. atrosanguinea* (Späth) C. K. Schneid. Purple Crab. **H** Very rare

First record, Mrs G. H. Read 1992, Dockens Water W of Splash Bridge, by Broomy Inclosure 2011, VC11, one medium-sized tree in scrub, comm. *GHF.*

M. prunifolia BORKH. Plum-leaved Apple. **H** Very rare

First record, W. G. Helyar 1992, Silchester Common 6262, VC12, two trees on bank of old gravel-workings, det. *NRG* (as a cultivar or hybrid of this species).

M. sargentii REHDER **H** Very rare

First record, Mrs J. Fryer 1980, one small bush, bird-sown in scrub around Hatchet Pond 3601, VC11, det. *EJC.*

M. hupehensis hort. Hupeh Crab. **H** Very rare

VC11: Hale Purlieu 1918, two small, bird-sown trees on slope above stream on sandy heath, Hb.RPB 1986, det. *CRL,* who comments that this agrees with the tree grown under that name by Hillier Nurseries, but it is not the true crab of that name, which he has seen wild in China. He suspects it could be an unnamed species which arrived undetected from China, or else a hybrid or a seedling sport of a named species. The local nursery at Hale has never dealt with this particular tree. The ripe cherry-sized fruits are a glossy dark red.

Undetermined **Malus** hybrids

Several other ornamental crabs are gradually becoming established in the wild, doubtless bird-sown. The following trees are so far indeterminate:

VC11: Gorley Hill 1611, edge of gravel-pit, on hillock; Hightown Common 1705, edge of heath; Row Down, Blackwell Common 4301, on edge of heath, *RPB* 1990.

Sorbus aucuparia L. Rowan. **N,H** Locally common Map 178

Open heathy woods, and heathland. A typical tree of wooded valleys, and of

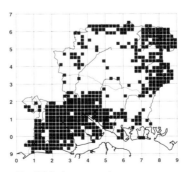

Map 178 Sorbus aucuparia

holly scrub, on the plateau gravels in the New Forest. Also common, and appearing native, on the Lower Greensand and the N and SE Tertiaries. Scarce or absent from the chalk. Can be bird-sown from planted trees on waste land and railways. It is often suggested that it is an introduction in S England but, although often planted, no reason can be found to regard it as other than native in old woodland on acid soil.

S. aucuparia x S. intermedia **H?** Very rare or extinct

VC11: Ashley, *PMH & HTB* 1933, Hb.BM, det. *AJR* 1979.

S. x thuringiaca (ILSE) FRITSCH (*S. aucuparia* x *S. aria*) **N** Very rare or extinct

VC12: 'West End coppice, a wood by the roadside about two miles from Farnboro' station', *WWR c.*1848, ?Hb.BM (ms note in *WAB*'s copy of *Phytologist,* 3, catalogued as '*Flora Hantoniensis*' in library at Royal Botanic Gardens, Kew). Not reported since *Fl.Hants* (pp. 150–151) and most of the former open country around Farnborough is now built on. However it does occur in Rake Hanger, VC13, in places only *c.*200m from the Hants border.

S. intermedia (EHRH.) PERS. Swedish Whitebeam. **H** Occasional

Planted in ornamental grounds and dispersed by birds; generally as isolated trees.

VC11: Marlborough Deep, Wootton 2298, *RPB* 1977; Brownhill Inclosure 2300, *RPB* 1977; Portchester Castle 6204, *EAP* 1981. Also 0890, 1608, 1690, 2498, 2402, 3226, 3696, 4008, 4498, 4826, 5024, 5614, 5898, 6206, 6402, 6604, 7098. VC12: Swallick Farm, Cliddesden 6548, old railway, Hb.AWW 1962; Selborne Hanger 7333, *AB* 1964. Also 4632, 8452.

S. aria (L.) CRANTZ Common Whitebeam. **N,H** Locally common Map 179

In woods, scrub and hedges; common on the chalk, especially in escarpment woodland of beech, ash and yew. Frequent on the acid soils of the high plateau gravels in the northern New Forest, often with rowan within largely pure holly clumps. Occasional and local elsewhere, and then often planted. Native in the Hythe Beds woodland along the borders of Sussex and Surrey, near where the hybrid with *S. aucuparia* (*S.* x *thuringiaca* (*q.v.*)) occurs. Rare in Malmstone hangers in VCs 11 and 12.

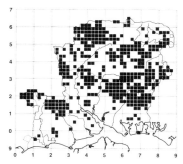

Map 179 Sorbus aria

S. torminalis (L.) CRANTZ Wild Service-tree. **N,H** Local Map 180

In woods and copses on the Tertiary clay soils of the estuaries near the coast, and in the New Forest, where it is occasional to locally frequent. Rather rare on the northern Tertiary clays, and on Gault at Gully Copse. When in woods, it is regarded as an excellent indicator of ancient woodland, though occasionally it is planted. Often only a single tree is found in a site, but in some places it forms stands of small trees through root-layering.

VC11: Gritnam Wood 2806, *SRD & FR* 1975; Tile Barn, Brockenhurst 2901, *AEB* 1988; Spillman's Copse, Bartley 3113, *RPB* 1974; Curbridge 5111, *RPB* 1967; Carpenters Copse 5809, N of Fareham, *FRS* 1982. **VC12**: Redlands Copse 5662, *VF* 1974; Pamber Forest 6160, *PB* 1982; Gully Copse, NE of Bentley 8045, *CRH & RBG* 1985.

In the eighteenth century, according to Dr A. Hunter (*Silva*, Notes, p.182),

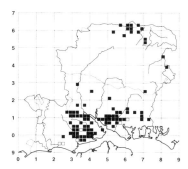

Map 180 Sorbus torminalis

its fruit was 'sold in the London markets in autumn', and had 'an agreeable acid flavour'; Evelyn himself noted that, with new wine and honey, it made 'a conditum of admirable effect to corroborate the stomach'; he also recorded that the timber was useful for the joiner, of which he had 'seen a room curiously wainscotted', and that it had many other uses (*Silva*, p.183).

Amelanchier lamarckii F.-G. SCHROEDER Juneberry. **H** Locally frequent Map 181

First records, G. W. Pierce, near West Wellow, VC8/11, and G. A. R. Watts, canal-bank at Pondtail, Fleet *c.*8253, VC12, 1932 or 1933 (both *Proc.Hants Fld Club* 12: 294, as *A. canadensis* Medik.).

In open woods and plantations on sandy and gravelly soils, and on heathland. Originally planted, but widely dispersed by birds, and thoroughly naturalized. Increasing in the New Forest, Woolmer Forest, and the NE Tertiaries. VC11: 42 ☐; VC12: 31 ☐.

VC11: Mark Ash Wood 2407, *RMV* 1988; Castle Hill, Chilworth 4016, *RPB* 1976; Heath Common, Petersfield 7522, *MS–W* 1982. **VC12**: Shortheath Common 7736, *AMo* 1977; Kingsley Common 7938, *FR* 1992; The Chase, Woolton Hill 4462, *NFC* 1979; Fleet Pond 8254, *CRH* 1983–92.

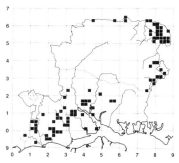

Map 181 Amelanchier lamarckii

Genus Cotoneaster

Many species are now grown in gardens and, having berries beloved of birds, are bird-sown into the countryside. These have only recently begun to be studied in Hants but the following have been identified:

[**Cotoneaster affinis** LINDL. Purpleberry Cotoneaster.

The record for Hurn Forest, VC11,

RPB & RMW 1985 (*Watsonia* **17**: 471) is an error for *C. transens.*]

C. transens KLOTZ Godalming Cotoneaster. **H**

First British record, R. P. Bowman & R. M. Walls 1985, Hurn Forest 1001, VC11, edge of ride in conifer plantation, Hb.RPB, redet. *JF* 1991 (*Watsonia* **19**: 146).

C. frigidus WALL. ex LINDL. Tree Cotoneaster. **H**

First record, Mrs J. Fryer 1986, pathside, Wheatham Hill, Steep 7427, VC12, Hb.JF.
  VC11: Stockbridge 3533, old railway trackside, *SAL* 1988, Hb.JF, det. *JF*.

C. x watereri EXELL (*C. frigidus* x *C. salicifolius*) Waterer's Cotoneaster. **H**

First record, Mrs J. Fryer 1985, Ashford Hangers, Steep 7326, VC12, det. *JRP & CAS* (*Watsonia* **18**: 219).
  VC11: Ipley Inclosure 3608, *RMV* 1987, det. *JF*. **VC12**: Also 4832.

C. salicifolius FRANCH. Willow-leaved Cotoneaster. **H**

First record, Mrs J. Fryer 1985, Wheatham Hill, Steep 7427, VC12, Hb.JF, conf. *BH*.
  VC11: Ports Down 6606, chalk grassland, probably bird-sown, *RRa* 1993, det. *JF*.

C. dammeri C. K. SCHNEID. Bearberry Cotoneaster. **H**

First record, R. A. Barrett 1993, Ports Down 6606, VC11, probably bird-sown, det. *JF*.

C. lacteus W. W. SM. Late Cotoneaster. **H**

First record, Mrs S. A. Lister 1988, Magdalen Hill, Winchester 5029, VC12, Hb.JF, det. *JF*.

[**C. congestus** BAKER Congested Cotoneaster

The record for Mogshade Hill 2309, VC11, Hb.RPB 1988 (*Watsonia* **17**: 471) is an error. Specimen redet. *JF* 1993 as *C. sherriffii*.]

C. sherriffii KLOTZ **H**

First British record, R. P. Bowman 1988, Mogshade Hill, New Forest 2309, VC11, two bushes on N road-bank W of bridge over underpass, Hb.JF, Hb.RPB 1992, 1993, det. *JF*.

C. integrifolius (ROXB.) KLOTZ (*C. thymifolius* Wall. ex Lindl.; *C. microphyllus* Loddiges non Wall. ex Lindl.) Small-leaved Cotoneaster. **H**

First record, S. S. Southwell & R. P. Bowman 1957, Noar Hill 7431, VC12, not seen recently.

Formerly confused with *C. microphyllus* Wall. ex Lindl.

VC11: Butts Lawn, Brockenhurst 2903, *PVJB & RPB* 1988, Hb.JF, Hb.RPB, det. *JF*. Also 7022. **VC12**: Also 4446, 4636.

[**C. nitidus** JACQUES Distichous Cotoneaster.

VC11: On bank of path behind beach, Warsash *c*.4905, *BAG* n.d., det. *JF*, but possibly planted (*Alien Pl.Brit.Is.*, p.153).]

C. horizontalis DECNE. Wall Cotoneaster. **H** Occasional

First record, Mrs M. P. Yule 1960, N of Christchurch, tetrad 1494, VC11.

One of the two longest-naturalized and still the commonest species in such places as chalk slopes, but also on roadsides on a variety of soils.

VC8: 0618. **VC11**: Also 0890, 1404, 1604, 2014, 2200, 2412, 2610, 2802, 3096, 3008, 3202, 3226, 3400, 3424, 3600, 4614, 4624, 4626, 5004, 5406, 5802, 6206, 6224, 6606. **VC12**: Ashford Hangers, Steep 7426, *JF* 1986. Also 3038, 3046, 4830, 5044, 5228, 7224, 7430.

C. divaricatus REHDER & E. H. WILSON Spreading Cotoneaster. **H**

First record, R. P. Bowman 1988, Fleetend, Warsash 5005, VC11, Hb.RPB, det. *JF*.

C. nitens REHDER & E. H. WILSON Few-flowered Cotoneaster. **H**

First record, Mrs S. A. Lister 1988, Winchester 4726, VC11, Hb.JF, det. *JF* (*Alien Pl.Brit.Is.*, p.153).

C. lucidus SCHLTDL. Shiny Cotoneaster. **H**

First record, Mrs J. Fryer 1986, Pitt 4529, VC11, Hb.JF (*Alien Pl.Brit.Is.*, p.153)
VC11: Also 4626.

C. villosulus (REHDER & E. H.

WILSON) FLINCK & HYLMÖ Lleyn Cotoneaster. **H**

First record, Mrs J. Fryer 1986, Pitt 4529, VC11, several plants, Hb.JF, det. *BH* (*Alien Pl.Brit.Is.*, p.156).

[**C. acuminatus** LINDL.

The record for Ampfield wood, VC11, *RCS* 1983 (*BSBI News* 37: 15) is an error and is referable to the following species.]

C. laetevirens (REHDER & E. H. WILSON) KLOTZ Ampfield Cotoneaster. **H**

First record, R. C. Stern 1983, Ampfield Wood 4123, VC11, E end near Hursley, refound *JF* 1987, Hb.JF, det. *BH* 1989 (*Alien Pl.Brit.Is.*, p.152).

C. simonsii BAKER Himalayan Cotoneaster. **H** Local and occasional, but under-recorded

First record, R. P. Bowman 1953, Crockford Bridge 3498, VC11, scrub in old marl-pit, Hb.RPB, det. *JRP* 1986.

Well naturalized in scrub, by roadsides and wooded streams, especially on heathland.

VC11: Also 1800, 2000, 2402, 2618, 2818, 3006, 3210, 3806, 4826, 7422. **VC12**: Old Stoner Hanger, Steep 7325, Hb.JF 1987. Also 5032, 7224, 7826, 8060, 8254. Many previous records have been disregarded in the interest of accuracy.

C. bullatus BOIS Hollyberry Cotoneaster. **H**

First record, Mrs J. Fryer 1986, St Catherine's Hill, Winchester 4827, VC11, trackside, det. *BH*.
VC11: Also 2004, 6606. **VC12**: Fleet Pond 8154, three shrubs, bird-sown in woodland on W side, *CRH* 1992, det. *KWP*.

C. 'Firebird' HOOFTMAN (*C. bullatus* x ?*C. franchetii*) **H**

First record, Mrs J. Fryer 1989, Wheatham Hill, Steep 7427, VC12, Hb.JF, det. *BH* (*Alien Pl.Brit.Is.*, p.151).

C. rehderi POJARK. Bullate Cotoneaster. **H**

First record, Mrs J. Fryer 1986, Ashford Hangers, Steep 7426, VC12, Hb.JF, det. *BH* (*Alien Pl.Brit.Is.*, p.154).

VC11: Ports Down 6606, chalk grassland, probably bird-sown, *RBa* 1993, det. *JF*.

[**C. moupinensis** FRANCH. Moupin Cotoneaster.

VC11: Recorded in *Alien Pl.Brit.Is.* (p.153), but no details traced and status unknown.]

C. dielsianus E. PRITZ. ex DIELS Diels' Cotoneaster. **H**

First record, Mrs J. Fryer 1985, Wheatham Hill, Steep 7427, VC12, Hb.JF, det. *JRP & CAS* (*Watsonia* 18: 218).

VC11: Burley golf-course 2102, Hb.RPB 1987, det. *JRP*. Also 2200, 4626, 5408, 7006. **VC12**: Also 6448.

C. sternianus (TURRILL) BOOM Stern's Cotoneaster. **H**

First records, Mrs J. Fryer 1987, Harefield Road, Winchester 4732, and Ashford Hangers, Steep 7326, VC12, Hb.JF, det. *BH* (*Alien Pl.Brit.Is.*, p.155).

VC11: A35 Markway Hill 2402, Hb.RPB 1992, det. *JF* (*Watsonia* 19: 286); Ports Down 6606, chalk grassland, probably bird-sown, *RBa* 1993, det. *JF*.

C. amoenus E. H. WILSON Beautiful Cotoneaster. **H**

First record, Mrs S. A. Lister 1988, B3420 Harestock 4632, VC12, chalky roadside bank, Hb.JF, det. *JF* (*Alien Pl.Brit.Is.*, p.149).

C. hummelii FLINCK & HYLMÖ **H**

First record, Mrs S. A. Lister 1987, Winchester 4726, VC11, between viaduct and traffic lights, Hb.JF, det. *JF* (*Alien Pl.Brit.Is.*, p.152).

C. perpusillus (C. K. SCHNEID.) FLINCK & HYLMÖ **H**

First record, Mrs S. A. Lister 1988, Winnall, Winchester 4829, VC12, bird-sown, Hb.JF, det. *JF* (*Alien Pl.Brit.Is.*, p.154).

C. vilmorinianus G. KLOTZ **H**

First record, R. A. Barrett 1993, Ports Down 6606, VC11, on chalk grassland, probably bird-sown, det. *JF* (*Alien Pl.Brit.Is.*, p.156).

Undetermined **Cotoneaster** species

VC11: Ferry Road, Sinah Warren,

Hayling Island 6999, single shrub under oak on roadside, *PS & WFS* 1994. *JF* and *BH* agree that this is a sp. nov. belonging to series Acuminati T. T. Yu., as yet undescribed.

Pyracantha coccinea M. ROEM. x **P. rogersiana** Hybrid Firethorn. **H**

VC11: Durns Town, Sway 2898, one bush on edge of old pit on heath, *GHF* 1992, det. *ACL* as probably this garden hybrid.

P. rogersiana (A. B. JACKS.) COLTM.-ROG. Asian Firethorn. **H** Overlooked?

VC11: Dibden Bay 4109, bird-sown bush on reclaimed land, Hb.RPB 1991.

Mespilus germanica L. Medlar. **D** Very rare

First record, H. L. Green, single tree, cut down in 1924, Pains Hill, near Lockerley, VC11 (*Suppl.Fl.Hants*, p.44).

VC11: Curbridge 5111, copse on bank of tidal R. Hamble, a single well-grown bush flowering and fruiting freely amongst native trees and shrubs and probably bird-sown, Hb.RPB 1968, moribund 1988; two trees in hedge of lane near Flexford Mill Cottage, Sway 2896, *GY* 1982.

Crataegus monogyna JACQ. ssp. **monogyna** Hawthorn. **N,D** Very common

Abundant and universal, in woodland, scrub, heathland, hedges, and on neglected chalk grassland, which it can easily overrun. Extensively planted as a hedge.

C. x media BECHST. (*C. x macrocarpa* sensu D. H. Kent, non Hegetschw.; *C. monogyna* x *C. laevigata*) **N,D** Rare

Usually with parents; commoner than *C. laevigata*.

VC11: Efford Bridge, Pennington 3094, Hb.RPB 1957, det. *RM*; Setley gravel-pit 3099, *RPB* 1957; Pennington Common 3095, two bushes in open scrub on heath, *RPB* 1990. VC12: Abbotts Ann *c*.3242, *MPY & JDG* 1968; West Down, Chilbolton 3838, edge of woodland, *WMK* 1975; Alice Holt Forest, frequent on W edge, *AB* 1976; Bins Wood *c*.7636, *FR* 1986; Sheephouse Copse 7545, by old trackway, *CRH* 1985–90. There are a few other unconfirmed records.

C. laevigata (POIR.) DC. (*C. oxyacanthoides* Thuill.) Midland Hawthorn. **N,D** Rare Map 182

Borders of woods, old woodland and nearby hedges. Distinctly rare and local, and mostly confined to the Gault and Upper Greensand clays, especially at Alice Holt Forest. It is common just to the E in Sussex. Rarely native outside ancient woodland but, strangely, absent from the New Forest. The scattered records in W Hants are likely to be introductions.

VC11: Ratlake, Ampfield Wood 4123, *EL* 1960, det. *AWW*; A3051 Burridge 5110, small bush in hedge, *AAB* 1989, Hb.RPB. VC12: Standfast Farm, Hawkley Hurst 7530, *AB* 1969; Goose Green Inclosure, Alice Holt Forest 8040, etc., *AB* 1978; *FR* 1988; Tadpole Lane, Ewshot 8250, *CRH* 1984.

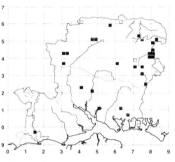

Map 182 Crataegus laevigata

FABACEAE

Robinia pseudoacacia L. False-acacia. **H** Local

First record, R. P. Bowman 1955, Anderwood Inclosure 2405, VC11.

Introduced in plantations on acid soil, locally naturalized and spreading on sandy waste land and tips in the SW and NE heathland areas. VC11: 28 □; VC12: 15 □.

VC12: Near Brook House 8156, *AB* 1980.

Galega officinalis L. Goat's-rue. **H** Very local

First records, R. P. Bowman 1956, Standon 4227, patch on grass verge, and C. D. Drake 1956, Western Shore, Southampton, VC11.

An alien originating from gardens; increasing. On disturbed soil, in gravel-pits, tips and waste places,

mostly in the built-up areas of S Hants. VC11: 31 □; VC12: 3 □.

VC11: Wicor 5905, *EAP* 1981; Swaythling Station 4415, *DEA* 1982; Bartley Water, Eling 3512, *RPB* 1984. VC12: Ovington 5631, *GHF* 1981 (*Watsonia* 14: 422); Yateley 8062, stream-bank, *ARGM* 1987; Hazeley Heath 7657, *CRH* 1988; Hogmoor Inclosure 7835, *AB* 1962 (*Watsonia* 14: 422).

Colutea arborescens L. Bladder-senna. **H** Rare

First record, A. W. Westrup 1950, tips, Ferry Road, Eastney 6799, VC11, Hb.AWW.

Garden escape, in waste places or on tips.

VC11: Peartree Green, Itchen 4311, *MS* 1982. Also 1492, 3612, 4010, 4414, 6098, 6400, 6602. VC12: A303, Andover 3644, *MFW* 1991. Also 8058, 8452, 8646.

Astragalus danicus RETZ. Purple Milk-vetch. **N** Very rare

First record, W. A. Payn 1940, roadside near Danebury 3337, VC12 (*Proc.Hants Fld Club* 15: 65), *GVD* 1962, destroyed by roadworks *c*.1970.

Very rare, in chalk turf.

VC12: Dunch Hill 2048, 2148, *RPB* 1970, 1980, 1988, not refound 1993; Shipton Bellinger 2345, *RPB* 1970, 1993–94.

A. glycyphyllos L. Wild Liquorice. **N** Very rare

First record, F. I. Warner 1873, Stratton Wood near Micheldever Station, VC12 (*Fl.Hants*, p.107).

Amongst scrub and on rough banks, on chalk.

VC11: Farlington Redoubt 6806, chalk slope of fortification, *LFM & WSL* 1954 (destroyed by excavation of chalk for A27); hedge near Crookham (Crookhorn?) Lane, *JLW* 1963, Hb.AWW, may be the same, or another site nearby. VC12: Lythe Hill 7224, *AB* 1963, small relic; Micheldever Wood, *PMH & ECW* 1940 (probably destroyed by forestry work); South Wonston 4735, railway spoil-heaps, *RP* 1967, Hb.AB; *PB* 1980; Monk Wood, Alton 7439, *AB* 1964.

Onobrychis viciifolia SCOP. Sainfoin. **N,D** Locally frequent Map 183

Locally common or occasional in chalk

grassland, especially by tracks and roadsides, but dwindling as it is no longer cultivated. Rare off the chalk.

VC8: A354, Martin Down 0320, *RPB* 1974–92. **VC11**: Priory Road, St Denys 4313, railway, *RPB* 1967, *PS* 1991; Fort Purbrook 6706, abundant, *EAP* 1981. **VC12**: Penton Mewsey *c*.3246, *BRB* 1968; along the old 'Portway' road, 2440–2541, *MFW* 1990; Andwell 6852, *AJPB* 1991.

[The agricultural cultivar '*O. sativa* Lam.' was sown on the B3006 S of Selborne 7432 by the Selborne Association, and on the Alresford bypass, tetrads 5630–6030, by HCC.]

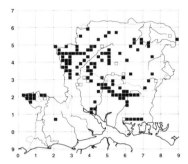

Map 183 Onobrychis viciifolia

Anthyllis vulneraria L. ssp. **vulneraria** Kidney Vetch. **N** Locally common Map 184

First record, Gilbert White 1766, Selborne, VC12 (*White's Jnls* **1**: 205).

Common in chalk grassland. Occasional on slipped clay beneath seacliffs, and in turf over shingle or masonry rubble along the coast. Rarely off the chalk, along gravelly banks of new roads.

VC11: Hordle Cliff 2692, *MR* 1976; Hurst Castle 3189, *SNHS* 1961, *RPB* 1991; Beaulieu old airfield 3400, 3500,

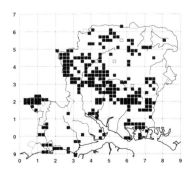

Map 184 Anthyllis vulneraria

RPB 1979–87; Calshot 4701, reclaimed land, *SNHS* 1974.

[ssp. **carpatica** (PANT.) NYMAN var. **pseudovulneraria** (SAGORSKI) CULLEN **D**

An alien in grass-seed mixture sown by HCC on Alresford bypass, tetrads 5630, 5830, 6030, VC12, *AB* 1991, det. *JRA*.]

Lotus glaber MILL. (*L. tenuis* Waldst. & Kit. ex Willd.) Narrow-leaved Bird's-foot-trefoil. **N,C** Local Map 185

Local in wet brackish pastures, and on sea-walls. Sporadic, and usually a colonist of bare and disturbed ground, inland; in gravel-, chalk- and clay-pits, disused railways, chalk roadside verges, and open woodland rides.

VC11: Clay-pits, Denmead 6511, Hb.*AWW* 1957; Eling Shore 3712, slightly brackish pasture, Hb.*RPB* 1955, *CC* 1989; Fields Heath, Fawley 4502, gravel-pit, *JO & PS* 1986. **VC12**: Duck Street *c*.3248, *GDF* 1969; Hare's Farm, Hartley Wintney 7657, *HJMB* 1988.

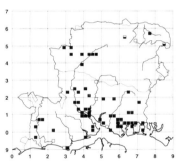

Map 185 Lotus glaber

L. corniculatus L. Common Bird's-foot-trefoil. **N** Common

Very common in dry open grassland, especially on chalk, sand and gravel.

L. pedunculatus CAV. (*L. uliginosus* Schkuhr) Greater Bird's-foot-trefoil. **N** Locally very common Map 186

Common in marshes, wet pastures, ditches, stream-banks, mildly acid bogs, and swampy open woods. Largely absent from the chalk.

L. subbiflorus LAG. (*L. hispidus* auct., non Desf. ex DC.) Hairy Bird's-foot-trefoil. **N** Very local and rare Map 187

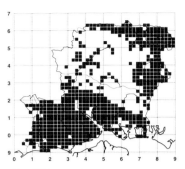

Map 186 Lotus pedunculatus

In sparse turf and bare, disturbed sand and gravel near the sea about Bournemouth and Christchurch. Inland, at:

VC11: Avon Causeway 1397, *RPB* 1983; Avon Forest Park 1202, *RPB* 1988; Blashford gravel-pits 1507, *RPB* 1981, Goatspen Plain gravel-pits 2201, *RPB* 1971, not seen 1988; Wilverley Post 2401, *MAJ* 1991; Sway 2799, *c*.20 plants at foot of reservoir, *RPB* 1991; track W of Frame Heath Inclosure 3303, *TGE* 1991. **VC12**: The Warren, Oakhanger 7735, on disturbed sand, Hb.AB 1974 (*Watsonia* **10**: 423), grown over by 1990.

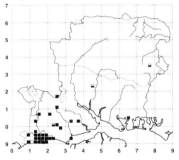

Map 187 Lotus subbiflorus

L. angustissimus L. Slender Bird's-foot-trefoil. **N** Very rare

In bare sand or fine gravel, and in short open turf, near the coast and in the Avon Valley.

VC11: Wick, Christchurch 1592, sandy edge of pond, *TWa* 1989, Hb.RMW, det. *JRA*; Spinnaker Lake, Blashford 1507, old gravel-pit, *FDR* 1963, Hb.*AWW*, scarce, with *L. subbiflorus*, *AB & JO* 1984, abundant in two places following dredging works, *RMW & RPB* 1988, very few, *RPB* 1994; Titchfield Haven 5302, old gravel-pit, *SJE & JAN* 1986, Hb.HCMS, 50–60 plants, *RPB* 1992, *c*.1000 plants, *RPB* 1994.

Tetragonolobus maritimus (L.) ROTH   Dragon's-teeth.   **C**   Very rare

First British record, F. Stratton 1875, Forest Farm, W of Winchester, grassy strip by an arable field, (*J.Bot.* **13**: 179). Probably what is now known as Forest of Bere Farm, 4029, VC11.

Possibly introduced in grass-seed mixtures.

VC11: Farley Mount (also in 4029), plantation-ride, *PMH* 1913, Hb.BM (as *Lotus siliquosus* L.); Collyer's Pit, Widley 6606, on bank of track, *DPJS & JMC* 1987. **VC12**: Noar Hill 7431, chalk-pit, *JM* 1970; in an adjacent chalk-pit, *JAB* 1980, *AB* 1994; in a third place, one year only, *RL* 1984.

Ornithopus perpusillus L.   Bird's-foot.   **N**   Locally common   Map 188

In short turf, and on bare sand or gravel, dry heathland and dunes; also in unfertilized lawns on sand in the NE.

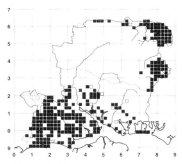

Map 188 *Ornithopus perpusillus*

Hippocrepis comosa L.   Horseshoe Vetch.   **N**   Locally frequent   Map 189

In open, chalk grassland, mainly in

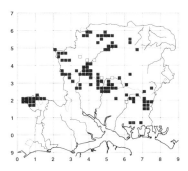

Map 189 *Hippocrepis comosa*

compact or eroded turf, colonizing bare chalk in places. Soon ousted by rank grass. Almost absent from NE Hants.

Securigera varia (L.) LASSEN (*Coronilla varia* L.)   Crown Vetch.   **H**   Very rare

First record, J. F. Rayner 1915, about Southampton, VC11 (*Suppl.Fl.Hants*, p.24).

A garden escape, naturalized in waste places, railway banks and sand-pits, but often transient.

VC11: Rayner's record has been confirmed at Millbrook 3812, *CDD* 1967, and a Bargate Street building-site 4111, *EH & PE* 1960, but both stands are now gone. It was found at Knapp Mill, Christchurch, *ER & NDS* 1925, and at Owslebury Bottom, *GWP* 1928 (both *loc.cit.*), the latter confirmed at 5124, *ARGM* 1980. Other records are: Bickton Mill 1412, *RPB* 1975, now gone; Bransgore 1998, *KK* 1977; Sherfield English 3023, disused sand-pit, *RPB* 1963, now gone; Shawford 4724, railway cutting, *NEGC* 1941 (*Rep.B.E.C.* for 1941–42, p.485).

Vicia orobus DC.   Wood Bitter-vetch.   **N**   Very rare or extinct

Old grassland, banks or scrub. 'In considerable plenty, though limited to a confined area, between Lyndhurst Station and Brockenhurst, 1875–79', J. Groves, Hb.BM, (*Fl.Hants*, p.110). This has been searched for without success. In future, it should be sought after scrub clearance along the line of an ancient trackway between these places (see Old Series one-inch OS maps, sheets 11, 15, edn 1, 1810, 1811).

V. cracca L.   Tufted Vetch.   **N**   Very common

First record, Gilbert White 1766, Selborne, VC12 (*White's Jnls* **1**: 212).

Common in hedges, scrub, wood-borders, rank grass, meadows, chalk downs and fens.

V. tenuifolia ROTH   Fine-leaved Vetch.   **D?**   Very rare

First record, Mrs G. Lyall 1969, hedgerow on road from Cheriton to Tichborne Park 5830, VC12, det. *JEL* (*Watsonia* **10**: 423), *DNT* 1977, *MT* 1991.

This is a perennial which comes up in the same place at intervals, but according to *EJC* does not produce seed in this country. He suggests it may have been a fodder-crop.

V. sylvatica L.   Wood Vetch.   **N** Very rare

First record, Gilbert White 1768, Fyfield, VC12 (*White's Jnls* **1**: 247).

Edges of woods and clearings, and in scrub over the chalk.

VC8: Boulsbury Wood 0715, 0814, Miss Liddell *c*.1950 (*Fl.Wilts*, p.210), *WI* 1975, *AB & JO* 1984. **VC11**: Hedgemoor Copse 2630, *LFS* 1966, not seen, *FR & APNH* 1980; Bottom Copse, Corhampton 5820, *PAB* 1995, conf. *RPB*. **VC12**: 'In a wood near the east turnpike at Appleshaw', *WBo* 1805 (*Bot.Guide* **1**: 320); Long Copse, Appleshaw 2948, in very dark beech- and larch-plantations, not flowering, *ILR* 1991, comm. *CC*, det. *FR* (*Watsonia* **19**: 144) (quite possibly the same site, or close to where Borrer discovered it).

V. hirsuta (L.) GRAY   Hairy Tare.   **N**   Common

On waste ground and in long grass, disturbed bare soil, borders of arable, and shingle beaches.

<V. parviflora CAV. (*V. tenuissima* auct., non (M. Bieb.) Schinz & Thell.) Slender Tare.   **C**   Extinct

First record, H. Reeks 1870, East Woodhay, VC12 (*Fl.Hants*, p.110, as *V. gracilis* Loisel.).

VC11: Recorded (as *V. gracilis* Loisel.) at Southampton Docks, *FIW* 1873 (*loc.cit.*); Milford, *PTBB* 1928 and Rowner, *MTH* (both *Suppl.Fl. Hants*, p.34). There are no confirmed records since.**>**

V. tetrasperma (L.) SCHREB. Smooth Tare.   **N**   Frequent and locally common

Frequent in open long grass, on bare disturbed ground and around arable fields.

V. sepium L.   Bush Vetch.   **N** Common

Along wood-borders and rides, in scrub lining streams, on downland and along hedgerows; on neutral and all basic soils, particularly chalk.

V. sativa L. ssp. **nigra** (L.) EHRH. (ssp. *angustifolia* (L.) Gaudin; *V. angustifolia* L.)   Narrow-leaved Vetch.   **N**   Common

In grassy places, meadows, verges, grass heaths, waste ground and railway banks; especially on sand or gravel.

ssp. **segetalis** (THUILL.) GAUDIN
Common Vetch.   **N?,D**   Apparently
common, but under-recorded

In grassland, hedgerows, verges, field-
borders, pastures, open woods, railway
banks, arable and waste ground.

ssp. **sativa** L.   **D**   Rare or under-
recorded

An escape from cultivation; waste
places, gravel-pits, newly-made verges,
tips.
    VC11: Blashford gravel-pits, rubble-
tip 1506, Lee gravel-pit 3517 and Lee
Lane, Nursling tip 3617, all Hb.RPB
1975, det. *FR*; Milford on Sea 2891,
waste land near cliffs, *RPB* 1977;
beside A3 below Windmill Hill, Horndean 7015, *AB* 1983. Also 3612, 3620,
3434. **VC12**: Roadside below Noar Hill
7532, *AB* 1982.

V. lathyroides L.   Spring Vetch.   **N**
Very local   Map 190

Local and sparse, in short turf on sand
and shingle along the coast. Very rare
on sandy heaths inland.
    VC11: Mudeford 1891, sandy turf
under pines, abundant, *RPB* 1989;
Sinah Common dunes 6899, Hb.AWW
1950, *EAP* 1980; Sandy Point, Hayling
Island 7498, *AB, EAP & FR* 1980;
Calshot beach 4801, *RPB* 1966, apparently lost since; East Wellow 3018,
weed in garden lawn, *RMV* 1983, det.
RPB. **VC12**: Kingsley Common 7938,
AB 1966; Trottsford Farm 8038, roadside, *WEW* 1961, *GM* 1993; Woolmer
Forest railway 7832, *AB* 1966–88.

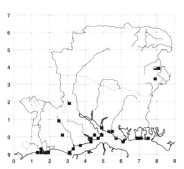

Map 190 Vicia lathyroides

V. lutea L.   Yellow Vetch.   **C**
Very rare or extinct

Casual on waste ground and on bare
sand or gravel in pits. Rarely known to
persist for long.
    VC11: Nursling gravel-pit 3616, in
fair quantity, *RPB* 1951, now lost;

Southampton 4012, waste ground, *MJC*
1956, *CDD* 1961; North Boarhunt sand-
pit 6011, Hb.AWW 1955, Blashford
gravel-pit 1506, Hb.AWW 1963;
Horsea Island 6304, one locality in SW,
CMcL, last seen 1967.

<V. bithynica (L.) L.   Bithynian
Vetch.   **N?**   Extinct

Scrub, rough grassland and hedges by
the coast. First found by J. E. Kelsall
in 1889, in a ditchside in a cultivated
field at Bridgemary near Gosport, but
Townsend doubted it was native
(*Fl.Hants*, excl.sp., p.116). Last seen at
Bassett, *JFR* 1915, and Milford on
Sea, *PTBB*, (both *Suppl.Fl.Hants*,
p.35). It probably was native, as it is in
similar coastal-scrub sites in Kent.>

Lathyrus japonicus WILLD. ssp.
maritimus (L.) P. W. BALL   Sea
Pea.   **N**   Very rare

First record, G. Halliday 1953, Hurst
Beach 3090, VC11, seen *JHo* 1963, not
refound *RER* 1973 (*Watsonia* 11: 247–
251).
    On shingle beaches.
    Refound after 30 years in another
site at Hurst Castle spit 3189, three
small leafy patches, *GDF* 1993, one of
which flowered, *MEY* 1994 (*Watsonia*
20: 293).

L. linifolius (REICHARD) BÄSSLER (*L.
montanus* Bernh.)   Bitter-vetch.   **N**
Locally common   Map 191

First record, Gilbert White 1766,
Selborne, VC12 (*White's Jnls* 1: 194).
    Common on acid soil, in woods and
scrub, bushy heaths, and under
bracken; also on railway banks. Local in
woods and hedgerows on other soils.
Generally rare on the chalk superficials.

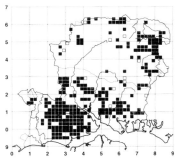

Map 191 Lathyrus linifolius

L. pratensis L.   Meadow Vetchling.
N   Very common

In grassland, verges and field borders.

<L. palustris L.   Marsh Pea.   **N**
Extinct

Fenny places. Formerly at Botany Bay,
Sholing 4510 or 4511, VC11, W. L.
Notcutt 1842 (*Fl.Hants*, p.114), no
record since; now extinct in SE
England due to drainage.>

L. tuberosus L.   Tuberous Pea.
D,C   Rare

An alien often introduced in chicken-
food and probably dispersed by birds.
In rough grass and waste places, often
transient but can persist through rank
grass.
    VC11: Netley Common 4711, grassy
area, in bracken, *PAB* 1991, Hb.RPB;
Lower Swanwick brick-pits 5009,
Hb.AWW, established since *c*.1945,
PWKP 1962; Lymington 3195,
Hb.AWW 1960; Horsea Island 6304,
Hb.AWW 1962; Crampmoor *c*.3822,
AW 1942 (*Proc.Hants Fld Club* **15**:
306); Owslebury–Twyford area, *HFC*
1943 (*Proc.Hants Fld Club* **16**: 61)
perhaps *PMH*'s record of 1930; Stanpit 1692, *MPY c*.1960–70; E of Buckholt Farm 2831, *RMV* 1987. **VC12**:
Wallers Ash 4936, in rank grass over
tunnel, *AB* 1968 (*Watsonia* **10**: 423),
GHF 1977; Penton Mewsey 3347,
border of cornfield, *GDF* 1973; Fullerton Station 3839, Hb.RPB 1975;
Micheldever 5041, border of bean-
field, *RPB* 1969; Tidbury Ring 4642,
in plantation of Corsican pine (*Pinus
nigra* ssp. *laricio*), *WJLP* 1940.

L. grandiflorus SM. (*L. tingitanus*
auct., non L.)   Two-flowered Everlasting-pea.   **H**   Very rare

First record, C. R. Hall 1993, Norris
Hill, Fleet 8353, VC12, large patch in
scrub.

L. sylvestris L.   Narrow-leaved
Everlasting-pea.   **N**   Rare   Map 192

First record, J. Goodyer ms, not later
than 1664, Hampshire (*Merr.Pin.*,
p.70).
    On borders of bushy woods and
hangers, on chalk; also on a few railway
banks.
    VC11: Holmsley railway bank 2201,
GARW 1932; Breamore Wood 1419,
RPB 1977. **VC12**: Lane to hanger,
Lythe Farm 7224, Hb.AWW 1960,
abundant, *AB* 1963; Ashe Arch, Overton 5350, all over embankment, *AB*
1970; Sparrow's Hanger, Selborne
7433, *AB* 1963, 1990; Kingsley 7838,

old railway bank, now in a garden, *AB* 1976, 1986; S side of Wheatham Hill 7426, *FR* 1985.

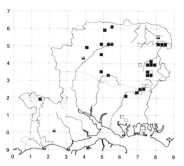

Map 192 Lathyrus sylvestris

L. latifolius L.   Broad-leaved Everlasting-pea.   **H**   Occasional

First record, J. F. Rayner 1915, Millbrook Station 3912, VC11, reclaimed land (*Proc.Hants Fld Club* **10**: 110).

On railway banks, roadsides and grassy waste-ground. VC11: 27 □; VC12: 28 □.

VC11: Wide Lane, Eastleigh 4416, railway banks, *CDD* 1958; A35 Vinney Ridge 2505, *RPB* 1987–88. **VC12**: Old Burghclere 4756, disused railway, *NFC* 1974; A32 between Andover and Ludgershall 3047, *GDF* 1984.

L. heterophyllus L. var. **unijugus** KOCH   Norfolk Everlasting-pea.   **C** Very rare

First record, A. R. G. Mundell 1987, Yateley 8161, VC12, beside flooded gravel-pit, det. *ACL & FR*. The record for Kingsley 7838, VC12, Hb.AB 1963 (*Watsonia* **10**: 423) was subsequently found to be an error for *L. sylvestris*.

L. hirsutus L.   Hairy Vetchling. **C,D**   Very rare

VC11: Crammoor *c*.3822, *AW* 1942 (*Proc.Hants Fld Club* **15**: 306). **VC12**: Chilbolton 4037, derelict camp, Hb.RPB 1968, det. *GAM*.

L. nissolia L.   Grass Vetchling.   **N** Local   Map 193

Local, but increasing. In rank grass, often on disturbed land, such as gravel-pits, road and railway banks; waste places, open rides and pastures, including coastal grassland.

VC11: Marchwood 3810, roadside verge, *PS* 1991; Fleetend, Warsash 5005, grassy gravel-pits, *RPB* 1988;

Farlington Marshes 6905, Hb.AWW 1951, *AB* 1986. **VC12**: Little Hawstead, Steep 7425, abundant in meadow, *AB* 1979, 1990; Bordon–Bentley old railway 7942, large patch, *ANHS* 1970; Andover 3844, roadside verges A303/A3093 interchange, *MFW* 1991; Farnborough Airfield 8453, 8553, *JK & ARGM* 1985 (*RAE Survey*).

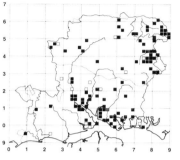

Map 193 Lathyrus nissolia

L. aphaca L.   Yellow Vetchling. **N,C**   Rare   Map 194

On borders of cornfields or grassy places on chalk, and also on waste ground. In some places it is obviously a casual, e.g. Farnborough 8653, VC12, introduced with bird-seed, *ARGM* 1973 (*RAE Survey*). However there are many old records, and in six places these are from adjacent tetrads which suggest it is native. They are:

VC11: Southampton Western Docks 4012, reclaimed land, *CDD* 1958, *MMcK* 1965; IBM Cosham 6504, *PAB* 1989; Eastney 6799, *TER c*.1960, *AB* 1967; field on Horsea Island 6304, Hb.AWW 1950, last seen by *CMcL* 1976, but reappeared on reclaimed land to the north. **VC11/12**: Winchester, four records in contiguous tetrads: 4626, 4630, 4828, 5028; and, most important, **VC12**: Froyle, where *CL*,

and later *MRA*, found it over the years in several places in four adjacent tetrads: 7442, 7446, 7642 and 7644; moreover, in 7642 it was plentiful as a cornfield weed, *CL* 1964, seen *GHF* 1980.

[**Ononis reclinata** L.   Small Restharrow.   (Sched.8)

Milford on Sea , VC11, *HBr* 1910 (*Milf. Rec.Soc.*, p.10). This record is insufficiently documented for acceptance.]

O. spinosa L.   Spiny Restharrow. **N**   Very local   Map 195

Very local on chalk-down slopes, on tufa alluvium, coastal pastures on wet clay, and earthen sea-walls; formerly rare on roadside verges in New Forest. Concentrated in two widely-separated areas: the SE coast from Hayling to Cosham, and the upper Test Valley.

VC11: Grass verge of A31, Winding Stonard, Ocknell 2410, Hb.RPB 1975 (lost after road-widening); Badminston Common 4602, probably introduced with imported rubble, *RPB* 1988; Hilsea Lines 6604, *EAP* 1980. **VC12**: Bransbury Common 4141, 4142, *RPB* 1985.

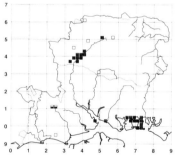

Map 195 Ononis spinosa

O. repens L. ssp. **repens**   Common Restharrow.   **N**   Locally common Map 196

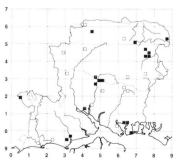

Map 194 Lathyrus aphaca

Map 196 Ononis repens ssp. repens

Common on chalk grassland and verges, on the seashore and dunes; occasional and widespread on sandy and gravelly roadsides.

Melilotus altissimus THUILL. Tall Melilot. **C,D** Locally frequent Map 197

Widespread, especially on chalk; in disturbed grassland or bare ground by roads, waysides, field-borders and leys. Increasing along motorways. More prevalent in rural areas and less frequent in towns than the next species. In *Fl.Hants* (p.99) this plant is considered 'rather rare'.

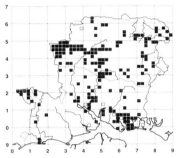

Map 197 Melilotus altissimus

M. albus MEDIK. White Melilot. **C** Locally frequent Map 198

A later arrival than the previous and the next species, with few records in *Fl.Hants*, which terms it 'very rare'. Now increasing and locally quite plentiful but transient, on waste and disturbed ground and bare roadside verges, especially around ports.

VC11: Portsmouth Station 6400, Hb.AWW 1951; Dibden Bay 4208, firm mud and shingle on polders, *RPB* 1974; very noticeable along some stretches of the M27 (*RPB*), and A3 (*AB* 1990). **VC12**: Bordon area,

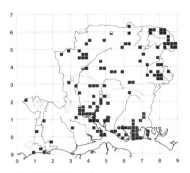

Map 198 Melilotus albus

common since 1960, *AB*; Cricket Hill, Yateley 8159, *DEA* 1986.

M. officinalis (L.) LAM. Ribbed Melilot. **C,D** Locally frequent

Widespread, especially on waste ground in and near towns. This and *M. altissimus* have possibly been confused by some recorders, but they do occur together. Townsend described *M. officinalis* (*Fl.Hants*, p.100) as 'rare' and confined to 'cultivated fields' or 'introduced with the crop'.

M. indicus (L.) ALL. Small Melilot. **C** Rare

First record, D. H. Scott 1910, W side of Tangier Park, VC12 (*Suppl. Fl.Hants*, p.31).

Rare but increasing, on disturbed ground, especially around Portsmouth. **VC11**: Winchester, *RLMS* 1930 (*Proc.Hants Fld Club* **10**: 297); Ferry Road, Eastney 6899, Hb.AWW 1950; Sinah Common 7099, established in short grass, *AB* 1977 (but overgrown 1986); Calshot 4801, reclaimed land, Hb.RPB 1975; Mill Lane, Romsey 3421, Hb.RPB 1980. Also 1404, 1412, 1692, 3620, 3812, 4414, 5012, 6400, 6404, 6600. **VC12**: Dogmersfield *c.*7650, garden weed, *AJSt* 1964; Aldershot 8550, roadworks, *TD & ARGM* 1990 (*Watsonia* **19**: 144).

Medicago lupulina L. Black Medick. **N,C,D** Very common

In short grass in meadows, waysides and waste places, on all except very acid heathy soils.

M. sativa L. ssp. **sativa** Lucerne. **D** Frequent

Widespread in waste places and verges, often as a relic of cultivation. May persist for some years, but usually transient.

ssp. **falcata** (L.) ARCANG. (*M. falcata* L.) Sickle Medick. **C** Very rare

First record J. F. Rayner 1907, Southampton Docks (*Proc.IoW N.H.S.* 1: 242).

VC11: Southampton Western Docks *c.*4111, *CDD* 1956; Middle Chine, Bournemouth 0790, *HB* 1953, *MPY* 1966.

ssp. **varia** (MARTYN) ARCANG. (*M.* x *varia* Martyn; *M. sativa* ssp. *sativa* x ssp. *falcata*) Sand Lucerne. **C,D** Very rare

VC11: Southampton Western Docks Gate *c.*4111, *WFB* 1965.

M. polymorpha L. Toothed Medick. **N,C** Rare

In turf over stabilized shingle on the coast, and as a casual on tips or in shoddy. VC11: 9 □; VC12: 1 □.

VC11: Hengistbury, Mudeford and Keyhaven, *KG* 1950, Hb.AB; Hurst Castle 3189, Hb.RPB 1975, *RPB* 1991; Mayflower Park, Southampton 4111, in short coastal turf, obviously native, *RPB* 1991; Lifeboat house, Eastney 6899, *EAP* 1980–89, det. *FR*; Sinah Common 6899, sandy roadside, *RFG* 1990. **VC12**: Still at Blackmoor fruit farm, 17 years after use of shoddy, *AB* 1991.

M. arabica (L.) HUDS. Spotted Medick. **N,C** Locally frequent Map 199

Frequent near the coast in short grassland, pastures, verges, banks and disturbed places. Rare and scattered further inland, mainly around Alton.

VC11: Shelley Farm, Ower, *GC* 1987; Manor Farm, Hayling Island 7100, Hb.AWW 1956; Chilcomb 5028, *YD* 1983. **VC12**: Isington Mill 7742, AB 1977; Doles Wood *c.*3650, *GDF* 1984; still at Blackmoor fruit farm, 17 years after use of shoddy, *AB* 1991.

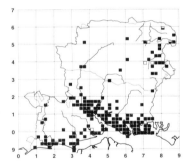

Map 199 Medicago arabica

Trifolium ornithopodioides L. Bird's-foot Clover. **N** Locally frequent Map 200

Fairly frequent in compact turf on coastal sand or gravel; widespread on verges, grassy borders of heathland and on banks in the New Forest. Rare on sandy heaths in the NE. Usually very dwarfed, but a more vigorous form occurs occasionally in grassy salt-marshes.

VC11: Southsea Common 6398, near the Naval Monument, Hb.AWW 1959, *EAP* 1980; Kingston North Common 1403, *RAF* 1985; N of Heath Pond, Petersfield 7522, *MS-W* 1975, *FR* 1994. **VC12**: Kingsley Common 7938, *AWW* 1963; Kennels Lane, Southwood 8454, *TD & ARGM* 1992, Hb.AB.

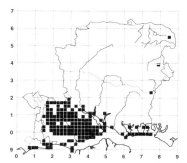

Map 200 Trifolium ornithopodioides

T. repens L.   White Clover.   **N,D** Very common

Universal in grassland and waste ground, on all soils. A form is frequently cultivated in clover leys.

T. hybridum L.   Alsike Clover.   **D** Common

A crop-plant, formerly much culti-vated and now widespread on banks and in waste places. No distinction has been made in the records between ssp. *hybridum* and ssp. *elegans* (Savi) Asch. & Graebn., although both may occur.

T. glomeratum L.   Clustered Clover.   **N**   Very local and rare Map 201

In gravelly and sandy turf near the coast, or up river valleys, especially the R. Avon.
   VC11: Burton Road, Christchurch 1793, *RPB* 1977; B3347 Kingston 1502, *RPB* 1981; Ringwood 1404, old railway, *RPB* 1981; Hinton 2094, rail-way bridge with imported gravel, *MPY c*.1960–70, *AB* 1977; near B3055, Widden Bottom 2899, grassy path to railway, abundant, *VS* 1992; Hatchet Pond 3601, *DEG* 1981; Lepe *c*.4498, *CDD* 1960; Redbridge 3613, *RPB* 1977; Markway Hill 2402, side of old road, *RPB* 1991; Sway 2799, in turf on and around reservoirs, *RPB* 1991; East End 3697, banks and short turf at road-triangle, *RPB* 1991. Far inland only on N side of Heath Pond, Petersfield 7522, *JLSL* 1975, Hb.AB, 7523, *FR*

1993–94, locally abundant with *T. subterraneum*.

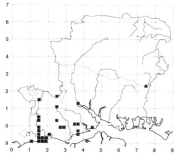

Map 201 Trifolium glomeratum

T. suffocatum L.   Suffocated Clover. **N**   Very rare but locally plentiful

In turf on shingle beaches, or bare ground, near the coast.
   VC11: Middle Chine, Bournemouth 0790, *AJB* 1990; Hengistbury Head and Stanpit Marsh 1691, *FAW* 1987 ; Mudeford *c*.1892, *AWW* 1960, Little Haven 1891, few plants in gravelly car-park area, *FAW* 1991; near Hurst Castle 3189, *JHL* 1969, *RPB* 1989; South Hayling 7098, behind the beach-huts, *AWW, FR & AB* 1950–85, *c*.250 plants, *RPB* 1992; Westfield 7198, 7298, on shingle, turf and small sand-dune, abundant, *FR* 1994; entrance to Sinah Common, Ferry Road 6999, *AB* 1977; Sandy Point, Hayling Island 7598, *AB, EAP & FR* 1980; Eastney 6899, *AB* 1963, *FR* 1993.

T. fragiferum L. ssp. **fragiferum** Strawberry Clover.   **N**   Locally frequent   Map 202

Frequent in brackish pastures and turf near the coast. Sporadic elsewhere, in damp alluvial grassland and on clay; also on verges and in old marl-pits in the New Forest.

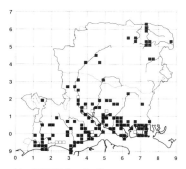

Map 202 Trifolium fragiferum

VC11: B3056 at Matley Passage 3307, *RPB* 1970; Hilsea Lines 6604, abundant in grassland, *DPJS* 1990. **VC12**: The Fish Pond, Froyle 7542, *CL* 1947, Hb.HCMS, *AB* 1976; beside A32, Hook 7253, *ARGM* 1987; Princes Avenue, Aldershot 8752, along edge of sports field, *ARGM & CRH* 1990.

T. aureum POLLICH   Large Trefoil. **C,D**   Very rare

First record, G. A. R. Watts 1932, canal-bank, Pondtail *c*.8253, and as a garden weed in Fleet, VC12 (as *T. agrarium* in *Watts MSS*).
   Usually a casual, with an affinity for the Aldershot area where it persists. It was a fodder-plant, and possibly emanates from the huge heap of cavalry horse-manure once on Laffan's Plain, which used to be dispersed to gardens, doubtless along the canal-towpath.
   VC11: Holmsley old railway 2300, one plant, *MPY* 1969. **VC12**: Yateley 8158, dump, *DNT* 1968; Aldershot 8751, dump, *DNT* 1962 (now built over); Aldershot 8852, many plants on waste land, *TD* 1979, few now surviv-ing, as site planted with trees, *ARGM* 1985.

T. campestre SCHREB.   Hop Trefoil. **N**   Common

In dry grassland on most soils, but especially on chalk.

T. dubium SIBTH.   Lesser Trefoil. **N**   Very common

Abundant throughout, in dry grassland.

T. micranthum VIV.   Slender Trefoil.   **N**   Locally common   Map 203

Widespread, and locally not uncom-mon, in short dry turf on pastures,

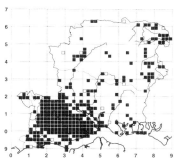

Map 203 Trifolium micranthum

175

commons, road-banks and verges, chiefly on sand or gravel; also in lawns and parks.

VC11: Nursling 3614, turf on river terrace, *RPB* 1976. **VC12**: Hawkley Hurst 7530, in lawn, *AB & GL* 1970; cricket-ground, Fleet 8053, *GARW* 1945 (*Watts MSS*), *CRH* 1991.

T. pratense L. Red Clover. **N,D**
Very common

Universal in grassland and waste ground, on all soils.

T. medium L. Zigzag Clover. **N**
Locally frequent Map 204

Widespread and frequent on heavy, basic soil; along wood-borders and rides; railway, road- and stream-banks; in scrub on heaths; bushy pastures and marl-pits; at the foot of the Malmstone hangers.

VC11: A35, Holmsley Station 2300, *RPB* 1979; Hollybrook Cemetery 4015, *RPB* 1984. **VC12**: Below Temple Hill, Selborne 7632, *AB* 1960–90; Ashford Hill meadows 5662, *PB* 1982.

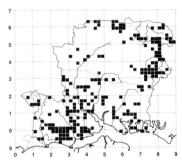

Map 204 Trifolium medium

T. incarnatum L. ssp. **incarnatum**
Crimson Clover. **D** Very rare

Once grown as a crop, this has become a rare casual.

VC11: Great Funtley Farm, near Fareham 5508, Hb.AWW 1951. **VC12**: Edge of Bramshot golf-course *c*.8354, *GARW* 1943 (*Watts MSS*), since built over; Sherfield, *NEGC c*.1940; Hackwood Lane, Cliddesden 6348, Hb.AWW 1962; Hatchwarren Lane, Basingstoke 6249, on disturbed ground, *JR* 1981–82. **VC11/12**: Petersfield 7323, bank beside slip-road to A3 bypass, *PAH* 1994.

T. striatum L. Knotted Clover. **N**
Locally frequent Map 205

Fairly frequent in dry turf on sand,

gravel and firm clay, on verges, banks, pastures and pits; on sea-walls, dunes and shingle. Rarely on chalk.

VC11: Lower Test 3614, on gravel terrace, *RMV* 1986. **VC12**: Kingsley 7938, *AB* 1980; Silchester Common 6562, *PB* 1988.

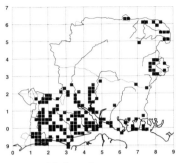

Map 205 Trifolium striatum

T. scabrum L. Rough Clover. **N**
Very local Map 206

Local, in turf, on coastal sand and shingle, also on verges in New Forest and old airfields. Very rare far inland.

VC11: Calshot Spit 4801, *RPB* 1966, 4802, *HFG* 1990; Stoney Cross old airfield 2412, *RPB* 1981; Weston Shore, Southampton 4409, *MS* 1974. **VC12**: Bentley Station 7943, *AWW* 1963.

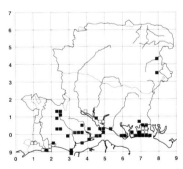

Map 206 Trifolium scabrum

T. arvense L. Hare's-foot Clover. **N** Locally frequent Map 207

First record, M. de Lobel not later than 1616, Southsea Castle, Portsmouth 6498, VC11 (*Ray Syn.*, p.330).

Frequent on bare or disturbed, sandy or gravelly, acid ground in heathland areas; coastal sands and shingle, or reclaimed land; not on chalk.

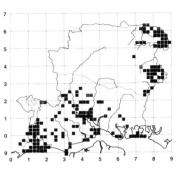

Map 207 Trifolium arvense

T. squamosum L. Sea Clover. **N**
Very rare

On earthen sea-walls, a declining habitat in this area.

VC11: Cams Bay, Fareham 5804, one plant in short turf, *DPJS* 1989; IBM North Harbour, Cosham 6405, five plants in sparse turf on reclaimed land, *RBa* 1991 (*IBM List*, p.9); Great Salterns, Portsmouth 6701, sea wall, Hb.AWW 1959, few plants *DPJS* 1992, Hb.RPB; Ports Creek area *c*.6604, *AWW* 1951; Farlington Marshes 6905, sea-wall, Hb.AWW 1957, 6803 grassy bank near lagoon, plentiful over 60m, *RPB* 1976, not seen recently, but at another site 6804, Hb.AWW 1955, plentiful in grassland, *NAS* 1994. Not refound in the localities given in *Fl.Hants* (p.102) and *Suppl.Fl.Hants* (p.32): Hamble banks between Curdridge and Swanwick and Bursledon; Gosport; Hill Head; Bridgemary and South Hayling.

T. subterraneum L. Subterranean Clover. **N** Locally frequent Map 208

Frequent in the south, in turf on sand, gravel and shingle; on verges, grassy heathland, banks, seashores and dunes.

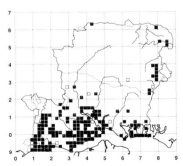

Map 208 Trifolium subterraneum

Very local or rare on NE heaths, which are ungrazed.

VC11: Rockford Green 1608, *RPB* 1988; Pennington Marshes 3292, *MR* 1976. **VC12**: The Chase, Woolton Hill 4262, *AR* 1969; Church Field, Blackmoor 7733, *AB* 1984; Fleet Cricket Ground 8053, *CRH* 1991, Hb.AB; Aldershot 8551, track beside playing fields, *TD* 1991.

Lupinus arboreus SIMS   Tree Lupin.   **H,C**   Very locally frequent

First record, Lady Anne Brewis 1923, old railway, Kingsley 7838, VC12.

On sandy or gravelly banks and dunes, often originally planted. It can become invasive.

VC11: Sinah Common dunes 6899, 6999, *DWF* 1958, where it was rapidly overwhelming the native flora before an infestation of aphids destroyed most bushes, *RPB* 1981–85; now established at Bournemouth; Christchurch; and on cliffs from Highcliffe to Barton on Sea. Also 1096, 1406, 1492, 1494, 2096, 2812, 3018, 3406, 4806, 7298, 7498. **VC12**: Established on the old Bentley–Bordon railway. Also 7634, 8260, 8450.

L. polyphyllus LINDL.   Garden Lupin.   **H**   Occasional

Persisting in a few waste places.

Laburnum anagyroides MEDIK. Laburnum.   **H**   Occasional

Occasionally self-sown on waste land, levelled tips, etc.

Cytisus striatus (HILL) ROTHM. Hairy-fruited Broom.   **D**   Very rare

First record, Lady Anne Brewis 1979, Longmoor Ranges 7931, VC12, det. *EJC*.

Recently sown and established on dry banks.

VC12: Sheet 7524, *AB* 1980; Aldershot 8852, *GHF* 1980, *CRH* 1991.

C. scoparius (L.) LINK ssp. **scoparius** (*Sarothamnus scoparius* (L.) Koch) Broom.   **N**   Locally very common

First record, R. Turner 1664: 'My father's grounds at Holshot in Hampshire [VC12] are never free from it altogether' (*Turn.Bot.*, p.53).

Disturbed sand or gravel, on heaths, embankments, pastures and pits. Generally in an acid pocket when on chalk.

Genista monspessulana (L.) L. JOHNSON (*Teline monspessulana* (L.) K. Koch)   Montpellier Broom.   **H** Very rare

First record, R. P. Bowman 1966, Casbrook Common, Michelmersh 3524, VC11, track through sand-pits.

An escape from cultivation.

VC11: M27 embankment, Rownhams Service Station 3917, *RCS* 1980; The Kench, Hayling Island 6999, *EAP* 1986.

G. tinctoria L. ssp. **tinctoria** Dyer's Greenweed.   **N**   Local   Map 209

First record, Gilbert White 1766, Selborne, VC12 (*White's Jnls* 1: 204).

In rough pastures, ancient meadows, field-borders, grass-heaths, old clay-pits and thickets, on heavy, slightly acid soils, particularly clay. Probably in acid pockets when on chalkland. Since the 1960s it has declined considerably through loss of old pastures.

VC8: Martin Down 0518, *PET* 1990. **VC11**: Setley Common, Roydon Woods 3100, *RPB* 1991; NW Hayling Island 7102, abundant, *EAP* 1984. **VC12**: Ashford Hill meadows 5662, *PB* 1982; S of Moulshay Farm, Sherfield Hill 6755, grassy ride near stream, *ARGM* 1980.

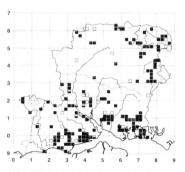

Map 209 Genista tinctoria ssp. tinctoria

G. anglica L.   Petty Whin.   **N** Locally common

On moist heaths and the fringes of bogs. Abundant in the New Forest, frequent but declining in the NE, and quite rare elsewhere (e.g. in Woolmer Forest) probably due to lack of grazing.

VC11: Baddesley Common 3921, few plants, *RPB* 1991; Purbrook Heath 6607, Hb.AWW 1951. **VC12**: Bransbury Common 4141, 4142, *RPB* 1974; Conford 8233, *AB* 1984; Hawley Common 8358, *CRH* 1983–87.

Ulex europaeus L.   Gorse.   **N** Frequent and locally very common

On heaths, especially beside tracks and verges. In waste ground and pits, leached soil on chalk downs, dry open woods, and clearings on acid soil. Also a colonizer of motorway-banks. A spectacular feature of New Forest roads in spring, but reduced by clearance along unfenced roads in recent years for road safety. Large areas are also burnt rotationally to improve grazing. In John Evelyn's day it was deliberately sown because 'no provender...makes horses so hardy as the young tops of these Furzes; no other wood so thick, nor more excellent fuel...If we imitated this husbandry, we might exceedingly spare our woods.' (*Silva*, p.410). Presumably this is why Gilbert White sowed it on top of Selborne Hanger causing an impenetrable thicket of which it has now been relieved by the National Trust.

U. gallii PLANCH.   Western Gorse. **N**   Very rare

First record, F. Rose 1980, Sandy Point, Hayling Island 7498, Hb.AB, det. *PMB*.

Dry heaths.

VC11: Turf Hill car-park, NW of Rushy Flat 2117, one bush, *RMV* 1985, Hb.RPB, det. *PMB*. These are the only two records confirmed since this species was redefined by M. C. F. Proctor (*Watsonia* 6: 177–187). All old records are doubtful.

U. minor ROTH   Dwarf Gorse.   **N** Locally common   Map 210

First British record, T. Johnson 1641, 'South Sea Castle' 6498, VC11 (*Merc.Bot.*, pt.2, p.21).

Common on nearly all heathland, very local on chalk superficials.

VC8: Tidpit Common Down 0618, *FR* 1978. **VC11**: Ringwood Forest

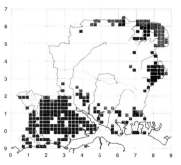

Map 210 Ulex minor

1006, *RPB* 1985; Browndown Common 5899, *MB* 1986–87. **VC12**: Great Park, Weston Patrick 6944, on rides, *FR* 1978; there is a post-1930 record for tetrad 7636; strangely absent from Shortheath Common 7736, *FR* 1970–94.

ELAEAGNACEAE

Elaeagnus umbellata THUNB. (*E. angustifolia* auct., non L.) Elaeagnus. **H** Very rare

First record, R. P. Bowman, 1988, Ferry Road, Sinah Common, Hayling Island 6999, VC11, in scrub on shingle behind old wartime building, a single shrub 6m high, probably bird-sown, *RBa & GHF* 1992, conf. *EJC* (*BSBI News* **68**: 37–39).

HALORAGACEAE

Myriophyllum verticillatum L. Whorled Water-milfoil. **N** Very rare

In ditches, streams and ponds. Greatly decreased from former times. The most recently recorded site is Mans Bridge, Swaythling 4415, VC11, old reservoir, *CDD* 1960, last record, Hb.RPB 1975. There are 17 old records.

M. aquaticum (VELLOSO) VERDC. Parrot's-feather. **H** Rare

First record, Mrs K. Coxhead 1977, Oliver's Battery 4527, VC11, spontaneous in garden pond, det. *EJC*.

An aquarists' weed which is likely to spread further.

VC11: Ashley Heath 1003, *RPB* 1977, dominant in a drain, over 220m by 1983; Nomansland 2517, roadside pond, *VW* 1983, conf. *RPB*; Bartley 3013, shaded pond, *RPB* 1990; Meon Navigation, Little Posbrook 5304, 5405, frequent over 2km of the canal, *RPB 1989*. Also 1492, 3292, 4096, 6804.

M. spicatum L. Spiked Water-milfoil. **N** Locally frequent Map 211

In slow-flowing rivers and streams, ponds and drains in water-meadows; largely in basic, or only mildly acid, waters, including those of the Lower Greensand and the NE Tertiaries. Locally common along the main river valleys in the SW and NE, but mostly absent from the New Forest, where

some records may relate to *M. alterniflorum.*

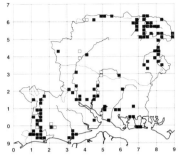

Map 211 *Myriophyllum spicatum*

M. alterniflorum DC. Alternate Water-milfoil. **N** Locally frequent Map 212

In ponds and streams, especially those flowing from valley bogs in distinctly acid, mainly oligotrophic waters. Typical and common throughout the New Forest, and the commoner water-milfoil in the Fleet–Aldershot heaths.

VC11: Gravelly Marsh, Beaulieu Estate 4197, small pond, *RPB* 1984; Hatchet Pond 3601, *RPB* 1988. **VC12**: Stream dividing the Slab from The Warren, Oakhanger 7735, *AB* 1970–84; Fleet Pond, *GARW* 1932 (*Watts MSS*); *ARGM & CRH* 1985, and in small pool, 1989–90, both in 8255; Trilakes, Yateley 8261, *AB* 1978; Yateley Green 8160, *WEW, ECW & JEL* 1961, *ARGM* 1987; Spring Lakes, Aldershot 8851, *AB* 1980, *CRH* 1991; Warren Heath 7659, *ARGM* 1985.

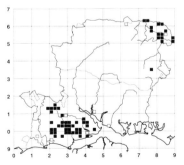

Map 212 *Myriophyllum alterniflorum*

LYTHRACEAE

Lythrum salicaria L. Purple-loosestrife. **N** Locally common

First record, Gilbert White 1766, 'At Whorwell' *c.*3840, VC12 (*White's Jnls* 1: 214).

Waterside margins, fens, wet meadows, marshy woods, and ditches. Common throughout the major river-valleys and stream-networks, on basic to mildly-acid soil, but strangely scarce in the SE.

L. hyssopifolia L. Grass-poly. **C**? Probably extinct (Sched.8)

VC11: Hayling Island, *MTH* 1921 (*Rep.B.E.C.* for 1921, p.382), *GB* 1929 (*Suppl.Fl.Hants*, p.47). This was probably only a casual occurrence, but the record is significant as this species was found as recently as 1987 across Emsworth Channel in Thorney Island, VC13, just over the county boundary in W Sussex where it is regarded as native.

L. portula (L.) D. A. WEBB (*Peplis portula* L.) Water-purslane. **N** Locally common Map 213

In wet, acid places, drying out in summer, e.g. depressions on heaths, tracks, muddy pond-edges. Very common in the New Forest; occasional to frequent on the other Tertiary sands and on the Lower Greensand.

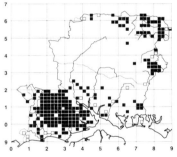

Map 213 *Lythrum portula*

THYMELAEACEAE

Daphne mezereum L. Mezereon. **N** Very rare

In woodlands on chalk and other basic soils. Decreased from over 20 sites in *Fl.Hants* (p.362) and *Suppl.Fl.Hants* (p.93).

VC11: W edge of wood by St Clair's Farm, Corhampton *c.*5721, *GARW* 1936 (*Watts MSS*), also recorded in SU52, *GGP* 1948, last known record for S Hants. **VC12**: Old Down Wood, Ropley, one plant last seen *SS* 1960; Butter Wood, Greywell 7151, 11 plants, *NEGC* 1943, a few *FR* 1946, now gone; Greywell Moors 7150, *c.*40 plants, *AJB* 1986–90, *HFG* 1992. A small colony is still near Selborne (but not at Gilbert White's site in the Hanger).

D. laureola L.   Spurge-laurel.   **N**
Locally frequent   Map 214

First record, Thomas White 1754, Selborne, VC12 (*White's Jnls* **1**: 31). In woods, mainly of beech; frequent on the chalk but scattered in woodland on other base-rich soils. Most common on the hangers from Langrish to Selborne.
   VC11: Horsea Island 6304, general and increasing on the S side, *CMcL* 1970; Roydon Woods 3100, *RPB & FR* 1978; Burnt Grove, Romsey 3320, *AG* 1974.

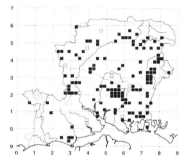

Map 214 Daphne laureola

ONAGRACEAE

Epilobium hirsutum L.   Great Willowherb.   **N**   Frequent and locally very common

In fens, marshes, riversides, and ditches on heavy soil. Plentiful in all suitable habitats.

E. parviflorum SCHREB.   Hoary Willowherb.   **N**   Frequent and locally common

In marshes, streamsides, waste ground; common except on dry soil.

E. montanum L.   Broad-leaved Willowherb.   **N,C**   Common

Woods, hedgebanks, old walls, waste ground; almost ubiquitous, but also now very much hybridized with *E. ciliatum*.

E. lanceolatum SEBAST. & MAURI   Spear-leaved Willowherb.   **N,C**   Rare   Map 215

On old walls, bare sandy hedgebanks and in gravel-pits, usually on base-rich soil. Rare on the Lower Greensand and to NE of the New Forest.

VC11: Avon Bridge, Christchurch 1692, *LBH c*.1943; old gravel-pits, Kimbridge 3225, Hb.RPB 1965; Shootash 3221, Hb.RPB 1966; Ashurst railway bank 3309, *RPB* 1966; West Town, Hayling Island 7099, *RMB* 1969; all impermanent. **VC12**: Infrequently in hollow lanes around Liphook and Bramshott on the Bargate Beds, but is apt to be overgrown or scraped off during roadside maintenance. Liphook 8231, on vestigial piece of hedgebank, *AB* 1971, may be J. G. Baker's site in *Fl.Hants* (p.155); Blackmoor 7733, *AB* 1968, Hb.AB 1971, det. *FDG* (*Watsonia* **10**: 425); Headley Rectory garden-wall 8236, abundant, *FR & AB* 1983.

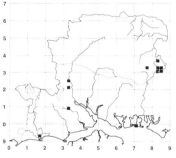

Map 215 Epilobium lanceolatum

E. tetragonum L. ssp. **tetragonum**
(*E. adnatum* Griseb.)   Square-stalked Willowherb.   **N,C**   Locally common

A colonist of bare, dry waste-ground, walls, clearings and tracks in woodland, and open marshy places. Fairly common, especially in the S.
   Although there are records for both this and the following subspecies, it should be noted that recent taxonomic treatment (*New Fl.*, p.528) does not recognize them as such since, apparently, many intermediates occur.

ssp. **lamyi** (F. W. SCHULZ) NYMAN
N,C   Very rare or overlooked
VC11: Brambridge, *EST* 1924 (*Suppl.Fl.Hants*, p.48). **VC12**: Long Sutton 7447, *FDG* 1966; Odiham *c*.7452, *FDG* 1966; Alton 7138, Hb.AB 1971, det.*FDG*.

E. obscurum SCHREB.   Short-fruited Willowherb.   **N,C**   Locally common

Damp woodland tracks, marshes, stream-banks, road-ditches. Common on acid soil.

E. roseum SCHREB.   Pale Willowherb.   **N,C**   Very local and rare   Map 216

In damp, open woods, dry beds of streams and ponds, waste ground and gardens. Scattered mostly in N of Hants; rare in the S, and concentrated around towns.
   VC11: East Dean 2626, streambank, *RPB* 1964; Wittensford 2814, on verges, *EAP* 1985; Middle Road, Winchester 4729, *DEA* 1981; dried-up bed of Wool Pond, Langrish 7023, Hb.AB 1976. **VC12**: A common weed in Basingstoke, *NEGC c*.1940; Bush Down 7234, plentiful in ride, *AB* 1964; Ashford Hill 7326, *FDG* 1964; car-park N of Fleet Pond 8155, *AB* 1985.

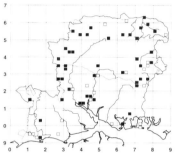

Map 216 Epilobium roseum

E. ciliatum RAF. (*E. adenocaulon* Hausskn.)   American Willowherb.   **C**   Common

First records, G. M. Ash & N. Y. Sandwith 1935, Hook Common and Fleet Pond, VC12, Hb.BM (*J.Bot.* **73**: 179). First recorded in the British Isles in 1891, but more widespread introductions are thought probable during the two World Wars.
   A ubiquitous weed of damp woods, streamsides and waste ground; our commonest willowherb.

E. palustre L.   Marsh Willowherb.   **N**   Locally common   Map 217

In fens, mildly acid valley-bogs, flushes and marshy meadows. Locally common in the New Forest and other Tertiary strata, on Lower Greensand and in the Test Valley.
   VC11: Stony Moors, Holmsley 2199, in base-rich flushes, *FR* 1983; Titchfield Haven 5302, *RPB* 1988. **VC12**: Ashford Hill meadows 5662, *PB* 1982; Woolton Hill 4361, *NFC* 1981; Cooper's Copse, Rotherwick 7057, in flush, *AJPB* 1991.

NOTE. Hybrids, involving almost all the above *Epilobium* species in many combinations, have been recorded tentatively though rather infrequently, usually in open, disturbed habitats.

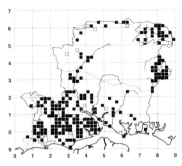

Map 217 Epilobium palustre

E. brunnescens (COCKAYNE) P. H.
RAVEN & ENGELHORN (*E. nerteroides* auct., non A. Cunn.) New Zealand Willowherb. **H** Very rare

First record, Mrs D. H. S. White 1964, damp waste ground near Longmoor Camp *c*.7830, VC12, Hb.BM (*Watsonia* 13: 334).

On damp, stony or waste ground; an invader from gardens.
VC11: Lymington Marina 3394, on damp stonework, *DEA* 1968; disused railway, Burley 1801, *RPB* 1975.
VC12: By Zebon Copse, Crookham 8051, on disturbed ground, *CRH* 1991.

Chamerion angustifolium (L.)
HOLUB (*Chamaenerion angustifolium* (L.) Scop.) Rosebay Willowherb. **N,C** Very common

First record, J. Goodyer 1618, Winchester, VC11/12 (*Early Brit.Bots*, p.111)

In woodland clearings, hedgebanks, on railways, waste ground and disturbed heathland. Abundant throughout Hants.

Ludwigia palustris (L.) ELLIOTT
Hampshire-purslane. **N** Rare
Map 218 Plate IV

First British record, J. Goodyer 1645, 'I have long observed this plant, as I found it growinge in the rivulett on the east side of Petersfield,...a heathy comon about the middest thereof', VC11 (*Early Brit.Bots*, p.188).

In ponds, shallow streams, marshy hollows and especially old marl-pits, sometimes where overshaded, not in markedly acid places. Very locally

abundant in the SE New Forest, to which it is now almost confined in the British Isles, but refound in E Sussex in 1991, where previously in two sites 1829–76. In Jersey it persisted until 1926, but in Essex it disappeared soon after discovery in 1976. Although stated to be chiefly perennial, E. J. Salisbury (*Watsonia* 9: 33) found it often as an annual when growing on mud. As an aquatic perennial, the vegetative increase is rapid and it frequently becomes dominant in shallow ponds, successfully overwintering in the relatively mild, local climate.
VC11: Last recorded at Petersfield 7522, 7523, 'in marshy spots into which expanded at intervals the shallow stream which drains the great pond', *WAB* 1848 (*Phytologist* 3: 365) and *WBo* n.d., Hb.BM. First record for New Forest: *WBo* 1843, near Brockenhurst Bridge 3003, where it still occurs. Subsequently it was found near Lyndhurst Road Station *c*.3310, 1878–88; between Lyndhurst and Holmsley and White Lawn in 1879 and between Rufus Stone and Minstead *c*.2711, 1883–1924. Also SE of Lyndhurst, *PMH* 1930–33 (*Proc.Hants Fld Club* 12: 295), probably the same as Matley Passage 3307, *GARW* 1932 (*Watts MSS*), *ALJ* 1939, where refound, *RPB* 1991.

Records show there has been a continuing expansion of its New Forest range, as a result of dispersal to new sites, presumably by grazing animals, waterfowl, or even on footwear. Recorded at Sowley Pond 3796, *FR* 1945; dominant in ponds at East End 3697 and East Boldre 3699, in 1952, Hb.RPB 1953; reaching Hatchet Pond 3601, in 1955; near Lymington River, Roydon Woods 3102, *AEB c*.1981; E of Pilley Bailey 3398, *AJB* 1983; in pond at Fletchers Green 2804, *JO* 1987 and near Mopley Pond 4501, *RPB* 1990.

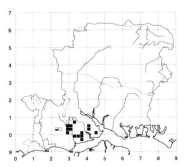

Map 218 Ludwigia palustris

The most westerly site, Burley 2202, *RPB* 1970, has died out.

Miller's Pond, Sholing 4510, *RPB* 1958–65, where probably an aquarists' introduction, was infilled.

Oenothera glazioviana MICHELI ex
C. MART. (*O. erythrosepala* Borbás) Large-flowered Evening-primrose. **H,C** Locally common Map 219

First record, G. C. Druce 1878, Blackwater Sewage Works, VC12, Hb.BM. (First for Britain, and one of the earliest in Europe, 1866, herbarium sheet labelled '*JRE*', name unknown, Niton, Isle of Wight, Hb.OXF, det. *KR*.)

Although this species reached Britain from N. America later than *O. biennis* (*q.v.*), it is now much commoner. It occurs in similar situations.
VC11: Hayling Island 7498, *AB* 1980, Hb.KTU. **VC12**: Aldershot 8452, *ARGM* 1980, Hb.KTU.

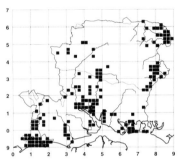

Map 219 Oenothera glazioviana

O. fallax RENNER (*O. glazioviana*
(female) x *O. biennis* (male)) Intermediate Evening-primrose. **C** Very rare or under-recorded

First record, R. P. Bowman 1978, Baffins, Portsmouth 6701, VC11, Hb.RPB, det. *KR*.
VC11: Mogshade Hill 2309, roadbank at under-pass, Hb.RPB 1987, det. *JCB*; Exbury 4200, *RPB* 1980, det. *KR*. **VC12**: Longmoor 7931, old railway, *AB* 1980, det. *KR*; the Slab, Bordon 7835, on disturbed sand, *AB* 1980, det. *KR*.

O. biennis L. Common Evening-
primrose. **H,C** Very locally frequent

First record, E. D. Marquand 1904, Lymington watershed, VC11 (*Fl. Hants*, p.157).

A garden plant believed to have arrived via continental Europe.

On disturbed, sandy ground, sand-dunes and waste ground. Common on the disturbed military training-ground of Woolmer Forest, VC12, *AB*, det. *KR*. Other records are more scattered and may originate from gardens. VC11: 27 □; VC12: 22 □.

VC11: Ashley Heath 1004, on tip, *RPB* 1980, det. *KR*; Shirley Warren 3914, *RPB & AEWy* 1992. **VC12**: Fullerton Station 3839, *RPB* 1980, det. *KR*; A3, Stodham Lane 7725, *GHF* 1977.

O. cambrica ROSTAŃSKI (*O. novae-scotiae* auct., non R. R. Gates; *O. parvi-flora* auct., non L.) Small-flowered Evening-primrose. **C** Rare or under-recorded Map 220

First record, J. E. Lousley 1958, Southampton Docks, VC11, Hb.RNG, det. *KR* 1977.

On waste ground, sand-dunes and disturbed, sandy heathland. On his visit to England in 1977, K. Rostański discovered this new species growing among *O. glazioviana* and *O. biennis* and freely hybridizing with them. Woolmer Forest contains every possible combination of the three species, the hybrids looking quite different according to the sex of the individual parents, each having a unique chromosome system. All previous records of *O. parviflora* and *O. ammophila* Focke probably belong here. Since *Oenothera* species are of N American (not European) origin, *O. cambrica* must have arisen in Europe (and probably in Britain), as it is not known in N America. It is probably of hybrid or mutant origin.

VC11: Hengistbury Head 1890, Hb.RPB 1985, det. *JCB*; Langstone *c*.7104, above salt-marsh, *AB* 1982, det. *KR*. **VC12**: Woolmer Forest 7832, *AB* 1978, det. *KR*; Aldershot 8751, *ARGM* 1980, det. *KR* (*Watsonia* 15: 131).

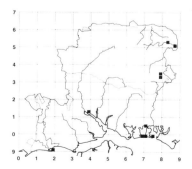

Map 220 Oenothera cambrica

O. stricta LEDEB. ex LINK (*O. odorata* auct., non Jacq.) Fragrant Evening-primrose. **H,C** Very rare

First record, J. F. Rayner 1905, High-field kitchen-garden, Southampton *c*.4214, VC11, (*Suppl.Fl.Hants*, p.48).

A colonist which is now well established around Bournemouth.

VC11: Bournemouth, E cliff, *NDS* 1935; Bournemouth 0890, 1091, 1291, 1494, *MPY* 1960–66, 0790, *RPB* 1978. **VC12**: Farnborough Airfield 8654, on old air-raid shelters, *ARGM* 1980, Hb.AB, det. *KR* (*Watsonia* 13: 334), site destroyed *c*.1988.

O. rubricaulis KLEB. **C** Very rare

First record, J. E. Lousley 1958, a casual at Southampton Docks, VC11, Hb.RNG, det. *KR* 1979.

Circaea lutetiana L. Enchanter's-nightshade. **N,C** Common

First record, Gilbert White 1765, 'in great plenty in the hollow lanes', Selborne, VC12 (*White's Jnls* 1: 164).

Woodland and tall hedgebanks, and as a weed in shady waste-ground or gardens; mainly on basic soil. Common throughout Hants, except in the New Forest where it is only occasional.

<**C. x intermedia** EHRH. (*C. lutetiana* x *C. alpina* L.) Upland Enchanter's-nightshade. **C** Extinct

VC11: Highfield, Southampton *c*.4215, weed introduced, probably introduced with garden plants from Scotland, *JFR c*.1905 (*Suppl.Fl.Hants*, p.48).>

CORNACEAE

Cornus sanguinea L. (*Thelycrania sanguinea* (L.) Fourr.) Dogwood. **N** Very common to local

In open woods, scrub and hedges; on chalk and other basic soils. Very common except in the SW.

C. sericea L. (*Thelycrania sericea* (L.) Dandy) Red-osier Dogwood. **H** Very rare, but under-recorded

Naturalized near rivers and streams. **VC11**: 3226. **VC12**: 4638, 7624.

SANTALACEAE

Thesium humifusum DC. Bastard-toadflax. **N** Very local Map 221

First British record, J. Goodyer 1620,

'on the side of a chalkie hill in an inclosure....as you goe from Droxford to Poppie hill in Hampshire', VC11 (*Ger.em.Johns.*, p.555).

In chalk grassland, semi-parasitic on small grasses of short turf, e.g. where *Festuca ovina* is dominant. Now very local and rather rare, becoming overgrown with scrub. As the downs are overgrown or ploughed, *Thesium* decreases.

VC8: Bokerley Ditch, Martin Down 0518, *RMV* 1988. **VC11**: Yew Hill, Compton 4526, *SNHS* 1968; Hazeley Down 5025, *RPB* 1984; Ports Down from Paulsgrove to Drayton, *FR* 1978–81. **VC12**: Isle of Wight Hill 2536, *GDF* 1988; Bransbury Common 4141, on chalky ridges, *FR* 1981; Danebury Hill 3237, plentiful, *FR* to 1992; margin of Harewood Forest 4045, *DEA & RJP* 1976.

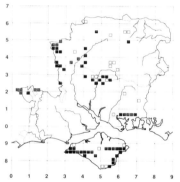

Map 221 Thesium humifusum

VISCACEAE

Viscum album L. Mistletoe. **N,H** Locally frequent Map 222

First record, Gilbert White 1766, Selborne, VC12 (*White's Jnls* 1: 193). A later record by White in 1780 mentions the host-species: 'missel-toe grows on the bough of the medlar: it abounds in my hedges, on the maple', (*White's Jnls* 2: 338). Two large maples with mistletoe survive from these hedges at 7433, *AB c*.1993.

On various hosts, mainly planted trees, and on these often very plentiful. From these sources most mistletoe on native trees is probably bird-sown. Locally common but very scattered. Alien host-trees in order of frequency are lime, poplar, apple, sycamore and false-acacia. Hawthorn is the most-recorded native host, then crack willow, field maple, common white-beam and rowan (once). There are no

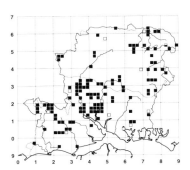

Map 222 Viscum album

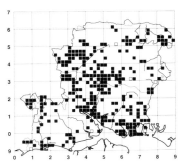

Map 223 Mercurialis annua

records on oak since *Fl.Hants* (p.189). Used medicinally to this day.

VC11: R. Test, Nursling 3516, on crack willow, *RPB* 1978; Ratlake 4123, on several sycamore trees, *EL* 1960; near Woodgreen Common 1717, on false-acacia, *JO* 1984; Sparsholt 4531, abundant on limes in avenue, *FR* 1982. **VC12**: North Warnborough 7351, on hybrid black poplar, *ARGM* 1976; Island Farm, Stoner 7325, *AB* 1979; Hurstbourne Priors churchyard 4346, mostly on lime, *RP* 1984.

CELASTRACEAE

Euonymus europaeus L.   Spindle. **N**   Locally common

First record, Gilbert White 1766, Fyfield, VC12 (*White's Jnls* 1: 206).

In woods, hedgebanks and scrub. Widespread, but commonest on the chalk and Malmstone. In the New Forest, mainly along streams on the better soils, perhaps often on deposits of silt, washed down over stream-banks. The wood is very hard: apart from making spindles from which, as Evelyn correctly observed, it derives its name, it was used to make other things such as virginal-keys and tooth-picks (*Silva*, p.412).

AQUIFOLIACEAE

Ilex aquifolium L.   Holly.   **N,H** Very common

In dry woodland and hedges and as bushes on the downs; it may also be found planted almost anywhere. Common throughout, but nowhere more abundant than in the older New Forest woodlands, where it grows to a great size with trunk more than 1m diameter. Both here and at Holly Hills and Holm Hills, Liphook, it may form woods on its own. Its use in former

times as a nurse-tree, to protect seedling beech-trees from animals, has led to an understorey of inhibited hollies in some woods. When it invades heath, it acts as a soil improver. 'The timber of the Holly...is the whitest of all hard woods, and therefore used by the Inlayer...It makes the best handles and stocks for tools...and of the bark is composed our bird-lime.' (*Silva*, pp.388–389).

BUXACEAE

Buxus sempervirens L.   Box. **N,H**   Very rare

First record, Lady Anne Brewis 1923, Noar Hill 7431, VC12.

Very often introduced as game-cover or bird-sown from gardens, but the truly wild box grows on steep, unstable limestone. This condition is found on the landslip of Noar Hill 7431, where there are four bushes, conf. *CRL* 1981. *FR* considers these to be native, as at Box Hill in Surrey. Another bush on Stoner Hill, in a steep beech-hanger, 7326, VC12, *FR* 1977, may also be native. The wild box features as boundary marks in Anglo-Saxon Charters, from Ecchinswell and East Meon (*Hist.Countryside*, p.210). The wood is intensely hard and weighty, and was much used for every kind of instrument, while sections of the root produced patterns useful in inlay (*Silva*, p.377). To this day, the sawdust is used to clean rings.

EUPHORBIACEAE

Mercurialis perennis L.   Dog's Mercury.   **N**   Very common to local

Woods and hedgebanks; abundant on all base-rich soils. Often carpets the ground in beechwoods on the chalk, where the canopy is thin. Rare in grazed woodland in the New Forest: evidently cannot withstand trampling.

M. annua L.   Annual Mercury.   **C** Locally common   Map 223

First record, W. L. Notcutt 1844, Church Lane, Fareham, VC11 (*Fl.Hants*, p.368).

A thoroughly established colonist of arable and bare ground still on the increase, this plant emanates from the ports and the gardens of towns, in and around which it is abundant, especially those on the chalk.

Euphorbia oblongata GRISEB.   **H** Very rare

First record, J. R. W. Hollins 1993, Ports Creek, Hilsea 6504, VC11, grass bank on S shore, a small vigorous colony, det. *RBa & EJC* 1994.

E. platyphyllos L.   Broad-leaved Spurge.   **C**   Rare   Map 224

First records, T. Yalden *c*.1770, 'about Matterly Farm...in cornfields... common', *c*.5429, and 'at Selburn in Mr [Gilbert] White's field', both VC12 (*Ray Syn.MS*, pp.177, 312).

Arable land on heavy, generally calcareous soils. Rare, but still appears widely around Selborne when left unsprayed.

VC8: Martin Down 0519, in cornfield, *CDD* 1982; Knoll Farm, Damerham 0917, *RPB & JO* 1986. **VC11**: Ridge Farm, Curbridge 5210, *PAB* 1985; near Soake, Cowplain 6711, *DPJS* 1987; Lovedean 6812, *DPJS* 1987. **VC12**: Plentiful in field below Noar Hill 7532, *AB* 1986; Bramshill 7562, on tipped soil, *AJB* 1987; Up Nately 7051, set-aside field, *CRH* 1993.

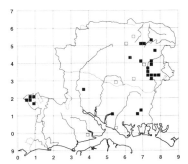

Map 224 Euphorbia platyphyllos

E. helioscopia L.   Sun Spurge.   **C** Common to locally frequent

Cultivated and disturbed ground; common on a wide range of soils except in the New Forest.

E. lathyris L.   Caper Spurge.   H   Rare

A garden escape on waste ground and tips, in old quarries, or as a garden weed. Uncommon and rarely persisting. VC8: 1 □; VC11: 15 □; VC12: 12 □.

VC8: Martin, in old lane, *VHP* 1962 (*Rep.S'ton N.H.S.*, p.8). VC11: Stockbridge 3534, old chalk-pit, *GDF* 1984; M27 Nursling 3716, N bank E of interchange, *RFG* 1990. VC12: Roman wall of Silchester 6462, *PB* 1982; Hurstbourne 4446, abundant in chalk-pit, *AB* 1968; Eversley Centre 7861, *CRH* 1990.

E. exigua L.   Dwarf Spurge.   C   Locally common   Map 225

First record, Gilbert White 1765, 'in the lane leading to the North-field', Selborne, VC12 (*White's Jnls* 1: 166).

Once an abundant cornfield-weed of the chalk, it is still often one of the few weeds in an otherwise clean crop. Also a rare colonist of bare places.

The following three records from localities on non-basic soil are all close to roads or other sites where cement was probably used. VC11: Near A35, Plain Heath 2198, on bare clay, *RPB* 1979; Beaulieu old airfield 3500, *c.*50 plants on bed of old runway, *RPB* 1987; Hatchet Pond 3601, roadside verge, *HJMB* 1983.

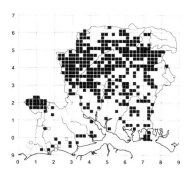

Map 225 Euphorbia exigua

E. peplus L.   Petty Spurge.   C   Common

Cultivated and waste ground, especially in gardens. Common though rather less general than *E. helioscopia* but more frequent in the New Forest.

E. portlandica L.   Portland Spurge.   N   Very rare

First record, W. A. Bromfield 1848, 'Very abundant on the wide flat beach at Stokes Bay', *c.*5898, VC11 (*Phytologist* 3: 821).

On shingle-beaches.

VC11: Stanswood Bay, a small population on semi-stabilized shingle, *RPB & JPFV* 1984 (*Watsonia* 16: 189), the first Hants record for 60 years, increased by 1991, *RPB & FR*. No longer at Calshot Spit, Stokes Bay or on Hayling Island.

E. paralias L.   Sea Spurge.   N   Very rare

On sandy beaches and dunes.

VC11: Now persisting only at Needs Ore Point 4297, *c.*500 plants, *RPB* 1992; Lepe Beach 4598, 12 plants on sandy shingle, N roadside, *PS & RPB* 1995; Gunner Point 6999 and Sandy Point 7599, Hayling Island. No longer at Milford on Sea, where collected by *HT* 1935, Hb.RDG, nor Hurst Beach, two large colonies, *FML* 1930 (*Proc. Hants Fld Club* 10: 300), nor Stone Point, Lepe 4698, last record, *CDD* 1960.

E. esula L.   Leafy Spurge.   C   Very rare

First record, A. W. Westrup *c.*1960, Broxhead Common 8037, VC12, roadside, Hb.AWW, det. *AR-S* 1990, habitat destroyed by fire *c.*1980, *AB*.

Roadsides and paths.

VC12: Chilbolton Down 4136, patch of 40 stems near woodland, *RMV* 1990, Hb.AB, det. *AR-S*.

E. x pseudovirgata (Schur) Soó (*E. uralensis* auct., non Fisch. ex Link; *E. esula* x *E. waldsteinii* (Soják) Czerep.) Twiggy Spurge.   C   Rare

First record, P. M. Hall 1937, between Owslebury and Baybridge *c.*5123, VC11, Hb.BM, Hb.K, det. *AR-S*.

Thought to have been introduced with fodder in places where horse-droppings might have occurred, e.g. roadsides and paths. Habitat similar to *E. esula*.

VC11: Soberton 6217, *PMH* 1940, Hb.BM, Hb.AWW 1957; Meonstoke 6120, old railway-bank, Hb.AWW 1958. VC12: Badshot Lea 8649, known many years, *TD & ARGM* 1980, Hb.AB.

The above records were all det. *AR-S* 1990. A few others, made under the false name of *E. uralensis*, cannot

now be redetermined in the absence of specimens.

E. cyparissias L.   Cypress Spurge.   N?,H,C   Very rare

First record, F. I. Warner 1871, Botley churchyard 5111 or 5112, VC11 (*Fl.Hants*, excl.sp., p.368).

In a few places in grassland or cleared woodland, mainly on chalk.

VC8: Kingstown Copse, Martin 0819, hill-top wood, dominant over small area in clearing, *DWF c.*1965. VC11: Avon Common 1298, on sand under bracken, *RPB* 1983; Yew Hill, Compton 4526, grassy place, *WFB* 1966 (*Rep.S'ton N.H.S.*, p.11). VC12: Isle of Wight Hill 2437, *RAT* 1966 (*Suppl.Fl.Wilts*, p.50), Hb.RPB; Warren Bottom Copse, Hannington 5554, formerly abundant in clearing, now ploughed, but survives on edge of field, Hb.AB 1980. Also 5228, 5252, 5450, 6840.

E. amygdaloides L. ssp. amygdaloides   Wood Spurge.   N   Locally common   Map 226

First record, ?W. Bayley *c.*1570–72, 'In cops by Cathe [?St Catherine's Hill] of ii sorts' Winchester, VC11/12 (ms note thought to be by Dr Walter Bayley under *Tithymalus masculus* on p. 605 of a copy of Du Pinet's *Historia Plantarum*, 1561, Botany Library, BM(NH) (see *Early Brit.Bots*, pp.235–236)).

In woodland on all except very acid or wet soil. Common throughout, except in districts with few old woodlands (e.g. NW of Winchester, and the Gosport–Portsmouth–Hayling Island area). It is one of the few Ancient Woodland plants that remains common in the old unenclosed, grazed, woodlands of the New Forest, presumably because of its acrid taste.

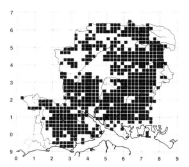

Map 226 Euphorbia amygdaloides ssp. amygdaloides

RHAMNACEAE

Rhamnus cathartica L. Buckthorn. **N** Locally common Map 227

First record, Gilbert White 1766, Fyfield, VC12 (*White's Jnls* 1: 206).

In scrub and open woods on the chalk, and also in fen carr. Very local in hedges and scrub on other soils, and by streams in the New Forest.

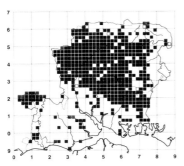

Map 227 Rhamnus cathartica

Frangula alnus MILLER Alder Buckthorn. **N** Locally common Map 228

First record, R. Turner 1664. 'In Hampshire we usually know it by the name of Dogwood...It grows commonly in moist woods and boggy places, as in a wood called Dane-Moor' (*Turn.Bot.*, p.8). Townsend was in error in attributing this record to *Rhamnus cathartica*. 'Dogwood' is an old Hampshire name for *Frangula* (*Engl.Fl.*, p.135), and it is still at Danmoor 7360, VC12, *CRH* 1992.

In scrub, heathland, and open woodland on very acid, sometimes ill-drained soil. Occasionally in fen carr. Common in the New Forest, and on the Tertiary sands of the north. On the Lower Greensand, only common at Conford. It makes the best charcoal for small-arms

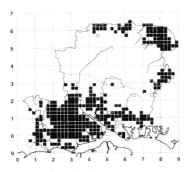

Map 228 Frangula alnus

gunpowder, and was collected for this purpose during World War II.

VITACEAE

Parthenocissus quinquefolia (L.) PLANCH. Virginia-creeper. **H** Rare

First record, Miss W. F. Buckle 1962, Southampton 4112, *c*.4210, *c*.4212, VC11.

Sometimes establishes itself on waste ground, or in sandy places.

VC11: South Hayling 7099, on sandy waste-land, *AB* 1977, flowered 1982, still present, *RBa* 1994 (*BSBI News* 68: 37). Also 5004. VC12: Eelmoor Flash 8452, two large plants, *ARGM* 1979–92. Also 4638, 5832, 7238.

LINACEAE

Linum bienne MILL. Pale Flax. **N** Very local and rare Map 229

On dry grassland and banks, generally on the chalk. Rare and often impersistent, except near the SE coast and at a recently-established New Forest site. Pre–1930 records show that its range has contracted in the SW coastal area.

VC11: Plentiful on Ports Down, where it has spread along the chalk banks of new roads; Stoney Cross Plain 2412, on W roadside, *RPB* 1990; Beaulieu old airfield 3500, Hb.RPB 1981, widespread along old runways by 1990; Hilsea Lines 6604, *EAP* 1983. VC12: Noar Hill 7431, *MS-W* 1970; Shalden Green 7043, roadside, *MO* 1983.

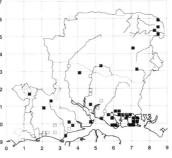

Map 229 Linum bienne

L. usitatissimum L. Flax. **D** Occasional

A relic of cultivation or from bird-seed. VC11: 11 □; VC12: 12 □.

L. catharticum L. Fairy Flax. **N** Locally common

First record, J. Goodyer before 1617, St Cross, Winchester, VC11: 'On the second of October 1617. going by...[the shop of] an Apothecary of Winchester in Hampshire, I saw this herbe lying on his stall, which I had seene growing long before...he told me that it was called Mill-mountain...'; and that he had been at a house 'at Saint Crosse a mile from Winchester' and had seen a man 'have this hearbe in his hand'. According to Goodyer 'It groweth plentifully in the unmanured inclosures of Hampshire, on chalkie downs.' (*Ger.em.Johns.*, pp.559–560).

Abundant on chalk grassland; on verges enriched by road-grit and other basic grassland, especially on the Headon marls of the New Forest, where it is frequent; also on dry, slightly acid grassland and heathland, as in the NE.

Radiola linoides ROTH Allseed. **N** Very locally frequent Map 230

On bare sand and gravel on heaths, in places which are flooded in winter, such as by tracks, ditches and edges of ponds. Common in the New Forest, but very local elsewhere.

VC8: Lopshill Common 0913, *RPB* 1985; Canada Common 2817, *RPB* 1977; Plaitford Common 2718, abundant, *FR* 1991. VC11: Hengistbury Head 1690, on damp base of sand-face, *RPB* 1990; Tantany Wood 3603, open glade, *RFG* 1991; Sandy Point, Hayling Island 7498, *FR* 1980. VC12: Mill Wood 7362, in quantity, *WEW* 1957, not seen 1986; Heath Warren 7660, *PB* 1983, *CRH* 1992; Woolmer Forest *c*.7832, 8031, *AB* 1986; Crookham Bog 8252, *ARGM & CRH* 1983; Odiham Common 7552, under pylons, *AJPB* 1988.

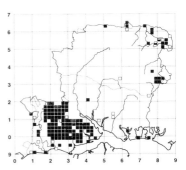

Map 230 Radiola linoides

POLYGALACEAE

Polygala vulgaris L. Common Milk-wort. **N** Locally common Map 231

In grassland and open scrub on chalk and other base-rich soils; in fens and on verges and railway banks. Locally it is now quite rare due to the loss of old meadows through grassland 'improvement'.

Two taxa are described in *New Fl.* (p.552): ssp. *vulgaris* and ssp. *collina* (Rchb.) Borbás (*P. oxyptera* Rchb. var. *collina* Rchb.). Although in the early days of the Hants recording scheme scattered records were made of this latter taxon, especially in chalk grassland or on the Headon Beds and in lime-enriched verges in the New Forest, we do not now consider that the two are sufficiently distinct to be recorded separately.

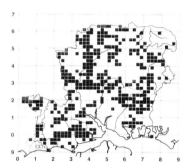

Map 231 Polygala vulgaris

P. serpyllifolia HOSÉ Heath Milk-wort. **N** Locally common Map 232

A strict calcifuge, very common on heaths and in acid grassland, and rides of heathy woods, especially in the New Forest, and on the Lower Greensand and the Tertiary sands of the NE. On

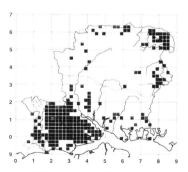

Map 232 Polygala serpyllifolia

chalk, only where overlain by acid drift.

P. calcarea F. W. SCHULTZ Chalk Milkwort. **N** Local Map 233

In chalk grassland, mainly in the W. Local but sometimes abundant, e.g:
VC8: Martin Down 0518, *RMV* 1988. VC11: Broughton Down 2833, *GDF* 1972; Farley Mount 4129, *RMV* 1986; Lower Brook 3327, in chalk-pits, *RPB* 1989. VC12: Ladle Hill 4756, *FR* 1987; West Down, Chilbolton 3838, *FR* 1972; Micheldever Spoil Heaps 5244, on bare chalk, *GHF* 1982.

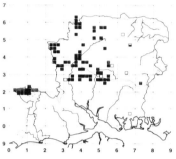

Map 233 Polygala calcarea

HIPPOCASTANACEAE

Aesculus hippocastanum L. Horse-chestnut. **H** Common

Widely planted and frequently self-seeding.

A. carnea ZEYH. Red Horse-chest-nut. **H** Very rare

Widely planted for ornament; originating in cultivation, probably from *A. hippocastanum* x *A. pavia* L. (*New Fl.*, p.554).
VC12: Self-sown at Aldershot (*Alien Pl.Brit.Is.*, p.204).

ACERACEAE

Acer platanoides L. Norway Maple. **H** Local

Frequently planted, and often self-seeding.

A. campestre L. Field Maple. **N** Common

In woodland and hedges on basic soil. Large trees can occur, such as in parts of the New Forest, where it is mainly along streams in ancient woods, on the chalk escarpment from Petersfield to

Selborne, and along the Malmstone. In the western Weald it ceases to be common east of the Gault, and thereafter may be found chiefly on the Bargate Beds. Hunter comments that 'the timber is far superior to Beech for all uses of the turner...and is employed often by those who make musical instruments...' (Notes, *Silva*, pp.191–192).

A. pseudoplatanus L. Sycamore. **D** Very common

An alien, introduced in mediaeval times and now completely naturalized in woodland, except on very poor, acid soil. Its proliferation tends to drive out other plants; however it is still absent from most of the old New Forest woodlands. Beautiful modern furniture is made from the wood, which takes a fine polish. If impregnated with preservative including a grey dye, it is known as 'harewood' (A. F. Mitchell, pers.comm.).

OXALIDACEAE

Oxalis acetosella L. Wood-sorrel. **N** Locally very common Map 234

In woodland, especially beech and oak, in coppice, wet alder-carr, and on shaded hedgebanks. On soils rich in humus, ranging from the acid New Forest and Lower Greensand areas, to chalk woodland. Common, but mainly absent from the deforested central chalk and from near the sea.

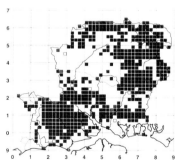

Map 234 Oxalis acetosella

Alien **Oxalis** spp.

These are all garden escapes in origin. Many are well established but it is difficult to decide when to class them as 'established aliens' as they are much under-recorded. The following species are tentatively included in that category:

O. valdiviensis BARNÉOUD   Chilean Yellow-sorrel.   **H**   Very rare

First record, Mrs M. P. Yule 1960, Stanpit 1692, VC11.

O. corniculata L.   Procumbent Yellow-sorrel.   **H**   Locally frequent

First record, E. F. Linton 1896, Bournemouth, VC11, Hb.BM.
  Commonly grown in gardens, it has escaped to paths, walls, waste and cultivated ground, etc. VC11: 30 ☐; VC12: 21 ☐.

O. exilis   A. CUNN. (*O. corniculata* var. *microphylla* Hook. fil.)   Least Yellow-sorrel.   **H**   Very rare

First record, R. Findlay 1926, Beaulieu Abbey 3802, VC11, Hb.K.
  A weed.
  VC11: Hillier Nurseries, Ampfield, *CRL* 1968; Ashley Lodge 2014, Hb.RPB 1977; Sports Centre, Southampton 4015, bank of bowling-green, *RMV* 1989. **VC12**: Church Crookham 8152, plentiful in garden lawn, *ARGM* 1988–92.

O. stricta L. (*O. europaea* Jord.) Upright Yellow-sorrel.   **H**   Local

First record, E. F. Linton 1896, Pithouse Farm, Hurn 1398, VC11, garden weed, Hb.BMH, *BW* 1955, Hb.BM.
  A frequent weed of cultivation in gardens. VC11: 11 ☐; VC12: 19 ☐.

O. articulata SAVIGNY (*O. floribunda* auct., non Lehm.)   Pink-sorrel.   **H** Local

First record, J. W. Wyatt 1935, Milford 2892, VC11, Hb.K.
  A garden weed, sometimes escaping on to waste ground. VC11: 25 ☐; VC12: 3 ☐.

O. debilis KUNTH (*O. corymbosa* DC.) Large-flowered Pink-sorrel.   **H** Under-recorded

First record, D. P. Young 1958, Southampton University Botanic Garden 4215, VC11 (*Watsonia* 4: 62).
  The chief pest species in gardens, proliferating by bulbils. Often confused with *O. articulata*. VC11: 10 ☐; VC12: 2 ☐.

O. latifolia KUNTH   Garden Pink-sorrel.   **H**   Very rare or under-recorded

First record, D. C. McClintock 1954,

West Downs School, Winchester 4629, VC11, Hb.BM.
  A garden weed. VC11: 5 ☐.

O. tetraphylla CAV.   Four-leaved Pink-sorrel.   **H**   Very rare

First record, Mrs M. P. Yule 1960, Stanpit 1692, VC11.

O. incarnata L.   Pale Pink-sorrel.   **H**   Very rare or under-recorded

First record, R. P. Bowman 1958, King's Park Road, Southampton 4212, VC11, Hb.RPB, det. *DPY*.
  A garden weed. VC11: 5 ☐.

O. lasiandra ZUCC.   **H**   Very rare

First record, D. C. McClintock 1971, weed in overgrown, abandoned nurseries, Christchurch 1893, VC11, Hb.BM, no record since.

GERANIACEAE

Geranium endressii J. GAY   French Crane's-bill.   **H**   Rare

First record, Mrs A. G. Padwick 1943, 'dark hollow', Petersfield, VC11/12, Hb.GF/TJF.
  A garden escape.
  VC11: Coombe Cross, East Meon 6621, Hb.AWW 1954. Also 1404, 4022. **VC12**: Kingsclere 5258, stream-bank, *WMK* 1971. Also 5646, 6854, 7054.

G. x oxonianum YEO (*G. endressii* x *G. versicolor*)   Druce's Crane's-bill.   **H**   Very rare

First record, R. P. Bowman 1975, A33 Compton 4625, VC11, road-cutting below gardens.
  A garden escape.
  VC12: Fleet Pond 8154, *ARGM* 1983, *CRH* 1991; by Bourley Road, W of Aldershot 8350, *ARGM* 1986.

G. versicolor L. Pencilled Crane's-bill.   **H**   Rare

First record, Miss W. G. Beddington 1917, Michelmersh churchyard 3426, VC11, abundant (*Suppl.Fl.Hants*, p.26), *c.*12 plants, *RPB* 1974, not seen recently.
  A garden escape.
  VC11: Love Lane, Petersfield 7523, *MS-W* 1977. Also 1404, 2294, 3030, 3428. **VC12**: Heron Wood, Aldershot 8749, *CRH* 1989. Also 3456, 3854, 4436, 5634, 6230, 6842.

G. rotundifolium L.   Round-leaved Crane's-bill.   **N,C**   Rare

First record, Miss F. Davidson 1928, Silchester, VC12 (*Suppl.Fl.Hants*, p.26).
  Dry, open banks and waste ground, generally on sand or chalk. Many of the records are probably casuals, but it is native on Hayling Island, where Westrup found it in four places. This is interesting, because it is much commoner on the Isle of Wight, the only place where Townsend knew it.
  VC11: Broughton (introduction), *HMS* 1935 (*Rep.B.E.C.* for 1935, p.25); Bournemouth 0890, *KG* 1954, Hb.AB; near Eastern Road, Farlington 6704, *AWW* 1960; Sinah Common golf-links 6999, *AWW* 1956, *EAP* 1980; Gunner Point, Hayling Island 6999, shingle-beach, *RPB* 1975–88; waste ground near Great Salterns Lake, Portsmouth 6702, *DPJS* 1991, Hb.RPB. Also 6206, 7098, 7298. **VC12**: Old Bordon–Kingsley railway 7838, *AB* 1968 (*Watsonia* 10: 422–423), 7837, *AB* 1980; Rake 8027, *FF* 1973, *AB* 1986. Also 8438.

G. pratense L.   Meadow Crane's-bill.   **N,H**   Local   Map 235

First record, Gilbert White 1765, 'in the lane leading to the North-field', Selborne, VC12 (*White's Jnls* 1: 166).
  On roadside verges and in meadows, on basic soil, or along streams flowing from chalk. Widespread, but not common; most plentiful on chalk in the NW. Probably native in some old pastures, as at Tichborne Common, VC12. Garden escapes have been excluded, as far as possible, from the map.
  VC8: A354, Martin Down 0320, *RPB* 1984–92. **VC11**: Roman road, Ashley Down, 3929, 4029, *FR* 1979; Ports Down 6106, *EAP* 1984. **VC12**: Still along the Oakhanger Stream to 7837, as

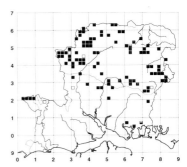

Map 235 Geranium pratense

recorded by Bromfield 1848, *AB* 1986, *FR* 1994; Roman road near Moody's Down Farm 4238, *RPB* 1969, *FR* 1979; Weston Patrick 6846, *FR* 1979; A303, Thruxton 2945, *MFW* 1990.

G. sanguineum L.   Bloody Crane's-bill.   **H**   Rare

Rarely naturalized, usually a transient garden-escape.

VC11: Tetrads 1092, 1612, 3816, 4012, 4014, 6604. VC12: 4636, 6850, 8254, 8450.

G. columbinum L.   Long-stalked Crane's-bill.   **N,C**   Locally frequent   Map 236

First British record, J. Goodyer 1654, 'In several places of Hampshire' (*Merr.Pin.*, p.45).

In grassland, scrub, waste and cultivated ground, mainly on the NW chalk, but also on the Bargate Beds of the western Weald, and on old railway lines and other artificial sites.

VC11: Hinton Admiral Station 2094, abundant, *AB* 1977; Beaulieu old airfield 3500, on remains of rubble, *RPB* 1972; Hale 1618, *JO* 1982. VC12: South Tidworth 2446, border of corn-field, *RPB* 1973; on a small road from B3004 to Standford, 8134, *AB* 1964 (Bargate Beds); Barford, Headley 8437, Hb.AWW 1963 (Bargate Beds).

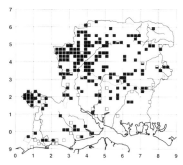

Map 236 Geranium columbinum

G. dissectum L.   Cut-leaved Crane's-bill.   **N,C**   Very common

On cultivated and waste land, roadside verges and banks.

G. x magnificum HYL. (*G. ibericum* Cav. x *G. platypetalum* Fisch. & C. A. Mey.)   Purple Crane's-bill.   **H** Very rare or under-recorded

First record, E. A. Pratt 1983, N of Fort Southwick 6207, VC11, E road-side, det. *ALG*, still there, *RPB* 1991.

This large, purple-blue cranesbill is quite sterile but spreads vegetatively from dumped garden-refuse.

VC11: Belney Farm, Southwick 6409, E roadside verge, *EAP* 1984, det. *ALG*.

G. pyrenaicum BURM. fil. Hedgerow Crane's-bill.   **C**   Locally frequent   Map 237

An invader, spreading from the W. Considered very rare by Townsend, now widespread and fairly common on banks, waste places and roadside verges, on light soil.

VC11: Rockbourne Roman Villa entrance 1117, *DEA* 1987; East Tytherley 2929, grass verge, *RPB* 1977; Bickford Lane, Southwick 6208, *JLSL* 1977. VC12: Roadside between Winchester and Easton, *Watts MSS* 1935, 4930, *ARGM* 1980; Danebury Down 3337, *RPB* 1984; Arford 8236, abundant on corner, *AB* 1970, *CRH* 1988; The Chase 4463, old railway, *NFC* 1982.

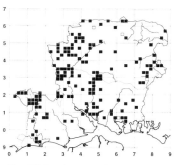

Map 237 Geranium pyrenaicum

G. pusillum L.   Small-flowered Crane's-bill.   **N**   Locally frequent   Map 238

Open, dry banks, roadside verges, and

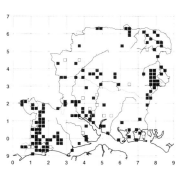

Map 238 Geranium pusillum

disturbed ground, on sand and gravel. Very locally common on the Lower Greensand and Tertiary sands of the NE and SW, otherwise scattered.

VC11: Gardeners Lane, Romsey 3420, *GC* 1987; Rum Bridge, Totton 3512, bank in recreation-ground, *RPB* 1991. VC12: Weyhill *c.*3046, *GDF* 1984; common in the Woolmer Forest area, *AB*; Hazeley Heath tip 7657, *CRH* 1990.

G. molle L.   Dove's-foot Crane's-bill.   **N,C**   Very common

In dry grassland, arable and waste places.

G. lucidum L.   Shining Crane's-bill.   **N,C**   Very local   Map 239

Requires a calcareous, but rather sandy soil, and a sheltered, but not too shaded, site. In lanes bordering the chalk, particularly in the Breamore–Fordingbridge area, and, very noticeably, on the Malmstone and Bargate or Sandgate Beds of the western Weald. In addition it occurs on walls or amongst gravestones.

VC11: Middle Road, Winchester 4729, *DEA* 1981; gravestones, Nursling 3516, *RPB* 1984; Hythe 4108, new gravel-path over pipeline, *RPB* 1988; Hyde 1612, shady banks of streams and roads, *RPB* 1977; Petersfield 7523, *MS-W* 1975; Catherington Retreat House 6914, *MD* 1981. VC12: Frogmore Lane 8460, abundant, *WEW* 1957; abundant on both sides of Frensham Lane 8238, *PEH & AB* 1977–86; Primrose Lane, Rake 8027, *FF* 1968, *AB* 1986; lane above Holybourne church 7341, *JLSL* 1976; Ashford Chace 7326, road-bank, *FR* 1980; Middle Wallop 2936, hedgebank, *GDF* 1987; various places on the Hogmoor housing estate 7834, *SP* 1988.

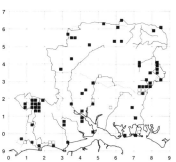

Map 239 Geranium lucidum

G. robertianum L. Herb-Robert.
N Very common

In woodland, hedgebanks, shingle, and as a garden weed. Most abundant on basic soil.

ssp. maritimum (BAB.) H. G. BAKER
N Very rare

VC11: Cadland 4699, mobile shingle-beach, *CDD* 1968, RPB 1986–93.

G. purpureum VILL. ssp. **forsteri** (WILMOTT) H. G. BAKER Little-Robin. **N** Rare Map 240

First record, W. Borrer 1829, Stokes Bay 5898, Hb.BM, refound *EH* 1958, conf. *AWW & EFW*, Hb.AWW.

On both stabilized and mobile areas of shingle-beaches, and on rubble and concrete buildings close to the sea; rare, but locally plentiful in some sites. With one exception (see below), all records of *G. purpureum* are of what has been separated as ssp. *forsteri*.

VC11: Hurst Castle 3189, 3190, *RPB* 1984; Stansore Point to Stanswood Bay 4698, 4699, *MR* 1976, *RPB & PFY* 1993; Calshot Spit 4802, *RPB* 1966, *HFG* 1990; Sinah Common golf-links 6999, 7099, *EAP* 1982, also on the shore at Gunner Point, Hayling Island 6998, *AB* 1986, abundant over *c*.400 x 20m, *RPB* 1988; Langstone Harbour, South Binness 6903, and Long Island 7003, *MB* 1966, *CJT* 1988.

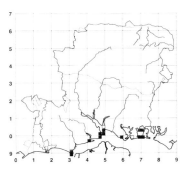

Map 240 Geranium purpureum ssp. forsteri

ssp. purpureum

A specimen from bushes by golf-club-house, Sinah Common 7099, Hb.AWW 1958, was conf. *EFW* as ssp. *purpureum*, and believed to be from the site found by *DWF* the same year. This area is now very overgrown with brambles, and all plants recently found here are ssp. *forsteri*. P. M. Benoit has grown both forms from seed and

doubts whether, from the evidence he has seen so far, it is worthwhile trying to divide them into two subspecies. However *RPB*, who has also cultivated both taxa, finds that plants from the S Hants shingle-beaches differ in both habit of growth and in sculpturing of the mericarps from those originating from Prawle Point, Devon, which are considered to be ssp. *purpureum*. Clearly, the widely-separated British populations require further study before a firm conclusion can be reached on their identity.

G. phaeum L. Dusky Crane's-bill.
H Very rare

First record, Miss Walters 1870, near the Red House, Ladwell Hill, Hursley 4223, VC11 (*Fl.Hants*, excl.sp., p.90).

VC11: Ashley Heath 1205, disused railway, Hb.FAW 1988, not seen *RPB* 1991; Michelmersh churchyard 3426, *WGB* 1917 (*Suppl.Fl.Hants*, p.26), *RPB* 1958, no record since. Also 1894.
VC12: Upper Clatford 3442, *DWF* 1966, *AO* 1975; Ramsdell *c*.5856, *EAB* 1967; The Vyne *c*.6256, *EAB* 1967.

G. retrorsum L'HÉR. ex DC. **C** Very rare

First record, Hon. E. R. Palmer 1960, well established by the main line, Bordon Station 7836, VC12, det. *JEL* (*Proc.B.S.B.I.* 4: 413–414), later tentatively identified as *G. potentilloides* L'Hér. ex DC. (*Proc. B.S.B.I.* 5: 224–226; *Alien Pl.Brit.Is.*, p.212), but the original determination was finally conf. *PFY* 1992.

When this area was bulldozed for an industrial estate, some roots were removed by *AB*, and later replanted as near as possible to the original site on the former line at 7836 (now a walk) where, by 1992, it had become re-established.

<**Erodium maritimum** (L.) L'HÉR. Sea Stork's-bill. **N** Extinct

First record, Miss M. T. Hillard 1921, south shore near ferry, Hayling Island 6899, VC11 (*Suppl.Fl.Hants*, p.28).

Seen in 1933 by *HPF* with *HFC* (*Proc.Hants Fld Club* 12: 301–302). Unfortunately there are no specimens to support these records. Much of the sandy shore here has now been washed away.>

E. moschatum (L.) L'HÉR. Musk Stork's-bill. **N,C** Very rare

Cultivated fields and waste places, generally near the sea.

VC11: *Fl.Hants* (pp.88–89) and *Suppl.Fl.Hants* (p.28) have five records which appear native: near Southsea under hedges, 1846; Chewton Village in plenty 1879; Ashley and near the Plough Inn, Hordle, 1894; South Hayling, 1920; Ashley *c*.2595, *AHM* 1928 (*Milf.Rec.Soc.*, p.29). All post-1930 records are of shoddy- or mill-aliens except the following: East Overcliff Drive, Bournemouth 1091, one plant, Hb.RPB 1993; Knapp Mill, footpaths in waterworks 1593, *RMW* 1981; West Cliff, Hythe 4108, gravelly bank by footbridge, Hb.RPB 1990, det. *EJC*; B2177 Portsdown Hill Road, Widley 6606, short turf in N verge, frequent, *DPJS* 1991, Hb.RPB (*Watsonia* 19: 144).

E. cicutarium (L.) L'HÉR. Common Stork's-bill. **N,C** Locally common

On open sand or gravel, on dunes, beaches, roadside verges and arable. Widespread, but commonest on heath-land or near the coast.

VC11: The true identity of plants on some dunes is uncertain. Tetrads 4698, 5898, 6698, 7098, 7298.

[**E. lebelii** JORD. (*E. glutinosum* Dumort.) Sticky Stork's-bill.

A record for South Hayling, *FBr* (*Suppl.Fl.Hants*, p.28), is not supported by a specimen and cannot be confirmed. Plants seen recently at this locality are glandular forms of *E. cicutarium* but, as suitable habitat exists, *E. lebelii* might occur there.]

BALSAMINACEAE

Impatiens noli-tangere L. Touch-me-not Balsam. **H** Very rare or extinct

First record, J. F. Rayner 1930, Matley 3307, VC11 (*Proc.Hants Fld Club* 10: 299).

In wet woodland. Plentiful at Matley until about 1973, dwindled since then and probably now lost through over-shading or grazing, last record, 1986.

VC12: Stoner Hill 7326, roadside through woods, Hb.AWW 1960.

I. capensis MEERB. Orange Balsam.
H,C Locally common Map 241

First record, Miss Barter 1835, 'wild in the Warden's garden, Winchester',

VC11 (through which R. Itchen runs) (*Fl.Hants*, excl.sp., p.90). However, it is considered that the records in *Fl.Hants* are more likely to have been of this than of the previous species.

It is now invasive beside rivers and ponds and in wet woodland such as willow holts. Although still increasing, it is almost absent from the New Forest and the SE.

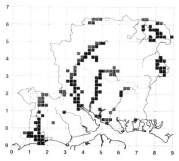

Map 241 Impatiens capensis

I. parviflora DC.   Small Balsam. **H**   Rare

First record, Miss S. G. Rooke 1924, Holdenhurst 1295, VC11 (*Proc.IoW N.H.S.* 1: 241).

In shady ditches, and under bushes. Rare as yet, but increasing greatly on the eastern border.

VC8: West Wellow 2820, shaded roadside ditch, *RMV* 1991. **VC11**: Bassett Wood 4216, *BL* 1967; Exbury Gardens 4299, *RFG* 1990. Also 3414, 3426. **VC12**: S of Hatherden *c*.3448, *BRB* 1965; spread along Longmoor roadside ditch, through three tetrads, 8030, 8430, *AB & RPB* 1974–77; Conford 8232, near ford, *RPB* 1974; lane near Stodham Park 7726, abundant, *AB* 1986; Vigo Lane, Blackbushe 8159, *VK* 1985. Also 7260, 7624, 7660, 7828, 8034, 8048, 8432.

I. glandulifera ROYLE   Indian Balsam.   **H,C**   Locally common Map 242

First record, Miss C. E. Palmer 1900, Odiham, VC12, Hb.OXF. (*Suppl. Fl.Hants*, p.29).

Spreading invasively along waterways, also on waste ground.

VC11/12: R. Rother 7728 to Sussex border 7723, *FR* 1991. **VC11**: R. Blackwater, Nursling 3515, *SS* 1969; Mallards Moor, Bursledon 4709, *DEA* 1984. **VC12**: R. Test, Longparish *c*.4344, *RPB* 1950; Basingstoke Canal

7552, *RPB* 1972; Broad Oak 7552 to Fleet 8053, widespread along the canal, *CRH* 1992.

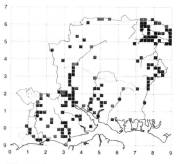

Map 242 Impatiens glandulifera

ARALIACEAE

Hedera helix L. ssp. **helix** Common Ivy.   **N**   Abundant

In woods and hedgebanks, often as an extensive carpet beneath dense canopies. It flowers only when it can climb up to the light.

ssp. **hibernica** (KIRCHN.) D. C. MCCLINT. (*H. hibernica* (Kirchn.) Bean)   Atlantic Ivy.   **N**   Underrecorded

First record, H. McAllister 1978, Hillier's Arboretum, Jermyn's Lane, Ampfield *c*.3723, VC11, (definitely wild).

This is the wild ivy of Ireland, the West, the Isle of Wight, and the S coastal region of Hants. It does not reach very far inland, but more work is needed to establish its distribution. Both ssp. *hibernica* and cultivar 'Hibernica' (see below) are tetraploid, and are the only ivy taxa in Hants so far identified as host to *Orobanche hederae* (ivy broomrape) (*q.v.*).

VC11: Sinah Common, Hayling Island 7099, *AB* 1984, det. *HMcA*; Eling 3612, path through churchyard, *AB* 1982, det. *HMcA*; Emsworth 7305, *AB* 1983, det. *HMcA*; Walhampton 3395, *AB* 1989; Old Street, Stubbington 5403, *KGM & AB* 1991; Manor Farm, Boarhunt 6008, *KGM & AB* 1991; also in the New Forest, SU21, 30, *HMcA* 1978.

H. 'Hibernica'   Irish Ivy.   **H** Under-recorded

A commonly naturalized cultivar, spreading from gardens.

VC12: Yateley Common 8059, under trees, *ACL* 1983; Old Stoke

4837, roadside hedge, *AB* 1979, det. *HMcA*; Oakley Park 8154, naturalized in woodland, *CRH* 1992; woodland S and W of Fleet Pond 8154, 8155, 8254, *CRH* 1992, det. *KWP*; Church Crookham 8252, in woodland, *CRH* 1992.

APIACEAE

Hydrocotyle vulgaris L.   Marsh Pennywort.   **N**   Locally common Map 243

Wet heaths and less-acid parts of bogs, open ditches and marshy meadows on peat and in fens. Avoids heavy shading. Abundant in the New Forest, on the Lower Greensand, and on the NE Tertiary sands.

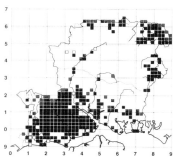

Map 243 Hydrocotyle vulgaris

Sanicula europaea L.   Sanicle.   **N** Locally common

Woodland on moderately-basic to calcareous soils. Common in all wellwooded parts of Hants, but restricted, in the New Forest, to ungrazed woods and old marl-pits, or to streamside, alluvial areas in grazed woods.

Eryngium maritimum L.   Seaholly.   **N**   Very rare   Map 244

First record, J. Goodyer 1618, 'One plant at Titchfield Bay' *c*.5302, VC11 (*Early Brit.Bots*, p.110).

Maritime sand-dunes and sandy beach-ridges; in open vegetation with marram, lyme-grass, etc. Now reduced to five or six small populations at Needs Ore Point 4297, Hill Head 5202, Eastney 6798, 6898. At Sinah Common 6999, where a once large population had shrunk through invasion by the sea, excessive trampling and competition from *Lupinus arboreus*, there has been a notable increase to over 100 fine plants, *FR* 1994. There is also a good population at Sandy Point,

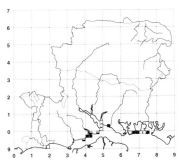

Map 244 Eryngium maritimum

Hayling Island 7498, 7598, protected by railings, *FR* 1992. Formerly also at the mouths of Christchurch Harbour and Southampton Water.

<E. campestre L. Field Eryngo. **N,C?** Extinct (Sched. 8)

First record, Mrs O. Baring 1913, Worthy Down, VC12, (*Hants Chron.*, 1 Feb. 1913)

Formerly in chalk grassland and a cornfield.

VC11: Possibly introduced: grassy field near Milton, *JEK* 1921; Tanners Lane, Pylewell 3695, one plant in lane outside a garden, *RAF & JNBM* 1983, destroyed 1985. **VC12**: Formerly native: Worthy Down 4535, the large patch on downland by a Roman road was ploughed *c*.1950, but survived on the verge until 1978 when choked out by brambles; Mapledurwell 6850, a small patch in a cornfield on a Roman road, *NT* 1943 (*Rep.B.E.C.* for 1943–44, p.725). It seeded into the recorder's garden but is probably now extinct; last seen 1968.>

Chaerophyllum temulum L. (*C. temulentum* L.) Rough Chervil. **N** Very common to local

Hedgebanks, scrub and borders of woods, on dry, mostly basic, soil. Very common except in the New Forest and other heathland, where it is local; succeeds *Anthriscus sylvestris* in flowering.

Anthriscus sylvestris (L.) Hoffm. Cow Parsley. **N** Very common

Roadside verges, hedgebanks, rank grassland and open woods. Abundant, except in the New Forest where it is scarce even on apparently suitable lanesides and borders of woods.

A. caucalis M. BIEB. Bur Parsley. **N** Very local Map 245

Dry, sandy, open banks and roadsides, especially near the sea. Rare inland, except around Oakhanger and Sleaford, VC12.

VC11: Mudeford 1891 or 1892, *MPY* 1960; Hurst Castle spit 3189, 3190, *RPB* 1978; frequent on Hayling Island, as at Sandy Point 7598, *FR* 1984; Avon 1498, one plant on border of barley-field, *RPB* 1991. **VC12**: B3004 Lode Farm, Kingsley 7737, abundant on both sides of the road, *AB* 1985.

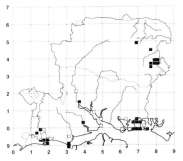

Map 245 Anthriscus caucalis

Scandix pecten-veneris L. Shepherd's Needle. **C** Very rare Map 246

First record, Gilbert White 1766, Selborne, VC12 (*White's Jnls* 1: 194).

A cornfield weed, especially of the chalk, once 'very common' (*Fl.Hants*), but now nearly extinct. There are enough records of this plant since 1960 to mark the boundary of the chalk in NE Hants, but it has now nearly all gone. In VC11, records often appear to be on clay or gravel.

VC11: Field at Inchmery, Lepe *c*.4398, *SS* 1972; E of Ridge Copse, Romsey 3418, in cornfield, *RPB* 1962; open space near Barton Common 2492, *JLeR* 1981. **VC12**: Snoddington Hill 2444, *AO* 1976; Ashford Hill 5561, in field of chamomile, on clay, *PB* 1987;

Tadley 6060, conserved in vegetable-patch, *RWa, PB & AB* 1989–91; South Side Farm, Longparish 4443, *GC* 1986; Battledown Farm, Kempshott 5950, *GC* 1986.

Myrrhis odorata (L.) SCOP. Sweet Cicely. **D** Very rare

First record, Miss M. T. Hillard 1919, neglected ground and margin of oat-field, Hayling Island (*Suppl.Fl.Hants*, p.50).

A garden outcast, grown as a pot-herb for its aniseed flavour; rarely established.

VC11: NE Bournemouth *c*.1094, *MPY c*.1960; Beacon Hill, Warnford 5922, Hb.AWW *c*.1960. Also 4228. **VC12**: Stokehill Farm 3951, firmly naturalized down lane from house, *GDF* 1983 (*Watsonia* **15**: 397); Four Marks 6636, roadside, *AB* 1969 (*Watsonia* **10**: 425).

Coriandrum sativum L. Coriander. **D,C** Very rare

Generally a casual on tips and waste ground, or on the strand-line of shores; rarely persisting.

VC11: Dunbridge Station 3126, *WAP* 1932 or 1933 (*Proc.Hants Fld Club*, **12**: 295); Hythe sea-wall *c*.4208, Hb.AWW 1962. **VC12**: Plentiful and persisting in a cornfield S of Weston Colley 4938, *EAB* 1955 (*Watsonia* **10**: 425).

Smyrnium olusatrum L. Alexanders. **D** Very locally frequent Map 247

Rare inland but common near the coast on roadside verges, hedgebanks and waste ground.

VC11: Sopley churchyard 1596, *MPY c*.1961. **VC12**: Beech, Alton 6838, in hedge, *JM* 1974. det. *EJC*.

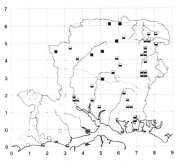

Map 246 Scandix pecten-veneris

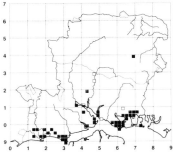

Map 247 Smyrnium olusatrum

<S. perfoliatum L.   Perfoliate Alexanders.   **H**   Extinct

VC12: Lane two miles E of Basingstoke, *RMz* 1932, Hb.BM.>

Conopodium majus (GOUAN) LORET   Pignut.   **N**   Frequent and locally common

In deciduous woodland, shady, unimproved pasture, and grass-heath under bracken, on clayey and sandy soils. Decreasing with 'improvement' of grassland.

Pimpinella major (L.) HUDS. Greater Burnet-saxifrage.   **C,N?** Very rare or extinct

Townsend excluded this species due to lack of confirmed records, but considered its absence remarkable (*Fl.Hants*, excl.sp., pp.187–188). Rayner gives five records, that for Sherborne St John, VC12, by *HLG* he accepted as confirming it for Hants. It was also recorded in the latter area, tetrad 6054, by *EAB* 1957, 1967, but a careful search for it there by *MJS* in 1992 was unsuccessful. Other records, presumably as aliens or casuals, exist, as in 'rough grassy ground formerly cultivated, Bassett', *JFR* 1919; Millbrook Road, Southampton 3813, *WFB* 1965 (*Rep.S.N.H.S.*, p.12) and Coombe near East Meon *c*.6620, *GWSP* 1939 (*Proc.Hants Fld Club* **15**: 67), all VC11. Also, 'within two miles of Burghclere Station', SU45, VC12, *PCH & MMcC-W* 1957, *BSBI* field meeting. However, although *P. major* was crossed off two cards at this meeting, no specimen was collected and *PCH* now has no recollection of this record – we suspect a slip of the pen! The continuing virtual absence of this species in Hants is remarkable, as it is locally common in Kent and E Surrey. It is, however, rare in N. Berks, rarer still in Sussex (one permanent site near Eastbourne), in Dorset, and in Wilts, where there is one site within a few kilometres of the Hants border at Collingbourne Wood 2753, *JDG* 1956. If it does appear as a native in Hants, it is likely to be in woodland in the NW corner.

P. saxifraga L.   Burnet-saxifrage. **N**   Locally very common

Dry grassland; abundant on the chalk downs, common on other basic soils. In the New Forest mostly confined to the Headon Beds, railways and roadside verges.

P. affinis LEDEB.   **C**   Very rare

First British record, R. M. Veall 1990, Nelson Hill, Southampton 4112, VC11, Hb.RPB, det. *MJS*.

Native of Turkey, Caucasus and Iran, thought to have been introduced with grass-seed; in 1991, numerous large, sprawling plants were seen here for 100m along the path by *RPB, EJC, ALG & PAH* (*Alien Pl.Brit.Is.*, p.221).

Aegopodium podagraria L. Ground-elder, Goutweed.   **D**   Very common

An old, medicinal herb found on roadside verges, waste ground, in gardens, borders of woods and plantations, wherever man's activities have carried it. It occurs on a wide range of well-drained soils, and is a serious garden-weed, difficult to eradicate as the far-creeping rhizomes penetrate deeply and small fragments regenerate quickly.

Sium latifolium L.   Greater Water-parsnip.   **N**   Very rare or extinct

Rivers and streams on basic strata. In *Fl.Hants* (pp.176–177) and *Suppl.Fl.Hants* (p.50) it is recorded along the Rivers Stour, Avon and Enborne and, erroneously, the Whitewater and the Basingstoke Canal at Odiham – specimens from the last two in Hb.OXF being *Berula erecta*, teste *CRH* 1993. Its disappearance, taken with that of *Oenanthe aquatica*, suggests pollution or excessive clearing out of streams. It is still locally plentiful in Sussex and in SE Kent, however, where similar factors obtain. Last records:

VC11: R. Stour, Iford 1393 (old bridge), *LBH* pre-1945. **VC12**: Wallop Brook, S of Nether Wallop 3035, *LFS* 1966.

Berula erecta (HUDS.) COVILLE Lesser Water-parsnip.   **N**   Locally frequent   Map 248

First British record, J. Goodyer 1620, 'plentifullie in the River by Droxford' 6018, VC11 (*Early Brit.Bots*, p.116).

Ditches, streams, canals and ponds on basic strata. Frequent to locally common along the main river valleys. Rare in the New Forest.

VC11: Marlborough Deep, Wootton 2298, *FEWV c*.1956, *RPB* 1986; Warblington 7305, Hb.AWW 1957. **VC12**: Chilbolton Common 3940, *MFW* 1991; stream at base of The Warren, Hawkley 7328, *MS-W* 1970, *AB* 1991.

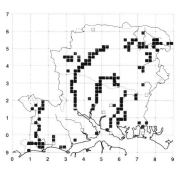

Map 248 Berula erecta

Crithmum maritimum L.   Rock Samphire.   **N**   Locally frequent Map 249

Maritime; on shingle-beaches, sand-dunes, sea-walls and stonework. Like all plants on beaches, it now suffers from trampling, although perhaps increasing in artificial habitats.

VC11: Southbourne 1591, behind promenade, *RPB* 1988; Pennington Marshes 3292, on sea-wall, *MR* 1976; Needs Ore Point 4297, *RPB* 1984; around Hayling Island and Langstone Harbour, and still on a small beach just N of the Harbour Station, Portsmouth 6200, *FR* 1970.

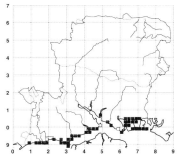

Map 249 Crithmum maritimum

Oenanthe fistulosa L.   Tubular Water-dropwort.   **N**   Local   Map 250 (overleaf)

First record, Gilbert White 1768, Selborne, VC12 (*White's Jnls* 1: 249).

Streams and ditches choked with other vegetation, ponds, fens, wet meadows and flushed bogs, if not too acid. Frequent in the New Forest, local in the Avon Valley, Forest of Bere and NE border areas. Scattered elsewhere.

VC11: Ruddy Mead, Lower Test 3614, *RPB* 1981; Roydon Woods 3000, *FR* 1980. **VC12**: Ron Ward's Meadow, Tadley 6060, *PB* 1983; Tundry Pond 7752, *CRH* 1987.

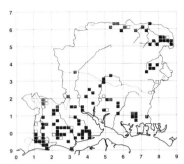

Map 250 Oenanthe fistulosa

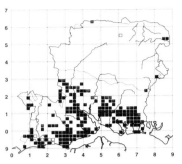

Map 251 Oenanthe pimpinelloides

[O. silaifolia M. BIEB. Narrow-leaved Water-dropwort.

One old record is 'East Hoo, in y^e parish of Subberton [Soberton]...in a hedgerow' [East Hoe 6315, VC11], J. Goodyer 1620, as *O. angustifolia* Lobel (How's ms note to *Phyt.Brit.*, p.81). Townsend in *Fl.Hants* (p.179) relied on Merrett's authority for assuming the record referred to this species. We feel this is too uncertain as it could have been one of several different umbellifers. A recent record for Stanpit Marsh 1692, *FAW* 1986–87, det. *BM* (*Fl.Christchurch*, p.57), is considered to be an error for *O. lachenalii*, which occurs at the precise site given for this species. In 1974 it was found in small quantity in a meadow in the Isle of Wight NE of The Wilderness, *FR & FRS* (*Fl.IoW*, p.57), but now seems to have disappeared.]

O. pimpinelloides L. Corky-fruited Water-dropwort. **N** Locally common Map 251

Dry or damp meadows, brackish grass-land near the coast, roadside verges, occasionally on grass-heaths; on heavy, non-calcareous soils. Common throughout much of S Hants – where, with Dorset and Somerset, it is perhaps more common than anywhere else in Britain – but very rare N of the line West Tytherley–Horndean.

VC11: A326 Eling 3612 to Dibden 4105, abundant on roadside verges since road construction, *RPB* 1974; Tipner 6303, *FR & EAP* 1982; Pulens Lane, Sheet 7523, in hedge (relic of marshes), *SPi c.*1970, extending into Pulens Crescent, *MS-W* 1976. **VC12**: Highclere 4462, in meadow, *ILR* 1991; Queens Road, Longmoor 8131, edge of marsh, Hb.AB 1970 (*Watsonia* **10**: 425); Farnborough Airfield 8653, *ARGM* 1980, seed sown nearby on Cove Hill when site built-over 1987, 24 plants *CRH & ARGM* 1993.

O. lachenalii C. C. GMEL. Parsley Water-dropwort. **N** Very local Map 252

Brackish grassland, salt-marshes, creeks by the coast and in estuaries. There are no recent inland records. It overlaps in habitat with *O. pimpinelloides* but is more restricted.

VC11: Marwell, *GWP* 1930 (*Proc. Hants Fld Club* **10**: 297); Pennington Marshes 3292, *MR* 1976; Bailey's Hard 3901, *RPB* 1985.

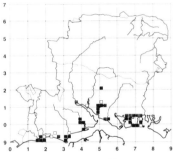

Map 252 Oenanthe lachenalii

O. crocata L. Hemlock Water-dropwort. **N** Locally very common Map 253

Marshes on inorganic silt, ditches,

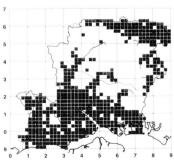

Map 253 Oenanthe crocata

streamsides, alder or willow carr and other wet woods.

O. fluviatilis (BAB.) COLEMAN River Water-dropwort. **N** Local Map 254

Slow-to swift-flowing rivers and streams, usually in calcareous water of moderate depth. Shy-flowering, often with submerged stems only. The 1991 *NRA Survey* of the Rivers Test and Itchen produced continuous records but did not cover the lower reaches to the river mouths. Unknown in the R. Meon. Falling water-level appears to have driven it out from one stream in the Lower Test, VC11. Re-invigorated by dredging in the Basingstoke Canal, VC12, as far E as Coxmoor Wood 7851 (*CRH* 1986), by 1991 it had declined and was plentiful only near Tundry Hill 7752, and North Warnborough 7351, 7352; it remains to be seen whether it will survive the turbidity caused by constant motor-boat traffic.

VC11: R. Avon, Sopley 1596, *AEB* 1982; Lymington River, Boldre Bridge 3198, *AEB* 1981–92; R. Dun, Mottis-font 3225, *KAH* 1982. **VC12**: Sherfield on Loddon 6858, *IMcD* 1971.

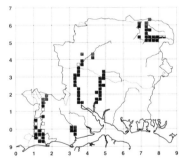

Map 254 Oenanthe fluviatilis

O. aquatica (L.) POIRET Fine-leaved Water-dropwort. **N** Very rare or extinct

Ponds, ditches and sluggish rivers. *Fl.Hants* (p.180, as *Œ. phellandrium* Lam.) states 'not uncommon in W. and central parts', and has many records for the R. Stour, Lymington water-shed, and the Rivers Test, Itchen and Meon. This recording scheme has produced only three records for the Stour, and one for the Lymington watershed, none very recent:

VC9: R. Stour, Kinson 0697, *MPY* 1964 (destroyed by bridge-alterations according to *ESH*). **VC11**: Iford 1493, *ESH* 1964; R. Stour, Stanpit Marsh 1692, *MPY* 1960; Keyhaven Marshes

3191, *PE* 1959, *CDD* 1968. Its disappearance is remarkable, but is paralleled by the loss of an associated species, *Sium latifolium* (*q.v.*). The record for Farringdon 7235, VC12, *AB* 1976 (*Watsonia* **11**: 395) is an error.

Aethusa cynapium L. Fool's Parsley. **C** Common

Waste ground, cornfields and other arable land, on well-drained soils. Both ssp. *cynapium* and ssp. *agrestis* (Wallr.) Dostál may occur, but they have not been distinguished in our records.

Foeniculum vulgare MILL. Fennel. **N?,D** Local Map 255

On banks, roadsides, bare waste-ground and by railways. Frequent locally near the coast and estuaries but rare inland.
    VC11: Near Hythe Pier 4208, *MR* 1976. **VC12**: Aldershot 8751, waste ground and railway bank, *TD & ARGM* 1980.

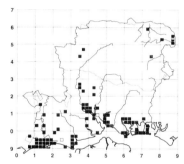

Map 255 Foeniculum vulgare

Silaum silaus (L.) SCHINZ & THELL. Pepper-saxifrage. **N** Locally common Map 256

First record, Gilbert White 1766, Selborne, VC12 (*White's Jnls* 1: 211).
    Old grassland, grass-heaths, old

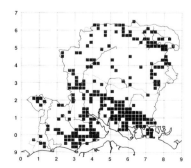

Map 256 Silaum silaus

marl-pits and roadside verges, nearly always on heavy clay. Common near the coast, and on the Tertiary and Gault clays, but rare on chalk or sand. The map corresponds well with the position of the clay.

Conium maculatum L. Hemlock. **N** Locally common

Disturbed ground along hedges, on waste ground, and in damp woods; also on dredged spoil on river-, stream- and ditch-banks. Widespread; common along the main valleys, but scarce in the New Forest and on much of the dry chalk-uplands.

Bupleurum tenuissimum L. Slender Hare's-ear. **N** Very locally frequent Map 257

Dry banks, especially inside sea-walls and upper margins of short-turf salt-marshes, often beside tidal drains. Frequent around Langstone Harbour and Hayling Island, rare elsewhere. Lost from two sites on the Test estuary.
    VC11: Black Water, Needs Ore 4197, *FR* 1975, refound *RPB* 1994; mouth of R. Hamble, Hook-with-Warsash 4805, *CRC* 1983; Cracknore Hard 4010, *RPB* 1984; Langstone 7104, continuous belt behind sea-wall, *EAP* 1984.

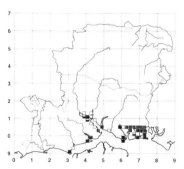

Map 257 Bupleurum tenuissimum

B. rotundifolium L. Thorow-wax. **C** Very rare or extinct

First record, Gilbert White 1766, Fyfield, VC12 (*White's Jnls* 1: 210).
    Formerly a rare weed of cornfields on chalk, now extinct in cornfields. Two recent records appear to be associated with compost. Some plant nurseries cultivate it.
    VC11: Chidden 6517, *PJR* 1974, seed from here was sown at Butser Ancient Farm 7118, and in 1991 when the farm was resited NE of Bascombe

Copse, Chalton Lane 7216, harvested seed was resown there – plants derived from these sowings still survive; Wecock Farm, Lovedean 6812, three plants at base of grassy manure-heap at edge of field, along footpath, *DPJS* 1987, Hb.RPB (*BSBI News* **60**: 34). **VC12**: Swarraton *c.*5636, *PMH* 1931, Hb.BM; Fob Down Farm, Alresford 5733, *AHC* 1938, Hb.RNG; Mapledurwell *c.*6850, first in cornfield, later in adjacent garden, *NT* 1940, *AWW* 1963; Monkwood *c.*6630, *CWMB* 1965, conf. *ECW* (*Proc.B.S.B.I.* 6: 240); appeared in a Four Marks garden 6634, *HTa* 1991, Hb.AB, conf. *EJC*.

Apium graveolens L. Wild Celery. **N** Very local Map 258

Brackish marshes and creek-banks on the coast, and tidal rivers. It is frequent in these habitats, but there are now no inland records as given in *Fl.Hants* (p.173).
    VC11: Eight Acre Pond, Normandy 3293, *ERB* 1990; Lower Test, Redbridge 3614, *RPB* 1977; Langstone 7104, in creek, *RPB* 1978.

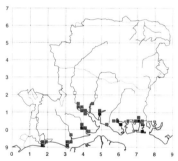

Map 258 Apium graveolens

A. nodiflorum (L.) LAG. Fool's Watercress. **N** Locally very common

First British record, J. Goodyer 1619, 'plentifullie by the lakes and rivers sides at Droxford', VC11 (*Early Brit.Bots*, p.114).
    In streams, ditches, ponds and marshes, both freshwater and brackish; mostly in base-rich waters. Very tolerant of pollution and eutrophication.

A. inundatum (L.) RCHB. fil. Lesser Marshwort. **N** Locally frequent Map 259

Shallow ponds with margins usually exposed in summer, also sluggish streams on heathland; in moderately acid waters. Common in the New Forest, occasional on the Tertiaries and Lower Greensand in the NE.

VC11: Jockstrill Common, Sopley 1597, *JO & RPB* 1987; Kentford Lake 3219, *RPB* 1958. **VC12**: Foxlease 8256, *ARGM* 1978; shallow pond, Woolmer Forest 7832, *AB* 1984; Bagwell Green, Winchfield 7653, abundant, *AJB* 1986; massively declined in the Basingstoke Canal due to dredging, *CRH* 1992.

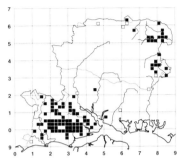

Map 259 Apium inundatum

Petroselinum crispum (MILL.) NYMAN ex A. W. HILL   Garden Parsley.   **D**   Very rare

VC11: Hurst Castle 3189, *SNHS* 1966. Recorded by W. A. Bromfield in 1838, as abundant on the shingle and being gathered for domestic purposes. It is now more confined to the crumbling, concrete emplacements.

P. segetum (L.) KOCH   Corn Parsley.   **N,C**   Rare   Map 260

First British record, J. Goodyer 1620 to 1625, 'in the wheate ershes about Mapledurham in Hampshire', *c.*7321, VC11 (*Early Brit.Bots*, pp.121–122).

Cornfields and disturbed ground on chalk, and on dry banks near the coast. Very scattered, and much decreased

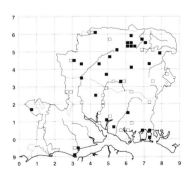

Map 260 Petroselinum segetum

since *Fl.Hants* (p.174) due to modern farming methods.

VC8: South Allenford, Damerham 0716, headland of wheat-field, *JO* 1987. **VC11**: Farlington Marshes 6804, *MB* 1975, *FR* 1990; Hursley 4325, border of cornfield, Hb.RPB 1975; Saltgrass Lane, Keyhaven 3091, *MEY* 1980, six plants, *RPB* 1991; Northney Road, North Common, North Hayling 7204, *GHF* 1977; Bere Copse, Soberton 6014, *HCC* 1985. **VC12**: Highclere 4458, *RJH* 1987; Severalls, Manydown Estate 6052, *GC* 1986; Abbotts Ann 3243, *JRM* 1994.

Sison amomum L.   Stone Parsley.   **N**   Locally common   Map 261

On grassy verges, alongside hedges, scrub-borders, old pastures, and banks on coastal, alluvial marshes. Mainly on heavy clay. Common near the coast and on the Gault, the London Clay and the Headon Beds.

VC11: Eling 3612, *RPB* 1978. **VC12**: Ashford Hill meadows 5662, *PB* 1983.

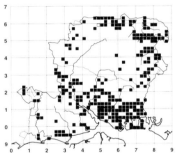

Map 261 Sison amomum

Carum verticillatum (L.) KOCH   Whorled Caraway.   **N**   Very rare

First record, R. P. Bowman 1966, Long Aldermoor, Minstead 2709, a small patch in marshy acid grassland; still prospering, *AB* 1983.

No recent record.

Boundway Hill 2698, one plant, *FR* 1976, not refound. The New Forest is a new and intriguing site for this Oceanic-southern species which is almost confined to W Britain, but it is paralleled by similarly isolated sites near Wareham in Dorset and it was formerly also in Surrey.

Angelica sylvestris L.   Wild Angelica.   **N**   Locally very common

In fens, marshes, wet meadows, riversides, moist, open woods and their rides.

Pastinaca sativa L. var. **sylvestris** (MILL.) DC.   Wild Parsnip.   **N**   Locally very common

In rank grassland, scrub, waste ground, and on verges. Very common on chalk, frequent on valley gravels and other light, mainly basic, soils.

Heracleum sphondylium L. ssp. **sphondylium**   Hogweed.   **N**   Very common

Roadside verges, waste land, hedges, borders of woods or clearings, and rank grass in meadows. Abundant throughout, except on the open New Forest.

H. mantegazzianum SOMMIER & LEVIER   Giant Hogweed.   **H**   Occasional

An established garden-escape, widely scattered and occasionally plentiful in moist, shady, grassy places or on waste ground. VC11: 17 □; VC12: 13 □.

VC11: Hilsea Lines 6604, woodland path, *EAP* 1980. **VC12**: Wonston 4739, marsh along stream, *RPB* 1966; Weyhill *c.*3046, *GDF* 1984.

Torilis japonica (HOUTT.) DC.   Upright Hedge-parsley.   **N**   Common

Roadside verges, hedgebanks, scrub and open woods. Common throughout the county, succeeding rough chervil in flower in July–August.

T. arvensis (HUDS.) LINK   Spreading Hedge-parsley.   **C**   Very rare   Map 262

First British record, J. Goodyer before 1664, 'amongst wheat, plentifully, near Petersfield', VC11/12 (*Merr.Pin., p.24*).

It once infested cornfields, principally on the chalk, but is now restricted to a very few sites.

The most recent records are: **VC11**: Upper Hamble Country Park, Botley 5011, arable field, *MJS* 1987 (*Watsonia*

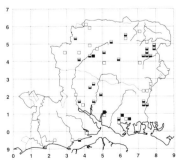

Map 262 Torilis arvensis

18: 220); Boarhunt 6109, corner of field, *JRw* 1991, Hb.RPB; near Miller's Coppice, Southwick 6407, *JRw* c.1983. **VC12**: Southside Farm, Longparish 4443, *PHC & AJB* 1986; Deane Down Farm 5550, edge of corn-field, Hb.AWW 1962; Roundwood c.5044, *WMB* 1969; Fair Oak 5561, *PB* 1993.

T. nodosa (L.) GAERTN. Knotted Hedge-parsley. **N** Rare Map 263

First record, W. L. Notcutt 1844, Titchfield churchyard 5405, VC11 (*Fl.Hants*, p.185).

On dry banks in a few coastal and inland sites. Given as 'frequent' in *Fl.Hants*, but now rare.
VC11: Portchester c.6004, *AWW* 1950; beside A35, Lyndhurst Road Station 3310, *RPB* 1962; Gosport ferry 6299, edges of lawns, *MJS* 1991 or 1992, comm. *EJC*; Farlington Marshes 6804, sea-wall, *MB* 1974, Hb.AWW; Southsea 6598, *EAP* 1983; South Moor, Langstone 7104, inner side of sea-wall, Hb.RPB 1990. **VC12**: Grateley c.2840, *BHSR & NDS* 1966; Basingstoke area, tetrads 5842, 6052, 6252, 6446, *EAB* 1964–66.

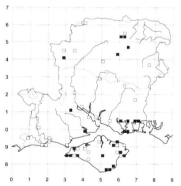

Map 263 *Torilis nodosa*

<Caucalis platycarpos L. Small Bur-parsley. **C** Extinct

First record, T. Yalden c.1770, 'about Matterly Farm...frequent in corn-fields', c.5429, VC12 (*Ray Syn.MS*, pp.177, 219).

An annual, native of S and E Europe, this cornfield weed of chalk soils was classed as 'very rare' in *Fl.Hants* (p.184). Although some of the old records refer to it as locally plenti-ful, there are no records since 1934 so it is presumed extinct.
VC11: Lockerley Mill 2926, *BG*

1934 (*Proc.Hants Fld Club* **15**: 67, as *C. daucoides* L.); 'One or two spots on the Eastney glacis, *EHW* 1900–08, plenti-ful May 1911', 6899, (annotated *Fl.Hants*). **VC12**: Andover, *MLW* 1912, Hb.BM; near Andover, *WS* 1934, Hb.BM.>

Daucus carota L. ssp. **carota** Wild Carrot. **N** Common

First record, J. Goodyer 1618, 'Drox-ford', VC11 (*Early Brit.Bots*, p.112).
Grassland, banks, borders of fields, waste ground and roadside verges. Very common on the chalk, but also on the dry, less-acid soils throughout, including the coast.

[ssp. **gummifer** (SYME) HOOK. fil. Sea Carrot.

No confirmed records exist.]

GENTIANACEAE

Cicendia filiformis (L.) DELARBRE Yellow Centaury. **N** Very local Map 264 Plate V

Heaths, on bare tracks, flood hollows, edges of ponds, ditches and on damp, sandy or gravelly soil, mud and clay, where inundated in winter. In the New Forest only, where it is widespread and sometimes abundant when conditions suit it. S Hants, W Cornwall and NW Pembs are now its major strongholds in Britain.
VC11: Hatchet Pond 3601, *FR* 1987; W of Shirley Holms 2998, *GH* 1969; near Ipley Inclosure 3608, *RPB* 1980; S of Wood Crates 2707, *FR* 1975; Burley Moor 2104, damp track-side, *JO* 1987; Blackwell Common 4301, disturbed soil over gas-main, *RPB* 1990. **VC12**: *Fl.Hants* (p.256) has records for 'near Andover' in 1856, and

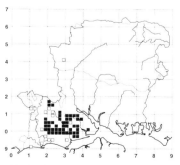

Map 264 *Cicendia filiformis*

Grateley. Not recorded since.

Centaurium erythraea RAFN Common Centaury. **N** Frequent and locally common

Dry grassland on heaths, commons, pastures and chalk downs. Also in old pits and open, woodland rides and clearings. Especially common in the SW.

var. **sublitorale** (WHELDON & C. E. SALMON) UBSDELL Very rare

Damp, sandy hollows on the SE coast, in Hayling Island. Although the origi-nal identification, as *C. littorale* (Turner) Gilmour, for long went unchallenged, this small population with distinctively narrow stem-leaves has been reclassified by R. A. E. Ubsdell after examination of S Hants specimens in Hb.BM (*Watsonia* **11**: 24). In 1981, E. A. Pratt carried out a biometrical study of the Sinah Common plants which shows that, although they are nearer to *C. littorale* in some distinguishing characters, overall they are more likely to be a vari-ant of *C. erythraea* (*J.Portsmth & Dist.N.H.S.* **3** No.3, 1982, pp.88–89). Subsequently, D. Eaton of Portsmouth Polytechnic measured the pollen-grain diameter and found it corresponded with that of *C. erythraea* (pers.comm).
FR and *DEA* suggest that the Hayling plants may be the product of past hybridization between *C. erythraea* and *C. littorale*. The latter is unknown in the British Isles south of Carmarthenshire, but it occurs along the continental coast of NW Europe as far west as the Pas de Calais and Normandy.
VC11: Sinah Common, one plant only, *JEL* 1936, Hb.RNG, det. *JSLG* (as '*C. littorale* near var. *occidentale* (Wheldon & C. E. Salmon) Gilmour') (*Proc.Hants Fld Club* **15**: 68), redet. *RPB* 1992. Sinah Common golf-links 6999, old shingle-quarry, Hb.AWW 1960 (probably *JEL*'s site), few plants *EAP* 1982, 78 in 1984, 192 in 1986, 22 in 1987, none in 1988. The reason for the fluctuation in numbers is not clear, but it may be due to low seed-set or poor germination in unfavourable years. Similar plants are known at Sandy Point, Hayling Island 7498, *EAP* 1980, *FR* 1992, Hb.RPB.
Plants identified as var. *capitatum* (Willd. ex Cham.) Melderis, found on Milford cliffs, VC11, *AHM* 1910 (*Milf.Rec.Soc.*, p.27), need refinding for correct determination.

C. pulchellum (Sw.) DRUCE Lesser Centaury. **N** Local Map 265

In rather calcareous grassland, short, open turf on ditch-banks, old marl-pits, former airfields, damp sandy salt-marsh turf, and open, woodland rides on chalk. Frequent in the southern New Forest on the calcareous Headon marls; occasional on the coast, but rare elsewhere.

VC8: Kitt's Grave, Martin Down 0320, spreading along tracks, *GDF* 1992. **VC11**: Hatchet Pond 3601, *FR* c.1980; Gilkicker Point 6097, *RPB* 1977; NW Hayling Island 7103, *FR* 1978; West Wood, Sparsholt 4230, *RPB* 1966; NW of Ashley Hole 2015, on bare chalk, old bombing range, *RPB* 1986. **VC12**: Shoulder of Mutton Hill, above Ashford 7326, *FBr* 1929 (*Suppl. Fl.Hants*, p.70), *FR* 1976; Hampage Wood 5430, *FR* 1985; Blackbushe Airfield 8158, *VK* 1984; Butter Wood 7052, *AJPB* 1986; Bramshill 7660, on track with *Radiola linoides*, *FR* 1989.

C. tenuiflorum (HOFFMANNS. & LINK) FRITSCH Slender Centaury. **N** Very rare or extinct (Sched. 8)

First and only record, H. Hawkes 1883, Portsmouth?, VC11, det. *FT* (*Fl.Hants*, p.255, as *Erythraea tenuiflora* Link).

It is clear that Townsend saw, and determined as this species, a specimen in J. Woods' herbarium which was accompanied by the note: 'Mr Hawkes of Portsmouth wishes to know whether this is *Erythraea Centaureum*'. The specimen has not been traced and the date of collection is not given. It is just possible that this very rare plant may be refound in a grassy salt-marsh somewhere in the Portsmouth area. It is still on a clayey shore bank at King's Quay in the north of the Isle of Wight (*CRP* in litt. to *FR* with specimen).

Blackstonia perfoliata (L.) HUDS. Yellow-wort. **N** Locally frequent Map 266

First record, Gilbert White 1767, 'in plenty up the sides of the steep cartway in the Kings field beyond Tull's', Selborne, VC12 (*White's Jnls* 1: 181).

In chalk grassland, or in chalk cuttings and verges; fairly frequent. Occasionally near roads or other places where chalk has been imported; in the New Forest on the Headon Beds and on the NE heaths, associated with concrete tracks, etc.

VC11: Blackhamsley Hill 2800, *RPB* 1972; Hurst Castle 3189, *RPB* 1961–88; Calshot 4701, 4801, spreading on reclaimed land, *SNHS* 1984; S of Knowle Hospital 5509, on roadbank, *ARLo* 1987. **VC12**: Rookery Dell, Monk Sherborne 6056, *PB* 1982; Hartfordbridge Flats 8158, *CRH* 1986; RAE Pyestock 8354, abundant, and Farnborough Airfield 8453, 8553, 8654, *ARGM* 1974–91, possibly due to imported soil.

Gentianella campestris (L.) BORNER Field Gentian. **N** Very rare

Dry, heathy grassland invaded by heather; in the New Forest on Headon clays or where overlain by plateau gravels. Rare but locally abundant; these large populations can drop dramatically in dry summers.

VC11: Holmsley, old airfield, extending from Magpie Green 2000, *RGL* 1977, to Plain Heath 2198, *RPB* 1979, also 2199, 2299, *AEB* 1979; S of Markway Inclosure 2401, *AEB* 1983, 2402, *RPB* 1985; Spy Holms 2302, *RPB* 1985; Whitten Bottom 2001, roadside verge, *RPB* 1987. Formerly at Breamore Down 1320, Newtown c.2193 and Hinton c.2195 (*Fl.Hants*, p.260) and Ashley c.2594 (*Suppl.Fl. Hants*, p.70). **VC12**: Refound after 75

years in old, herb-rich grassland N of the Temple, Highclere Park 4560, hundreds of plants, *AJB* 1986, det. *FR* (*Watsonia* 18: 221). Old records for six other localities where it has not been refound.

G. germanica (WILLD.) BORNER Chiltern Gentian. **N** Very rare Map 267

Chalk grassland, cuttings, old chalk-pits, open scrub. Now confined to the NW downs along and S of the Berks border.

VC12: Ashmansworth 4158, *NP* 1956, *FR* 1973; 4157, *NP* 1955, Hb.ABD, *RPB* 1969, now ploughed; Great Litchfield Down, disused railway 4654, thousands of plants, *RPB* 1969; new A34 verge 4655, numerous, *PB* 1980; disused railway N of Old Burghclere 4759, *MBo* 1976; Ecchinswell chalk-pit, *PMH* 1937 (now gone), Hb.BM; S of Faccombe 3957, *FP* 1958; Worthy Down 4434, *JCDa* in litt., 1940 (since ploughed).

G. x pamplinii (DRUCE) E. F. WARB. (*G. germanica* x *G. amarella*) **N** Very rare

VC12: North Sydmonton, *ABJ* 1895, Hb.OXF; Ashmansworth to East Woodhay 4158, *NP* 1955; Great Litchfield Down 4654, disused railway, *RPB* 1980; Walbury Hill 3761 (Berks), *MBo & VF* 1975, conf. *FR*.

G. amarella (L.) BORNER ssp. **amarella** Autumn Gentian. **N** Locally common Map 268

First record, Gilbert White 1768, Selborne, VC12 (*White's Jnls* 1: 254).

In short, chalk turf on downs, banks, chalk cuttings, and sunny, woodland rides. In the SW, in the New Forest only, where it is very local on the Headon Beds in old marl-pits and on verges.

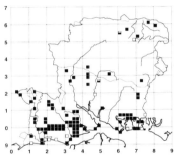
Map 265 Centaurium pulchellum

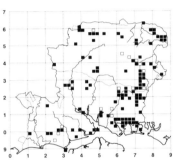
Map 266 Blackstonia perfoliata

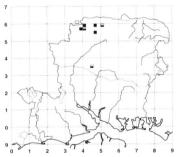
Map 267 Gentianella germanica

VC11: Marlpit Oak 2899, *RPB* 1957; Plain Heath, old airfield 2198, *RPB* 1979; Ocknell Plain 2211, edge of old airfield, *RPB* 1991.

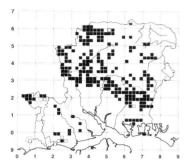

Map 268 Gentianella amarella ssp. amarella

G. anglica (PUGSLEY) E. F. WARB. ssp. **anglica**   Early Gentian.   **N,C** Very rare (Sched. 8)   Map 269

First record, E. H. White 1929, Horndean Down 7015, VC11 (*Suppl.Fl. Hants*, p.71, as *G. lingulata* C. Agardh var. *praecox* (Towns.) Wettst.). Occurs very sparsely on chalk downs, often on banks facing south, but only where the turf is very short or even where the chalk is weathered bare. Although the populations fluctuate, most of them are declining and the conclusion cannot be avoided that lack of grazing is responsible. In striking contrast, in the Isle of Wight *G. anglica* is so much more common that *Fl.IoW* (p.66) describes it as 'frequent to common' and *G. amarella* only as 'frequent'.

VC8: Martin Down 0419, old ranges, Hb.RPB 1967, *FR* 1988; Kitt's Grave, Martin Down 0320, *RPB* 1982. **VC11**: NW of Ashley Hole 2015, bare chalk at old bombing range, seeds probably brought in with imported

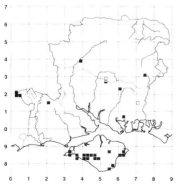

Map 269 Gentianella anglica ssp. anglica

chalk, *RPB* 1986, *c*.1500 plants, *RPB* 1992, *c*.2800 in 1994; near Paulsgrove chalk-pit 6306, *MB* 1975; Beacon Hill, Warnford 6023, one plant, *L-Lo* 1980. **VC12**: Noar Hill 7431, *CL* 1951 (*Watsonia* **2**:346), *ARGM* 1988, *SP & FR* 1994; Cheesefoot Head 5227, *HWP & PMH* 1934 (*Proc.Hants Fld Club* **15**: 68), *EM-R* 1954, Hb.K; West Down, Chilbolton 3838, bank near road, *RPB* 1967 (*Rep.S'ton N.H.S.*, p.14), not seen since.

Gentiana pneumonanthe L. Marsh Gentian.   **N**   Rare   Map 270 Plate VI

Grassy, wet heaths with *Molinia caerulea* in the *Erica tetralix*-zone bordering valley bogs. Very local in the New Forest, where plentiful most years in the main sites, but very rare as outliers, and on the heaths of the Moors River and Thames Basin. Populations at several sites are quite low, and regular grazing or occasional burning seem necessary for their maintenance.

VC11: Ashley Heath 1004, *MPY & ESH c*.1960–70; East Parley Common 1099, solitary plant, *RMW c*.1982, *RPB* 1991; Baddesley Common 3921, a relic, *KC* 1962, one plant, *RPB* 1984, none 1992. **VC12**: Bartley Heath 7253, plentiful, *ARGM* 1973–92; Hook Common 7253, plentiful, *GARW* 1933 (*Watts MSS*), much declined, *ARGM* 1987, six plants, *CRH* 1995. Formerly at Hazeley Heath 7558, *GARW* 1936 (*loc.cit.*), and Farnborough Airfield 8453, the main colony of which was destroyed in 1941 when Cove Reservoir was drained, last record *GEB c*.1960, one plant. Rose Kingsley (*Proc.Hants Fld.Club* **8**: 132), mentions it at Bramshill, *c*.1870, comm. *CRH*.

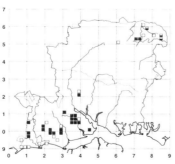

Map 270 Gentiana pneumonanthe

APOCYNACEAE

Vinca minor L.   Lesser Periwinkle. **N?,H**   Locally frequent   Map 271

First record, Gilbert White 1766, 'Shrub-wood', Selborne, VC12 (*White's Jnls* **1**: 190), still on this hanger 7533, *AB* 1975.

On wooded hedge- and ditch-banks, in thickets. It often spreads as a dense mat in copses, but so much has been discarded from gardens or planted in woods for ground-cover that it is difficult to tell if it is native.

VC11: Netley Marsh 3112, copse along stream, *RPB* 1982; throughout Wool Copse, Langrish 7023, *RMD* 1964, *AB* 1976. **VC12**: Copse in Linchborough Park, Woolmer Forest 8133, *AB* 1988; Weston Common woods 6944, carpeting the ground, *CRH* 1985.

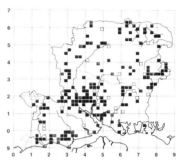

Map 271 Vinca minor

V. major L.   Greater Periwinkle.   **H** Local and occasional

Always a garden outcast, this occurs in hedges, verges, tree-belts and refuse-tips; generally near houses or roads. VC8: 2 □; VC11: 45 □; VC12: 47 □.

SOLANACEAE

Nicandra physalodes (L.) GAERTN. Apple-of-Peru.   **C**   Rare

First record, F. Bentley 1957, Farlington *c*.6704, VC11, on waste ground.

A common casual of bird-seed and formerly of shoddy, which sometimes persists. VC11: 9 □; VC12: 8 □.

VC11: Swaythling, plentiful and apparently established, on consolidated waste-ground, *JEL* 1958, Hb.BM; Shappen, Burley 2102 and Butt's Lawn, Brockenhurst 2902, garden weed, *RPB* 1987. **VC12**: Kingsley fruit farm, 7739, coming up regularly, probably from former shoddy, *AB* 1966; RAE Farnborough 8654, persisted three years in flower-beds, *JK* 1980, reappeared *ARGM* 1992; Eelmoor Marsh 8453, where soil dumped on track, *ARGM* 1992.

Lycium barbarum L. (*L. halimifolium* Mill.) Duke of Argyll's Teaplant. **H** Occasional

Often planted by the sea, or in hedges, and sometimes spread by birds into waste places. VC11: 22 □; VC12: 16 □.
VC11: Pylewell Shore 3695, *RPB* 1974. **VC12**: Vernham Row 3256, *GDF* 1981.

L. chinense MILL. China Teaplant. **H** Very rare

First record, Lady Anne Brewis 1970, bird-sown on a bombsite, Alton *c*.7238, VC12, now built-on.
VC12: Roadside hedge, Shipton Bellinger 2344, *RPB* 1975, det. *FR* (*Watsonia* **18**: 222).

Atropa belladonna L. Deadly Nightshade. **N** Local Map 272

First record, R. Turner 1664, 'near Alton in Hampshire', VC12 (*Turn.Bot.*, p.224).

In open scrub on downs, and in clearings in beech-wood on the chalk, with one or two sites on Malmstone; locally frequent on the W and E downs, including the Wealden Edge hangers; more restricted on the N and central chalk. It disappears as clearings become overgrown. There are no recent records on other soils, or on ruins.
VC11: Standon 4226, beech-wood, *RPB* 1975; Coombe Wood, East Meon 6718, *JRw* 1991. **VC12**: Noar Hill 7431, on cleared landslip, *AB* 1982; Bush Farm near Nether Wallop 2636, by road, *GDF* 1988; Snoddington *c*.2444, *MFW* 1989; Hawkley Hanger 7329, *DPJS & JMC* 1988; Micheldever Spoil Heaps 5244, *HFG* 1991, conf. *AJB*; The Warren, Hawkley 7328, *AB* 1993.

Deadly poisonous; still used medicinally for enlarging the pupils of the eyes.

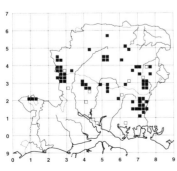

Map 272 Atropa belladonna

Hyoscyamus niger L. Henbane. **N,D,C** Rare Map 273

First record, Gilbert White 1766, Selborne, VC12 (*White's Jnls* 1: 194).

On disturbed or bare soil, verges, waste or arable ground, and formerly on the seashore. Strangely, it cannot be found on the seashore now, although it still has that habitat on the Isle of Wight. In *Fl.Hants* (p.265) it was described as 'locally abundant' and, earlier, in *Gerard's Herball* (p.283) as found 'almost everie where by highwayes, in the borders of fields, about dung-hills and untoiled places'. Nowadays it is widespread, but infrequent and often transient. Perhaps the gradual disappearance of dunghills with the reduction in the use of animal manure is the key to its decline.
VC11: Near Shawford Station 4725, in field of pigs, *CDD* 1960; Houghton 3431, potato-patch by disused railway, 50 plants, *RPB* 1977; Wheely Down 6123, in patch of nettles, *JF* 1984; Catherington Lith, Horndean 7014, *JOc* 1990. **VC12**: Moundsmere Farm 6243, plentiful, *AB* 1965, *PJ* 1973; Blackbushe 8159, one plant, *CRH* 1986; Winchester, bulb farm 5029, *GC* 1989; Bell Street, Whitchurch 4648, building site, *JR* 1991; Malshanger 5752, in unsprayed arable, *JCo* 1957, *WGH* 1976–93; Wootton St Lawrence 5753, abundant, *FR* 1993.

It was used to mitigate 'all kinde of paine', and 'To wash the feet in the decoction of Henbane causeth sleepe..., and also the often smelling to the floures. The leaves, seed and iuyce taken inwardly causeth an unquiet sleep...and is deadly to the party.' (*Ger.em.Johns.*, p.355).

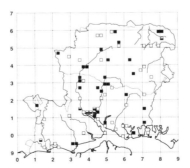

Map 273 Hyoscyamus niger

<Salpichroa origanifolia (LAM.) THELL. Cock's Eggs. **C** Extinct

VC11: Hayling Island beach, *DW* 1949–51, Hb.BM.>

Solanum nigrum L. ssp. **nigrum** Black Nightshade. **N?,C** Frequent and locally common

A common weed of cultivation and waste places, especially on acid soil.

ssp. **schultesii** (OPIZ) WESSELY **C**

VC11: Southampton Docks, *JEL* 1958, Hb.BM, Hb.K, det. *JME*; Blackhorse Lane, Shedfield 5614, amongst maize-crop, *PJSe* 1993, Hb.RPB.

S. sarachoides SENDTN. Leafy-fruited Nightshade. **C** Very rare

First record, A. W. Westrup 1962, North Hayling 7302, VC11, arable field (abundant, *AB* 1975).

A casual, in sandy places, which can persist and multiply.
VC11: Christchurch, garden weed, *JRo* 1963, Hb.BM; two plants on a sandy shingle-spit, between Tanners Lane 3695 and Sowley Shore 3795, *IG* 1985. VC12: Hazeley Heath dump *c*.7656, *DEB* 1962; the Slab, Bordon 7835, old sand-pit once used for tipping, abundant and persistent, *AB* 1974–84; Osbornes Farm, Sleaford 8038, *AB* 1989, det. *EJC*; Aldershot 8550, disturbed soil, *ARGM & TD* 1990.

S. dulcamara L. Bittersweet. **N** Very common

In hedges, scrub, moist woods and fens, shady streamsides, ditches and pond-margins; also on bare gravelly banks and beaches.

var. **marinum** BAB.

VC11: This has been recorded from the shingle of Hurst Castle spit 3189 or 3190, Browndown 5898, and Hayling Island 6899, 7098. It may now have been destroyed by trampling or erosion by the sea.

Datura stramonium L. Thornapple. **C,H,D** Local Map 274

First record, R. S. Hill 1836, rubbish-heaps at The Vyne, VC12, Hb.BM (*Fl.Hants*, excl.sp., p.266).

On arable or disturbed sandy ground, and on the Malmstone; found particularly in potato-fields. The seeds can germinate after lying in the ground for a very long time – experiments have shown them to have over 90 per cent viability after being buried for nearly forty years (*Weeds & Aliens*, pp.327–328). A native of N America and at one time a common weed of shoddy, it can persist wherever the ground is not regularly cultivated or overgrown. All records known to derive from shoddy are excluded from the map. Widespread but uncommon, it appears most frequently in the sandy waste and arable ground around Woolmer Forest, where it seems to be truly naturalized.

VC11: Romsey 3522, potato-field, *RPB* 1975; Bargain Farm, Nursling 3715, border of arable field, *RPB* 1985; Hightown Reservoir 1805, *RMW* 1982; Tipner 6303, *FR & EAP* 1981. **VC12**: Priory Farm, Selborne 7434, *AB* 1981 and for many years before and after; Upper Clatford *c.*3442, waste ground by river, *GDF* 1983; Chilbolton Common 3940, near car-park, *AJB* 1989; Yateley Heath Wood 7958, *AB* 1986; North Camp, Farnborough 8753, disturbed roadside soil, *CRH & ARGM* 1991, 56 counted, *TD* 1991.

An ointment made from it was used for 'all manner of burnings or scaldings' (*Ger.em.Johns.*, p.349).

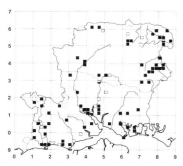

Map 274 Datura stramonium

var. tatula (L.) TORR.

The purple-flowered variant, hardly ever known to seed itself and persist.

VC12: Basingstoke and Old Basing, *NEGC* 1941; Ragmore Farm, Barnet Side 7128, *JF* 1984, many years after shoddy was last used.

CONVOLVULACEAE

Convolvulus arvensis L.   Field Bindweed.   **N,C**   Very common

On arable and waste ground, disturbed verges, gardens, etc.

Calystegia soldanella (L.) R. BR. Sea Bindweed.   **N**   Very local   Map 275

First record, J. Goodyer 1633: 'In Hampshire....they make use of this for

Scurvie-grasse', (*Ger.em.Johns.*, p.839)

Dunes and beaches of sand or shingly sand; scattered along the coast. It has decreased but seems more resilient to trampling than some other dune-plants.

VC11: Hengistbury Head 1891, *CEP* 1967; Stone Point, Lepe 4698, *RPB* 1989; Sandy Point, Hayling Island 7498, *AB, EAP & FR* 1980; *FR* 1990; Sinah Common 6998, plentiful, *FR* 1994.

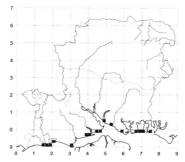

Map 275 Calystegia soldanella

C. sepium (L.) R. BR. ssp. **sepium** Hedge Bindweed.   **N**   Common

On hedges, in scrub and in open carr.

ssp. **roseata** BRUMMITT   **N**   Very rare

First record, N. D. Simpson 1940, Keyhaven 3090, VC11, Hb.NDS, det. *RKB*.

Specific to brackish marshes.
VC11: Browndown 5899, Hb.AWW 1952, det. *RKB*.

C. x scanica BRUMMITT (*C. sepium* x *C. pulchra*)   Very rare

First record, Lady Anne Brewis 1983, Liss Forest 7829, VC12, side of a wood, near houses, schizopetalous, Hb.AB, Hb.K, det. 'probable' *RKB*.

C. x lucana (TEN.) DON (*C. sepium* x *C. silvatica*)   **C**   Very rare

First record, Miss W. F. Buckle 1965, Castle Way, Southampton 4111, VC11, det. *DHK*.

C. pulchra BRUMMITT & HEYWOOD (*C. dahurica* sensu Walters & D. A. Webb non (Herb.) Don)   Hairy Bindweed.   **H**   Very local   Map 276

First record, Lady Anne Brewis 1923, garden at Wonston 4739, VC12, later destroyed.

In gardens and hedges near houses,

frequently having been transported with earth. Only a few records in VC11, but well established in the Fleet–Farnborough area, and elsewhere in the NE, presumably having spread from London.

VC11: Finchdean 7312, *AWW* 1951. **VC12**: Oakhanger 7635, *AB* 1966 (*Watsonia* 10: 427); on various bridges over the M3 from Camberley (VC17) to Hatch 6651, but particularly abundant at Andwell 6952, *AB* 1980; the presumption is that they were banked up with soil from the same source.

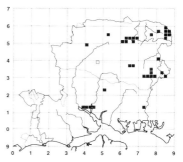

Map 276 Calystegia pulchra

C. silvatica (KIT.) GRISEB.   Large Bindweed.   **H**   Locally common

First record, G. A. R. Watts 1942, Kenilworth Road, Fleet 8154, 8254, VC12 (*Watts MSS*).

In hedges, scrub and waste places, edges of refuse-tips and railways. Now widespread, emanating from the towns.

CUSCUTACEAE

Cuscuta europaea L.   Greater Dodder.   **N**   Very rare

Parasitic, generally on *Urtica dioica*, in wet places. There are very few Hants records of this species, and some may be errors. Only one record has been made in recent years:

VC12: Ashford Hill 5662, on *U. dioica* on the bank of a stream, *PB* 1988 (*Watsonia* 18: 222).

C. epithymum (L.) L.   Dodder.   **N** Locally common   Map 277

On heaths, where it is a common parasite on *Calluna, Ulex* and *Teucrium*; also in scattered sites on the chalk, on downs or edges of arable fields, and on dunes, where it lives on *Trifolium* and *Thymus* and various other hosts.

VC11: Broughton Down 2833, *HOS* 1983; Browndown Point 5799, on *Rosa*

pimpinellifolia, *Teucrium scorodonia*, *Silene nutans*, etc., *RPB, EJC & EAP* 1989; Sandy Point, Hayling Island 7498, *DB* 1975. **VC12**: Ashmansworth 4057, on *Galium verum*, *RPB* 1969; Warren Hill 2547, extensive patch on *G. verum* and other chalk plants, *MFW* 1990.

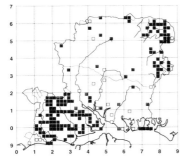

Map 277 Cuscuta epithymum

MENYANTHACEAE

Menyanthes trifoliata L.   Bogbean. **N**   Locally common   Map 278

First record, Gilbert White 1766, 'in Bean's pond' Oakhanger, VC12 (*White's Jnls* 1: 199). This may be the pond on Shortheath Common 7736 but this is not certain. See also *Vaccinium oxycoccos* (p. 140).

Central zones of valley bogs, acid pools, wet fen-meadows and their ditches. Common in the New Forest, local in the major river valleys, the Thames Basin and Woolmer Forest, rare elsewhere. Declining in the chalk wetlands with improvement and drainage of old meadows.

VC11: Emer Bog 3921, *RPB* 1961, 1992; Purbrook 6607, surviving bog, *MB* 1975. **VC12**: Itchen Stoke Mill 5631, *FR* 1986; Chilbolton Common 3840; *RPB* 1967, *FR* 1984; Ashford

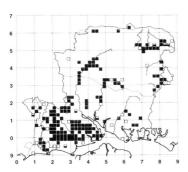

Map 278 Menyanthes trifoliata

Hill meadows 5662, *PB* 1984; High-clere Park 4361, *NFC* 1980.

Nymphoides peltata KUNTZE Fringed Water-lily.   **N?,H**   Very local

First record, R. Appleton 1837, pond between Old Basing and Nateley, VC12 (*Brit.Phaen.Bot.* 3: no.161, as *Villarsia nymphaeoides*; *Fl.Hants*, excl.sp., p.261).

In lakes and sluggish streams, either introduced through discards from garden ponds, or brought naturally by waterfowl; it rapidly becomes rampant. Possibly native in some sites.

VC11: Near R. Avon, Purewell 1693, *JG* 1967; Blashford gravel-pits, in three lakes, 1407, 1506, 1507, 1607, *RPB* 1973, 1984; Whitten Pond, Burley 2001, *RPB* 1987; Fort Brockhurst and Fort Elson, Gosport 5902, *RPB* 1987. Also 1492, 2206, 2208, 3698, 4400, 6816. **VC12**: Hollybrook Lake 8035, *AB* 1978; Bourley Bottom 8250, *ARGM* 1978, *CRH* 1991 (transplanted from Bourley into Rushmoor Flash, Basingstoke Canal 8552, by *ARGM* 1980); Cove Brook 8658, *JES* 1987; Ecchinswell 5060, *PB* 1987. Also 4460, 7636, 8252, 8452, 8458, 8652, 8850.

HYDROPHYLLACEAE

Phacelia tanacetifolia BENTH. Phacelia.   **C**   Very rare

First record, Mrs F. Finucane 1973, weed in grass at Berry Grove Farm, Liss 7728, VC12, det. *JEL* (*Watsonia* 18: 221).

VC11: Whiteknap, Romsey 3720, garden weed, *MTu* 1977, Hb.RPB, det. *EJC*; Winchester 4628, in garden, *SAL* 1985. **VC12**: All over a garden in Kingsley 7838, *AMa* 1982–88, det. *FR* (*loc.cit.*); Park Corner, Crondall 7748, *ARGM* 1990.

BORAGINACEAE

Lithospermum purpureo-caeruleum L.   Blue Gromwell.   **H** Very rare

First records, D. P. J. Smith 1992, near A3, Hilsea 6504, VC11, dry rocky bank on old fortifications, large patch, Hb.RPB, and R. A. Barrett 1992, Droxford 6118, VC11, two plants on verge of track, Hb.EJC, both det. *EJC*.

L. officinale L.   Common Gromwell.   **N**   Locally frequent Map 279

First record, Gilbert White 1765, Selborne, VC12 (*White's Jnls* 1: 165).

In open scrub on downs, open woods and their rides, and on banks. Restricted to the chalk; widespread, but only locally common. Follows scrub-clearance.

VC8: Near A354 Martin Down 0319, *RMV* 1990. **VC11**: Noads Copse 2532, *RPB* 1984; West Wood, Sparsholt 4129, 4130, *RMV* 1988; Corhampton golf-course 5819, in woodland clearing, *AB* 1985. **VC12**: Noar Hill Common 7230, *SP* 1980; M3 Farleigh Wallop 6047, on embankment, *GHF* 1981; Bradley Wood 6441, *ANHS* 1987; near Alresford 5930, *ARGM* 1988; Sutton Common 7445, *CRH* 1990; Old Stockbridge Road, Middle Wallop 3040, under hedgerow, *MFW* 1991.

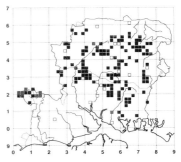

Map 279 Lithospermum officinale

L. arvense L.   Field Gromwell.   **C** Local   Map 280

Borders of cornfields and other arable land on chalk. Widespread but disappearing wherever cornfields are sprayed.

VC8: Fairly plentiful in a field between Toyd Farm and Grans Barrow 0820, *JO* 1988. **VC11**: Ashley Down 3929, *RPB* 1977; Broughton Down 2832, abundant in barley-field head-

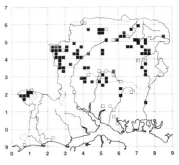

Map 280 Lithospermum arvense

land, *RPB* 1987. **VC12**: Ashley Warren 4856, *PB* 1979; Hampshire Gap 2440, edge of cornfield, *RPB* 1985; Tidworth 2246, *MFW* 1989.

Echium vulgare L. Viper's-bugloss. **N** Locally frequent Map 281

First record, Gilbert White 1765, Selborne, VC12 (*White's Jnls* **1**: 166).

On dry, bare soil, i.e. chalk, sand or gravel, but, inland, dependent on either rabbit-grazing or periodic disturbance. It can, therefore, be abundant for a time on bare chalk or sandy tracks but may subsequently be overgrown. Locally common on coastal shingle and sand-dunes; rare in the SW.

VC11: Sinah Common dunes 6999, *RPB* 1972, *FR* 1994; Mizmaze Hill 1420, *RPB* 1984; A3, Butser Gap 7118, on bare chalk, *AB* 1980. **VC12**: Woolmer Forest 7832, *AB* 1987; Hawley Common 8458, dozens by newly-surfaced military track, *CRH* 1988; Grateley 2640, *MFW* 1989.

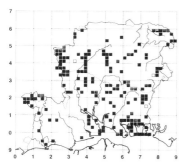

Map 281 Echium vulgare

Pulmonaria officinalis L. Lung-wort. **H,D** Rare

Sometimes introduced into woods or escaped from gardens into waysides and waste places. VC11: 7 □; VC12: 7 □.

VC11: Near Gosport, Ampfield 3921, wood S of railway, *FEWV* 1958 (*Rep.S'ton N.H.S.*, p.5). **VC12**: Near Woolton Hill 4260, on bank of brook, *WMK* 1975; Brook Farm, Ashford Hill 5562, *VF* 1982.

'The leaves are used among pot-herbes. The roots are also thought to be good against the infirmities and ulcers of the lungs.' (*Ger.em.Johns.*, p.809.).

P. longifolia (BASTARD) BOREAU Narrow-leaved Lungwort. **N** Local Map 282 Plate VII

First record, J. Goodyer 1620, 'in a wood by Holbury House in the New

Forrest' (*Ger.em.Johns.*, p.809). Still extant at 4203, VC11, *RPB* 1985.

In woods and plantations, especially in grassy rides and on ditch-banks; on hedge- and railway-banks, bushy streamsides, in scrub on heaths, and in old marl-pits and open bracken. On fertile clay and loam soils, especially on the Headon Beds; widespread in the central and southern New Forest, and just beyond. In Britain, this species is confined as a native to the basin of the prehistoric Solent River, on Tertiary formations in E Dorset, SW Hants, and the northern half of Wight.

VC11: Upper Pennington Common 2995, *RPB* 1960; N of Frame Heath Inclosure 3403, on railway bank, *APHo* 1976; Burley Beacon 2002, *AEB* 1986; Pound Lane, Colbury 3511, *RB* 1967, RPB 1986–93; Keeping Copse 3901, 4000, *SNHS* 1955; East End 3697, *ARGM* 1980; Setley Common, Roydon Woods 3100, *FR* 1986.

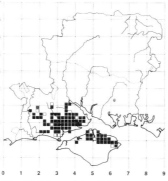

Map 282 Pulmonaria longifolia

Symphytum officinale L. Common Comfrey. **N,D** Locally common Map 283

Banks of rivers and streams, edges of ponds, marshes, wet woodland clearings, fen carr. Common in all basic

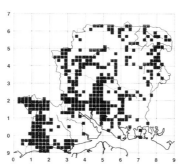

Map 283 Symphytum officinale

wetlands, with scattered occurrences in dry, grassy verges, etc.

The mucilaginous roots were used as an ancient cough mixture and for healing wounds (*Ger.Herb.*, p.661).

S. x uplandicum NYMAN (*S. officinale* x *S. asperum*) Russian Comfrey. **D** Locally common

First record, J. F. Rayner 1928, Ashley Wood *c*.3830, VC11 (*Suppl.Fl.Hants*, p.71, as *S. peregrinum* Ledeb.).

This artificial hybrid, bred for cattle-fodder and also ploughed in as 'green manure', has become a weed and is to be found on roadside verges, borders of arable fields, waste ground, open plantations, etc. It is commoner in the N half of the county, and reaches pest proportions on the R. Wey at Isington Mill 7642, VC12, *AB* 1986.

S. 'Hidcote Blue' hort. ex G. THOMAS (*S. officinale* x *S. asperum* x *S. grandiflorum*) Hidcote Comfrey. **H** Very rare

VC12: Established in a wood N of Monk Sherborne 6057, *PHR* 1983, det. *ACL* (*Watsonia* **15**: 399).

S. asperum LEPECHIN Rough Comfrey. **H** Probably extinct

First record, Mrs M. Becher 1982, Walhampton 3395, VC11, two plants opposite the 'Wagon and Horses', det. *GAN*, seen up to 1988.

S. tuberosum L. Tuberous Comfrey. **H** Very rare

First record, I. A. Williams 1925 or 1926, near Liphook, VC12 (*Rep. Watson B.E.C.* **1925–26**, p.342).

VC11: Hedgemoor Copse, West Tytherley 2631, *RPB* 1966, conf. 1988, Hb.RPB (*Watsonia* **19**: 149); Bushy Copse 5325, dominant over a large area, *JRw* 1991. **VC12**: Alice Holt Forest, near Bentley, *WHS* 1951, det *JEL* (*Watsonia* **2**: 47).

S. grandiflorum DC. (*S. ibericum* Steven) Creeping Comfrey. **H** Very rare

First record, R. P. Bowman 1951, Compton 4625, VC11.

A ground-coverer, seldom far from gardens.

VC11: Also 3032. **VC12**: Conford 8233, *AB* 1961; near N bank of Micheldever Stream, Wonston 4739, *RMV* 1989; Cheriton 5728, lane leading to Hill House, *ANHS* 1989. Also 4054, 7826, 8230.

S. orientale L.   White Comfrey.   **H** Rare

First record, A. W. Westrup 1950, Portchester 6205, VC11, Hb.AWW.

Waste places, disturbed verges; almost confined to the SE coast.

VC11: A2030 Langstone Harbour 6703, Hb.RPB 1979, det. *EJC*; Medina Road, Wymering 6605, churchyard and roadside, *RBa* 1990–91. Also 6400, 6600, 6698, 7098, 7006. **VC11/12:** Near Hinton Ampner *c.*5927, *CWMB* 1961. **VC12**: The Grange, Northington 5636, *RAF* 1993; Claycart Bottom 8452, *TD* 1994, Hb.AB.

Anchusa arvensis (L.) M. BIEB. (*Lycopsis arvensis* L.)   Bugloss.   **N,C** Locally common   Map 284

First record, Gilbert White 1765, Selborne, VC12 (*White's Jnls* 1: 166).

Arable and bare waste-ground, mainly on sand or gravel. Rare on chalk. Locally common in the Avon Valley, the western Weald and the E Thames Basin; sparse and scattered elsewhere. Much less common as an arable weed than formerly.

VC11: Woodington Farm, East Wellow 3020, *RMV* 1983. **VC12**: Near Headley 5063, *NFC* 1973; Andover Airfield 3345, base of security-fence, *MFW* 1991.

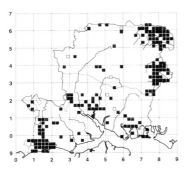

Map 284 Anchusa arvensis

<Cynoglottis barrelieri (ALL.) VURAL & KIT TAN (*Anchusa barrelieri* (All.) Vitman)   False Alkanet.   **H** Extinct

VC11: Dibden Purlieu 4106, in an old sand-pit with *Echium vulgare*, *RPB* 1963, Hb.BM, det. *GAM*. Later lost to a new housing estate.>

Pentaglottis sempervirens (L.) TAUSCH ex L. H. BAILEY   Green Alkanet.   **D,H**   Local and occasional

First record, H. Reeks *c.*1875, Thruxton, VC12 (*Fl.Hants*, excl.sp., p.326).

An old herb, now fully naturalized on roadsides, scrub near habitations and in waste places. Widespread and locally frequent. VC11: 39 □; VC12: 58 □.

VC11: Ashley church 3830, on roadsides, *RPB* 1984. **VC12**: Up Nately 7052, *HJMB* 1988.

The roots produce a red dye which was used 'to colour sirrups, waters, gellies, and such like confections', and for 'womens paintings' (*Ger.em.Johns.*, p.801).

Borago officinalis L.   Borage. **H,D**   Occasional

Waste and disturbed ground, generally on the chalk; often only transient. VC11: 31 □; VC12: 23 □.

VC11: Near Fort Southwick, Ports Down 6206, *RPB* 1990. **VC12**: A34, Bradley Wood 4652, abundant on a bank of chalk raised in construction of the new road having been removed from the old railway nearby, *RPB & AB* 1969; Andover 3646, rough ground S of A3093, persisting many years, *MFW* 1991.

Trachystemon orientalis (L.) G. DON   Abraham, Isaac and Jacob.   **H** Very rare

First record, Mrs F. Finucane 1968, Chiltley Lane, Liphook 8430, VC12, still there, *ARGM* 1979.

VC12: Selborne 7433, on earth-spoil removed during enlargement of car-park into ground where *Trachystemon* had once been introduced, *JG* 1960s. It reappeared and was still there in 1988, *AB*.

<Mertensia maritima (L.) GRAY Oysterplant.   **N**   Extinct

'The very rare Sea Gromwell (Steinhammera maritima) has been seen on the half dry beach just within reach of the salt spray...' at Netley, VC11, 1858 (*Phytologist N.S.* 2: 545; *Fl.Hants*, excl.sp., p.325).>

Plagiobothrys scouleri (HOOK. & ARN.) I. M. JOHNST.   White Forget-me-not.   **C**   Very rare

First record, Miss A. L. Hale & Miss E. S. Haines 1982, Setley gravel-pit

3099, VC11, abundant in bare, wet, sandy hollows, Hb.RPB, det. *AOC* (*Watsonia* 17: 191).

Native of western N America, where it occurs on damp, sandy, sometimes saline ground.

VC11: Beaulieu old airfield 3500, flood hollow on bed of old perimeter-track, Hb.RPB 1987, Hb.BM, det. *AOC* (*loc.cit.*).

Myosotis scorpioides L.   Water Forget-me-not.   **N**   Locally very common

Streamsides, ditches, ponds, marshes, swampy, open woods; common in all except very acid wetlands.

M. secunda A. MURRAY   Creeping Forget-me-not.   **N**   Locally common Map 285

Swampy sides of streams and ditches on heathland, and in wet rides of woods; in boggy pastures, pools and flushed bogs; generally, but not always, on acid soil. Common in the New Forest, much less so on the NE Tertiary and Wealden heathlands; very local or rare elsewhere.

VC11: Breamore Marsh ponds 1518, *MS-W* 1976; Mellishes Bottom, Wickham Common 5910, edge of pond, *RPB* 1989. **VC12**: Great Pen Wood 4462, *NFC* 1968; Micheldever Stream 5139, *TCGR* 1988.

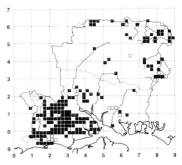

Map 285 Myosotis secunda

M. laxa LEHM. ssp. **caespitosa** (SCHULTZ) HYL. ex NORDH. (*M. caespitosa* Schultz)   Tufted Forget-me-not.   **N**   Locally common

On marshy streamsides and pond-margins, ditches and boggy pastures; fairly common on all moderately-acid, wet soils, sparse and local elsewhere. Perhaps over-recorded due to confusion with small-flowered *M. scorpioides*.

M. sylvatica HOFFM. Wood Forget-me-not. **N,H** Very local Map 286

Open bushy woods and clearings, wooded calcareous streams, and borders of scrub on chalk-grassland slopes; sometimes garden escapes are washed down streams. Undoubtedly native on the chalk slopes of the far NW, and in the E along the R. Rother and its tributaries, from its watershed at Noar Hill, Hawkley, and Ashford Chace, and by the R. Deadwater. Elsewhere it is difficult to know whether it is a garden escape, as the two types are often indistinguishable. It has been the intention to exclude all doubtfully indigenous records from the map, but some may still have slipped through.

VC11/12: Along the R. Rother, from Sheet 7624, VC11, up to Burhunt 7532, VC12, *AB* 1982. **VC12**: Chalk hangers above Ashford Chace 7326, 7426, abundant for over 2km, *FR* 1986; R. Deadwater at Hollywater 8033, *AB* 1973; Pilot Hill 3959, 4059, *RPB* 1963, *FR* 1975; woodland near Vernham Dean, 'undoubtedly native', *PMH* 1934, *GDF* 1981, and at Hampshire Gate 3354, where *PMH* considered them doubtfully native as some flowers were white or pink; Combe Wood 3559, *FR* 1984; Faccombe Wood 3856, *FR* 1976.

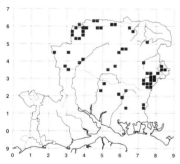
Map 286 Myosotis sylvatica

M. arvensis (L.) HILL Field Forget-me-not. **N,C** Common

In arable fields, waste ground, bare banks, clearings and paths in woods, gardens. Very common, especially on light or basic soils.

M. ramosissima ROCHEL Early Forget-me-not. **N** Local and occasional Map 287

On dry, bare ground, banks, open, short turf, and dunes; on sand or gravel. Also on ant-hills, especially in chalk grassland. Widespread, but infrequent, and

only common in Woolmer Forest. It seems to be absent from the Aldershot area and very scarce in the New Forest.

VC11: Moyles Court 1608, road-triangle, *RPB* 1992; Sandy Point, Hayling Island 7498, *AB, EAP & FR* 1980; foot of Broughton Down 2932, *RPB* 1988. **VC12**: Ashford Hill meadows 5662, *FR* 1983; Heckfield Heath 7261, *CRH* 1988; Warren Hill 2448, N face, *MFW* 1989.

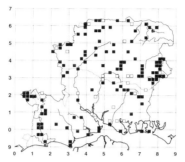
Map 287 Myosotis ramosissima

M. discolor PERS. Changing Forget-me-not. **N** Locally frequent

In open, short turf, disturbed and bare ground around fields, pits and verges. Widespread and locally common on dry, light sandy or gravelly soil; on chalk, frequent only in the NW.

VC11: Common Marsh, Stockbridge 3534, banks of old pits, *RPB* 1985; Shedfield 5514, *AWW* 1956. **VC12**: Rookery Dell, Monk Sherborne 6056, *PB* 1982; Hazeley Heath 7657, *CRH* 1988; Woolmer Forest 7831, *AB* 1988.

Cynoglossum officinale L. Hound's-tongue. **N** Locally frequent Map 288

First record, Gilbert White 1766, Selborne, VC12 (*White's Jnls* 1: 190).

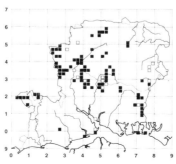
Map 288 Cynoglossum officinale

In dry, chalk grassland, especially in broken turf around warrens, and in open scrub; widespread, but now local, owing to grassland 'improvement', rabbit-decline and ploughing. Rare in dune-turf on the coast.

VC11: Stansore Point 4699, *RPB* 1963; old railway-track, Set Thorns 2600, *DEA* 1986; Sandy Point, Hayling Island 7598, *AB, EAP & FR* 1980. **VC12**: Harewood Forest, by Augurs Hill Copse 3842, *MFW* 1991; Chilbolton Common 3839, *RPB* 1992.

VERBENACEAE

Verbena officinalis L. Vervain. **N** Frequent and locally common

First record, Gilbert White 1766, Selborne, VC12 (*White's Jnls* 1: 212).

In chalk grassland, especially in disturbed or bare places, along tracks and banks, on verges and dry, bare, gravelly soil, often on old airfields or where limestone chippings have been spread, and on crumbling tarmac. Widespread, but common only in the chalklands of the W and SE.

VC11: Beaulieu old airfield 3400, *RPB* 1983; Fareham 5907, verge of M27 exit-road, *EAP* 1985; R. Avon, South Charford Farm 1718, on dredgings, *JO* 1983. **VC12**: Weyhill 3146, *GDF* 1984; Farnborough Airfield 8453, on sandy soil, *ARGM* 1977–89; Fleet Pond 8255, 15 plants amongst heather, *CRH* 1986–91; Sheephouse Copse 7545, *ANHS* 1991.

LAMIACEAE

Stachys officinalis (L.) TREVIS. (*Betonica officinalis* L.) Betony. **N** Locally common

First record, Gilbert White 1765, Selborne, VC12 (*White's Jnls* 1: 161).

In open woods, clearings and rides, grass-heaths, rough pastures, on predominantly acid soils; widespread and fairly common, except on the downs, where it is generally on leached slopes or chalk superficials. Absent from the Wealden Edge hangers. White flowers in Little Hawstead meadow, Steep 7425, VC12, *AB* 1990.

< **S. germanica** L. Downy Wound-wort. **N** Extinct (Sched. 8)

Formerly N of Itchen Abbas 5234, VC12, W. W. Spicer 1850–72, Hb.BM, field ploughed soon after (*Fl. Hants*, p.308).>

S. sylvatica L.   Hedge Woundwort.
N   Very common

In open woods and their borders, scrub, hedges, shady waste places and gardens.

S. x ambigua SM. (*S. sylvatica* x *S. palustris*)   Hybrid Woundwort.
N,H?   Occasional

Can occur anywhere where both parents grow, or sometimes without them in circumstances suggesting cultivation.

VC8: B3078 Lower Breach Copse 1115, frequent over 50m along wooded roadside, Hb.RPB 1991. **VC11**: Warwickslade Cutting, Poundhill Heath 2805, Hb.RPB 1981; Segensworth Lane, Titchfield 5207, Hb.AWW 1962. Also 1406, 3206, 3404, 4000, 5202, 6008, 6408, 6614. **VC12**: Queens Road, Longmoor 8131, with both parents, *AB* 1963–86; Selborne, in two streets, without parents, 7333, *AB* 1961, 7433, *SP* 1985; Sutton Common 7344, in ditch under roadside hedge, *ANHS* 1991. Also 5828, 6854, 7236, 7842, 8036.

S. palustris L.   Marsh Woundwort.
N,C   Locally common

On banks of rivers and streams, ditches, and marshes; also borders of arable fields and verges on the clay. Widespread and often common except on very acid soil.

S. arvensis (L.) L.   Field Woundwort.   **C**   Locally frequent

First record, R. S. Hill 1839, Oakridge, Basingstoke, VC12, Hb.WARMS.

In arable fields, bare, disturbed ground and gardens. Usually on rather acid, sandy or gravelly soil where it is widespread and locally frequent. Occasional on the chalk.

Ballota nigra L. ssp. **foetida** (VIS.) HAYEK   Black Horehound.   **N?,C?** Locally common

First records, W. L. Notcutt 1844, Wickham, Titchfield, Cattisfield, etc., VC11, (*Fl.Hants*, p.307).

On roadside verges, hedgebanks, borders of fields, waysides and waste ground; around farmyards. A nitrogen-lover, tending to be found in rather disturbed situations.

<**Leonurus cardiaca** L.   Motherwort.   **D**   Extinct

First record, Gilbert White 1766,

Selborne, VC12 (*White's Jnls* **1**: 213).

An old herb used for asthma and other ailments which was formerly occasionally to be found near villages. There are ten old records, of which only two survived into this recording period. Of these, the one at Bickton Mill 1412, VC11, was last seen by *VHP* in 1962. Specimens from Gilbert White's 'Forest side' site, opposite Oakhanger Chapel 7736, VC12, were collected by *JEL* in 1935, Hb.RNG, but it no longer occurs there.>

Lamiastrum galeobdolon (L.) EHREND. & POLATSCHEK ssp. **montanum** (PERS.) EHREND. & POLATSCHEK (*Galeobdolon luteum* Huds. ssp. *montanum* (Pers.) Dvor kov)   Yellow Archangel.   **N** Locally common

First record, Gilbert White 1768, Selborne, VC12 (*White's Jnls* **1**: 238).

In ancient woodland, copses, hedgerows and wooded streams descending from ancient woodland. Common in well-wooded districts on the chalk and other basic heavy soils; occasional elsewhere. A similar plant but with variegated leaves, described as ssp. *argentatum* (Smejkal) Stace (*Galeobdolon argentatum* Smejkal), is grown as ground-cover and occurs as an established alien from garden throw-outs.

Lamium album L.   White Deadnettle.   **N,C**   Common

A perennial of roadside verges, hedgebanks, waysides and waste land, but not an agricultural weed.

L. maculatum (L.) L.   Spotted Dead-nettle.   **H**   Occasional

First record, W. Willis 1890, list of plants in the neighbourhood of Alresford, VC12 (*Fl.Hants*, excl.sp., p.315).

A garden escape, sometimes established on verges near houses or on rubbish-tips. VC11: 20 □; VC12: 11 □.

L. purpureum L.   Red Dead-nettle.   **C**   Common

An annual weed of cultivated fields, gardens, disturbed and waste ground.

L. hybridum VILL.   Cut-leaved Dead-nettle.   **C**   Very local and rare Map 289

First record, F. Townsend *c*.1872, Shedfield Lodge 5513, VC11 (*Fl.Hants*, p.312).

On cultivated or disturbed ground. A rare agricultural weed.

VC11: Near Harbridge *c*.1410, *ESH* 1965; Droxford *c*.6018, *AWW* 1952; Gardeners Lane, Romsey 3319, edge of crop of winter wheat, *GC* 1987 (*Watsonia* **18**: 223); Flanders Farm, West End 4814, *PS* 1990. **VC12**: W of Nether Wallop 2536, frequent in arable field, *RMV* 1988; near Marsh House, Bentley 7944, several in arable field, *AB* 1969; bank of R. Whitewater, North Warnborough 7352, *AB* 1984.

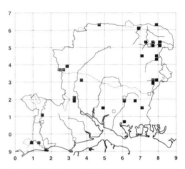

Map 289 Lamium hybridum

L. amplexicaule L.   Henbit Deadnettle.   **C**   Locally frequent

First record, Gilbert White 1766, Selborne, VC12 (*White's Jnls* **1**: 200).

In arable fields and gardens on light sandy, gravelly or chalky soils; fairly common on the NW chalk, local and scattered elsewhere. A decreasing weed in many areas, due to increased agricultural efficiency.

Galeopsis angustifolia EHRH. ex HOFFM.   Red Hemp-nettle.   **N,C** Local and occasional

First records, W. L. Notcutt 1844, over the tunnel near Fareham; near Bedenham, (*Fl.Hants*, p.310) and Miss C. R. May 1844, Cotters-Dean [Coulters Dean] Buriton 7419, VC11 (*May Ptgs Cat.*: 664).

This is a vanishing cornfield-weed on chalk. It can still be found in small quantity, usually if there has been a halt to crop-spraying, or in unsprayed sites such as chalk-pits, cuttings, or old railways.

VC11: Buckholt 2831, *RMV* 1987; Old Winchester Hill 6420, arable field, *RPB* 1987; Stanswood Bay 4699, ten plants on shingle at back of beach, *RPB* 1986; Nine Mile Water Farm 3034, *GDF* 1981. **VC12**: Augurs Hill Copse 3842, in field, *DMa* 1987; cornfield above Coneycroft Hanger,

Selborne 7333, *AB* 1964; Steventon Warren Farm 5445, 'set-aside' arable, *PJW* 1991; Micheldever Spoil Heaps 5244, *RMa* 1991.

[**G. ladanum** L. Broad-leaved Hemp-nettle.

There are no confirmed modern records and, after examining specimens in Hb.BM., *EJC* re-determined several old records as *G. angustifolia*.]

G. speciosa MILL. Large-flowered Hemp-nettle. **C** Very rare

On bare or disturbed soil on verges, and borders of arable ground; a transient weed.
VC11: Satchell Lane, Hamble *c*.4708, *c*.50 plants, *DBF* 1964 (*Rep. S'ton N.H.S. General Records*, p.2); Chilworth *c*.4018, roadside, *CDD* 1953. VC12: Winchester Station 4729, patch in new border, *DEA* 1978–81 (*Watsonia* **13**: 338). There are two records for VC11 and one for VC12 in *Suppl.Fl.Hants* (p.85).

G. tetrahit L. *sensu lato* (incl. *G. bifida* Boenn. *q.v.*)

In damp rides and clearings in woods, especially after coppicing; in hedgerows, on streamsides, borders of cultivated fields and waste ground. Widespread and generally common, but scarce over the central and western downland. Frequently found along paths in pheasant-coverts.

G. tetrahit L. *sensu stricto* Common Hemp-nettle. **N,C** Locally common

This appears to be slightly more frequent than *G. bifida* in the NW, and less so in the S.

G. bifida BOENN. Lesser Hemp-nettle. **N,C** Locally common

First records, R. A. Pryor *c*.1874, Brookwood [Brockwood], VC11 and Ropley Dene, VC12 (*Fl.Hants*, p.311).
In similar habitats to the previous segregate, but apparently scarce in the NW, although the overall distribution-pattern of both is similar.

Melittis melissophyllum L. Bastard Balm. **N** Rare Map 290

An inhabitant of ancient woodland, where it grows in glades and rides, often near streams, where it can get some light, and in hedgerows which are relics of woodland. On basic clay soils,

especially on the calcareous Headon Beds. Now rare, in the New Forest and in one or two other sites in the SW. It has declined greatly over the last 20 years, mainly through overshading, but it can reappear after scrub clearance and coppicing.
VC8: Whitsbury Wood *c*.1318, *IMG* 1957 (*Fl.Wilts*, p.462); Whitsbury Down *c*.1221, in lane, *EFP* 1959 (*Suppl.Fl.Wilts*, p.47). VC11: Brownhill Inclosure 2399, *RPB* 1977, now scarce; Wootton Coppice Inclosure 2499, *MPY* 1964, *FR* 1983; Holmsley Inclosure 2200, *RPB* 1970, barely surviving, *AEB* 1987; Newlands Copse, Roydon Woods 3201, *MRB* 1988; Bakers Copse, Roydon Woods 3001, *SK* 1989; Ratlake 4123, *EL* 1937, 1985; Sack Copse, Sherfield English 2821, 2822, *JHow & ILR* 1992. Other modern sites lost or not refound: lane near Breamore Wood *c*.1419, *RCA* 1939, *FDR* 1963, (lane since bulldozed); Ocknell Inclosure 2411, *JRu* 1950; Pinnick Wood 1907, *RPB* 1957–71; near Anses Wood 2212, *AG* 1975; near Rodlease House, Boldre 3298, wooded bank near road, *AMD & JMD c*.1955–65 (later obliterated); Brokes Copse 2824, *RPB* 1964, ploughed 1965; Ampfield Wood 4024, *PE* 1968; near Pennington *c*.3094, *GESB* 1936.

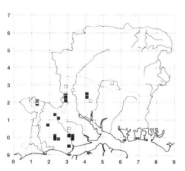

Map 290 Melittis melissophyllum

Marrubium vulgare L. White Horehound. **D,C** Very rare

First record, Gilbert White 1768, Selborne, VC12 (*White's Jnls* **1**: 249), 'on several parts of Shortheath, Selborne', *WAB* 1850. Bromfield suggests 'perhaps once cultivated there' (for cough mixtures) (*Fl.Hants*, p.306). Canon J. Vaughan found it there in 1877 but it is now extinct at that site.
On roadside verges and in waste places. Though probably a native on the Isle of Wight, inland it is a relic of

herbaries, and it was formerly a shoddy weed.
VC11: Frogham 1712, *JG* 1960, *RPB* 1992; waste ground S of Petersfield *c*.7422, *GARW* 1933 (*Watts MSS*). Formerly on Portsea Isle, *EHW* 1903–08. VC12: Roadside near Conford Moor 8232, *ALJ* 1954.

Scutellaria galericulata L. Skullcap. **N** Locally common Map 291

On banks of rivers and streams, ponds, marshes, wet, open woods and carr; fairly common along the main river-valleys in the W and NE; very local or rare elsewhere.
VC11: Near Baddesley Common 3820, abundant in marshy pasture, *RPB* 1984. VC12: Netherton Bottom 3756, *NFC* 1968.

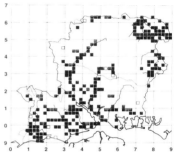

Map 291 Scutellaria galericulata

S. x hybrida STRAIL (*S. galericulata* x *S. minor*) **N?** Probably extinct

VC11: Weston *c*.4409, *EFL* 1900, Hb.CGE; Hatchet Pond 3601, bank of borrow pit at NE end, *FHP* 1963, Hb.CGE.

S. minor HUDS. Lesser Skullcap. **N** Locally common Map 292

First record, Gilbert White 1769, Selborne (*White's Jnls* **1**: 292).

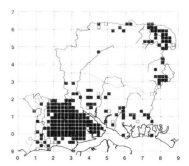

Map 292 Scutellaria minor

In bogs, ditches on heaths, wet, open, grassy woods, especially in rides; always on acid soil. Very common in the New Forest, frequent in the western Weald and the NE Tertiaries, scarce elsewhere.

Teucrium scorodonia L.   Wood Sage.   **N**   Locally very common

In open, heathy woods and plantations, especially on banks and in rides; borders of heaths and acidic pastures; amongst scrub behind sea-beaches. Very common, except on the chalk where it is only occasional on superficial deposits. Absent from the E chalk hangers.

<T. chamaedrys L.   Wall Germander.   **D**   Extinct

VC11: It '..covers the old chalk pit at bottom of Stakes Lane....Upham' 5319, Miss A. Woodhouse 1888 (*Fl.Hants*, excl.sp., p.316), *GWP* 1930 (*Proc. Hants Fld Club* **10**: 297). **VC12**: Burghclere 4660, disused station, a garden plant established for 20 years, *EG* 1976, now gone.
  A herb, 'which delivereth the bodie from all obstructions or stoppings' (*Ger.em.Johns.*, p.657).>

T. botrys L.   Cut-leaved Germander. **N,C**   Very rare (Sched. 8)   Plate VIII

First record, Miss C. R. Scott 1911, by railway near Popham Beacons [Micheldever Spoil Heaps] (*Suppl.Fl. Hants*, p.86).
  On bare, chalk banks, clearings in woods and edges of fields; always on chalk and confined to very few sites.
  VC12: Micheldever Spoil Heaps 5143, 5144, 5244, *SJE* 1985, *HFG* 1991. There are still at least 1000 plants on the bare chalk, but it has obviously decreased since 1927, when it was described as 'enormously plentiful...for quite a mile northwards, covering the chalky spoil banks wherever they exist.'; Freefolk Wood 4944, in clearing, *WJLP* 1942–61, then ploughed; Augurs Hill Copse 3842, edge of arable field, *WS* 1933, plentiful, *HFG* 1992.

Ajuga reptans L.   Bugle.   **N** Common

In damp woods, copses, shady, roadside verges and old, wet meadows. Sometimes a pink form is found, as at Blackmoor Wood 7732, and Noar Hill 7431, VC12, *AB*.

A. chamaepitys (L.) SCHREB. Ground-pine.   **N or C**   Very rare (Sched. 8)   Map 293

First record, T. Yalden *c*.1770, 'on Long-wood rabbit warren near the Warren House, a few scattered plants' 5326, VC11 (*Ray Syn.MS*, p.244).
  On open chalk around edges of cornfields and other arable ground, and along adjacent bare tracks. Probably only about two sites are still extant.
  VC11: Dean 5719, Hb.AWW 1957, not seen *RPB* 1984; W of Farlington Redoubt 6806, in chalky furrows, *RE* 1930. **VC12**: Augurs Hill Copse 3842, edge of arable field, *WS* 1933, *HFG* 1992; by A303 W of Micheldever Station 5042, near gate into cornfield, *WMK* 1972; SE of Freefolk Wood 5043, *PB & FR* 1985; field W of Bramdown Copse 5247, *MMcC-W* 1956.

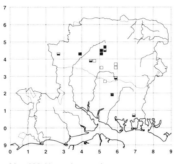

Map 293 Ajuga chamaepitys

Nepeta cataria L.   Catmint.   **N** Rare   Map 294

First record, Gilbert White 1766, Fyfield, VC12 (*White's Jnls* **1**: 206).
  In hedgerows, on road-banks, verges of lanes, borders of fields and chalk-pits. It has decreased since *Fl.Hants* (p.302), and is now confined to the chalk whereas it used to extend a little further. It is liable to be shaded out in overgrown hedges and then reappear years later after trimming or soil-disturbance.
  VC8: Kites Nest Farm, Martin 0617, edge of arable in two places, *JO* 1986; Tidpit Common Down 0617, 0618, scattered plants, *JO* 1986; S of Tidpit 0718, *JO* 1986. **VC11**: Port Lane, Hursley 4426, *RPB* 1950, 1976; Horsea Island 6304, Hb.AWW 1950, *CMcL* 1979 states there were several sites, some of them now destroyed; Deacon Hill 5027, headland of wheat-field on N side of Roman Road, *RPB* 1984; near Hanging Wood 3929, *JRw* 1991. **VC12**:

Quidhampton *c*.5250, both sides of the road, *EAB* 1962; Nether Wallop 3037, hedgebank in lane to airfield, *RPB* 1967 (*Rep.S'ton N.H.S.*, p.14); Chilbolton 4039, roadside hedgebank, *RPB* 1969 (*Rep.S'ton N.H.S.*, p.11); Greywell 7151, *AJPB* 1991.

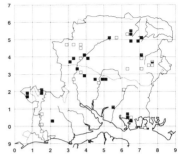

Map 294 Nepeta cataria

Glechoma hederacea L.   Ground-ivy.   **N**   Very common

Plentiful in hedgerows, woods, scrub, borders of fields and shady grassland.

Prunella vulgaris L.   Selfheal.   **N** Very common

In acid and chalk grassland, verges, old pastures, fens, woodland rides, and waste places.

P. x intermedia LINK (*P. x hybrida* Knaf; *P. vulgaris* x *P. laciniata*)   **N** Very rare

VC11: Near Brockenhurst, *JAR* 1911, Hb.BM; Farley Mount 4129, near carpark, *AHA* 1985. **VC12**: Old recorded sites at Shipton Bellinger and Shalden Hollow, Alton, with the parents, both probably now lost.

P. laciniata (L.) L.   Cut-leaved Selfheal.   **N**   Very rare or extinct

First record, Miss K. A. Childs *c*.1920, Shalden Hollow near Alton, VC12, Hb.HCMS, with *P. x hybrida* [= *P. x intermedia*] (Shalden Hollow has since disappeared).
  On chalk grassland or bare chalk.
  VC11: Near Crab Wood (Farley Mount), *HTB* 1930 (*Rep.B.E.C.* for 1930, p.366); seen 4129, with hybrid, *WMB* 1958; roadside 4229, *MPY* 1969, last seen 1974. **VC12**: N of A30, near Leckford 3835, in field, *ADuSB* 1932–36; near Shipton Bellinger *c*.2244, old camp-site, *JDG, PMH & ECW* 1937, Hb.BM. Gone from all these sites, and perhaps now extinct.

P. grandiflora (L.) SCHOLLER Large Selfheal. **H** Very rare

VC11: Near Beaulieu Road Station, two large plants on railway embankment, *WL* 1971, det. *EJC* 1985 (*BSBI News* **41**: 20); W of Studland Common, Milford on Sea 2792, several large plants on floor of old pit, *AEB & CB* 1994, Hb.RPB, conf. *EJC*.

Melissa officinalis L.   Balm.   **D** Occasional

Waste places and waysides, mostly near habitations as a garden outcast. VC11: 27 □; VC12: 9 □.

VC11: Near Eling Mill 3612, by railway line near wharf, *RPB* 1986; Southampton Common 4113, near nursery, *CDD* 1960. VC12: Upper Clatford 3543, *GDF* 1983; Gaston Copse 7148, *ANHS* 1984.

Satureja montana L.   Winter Savory.   **D** Very rare

First record, Miss C. E. Palmer 1900, Beaulieu Abbey 3802, VC11, from a specimen erroneously labelled *Hyssopus* in Hb.OXF from her collection, det. *JCM* 1919 (*Rep.B.E.C.* for 1919, p.573). In 1920, C. E. Britton reported a herbarium sheet from this locality dating back to August 1873 (*J.Bot.* **58**: 295) but this has not yet been traced. Still abundant, *WFS* 1989 (*Wild Fl. Mag.* **1990**: 12).

Clinopodium ascendens (JORD.) SAMP. (*Calamintha sylvatica* Bromf. ssp. *ascendens* (Jord.) P. W. Ball; *C. ascendens* Jord.)   Common Calamint. **N,D** Very local   Map 295

First record, J. Woods 1824, near Netley, VC11 (*Fl.Hants*, p.301).

On dry, bare hedgebanks, verges and old walls; widespread, but generally uncommon on the chalk, where it is native. It may reappear after hedge-cutting or disturbance of overgrown road-banks. It can also be a relic of cultivation.

VC11: B3347 near Court Farm, Sopley 1597, *RPB* 1990; Exton 6020, laneside bank, *HCA–H* 1975; Fort Cumberland, Eastney 6899, *EAP* 1987. VC12: Penton Mewsey *c*.3246, *GDF* 1973; West Tisted *c*.6428, *MB* 1966.

<**C. calamintha** (L.) STACE (*Calamintha nepeta* (L.) Savi ssp. *glandulosa* (Req.) P. W. Ball)   Lesser Calamint.   **C** Extinct

First record, Miss K. Smith and Mr Sanders 1926, Hazeley Camp, Twyford, VC11 (*Suppl.Fl.Hants*, p.83).

VC11: Hazeley Down, near Twyford 5025, on site of old army camp, *GARW* 1933 (*Watts MSS*), no record since.>

C. vulgare L.   Wild Basil.   **N** Locally common

In hedges, verges, open scrub, woodland rides and borders, and rank grassland. Widespread and very common on the chalk; occasional outliers on other soils.

C. acinos (L.) KUNTZE (*Acinos arvensis* (Lam.) Dandy)   Basil Thyme. **N,C** Locally frequent

First record, J. Dale *c*.1650, 'in Salisbury feild neere Basing stoake', VC12 (How's ms note on fol.1 of his copy of *Phyt.Brit.*, as *Acinos Anglica flore albo*).

On arable and bare ground, verges, banks, railway- and road-cuttings. Almost confined to bare soil on the chalk. Widespread and locally frequent, but probably less common than in Townsend's day. VC8: 7 □; VC11: 22 □; VC12: 69 □.

VC11: Beaulieu old airfield 3400, abundant on bed of former runway, *RPB* 1990; Fort Nelson, Ports Down 6007, in disturbed, broken turf, *RPB* 1988. VC12: Tothill old railway 4462–4661, *VF* 1982; Tidworth *c*.2246, *MFW* 1989. Rarely on sand: in Blackmoor Park 7832, until overshadowed by rhododendrons, *AB c*.1945; Farnborough Airfield 8653, on sandy bank, *JK & ARGM* 1981, since lost.

<**Hyssopus officinalis** L.   Hyssop. **D** Extinct

Formerly long-naturalized on the ruins of Beaulieu Abbey 3802, VC11 (*Fl. Hants*, excl.sp., p.315). Not refound 1927 (*Suppl.Fl.Hants*, p.vii) nor since.>

Origanum vulgare L.   Marjoram. **N** Locally common   Map 296

Common in open scrub, verges, hedgebanks, rank grassland, chalk-pits, and open woodland rides and clearings on the chalk. Anywhere off the chalk it is usually associated with introduced soil.

VC11: Palmer's Ford 1000, track by sewage-works, *RPB* 1991; Weston Lane, Nursling 3615, by railway bridge, *RPB* 1974; M275 Tipner 6302, *DPJS & RPB* 1991. VC12: There are a few sites on the NE heaths: Blackbushe 8059, several patches, *VK* 1985–88; Fleet 8353, roadside verge, *TD & ARGM* 1980–88; Aldershot 8450, becoming swamped by scrub, *TD & ARGM* 1980.

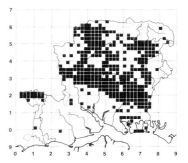

Map 296 Origanum vulgare

Thymus vulgaris L.   Garden Thyme.   **D** Very rare

A culinary herb.
VC11: Walls of Wolvesey Palace, Winchester 4829, *CRL* 1969.

T. pulegioides L.   Large Thyme. **N** Locally frequent   Map 297

On grassy heathland, in verges, old marl- and gravel-pits; leached and

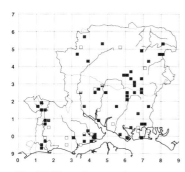

Map 295 Clinopodium ascendens

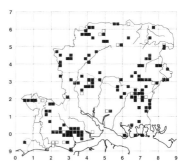

Map 297 Thymus pulegioides

superficial soils on the chalk; also in chalk grassland, on disused railways, etc. Everywhere scarcer than *T. polytrichus*, except in the southern New Forest where it largely replaces it. Three sites are in churchyards.

VC11: South Gorley 1711, Hb.RPB 1976; Beaulieu old airfield 3500, Hb.RPB 1981; Butser Hill 7120, *FR* 1991. **VC12**: Tichborne Down 5930, *ARGM* 1988; N of Isle of Wight Hill 2538, *GDF* 1988; brickwork of railway bridge, Broad Road, Andover 3043, *MFW* 1991; Noar Hill 7431, with *T. polytrichus*, *FR* 1982; Ashford Hill 5662, in meadow, *PB* 1982; Bourley 8249, *CRH* 1983, 1991.

[**T. pulegioides x T. serpyllum** L.

Farley Mount, VC11, *HG & JGr* 1929, Hb.BM (*Suppl.Fl.Hants*, p.83, as *T. x oblongifolius* Opiz.). C. D. Pigott rejected all records of this hybrid in the British Isles (*Hybr.Fl.Brit.Is.*, p.390). *T. serpyllum* is restricted to the Breckland of E Anglia.]

T. polytrichus A. KERN. ex BORBÁS ssp. **britannicus** (RONNIGER) KERGUÉLEN (*T. praecox* Opiz ssp. *arcticus* (Durand) Jalas; *T. drucei* Ronniger) Wild Thyme. **N** Locally common   Map 298

In short turf of dry grassland, in verges, on banks, etc.; widespread and common over much of the chalk. Local on other, mainly gravelly soils, and on sand or shingle along the coast. There is a possibility that some of the records along the western border of the New Forest may be *T. pulegioides*.

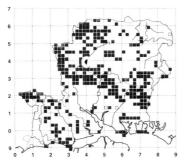

Map 298 Thymus polytrichus ssp. britannicus

Lycopus europaeus L.   Gipsywort. **N**   Locally common

By rivers, streams, ditches, ponds, in marshes and wet, woodland rides. Common in most wetlands.

Mentha arvensis L.   Corn Mint. **N,C**   Frequent and locally common Map 299

In borders of arable fields, shallow ditches, disturbed soil in verges, and damp, woodland rides.

With the exception of *M. arvensis*, *M. aquatica*, *M. x verticillata* and *M. pulegium*, *Mentha* taxa are probably all either ancient or recent escapes or throw-outs from gardens.

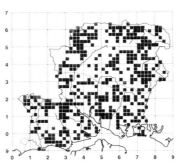

Map 299 Mentha arvensis

M. x verticillata L. (*M. arvensis* x *M. aquatica*)   Whorled Mint. **N** Locally frequent

First record, J. Lightfoot *c*.1770 (as *M. x gentilis*), Hartley Bridge, VC12, Hb.K, det. *RMH* 1990.

A natural hybrid, occurring in ditches, stream-banks, and wet, grassy places. It seems to be commoner in the SW, but that could well be due to recording bias.

M. x smithiana R. A. GRAHAM (*M. arvensis* x *M. aquatica* x *M. spicata*) Tall Mint. **D**   Rare

A garden outcast in streams, ditches, waste ground and tips, but it seems to have flourished best in the wet places. **VC11**: Near R. Test, Nursling 3614, Hb.RPB 1981, det. *RMH*; Blashford 1506, *RPB* 1981. Also 3814, 4012, 4296. **VC12**: Greywell, *GARW* 1934 (*Proc.Hants Fld Club* **15**: 69); Overton Mill 5150, *WEW* 1957, det. *RAG*; near Winchfield Station, *ALS* 1932 or 1933 (*Proc.Hants Fld Club* **12**: 296), same site as 'roadside ditch...Winchfield', *GARW* 1934 (*Watts MSS*), still there 7654, *ARGM* 1980, Hb.AB; Waggoners Wells 8534, abundant in stream and at lakeside, but a shy flowerer, *AB* 1976–82. Also 7050, 7452, 7852.

M. x gracilis SOLE (*M. x gentilis* auct., non L.; *M. arvensis* x *M. spicata*) Bushy Mint. **D**   Rare

First record, E. D. Marquand *c*.1879, near Brockenhurst, VC11, Hb.NMW.

Generally an ancient garden throwout and, as such, to be found in ditches, borders of fields, roadsides and on tips.

VC9: 0494. **VC11**: East Meon, *FE* 1932 or 1933 (*Proc.Hants Fld Club* **12**: 296); Ringwood *c*.1405, *NDS* 1934 (*Atlas Brit.Fl.Crit.Suppl.*, p.65); Timsbury *c*.3424, *PMH* 1939, Hb.NMW; Buddle Green, North Gorley 1611, edge of green on streamside near cottages, *RPB* 1981, Hb.K, det. *RMH*; Kingston North Common 1402, in rank herbage, *RPB* 1986, det. *RMH*; Hungerford, Fordingbridge 1612, wet ditch along roadside hedge, Hb.RPB 1981, det. *RMH*; near Bloodoaks Farm, Bramshaw 2616, 2716, along stream-bed, *RPB & JO* 1990. Also 1490, 1604, 3096. **VC12**: Empshott Green 7431, *AB* 1970, det. *RMH*; Quarley Manor Farm 2642, *RPB* 1969, det. *RMH*; derelict cottage-garden near Bramdean, *GARW* 1934 (*Rep. B.E.C.* for 1934, p.837); Micheldever *c*.5038, far from houses, *CW* 1943, det. *ALS* (*Watsonia* **1**: 51, as *M. x cardiaca* (Gray) Baker); Sleaford tip 8038, *AB* 1970, det. *JEL*.

M. aquatica L.   Water Mint. **N** Locally very common

On banks of rivers, in streams, ponds, ditches, marshes, wet, open woods and carr; common in all wetlands.

M. x piperita L. (*M. aquatica* x *M. spicata*)   Peppermint. **D**   Rare

On damp roadsides, in ditches and on tips.

nv. **piperita**

VC11: Soberton 6012, Hb.AWW 1961; B3081 Ebblake, Ringwood Forest 1007, marshy verge, Hb.RPB 1985, det. *RMH*. Also 1406, 1604, 4218. **VC12**: Shipton Bellinger 2344, in ditch, *GDF* 1982, det. *RMH*; ditch near beginning of Hitches Lane, Crookham 7952, *GARW* 1933 (*Watts MSS*), not found *ARGM* 1980. Also 4834.

nv. **citrata** (EHRH.) BRIQ.

VC11: Burton *c*.1694, *CDD* 1968. Also 1894. **VC12**: Sleaford tip 8038, *AB* 1970, det. *JEL*.

M. spicata L.   Spearmint. **D** Frequent

First record, Miss M. T. Hillard 1919, Foxbury Waste, near Exton, VC11 (*Suppl.Fl.Hants*, p.81).

Waste places and roadside verges, sometimes in quite remote areas; widespread and fairly frequent. This is the commonest garden mint, and is often found as a garden-outcast. 119 records, of which *c*.22 are of the hairy form, formerly identified as *M. longifolia* (L.) Huds., but some of these are probably *M.* x *villosonervata* (*RMH*).

M. x **villosa** HUDS. (*M.* x *niliaca* auct., non Juss. ex Jacq.; *M.* x *cordifolia* auct.?, *an* Opiz ex Fresen.; *M. spicata* x *M. suaveolens*)   Apple Mint.   **D**   Occasional

Waste places, tips, and roadsides. VC8: 1 □; VC11: 16 □; VC12: 19 □.

nv. **alopecuroides** (HULL) BRIQ.

VC11: Lee gravel-pit 3617, Hb.RPB 1983, det. *RMH*; waste land opposite Fort Nelson 6006, Hb.AWW 1963, det. *RMH*, *RPB* 1986. VC12: Itchen Abbas 5232, *HJMB* 1988.

nv. **villosa**

VC11: Priestlands Lane, Lymington 3195, rough, wet field by gardens, Hb.AWW 1962, det. *RMH*, who says 'but this form should perhaps be regarded as distinct'. The leaves are elliptic-ovate.

nv. unnamed

VC12: A mint which has puzzled generations of botanists grows down the Oakhanger Stream at Selborne, from Dorton Cottage 7433 to the Priory Farm 7534, Hb.AB 1968. *RMH* determined it as an unnamed nothovariety of *M.* x *villosa*, with the same parentage. It does not look at all like nv. *alopecuroides* but is similar to nv. *villosa* (*Watsonia* 10: 428).

M. x **villosonervata** OPIZ (*M. spicata* x *M. longifolia*)   Sharp-toothed Mint.   **D**   Very rare or under-recorded

VC11: Dunwood, roadside dump 3022, 1976; Calshot 4701, 1986; Northney, North Hayling 7203, 1988. VC12: Shipton Bellinger 2345, 1974. All Hb.RPB, det. *RMH*.

M. suaveolens EHRH. (*M. rotundifolia* sensu Robson et auct., non (L.) Huds.)   Round-leaved Mint.   **D**   Very rare

Much confused with *M.* x *villosa* nv. *alopecuroides*, this is not native in Hants.

VC11: Refuse-tip, Burton Common 1995, Hb.RPB 1985, det. *RMH*; R. Mude, Burton 1894, on bank S of railway bridge, Hb.FAW 1987, conf. *RPB* 1991. VC12: East Woodhay 4060, abundant on floor of chalk-pit, *WMK* 1975: this is Reeks's old station in *Fl.Hants* (p.294). These are the only three authentic modern records.

M. pulegium L.   Pennyroyal.   **N**   Rare (Sched. 8)   Map 300

First record, R. S. Hill 1839, pond on Burgh heath, VC12 (*Fl.Hants*, p.297).

On margins of ponds, grassy flood hollows and flushed short turf, ditch-channels and old marl-pits; often in heavily trodden, grazed sites. Now almost confined to the New Forest which probably supports the largest remaining population in NW Europe due to the continuance of an ancient grazing-regime ensuring maintenance of a suitable habitat.

VC8: Stock's Cross 2715, *RPB* 1980, plentiful, *FR* 1994. VC11: Pilley Pond 3398, *GHF* 1977; Cadnam Green 2914, *RPB* 1976, *FR* 1991; East End 3697, *WMK* 1983, *HFG* 1991; Pennington Common 3095, Hb.AWW 1963, last seen *JMD c*.1984; probably gone from Breamore Marsh ponds 1518, *BW* 1953, Hb.AWW 1958, last record *FR* 1969. VC12: Edge of pond near Bramshill Police College 7558, *BMe* 1977 (*Watsonia* 18: 430), is probably the last record in VC12, habitat overgrown, *CRH* 1986; Cove 8355, sandy lay-by in heathland, *AWh* 1977, Hb.AB, det. *FR* (*Watsonia* 13: 338), later admitted to be a garden throw-out which did not persist. Also near Fleet Pond 8154, naturalized in mown garden lawn on site of former heathland where not deliberately introduced, teste *ARGM* 1984, lawn later dug up.

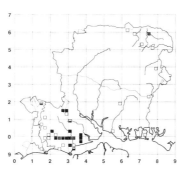

Map 300 Mentha pulegium

M. requienii BENTH.   Corsican Mint.   **H**   Very rare

Naturalized from gardens. In damp crevices between paving stones.

VC11: Rockbourne 1118, *FDR* 1964; 1117, *MPY* 1966; Southbourne *c*.1491, *WFB* 1962.

Salvia pratensis L.   Meadow Clary. **H**   Very rare (Sched. 8)

First established record, R. A. Titt 1966, Isle of Wight Hill [Porton Ranges] 2437, VC12 (*Suppl.Fl.Wilts*, p.46).

On chalk grassland. In 1986, at the above site, the then *NCC* found thousands of rosettes over an area 15m square. It is thoroughly established, but there was once a house and garden on the site. There are 11 other old records and one recent one, as casuals.

S. verbenaca L. (*S. horminoides* Pourr.)   Wild Clary.   **N,C?**   Rare   Map 301

First record, Gilbert White 1766, Fyfield, VC12 (*White's Jnls* 1: 206).

On grassy banks or bare soil on the chalk; also in verges, about ruins and fortifications, and in churchyard-turf, to which it may have come with imported stone from Portland where it is common. In Hants it is very scattered and quite rare; the many records in *Fl.Hants* (p.303) suggest that it has decreased.

VC11: Sopley churchyard 1596, *RPB* 1984; Fort Cumberland 6899, *EAP* 1981 ('abundant on Portsmouth fortifications', *EHW*'s annotated *Fl.Hants*, *c*.1930); Nelson Lane, Ports Down 6106, chalk turf on roadside bank, *JSt* 1985. VC12: Longstock 3536, grassy roadside bank, *AR* 1975; Bere Hill, Whitchurch 4648, along footpath above houses, *RPB* 1966.

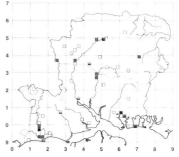

Map 301 Salvia verbenaca

<**S. verticillata** L.   Whorled Clary. **H**   Extinct

VC12: Railway bridge by Bramshot

Links, near Fleet 8355, six plants, *GARW* 1932 (*Watts MSS*). No record since. Four older VC11 records in *Suppl.Fl.Hants* (p.84).>

HIPPURIDACEAE

Hippuris vulgaris L.   Mare's-tail.   **N**   Locally frequent   Map 302

In rivers and ponds, usually in well-oxygenated, calcareous water. Locally common in the Test and Itchen valleys, and the Basingstoke Canal; local in chalk streams or springs elsewhere.

VC11: Stanpit Marsh 1692, *RPB* 1985; R. Test, Great Bridge 3523, *RMV* 1987; Bishop's Waltham 5517, millpond, *RPB* 1972. **VC12**: Hawkley 7428, *MS-W* 1970; Great Pen Wood 4462, small pond, *NFC* 1982; R. Whitewater, Greywell Moors 7150, pond by spring, *FR* 1983; Springlakes 8851, *JES* 1986.

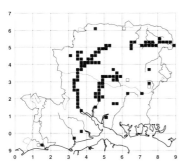

Map 302 Hippuris vulgaris

CALLITRICHACEAE

Callitriche stagnalis Scop.   Common Water-starwort.   **N**   Frequent and locally very common

In ponds, open, muddy ground, wet tracks in woods and meadows; common in suitable habitats, and apparently with a wide soil and water pH range, from basic to acid.

C. platycarpa Kütz.   Various-leaved Water-starwort.   **N**   Locally frequent

In rivers, streams and ponds, especially in shallow reaches which are silted up with mud; in basic to mildly-acid water. Probably often confused with the previous and with the next two species.

C. obtusangula Le Gall   Blunt-fruited Water-starwort.   **N**   Locally frequent   Map 303

In rivers and streams, mainly in peaty and base-rich waters, especially those of the chalk valleys, where very common; also more locally in mildly-acid water.

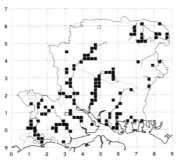

Map 303 Callitriche obtusangula

C. brutia Petagna (*C. intermedia* Hoffm. ssp. *pedunculata* (DC.) A. R. Clapham)   Pedunculate Water-starwort.   **N**   Very locally frequent, but under-recorded

First record, H. Groves & J. Groves 1886, moist roadside near Hythe, VC11, Hb.NMW (as *C. hamulata* var. *pedunculata*), det. *CDPr* 1990.

In shallow, seasonal ponds, ditches and flood hollows on heathland and probably also in deeper ponds; in the New Forest and Avon Valley. Very difficult to separate from *C. hamulata* unless terrestrial fruiting specimens can be found, and for this reason the VC12 records of *C. hamulata* need revision. VC8: 2 □; VC11: 56 □; VC12: 1□.

VC8: Furzley Common 2816, flood hollows, *RMV* 1991, Hb.CGE, det. *CDPr*. **VC11**: Kingston North Common 1503, edge of pond, Hb.RPB 1991, det. *CDPr*; Pennington Marshes 3292, flood-pool on levelled tip, Hb.RPB 1993; pool W of A337 New Park, Brockenhurst 3004, *CDP* 1950, Hb.CGE, det. *CDPr* 1990; in 49 tetrads in the New Forest, *RPB & RMV* 1991–93, det. *CDPr & RPB*. **VC12**: Woolmer Pond 7832, with fruits on newly-created, open, sandy shore, *FR* 1994.

C. hamulata Kütz. ex W. D. J. Koch (*C. intermedia* ssp. *hamulata* (Kütz. ex W. D. J. Koch) A. R. Clapham)   Intermediate Water-starwort.   **N**   Locally frequent   Map 304

In rivers and streams of varying depth and velocity. Largely restricted to acid waters, as the majority of records in the SW and NE indicate. Scattered records elsewhere may be the result of confusion with submerged plants of *C. obtusangula*.

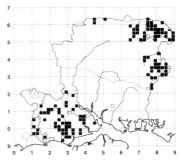

Map 304 Callitriche hamulata

PLANTAGINACEAE

Plantago coronopus L.   Buck's-horn Plantain.   **N**   Locally common   Map 305

In short turf or bare ground, in dry sandy or gravelly pastures, heaths, paths, roadsides, banks of old pits, and on sand-dunes and shingle along the coast. Common everywhere on sand and gravel, except in the central part of northernmost Hants.

VC12: Silchester Common 6262, *PB* 1980.

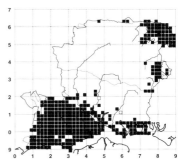

Map 305 Plantago coronopus

P. maritima L.   Sea Plantain.   **N**   Locally frequent   Map 306

In grassy salt-marshes, mud-flats, dune-turf on sand or shingle; common along the coast and in estuaries; occasionally inland in the S New Forest, in old marl-pits or on heaths, in sparse turf sometimes flushed by drainage-flows.

VC11: Crockford Bridge 3499, *RPB* 1980; Whitten Bottom 2000, in gully, *RPB* 1979.

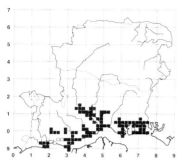

Map 306 Plantago maritima

P. major L.   Greater Plantain.   **N,C** Abundant

Open, much-trodden grassland in roadside verges, waysides, pastures, lawns and waste places; on bare soil along paths or around cultivated fields. It is an indication of excessive trampling on grass-paths. The common plant is said to be ssp. *major*. A very robust form, which may be ssp. *intermedia* (Gilib.) Lange, occurs on muddy banks of freshwater and tidal rivers, and requires further study.

P. media L.   Hoary Plantain.   **N** Locally common

Old grassland on the downs, in dry pastures, roadside verges, churchyards and lawns; widespread and abundant on the chalk, scattered and local on other basic soil.

P. lanceolata L.   Ribwort Plantain. **N,C**   Abundant

In grassland on all types of soil, also a weed on cultivated ground.

Littorella uniflora (L.) ASCH. Shoreweed.   **N**   Local   Map 307

On shallow, gravelly or sandy beds and margins of lakes, ponds and streams on heathland; also on heaths in the lower level of small flood hollows which are often quite dry in summer, where it forms a compact sward. Frequent in the New Forest, rare in the NE.
  VC11: Hengistbury Head 1690, edge of small pond, *RPB* 1990; Longcross Plain 2415, *RPB* 1961; Ober Heath 2703, *JO & RMW* 1987. **VC12**: Ewhurst Lake *c*.5757, *WEW* 1958, not refound *FR & PB* 1993; Silchester Common 6262, *WGH* 1992; Woolmer

Pond 7831, Hb.AWW 1951, *FR* 1994, locally abundant on newly-created, open sandy shore; Fleet Pond 8255, *GARW* 1932 (*Watts MSS*), *VL* 1951, reappeared after management, *CRH* 1989; Bourley Bottom 8250, *ARGM* 1977, *CRH* 1987; Basingstoke Canal, Pondtail 8253, *VL* 1960, the only post-dredging record is Puckridge 8452, *CRH* 1988–92.

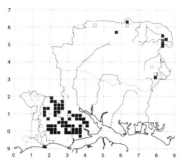

Map 307 Littorella uniflora

BUDDLEJACEAE

Buddleja davidii FRANCH.   Butterfly-bush.   **H**   Locally common

First record, A. W. Westrup 1950, E Southsea *c*.6698, VC11.
  This popular garden plant found an ideal habitat for dispersal in the bombsites of World War II. It is not surprising, therefore, that the chief centre from which records show it radiating is Southampton. It colonizes waste ground, walls, railways, old chalk-pits, and bare, coastal reclaimed land. It is mainly in built-up areas, but increasingly in rural ones.

OLEACEAE

Fraxinus excelsior L.   Ash.   **N** Very common

First record, Survey of the manor of East Meon in 1647, 'a great ash standing on the side of Butser Hill', VC11 (*VCH Hants* 3: 67).
  In woods and hedges. Common to abundant throughout Hants, except on acid soils. Characteristic of shallow soil on chalk, where it is an important colonist of ungrazed grassland, and also acts as a precursor to the natural regeneration of beech-woods. Plentiful also on deep, moist, base-rich soil on the Malmstone (often with wych elm), at the foot of the chalk scarp, and on the Gault and other clays. In the New Forest, only on alluvial soil in valley

woods, especially on the Headon Beds, and not abundant. Probably commoner now than in prehistoric times, as its sites seem then to have been occupied by wych elm and small-leaved lime, and its pollen record suggests that it was by no means abundant in prehistoric times.

Ligustrum vulgare L.   Wild Privet. **N**   Locally very common

In woods, scrub and old hedges; often dominant in the shrub-layer of beech- and ash-woods on chalk; a colonist of neglected chalk-grassland; also in dry carr and along wooded streams here and there on the Headon Beds and other base-rich Tertiary strata. Occasionally planted as a hedge.

var. **auriflorum** HÖFKER

VC11: Duncoombe Wood, East Meon, single bush, apparently wild, *FE* 1931 (*Proc.Hants Fld Club* 12: 82, as var. *floreluteo*).

L. ovalifolium HASSK.   Garden Privet.   **H**   Occasional

The usual plant in hedges. Not truly naturalized. Much confused with *L. vulgare*.

SCROPHULARIACEAE

Verbascum blattaria L.   Moth Mullein.   **C,H**   Rare

Casual only. VC11: 7 □; VC12: 4 □.
  VC11: Hilsea Lines 6504, white-flowered plant by path through wood, *RPB* 1990. **VC12**: Aldershot 8650, plentiful on waste land cleared for building, *TD & ARGM* 1980; Wolverton Wood 5559, by ride at entrance, *PB* 1988.

V. virgatum STOKES   Twiggy Mullein.   **H**   Very rare

First record, B. King 1879, gravelly banks at Highcliffe, VC11 (*Fl.Hants*, excl.sp., p.288).
  VC11: South Hayling; plants persisted for over 60 years, having been recorded first by *MTH* in 1921 (*Suppl.Fl. Hants*, p.75), and last by *AB* in 1982, by the road to Seager House 7098, where it was destroyed by 'tidying up' in 1984; also long established on a building site 7198, until built on in the 1960s, *AB*. Five other isolated records since 1929 are all on the south coast, the last being Brownwich Farm 5103, *RPB* 1984–85, and Titchfield

Haven 5302, *JAN & RPB* 1986–87. Also 3090, 4010.

V. phlomoides L.   Orange Mullein. **H**   Rare

First record, G. A. R. Watts, 1938, Hazeley Heath *c.*7657, VC12 (*Proc.Hants Fld Club* **15**: 68).

An earlier, unconfirmed record, 'single specimen on the chalk near Fullerton', VC12, C. B. Clarke 1866, is entered with a query in *List Flg Pl. Andvr* (p.71).

An increasing garden-escape, on waste ground near houses, refuse-tips, and disturbed roadsides.

VC11: Lord's Hill 3816, *WFB & RPB* 1975, det. *IKF*; M27 Lark Hill, Ports Down 6106, abundant on N bank of motorway, *RPB* 1990. Also 3292, 3406, 3614, 3618, 4004, 4806, 6098, 6404, 6696, 6600, 6602, 6604, 6898. **VC12**: Aldershot 8751, disused railway-sidings, some white-flowered, *GHF & ARGM* 1981, site built over 1986; M3 roundabout, Dummer 5846, Hb.AB 1980, det. *EJC*. Also 5042, 7238, 7658, 8058, 8236.

V. thapsus L.   Great Mullein.   **N,H** Frequent and locally common

Bare and disturbed soil on downs, banks, verges in woodland clearings, and along railways; common and sometimes abundant, especially on chalk.

V. x semialbum CHAUB. (*V. thapsus* x *V. nigrum*)   **N**   Very rare

There are unlocalized records for VC11 and VC12 in *Hybr.Fl.Brit.Is.* (p.361).

VC11: Near Common Marsh, Stockbridge 3534, levelled, tipped chalk-soil on waste ground W of road, Hb.RPB 1987, det. *IKF*. **VC12**: West Down, Chilbolton 3839, *ANHS* 1983, one plant, carefully identified but not collected.

V. nigrum L.   Dark Mullein.   **N** Locally common   Map 308

Roadside verges, grassy banks, borders of fields and rank grassland; on dry chalk and other light soils, especially sands and gravels. Widespread and common, becoming rare in the S and NE.

V. lychnitis L.   White Mullein. **C,H**   Very rare

First record, [T. Garnier] 1799, Hambledon, VC11, roadsides and waste ground, very rare (*Hants Repos* **1**: 118; *Fl.Hants*, excl.sp., p.288).

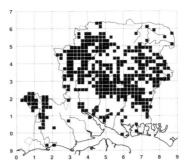

Map 308 Verbascum nigrum

Not native in Hants, but is native though rare in W Sussex in open chalk woods and locally common on the chalk in Kent.

VC11: The only recent, verified records are Peartree Green, Southampton 4311, bank of tipped railway-ballast, *SNHS* 1981, det. *GAM* (*Rep.S'ton N.H.S.*, p.4), 19 rosettes, *MS* 1984, two flower-spikes and seedlings, *MS* 1994 (*Newsletter S'ton N.H.S.*, Dec.1994, p.7); Eastleigh 4517, ballast by railway, *PS* 1994. There is an unconfirmed record N of Shawford 4726, on disused railway, comm. *MS c.*1960, and one for Sholing, not far from Peartree Green (*Suppl.Fl.Hants*, p.75).

Scrophularia nodosa L.   Common Figwort.   **N,C**   Common

Damp woods and scrub, shady hedge-banks; sometimes in waste places and along railway tracks; less common on very acid soil.

S. auriculata L. (*S. aquatica* auct., non L.)   Water Figwort.   **N,C** Locally common   Map 309

Banks of rivers and streams, ponds, ditches, marshes and damp rides. Also in drier sites, such as pits and open

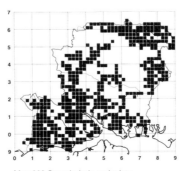

Map 309 Scrophularia auriculata

hangers on the chalk, and along railway tracks. Common in the river valleys.

<S. vernalis L.   Yellow Figwort.   **H** Extinct

First records, Mrs Sidebottom 1931, near Broughton (*Rep.B.E.C.* for 1931, p.661) and G. W. Pierce 1931, East Tytherley 2928, VC11, a very large colony (*Proc.Hants Fld Club* **12**: 83), wall of churchyard, *PMH* 1932, Hb.BM (all relate to the same site). Seen *AB c.*1970, searched for in vain by *RPB* 1983.>

Mimulus moschatus DOUGLAS ex LINDL.   Musk.   **H**   Rare

First record, F. Browning 1924, on the Loddon near Basingstoke, VC12 (*Proc.IoW N.H.S.* **1**:261).

Muddy edges of ponds and wooded swamps. Slowly spreading, and plentiful in some sites.

VC11: Near Shatter Ford 3505, *NDS* 1933, abundant over area *c.*2 x 2.5m, *RPB* 1990; Mill Lawn, Burley 2203, stream flowing from bog, *RMW & RPB* 1987; Ampfield *c.*3923, *PMH* 1928, Hb.BM. Also 1610, 1612, 2802, 3218, 3802, 4216. **VC12**: North Warnborough 7252, *GHF* 1977, *HWT* 1988. Also 7828.

M. guttatus DC.   Monkeyflower. **H**   Locally frequent   Map 310

First record, C.B. Clarke 1866, 'Whitchurch to Long Parish [VC12], in the swamps' (*List.Flg.Pl.Andvr*, p.73, as *M. lutens* L.).

Muddy margins of rivers, streams and ponds. Most frequent along the R. Itchen and R. Meon, more local on the R. Test and R. Avon, and the rivers draining the Thames Basin and the western Weald; scattered and rare elsewhere.

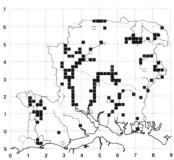

Map 310 Mimulus guttatus

M. x robertsii SILVERSIDE (*M. guttatus* x *M. luteus* L.)   Hybrid Monkeyflower.　**H**　Rare

First record, R. Meinertzhagen 1930, Warnford Lake 6222, VC11, Hb.BM.

In similar situations to *M. guttatus*, but still rare.

VC8: Allen River, Damerham 1015, 1016, Hb.RPB 1976, 1979, det. *EJC*. **VC11**: Barton on Sea 2392, streamlet below cliff, Hb.RPB 1986, det. *RHR*; Marshcourt River, Common Marsh, Stockbridge 3534, Hb.RPB 1989, det. *AJS* 1991. Also 1610, 1612. **VC12**: Stream running into Wallop Brook 2938, *RMV* 1988–89, Hb.AB. Also 2844, 3044, 3446, 3646.

Limosella aquatica L.　Mudwort. **N**　Very rare

Muddy edges of ponds and flood-channels which dry out in summer.

VC11: Breamore Marsh ponds, 1517, 1518, *BG* 1934, *RPB* 1983, *CC* 1991; Wick Meads 1592, *RMW* 1991; Stanpit Marsh 1692, in tidal drain-channel, *RPB* 1971, *WGH* 1987; R. Avon, Ham Common 1498, plentiful in mud, *AJB* 1986; Ellingham Lake 1407, drained bed of flooded gravel-pit, *RPB* 1987–88; Bramshaw Telegraph 2216, seasonal pond N of road, *RPB* 1991. Formerly at three other sites. **VC12**: Hook Common 7153 or 7253, one plant in peaty cart-rut, *NEGC* 1942 (*Rep.B.E.C.* for 1941–42, p.498); Wash Water by the Enborne Stream (R. Enborne) 4563, *WBe & ABJ* 1906, Hb.BM (doubtless the same as 'Muddy flat bordering the Enborne near Wash Bridge, on the Hants as well as the Berks bank' in *Suppl.Fl.Hants*, p.77). No record there since.

Calceolaria chelidonioides KUNTH Slipperwort.　**C or H**　Very rare

First record, Miss S. Mold 1963, Sway, garden weed, VC11, comm. *DMcC*, Hb.RNG, det. *JEL* as *C. tripartita* Ruíz & Pav. (*Proc.B.S.B.I.* **5**: 339).

An aggressive garden weed, from S America.

Antirrhinum majus L.　Snap-dragon.　**H**　Rare

Established and naturalized on a few old walls, elsewhere a transient garden-escape.

VC11: Portchester Castle 6204; Winchester 4828; Titchfield Abbey 5406. **VC12**: Old Basing 6652.

Chaenorhinum minus (L.) LANGE Small Toadflax.　**C**　Locally common

First record, Gilbert White 1766, 'The least toad's flax, *linaria Antirrhinum dicta*', Selborne, VC12 (*White's Jnls* **1**: 211).

An arable weed of the chalk, where it is still quite common, and especially associated with the limestone ballast and clinkers of old railways. On other soils it can often be seen to follow these railways, as in the New Forest on the former Brockenhurst–Ringwood line.

Misopates orontium (L.) RAF. Weasel's-snout, Lesser Snapdragon. **C**　Locally frequent　Map 311

Arable fields, disturbed ground and gardens on light, sandy or gravelly soils. Distribution very discontinuous, but locally common on the Tertiaries of the SW, and on the Wealden sand; widespread but infrequent on the chalk and N Tertiaries. Once a common arable weed, it has declined wherever crop-spraying is carried out.

VC11: Potato-field, Shelley Farm, Ower 3217, *GC* 1987; Timsbury 3425, plentiful garden weed, *AJRa & RPB* 1988–89. **VC12**: Strawberry field near Kingsley 7837, *AB* 1987; Farnborough 8652, many plants among cinders on waste land, *TD* 1978; NE of Liss 7928, arable, *FR* 1980.

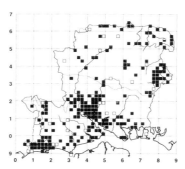

Map 311 *Misopates orontium*

Cymbalaria muralis P. GAERTN., B. MEY. & SCHERB. ssp. **muralis**　Ivy-leaved Toadflax.　**H**　Frequent

First record, Miss C. R. May 1837, wall outside the park, Breamore *c.*1518, VC11 (*May Ptgs Cat.* no.600).

On old walls, rubble-heaps and masonry; widespread. A white-flowered form occurs, as at Rockbourne church-yard 1118, VC11, *RPB* 1984, and Sheet House 7524, VC12, outer wall, *AB* 1990.

Kickxia elatine (L.) DUMORT. Sharp-leaved Fluellen.　**C**　Locally common

First record, Gilbert White 1765, 'in my Ewel-close a wheat-stubble', Selborne, VC12 (*White's Jnls* **1**: 166).

Cornfields and other arable land on chalk, also on bare disturbed roadsides; it can also tolerate neutral and mildly acid soil so its range is wider than *K. spuria*.

K. spuria (L.) DUMORT.　Round-leaved Fluellen.　**C**　Locally frequent

First record, Gilbert White 1765, 'in my Ewel-close a wheat-stubble', Selborne, VC12 (*White's Jnls* **1**: 166).

An arable weed, almost confined to the chalk, where it seems to have been more resistant to spray than have others. It has been found curtaining a gravelly ditch-bank at Little Somborne 3832, VC11, *RPB* 1966.

Linaria vulgaris MILL.　Common Toadflax.　**N,C**　Common

On waste ground, verges, hedgebanks, grassy borders and bare ground around arable fields, and in rank grassland; prefers sand and chalk to clay.

L. x sepium ALLMAN (*L. vulgaris* x *L. repens*)　**N,C**　Rare

VC11: Barton Common 2492, *KK* 1977; Browndown 5899, Hb.AWW 1957, 1960; Windmill Hill, Clanfield 7116, Hb.AWW 1963. **VC12**: Recorded on the disused Winchester–Newbury railway cuttings 4833–4650 during 1967–72, but not reported since the habitat became over-grown and partly destroyed.

L. purpurea (L.) MILL.　Purple Toadflax.　**H,C**　Locally frequent

First record, F. I. Warner *c.*1860, old walls in Symonds Street, Winchester 4829, VC11 (*Fl.Hants*, p.273).

A garden escape, though there are early records of its being 'sown with the corn' (*loc.cit.*). Usually on walls, waste land or railways. Common around the main urban areas, and increasing. VC11: 55 ☐; VC12: 22 ☐.

VC11: A33 Compton 4624, on chalk banks, *RPB* 1975. **VC12**: Farnborough Airfield 8654, *ARGM* 1978.

L. repens (L.) MILL.　Pale Toadflax. **N,H**　Very local　Map 312

First record, T. Yalden *c.*1770, 'about 2 miles from Southampton, in the hedge of a common, on the right hand of the turnpike or road going from Southampton to Rumsey', VC11 (*Ray Syn.MS*, p.282).

On bare chalk or sand, on maritime shingle amongst bushes, on dry hedge-banks or roadsides. It still occurs along the coast, around Marchwood and the E Solent, and on Hayling Island; it is now commonest around Gilkicker Point 6097, VC11, *MB* 1976, *EAP* 1983. For many years it was abundant on the chalk cuttings of the Winchester–Newbury railway and, although this is largely overgrown and has been partly incorporated with the A34, it still exists in open spots of the disused railway, *PB* 1992; also in places on the A34 verges, e.g. at 4651, VC12, *AB* 1986.

VC11: Morestead Down, on bare chalk 5026, *WGH* 1981; Old Winchester Hill 6420, border of arable field and disturbed chalk-grassland, *RPB* 1987. **VC12**: Woolmer Forest 7832, on bare sand, *PLeB* 1973.

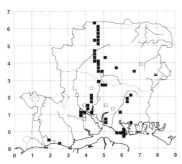

Map 312 Linaria repens

Digitalis purpurea L. Foxglove. **N** Locally abundant

In open woods, where it is often abundant in clearings; in hedgebanks, bushy heaths, sand- and gravel-pits. Very common on all acid soil; local on superficial soils over the chalk, and on the slightly basic Malmstone.

Erinus alpinus L. Fairy Foxglove. **H** Very rare

First record, N. E. G. Cruttwell 1941, 'up the side of a house', Lasham 6742, VC12 (*Rep.B.E.C.* for 1941–42, p.498), *EAB* 1957.

An alien which people delight in sowing on old walls.

VC11: Hale House, Hale 1718, flowers white, *JO* 1986; Lyndhurst car-park 2908, on old wall, *RCS* 1981. **VC12**: Hurstbourne Tarrant 3852, flint wall, *WMK* 1969, *GDF* 1970.

Veronica serpyllifolia L. ssp. **serpyllifolia** Thyme-leaved Speed-

well. **N** Frequent and locally common

Short grassland in pastures, on lawns, woodland clearings and damp rides; damp, bare soil in pits and verges.

V. officinalis L. Heath Speedwell. **N** Frequent and locally common

In open, acidic woods, dry grassy banks and tracks on heaths; on superficial soils and leached areas over the chalk, both on the downs and in woodland.

V. chamaedrys L. Germander Speedwell. **N** Very common

Open woods, copses, hedgebanks, verges, and in coarse grassland everywhere.

V. montana L. Wood Speedwell. **N** Locally common

Generally characteristic of ancient woodland and, if in the open, may be a relic of this. Very common on the Malmstone hangers, but scarce on the NW chalk where woods are few. A persistent weed in flower-beds, 36 St Mary's Road, Liss 7728, VC12, *FR* to 1994.

V. scutellata L. Marsh Speedwell. **N** Locally common Map 313

First record, Miss G. E. Kilderbee 1848, Bisterne Common, VC11 (*Fl.Hants*, p.281).

Pond-margins, wet, grassy hollows and ditches on heaths, boggy pastures and marshes; almost always on acid soil. Common in the New Forest, more local on other Tertiary soils in the SW, Forest of Bere and Thames Basin, and in Woolmer Forest.

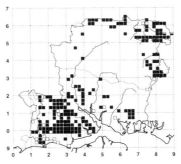

Map 313 Veronica scutellata

var. **villosa** SCHUMACH. Underrecorded?

VC11: Crockford Bridge 3598, *LWF*

n.d., det. *FHP*. **VC12**: Heckfield *c.*7260, *VEM* 1921, Hb.RDG; Bartley Heath 7252, *AJPB* 1986; marshy field near Liphook, *ECW* 1938, Hb.BM; Foxlease meadows 8257, plentiful, *CRH* 1991. Also 8052, 8254, 8452.

V. beccabunga L. Brooklime. **N** Locally common

In streams, ponds, ditches, marshy meadows, and wet gravel-pits. Common, except in very acid waters.

V. anagallis-aquatica L. Blue Water-speedwell. **N** Rare

In small streams, usually those rising from the chalk; now probably rare.

The pure strain has been seen only in the following sites: **VC8**: Allen River 0719, 0818, Hb.AB 1979. **VC11**: Near Ashurst Bridge 3312, *RMV* 1990, Hb.AB; Bedhampton 7006, Hb.RPB 1990; streams at Langstone 7105, Warblington 7305 and Emsworth 7506, 1982; Warnford Lake 6222, 1983; Cheriton, source of R. Itchen 5827, Hb.AB 1975. **VC12**: R. Enborne 4863, 5063, 1976; Tichborne 5731, 1978; Truncheants Stream 7237, 1965; R. Hart 7755, 1978; R. Wey 8144, 1965; all *AB*. Selborne 7232, *SP* 1982; stream running into Wallop Brook 2938, *RMV* 1988–89. Also 6852, 7050. Elsewhere in Hants it seems to have been quite ousted by the robust hybrid with *V. catenata*.

V. x lackschewitzii J. B. KELLER (*V. anagallis-aquatica* x *V. catenata*) **N** Locally abundant Map 314

First record, E. F. Linton 1893, Sopley, VC11, Hb.BM, det. *EBBa*.

This is now the usual water speedwell in all the larger rivers of Hants, and their tributaries; in shallow ponds and drains in water-meadows. It occurs in all basic waters, and has become a

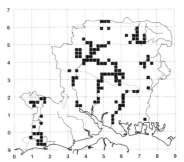

Map 314 Veronica x lackschewitzii

rampant weed which is subject to control. Some back-crosses are at least partially fertile (*Exper.taxonomy Veronica*).

V. catenata PENNELL Pink Water-speedwell. **N** Very local Map 315

First record, Miss C. E. Palmer 1893, Odiham Common, VC12, in dry ditch, Hb.BM, det. *JHB*.

In shallow, muddy ponds and ditches on the clay; silt and shingle on margins of slow-flowing streams and rivers, in basic to mildly-acid waters; salt-marshes. Widespread, but frequent only in the Avon Valley and less so in the Lower Test, rare elsewhere.

VC11: South Charford 1618, muddy stream, *RPB* 1966; mouth of Wallington River 5806, on mud under bypass, *AB* 1978; Haskell's Pond, Kingston North Common 1402, *RPB* 1984; Wick 1591, waterside of large dyke, *JOM* 1970. **VC12**: Farringdon meadows 7235, in small pond, *AB* 1976; R. Wey 8044, *AB* 1976, Broad Oak 7552, in small pond, *AB* 1977.

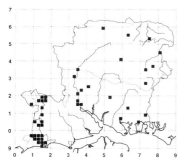
Map 315 Veronica catenata

V. arvensis L. Wall Speedwell. **N,C** Common

On walls and masonry, in short turf on dry banks, on dunes and shingle; on bare sandy soil, and in arable.

V. agrestis L. Green Field-speedwell. **C** Occasional Map 316

First record, Miss C. R. May 1835, kitchen-garden, Breamore Rectory, VC11 (*May Ptgs Cat*. no.623).

In arable fields and gardens, mostly on sandy soil. Rather uncommon in the NE and SW; not much recorded elsewhere.

VC11: Milford on Sea 2991, garden weed, *RMB* 1979; East Wellow 3018, in garden, *RMV* 1985, Hb.RPB; flower-bed behind Burley Manor 2103,

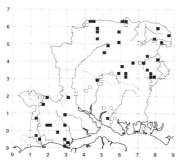
Map 316 Veronica agrestis

EAP 1987; Titchfield Common 5206, allotment, *RMV* 1988, Hb.RPB. **VC12**: Alton 7238, old allotments, *JLSL* 1978; Silchester Common 6262, *PB* 1980; old railway between The Chase and A343, 4462, *VF* 1982; Headley 5162, gravel-workings, *PB* 1987.

V. polita FR. Grey Field-speedwell. **C** Locally frequent Map 317

An arable weed, not uncommon on the chalk, but much more scarce away from it.

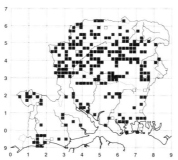
Map 317 Veronica polita

V. persica POIR. Common Field-speedwell. **C** Common

Cultivated and disturbed waste-ground, bare verges. Townsend observes: 'This species, now so generally distributed throughout the country, was first introduced about 1820. It is a native of Eastern Europe and Central Asia'. (*Fl.Hants*, p.278, as *V. buxbaumii* Ten.).

V. filiformis SM. Slender Speedwell. **H** Frequent

First record, P. M. Hall, N. D. Simpson & E. C. Wallace, 1935, garden outcast, Kingsley, VC12, Hb.BM.

First introduced as a rock-garden plant, it is now widespread and increasing rapidly. Locally common in lawns, verges and churchyards, where regularly mown. Also on grassy riverbanks and revetments.

VC11: Ellingham churchyard 1408, *RPB* 1984. **VC12**: Norris Hill, Fleet 8353, *ARGM* 1979.

V. hederifolia L. Ivy-leaved Speedwell. **N,C**

Cultivated and waste ground, gardens, waysides, hedgebanks, and sides of tracks through woods. No attempt has been made to map the two subspecies.

ssp. **lucorum** (KLETT & RICHT.) HARTL (*V. sublobata* M. A. Fisch.)

Frequent and locally common.

ssp. **hederifolia**

Somewhat less common but may also be widespread and has been noted at: **VC11**: West Tytherley and Broughton *RMV* 1988; Titchfield Abbey 5406, *RPB* 1988. **VC12**: Conford 8232, *AB* 1972, det. *BM*; Yateley 8160, *ARGM* 1987.

V. longifolia L. Long-leaved Speedwell. **H** Very rare

A garden escape.

VC12: Established on top of Waller's Ash Tunnel 4936, *AB* 1968 (*Watsonia* **10**: 427); Norris Hill 8353, *TD* 1979, *ARGM* 1988; Farnborough 8853, roadside, *ARGM* 1980.

<**V. spicata** L. Spiked Speedwell. **N** Extinct (Sched. 8)

Formerly at Bishopstoke, VC11, T. Garnier 1839 (*Fl.Hants*, p.279).

Townsend examined Garnier's specimens in Hb.BM, and stated they belonged to the var. α *genuina* Syme (ssp. *spicata*). Townsend also gives a record by Miss C. M. Yonge: 'Cranbury park (near Otterbourne, about three miles from Bishopstoke; possibly Dean Garnier's station) in dry gravelly soil'. Bromfield thought it probable that *V. officinalis* was mistaken for it at Cranbury Park (*Phytologist* 3: 654). There have been no records since. This was a strange, but apparently correct, record for a strong calcicole of very local occurrence in Britain. Possibly it once occurred (like *Antennaria dioica*) on the formerly extensive chalk grasslands of central Hants, now reduced to fragments.>

V. paniculata L. (*V. spuria* auct., non L.)   **H**   Very rare

VC11: Teglease Down 6520, chalk-pit, Hb.AWW 1961.

<**Melampyrum cristatum** L. Crested Cow-wheat.   **N**   Extinct

Formerly by Netley Abbey, and in woods between Clanfield and East Meon, VC11, 'most abundant' (*Fl. Hants*, p.287). Last record, Stratton, near Micheldever, VC12, 'in considerable plenty', *HPF* 1904 (*loc.cit.*). These Hants records, far from its main range in eastern England, suggest that this species was once much more general on the borders of calcareous woodlands, and that woodland clearance has caused its present extreme restriction.>

<**M. arvense** L.   Field Cow-wheat. **C**   Extinct (Sched. 8)

Formerly a weed of cornfields. There are three old records, the last of which was in a field near Boyes Copse, Owslebury 5022, VC11, *GWP* 1927 (*Suppl.Fl.Hants*, p.78). It is still in the Isle of Wight.>

M. pratense L.   Common Cowwheat.   **N**   Map 318

First record, Gilbert White 1766, Fyfield, VC12, 'in great plenty in all the woods' (*White's Jnls* 1: 206).

ssp. **pratense**   Locally common

In woods, borders of heaths and shady road-banks, generally on acid soil. Fairly common, especially in the New Forest. The map shows both subspecies.

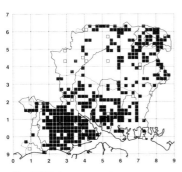

Map 318 Melampyrum pratense

ssp. **commutatum** (TAUSCH ex A. KERN.) C. E. BRITTON   Rare or under-recorded

First record, Miss K. A. Childs 1949,

Ackender Wood, Alton 6938, VC12, Hb.HCMS, det. *FR*. The wood is now coniferized.

Restricted to calcareous woodland.

VC8: Boulsbury Wood 0814, *FR* 1976; Bovis Row, Damerham 0814, *RPB* 1984. VC11: Dundridge 5718, *AJES* 1959; Frenchmoor 2627, Hb.RPB 1975, det. *FR*; SW of Roundhill Farm, Breamore 1317, *RPB* 1976. Also 2432, 3026, 3628, 3630, 5818. VC12: Danebury Hill Wood 3237, *AJES* 1959; Vinney Copse 7345, roadside, Hb.AB 1975, det. *FR* (*Watsonia* 11: 397); formerly at Shrub Hanger, Selborne 7533, *AB c.*1922.

Euphrasia anglica PUGSLEY   Glandular Eyebright.   **N**   Locally frequent   Map 319

Grass-heaths, roadside verges and pastures on acid soil. Common in the New Forest, rare in heathy grassland in the SE, NE, and in Woolmer Forest.

VC11: North Ripley 1700, old pasture, *RPB* 1991; Matley Passage 3307, grassy roadside, *PMH* 1934; Havant Thicket 7109, Hb.AWW 1959, det. *PFY*; Queen Elizabeth Forest 7320, Hb.AWW 1956. VC12: Near Bourley Reservoirs 8249, *GHF* 1981, *CRH* 1991; Ashford Hill meadows 5662, *FR* 1985; Blackmoor golf-course 7734, *AB* 1974; Yateley Heath Wood 8056, abundant in ride, *AB* 1980.

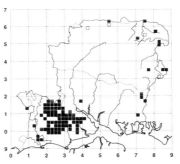

Map 319 Euphrasia anglica

E. x glanduligera WETTST. (*E. anglica* x *E. nemorosa*)   **N**   Very rare

VC11: Matley Passage 3306, Hb.RPB 1978, det. *AJS*.

E. anglica x E. confusa   **N**   Very rare

VC11: Rowbarrow 3504, grass-heath with open bracken, Hb.RPB 1991, det. *AJS*.

E. anglica x E. ?micrantha   **N**

VC11: Denny Bog 3404, Hb.AWW 1959, det. *PFY*.

E. arctica LANGE ex ROSTRUP ssp. **borealis** (F. TOWNS.) YEO (*E. borealis* (F. Towns.) Wettst., *E. brevipila* auct., non Burnat & Gremli ex Gremli)   **N**   Very rare

First record, E. F. Linton 1895, 'Herne', VC11 (as *E. borealis*, conf. *RvW*) (*Fl.Hants*, p.282).

In moist meadows.

VC8: South End, Damerham 1015, Hb.RPB 1977, det. *PFY*. VC11: Common Marsh, Stockbridge 3534, Hb.RPB 1989, det. *AJS*; R. Meon, St Clair's Farm, Soberton 6015, watermeadow (now dry), *EM–R* 1938, Hb.K, det. *PFY*; Holmsley *c.*2200, wet field, *MCFP* 1951, Hb.CGE, det. *PFY*; Lye Heath, Southwick 6408, fen-meadow, Hb.RPB 1985, det. *AJS* (*Watsonia* 17: 192). VC12: Winnall Moors, Winchester 4830, grassy path along stream, Hb.RPB 1985, det. *AJS* (*Watsonia* 17: 476); Bransbury Common 4141, Hb.RPB 1988, det. *AJS* (*Watsonia* 18: 222–223).

E. arctica ssp. **borealis** x **E. nemorosa**   **N**   Very rare

VC11: Common Marsh, Stockbridge 3534, Hb.RPB 1989, det. *AJS*. VC12: Bransbury Common 4141, *FR* 1988, Hb.RPB, det. *AJS* (*Watsonia* 18: 223).

E. tetraquetra (BRÉB.) ARROND. (*E. occidentalis* Wettst.)   Sea-coast Eyebright.   **N**   Very rare

First record, E. F. Linton 1896, Hengistbury Head, VC11, Hb.BM, det. *HWP*.

Cliff-tops and dunes on the coast, or in short turf not far inland.

VC11: Hayling Island, *NDS* 1957, Hb.BM, det. *HWP*, Sinah Common 6999, shingle hollow on golf-links, Hb.AWW 1961, det. *PFY*; Sinah, South Hayling, *PMH* 1936, det. *HWP* (as 'probably this'); Marlborough Deep 2298, *NDS* 1940, conf. *PFY* 1952; Barton on Sea 2492, on golf-course and fields along cliff-top, *PFY* 1951; Hordle Cliff 2692, grassy bank at base of undercliff, Hb.RPB 1990, det. *AJS*; Studland Common, Milford on Sea 2792, Hb.RPB 1989, det. *AJS*; near Ocknell Pond, Stoney Cross old airfield 2312, Hb.RPB 1991, det. *AJS*.

A hybrid, of which *E. confusa* may be the other parent, occurs at Studland Common 2792, and at Ashley, New

Milton 2594, a population is present possibly involving both *E. nemorosa* and *E. micrantha*, Hb.RPB 1989–90, det. *AJS*.

E. tetraquetra x E. nemorosa   N
Very rare

VC11: Hordle Cliff 2692, Hb.RPB 1990, det.*AJS*; Stansore Point 4698, Hb.RPB 1992, det. *AJS*; Sinah Common golf-links 6999, Hb.AWW 1961, det. *PFY* as apparently this hybrid.

E. nemorosa (Pers.) Wallr.
Common Eyebright.   N   Locally very common

Grassland, in pastures, on chalk downs, roadside verges, banks, grassy heaths, woodland rides and in open scrub. Common generally, except on improved agricultural land. Semi-parasitic on grass, as are all other eyebrights.

E. nemorosa x E. pseudokerneri   N   Occasional

Recorded where both parents occur together.
VC8: Martin Down 0418, Hb.RPB 1986, det. *AJS*. **VC11**: Fawley Down 5227, Hb.PFY 1957; North Hayling 7103, chalk bank of disused railway, Hb.RPB 1986, det. *AJS*.

E. nemorosa x E. confusa   N
Very rare

VC11: Ossemsley Ford, Holmsley Station 2300, Hb.RPB 1986, det. *AJS*; Magpie Green, Thorney Hill 2100, grass-heath, Hb.RPB 1987, det. *AJS*; Pennington Common 3095 and Pitts Deep 3795, both Hb.RPB 1990, det. *AJS*.

E. nemorosa x E. micrantha   N
Very local, but under-recorded

VC11: Avon Forest Park, St Leonards 1202, grass-heath by car-park, Hb.RPB 1990; B3056 near Pig Bush 3605, Hb.RPB 1991, det. *AJS*; near Hatchet Pond 3601, on S side, *AJS* 1979; Norleywood 3697, Hb.AJS 1980; Turf Hill 2117, Hb.RPB 1986, det. *AJS*. **VC12**: Blackbushe Airfield, Yateley 8159, on heathland, *FR & CRH* 1988, Hb.RPB, det. *AJS*, 'very close to *E. micrantha*' (*Watsonia* 18: 222).

E. pseudokerneri PUGSLEY   Chalk Eyebright.   N   Very locally frequent
Map 320

First record, W. L. Notcutt 1842, Maindell chalk-pit, near Fareham, VC11, Hb.MANCH (*Bot.J.Linn.Soc.* 48: 515).

In short turf and open scrub on chalk downs, and in chalk-pits. Frequent on Ports Down; very local on other downs, and rare in VC12.
VC8: Martin Down 0518, 0618, *FR* 1978. **VC11**: Paulsgrove 6306, above chalk-pit, Hb.RPB 1986, det. *AJS*; Catherington 6815, Hb.AWW 1951; Beacon Hill, Warnford 6022, abundant, *FR* 1987; Butser Hill 7020, 7220, *FR* 1991. **VC12**: Micheldever Spoil Heaps 5143, on railway banks, *NCC* 1978; Inkpen Hill 3662, Hb.PFY 1974; N of Overton 5151, *FR* 1976; West Down, Chilbolton 3838, *FR* 1972 (*Watsonia* 11: 397).

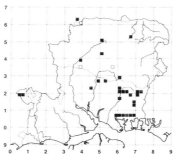

Map 320 Euphrasia pseudokerneri

forma elongata PUGSLEY

VC12: Mapledurwell Fen 6752, *FR* 1976, Hb. AB, det. *PFY* (a specimen from near Hatch 6752, in Hb.AWW 1963 is probably this form, *RPB*).

E. confusa PUGSLEY   N   Rare

First record, J. F. Rayner 1924, Holmsley, VC11, margin of ditch (*Suppl.Fl.Hants* p.78).

On short turf, mainly on the Oligocene marls in the New Forest.
VC11: Roadside near Holmsley Station 2300, *PMH & AJW* 1938, det. *HWP, RPB* 1966; Stoney Cross 2312, old airfield, Hb.RPB 1991, det. *AJS*; Yewtree Bottom 2500, Hb.RPB 1990, det. *AJS*; Pennington Common 3095, *HF* n.d., Hb.RPB 1990, det. *AJS*; Hatchet Pond 3601, *WFB* 1964, det. *PFY*; Marlborough Deep 2298, Hb.RPB 1970, det. *PFY*; Long Slade Bottom 2701, Hb.RPB 1992, det. *AJS*; Beaulieu old airfield 3500, showing some characters of *E. micrantha*, Hb.RPB 1990, det. *AJS*; Milford on Sea 2792, bank in old sand-pit, a popu-

lation hybridized with some other undetermined species, Hb.RPB 1989, det. *AJS*. **VC12**: Near Walkeridge Farm, S of Kingsclere, Hb.NDS n.d.

E. confusa x E. micrantha   N
Very rare

VC11: Furzy Brow 3504, grass-heath, Hb.RPB 1987, det. *AJS*.

E. micrantha RCHB.   Slender Heatheyebright.   N   Rare   Map 321

First record, H. C. Watson 1875, near Fleet Pond, VC12 (*Fl.Hants*, p.283, as *E. gracilis* Fr.).

Heaths and roadside verges amongst heather, in short turf on clay, or on bare sand. Very local in the New Forest; three other scattered sites, two of them old. A. J. Silverside considers the New Forest populations to be much hybridized with *E. nemorosa*.
VC11: Crockford Bridge 3599, old marl-pits, Hb.RPB 1957, *FR* 1982; Holmsley Ridge 2100, levelled gravel-pit, Hb.RPB 1987; Clay Hill, Burley 2302, *JO* 1988, Hb.RPB; Beaulieu old airfield 3500, Hb.RPB 1990, det. *AJS*; Sinah, South Hayling, *PMH* 1936, det. *HWP, AWW* 1950. **VC12**: Longmoor airstrip 8031, *FR* 1979, Hb.AB (*Watsonia* 13: 337).

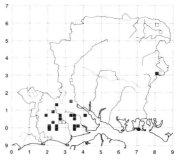

Map 321 Euphrasia micrantha

[**E. scottica** WETTST.

Three VC11 records in *Suppl.Fl.Hants* (p.78) are errors for either *E. micrantha* or a slender form of *E. nemorosa*.]

Odontites vernus (BELLARDI) DUMORT.   Red Bartsia.

First record, Miss C. R. May 1835, Breamore Marsh *c.*1518, VC11 (*May Ptgs Cat.* no.627).

Grassy waste-ground, arable fields, tracks, verges, woodland rides, pits; especially on the chalk.

ssp. **vernus** **N,C** Occasional

Mainly restricted to cornfields on the central and northern chalk, where it is quite frequent; in a few scattered sites elsewhere.

VC11: Near R. Avon, Breamore Mill 1617, Hb.RPB 1981; First Sea Lord Plantation, Lee 3617, Hb.RPB 1980. **VC12**: Thruxton 2844, *RPB* 1968; N of Micheldever Station 5144, *RPB* 1968.

ssp. **serotinus** (SYME) CORB. **N,C** Frequent and locally common

Common, almost throughout the whole range of habitats.

Parentucellia viscosa (L.) CARUEL Yellow Bartsia. **N,C** Very local and rare Map 322

Damp, acid, sandy hollows where water stands in winter, moist pastures and edges of bogs, airfields constructed on drained bogs, floors of gravel-pits; often near the coast, but there are inland sites in the New Forest, at Ampfield, and in the Woolmer Forest and Aldershot areas. The populations tend to wax and wane.

VC11: Stanswood 4600, 4601, locally plentiful, *RPB* 1984–90; Holmsley Ridge 2100, flood hollows on levelled gravel-pit, plentiful, *RPB* 1987; Stoney Cross 2412, 2512, flushed turf and bog near old road, *RPB & FR* 1975–87; Ampfield Wood 3924, grassy ride, *KC* 1978; Chilling-Hook 5104, disused gravel-pit, *PS* 1991. **VC12**: Longmoor airstrip 8031, *MS-W & JLSL* 1974 (*Watsonia* **10**: 428), *FR* 1991; Farnborough Airfield 8452, 8453, 8454, *ARGM* 1975–88, formerly plentiful, now scarce; Bramshill Plantation 7561, *CRH* 1986, since lost.

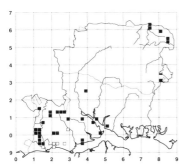

Map 322 Parentucellia viscosa

<Rhinanthus angustifolius C. C. GMELIN (*R. serotinus* (Schönh.)

Oborny) Great Yellow-rattle. **C** Extinct (Sched. 8)

Formerly in cornfields on the downs near Grateley, VC12, W. Hussey 1890; so abundant it was said to kill the crops, and had been known there many years previously (*Fl.Hants*, pp.286–287). The only record since is from Silchester, VC12, Miss F. Davidson 1906 (*Suppl.Fl.Hants*, p.78, as *R. major* Ehrh.>

R. minor L. Yellow-rattle. **N** Locally common

In grassy places on basic soil. Semi-parasitic on the grass so farmers control it. Widespread, and fairly common on the chalk, locally frequent elsewhere, but has declined due to grassland improvement. In addition to ssp. *minor* of old meadows, chalk-grassland plants have been separately defined as ssp. *calcareus* (Wilmott) E. F. Warb., and those of damp grassland and fens as ssp. *stenophyllus* (Schur) O. Schwarz. All three are recorded in the county, but they can intergrade and, pending a detailed study, it is not considered possible to distinguish them. Some botanists we know sow the seed thickly in their lawns, as the resultant growth of the plant reduces the need for frequent mowing.

Pedicularis palustris L. Marsh Lousewort, Red-rattle. **N** Local Map 323

First record, Gilbert White 1766, Selborne, VC12 (*White's Jnls* **1**: 197).

In peat valley-bogs, calcareous mires, edges of ponds, fens and marshy meadows; widespread; fairly common in the New Forest, very local in other Tertiary areas, and increasingly rare in alluvial wetlands, due to drainage or spread of scrub.

VC8: Lopshill Common 0913, one

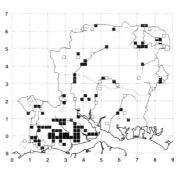

Map 323 Pedicularis palustris

plant in small bog, *RPB* 1989. **VC11**: Rockbourne 1216, fen-meadow, *RPB* 1979; R Test, Nursling 3615, marshy meadow, *RPB* 1953, no record since; Lye Heath 6408, Hb.AWW 1960, *FR* 1990. **VC12**: Chilbolton meadows 3940, *FR* 1984; Bransbury Common 4141, *FR* 1988; Easton *c*.5032, *AH* 1975; Stockbridge North Fen 3535, abundant, *FR* 1990; Ashford Hill meadows 5662, *PB* 1983; Greywell 7151, *FR* 1994; Fleet Pond 8254, *CRH* 1987; Hillside Farm, Odiham 7550, *CRH* 1988.

P. sylvatica L. ssp. **sylvatica** Lousewort. **N** Locally common Map 324

First record, Gilbert White 1768, Selborne, VC12 (*White's Jnls* **1**: 235).

On damp heaths, heathy pastures, and open plantation-rides. Common in the New Forest and Woolmer Forest and on the NE Tertiaries; rare on chalk superficials.

VC8: Lopshill Common 0913, *HWTi c*.1956 (*Fl.Wilts*, p.441), *HCC* 1986. **VC11**: Hengistbury Head 1690, *MPY c*.1960; Browndown 5899, *AWW* 1952; Sandy Point, Hayling Island 7498, *AB, EAP & FR*, 1980. **VC12**: Bransbury Common 4141, 4142, *FR* 1986; SE of Hurstbourne Tarrant *c*.3850, *GDF* 1983; Chawton Park Wood 6735, *AAB* 1981; Odiham Common 7451, *CRH* 1986; Woolmer Forest 7829, white-flowered form common, *FR* 1987.

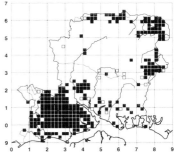

Map 324 Pedicularis sylvatica ssp. sylvatica

OROBANCHACEAE

Lathraea squamaria L. Toothwort. **N** Locally frequent Map 325

First record, Gilbert White 1772, Selborne, VC12 (*White's Jnls* **1**: 404).

In old woods and copses on the chalk and Malmstone; parasitic most often on *Corylus*, but also on *Acer*, *Ulmus*, *Tilia* and *Prunus laurocerasus*. Fairly frequent on chalk in the SE and N, and in the Wealden Edge woods; rare elsewhere.

VC11: Lowton's Copse, Clanfield 7018, *JRWH* 1987; near Hale Church 1718, on *P. laurocerasus*, *FEWV* 1961, *JO & RPB* 1987; near Owslebury 5022, side of bridleway, *RMV* 1987. **VC12**: Thornycombe Wood, Vernham Dean 3355, *APNH* 1980; Bradley Wood 6441, *ANHS* 1987; Payne's Peak Copse, Bramshill Park 7558, *MN* 1985; Gravelly Wood 7746, *CRH* 1988. Not seen for at least ten years in Gilbert White's locality at Dorton, Selborne 7433, *FR* 1994.

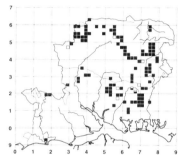

Map 325 Lathraea squamaria

L. clandestina L.   Purple Toothwort.   **H**   Very rare

First record, D. Smith 1958/59, Monks Brook, N of Swaythling 4416, VC11, comm. *DPJS* 1992, refound growing on *Salix fragilis* and *Alnus* over *c*.65m, *JE* 1982, comm. *KW* (*Rep.S'ton N.H.S.* p.17), extending to *c*.210m, *RPB, DS & DPJS* 1992.

Originating from nurseries, whence it has been introduced on planted *Salix* and *Populus* spp., as a root parasite. **VC11**: Chapel Lane, Timsbury 3425, edge of garden pond, introduced on roots of shrubs from nursery, *AJRa* 1989; Ampfield *c*.3923, *AO* 1975; Chandler's Ford *c*.4421, banks of garden stream close to nursery, *RED* 1961, comm. *FEWV* (*Rep.S'ton N.H.S.*, p.2). **VC12**: Near New Mill, Eversley 7662, on roots of *Salix* from a garden, *EHa* 1963; Newtown Gully 4763, *CL* 1963, *NFC* 1981; by R. Enborne 5063, *PB* 1988; Kingsclere 5259, on *Populus*, *RC* 1993.

Orobanche purpurea JACQ.   Yarrow Broomrape.   **N**   Very rare

First record, D. Marryat 1903, Shed-field *c*.5513, VC11, Hb.OXF (*Rep.B.E.C.* for 1924, p.664). There is a much earlier record, possibly this species, by J. Goodyer 1621,'*Nidus avis flore & caule violaceo purpureo colore* [Bird's nest with flower and stalk violet-purple in colour]...This I found wilde in the border of a field called Marborne, neere Habridge [Haw Bridge] in Haliborne [Holybourne]' *c*.7441, VC12 (*Ger.em.Johns.*, p. 228).

Parasitic on *Achillea millefolium*.
VC12: Stoke, St Mary Bourne 4051, nine spikes in a paddock, *PJC* 1976 Hb.AB, det. *AB* (*Watsonia* **12**: 174), *GDF* 1984, 32 spikes, *PB* 1991.

O. rapum-genistae THUILL. Greater Broomrape.   **N**   Rare   Map 326

Parasitic on *Ulex* and *Cytisus*. Greatly decreased, and now centred chiefly around the New Forest. In most sites it seems to be spasmodic and transient in its appearance.

VC11: Exbury 4201, *RPB* 1962; Otterwood 4101, *RBG* 1984; Dibden Bay 4108, *TWO* 1976; North Gate, Beaulieu 3804, *MR* 1975; Chilworth Common 4017, *DEA* 1975; Mockbeggar 1609, in old gravel-pit, *RPB* 1986, 280 spikes, *RPB* 1992, 430 spikes, *RPB* 1994 ; West Wood, Netley 4509, two dead stems on dying *Cytisus*, *PAB* 1986. **VC12**: Medstead 6436, *AWW* 1963, not seen since; Silchester Common 6262, *PB* 1987 (*Watsonia* **18**: 223); Ashford Hill meadows 5662, *PB* 1988.

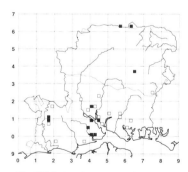

Map 326 Orobanche rapum-genistae

O. elatior SUTTON   Knapweed Broomrape.   **N**   Locally common Map 327

Parasitic on *Centaurea*, generally *C. scabiosa*, in rank chalk-grassland, on downs, banks, verges, open scrub and edges of arable fields; almost confined to the chalk, and commonest in the W.

VC11: Near Moorcourt 3517, *RPB* 1962; Fort Widley 6506, *EAP* 1982. **VC12**: Nether Wallop 2834, *RMV* 1988; Rookery Dell, Monk Sherborne 6056, *PB* 1982; Noar Hill 7331, *AB & FR* 1970–94.

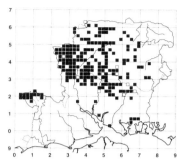

Map 327 Orobanche elatior

<O. alba STEPHAN EX WILLD. Thyme Broomrape.   **N**   Extinct

Parasitic on *Thymus*.
VC11: Crab Wood, Winchester *c*.4329, H T Baker 1934, det. *WHP* (*Rep.B.E.C.* for 1934, p.835, as *O. rubra* Sm.). P. M. Hall states (*Proc. Hants Fld Club* **15**: 69), 'the identification is not accepted in the absence of a voucher specimen, and the record is therefore excluded.' **VC12**: In 1963, Mrs J. Goater and B. Goater found two specimens near Micheldever Spoil Heaps, which they did not collect. However, they took such careful notes that *RPB* and *FR* accepted their record. The site was ploughed a few years later.**>**

O. hederae DUBY   Ivy Broomrape. **N,H?**   Very rare

First record, N. E. G. Cruttwell *c*.1940–45, Winchester, VC11/12 (*Fl. Bas.MS*, p.11).

Parasitic on *Hedera*. On or near the coast, mostly found on *H. helix* ssp. *hibernica* (Atlantic ivy). Inland, all records of *O. hederae* for which the host plant has been identified were on the cultivar *Hedera* 'Hibernica' (Irish ivy), which is commonly planted and naturalized.

VC11: B3054 Walhampton 3395, verge outside garden wall, *MBec* 1989, comm. *AEB*, det. *FJR* (on Atlantic ivy, det. *AB*); Lord's Hill, Southampton 3816, on planted ivy in school quadrangle, *PAB* 1986; Netley Castle 4508, on forecourt, *PS* 1991; opposite Wolvesey Palace, Winchester 4829, on old city-wall, *EAP* 1993. **VC12**: O.

hederae was seen in tetrad 4836, *JGD* 1968, and tetrad 6036, *RHJ* 1969, but the colour was not recorded.

forma **monochroma** BECK (entirely yellow)

VC11: Gardens in Winchester 4829, *AB* 1988, Hb.RPB, det. *DJHa* (*Watsonia* 17: 476); Middle Road, Winchester 4729, *DEA* 1992, comm. *AB*, Hb.RPB. **VC12**: Garden of Police House, Alresford 5832, *AAB* 1979, det. *FJR* (*Watsonia* 18: 223), again in 1991; Jacklyns Lane, Alresford 5832, *AAB* 1989; Old Alresford 5934, roadside, *ENi* 1989 (*Watsonia* 18: 429); Liss 7728, one plant in garden, *FR c*.1980.

The inland records of f. *monochroma* are all centred on Winchester and Alresford so it may have spread from some nursery, or it may be a wild flavistic form.

O. minor SM. Common Broomrape. **N,C** Locally frequent and occasional

Parasitic on various plants, notably legumes, also composites and even on some garden plants; in rough grassland, especially on chalk and gravelly soils, roadside banks and verges and in clover leys. More common and widespread than *O. elatior*; more frequent in the W than in the E.

var. **minor** and var. **compositarum** PUGSLEY are both recorded.

Orobanche sp. on *Eryngium maritimum*

Originally identified as *O. maritima* Pugsley from Sinah Common dunes 6899, a few plants on sea holly, *FR* 1951. There are no records since, and the dunes at this point have partly been eroded. *Eryngium* is now again locally abundant (1994) but the *Orobanche* was not seen in 1993 or 1994, *FR*. Another *Orobanche* found on *Eryngium* in 1859 at St Helens Duver, IoW – some 11km across Spithead – was recorded as *O. amethystea* Thuill, but was later declared by Pugsley to be *O. minor* Sm. (*Suppl.Fl.Hants*, p.79). Plants on this host in Kent were also recorded as *O. amethystea* (*Atlas Kent Fl.*, p.129). Unless or until it reappears, it seems best to leave this plant unnamed.

LENTIBULARIACEAE

Pinguicula lusitanica L. Pale Butterwort. **N** Locally frequent Map 328

In bogs, or the drainage ditches of former bogs; on flushed-clay heath and exposed, wet peat. Frequent and often plentiful in the New Forest, on both acid peat and peat over calcareous marl; very rare elsewhere.

VC8: Lopshill Common 0913, *HWTi c*.1956 (*Fl.Wilts*, p.447), *RPB* 1989. **VC11**: Hengistbury Head 1790, *LW* 1982; Dark Water, Lepe 4599, *RPB* 1984. Probably now gone, due to scrub encroachment, from both Gomer Pond fen 5899, *MB* 1976, and The Frenches 3022, *RPB* 1963, not seen 1974. Formerly extending into the Forest of Bere. **VC12**: Eelmoor Marsh, Laffan's Plain (now Farnborough Airfield), *GMG* 1919, *GARW* 1935 (*Watts MSS*), refound *ARGM* 1975 throughout ditch-system 8353, 8453, numbers reduced by 1988, but thousands again following ditch-maintenance, *ARGM* 1990–94.

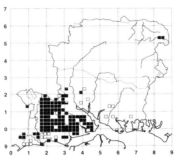

Map 328 Pinguicula lusitanica

P. vulgaris L. Common Butterwort. **N** Very rare Map 329

First records, T. Johnson 1633, 'groweth also in Hampshire' (*Ger.em. Johns.*, p.789), and 1634, 'in a bogge about the middle way between Sarisbury and Southampton', VC11 (*Merc. Bot.*, p.59).

In spongy turf in calcareous fen-meadows and boggy heaths, always in basic flushes.

VC11: Acres Down 2708, *AEB* 1984 (*Watsonia* 16: 191), plentiful *RPB* 1991, *FR* 1994. **VC12**: Laffan's Plain, Farnborough, *GMG* 1937, *HFC* visit, and 'peaty water cuts at W edge of Laffan's Plain', *GARW* 1938 (*Watts MSS*), Hb.BM, refound *ARGM* 1975 at Eelmoor Marsh 8353, 8453, plentiful 1989–91; Tichborne Common 5731, *RAB & ECW* 1966, *FR* 1978, *JRC* 1994; Mapledurwell Common, *RSH* 1849, largely destroyed by the M3 road construction but refound in the remaining fragment (now Mapledurwell

Fen) 6752, *PHB* 1967, where a few plants still survive, having been rescued as a result of habitat management by the HWT, *HFG* 1992, *FR* 1994.

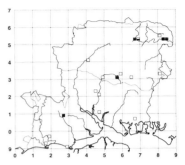

Map 329 Pinguicula vulgaris

[**Utricularia vulgaris** L. Greater Bladderwort.

Greywell *c*.7150, bog-stream, *CP* 1881, Hb.OXF (*Suppl.Fl.Hants*, p. 80). This specimen has now been determined by *PGT* as *U. australis*. No plants referable to this segregate have been found in Hants. All records in *Fl.Hants* (pp.327–328) are considered to be errors for *U. australis*.]

U. australis R. BR. (*U. neglecta* Lehm.) Southern Bladderwort. **N** Rare Map 330

First record, Sir Joseph Hooker 1875, Sopley, VC11 (specimens from this site were sent by the Revd H. M. Wilkinson to Charles Darwin and mentioned in his work on *Insectivorous Plants* (edn 2, p.395) (*Fl.Hants*, p.328)).

Ponds and deep ditches, or slow streams, in basic to slightly acid waters. It has recently invaded the Basingstoke Canal, VC12, in a truly impressive manner. Arriving from Surrey, it reached Ash Lock by 1987 and a colony was established at Aldershot (8752) in 1988. At the same time an introduction into Claycart Flash failed, but plants floated out into the canal and founded a flourishing colony near Claycart Bridge. Since then it has increased apace and, by 1991, had become extremely common from Aldershot (8752) to Eelmoor (8353) and locally dominant at a few sites. By 1992 it had reached Fleet and could then be found in every 1km square from 8052 to the Surrey border. It avoids the deeper water, but thrives in the margins for a metre out from the bank.

It is likely that plant-fragments are caught up on passing motor-cruisers and distributed to other parts of the canal where, in the less-disturbed waters, the drifted plants are able to flourish amongst emergent vegetation. The flowering population fluctuates widely. Not known to flower in the Hants section of the Basingstoke Canal.

VC11: Ponds on edge of Hurn Forest 1000, *RMW* 1985; Coward's Marsh, Christchurch 1594, Hb.AWW 1963; Marlborough Deep 2298, in one small pool, not flowering, Hb.RPB 1957, *AEB* 1985; North Stoneham 4317, *LC* 1964; Itchen Valley, above Mans Bridge 4415, drainage-stream in old water-meadows, *RPB* 1975. **VC12**: Easton Marsh and R. Itchen outside Durrington Mill 4830, *PMH* 1932–33, *AB* 1963 (at Durrington Mill); Short-heath Pond 7736, *AB* 1980, *FR* 1990; Woolmer Forest, in ponds, *AB* 1975; Knox's Pond, Bordon 8034, *CWa* 1983, flowered abundantly 1989; Fleet Pond 8254, in flower, *CWa & ARGM* 1975, *CRH* 1991; Greywell *c*.7150, bog-stream, *CP* 1881, Hb.OXF, det. *PGT*.

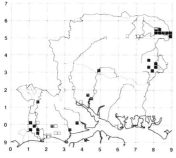

Map 330 Utricularia australis

U. intermedia HAYNE   Intermediate Bladderwort.   **N**   Very rare

Choked streams and pools in valley bogs, in very acid water; very seldom flowering in Hants.

VC11: Bog by railway near Beaulieu Road Station, Hb.AWW 1963 (specimen with flowers). Now confined to Shatterford Bottom 3405, 3406 and Denny Bog 3504 in the New Forest, *RPB* 1970–71. Although locally plentiful in parts of Denny Bog, it was estimated that about 40 per cent of the plants had been lost during previous Forestry Commission drainage (*Rep.S'ton N.H.S.*, p.9). A pool at Woodfidley Passage 3405, where it had been known since 1950, was drained at the same time, and it has not been

reported there since. Formerly at Miller's Pond, Sholing 4510, *FIW* 1873 (*J.Bot.* **11**: 274), pond filled in *c*.1966.

U. minor L.   Lesser Bladderwort.   **N**   Very locally frequent   Map 331

In the pools and choked drains of bogs; in flushed bogs, both acid and basic, and in canals. Confined to a few sites in the NE, and the New Forest, where it is locally frequent, especially in the S.

VC8: Furzley Common 2815, *FR* 1983. **VC11**: Ebblake, Ringwood Forest 1006, plentiful in bog-pools, *RPB* 1985; Upper Crockford Bottom 3499, *EAP* 1983; flush, Acres Down 2708, *FR* 1993. **VC12**: Fleet Pond 8254, *CWa & ARGM* 1975, *CRH* 1984–91; Farnborough Airfield, ditch on Eelmoor Marsh 8453, *ARGM* 1975–88; Basingstoke Canal at Puckridge 8452, *CRH* 1986, not since.

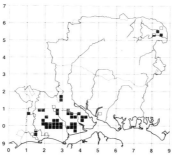

Map 331 Utricularia minor

CAMPANULACEAE

Campanula patula L.   Spreading Bellflower.   **N**   Very rare

First record, J. Goodyer, before 1664, 'In the pastures & hedgesides on the North-west of the Moor not far from the great bog neer Petersfield', VC11 (*Merr.Pin.*, p.103). This record is incorrectly given under *C. rapunculus* in *Fl.Hants* (p.245).

Gravelly or sandy pastures, banks and coppiced hedges. It may re-emerge after suitable conservation management. There are a number of records in *Fl.Hants* (pp.245–246) (although three of these almost certainly refer to *C. rapunculus* (*q.v.*)), and at the time of writing one hesitates to call it 'extinct', although it has made only two recent appearances, each of one year only, both in VC12. These are: Lawren's Lodge, Standford 8134, edge of lawn (once within Woolmer Forest), *P.Si*

1979, det. *FR* (*Watsonia* **13**: 338); lane behind St Mary's Church, Liss 7727, *RL* 1982. Formerly well known at Pinns Farm, Wellow 2920, VC8, *GWP* 1931 (*Proc.Hants Fld Club* **12**: 82), where there is a very suitable hedge-bank that might reveal it one day. An old record not in *Fl.Hants* is: Densham Wood, New Forest [probably Densome Wood, Woodgreen 1717 or 1817, VC11], *CRM* 1834 (*May Ptgs Cat.*, no.511). Still persistent in W Sussex E of Rogate, *FR* 1993.

C. rapunculus L.   Rampion Bellflower.   **D**   Very rare

Grassy verges and disturbed, gravelly soil. Doubtless originating from the former cultivation of its swollen roots as a winter salad. Goodyer's record in *Fl.Hants* (p.245) is an error for *C. patula* (*q.v.*); likewise that for *C. patula* at Nursling, and also those for Avon Tyrrell and near Sopley, must surely refer to this species.

Now persists in only two areas: **VC11**: B3347 Avon 1497, verges and road-banks, *JO & RPB* 1987, 1498, 1597, *RPB* 1993; Nursling gravel-pit 3515, 3516, *RPB* 1953–93; Test Lane, Nursling 3614, bank by new road, *RPB* 1979, transient.

C. persicifolia L.   Peach-leaved Bellflower.   **H**   Rare

First record, Lady Anne Brewis 1975, ruins of Bishop's Palace, Bishop's Waltham 5517, VC11.

VC11: Beaulieu old airfield 3500, white-flowered, under bramble, *RPB* 1990, conf. *EJC*. Also 1296, 2492, 7420. **VC12**: Combe 3660, grassy bank by church, *AB* 1976. Also 6846, 7238, 8030, 8058.

C. medium L.   Canterbury-bells.   **H**   Very rare

First record, J. F. Rayner 1924, Beaulieu Abbey 3802, VC11, old walls (*Proc.IoW N.H.S.* **1**: 256), still there, *EH* 1960, *RPB* 1983.

VC11: Bransgore 1896, *MPY* 1966.

<C. alliariifolia WILLD.   Cornish Bellflower.   **H**   Extinct

VC12: Sown by somebody along the old Bentley–Bordon railway, at Kingsley 7838, *AB* 1965–68 (*Watsonia* **10**: 428). It was destroyed when the railway was demolished.>

C. glomerata L.   Clustered Bellflower.   **N**   Locally frequent   Map 332

First record, Gilbert White 1765, 'in the lane leading to the North-field', Selborne, VC12 (*White's Jnls* 1: 166).

In open, chalk grassland on the downs, on banks and in old chalk-pits. Widespread, but diminishing through lack of grazing.

VC11: Hazeley Down 5025, *RPB* 1984; Butser Hill 7120, abundant, *FR* 1991. **VC12**: Ibthorpe 3653, woodland ride, *GDF* 1984; West Down, Chilbolton 3839, *RPB* 1992.

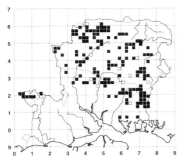

Map 332 Campanula glomerata

C. latifolia L.   Giant Bellflower.   **H** Very rare

First record, Miss W. F. Buckle 1966, Pilgrim's School, Winchester 4829, VC11, waste ground near stream. (There is an earlier record in *Suppl.Fl. Hants* (p.66) for Chestnut Grove, Steep, but this was probably a private house).

VC11: Testwood 3614, established on shady bank of stream near R. Test, *RPB* 1980, 1991, det. *EJC*. Alien in Hants, but still present and probably native as near to Hants as Braydon Forest in N Wilts, *FR*.

C. trachelium L.   Nettle-leaved Bellflower.   **N**   Locally common Map 333

First record, Gilbert White 1765, 'in

the lane leading to the North-field', Selborne, VC12 (*White's Jnls* 1: 166).

In woodland rides and clearings, wooded lanes and old hedgerows. Nearly always on the chalk, apart from a few sites on Malmstone.

VC11: Crab Wood 4329, *RMV* 1986.

C. rapunculoides L.   Creeping Bellflower.   **H**   Rare

A persistent garden-escape, with creeping roots. Borders of cornfields, roadsides and hedgerows. Very scattered and rather rare, though slightly more frequent around Broughton. VC11: 12 □; VC12: 12 □.

VC11: Holmsley, roadside outside keeper's lodge 2299, *JFR* 1918 (*Suppl. Fl.Hants*, p.66), *RPB* 1950; Houghton Drayton 3332, *RPB* 1965, 3331, 3332, border of field and tree-belt, abundant, *SNHS* 1992; two roadsides, Broughton 3133 and 3034, *RPB* 1968; Round Hat, Buckholt, near edge of copse 2732, *RMV* 1987. **VC12**: Freefolk Wood 5044, roadside, *JLSL* 1978; Appleshaw 2948, cornfield near railway, *RPB* 1968.

C. rotundifolia L.   Harebell.   **N** Locally common

On dry soils, i.e. chalk, gravel and sand; on downland, heathland, dry, heathy pastures, in open bracken, and on roadside verges. Widespread and fairly common, but generally absent from the clay.

Legousia hybrida (L.) DELARBRE Venus's-looking-glass.   **C**   Locally frequent   Map 334

In corn- and other arable fields on the chalk. Much declined since the advent of crop-spraying, but still one of the commoner chalk weeds. Rarely, on basic sandy or gravelly soil.

VC11: Moyles Court 1508, banks of

new gravel-pit, *AB* 1977; Sherfield English 3023, old sand-pit, *RPB* 1965; Roke Manor Farm, Romsey 3422, *GC* 1987; near Brownwich Pond 5103, border of cornfield, *RPB* 1989. **VC12**: Noar Hill 7431, on arable, *FR* 1982.

L. speculum-veneris (L.) CHAIX Large Venus's-looking-glass.   **C** Very rare

First record, G. W. Willis *c.*1940–1945, cornfield near Wootton St Lawrence, VC12 (*Fl.Bas.MS*, p.8). Originally found 1916, but misidentified (*GWW* ms note).

VC12: Sutton Down [not South Down] Farm 4537, in cornfield, *AB* 1977, det. *FR*; Lower Wootton 5753, on arable, *BMe* 1976, long established here and abundant, *JFi & FR* 1993 (*BSBI News* **66**: 38–39).

Wahlenbergia hederacea (L.) RCHB. Ivy-leaved Bellflower.   **N**   Rare Map 335

First record, W. Graves *c.*1777, Woolmer Forest, VC12 (*Fl.Londin.*, Tab.93).

Boggy grass along stream-banks and adjacent spring-line seepages; wet, grassy glades and open rides of woods. Very locally plentiful in the central New Forest, but concentrated in one main area. Rare in the NE near Aldershot.

VC11: Cadnam Common 2915, *RPB* 1960, *RPB & FR* 1994; Lyndhurst Hill 2807, *FR* 1976; Wood Crates 2608, *FR* 1994; Butts Lawn 2905, *MAS* 1984. Destroyed by M27 at Copythorne Common 3015 and by housing estate at Fernyhurst, Rownhams 3816 (last record *RPB* 1972). **VC12**: Shady bog, Fleet, *NEGC* 1941 (*Rep.B.E.C.* for 1941–42, p.495), beside Gelvert Stream 8254, *CWa & ARGM* 1975, very few left *CRH* 1988; Bourley water-catchment area 8249, 8250, 8350, local on mown ditch-sides,

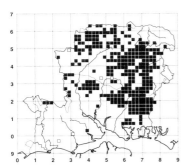

Map 333 Campanula trachelium

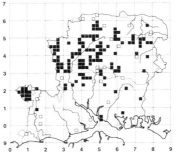

Map 334 Legousia hybrida

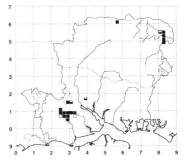

Map 335 Wahlenbergia hederacea

ARGM 1977–88 (*Watsonia* **13**: 338); Ashford Hill 5661, *PB* 1986, not seen since.

Phyteuma orbiculare L. (*P. tenerum* R. Schulz) Round-headed Rampion. **N** Very locally frequent Map 336

First British record, J. Goodyer 1618, Droxford, VC11 (*Early Brit.Bots*, p.111).

On grazed, chalk grassland and open scrub, especially on slopes, banks, earthworks and along tracks; much reduced in places by the ploughing of the downs. It survives best in our downland reserves. Formerly on a continuous diagonal belt of downland, from Leckford 3636, VC12, to Buriton 7419, VC11, with one outlier on the edge of Salisbury Plain, and one on Ports Down. This distribution is similar to that of the butterfly *Lysandra coridon* (Poda) (the chalk hill blue).
VC8: Martin Down 0518, *GMH* 1979, five plants, *PET c.*1988. **VC11**: Lime Kiln Lane, Butser Hill 7120, *MW* 1979, *FR* 1991; Beacon Hill, Warnford 6022, *FR* 1987. **VC12**: Chilbolton Down 4136, *AB* 1968–84.
NOTE. Our British plant and that of N France closely agree with *P. tenerum* R. Schulz and seems distinct from C European *P. orbiculare* L. which has large capitular bracts (F.R.).

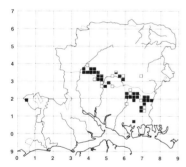

Map 336 Phyteuma orbiculare

Jasione montana L. Sheep's-bit. **N** Locally frequent Map 337

First record, J. Goodyer 1618, 'At Sheete' *c.*7524, VC11/12 (*Early Brit. Bots*, p.110).

Dry, sandy and gravelly heaths, road-banks, verges, disused railways, old pits, coastal dunes. It was formerly locally frequent in the Avon Valley, the NE Tertiary heaths, and Woolmer Forest; however, since the advent of myxomatosis in 1955, it has tended to become overgrown from lack of rabbit-

grazing. Scarce in the New Forest and always in artificial habitats. Locally plentiful in scattered coastal sites.
VC11: Near Burton Common 1995, *RPB* 1951; Mount Pleasant, Sway 2997, *AEB* 1990; Browndown 5799, *RPB* 1973; Sinah Common 6999, plentiful, *FR* 1994. **VC12**: By A325 Greatham 7831, *FR* 1988; Silchester Common 6262, *PB* 1980; roadside verge S of Tweseldown 8251, *CRH* 1984–91; Shortheath 7736, locally plentiful, *FR* 1994.

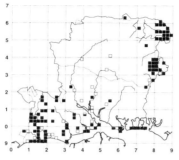

Map 337 Jasione montana

Lobelia urens L. Heath Lobelia. **N** Very rare

First record, J. Vorse 1903 or 1904, Hinton 2095, VC11, ms note comm. to *JFR* describing the discovery of this species by a schoolgirl picking wild flowers – a small patch in an opening amongst the firs, which increased to many hundreds of plants in later years (*Suppl.Fl.Hants*, p.65). Later, it was reported to grow in 'the moist ride of a tall pine wood...only one patch, slowly spreading', but allegedly 'a renowned botanist who once lived within walking distance of the locality introduced it by scattering seed brought from Devonshire' (Winchester Sci. & Lit.Soc. lecture (*Hants Chron.*, 1 Feb. 1913)).

On damp, acid, sandy soil, in grass-heath with bracken, or among planted conifers. The population fluctuates, being encouraged by soil-disturbance and the making of ruts and hollows which hold water. In this respect, *L. urens* is similar to *Radiola linoides*. Following a fire in 1965 which destroyed the conifer plantation, up to 200 plants were seen. In 1988, 260 plants appeared in the open grassland but, in 1989 – a very dry year – only about ten could be found. Following clearance-work by *HFG* during the winter of 1990, however, 120 flowering spikes appeared in 1991, 100 plants, *RPB* 1994. Formerly also found at

Burton Common 1995, *AWW* 1958; Christchurch, waste ground, *ER c.*1925 (*Fl.Bmth. App.2*, p.313), the last rather dubious in such a habitat.

RUBIACEAE

Sherardia arvensis L. Field Madder. **N,C** Locally common

First record, Gilbert White 1765, 'in a wheat field stubble', Selborne, VC12 (*White's Jnls* **1**: 167).

On arable, disturbed and bare soil, or where the vegetation is thin; on disused railway-tracks and old airfields. Widespread and common on the chalk, rather frequent elsewhere, generally where there is a little lime.

Asperula cynanchica L. ssp. **cynanchica** Squinancywort. **N** Locally frequent Map 338

First British record, J. Goodyer 1619, '[in the inclosures of Hampshire] in drie Chalkie grounds abundantly' (*Ger.em. Johns.*, p.1120).

In short turf of dry, chalk grassland, or even on bare chalk, especially on the downs, and the edge of Salisbury Plain. In *Fl.Hants* (p.198) it was considered extremely common in this habitat. Nowadays, many downs have been ploughed, and on some others the lack of grazing has reduced it but it is still plentiful in many sites. Untypical habitats are:
VC11: Stoney Cross old airfield 2412, *GHF* 1989. **VC12**: Bransbury Common 4141, on low, chalk ridge in fen-meadows, *FR* 1986.

It was used as a herb for 'the quinsey'.

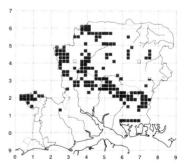

Map 338 Asperula cynanchica ssp. cynanchica

Galium odoratum (L.) Scop. Woodruff. **N** Locally common Map 339

First record, Gilbert White 1765, 'beechen Hanger', Selborne, VC12 (*White's Jnls* **1**: 164).

Woods and copses on base-rich soil. Very common in all wooded areas on the chalk, especially in open beech-woods; local elsewhere, in old woodlands on fertile clay or loam, and rare in the SW and throughout the coastal plain. **VC11**: Bakers Copse, Roydon Woods 3100, *FR* 1980. **VC12**: Aldershot 8551, plentiful in wood beside A325, *TD* 1987; common in woods and by sunken lanes on the Malmstone, *FR* 1994.

In the Middle Ages, this scented plant was strewn on floors.

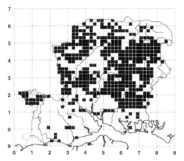

Map 339 Galium odoratum

G. uliginosum L. Fen Bedstraw. **N** Locally frequent Map 340

In fens, marshes, wet meadows, marshy ditches, wet, grassy heaths over Headon Beds. Widespread and frequent in the main valleys and other wetlands on alkaline to mildly-acid peat and clay.

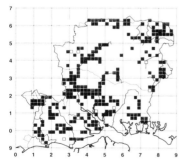

Map 340 Galium uliginosum

G. constrictum CHAUB. (*G. debile* Desv., non Hoffmanns. & Link) Slender Marsh-bedstraw. **N** Very locally frequent Map 341

First records, J. F. Rayner 1924,

Hatchet Pond, det. *GCD* (*Rep.B.E.C.* for 1924, p.438), and near Holmsley Bog; and Miss E. S. Todd 1924, Lyndhurst, VC11 (all *Suppl.Fl.Hants*, pp.xii, 52).

In grassy heaths, wet flood-hollows, drainage-channels, marshy pond-margins, gravel-pits, and muddy track-ruts; chiefly on base-rich clays. It is almost confined to the New Forest but since about 1970 it has spread widely at an accelerating rate to some 50 sites from the three original recorded sites. Overall there is now a large population. **VC11**: Hatchet Pond 3601, still extant *ARW & NIW* 1980; Fulliford Bog 3308, 3408, old stream channel, *NAS* 1987, *RPB* 1994; Bolderford Bridge 2803, in marshy pond W of track, *RPB* 1987.

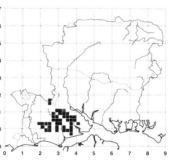

Map 341 Galium constrictum

G. palustre L. Common Marsh-bedstraw. **N** Locally common

First record, P. Collinson 1739, 'In going from Southampton...to Portsmouth after passing the Ferry [VC11]. At the entrance of the common or moor near a great pond...in the rill...among the rushes I found the Elephant Caterpillar [*Deilephila elpenor* L.] feeding on the Water Ladies bedstraw', (MS 323 in Linn.Soc.).

In marshy meadows, fens, stream-sides, ditches, wet grass-heaths and damp rides in woods. Common on the more acid soils, but more restricted in the chalk wetlands, where it is chiefly in the main valleys. It is no longer considered advisable to try to segregate ssp. *palustre* and ssp. *elongatum* (C. Presl) Arcang. unless supported by a chromosome count (*Pl.Crib*, p.91–92).

G. verum L. Lady's Bedstraw. **N** Locally common

Dry grassland on the downs, old pastures, hedgebanks, verges, and on

stabilized dunes in short turf. Common along the coast; very common on the chalk, but rather local on other soils. The few records in very acid areas are probably connected with the lime in concrete used for roads, e.g. Farnborough Airfield 8653, VC12, *ARGM* 1981.

G. x pomeranicum RETZ. (*G. verum* x *G. mollugo*) **N** Very rare

Mainly coastal and usually impersistent.

VC11: Park Shore 4096, *RPB* 1953; Sinah Common golf-links 6999, with parents, Hb.AWW 1950, *EAP & RPB* 1985. Also 4228, 5818, 7498. **VC12**: 6452.

G. mollugo L. ssp. **mollugo** Hedge-bedstraw. **N** Common

In hedges, verges, scrub, borders of woods and grassland; very common on the chalk and most other fertile soils.

ssp. **erectum** SYME (*G. album* Mill.) Upright Hedge-bedstraw. **N,C** Occasional

Very variable (*Pl.Crib*, p.92); not all identifications are now certain, but a large proportion of our records seem to be concentrated on the western chalk. Other records are scattered. J. E. Lousley (*Fl.Surrey*, p.298) states that it is a weed of agricultural seed-mixtures, and that most of the Surrey records are on roadsides. This would tally with two Hants records: A35, Markway Hill 2402, *RPB* 1985, VC11; and B3004, Conford 8232, *AB* 1971, VC12.

VC11: Stanswood Bay 4799, shingle-beach, *FR, RPB & GHF* 1991; Ashlett 4603, Hb.RPB 1986, det. *FR* 1991; Butser Hill 7120, *FR* 1991; Beacon Hill, Warnford 6022, Hb.AWW 1958. **VC12**: Down W of Ashdown Copse 2247, *AB* 1980, det. *FR*; Sidown Hill 4457, *FR, AB & PB* 1981; Button's Brow 7330, *AB* 1964, *FR* 1976–86.

G. pumilum MURRAY Slender Bedstraw. **N** Very rare

First record, Miss W. F. Buckle 1966, Yew Hill, Hursley 4426, VC11, det. *KMG* (*Rep.S'ton N.H.S.*, p.12), *c*.100 plants over a 45m extent at foot of down, Hb.RPB 1975.

In short turf in chalk grassland. **VC12**: Isle of Wight Hill 2437, *PJW* 1991 (*Watsonia* **19**: 150); Ladle Hill, Burghclere 4756, *FR* 1987, Hb.AB (*Watsonia* **17**: 192).

G. saxatile L.   Heath Bedstraw.   **N**
Locally common   Map 342

Dry grass-heath, often in open
bracken, pastures, open woods in rides
and clearings. Common on all acid soils
and occasionally on Clay-with-flints or
other acid deposits on chalk, e.g.:
   VC8: Martin Down 0618, *RMV*
1989. **VC12**: Chawton Park Wood
6736, 6836, *AB* 1976; Micheldever
Wood 5338, *JRw* 1991.

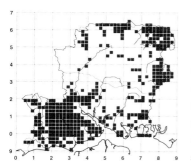

Map 342 Galium saxatile

G. aparine L.   Cleavers.   **N,C**
Abundant

In hedgerows, cultivated and waste
ground, scrub, woodland clearings,
marshes and bare shingle.

<G. tricornutum DANDY   Corn
Cleavers.   **C**   Extinct

Formerly a weed of cornfields and
other arable, mainly on the chalk.
Always rare, it is now thought to be
extinct as a result of changed farming
methods. **VC8**: Whitsbury 1218, *EMH*
1930. **VC12**: Oakley Park 5649, casual
in corn-stubble, *EAB* 1966.>

G. parisiense L.   Wall Bedstraw.
N,C   Very rare

First record, Miss M. McCallum-
Webster & Mrs D. K. Lang 1935, old
wall in Old Basing 6652, VC12 (*Rep.
B.E.C.* for 1935, p.31), still present,
AB 1989.
   On old walls and bare ground;
perhaps native in two sites, introduced
in another.
   VC12: Micheldever Spoil Heaps
5244, *HJMB & JEL* 1956, Hb.BM,
ECW 1957, *CC* 1991; Farnborough
8852, refuse-tip in old gravel-pit, *AB*
1981.

Cruciata laevipes OPIZ (*C. chersonen-
sis* auct., non (Willd.) Ehrend.; *Galium*

cruciata (L.) Scop.)   Crosswort.   **N**
Locally common   Map 343

First record, Gilbert White 1766,
Fyfield, VC12 (*White's Jnls* **1**: 206).
   In hedgebanks, verges, lanes, borders
of woods, rank grassland; on the chalk
and other basic and fertile soils on
farmland. Nevertheless, the distribution map is extraordinary, showing it
to be common only in the SE quarter,
extending to W of Southampton. We
agree with the authors of the Floras of
Sussex, Kent, Surrey and Berkshire
that there is some unexplained factor
here. In Wight it is similarly frequent
only in the E.

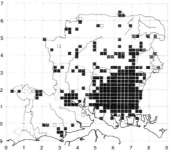

Map 343 Cruciata laevipes

Rubia peregrina L.   Wild Madder.
N   Rare   Map 344

In scrub and hedges on or near the
coast, and in old, overgrown marl-pits
in the southern part of the New Forest.
Locally frequent on wooded shores
between Tanners Lane and Lepe, and
in the Beaulieu River estuary; almost
confined to exposures of the calcareous
Headon Beds.
   VC11: Marlborough Deep 2298,
scrub in old marl-pit, *AEB & SRD*
1978, not seen recently; Hurst Castle

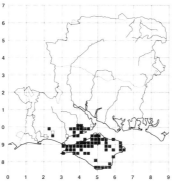

Map 344 Rubia peregrina

3189, at base of steps high up on walls,
AEB 1990;   Crockford Bridge 3598,
RPB 1953, *FR* 1982; Inchmery House,
Lepe 4498, *RPB* 1983.
   D. E. Allen suggests that William
Turner's record (1568), 'the fairest and
greatest that ever I saw groweth in the
lane besyde Wynchester, in the way to
Southampton' (*Turn.Herb.* edn 2,
p.118), was probably *R. tinctorum* L.,
known to have been cultivated around
Alresford and Winchester in the four-
teenth century for a dye for the wool
trade (*Watsonia* **14**: 178). Both this and
Miss C. M. Yonge's 1898 record at
Otterbourne (*Keble's Parishes*, p.219)
are very far outside the range of *R.
peregrina*.

CAPRIFOLIACEAE

Sambucus nigra L.   Elder.   **N,D,H**
Very common

A ubiquitous shrub in woods, scrub,
old hedges, waste ground and old pits,
especially on the chalk and other basic
soil. It was 'planted about conie-
burrowes for the shadow of the Conies'
(*Ger.em.Johns.*, p.1422).
   Every part of the elder was used
medicinally. 'The seeds...dried' were
'good for such as have the dropsie, and
such as are too fat, and would faine be
leaner'. A compress of pounded leaves
'doth asswage the paine of the gout'
(*Ger.em.Johns.*, p.1423). The modern
herbalist still uses elder: the bark as a
purgative, diuretic and emetic, the
leaves for bruises, wounds and
chilblains, and the flowers for colds,
influenza and hay fever (*Herb Guide*,
p.27).

'Laciniata'   **H**

Sometimes planted by HCC, possibly
also bird-sown.
   VC11: Meonstoke 6119, Hb.AWW
1952; Pauncefoot Hill, Romsey 3420,
AG 1975; lay-by on A3 near Buriton
7321, *CRL*, conf. *AB* 1971. Also 3414,
3430, 7200. **VC12**: 6628, 7450, 8252.

S. ebulus L.   Dwarf Elder,
Danewort.   **N?,D,H**   Very local
Map 345

First records, Gilbert White 1766
(*White's Jnls* **1**: 195) and 1778, 'among
the rubbish and ruined foundations of
the Priory' Selborne 7534, VC12,
(*White's Selb.* **2**: 5).
   A doubtful native, this plant is
found along roads or railways, in waste
places and old pits, seldom far from

houses or ruins and in Hants generally on the chalk. It is handsome enough to be grown in gardens today, and has succulent berries which can be bird-sown. It was used medicinally for the same complaints as elder, but it is poisonous, unlike *S. nigra*.

VC11: Marsh Court 3533, W roadside, Hb.AWW 1962, *DEA* 1991; Fir Copse Road, Farlington 6707, *EHW* 1908–48, since built over; Havant 7205, old railway bank, *AB* 1982, many plants, *DBa* 1992. **VC12**: Near West Down, Chilbolton 3838, verges and chalk-pit, *RPB* 1951–92; Leckford 3737, old railway track, *RMV* 1984; Goleigh Farm 7331, *AB* 1964; Higher Oakshott Farm 7328, *AB* 1964; Longmoor 7832, rifle-range No.3, (bird-sown?), *AB* 1979.

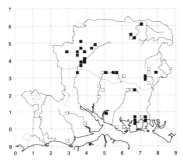

Map 345 Sambucus ebulus

Viburnum opulus L.   Guelder-rose. **N,H**   Common

In open woods, carr, scrub, wooded stream-banks, and hedges; usually in damp situations, but also in drier places such as chalk-pits.

VC12: Yellow-fruited bushes, presumably a cultivar (though a wild taxon, var. *flavum* Horwood, is known), The Chase, Woolton Hill, on disused railway 4463–4462, *NFC* 1982.

V. lantana L.   Wayfaring-tree.   **N** Locally common

In scrub, open woods and hedges; generally very common on the chalk, but *ANHS* spent one summer fruitlessly trying to find it in the Medstead–Four Marks–Bentworth area, where the chalk is topped with much Clay-with-flints, accounting for a large gap in the distribution. Rare in a few sites on other soils.

VC11: Bury Farm, Marchwood 3711, 3811, roadside hedge, *RPB* 1955; B3056 near Pig Bush 3605, *RPB* 1981;

Dilton Gardens, Roydon Woods 3200, hedge on gravel, *RJT* 1982. **VC12**: Conford 8232, *AB* 1971; Farnborough 8652, *DNT* 1969.

Of the wayfaring tree, John Evelyn wrote that it 'makes pins for the yokes of oxen', and 'the most pliant and best bands to faggot with'. It will also 'make an excellent gargle', and 'the leaves decocted to a lye, not only colour the hairs black, but fasten their roots...' (*Silva*, p.413).

V. tinus L.   Laurustinus.   **H** Under-recorded

Planted in shrubberies and parks, and sometimes self-sown, e.g. in tetrads 4416 VC11, 7256 VC12.

Symphoricarpos albus (L.) S. F. BLAKE (*S. rivularis* Suksd.)   Snowberry.   **H,D**   Frequent

Originally planted in woods as cover for pheasants, it spreads by suckers, or is dispersed by birds which eat the berries in a hard winter.

S. x chenaultii REHDER (*S. orbiculatus* Moench x *S. microphyllus* Kunth) Pink Snowberry.   **H**

VC12: R. Deadwater, Bordon 8035, on waste land, Hb.AB 1976, det. *EJC*.

Leycesteria formosa WALL. Himalayan Honeysuckle.   **H**   Rare

First record, E. A. Hamilton 1924, Chandler's Ford, VC11 (*Proc.IoW N.H.S.* 1: 250).

Occasionally bird-sown from gardens or shrubberies, but rather impermanent.

VC11: Gomer Pond 5899, in marshy scrub, *RPB* 1984. Also 1406, 2092, 2094, 2292, 3424, 3600, 3814, 4624. **VC12**: Fleet, *c.*8254 spontaneously in cleared woodland, *FGK 1956*, comm. *DHK*.

Lonicera nitida E. H. WILSON Wilson's Honeysuckle.   **H**   Rare

First record, J. R. Palmer 1965, Stanpit Marsh tip 1692, VC11.

Increasingly planted in hedges, or as cover for pheasants. Occasionally well naturalized and flowering, or springing from dumped hedge-clippings.

VC11: Pennington Common 3095, in scrub, *RPB* 1989. Also 3430, 3814, 3816, 4202, 5218, 6604, 7014. **VC12**: Shipton Bellinger 2444, *GDF* 1982. Also 2646, 5642, 5654, 5656, 7238, 7428, 7632, 8434.

L. japonica THUNB ex MURRAY Japanese Honeysuckle.   **H**   Very local

First record, Miss J. M. Douglas 1963, Normandy, Lymington 3394, VC11.

Becoming rampant in a few untrimmed hedges and places where garden rubbish is discarded, mostly near the coast.

VC11: Pilley 3297, lane near ford, *RPB* 1976, det. *EJC*. Also 1406, 2292, 3292, 3410, 4008, 4400, 4616, 5004, 5898, 6404, 6604, 7004, 7098. **VC12**: Alice Holt 8043, 8044, by railway, *AB* 1971. Also 8252.

L. periclymenum L.   Honeysuckle. **N**   Common

Common everywhere in woods, copses, scrub and hedges.

L. tatarica L.   Tartarian Honeysuckle.   **H**   Very rare

First record, R. A. Barrett 1990, Sinah Common, Hayling Island 6999, VC11, perhaps bird-sown, prominent in hedgerow, 1994, det. *EJC*, Hb.RPB (*Alien Pl.Brit.Is.*, p.295; *BSBI News* 68: 37–39).

ADOXACEAE

Adoxa moschatellina L.   Moschatel.   **N**   Locally common   Map 346

First record, Gilbert White 1766, Selborne, VC12 (*White's Jnls* 1: 193).

In woods, copses, old hedgebanks, wooded streamsides. Widespread and quite common in the chalk areas and on fertile loams, clays and fine silt. Rare in the SW and in areas devoid of old woodland relics, almost absent in the New Forest.

VC11: Beaulieu River, North Gate 3804, *RPB* 1958; Roydon Woods 3102, *FR* 1983; Ivy Wood, Brockenhurst 3102, in open forest, *FR* 1980.

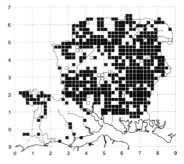

Map 346 Adoxa moschatellina

VALERIANACEAE

Valerianella locusta (L.) LATERR.
Common Cornsalad. **N,D,C**
Locally frequent   Map 347

First record, Gilbert White 1766, Selborne, VC12 (*White's Jnls* **1**: 193).

On cultivated and disturbed ground, bare banks of railways, roads and hedges; also on shingle and walls. Widespread, but commonest on the chalk. It can be grown as a salad-plant.

VC11: Holmsley 2300, disused railway, *RMB* 1969; A338 Ringwood 1405, verges at junction, *RPB* 1990. **VC12**: Abundant at mouth of Kingsley sand-pit 7837, *AB* 1990; Coleford Bridge, Farnborough 8755, plentiful by farm-gate (Hampshire bank of R. Blackwater), *CRH* 1991.

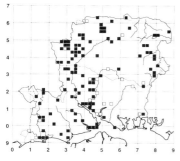

Map 347 Valerianella locusta

V. carinata LOISEL. Keeled-fruited Cornsalad. **N?,C** Rare Map 348

First record, E. H. White 1909, walls of Place House, Titchfield 5406, VC11 (his annotated copy of *Fl.Hants*).

In similar situations to *V. locusta*, but much rarer, although increasing in VC11 in recent years.

VC11: Fordingbridge Hospital 1414, *JO* 1986, Hb.RPB; A31 Poulner, Ringwood 1505, 1605, abundant on N bank of dual carriageway, Hb.RPB

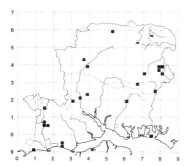

Map 348 Valerianella carinata

1990; East Wellow 3018, garden weed, *RMV* 1985, Hb.RPB; New Milton 2493, 2494, weed in pavement, *JLeR* 1989, Hb.RPB; Mill Lane, Droxford 6918, Hb.AWW 1952; Black Point, Hayling Island 7598, sand-dune bank, Hb.RPB 1989. **VC12**: Privett 6728, station yard, Hb.AWW 1958; Goodworth Clatford 3642, *AO* 1991; Kingsley 7837, abundant on chalk foundations of old railway; and Sleaford 8038, in sand-pit, *AB* 1980.

V. rimosa BASTARD Broad-fruited Cornsalad. **N?,C** Very rare

First record, J. H. Balfour 1837, Alresford, VC12, Hb.WARMS.

In similar situations to other cornsalads, but now very rare.

VC11: Romsey, *FBu* 1890, Hb.BM; East Meon *c*.6620, *AWW* 1958; South Hayling *c*.7298, *AWW* 1952; Sparsholt *c*.4230, *AO* 1969, det. *AB*; Bossington 3331, *GDF* 1972; Dibden Bay 4108, bank of polder, casual, Hb.RPB 1979, det. *CCT*; Compton Down 4526, border of cornfield, *SAL* 1986–88, conf. *PJW*. **VC12**: Penton Mewsey *c*.3246, *GDF* 1973; Overton *c*.5250, *WEW* 1958; Cow Down Copse, Newfound 5850, *WEW* 1956; Lord Wandsworth College 7446, *BFCS* 1953; field near Bramdown Copse, Overton 5247, over 100 plants, *JRM* 1994, Hb.AB.

V. dentata (L.) POLLICH Narrow-fruited Cornsalad. **C** Locally frequent   Map 349

In cornfields and other arable; widespread and locally frequent on the chalk, occasional on other fertile soils, but rare in the S.

VC11: Dilton Farm, Boldre 3300, *AEB* 1990, conf. *FR*; Chalton Down 7315, *EAP* 1983. **VC12**: East Woodhay 4060, *NFC* 1980; Sutton Common 7345, locally abundant on edge of field, *CRH* 1990.

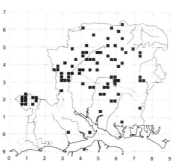

Map 349 Valerianella dentata

V. eriocarpa DESV. Hairy-fruited Cornsalad. **C** Very rare

First record, R. M. Walls 1993, base of East Cliff, Bournemouth 0990, VC11, Hb.RMW, conf. *RPB* (*Watsonia* **20**: 297).

Valeriana officinalis L. Common Valerian. **N,D** Locally common

Streamsides, marshes, damp, open woods; also in drier places in open scrub, chalk-pits, roadside verges, hedges, and in rank grassland on the downs. Widespread and common in the wetlands, less so elsewhere.

It is still an important medicinal herb, being widely used as a sedative.

V. dioica L. Marsh Valerian. **N**
Locally frequent   Map 350
First record, Gilbert White 1766, Selborne, VC12 (*White's Jnls* **1**: 197).

In wet meadows, fens, less-acid, flushed bogs, and open carr. Widespread and rather common in the New Forest, Forest of Bere, and the main river valleys; local in Woolmer Forest (in flushes on Sandgate Beds) and elsewhere, and decreasing wherever drainage and grassland 'improvement' is carried out.

VC11: Lower Test 3615, in two meadows, *RPB* 1980. **VC12**: Ashford Hill meadows 5662, *PB* 1983; Burhunt Valley 7532, *IM* 1986.

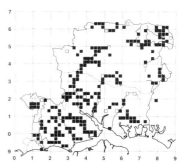

Map 350 Valeriana dioica

Centranthus ruber (L.) DC. Red Valerian. **H,D** Local

A handsome garden-plant, and an old medicinal herb. On old walls and ruins, cliffs, chalk-pits, chalk cuttings and banks, and on rubble. Frequent along the coast, but local everywhere else. VC11: 40 ☐; VC12: 7 ☐.

The 'poore people' of Gerard's day called it Setwall, and held it in such veneration as an antidote or 'counterpoison' and preservative medicine, that 'some woman Poet or other... made these verses:

> They that will have their heale
> Must put Setwall in their keale.'
> (*Ger.em.Johns.*, p. 1078).

DIPSACACEAE

Dipsacus fullonum L. (*D. fullonum* ssp. *sylvestris* (Huds.) P. Fourn.) Wild Teasel. **N,D** Locally common

In borders of fields, waysides, damp woodland clearings, stream-banks, newly-dug ditches; usually where soil has been recently disturbed. Widespread and generally common, especially on heavy clay and chalk. Rare inland in the SW.

D. pilosus L. Small Teasel. **N** Rare Map 351

First record, Gilbert White 1766, Selborne, VC12 (*White's Jnls* 1: 216).
Generally beside streams flowing from the chalk, disappearing as the wooded banks become too shaded, and reappearing if they are coppiced. The sites fall into six areas: R. Test and R. Dun flowing into it; Wallington River; western Weald, on or near streams flowing from the chalk, but generally on the Malmstone; London Clay over chalk at Horsedown Common, and the branch of R. Hart which rises in the chalk very near to this; London Clay at Silchester, with no stream nearby; woods on chalk around Herriard and Hawkley, also with no nearby stream.
VC11: R. Dun and Bitterne Grove, Mottisfont 3225, 3226, many plants, *KAH* 1982; Oakley Copse, Mottisfont 3328, *RPB* 1983; Wallington River, Boarhunt 5807, 5808, 5909, *AWW* 1952, *RPB* 1983. **VC12**: Dorton, Selborne 7433, *AB* 1984, where first recorded by Gilbert White; R. Hart

at Winchfield 7854, *CRH* 1986; Silchester, *RSH* 1858 (*Fl.Hants*, p.202), mound within Roman walls near wood 6362, *PB* 1980; Herriard Common 6544, *HCC* 1986; Hawkley Hanger 7329, over-shaded by scrub, *DPJS* 1987–89.

Knautia arvensis (L.) COULT. Field Scabious. **N** Locally very common Map 352

On grassy borders of fields and banks, roadside verges, dry rank grassland in pastures and on the downs. Very common on the chalk; frequent to occasional elsewhere, mainly on basic gravelly soils.
Gerard recommended scabious for 'infirmities of the chest'. (*Ger.em. Johns.*, p.725).

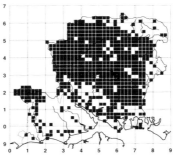

Map 352 Knautia arvensis

Succisa pratensis MOENCH Devil's-bit Scabious. **N** Locally very common Map 353

On damp, grassy heaths and old marsh-pastures, grass-rides of woods, drier fens; also in damp, chalk grassland. Very common in the New Forest and on other acid, wet soils, especially clay; locally frequent to occasional on the downs. In some old meadows in the

Avon Valley it flowers early before they are mown for hay.

Scabiosa columbaria L. Small Scabious. **N** Locally common Map 354

First record, Gilbert White 1766, Selborne, VC12 (*White's Jnls* 1: 216).
Very markedly confined to the chalk, and common wherever virgin turf remains on the downs, on roadside banks and verges, and in chalk-pits. Rarely, in alluvial meadows of the upper Test, e.g. Bransbury Common *c*.4141, VC12, *RPB* 1960. Outside the chalk area it is in artificial habitats beside roads or railways.
VC11: Beaulieu Road Station 3505, bed of former road at old camp-site, *RPB* 1987; A31 near Handy Cross 2107, *RPB* 1953–56.

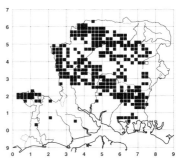

Map 354 Scabiosa columbaria

ASTERACEAE

Carlina vulgaris L. Carline Thistle. **N** Locally frequent Map 355

First record, J. Goodyer 1618, 'It growes on our Chalke Downes' (*Early Brit.Bots*, p.112).
On grazed, chalk grassland; fairly common, but becoming discontinuous through ploughing or lack of grazing.

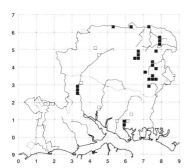

Map 351 Dipsacus pilosus

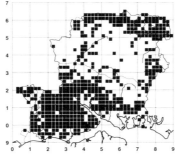

Map 353 Succisa pratensis

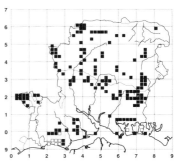

Map 355 Carlina vulgaris

Local on the Headon Beds, in old marl-pits and verges in the southern New Forest, and, rarely, on coastal shingle or rubble-remains.

Arctium lappa L.   Greater Burdock.   **N,C**   Very local and occasional   Map 356

In waste places and rubbish-tips; track-side verges, borders of woodlands on clay; around farmsteads and on gravelly river-banks. Local in the Avon Valley, lower Test and Itchen valleys, and by the R. Stour; otherwise rare.

VC11: Manor Farm, Michelmersh 3526, *RPB* 1966; Fryern Court farm-yard, Fordingbridge 1416, *JO* 1987; Chalk Lane, Albany Farm, N of Fareham 5709, *RPB* 1988. **VC12**: Mill Farm, Hartley Wespall 6957, *ECW* 1980; Binswood 7637, *FR* 1986; near Hartley Wintney *c.*7658, *UR* 1966; near Mallards Copse, Foxlease 8256, *CRH* 1985.

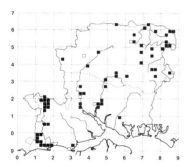

Map 356 Arctium lappa

A. minus (HILL) BERNH.   Lesser Burdock.   **N,C**   Common

On waysides, in rank grassland, woodland edges and disturbed ground in open woodland, and on waste ground. As well as ssp. *minus*, which is common throughout, there are scattered records of ssp. *pubens* (Bab.) P. Fourn. and ssp. *nemorosum* (Lej.) Syme but most of these have been insufficiently studied.

Carduus tenuiflorus CURTIS   Slender Thistle.   **N**   Local   Map 357

On beaches, bases of cliffs, grassy waste-ground along the coast and in estuaries; rather local and infrequent.

VC11: Sway 2799, on top of reservoir, *RPB* 1991; Pitts Deep 3795, *RPB* 1981; East Boldre 3700, on disturbed soil of roadside verge after gas-main installation, *RPB* 1981; Browndown 5799, 5898, on shingle, *MB* 1986–87.

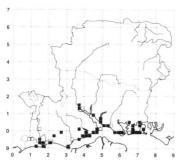

Map 357 Carduus tenuiflorus

C. crispus L. ssp. **multiflorus** (GAUDIN) GREMLI (*C. acanthoides* auct., non L.)   Welted Thistle.   **N,C** Locally common

On waysides, borders of fields, clearings in woods and disturbed ground along streams. Common over most of the chalk; very local and scattered elsewhere, chiefly on basic gravels.

C. x dubius BALB. (*C.* x *orthocephalus* auct., non Wallr. nec. Curtis; *C. crispus* x *C. nutans*)   **N,C**   Very rare

VC11/12: Cheesefoot Head *c.*5226, with both parents, *EM–R* 1954, Hb.K. **VC12**: Weyhill 3245, verge by airfield, *RPB* 1968.

C. nutans L.   Musk Thistle.   **N,C** Locally common

On disturbed and waste ground, grassland and roadside verges. Common on the chalk, especially in the W; frequent to occasional on gravelly or sandy soils, especially in the Avon Valley.

Cirsium eriophorum (L.) SCOP. Woolly Thistle.   **N**   Rare   Map 358

First record, J. Goodyer 1617, 'neare London highwaie on the east parte of Haliborne' [Holybourne] *c.*7441, VC12 (*Early Brit.Bots*, p.146)

In chalk grassland on the downs and on fragments of undisturbed turf; rare and scattered, and almost confined to VC12.

VC8: Martin Down 0419, *c.*20 plants on one-time arable land, last ploughed in 1957, *PET* 1990. **VC11**: Avon Forest Park, St Leonards 1202; *RMW* 1985; down N of Roman Road, Chilcomb 4927, *KC* 1970–84. **VC12**: Deane 5451, roadside verge, *EAB* 1962, *AB* 1972; Isle of Wight Hill 2437, *GDF* 1988; Beacon Hill, Old Burghclere 4557, *FR*, *PB & WGH*

1981; field near Lasham 6642, *CL* 1951 (*Watsonia* **2**: 344).

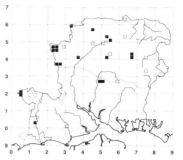

Map 358 Cirsium eriophorum

C. vulgare (SAVI) TEN.   Spear Thistle.   **N,C**   Very common

In pastures, verges, woodland clearings, and waste ground.

C. x sabaudum M. LOEHR (*C. vulgare* x *C. acaule*)   **N**

VC11: Recorded in *Hybr.Fl.Brit.Is.* (p.422), but no further details available.

C. x subspinuligerum PETERM. (*C. vulgare* x *C. palustre*)   **N**

VC11: Roadside between Brockenhurst and the station 3002, *GCD* 1882 (*J.Bot.*, p.247).

C. dissectum (L.) HILL   Meadow Thistle.   **N**   Locally common   Map 359

In meadows and bogs on acid soil, nearly always associated with some flushing or horizontal water-movement, supplying it with extra nutrients; also in fens. Very common in the New Forest, more local elsewhere; on calcareous peat at Bransbury, Chilbolton and Conford.

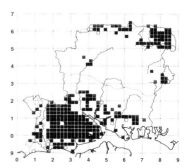

Map 359 Cirsium dissectum

VC11: Hookheath Meadows *c*.6407, *EAP* 1982. **VC12**: Blackwater Meadows 8460, *AWW* 1963, *ARGM* 1987.

C. x forsteri (SM.) LOUDON (*C. dissectum* x *C. palustre*)   N   Very rare

VC11: Near Holmsley, *JEK* 1929 (*Suppl.Fl.Hants*, p.59). **VC12**: Conford *c*.8232, *NYS* 1955; Silchester Common 6260, *BRB* 1968; Fleet Pond 8254, *CRH* 1984–87.

C. acaule (L.) SCOP. (*C. acaulon* (L.) Scop.)   Dwarf Thistle.   N   Locally common   Map 360

First British record, J. Goodyer 1620, 'on the Chalkie downes of Hampsheire plentifullie' (*Early Brit.Bots.*, p.118).

In short grassland on the downs, and in basic pastures, verges and old marl-pits. Common on the chalk; frequent on the Headon Beds in S New Forest, and local elsewhere.

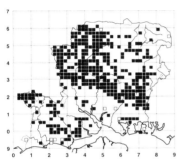

Map 360 Cirsium acaule

C. palustre (L.) SCOP.   Marsh Thistle.   N   Frequent and locally very common

In damp pastures, marshes, rides and clearings of wet woods; especially common on the clay, occasional on chalk-grassland slopes, in damper areas.

C. arvense (L.) SCOP.   Creeping Thistle.   N,C   Very common

First record, Miss C. R. May 1840, roadside, Tipner, VC11 (*May Ptgs Cat.*, no.469).

In neglected grassland, arable fields, roadsides and waste ground.

Onopordum acanthium L.   Cotton Thistle.   N?,H   Very local and rare   Map 361

This is a very handsome garden plant, and as such often cultivated. However, its distribution in Hants cannot be

readily reconciled simply with random garden escapes for the records show it is more frequent in the sandy regions of the NE and E. This is consistent with the concentration of records in East Anglia (*Atlas Brit.Fl.*, p.290), where P. J. O. Trist (*Fl.Breck.*, p.87) has boldly proclaimed it to be native. It is a biennial, occupying broken ground, and therefore rarely persists for long. Its occurrence in the NE on dumps could be linked, as with *Sigesbeckia serrata*, with the transportation of earth.

VC11: Burton Common 1995, gravel banks in tip, *RPB* 1977; Ullswater Road, West End 4514, disturbed ground, *PAB* 1990. **VC12**: Hazeley Heath tip *c*.7657, *GARW* 1935 (*Watts MSS*), 7458 *EH* 1961, 7557 *RPB* 1970; Farnborough Airfield 8554, 8654, on heaps of soil, *ARGM & JK* 1980; Pyestock Hill 8353, disturbed, old dump, *ARGM & TD* 1980–88, *CRH* 1991, plentiful; A339 near Wolverton *c*.5458, *PB* 1986–87.

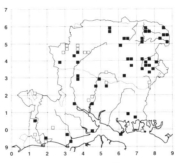

Map 361 Onopordum acanthium

Silybum marianum (L.) GAERTN.   Milk Thistle.   H,C,D   Rare

Has a tendency to turn up as a casual on refuse-tips, roadsides and waste ground, and as an unexpected weed in gardens. It was formerly cultivated for medicinal purposes, when it must have been commoner, for Gerard, who calls it 'our Ladies-Thistle', says 'It groweth upon waste and common places by high waies, and by dung-hils, almost every where.' (*Ger.em.Johns.*, p.1150). Some people grow it for its handsome leaves, and it was once a well-known shoddy-weed. VC11: 12 □; VC12: 10 □.

VC11: Lepe 4498, large colony behind beach, by roadside, *MR* 1976, *RPB* 1992. **VC12**: Silchester Common 6260, *PB* 1980.

Serratula tinctoria L.   Saw-wort. N   Locally common   Map 362

First record, Miss C. R. May 1837, hedge at Warrens, New Forest, VC11 (*May Ptgs Cat.*, no.459).

On grass-heaths, borders of scrub, open woods, and even on chalk downs. It is an interesting plant because it seems to like clay, heathland and chalk. Whether the clay and heathland that it inhabits are slightly basic, and the chalk slopes rather leached, requires study. Common in the New Forest, but local elsewhere.

VC8: Martin Drove End 0421, chalk-grassland bank, *RPB* 1989. **VC11**: St Catherine's Hill, Winchester 4827, *RMV* 1988; Wickham Common 5810, rare, *RPB* 1989. **VC12**: Watership Down 4957, *NFC* 1979; Tichborne golf-course 5831, *ARGM* 1988; Bartley Heath 7253, *AB* 1970, *CRH* 1989; Hazeley Heath 7657, *CRH* 1984, 1991.

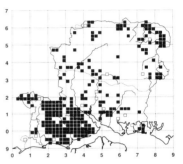

Map 362 Serratula tinctoria

Centaurea scabiosa L.   Greater Knapweed.   N   Locally common   Map 363

First record, J. Goodyer 1618, 'At Chawton' *c*.7037, VC12 (*Early Brit. Bots.*, p.110).

In chalk grassland, roadside verges, hedgebanks, and borders of fields. Very common on the chalk; local on basic gravelly soils, especially in the

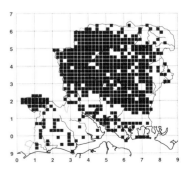

Map 363 Centaurea scabiosa

Avon Valley, along roads and railways, and in old pits.

C. cyanus L. Cornflower. **C,H**
Very rare

First record, Gilbert White 1766, Fyfield, VC12 (*White's Jnls* 1: 206).

A cornfield weed, now so rare that it is very seldom found in cornfields. Those found in waste places are generally garden escapes, although it can occur when arable soil is disturbed for roadworks.

VC11: Wellow district, common, *GWP* 1931 (*Proc.Hants Fld Club* **12**: 82); Dibden Bay 4108, on newly-made bank with other rare arable weeds, *RPB* 1979; Brownwich cliff 5202, thought to be border of a former cornfield, *SNHS* 1985. **VC12**: Monkwood, Ropley 6630, hayfield formerly a cornfield, several patches, *CWMB* 1954 (in litt. to *ECW*); cornfield near Oakridge Farm, Basingstoke 6353, *NEGC* c.1940, built on, *EAB* 1964; Tadley Place Farm 5959, large patch in cornfield, *EAB, AWW & AB* 1962, now destroyed; South Tidworth 2446, weedy barley-field, *DWF & MEY* 1968; Duck Street 3249, waste ground between cross-roads, *GDF* 1969; Battledown Farm, Basingstoke 5950, *PS* 1984; Micheldever 5143, one plant on road-widening, not persisting, *ARGM* 1983; edge of field by farm at S end of Green Lane, Fleet c.8051, *GARW* 1933 (*Watts MSS*); Dogmersfield c.7650, in crops, *DEB* 1962–63; A343 Over Wallop 2737, *RPB* 1977; Middle Wallop 2744, *WMK* 1977; Headley 5161, roadsides, *CL* 1964; bean-field, Hitches Lane, Fleet 7953, *GARW* 1942; N of Wishanger Common 8339, ten plants in carrot-field, *PLeB* 1973.

C. calcitrapa L. Red Star-thistle. **N?,C** Very rare

First records, W. L. Notcutt 1842, Peel Common and Ports Down, VC11 (*Fl.Hants*, p.212).

In chalk grassland or on gravel near the coast; at one time also a shoddy weed. This plant continued to be reported intermittently for c.90 years from Peel Common 5702, 1919; Chark Common 5702, to 1915; and Ports Down; with one instance each at Tipner and Hayling Island (all in *Suppl.Fl.Hants*, p.60); last seen on Ports Down *GARW* 1930 (*Watts MSS*) and *LP* 1934. The only record since is Browndown c.5898, one plant on consolidated shingle, *RJH* 1984.

C. nigra L. (incl. *C. nemoralis* Jord.) Common Knapweed. **N** Common

In grassland, on downs, in pastures, open woods, on roadside verges and waste ground. In Hants, the rayed form seems associated with ancient meadows.

C. x moncktonii C. E. BRITTON (*C. x drucei* C. E. Britton; *C. nigra* x *C. jacea*) **C** Very rare

VC11: Frogmore Lane, Southampton 3715, Hb.RPB 1976, det. *FR*, transient. **VC12**: Yateley Common, outside Blackbushe Airfield 8159, *AMS* 1967, Hb.AB 1968, det. *JEL* as a 'hybrid swarm' (i.e. hybrids retrogressing into *C. nigra*) (*Watsonia* **10**: 429). Not seen 1976 or since.

C. jacea L. Brown Knapweed. **C** Very rare or extinct

First record, Mrs A. M. Simmonds 1967, trackway on Yateley Common, outside Blackbushe Airfield 8159, VC12, together with the hybrid. Not seen 1976.

In grassland and waste places, probably introduced in grass-seed mixture. **VC11**: Mudeford c.1892, *KG* n.d. Also 2806, 3092.

Cichorium intybus L. Chicory. **N?,D,C?** Frequent

First record, Miss C. R. May 1834, field near the limekiln, Breamore 1519, VC11 (*May Ptgs Cat.*, no.503).

On roadside verges, borders of fields and waste ground. Stated in *Atlas Kent Fl.* (p.147) to be 'probably native... especially on chalky soils', but in Hants it seems no more common on the chalk than anywhere else. In most places it is an agricultural relic, being a fodder-crop and a salad-plant.

<Arnoseris minima (L.) SCHWEIGG. & KÖRTE Lamb's Succory. **N** Extinct

Formerly on sandy, but badly-drained fields or tracks. The habitat of this plant has practically ceased to exist and, as there have been no records since 1938, it is feared extinct.

Records since 1930 are: **VC11**: Hinton Admiral, *LBH* 1933. **VC12**: Yateley, *HWM* 1916, *JBLS* 1938 (*Rep.B.E.C.* for 1938, p.46), probably from the edge of Blackbushe Common 8058, from where there is a specimen in Hb.AB, collected *KG* 1937; 'Few in sandy field near Pondtail', Fleet; 'Very abundant in adjoining field near Bramshot Links club-house. Also in

clearing on wooded slope between Pondtail and Bramshot Golf Links'; and 'In two fields by Green Lane between Fleet and Crookham, with stems up to 15 inches', all *GARW* 1932 (*Watts MSS*); field at E end of Fleet Pond 8254, *GARW* 1938 (*loc.cit.*). The club-house was formerly in 8355, and the golf-course, which extended to the S, is long gone. *JEL* knew the 'Pond-tail clearing' site well, and found it completely overgrown after the war. The Green Lane site probably refers to 7953, where there are now housing estates.>

Lapsana communis L. ssp. communis Nipplewort. **N,C** Very common

In borders of woods, hedgerows, shady waysides, arable and waste ground; also on old walls and in gardens.

Hypochaeris radicata L. Cat's-ear. **N** Frequent and locally very common

Very common in acid to neutral grassland, but of lower frequency over much of the chalk, as it is untypical of old chalk-grassland.

H. glabra L. Smooth Cat's-ear. **N** Rare Map 364

On exposed, acid, sandy or gravelly soil on heaths, dunes, verges, and arable.

VC11: Hengistbury Head 1790, *CEP* c.1980; Black Common, Linwood 1809, both sides of track, *RPB* 1991; Sinah Common golf-links 6999, *DWF* 1958, *FR & ECW* 1981; Sandy Point, Hayling Island 7598, *AB, FR & EAP* 1980, *FR* 1993; Browndown 5899, *EJC, RPB & EAP* 1989. **VC12**: Military railway, Woolmer Forest 7832, *AB* 1982; N of Longmoor Camp 7931, plentiful on sandy ground, *FR* 1988; Riseley 7463, cornfield by ford, *WEW* 1957; field at E end of Fleet Pond

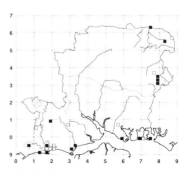

Map 364 *Hypochaeris glabra*

8254, with *Arnoseris minima*, *Hypericum humifusum* and *Filago minima*, *GARW* 1938 (*Watts MSS*).

Leontodon autumnalis L. Autumn Hawkbit. **N** Common

Common in grassland of all types.

L. hispidus L. Rough Hawkbit. **N** Frequent and locally common

In old grassland kept fairly short by grazing or mowing, on chalk or other basic soil.

L. saxatilis LAM. (*L. taraxacoides* (Vill.) Mérat) Lesser Hawkbit. **N** Locally common Map 365

In dry grassland on heaths, commons, pastures and roadside verges. Common on acid soil, especially in the SW; locally common on the chalk.

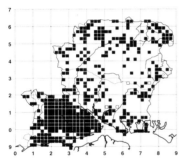

Map 365 Leontodon saxatilis

Picris echioides L. Bristly Ox-tongue. **N,C** Locally common Map 366

First record, Gilbert White 1766, Selborne, VC12 (*White's Jnls* 1: 204).

On roadsides, banks and clearings, waste ground and sea-walls; largely confined to stiff clay. Local on the Gault, the London Clay, and the

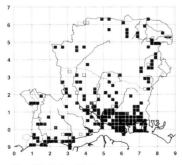

Map 366 Picris echioides

Headon Beds, but common only on the London Clay of the SE coast and its hinterland; occasional on chalk.

VC11: Horsebridge 3430, verge at bend in road, *RPB* 1987; Calshot 4801, reclaimed land by path, *RMV* 1986; Fort Nelson Picnic Place 6006, *RPB* 1986. **VC12**: Hawkley 7328, field at base of The Warren, *MS-W* 1974, *DBa* 1989; Wonston 4739, in clearing caused by gale, *ARL* 1989; Andover 3546, road-cutting, *MFW* 1991.

P. hieracioides L. Hawkweed Ox-tongue. **N,C** Locally frequent Map 367

First record, Gilbert White 1768, Selborne, VC12 (*White's Jnls* 1: 251). On bare or disturbed chalk or gravel, roadsides, railway banks, old pits, and scrub on the hangers. Common about Southampton, the Selborne area, and along certain roads and railways; otherwise local.

VC11: Hovercraft terminal, Southampton 4311, *MR* 1976; Ashlett Creek, Fawley 4701, *RMV* 1986. **VC12**: Oakshott Hanger 7327, *FR* 1987; Deadbrook Lane, Aldershot 8851, *CRH* 1990.

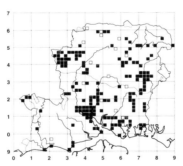

Map 367 Picris hieracioides

Tragopogon pratensis L. ssp. **minor** (MILL.) WAHLENB. Goat's-beard, Jack-go-to-bed-at-noon. **N** Locally common

In pastures, chalk grassland, waysides and grassy waste land; common on chalk and other basic soil.

T. x mirabilis ROUY (*T. pratensis* x *T. porrifolius*) Status unknown

Aldershot 8749, spontaneous in garden, *DNT* 1978.

T. porrifolius L. Salsify. **D** Very rare

A rare relic of cultivation with a slight

concentration around Portsmouth.

VC11: Milford on Sea 2991, plentiful on bank around car-park, *RPB* 1989; A31, Poulner, Ringwood 1605, plentiful on bank on N side, *RPB* 1990; London Road, Widley 6707, Hb.AWW 1960; Fareham 5406, *MBU* 1959; Craneswater Avenue, Southsea 6598, weed in drive, *EAP* 1992; Hilsea Lines 6604, *DPJS* 1990. Formerly abundant on military fortification at Eastney, *EHW* 1903–08 (*Suppl.Fl.Hants*, p.65). **VC12**: Basingstoke, waste ground, *NEGC* 1942 (*Rep.B.E.C.* for 1941–42, p.494); near Winchester Station 4730, on railway, *ADuSB* 1956, *UP* 1960; Greywell 7151, several plants by roadside, *AJPB* 1991–92.

Sonchus palustris L. Marsh Sow-thistle. **N?** Very rare

First record, Mrs S. P. Scott 1959, Gilbury Hard, Exbury 4100, VC11, some large stands in wooded margin of estuary-shore above high-water mark, on clay; still present *MSG* 1968, det. *DMcC*, comm. *AduSB* (*Watsonia* 8:59); 175 stems over *c.*230m, *RPB* 1985.

VC11: Lower Exbury 4198, *RPB* 1972; 4199, *RPB* 1989. It has been suggested that seed may have arrived on clothing of troops in boats prior to D-Day embarkation, but it is well established in a community similar to those on the Medway in Kent; it appears to be native and may previously have been overlooked.

S. arvensis L. Perennial Sow-thistle. **N,C** Frequent and locally common

In arable fields, bare banks of rivers and ditches, marshes, and along the drift-line on seashores and estuaries. In *Fl.Hants* (p.235) 'common in some parts', so it may have increased. Only moderately common in the extreme NE.

S. oleraceus L. Smooth Sow-thistle. **C** Frequent and locally common

On arable land and bare waste-ground, roadsides, at the foot of walls and edges of pavements; once used as a pot-herb.

S. asper (L.) HILL Prickly Sow-thistle. **C** Common

In similar habitats to *S. oleraceus* but distinctly commoner; also an old pot-herb.

Lactuca serriola L. Prickly Lettuce. **C** Locally frequent Map 368

First record, Mr & Mrs Starck 1918, Hythe–Fawley road, VC11 (*Suppl.Fl. Hants*, p.65).

On bare, disturbed roadsides and gravelly banks, derelict building-sites, coastal waste-ground and sea-walls. Frequent about Southampton, Portsmouth, Aldershot, Andover, Bournemouth and Christchurch; otherwise local, but perhaps spreading. **VC11**: Dibden Bay 4108, banks around polders, *RPB* 1970–89. **VC12**: Abundant on roadworks of the M3, Winchester 4929, 4930, *AB* 1985; Farnborough Airfield 8453, *ARGM* 1990.

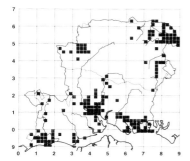

Map 368 Lactuca serriola

L. virosa L.   Great Lettuce.   **C** Very rare

First record, J. Goodyer 1618, 'on the walls and dry bancks of earth at Southampton', VC11 (*Early Brit.Bots*, pp.158–159).

Although *Fl.Hants* (p.234) and *Suppl.Fl.Hants* (p.65) list 12 records, some of these may relate to *L. serriola*, which was not listed in *Fl.Hants*.

There are three authentic modern records: **VC11**: Ashlett 4702, 4703, large stands on dredged shingle near path by power-station, *RPB* 1974–93. **VC12**: near R. Blackwater, Farnborough Street 8756, two plants, *CRH* 1991; Aldershot 8852, near former refuse-tip, *CRH* 1990, Hb.AB, det. *RNC*.

Cicerbita macrophylla (WILLD.) WALLR. ssp. **uralensis** (ROUY) P. D. SELL   Common Blue-sow-thistle.   **H** Rare

First record, Miss D. Fox 1942, Hartley Wintney 7656, VC12, on common, comm. *BW*, Hb.BM.

A garden throw-out, with far-creeping rhizomes, which can become established anywhere that people discard plants or garden soil.

VC11: Old Milton 2394, in small field, *AJM* 1946, Hb.BM; Huckwood Lane, Chalton 7415, Hb.AWW 1961. **VC12**: Bushy Leaze Wood, Alton 6838, side of track, *AB* 1976, Hb.AB 1992; St.John's Cross 3342, in lay-by, *AO* 1978; hedgerow surrounding Thruxton circuit/aerodrome 2745–2846, *MFW* 1989. Also 2848, 4830, 8236, 8432.

Mycelis muralis (L.) DUMORT. Wall Lettuce.   **N**   Locally common

First record, Gilbert White 1765, 'in a most shady part of the hollow lane...before you come to the nine-acre-lane', Selborne, VC12 (*White's Jnls* 1: 166).

In beech-woods on chalk and in other woods on basic to slightly acid soil where the herb-layer is sparse, as on banks of some wooded New Forest streams. Also on dry, shady road-banks and old walls. Common on the chalk and Malmstone, locally frequent elsewhere. Exceptionally in woodland of Scots pine and in an open, spruce plantation in the NE.

Genus **Taraxacum**   Dandelions The surface has barely been scratched in the recording of the innumerable dandelions in Hampshire. It is already clear that there are three areas where these are specially interesting: The New Forest, which is rich in *T. palustre*; the Thames Basin, i.e. meadows by the northern rivers which flow into the Thames and which share some of the remarkable dandelion flora of Oxfordshire and Berkshire; and the Test Valley, which has some of the same species – but whether this is because the source of the R. Test is only just over the watershed from that of the R. Loddon is a matter for speculation. The distribution of all but the *Erythrosperma* is intimately connected with river valleys. Eight species are endemic to the British Isles. Of the introductions, there are eight 'denizens' – introduced in grass-seed mixtures, and three 'colonists' or accidental introductions.

All our random collections have been identified or redetermined by either A. J. Richards or C. C. Haworth. *T. palustre* alone has been systematically mapped.

sect. **Erythrosperma** (H. LINDB.) DAHLST.

This is the group which used to be

known as *T. laevigatum* (Willd.) DC., Lesser Dandelion. They are small dandelions, in dry places:

T. acutum A. J. RICHARDS   **N**

VC11: Vineyard Hole, East Meon 6822, Hb.RPB 1976.

T. argutum DAHLST.   **N**

VC11: Sinah Common golf-links 6999, Hb.AB 1975.

T. brachyglossum DAHLST.) DAHLST.   **N**   Probably common

VC11: Sandy Point, Hayling Island 7498, *AB* 1976; Heath Common, Petersfield 7523, *AB* 1980; Goatspen Plain 2202, Hb.AMB 1981. **VC12**: All over Woolmer Forest, Hb.AB 1971; Noar Hill, *AB* 1977; Abbotstone Down 5836, *AB* 1972.

T. commixtum G. E. HAGLUND   **N**

VC11: Sinah Common golf-links 6999, Hb.AB 1976.

T. dunense SOEST   **N**

VC11: Sinah Common and beach 7098, on loose sand, Hb.AB 1975.

T. fulviforme DAHLST.   **N**

VC11: Sinah Common 6999, by the ferry, *AB* 1971; Twyford Down 4927, Hb.RPB 1976; Set Thorns Inclosure 2600, disused railway, Hb.AMB 1981. **VC12**: Faccombe, *GCD* 1931, Hb.OXF; Longmoor Station 7931, Hb.AB 1974.

T. glauciniforme Dahlst.   **N**

VC11: Butser Hill 7120, Hb.AB 1976; Sinah Common 6998, beach near golf-links, Hb.AB 1975. **VC12**: Abbotstone Down 5836, Hb.AB 1972; Wonston 4739, in crazy paving, Hb.AB 1980.

T. lacistophyllum (DAHLST.) RAUNK.   **N**   Common

VC11: Abbotsbury Farm, Timsbury 3623, Hb.RPB 1977; Sinah Common 7098, Hb.AB 1975; Butser Hill 7120, Hb.AB 1976. **VC12**: Ridges Green, Blackmoor 7832, Hb.AB 1972; Woolmer Forest 7932, Hb.AB 1974.

T. oxoniense DAHLST.   **N** Common

The commonest of the *Erythrosperma*, especially on the chalk hills.

VC11: N of Fernycroft 3606, old

camp-site, Hb.RPB 1977; Vineyard Hole, East Meon 6822, Hb.RPB 1976. **VC12**: Blackmoor Park 7832, Hb.AB 1969; Noar Hill 7331, Hb.AB 1971; Micheldever Spoil Heaps 5142, *KS* 1991.

T. rubicundum (DAHLST.) DAHLST. N   Probably common

VC11: Sinah Common 6899, *AB* 1971, 7098, *AB* 1975; Butser Hill 7120, *AB* 1976; Vineyard Hole 6822, Hb.RPB 1976; Deadman Hill 1916, Hb.RPB 1976; Twyford Down 4927, Hb.RPB 1976. **VC12**: Abbotstone Down 5826, *AB* 1972.

The Marsh Dandelions

In marshes, wet heath, damp, unimproved meadows and flushes. Sometimes on roadsides derived from damp meadows.

sect. **Palustria** (DAHLST.) DAHLST.

Only two species, both rare nationally.

T. anglicum DAHLST.   N   Very rare

VC12: Chilbolton Common 3840, in short turf on wet, alluvial pasture, Hb.RPB 1986.

T. palustre (LYONS) SYMONS (incl. *T. pollichii* Soest)   N   Rare   Map 369

VC11: Hatchet Pond, Beaulieu 3601, *AJR* 1969. *RPB* has since found this species quite widely in the New Forest. It inhabits the wet lawns on clay where the ponies graze, as a consequence of which it is very dwarf in stature. Common Marsh, Stockbridge 3534, Hb.RPB 1986.

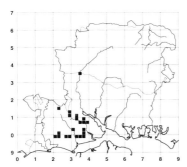

Map 369 Taraxacum palustre

sect. **Spectabilia** (DAHLST.) DAHLST.

Two of the commonest marsh dandelions are now included in one species:

T. faeroense (DAHLST.) DAHLST. (incl. *T. spectabile* sensu A. J. Richards, non Dahlst.)   N   Probably local

VC11: 19 □; VC12: 9 □.
    VC11: Chandler's Ford *c*.4220, *MPY* 1970; Common Marsh, Stockbridge 3534, Hb.RPB 1968; Baddesley Common 3821, Hb.RPB 1977; Wood Crates, Acres Down 2608, *RPB* 1971. **VC12**: Mabbotts Farm, Hawkley 7530, Hb.AB 1969; Conford Moor 8233, Hb.AB 1969; North Warnborough Common, *AB* 1977; top of Noar Hill 7331, an airborne achene presumably having drifted from a marsh, Hb.AB 1972.

sect. **Naevosa** M. P. CHRIST.

T. euryphyllum (DAHLST.) M. P. CHRIST.   N

VC11: Clay Hill, Lyndhurst 3005, Hb.RPB 1977; near Crampmoor, Romsey 3822, Hb.RPB 1977. **VC12**: Headley Park bridge 8138, Hb.AB 1971; Liss Forest 7730, in fields, Hb.AB 1977; Greatham 7731, field next to The Old Moor, Hb.AB 1977; Lodge Pond, Alice Holt Forest 8142, Hb.AB 1972.

T. maculosum A. J. RICHARDS (*T. maculigerum* sensu A. J. Richards, non H. Lindb.)   N

VC11: S of Lyndhurst Road Station 3310, Hb.RPB 1976; Mill Lawn Brook, Burley 2203, Hb.RPB 1977. **VC12**: North Warnborough Green 7252, Hb.AB 1977.

T. richardsianum C. C. HAWORTH N

VC11: Goatspen Plain 2202, Hb.AMB 1981. **VC12**: Ashford Hill 5562, damp meadow, Hb.AB 1984.

sect. **Celtica** A. J. RICHARDS

T. bracteatum DAHLST.   N

VC11: Common Marsh, Stockbridge 3533, Hb.RPB 1986. **VC12**: Lodge Pond, Alice Holt Forest 8042, Hb.AB 1977; Odiham Common 7451, Hb.AB 1977; North Warnborough Green 7252, Hb.AB 1978.

T. britannicum DAHLST.   N

VC11: Near A35, Plain Heath 2198, Hb.RPB 1980.

T. duplidentifrons DAHLST. (*T. raunkiaeri* Wiinst.)   N

VC11: Marsh near Sheet Mill 7624, *AB* 1971; Baddesley Common 3821, Hb.RPB 1977; Holmsley 2100, *AB* 1981; Goatspen Plain 2202, Hb.AMB 1981. **VC12**: Liss 7728, *AB* 1969; North Warnborough Green 7252, *AB* 1977.

T. excellens DAHLST.   N

VC12: Greatham End 7730, Hb.AB 1974.

T. fulgidum G. E. HAGLUND   N

VC11: Lower Test, Nursling 3614, Hb.RPB 1977. **VC12**: Hogmoor Inclosure, Bordon 7934, Hb.AB 1969; Odiham Common 7451, Hb.AB 1975; Broad Oak 7551, in field, Hb.AB 1977; North Warnborough Green 7252, Hb.AB 1977; Ron Ward's Meadow, Tadley 6060, Hb.AB 1991; Stockbridge North Fen 3535, Hb.AB 1991.

T. gelertii RAUNK. (*T. adamii* sensu A. J. Richards, non Claire)   N

VC11/12: Between Petersfield and Liss, probably on R. Rother SU72, *ESM* 1895, Hb.BM. **VC11**: Ruddy Mead, Nursling 3614, Hb.RPB 1976. **VC12**: Hogmoor Inclosure, Bordon 7934, Hb.AB 1969; Ashford Hill meadows 5662, *AB* 1990.

T. haematicum G. E. HAGLUND   N

VC11: Standing Hat, Balmer Lawn 3103, Hb.RPB 1977.

T. nordstedtii DAHLST. (incl. *T. litorale* Raunk.)   N   Probably locally frequent

This is probably the commonest of the marsh dandelions. VC8: 2 □; VC11: 23 □; VC12: 17 □.
    VC8: Lopshill Common 0913, Hb.RPB 1977. **VC11**: Sagles Spring, near Rockbourne 1216, Hb.RPB 1977; Dibden Bay 4008, Hb.RPB 1977; Baddesley Common 3821, Hb.RPB 1977. **VC12**: Huntingford 8238, Hb.AB 1977; Crookham Village 7953, Hb.AB 1970; Ashford Hill 5562, *AB* 1986.

T. ostenfeldii RAUNK. (*T. duplidens* H. Lindb.)   N

VC12: Yateley Common 8160, Hb.AB 1970.

T. subbracteatum A. J. RICHARDS N

VC12: Odiham Common *c*.7452,

Hb.AB 1977; Crookham Village 7953, *AB* 1975; North Warnborough Green 7252, *AB* 1975; N of R. Wey 8238, *AB* 1975; Lodge Pond, Alice Holt Forest 8042, *AB* 1977; Hogmoor Inclosure 7834, *AB* 1971; Greatham End 7736, *AB* 1971; Standford 8134, *AB* 1974.

T. tamesense A. J. RICHARDS   N

VC12: Central reservation of A30 at Hartfordbridge 7757, Hb.AB 1970. The situation indicates a relict meadow.

sect. **Hamata** H. ØLLG.

T. boekmanii BORGV.   N

VC11: Itchen Valley, N of Mans Bridge 4515, Hb.RPB 1976; Set Thorns Inclosure 2600, disused railway, Hb.AMB 1981. **VC12**: Liphook 8131, damp field, *AB* 1972.

T. hamatiforme DAHLST.   N

VC11: R. Avon, Moortown 1404, Hb.RPB 1976. **VC12**: Deanland Farm, Newnham 6954, Hb.AB 1972; Priory Valley, Selborne 7534, Hb.AB 1979; R. Wey, Huntingford 8238, Hb.AB 1977; Ron Ward's Meadow, Tadley 6060, Hb.AB 1991.

T. hamatum RAUNK.   N

VC11: S Winchester 4727, *AB* 1971. **VC12**: Hogmoor Inclosure, Bordon 7933, Hb.AB 1969; Empshott 7530, Hb.AB 1969; Liphook 8231, marshy place, Hb.AB 1971; Odiham Common *c.*7452, *AB* 1977; Chilbolton 3840, *RPB* 1986.

T. kernianum HAGEND., SOEST & ZEVENB.   D

VC12: Odiham 7350, *MMcC-W* 1978, Hb.E; Hazeley 7460, meadow by R. Hart, Hb.AB 1978.

T. lamprophyllum M. P. CHRIST. (*T. maculatum* sensu A. J. Richards 1972)   N

VC11: War Down 7219, roadside verge, *AB* 1976. **VC12**: Odiham Common 7451, Hb.AB 1975; R. Wey, Huntingford 8238, *AB* 1975; Mapledurwell Fen 6752, Hb.AB 1972; field by Basingstoke Canal 7451, *AB* 1977.

T. pseudohamatum DAHLST.   N

VC11: Holbury Mill, Lockerley 2826, Hb.RPB 1977; Lower Test, Nursling 3614, Hb.RPB 1977; A3 verge, War

Down 7220, Hb.AB 1976; Westfield Hall garden, Milford on Sea 2891, Hb.AMB 1981. **VC12**: Hogmoor 7834, old railway, *AB* 1971; Odiham Common 7451, Hb.AB 1977.

T. subhamatum M. P. CHRIST.   N

VC11: Keyhaven 2990, Hb.AB 1975; Nursling 3716, Hb.RPB 1977; Baddesley Common 3821, Hb.RPB 1977. **VC12**: Liphook 8231, marshy field, Hb.AB 1972.

sect. **Ruderalia** KIRSCHNER, H. ØLLG. & STEPANEK

In damp or dry meadows, gardens, waste ground, roadsides and dry heaths.

T. aequilobum DAHLST.   D

VC12: Leckford 3835 and 3636, *EGP* 1974.

T. alatum H. LINDB.   N

VC11: Holmsley 2098, old airfield, *AB* 1981; Milford on Sea 2891, cliff-top, Hb.AMB 1981. **VC12**: R. Hart, Hazeley 7460, Hb.AB 1978; Passfield 8234, Hb.AB 1974; Old Alresford 5833, Hb.AB 1976.

T. ancistrolobum DAHLST.   N

VC12: R. Hart, Hazeley 7460, *AB* 1978; Broad Oak 7551, Hb.AB 1975; Benhams Lane, Greatham 7831, Hb.AB 1971.

T. aurosulum H. LINDB.   D

VC12: Kingsley 7837, railway arch, Hb.AB 1971.

T. cherwellense A. J. RICHARDS   N

VC12: Odiham Common 7452, Hb.AB 1977.

T. cophocentrum DAHLST.   N

VC12: Ron Ward's Meadow, Tadley 6060, Hb.AB 1991.

T. cordatum PALMGR.   N

VC11: Sinah Common near ferry 6999, Hb.AB 1971; Warwick Slade 2706, Hb.RPB 1976. **VC12**: By Rother bridge, Sheet 7624, Hb.AB 1976; Ridges Green, Blackmoor 7831, Hb.AB 1972; R. Test, Gavelacre 4142, *AB* 1979.

T. croceiflorum DAHLST.   N

VC11: Sinah Common golf-links 7098,

Hb.AB 1975. **VC12**: Greatham End 7831, Hb.AB 1974; Pamber Forest 6260, roadside, *AB* 1975; R. Hart, Hazeley 7460, *AB* 1978.

T. dahlstedtii H. LINDB.   N

VC11: Sinah Common golf-links 7098, Hb.AB 1975. **VC12**: Pondtail Bridge, Fleet 8253, Hb.AB 1975; R. Test, Gavelacre 4142, Hb.AB 1979.

T. densilobum DAHLST. (*T. percrispum* M. P. Christ.)   C

VC12: Odiham 7350, *MMcC-W* 1978, Hb.E; East Stoke Farm 4837, Hb.AB 1980; Bordon 7834, bus-stop, Hb.AB 1979; R. Hart, Hazeley 7460, Hb.AB 1978.

T. ekmanii DAHLST.   N

VC11: Nursling Mill 3515, Hb.RPB 1977; Milford on Sea 2891, cliff-top, Hb.AMB 1981. **VC12**: Greywell 7150, churchyard, Hb.AB 1977; Broad Oak 7551, Hb.AB 1977; North Warnborough Green 7252, Hb.AB 1978; East Stoke Farm 4837, Hb.AB 1980.

T. expallidiforme DAHLST.   N

VC11: Sandy Point, Hayling Island 7498, Hb.AB 1976; Westfield Hall garden, Milford on Sea 2891, Hb.AMB 1981. **VC12**: Leckford 3839, *EGP* 1974; R. Test, Quidhampton 5150, Hb.AB 1979; Springs Meadow, Blackmoor 7632, *AB* 1972.

T. fasciatum DAHLST.   N

VC12: Crookham Village 7953, Hb.AB 1970; Ron Ward's Meadow, Tadley 6060, Hb.AB 1991.

T. insigne EKMAN ex M. P. CHRIST. & WIINST. (*T. ordinatum* Hagend., Soest & Zevenb.)   N

VC11: Goatspen Plain 2202, Hb.AMB 1981. **VC12**: The Warren, Hawkley 7228, *AB* 1969.

T. laeticolor DAHLST.   N

VC12: Wonston 4730, Hb.AB 1980; R.Test, Gavelacre 4142, Hb.AB 1979.

T. latisectum H. LINDB.   D

VC12: R. Test, Quidhampton 5250, Hb.AB 1979.

T. lingulatum MARKL. (*T. aequatum* Dahlst; *T. subpallescens* Dahlst.)   N

VC11: A3, War Down 7220, verge, *AB*

1976; Milford on Sea 2891, cliff-top, Hb.AMB 1981. **VC12**: Hogmoor, Bordon 7933, old railway, Hb.AB 1971; Queens Road, Longmoor 8131, Hb.AB 1971; Old Alresford 5833, Hb.AB 1976; Pamber Heath 6062, *AB* 1979.

T. longisquameum H. LINDB. (*T. adsimile* Dahlst.; *T. latispina* Dahlst; *T. mucronatum* sensu A. J. Richards et auct., non H. Lindb.) **N**

VC12: Mapledurwell Fen 6752, Hb.AB 1972; Huntingford 8238, Hb.AB 1975; Longmoor Station 7931, *AB* 1970; R. Hart, Hazeley 7460, *AB* 1978.

T. macrolobum DAHLST. (*T. lacerabile* Dahlst.) **N**

VC11: A3, War Down 7220, *AB* 1976. **VC12**: Mill Court 7541, Hb.AB 1975; Yateley Common 8460, *AB* 1970.

T. oblongatum DAHLST. (*T. perhamatum* Dahlst.) **N**

VC11: War Down 7220, in field, Hb.AB 1976; near Winchester College 4828, towpath, *AB* 1980. **VC12**: Queens Road, Longmoor 7830, in meadow, *AB* 1971.

T. pachymerum G. E. HAGLUND **D**

VC12: R. Test, Gavelacre 4142, Hb.AB 1979.

T. pallescens DAHLST. **D**

VC11: South Hayling 7098, beach beside golf-links, *AB* 1975. **VC12**: R. Wey, Huntingford 8238, *AB* 1975; Pamber Heath 6062, *AB* 1979; Frensham Pond Hotel 8439, *AB* 1977.

T. pannucium DAHLST. **N**

VC11: A3, War Down 7220, verge, Hb.AB 1976. **VC12**: Leckford 3835, *EGP* 1974; North Warnborough Green 7252, Hb.AB 1977; R. Alre, Old Alresford 5833, Hb.AB 1976.

T. pannulatiforme DAHLST. **N**

VC12: Near source of R. Test, Polhampton 5250, Hb.AB 1979; Stockbridge North Fen, 3535, Hb.AB 1991.

T. pectinatiforme H. LINDB. **D**

VC11: Sinah Common, car-park by ferry 6899, Hb.AB 1975; A3 verge, War Down 7220, Hb.AB 1976. **VC12**: Odiham Common 7451, Hb.AB 1975;

R. Test, Quidhampton 5150, Hb.AB 1979; Liss Forest 7730, in field, Hb.AB 1977; Frensham Pond Hotel 8439, Hb.AB 1977.

T. polyodon DAHLST. (*T. ardisodon* Dahlst.; *T. naeviferum* Dahlst.) **N**

VC11: Westfield Hall garden, Milford on Sea 2891, Hb.AMB 1981. **VC12**: Headley Park Bridge 8138, Hb.AB 1971; Sheet 7524, Hb.AB 1976; field next to Old Moor, Greatham 7231, Hb.AB 1977; Bramley Army Depot 6658, *AB* 1980.

T. procerisquameum H. ØLLG. (*T. procerum* sensu A. J. Richards et auct., non G. E. Haglund **C**

VC12: Benhams Lane, Greatham 7731, Hb.AB 1974; The Warren, Hawkley 7228, Hb.AB 1979; car-park, Frensham Pond Hotel 8439, Hb.AB 1977; Odiham 7350, *MMcC-W* 1978, Hb.E.

T. rhamphodes DAHLST. **D**

VC11: Sinah Common, tetrad 6898 or 7098, Hb.AB 1975.

T. sellandii DAHLST. **N**

VC11: Westfield Hall garden, Milford on Sea 2891, Hb.AMB 1981.

T. stenacrum DAHLST. **N**

VC12: Watership Down 4856, Hb.AB 1975; R. Hart, Hazeley 7460, Hb.AB 1978; North Warnborough Green 7252, *AB* 1978.

T. subexpallidum DAHLST. (*T. sublaciniosum* sensu A. J. Richards et auct., non Dahlst.) **N**

VC12: Bordon 7935, *AB* 1970; Benhams Lane, Greatham 7731, *AB* 1971; Leckford 3835, *EGP* 1974.

T. sublaeticolor DAHLST. **N**

VC12: Bordon 7935, Hb.AB 1975; Greywell churchyard 7150, Hb.AB 1977; R. Test, Quidhampton 5150, Hb.AB 1979; Odiham Common 7451, *AB* 1977.

T. subundulatum DAHLST. (*T. hemipolyodon* Dahlst.) **N**

VC12: Lodge Pond, Alice Holt Forest 8142, Hb.AB 1972; Odiham Common 7451, Hb.AB 1975; North Warnborough Green 7252, *AB* 1977.

T. undulatiflorum M. P. CHRIST. **N**

VC12: R. Test, Quidhampton 5150, Hb.AB 1979; Ron Ward's Meadow, Tadley 6060, Hb.AB 1991.

T. vastisectum MARKL. ex PUOL. **C**

VC11: Milford on Sea 2891, on cliff-top, Hb.AMB 1981.

T. xanthostigma H. LINDB. **N**

VC12: Springs Meadow, Blackmoor 7632, Hb.AB 1972; Wheatham Farm, Oakshott 7527, Hb.AB 1979; Bordon 7935, Hb.AB 1975; Benhams Lane, Greatham 7731, Hb.AB 1974; Leckford 3835, *EGP* 1974.

Crepis biennis L. Rough Hawk's-beard. **N?,C** Rare Map 370

On roadside verges, hedgebanks and rough grassland; sometimes a weed in a grass-crop. Mostly impermanent, but in E Hants it is firmly established in a few places, generally roadsides.
  VC11: Newgate Lane, Fareham 5704, *MB* 1968, 1976, Hb.AB; St Nicholas' Church, South Boarhunt 6008, Hb.RPB 1988, det. *FR*; Knapp Mill, Christchurch 1593, *RMW* 1981. **VC12**: Selborne, *JEW* 1954; Selborne, in two places, foot of Galley Hill 7433, and lane to King's Farm 7331, *AB* 1960, 1989; near Ashdown Copse 2446, *MFW* 1984.

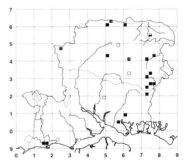

Map 370 Crepis biennis

<**C. nicaeensis** BALB. French Hawk's-beard. **C** Extinct

VC11: W of Sway Station 2798, in field of sown grass and clover, *EFL* 1890, Hb.BM (*Fl.Bmth*, p.137). **VC12**: Odiham, *CP* (*Suppl.Fl.Hants*, p.62). This was never more than a casual, and there are no modern records.>

C. capillaris (L.) WALLR. Smooth Hawk's-beard. **N,C** Common

Widespread and plentiful in grassland, arable and waste ground.

C. vesicaria L. ssp. **taraxacifolia** (THUILL.) THELL. ex SCHINZ & R. KELLER (ssp. *haenseleri* (Boiss. ex DC.) P. D. Sell)   Beaked Hawk's-beard. **N?,C**   Frequent and locally common

First record, E. J. Tatum 1886, Ford-ingbridge, VC11 (*J.Bot.* **34**: 135).

Bare ground and rough grass on roadside verges, tracks, disturbed stream-banks, arable fields, ley pastures, waste ground, and along rail-ways. This plant was not recorded in England until 1713, in the London area of Kent. Dillenius found it in Sussex in 1724, and it was present in Kent, Surrey, Sussex and Essex, as a rare plant, in the early 19th C. although it was sometimes confused with *C. foetida*. It may have arrived in the 18th C. at the Port of London as a weed in grass-seed, but E. J. Clement (pers.comm.) has suggested that seeds could have blown across the Channel from western France (where it is a common native), or that it could equally well have been a rare native in Kent and Sussex. Then, either the climate became more to its liking, or it received new vigour as a result of mutation, and it experienced a popula-tion explosion. Hants, Isle of Wight, Wilts, Berks and Somerset all acquired their first records in the 1880s. At first it was noticed that it preferred chalk, but in Hants it is now so common that it occupies practically all soils.

C. setosa HALLER fil.   Bristly Hawk's-beard. **C**   Very rare

First record, D. H. Scott 1910, between Dummer and Popham Lane, *c*.5745, VC12 (*Proc.IoW N.H.S.* **1**: 255).

Probably a casual from grass-seed or fodder.
VC11: Rum Bridge, Totton 3512, border of car-park and grassy banks along path, in plenty, *RMV* 1990, Hb.RPB; near Kingfisher Lake, Test-wood 3514, in coarse grass, *RMV* 1990 (both *Watsonia* **18**: 432). **VC12**: Hook Common 7253, on A32 embankment, *AB* 1980, det. *EJC*; Andover, *WAP* 1944 (*Proc.Hants Fld.Club* **16**: 194).

[**C. foetida** L.   Stinking Hawk's-beard.

Hayling Island, in several places, *MTH* 1919–20 (*Suppl.Fl.Hants*, p.61). This has never otherwise been recorded in

Hants; there are no specimens, and it must be borne in mind that it could be confused with *C. vesicaria*.]

Pilosella officinarum F. W. SCHULTZ & SCH.BIP. (*Hieracium pilosella* L.)   Mouse-ear Hawkweed. **N**   Frequent and locally common

In dry, short turf; it also spreads on bare banks and other open ground. Common on all light soils, but usually absent from improved grassland.

P. flagellaris (WILLD.) P. D. SELL & C. WEST ssp. **flagellaris** (*Hieracium stoloniflorum* auct., non Waldst. & Kit.) **C**   Very rare or extinct

First record, Miss V. M. Leather 1958, Pondtail Bridge, Fleet 8253, VC12, roadside verge, Hb.AB, det. *DPY*, lost by 1976 due to roadworks.

Said to be a foreign grass-seed weed, it has been a rather unsuccessful colonist in Hants. There are only four records, the others being: **VC11**: St Cross 4827, track of old railway, Hb.RPB 1970, det. *CEAA*, now shaded out. **VC12**: Chilbolton 4038, verge by cornfield track, *RPB* 1969, det. *CEAA*; Hartley Wood 7535, on ground cleared for planting, *AMM c*.1959, det. *BM*, long since overgrown.

P. x floribunda (WIMM. & GRAB.) ARV.-TOUV. (*Hieracium x floribundum* Wimm. & Grab.; *P. lactucella* (Wallr.) P. D. Sell & C. West x *P. caespitosa* (Dumort.) P. D. Sell & C. West) **C** Very rare

First record, R. P. Bowman 1991, B3056 Stephill Bottom to Pig Bush 3505, VC11, W verge in grass-heath with tussocks of *Calluna* and *Erica tetralix*, 45+ plants in 4 x 2m, Hb.RPB, det. *PDS*; in 1992, 134+ plants bearing 24 flowering stems.

Discovered on the site of military emplacements dating from the 1939–45 war, it may have been introduced during that period. Previously recorded in the British Isles only near Belfast, Northern Ireland, 1897–1910 (*Watsonia* **19**: 187–188).

P. aurantiaca (L.) F. W. SCHULTZ & SCH.BIP. (*Hieracium aurantiacum* L.; *H. brunneocroceum* Pugsley)   Fox-and-cubs. **H**   Occasional

First record, Miss M. T. Hillard 1919, near Fareham, VC11 (*Proc.IoW N.H.S.* **1**: 255).

Grassy verges on heaths and commons, usually near houses, and

along railways. Widely scattered records; probably usually spread by stolons from garden throw-outs, but perhaps seeds may also be wind-dispersed from gardens.
VC11: Magpie Green, Holmsley 2100, *MPY* 1963, *RPB* 1971; Avon Forest Park 1202, rampant, *RPB* 1985. **VC12**: Over Wallop 2938, main road, away from houses, *GDF* 1988; The Chase 4462–4463, old railway NW of A343, *VF* 1982; West Green, Yateley 8061, *ARGM* 1987; Hitches Lane, Fleet 7954, *GARW* 1943 (*Watts M.SS,* as *H. brunneocroceum*).

Most records probably refer to ssp. *carpathicola* (Nägeli & Peter) Soják (*H. brunneocroceum*). There are widely scat-tered records of ssp. *aurantiaca* (as *H. aurantiacum*) since 1950, but they are insufficiently documented to give any definite examples. The two subspecies are in any case doubtfully distinct.

Genus **Hieracium**   Hawkweeds

sect. **Sabauda** F. N. WILLIAMS

H. sabaudum L. (incl. *H. perpropin-quum* (Zahn) Druce and *H. bladonii* Pugsley). **N**   Locally common

In open woods, borders of heaths, shady roadsides and banks. Quite common on acid soil, especially on sand and loam; occasional on chalk or other basic soil.
VC12: A325, Bordon 7935, Hb.AB 1970, det. *CW* (as *H. perpropinquum* with some characters of *H. virgultorum* Jord.).

H. rigens JORD.   **N,C**   Very rare

First record, C. West 1956, waste ground, Southampton, by railway station, *c*.4112, VC11, Hb.CGE.

In Hants it is associated with rail-ways or with open woods or wooded banks.
VC11: Railway S of Beaulieu Road Station 3505, and Bishop's Dyke 3504, at foot of ancient bank E of railway, Hb.RPB 1987, det. *RCS*. **VC12**: Rail-way bank near Fleet Pond 8255, *VL* 1960, Hb.AB, det. *CW*, refound *CRH* 1986, Hb.AB, det. *RCS*; Basing Wood 6455 (on London Clay), beside forest road, *RCS* 1986.

H. salticola (SUDRE) P. D. SELL & C. WEST   **C**   Very rare

First record, Mrs M. P. Yule 1963, Burton Common *c*.1995, VC11, Hb.AWW, det. *PDS & CW*.

sect. **Umbellata** F. N. WILLIAMS

H. umbellatum L.   **N**   Locally frequent   Map 371

On heaths, in grass amongst bracken, or on tracks amongst heather; among bushes and on open, woodland banks. Fairly common on acid soil in the SW, commoner in Woolmer Forest and around Farnborough; rare elsewhere; var. *coronopifolium* Bernh. is occasional.

VC11: Hengistbury Head 1790, *JOM* 1970; Pig Bush 3604, in oakwood, Hb.RPB 1957, det. *AM*; Meyrick Park, Bournemouth 0891, behind tennis pavilion, *DEA* 1987. **VC12**: Near Hawley Lake 8357, gravel-path, *AB* 1976, det. *PDS*; Basingstoke Hospital 6153, *PB* 1980; Stony Down 6830, *RCS* 1983; var. *coronopifolium*, Tweseldown Racecourse 8251, *CRH* 1984.

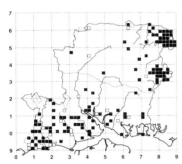

Map 371 Hieracium umbellatum

sect. **Tridentata** F. N. WILLIAMS

H. calcaricola (F. HANB.) ROFFEY   **N**   Very rare

First records, G. Halliday 1967, Holmsley Station 2300, VC11 and Lady Anne Brewis 1967, Whitehill railway cutting 7934, VC12, det. *CW*.

VC11: Clay Hill, Burley 2302, and Bagshot Moor 3600, on dry track, *WMK* 1974, det. *CW*; Highland Water Inclosure 2409, in ride, *JO* 1987, Hb.RPB, det. *RCS* 1991; Sinah Common 7099, in scrub on shingle at E end of lagoon, *AOC & DEA* 1984, Hb.CGE, det. *PDS*. **VC12**: Woolmer Road, Greatham 7831, *AB* 1968, det. *CW*; Basingstoke Canal, Fleet 8052, towpath, *AB* 1975, det. *PDS*.

H. eboracense PUGSLEY   **N**   Very rare

First record, Miss M. McCallum-Webster 1967, Whitehill railway cutting 7934, VC12, det. *PDS*.

VC11: There are unconfirmed records for: Romsey *c*.3622, 1965; Upper Hamble Country Park 4911 or 5010, 1987–88; and Sinah Common 7099, *c*.1975. **VC12**: Cooper's Bridge Farm, Bramshott 8333, roadside, Hb.AB 1975, det. *PDS*.

H. trichocaulon (DAHLST.) JOHANSS.   **N**   Locally common

On grassy heathland, in open woods, on shady roadsides and railway banks. Widespread and quite common on most acid soils, especially in the SW; thinly spread over the chalk, mostly on superficial soils.

VC8: Pinns Farm, East Wellow 2920, sandy road-bank, Hb.RPB 1975, det. *PDS*. **VC11**: Sinah Common 6999, roadside, *AB* 1976, det. *PDS*. **VC12**: Clere Wood, Highclere 4560, *AB* 1976, det. *PDS*.

H. cantianum F. HANB.   **N**   Very rare

First record, G. A. R. Watts 1938, banks of stream, E side of Fleet Pond, on W side of road 8254, VC12, det. *HWP* (*Watts MSS*).

sect. **Vulgata** F. N. WILLIAMS

H. pollichiae SCH.BIP. (*H. roffeyanum* Pugsley)   **C**   Very rare

First record, Lady Anne Brewis 1963, lane up Selborne Hanger 7333, VC12, Hb.AB, det. *PDS & CW* (*Watsonia* 10: 429), still there *AB* 1988.

H. lepidulum STENSTR.   **C**   Very rare

There is a record for SU42, VC11/12, in *Atlas Brit.Fl.Crit.Suppl* (p.116).

[**H. surrejanum** F. HANB.

Specimens in Hb.BM, collected from various sites around Fleet, including 'A mile or two S. of Fleet village', VC12, *ESM* 1898 (*J.Bot.* 41: 249) and labelled as this species, have been redet. *DJMcC* 1990 as closest to *H. diaphanum*, although they do not precisely correspond with that species as he understands it, *fide CRH* 1993.]

H. cheriense JORD. ex BOREAU   **C**   Very rare

First record, Lady Anne Brewis 1968, Silchester Common 6162, VC12, road-

side, Hb.AB, det. *PDS & CW* 1970 (*Watsonia* 10: 429).

VC12: Great Pen Wood 4461, roadside, Hb.AB 1976, det. *PDS*.

H. acuminatum JORD. (*H. strumosum* (Ley ex W. R. Linton) Ley)   **N?,C**   Very local and occasional   Map 372

First record, Mrs W. Boyd Watt 1945, Bournemouth, VC11 (*Proc.Hants Fld.Club* 16: 290, as *H. lachenalii* C. C. Gmel.).

On roadsides, railways and the edges of woods; commonest on the chalk, but in the western Weald it extends to the clay and sand.

VC8: Boulsbury Wood 0715, *AB* 1976, det. *PDS*. **VC11**: Denny Bog railway bank 3505, Hb.AWW 1956; Wootton *c*.2498, *MPY c*.1965, det. *PDS & CW*; Shawford 4625, roadside, *RHJ* 1975, Hb.AB; Fort Nelson, Ports Down 6007, Hb.RPB 1986, det. *RCS* 1991. **VC12**: Weyhill *c*.3046, *GDF* 1984, det. *AB*; Silchester Common 6262, roadside, Hb.AB 1968, det. *PDS & CW*; Micheldever Spoil Heaps *c*.5244, *VL* 1960, det. *CW*, Hb.AB 1978; A325, Whitehill Chase 7834, Hb.AB 1969, det. *PDS & CW*.

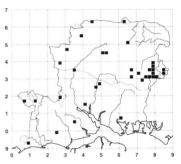

Map 372 Hieracium acuminatum

H. diaphanum FR. (*H. anglorum* (Ley) Pugsley   **C**   Very rare

First record, D. H. Scott 1927, banks of railway spoil, East Oakley, VC12 (*Suppl.Fl.Hants*, p.62, as *H. cacuminatum* Dahlst.).

VC11: Broughton Down 2833, on chalk banks, Hb. RPB 1965, 1975, det. *PDS*. **VC12**: Ewshot *c*.8250, roadside, *VL* 1960, Hb.AB, det. *PDS & CW*; Caesar's Camp, Aldershot 8350, *CRH* 1987, det. *RCS, CRH* 1995; sandy bank, Church Road, Fleet 8054, *CRH* 1995, det. *RCS*. Records of *H. surrejanum* from around Fleet, *ESM* 1898, Hb.BM may be referable here.

H. maculatum SM.   **C,H**   Very local   Map 373

First record, F. Townsend 1882, hedgebank on the high road at Meonstoke near the rectory 6120, VC11 (*Fl.Hants*, p.238).

This alien is a handsome garden-plant, and may well be of local hortal origin, but railways have played a large part in its distribution. It has been found in gardens, on old walls, railways, roadside banks and plantations.

VC11: The second record is for Exton, *CDa* 1924 (*Suppl.Fl.Hants*, p.63). In 1975 *HCA-H* reported it in 6120, just N of the railway bridge at Meonstoke, and by that time it occurred the whole way along the chalk gorge of the old Meon Valley railway, from Droxford to Privett, and was also seen at Southampton Central Station by *CW*. Seeds were very likely blown from the Meon Valley railway to Old Winchester Hill 6420, *JB* 1982, det. *PDS*. In an old walled garden in Catherington 6914, *MD* 1981; Horsea Island 6304, *AWW* 1958; Paulsgrove, Ports Down 6306, in old chalk-pit, *RPB* 1991. Also at Broughton Down 2833, *RMV* 1990, Hb.RPB, det. *RCS*, in same vicinity as several localities in VC12 (see below). **VC12**: The old Weyhill–Andover railway may have been a similar source of dispersal: a large patch at 3045, *MPY & JN* 1968, *GDF* 1984; Abbotts Ann 3242, *MPY & JDG* 1968; Snoddington Hill 2444, *GDF* 1982; and Shipton Bellinger 2345, beech plantation, Hb.RPB 1975, det. *PDS*. In 1989 *MFW* added 2346, 2440 and 2741, two of them on railways, and in 1991 at Wherwell 3840, roadside near old railway. This general area is near Broughton Down 2833 (see under VC11). In E of VC12, by railway bridge and at roadside, Alice Holt 8043, Hb.AB 1972, det. *CW*. Also abundant Liphook 8432, on old wall, Hb.AB 1967, det. *CW* (*Watsonia* 10:

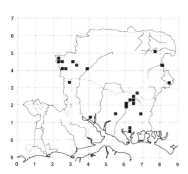

Map 373 Hieracium maculatum

429), whence blown to private garden in Liphook, *PSo* 1980.

H. scotostictum HYL.   **C,H**   Very rare

First record, J. Vorse 1922, Hinton Admiral, railway bank 2094, VC11 (*Suppl.Fl.Hants*, p.62, as *H. praecox* Sch. Bip.).

According to J. E. Lousley, this alien was probably introduced during the 1914–18 war (*Fl.Surrey*, p.328). Generally found near railways but probably also grown in gardens.

VC11: Hinton Admiral, railway bank, Hb.AWW 1956, also on railway bridge 2094, *RPB* 1991; garden in North View, Winchester 4729, *DEA* 1985, Hb.DJMcC, det. *PDS*. **VC12**: Isle of Wight Hill *c*.2537, *RAT* 1969, det. *K*, *GDF* 1988.

H. sublepistoides (ZAHN) DRUCE   **C**   Very rare or overlooked

First record, P. M. Hall 1934, S of Winchester on railway bridge *c*.4726, VC11, Hb.BM, det. *HWP*.

VC11: Sleepers Hill, Winchester 4628, one plant on shady roadside, *DEA* 1988, Hb.BM, det. *DJMcC*; roadside near King's Somborne 3632, *RCS* 1986, 3530, Hb.RPB 1985, det. *RCS* 1991; near Crooked Walk Lane, Ports Down 6207, on chalk slope, Hb.RPB 1990, det. *RCS*. **VC12**: Selborne *c*.7432, bank of lane, *PMH & AJW* 1937 (*Rep.B.E.C.* for 1937, p.486); Worthy Down 4534, beech-belt, *RPB* 1969, det. *CEAA*; Selborne 7433, Hb.AWW 1957.

H. grandidens DAHLST.   **C**   Very rare

First record, Lady Anne Brewis 1976, East Woodhay *c*.4060, VC12, Hb.AB, det. *RCS*.

H. exotericum JORD. ex BOREAU *sensu lato*   **N,C**   Locally frequent   Map 374

Widespread, generally on the chalk where often in shady lanes and open beech-woods. No specimens referable to *H. exotericum sensu stricto* have so far been found; the records listed below belong to allied species as yet unnamed.

VC11: Yew Hill, Hursley 4426, foot of chalk down, Hb.RPB 1975, det. *PDS*; St Cross, Winchester 4728, railway bridge, *JLSL* 1974, Hb.AB; Ports Down 6006, *AWW* 1950. **VC12**: Well 7646, *VL* 1960, det. *CW*; Redrice 3341,

MFW 1991; Hawkley Hurst 7530, *AB* 1969, det. *PDS*; Warren Bottom Copse *c*.5454, *WMK* 1975, Hb.AB, det. *CW*; Silchester Common *c*.6262, *AB* 1969; Waggoners Wells *c*.8634, *HJMB* 1986.

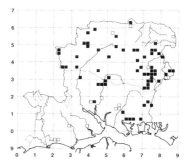

Map 374 Hieracium exotericum agg.

Undetermined **Hieracium** spp.

1. **VC12**: Andover Road, Winchester 4730, under beeches, *DEA* 1985, Hb.CGE, indet. *PDS*, but apparently an introduced European species.

2. **VC12**: Rowledge churchyard 8243, Hb.RCS 1986, indet. *JBev* 1994. Originally identified as *H. surrejanum* F. Hanb., this requires further study.

Filago vulgaris LAM. (*F. germanica* L., non Huds.)   Common Cudweed. **N,C**   Locally frequent.   Map 375

On bare, sandy or gravelly roadsides, heathland tracks, borders of arable fields or waste ground, and in old pits; chiefly on acid soil. Locally frequent in the SW, rare and sporadic elsewhere; certainly rarer than formerly.

VC11: Rockford Common 1608, old gravel-pit, *RPB* 1986; Passford House Farm, Mount Pleasant 2997, abundant on pit-banks, *RPB* 1991; Beaulieu old airfield 3500, *BSBI* 1983; Hillier's Arboretum, Abbotswood 3723, *HJMB* 1987. **VC12**: Edge of field near Fren-

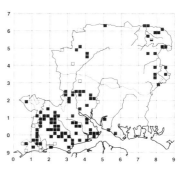

Map 375 Filago vulgaris

sham Pond Hotel 8339, abundant, *HCA-H* 1977; Headley 5162, gravel-workings, *PB* 1987; Yateley Common 8158, *AB* 1972, *CRH* 1991; Silver Fox Farm, Blackbushe 8059, *CRH* 1988; Sunny Hill Road, Aldershot 8450, *VL* c.1959, *ARGM* c.1980, since overgrown; Langley, Liss 8028, fallow field, *FF* 1991.

F. lutescens JORD. (*F. apiculata* G. E. Sm. ex Bab.) Red-tipped Cudweed. **N,C** Very rare (Sched. 8) Plate IX

On open, sandy ground, and formerly in sandy cornfields. Like *Pulicaria vulgaris*, this plant has suffered from the modern absence of grazing. From about 14 records in *Fl.Hants* (p.218) and *Suppl.Fl.Hants* (p.54), only three are comparatively modern, of which one alone is extant.
VC11: Hengistbury Head c.1690, *JEL* 1924–27. **VC12**: Winchfield c.7454, sandy field with *F. vulgaris*, *ALS* 1939; Broomhurst Farm 8156, several plants on sandy ground disturbed for road-widening, Hb.AB 1980 (*Watsonia* 13: 338), disappeared by 1981. Conservation work by the HWT in 1986, involving deliberate soil disturbance, led to two plants appearing in 1987. Other plants appeared 500m away, also in 1987, following disturbance of the soil when a street-lamp was erected. Seeds were collected from these and sown on the original site, resulting in 38 plants in 1988. Management of the site in most subsequent winters has produced a maximum count of 178 plants in 1992. The colony is extant, *CRH* 1995.

F. pyramidata L. (*F. spathulata* auct., non C. Presl) Broad-leaved Cudweed. **N** Very rare or extinct (Sched. 8)

On bare gravelly soil.
VC11: Ashley Heath c.1204, *MPY* c.1965, det. *BM*; Beaulieu Heath 3599, old gravel-pit near B3054, Hb.AWW 1957, site now filled in. **VC12**: West Down, Chilbolton 3838, c.50 plants in bare, gravelly, chalk soil in old gravel-pit used as a tip, Hb.RPB 1974, det. *JEL* (*Watsonia* 10: 429), site since levelled and overgrown.

F. arvensis L. Field Cudweed. **C** Very rare

First record, J. Ounsted 1986, Kingston North Common 1403, VC11, neglected, weedy, arable field, transient, Hb.RPB, det. *FR & JRPr*.

F. minima (SM.) PERS. Small Cudweed. **N** Locally common Map 376

First record, M. de Lobel before 1616, 'neere Petersfield', VC11/VC12 (ms note on fol.1 of W. How's own copy of his *Phyt.Brit.*, in library of Magdalen College, Oxford (*Early Brit.Bots*, p.280).
On dry, bare sand or gravel on heaths, roadside verges, old railway lines, tracks in old pits, and fallow fields. Only locally common, on acid soil, especially in the New Forest and Woolmer Forest, W of Aldershot and Bramshill Common.

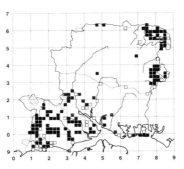

Map 376 *Filago minima*

<F. gallica L. Narrow-leaved Cudweed. **N** Extinct

The only record, Miss C. Davidson 1928, Exton, VC11 (*Suppl.Fl.Hants*, p.55).>

<Antennaria dioica (L.) GAERTN. Mountain Everlasting. **N** Extinct

First record, W. L. W. Eyre 1883, Swarraton, VC12, 'a considerable patch' (*Fl.Hants*, p.220).
Formerly in dry, chalk grassland; extinct through conversion of most of this habitat to arable or ley grasslands. Lane End Down, Beauworth 5525 or 5526 (Gander Down), VC11, *PMH* 1913 (*Rep.Winch.Coll.N.H.S.* 1927–31, p.14), 70 female heads in dense patch, *JNM* 1931 (*Proc.Hants Fld Club* 12: 82), *WHP et al* 1932 (*Rep.B.E.C.* for 1932, p.222). No record since.>

Anaphalis margaritacea (L.) BENTH. Pearly Everlasting. **H** Very rare

First record, Miss A. Woodhouse 1886, 'on the edge of a fir wood half a mile from Beacon Hill' (W of Warnford 6222), VC11 (*Fl.Hants*, excl.sp., p.240).
VC11: Salisbury Trench Inclosure 2514, opening amongst heather, by

gravel ride, *LC* 1966 (*Rep.S'ton N.H.S.*, p.12); Brockenhurst railway c.3102, *AMD & JMD* 1963; Brockenhurst–Lymington railway embankment, *JG* 1968, det. *RPB* (*Rep.S'ton N.H.S.*, p.14); Bagnum 1702, disused railway, *KK* 1970. **VC12**: Anton Lakes 3546, extensive patch, *MFW* 1992; near B3013, Yateley Heath Wood 8157, overgrown by plantation and last seen, *DEB* 1965.

Gnaphalium sylvaticum L. Heath Cudweed. **N** Locally frequent Map 377

First record, T. Bell Salter 1832, New Forest near Stoney Cross c.2511, VC11, Hb.QMC.
On dry, bare sand or gravel, or on Clay-with-flints over chalk. In sparse turf over heaths, mainly along tracks, and in bare rides in woods; in old sand-pits. It reappears in old sites when they are cleared. Rather rare in the SW and NW, but locally frequent in the NE.
VC8: Queens Copse, Melchet Park 2621, open, sandy track, *RPB* 1966. **VC11**: Pilley Bailey 3398, track on heath, *MR* 1976; Hyden Wood c.6818, *JRw* 1991; Ridley Plain 2006, track through heather, *RPB* 1970–89; Wilverley Plain 2501, reseeded lawn, *CB* 1988. **VC12**: Faccombe Wood 3955, *DEA & AB* 1975; Headley gravel-workings 5162, *PB* 1987; N end of Micheldever Wood 5337, *DEA* 1975; Monkwood 6730, in area cleared two years before, *AB* 1977, *EAP* 1983; Southwood 8354, c.400 to 1100 plants, *CRH* 1984–91; Bordon old railway 7836, *AB* 1989; Bramdean Common 6329, *PAB* 1988.

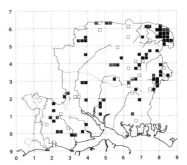

Map 377 *Gnaphalium sylvaticum*

G. uliginosum L. Marsh Cudweed. **N** Locally very common

In damp situations such as flood hollows, borders of arable fields, pond-margins, damp paths, track-ruts on heaths, and wet, woodland rides. Generally common, though less so on the chalk.

<G. luteoalbum L. Jersey Cudweed. **C** Extinct (Sched. 8)

Casual. Last record, F. H. Arnold 1886, Hayling Island, VC11 (*Fl.Hants*, p.220)>

Inula helenium L. Elecampane. **H,D** Very rare

First record, W. Pamplin 1848, by the roadside not far from Preston Candover *c*.6041, VC12 (*Phytologist* **3**: 431).

This handsome garden-plant exists as a rare outcast, generally by a road where it is a great survivor unless deliberately destroyed.
VC11: Christchurch, by the Priory, *NDS* 1929; Redbridge Lane, Nursling 3816, *RPB* 1952–88. Also 1604, 4498. **VC12**: Preston Candover, rough meadow on site of old garden, *NEGC* *c*.1940 (*Fl.Bas.MS*, p.7); Empshott Green 7430, *MS-W* 1971; foot of Worldham Hill 7538, known for years, *AB* 1989; Burghclere *c*.4761, *CL* 1962. Also 3444, 3642.

I. conyzae (GRIESS.) MEIKLE (*I. conyza* DC.) Ploughman's-spikenard. **N** Locally frequent Map 378

First record, Gilbert White 1766, Selborne, VC12 (*White's Jnls* **1**: 216).

Fairly common in short grassland and bare ground on the chalk; on hedgebanks, in scrub, old chalk-pits, waste land and on walls. Also, very locally, in gravelly places near the SW coast, along old airfield runways in the New Forest, and about ruins.

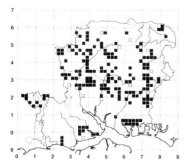

Map 378 Inula conyzae

I. crithmoides L. Golden-samphire. **N** Very locally frequent Map 379

First record, John Ray 1670, marsh near Hurst Castle, VC11 (*Ray Syn..*, pp.174–175).

In the upper parts of gravelly and muddy salt-marshes, often among *Atriplex portulacoides* (sea-purslane); also on the face of sea-walls. Almost confined to the shores of Portsmouth, Langstone and Chichester harbours.
VC11: Milford *c*.2991, *EC* 1945; Hurst spit 3189, 3190, plentiful, and Keyhaven Marshes 3191, *RPB* 1951–92; Needs Ore Point 4297, small patch on bank of creek in salt-marsh, *RPB* 1992; Langstone 7005, *EAP* 1983, *FR & RPB* 1993.

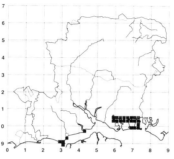

Map 379 Inula crithmoides

Pulicaria dysenterica (L.) BERNH. Common Fleabane. **N** Locally very common

First British record, ?W. Bayley *c*.1570–72, 'In diches evrywhere about Winchester', VC11/12 (ms note, thought to be by Dr Walter Bayley, under *Conyza media* on p.390 of a copy of Du Pinet's *Historia Plantarum* 1561, Botany Library, BM(NH) (see *Early Brit.Bots*, pp.235–236)).

On streamsides, in ditches, marshy meadows, fens, wet, woodland rides; common, particularly on wet clay. Occasional on quite dry roadside verges, even on the chalk. 'The Herbe burned, where flies, Gnats, fleas, or any venemous things are, doth drive them away.' (*Ger.em.Johns.*, p.485).

P. vulgaris GAERTN. Small Fleabane. **N** Rare (Sched. 8) Map 380 Plate X

Beside ponds, in marshy flood hollows, damp, grassy verges, shallow ditches and muddy track-ruts; nearly always in places inundated in winter but drying in summer. Constant grazing and disturbance by trampling of ponies and cattle seem necessary for its survival. It has almost died out throughout nearly

all NW Europe, with the exception of the New Forest, where the traditional grazing pattern has been maintained. Here it is frequently associated with *Persicaria hydropiper, P. minor, Mentha pulegium, Rorippa palustris* and *Plantago major*. A few plants survive in two sites in VC12, close to the Berks boundary. In 1990, a survey of the British population by the *HFG*, estimated that S Hants contained some 99 per cent of the total of about 10,000 plants. There is considerable annual fluctuation in population size in the New Forest as a whole and at individual sites (*Watsonia* **18**: 405–406).
VC11: Pithouse Farm, Hurn 1398, *NDS* 1931–54, *AJB & RPB* 1987; South Gorley 1610, *MPY* 1968, *GHF* 1992; Biddlecombe Farm, Cadnam 2913, 5000+ plants, *GDF* 1991; Cadnam Green 2914, *RPB* 1976–91; Bartley 3012, *RPB* 1962, *FR* 1982; Pooksgreen, Marchwood 3710, one plant, *SS* 1962, no record since; Brockenhurst South Weirs 2801, Hb.AWW 1957, *FR* 1987, *RPB* 1994. **VC12**: Springwater Farm, Bramshill 7462, *AMS* 1960, *ADRH* 1978, *FR & PB* 1982–83, 59 plants, *CC* 1993; Ashford Hill meadows 5662, *PB* 1988. At Bramshill, the fleabane was originally lost to road-widening, although *EAB & PHB* moved some plants to near Riseley Mill 7262, by the river; later refound at Springwater Farm in two nearby fields.

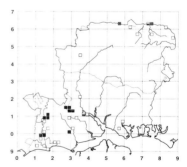

Map 380 Pulicaria vulgaris

Solidago virgaurea L. Goldenrod. **N** Locally common Map 381

First record, Gilbert White 1766, Selborne, VC12 (*White's Jnls* **1**: 212). On grass-heaths, in dry woods, borders of pastures, rocky lanes on the sand. Common on acid soil, but apparently infrequent in the central New Forest. It usually avoids chalk grassland although it is occasional on leached slopes of downs and on chalk superficials. All but absent from the Wealden Edge hanger woodlands, but it has been found on the Malmstone in Longmead Copse, Hawkley 7428, VC12, *APNH* 1980.

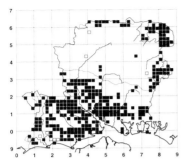

Map 381 Solidago virgaurea

S. canadensis L. (*S. altissima* L.) Canadian Goldenrod. **H** Local and occasional

A garden relic on roadsides, waste places, stream-banks and rubbish-tips. Outcast goldenrod is very persistent. Some records may well refer to one of the following species.

S. gigantea AITON ssp. **serotina** (KUNTZE) McNEILL (*S. serotina* Aiton, non Retz.) Early Goldenrod. **H** Rare or under-recorded

On roadsides and in waste places.
VC11: Test Lane, Redbridge 3614, Hb.RPB 1975, det. *CJ*. Also 3096, 3810, 3814, 4012, 4614, 6606, 6608. VC12: Near Broomhurst Farm, Fleet 8056, *AB* 1980. Also 7240, 7634, 7834, 7836, 7838.

S. graminifolia (L.) SALISB. (*S. lanceolata* L.) Grass-leaved Goldenrod. **H** Very rare or under-recorded

On roadsides and waste places.
VC11: Swaythling 4414, *WP* 1968. Also 4614, 4822. VC12: Andwell 6852, bridge over M3, *AB* 1980. Also 2846, 3244, 7252, 8434.

Aster novae-angliae L. Hairy Michaelmas-daisy. **H** Under-recorded

In waste places, sandy ground, roadsides near villages, railway banks, and tips. There are very few records.
VC11: 1604, 2492, 4214. VC12: 3044, 5038.

A. laevis L. Glaucous Michaelmas-daisy. **H** Very rare

VC11: 4614. VC12: Fullerton 3839, disused railway, Hb.RPB 1975, det. *PFY*. Also 7834.

A. x versicolor WILLD. (*A. laevis* x *A. novi-belgii*) Late Michaelmas-daisy. **H** Rare or under-recorded

VC11: Lee near Romsey 3617, refuse-tip, Hb.RPB 1977, det. *PFY*. Also 3094, 3298, 3416, 4216, 4614, 3832. VC12: 3838, 7834.

A. novi-belgii L. Confused Michaelmas-daisy. **H** Local and occasional

In similar sites to *A. novae-angliae*.
VC11: Titchfield Haven 5302, old gravel-pit, Hb.RPB 1975, det. *PFY*.

A. x salignus WILLD. (*A. novi-belgii* x *A. lanceolatus*) Common Michaelmas-daisy. **H** Under-recorded

First record, G. A. R. Watts 1932, Fleet Pond, E side 8254, VC12, det. *NYS* (*Watts MSS; Proc.Hants Fld Club* 12: 295), still there, *CRH* 1992.
VC9: 0494. VC11: 0894, 1204, 1412, 2200, 4210, 5008, 6000, 6404. VC12: By the Basingstoke Canal in Aldershot 8751, Hb.AB 1976, det. *PFY*. Also 4238, 7052, 7834.

A. lanceolatus WILLD. Narrow-leaved Michaelmas-daisy. **H** Local and occasional

On streamsides, in muddy willow-holts, even in the tidal zone; railway banks and refuse-tips; probably frequent, and the most established naturalized *Aster* species in Hants.
VC11: R. Test, Testwood 3614, Hb.RPB 1977, det. *PFY*. Also 0892, 1490, 1602, 3414, 3612, 3814, 4210, 4620, 4806, 5008, 5604, 6004, 6098, 6400, 6402, 6404, 6600, 6602, 6898, 7006. VC12: 4444, 6458, 7458.

A. tripolium L. Sea Aster. **N** Locally common

Common on coastal and estuarine salt-marshes or shores, sea-walls and reclaimed land; rarely in wet gravel-pits near the coast. VC11: 72 □.
VC11: Frequent on verges of the A3, from N of Bedhampton to Cowplain, having spread with the use of de-icing salt, *FR* 1988; Fields Heath gravel-pit 4502, *RPB* 1966; Nursling gravel-pit 3515, *RPB* 1962, infilled *c*.1970.

Erigeron glaucus KER GAWL. Seaside Daisy, Beach Aster. **H** Rare

First record, Mrs C. I. Sandwith 1942, established on cliffs at Bournemouth, VC11 (*Rep.B.E.C.* for 1945, p.29).
VC11: Bournemouth cliffs 0890, *MPY* 1966, *RPB* 1978; Hengistbury 1891, sand-spit, *RPB* 1985. Also 1090, 1290, 1490, 2092, 2292, 4498.

E. karvinskianus DC. (*E. mucronatus* DC.) Mexican Fleabane. **H** Very rare

Introduced on walls.
VC11: Kimbridge 3325, wall along stream, Hb.RPB 1975 (*Rep.S'ton N.H.S.*, p.12); Titchfield Square 5405, on walls and paving, *RFG* 1990. VC12: St John's Church, Winchester 4829, S wall of tower, *KC* 1987. Also 7250.

E. annuus (L.) PERS. ssp. **strigosus** (MÜHL. EX WILLD.) WAGENITZ (*E. strigosus* Mühl. ex Willd.) Tall Fleabane. **C** Very rare

VC12: Longmoor airstrip 8131, *AB* 1975–86, det. *EJC* (*Watsonia* 11: 399).

E. acer L. Blue Fleabane. **N** Frequent Map 382

First British record, J. Goodyer 1621, 'growinge wild on the walls at Winchester', VC11/12 (*Early Brit. Bots*, p.163).
In dry places, in pastures, on bare ground, banks, roadside verges, old pits and disused railways. Frequent, especially on the chalk, also on gravel and Headon clays, and locally on bare, sandy heathland. It appears to have increased since *Fl.Hants*, where it is described (p.226, as *E. acre*) as 'not common, though generally distributed'.

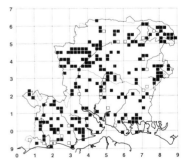

Map 382 Erigeron acer

Conyza canadensis (L.) CRONQUIST (*Erigeron canadensis* L.) Canadian Fleabane. **C** Locally common Map 383

First record, W. Wickham 1877, one casual at Binsted Wyck, VC12 (*Bell's Selb.* **2**: 370).

On bare, dry waste-ground, roadsides, railways, at the foot of walls, and on pavements; also on disturbed, sandy or gravelly heathland and arable, occasionally on chalk. Locally common around large built-up areas, in the Avon Valley, and on the NE heathlands, but only occasional elsewhere. Townsend regarded it as very rare but correctly predicted that it would multiply rapidly. His three records were all in the NE, rather suggesting that it reached Hants from Surrey and London, as indeed *Atlas Brit.Fl.* (p.281) bears out.

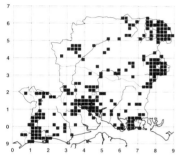

Map 383 Conyza canadensis

C. sumatrensis (RETZ.) E. WALKER (*Erigeron sumatrensis* Retz., *Conyza albida* Willd. ex Spreng.) Guernsey Fleabane. **C** Rare

First record, D. P. J. Smith & G. D. Kitchener 1994, by A3 Portsmouth 6401, VC11, amongst shrubs by footpath, conf. *EJC*, Hb.RPB.

Scattered plants have also been found along other roadsides in central Portsmouth.

VC11: Keswick Road, Woolston, Southampton 4311, two plants, *PS* 1994, conf. *EJC*. Also 3612, 4010, 4410, 4416.

C. cf. bilbaoana REMY **C** Very rare

First British record, P. D. Stanley 1994, Keswick Road, Woolston Southampton 4311, VC11, on waste ground, Hb.RPB, det. *EJC*.

This recently-recognized alien has been found in at least six other roadside and waste-ground sites close to the docks and waterfront in Southampton and may well spread outwards to other areas. It is thought to be a native of S America.

VC11: Also 4010, 4208, 4410, 4412.

Bellis perennis L. Daisy. **N** Abundant

Ubiquitous in short grassland on all soils.

Tanacetum parthenium (L.) SCH.BIP. (*Chrysanthemum parthenium* (L.) Bernh.) Feverfew. **D** Locally frequent

Originally introduced as a herb, today it is fairly common around built-up areas, in waste and disturbed ground, on walls or on tips. The double-flowered (*flore-pleno*) variety of gardens is more frequent in NE urban areas. It is still used as a cure for migraine.

T. vulgare L. (*Chrysanthemum vulgare* (L.) Bernh., non (Lam.) Gaterau) Tansy. **N,D** Locally frequent

On banks of rivers and streams, roadside verges, grassy borders of fields and commons. Native and common in some river valleys, frequent elsewhere, often originating from former cultivation, but these records are sometimes difficult to separate.

VC11: R. Blackwater, Nursling 3415, *RPB* 1952. **VC12**: R. Hart, Elvetham to M3 7755, *AB* 1978.

'In the spring time are made with the leaves hereof newly sprung up, and with egs, cakes or tansies, which be pleasant in taste, and good for the stomacke.. ..The seed of Tansie is a singular and approoved medicine against Wormes.' (*Ger.em.Johns.*, p.651). For the latter purpose, it is still in use.

Seriphidium maritimum (L.) POLJAKOV (*Artemisia maritima* L.) Sea Wormwood. **N** Very locally frequent   Map 384

First record, J. Gerard 1597, 'Sea

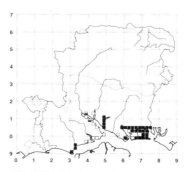

Map 384 Seriphidium maritimum

Mugwort groweth...at Portsmouth by the Isle of Wight', VC11 (*Ger.Herb.*, p.946).

On sea-walls, and the upper parts of shingly salt-marshes. Frequent on the shores of Portsmouth, Langstone and Chichester Harbours. Now rare in the W Solent; only in the lower Hamble estuary, and from Hurst to Pennington Marshes.

VC11: Hurst spit salt-marsh 3190, *RPB* 1984. Gone from Millbrook Point 3912, and Dibden Bay 4008.

Artemisia vulgaris L. Mugwort. **N?,D** Common

In waysides, hedges, borders of fields and waste ground. Very common everywhere except the New Forest. Used to this day as a digestive stimulant and as an aid to depression but in ancient times it was used to ease childbirth.

A. verlotiorum LAMOTTE Chinese Mugwort. **C** Rare

First records, J. Cadbury 1962, Langstone 7005, and Miss W. F. Buckle 1962, Millbrook 3812, VC11 (*Rep.S'ton N.H.S.*, p.8), both on refuse-tips.

In verges and hedges, and on tips. How this plant reached Europe is shrouded in mystery, but since its arrival it has spread widely. A very rare and local weed in SW China, it was first noticed in France in 1876, possibly as a result of French military operations in China. It may have been deliberately spread in Europe for medicinal use. In England, first collected on Hounslow Heath, Middlesex, VC21, in 1908, probably introduced as rhizomes mixed up with imported plants. J.P.M. Brenan considered that, as it flowers too late in this country to set seed, its propagation must be entirely through discarded rhizomes (*Watsonia* 1: 209).

VC11: Near Beauworth 5724, *RHJ* 1973, *GHF* 1977. Also 4210, 4806, 5824, 6000, 6002, 6404, 6600. **VC12**: Cheriton 5728, on bridleway, *KC* 1980. Also 5828.

A. absinthium L. Wormwood. **C,D** Very local and rare   Map 385

On waste ground, bare roadsides, railways and tips, especially near ports. Frequent about Southampton, less so around Portsmouth; rare elsewhere. It is still used in modern herbalism for indigestion and for worms.

VC11: Cracknore Hard Lane, Marchwood 4010, *RPB* 1984. **VC12**:

Vigo Lane, Blackbushe 8059, on tipped soil, *CRH* 1986–87.

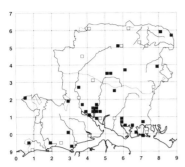

Map 385 Artemisia absinthium

<**Otanthus maritimus** (L.) Hoff-MANNS. & LINK   Cottonweed.   N
Extinct

First record, J. Goodyer 1621, 'one plant...on the seashoare on the south parte of the Iland of Haylinge', VC11 (*Early Brit.Bots*, p.148).
    VC11: Sand bank, Mudeford *c*.1891, *HMWi, BK & JGr* 1879 (*J.Bot.*, p.344); bank washed away, but the plant reappeared nearby. Not refound 1892 (*Fl.Hants*, p.216). If our climate is really getting warmer, this Mediter-ranean–southern Atlantic species may recolonize; it is still locally abundant on the Normandy coast, E of Cherbourg.>

Achillea ptarmica L.   Sneezewort.
N   Locally common   Map 386

In damp, grassy heaths and old pastures, acid marshes, and pond-margins; common on all acid soils, especially clay. The very few records for the chalk areas are probably from wet locations. 'The smell of this plant procureth sneezing.' (*Ger.em.Johns.*, p.606)

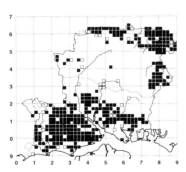

Map 386 Achillea ptarmica

A. millefolium L.   Yarrow.   N
Abundant

Ubiquitous in grassland of all types.

Chamaemelum nobile (L.) ALL.
Chamomile.   N,H   Locally frequent
Map 387

First record, Gilbert White 1766, Selborne, VC12 (*White's Jnls* 1: 215).
    In short, grazed turf on dry, grassy heaths, commons, old pastures and roadsides; confined to acid soil. Common in the New Forest; rare on the NE and SE Tertiaries. It is some-times used in lawns as it thrives on being trampled. This is probably why it is locally plentiful on some playing fields in VC12.
    VC8: Lopshill Common 0913, *RPB* 1986. **VC11**: Browndown 5899, *AWW* 1952. **VC12**: Hook Common 7252, *DEB* 1968; Hazeley Heath *c*.7458, *ECW & FR* 1975; several sports-fields in Aldershot and Farnborough, e.g. 8652, 8551, *ARGM* 1983–90, *CRH* 1993; Hartley Wintney cricket-ground 7656, *APHo* 1970, *HWi* 1993.

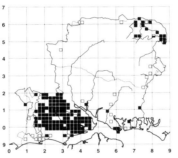

Map 387 Chamaemelum nobile

Anthemis arvensis L.   Corn
Chamomile.   C   Local   Map 388

An arable and waste-ground weed of the chalk. Frequent on the northern chalk in the 1960s; only a casual on the

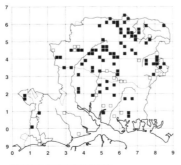

Map 388 Anthemis arvensis

sand. However, by the 1980s crop-spraying had reduced it considerably.
    VC8: Tidpit Common Down, Martin 0717, headland of wheat-field, *RPB* 1986. **VC11**: A338, Ellingham Cross 1408, on disturbed soil, Hb.RPB 1988. **VC12**: Worthy Down 4535, disturbed soil of oil-exploration site, *AB* 1988; Tichborne Down 5831, edge of arable field, *ARGM* 1988; Stapely Down 7448, *CRH* 1990, det. *FR*.

A. cotula L.   Stinking Chamomile.
C   Locally common   Map 389

First record, Gilbert White 1765, Selborne, VC12 (*White's Jnls* 1: 166).
    An arable and waste-ground weed, common on chalk and clay soils in the N, very local in the S.

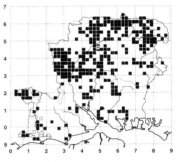

Map 389 Anthemis cotula

A. tinctoria L.   Yellow Chamomile.
D,H   Very rare

First record, G. C. Druce 1904, Southampton, VC11 (*Fl.Hants*, excl. sp., p.241).
    Rarely established, otherwise only a casual. Used as a dye.
    VC11: Established at IBM, North Harbour, Cosham 6404, in two patches, beside a brackish lake, *RBa* 1989. Also 4412, 4614. **VC12**: Hazeley Heath dump 7657, *GARW* 1936 (*Watts MSS*). Also 7038, 8650.

Chrysanthemum segetum L.
Corn Marigold.   C   Locally frequent
Map 390

First record, Gilbert White 1766, Selborne, VC12 (*White's Jnls* 1: 213).
    A cornfield weed of the sand, once common but steadily decreasing throughout the time of our recording, although it has withstood herbicide spraying longer than many other corn-field weeds. 'The stalks and leaves of Corne Marigold....are eaten as other pot-herbes are.' (*Ger.em.Johns.*, p.745).

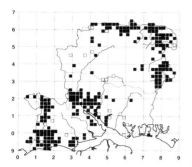

Map 390 Chrysanthemum segetum

Leucanthemella serotina (L.)
TZVELEV (*Chrysanthemum serotinum*
L.)   Autumn Oxeye.   **H**

VC12: A long-standing patch, at the
foot of Worldham Hill 7538, along
with *Inula helenium*, *AB* 1964–78, det.
DMcC.

Leucanthemum vulgare LAM.
(*Chrysanthemum leucanthemum* L.)
Oxeye Daisy.   **N,C**   Common

Native in old grassland; colonizes bare,
gravelly banks, roadside and railway
verges. Common on all fertile soils.
Gerard calls it 'Maudelen woort' and
says 'the herbe is good to be put into
vulnerarie drinkes or potions, as one
simple belonging thereto most neces-
sarie, to the which effect the best prac-
tised do use it' (*Ger.Herb.*, p.509).

L. x superbum (BERGMANS ex J. W.
INGRAM) D. H. KENT (*L.* x *maximum*
hort., non (Ramond) DC.; *Chrysanthe-
mum* x *maximum* hort., non Ramond;
L. lacustre (Brot.) Samp. x *L. maximum*
(Ramond) DC.)   Shasta Daisy.   **H**
Occasional

First record, R. P. Bowman 1958,
Miller's Pond, Sholing 4511, VC11, on
sandy waste-ground.
   A garden throw-out. In old pits, on
disturbed verges, and tips; also on
slipped clay on cliffs.
   VC11: Barton on Sea cliffs 2392,
RPB 1977. Also 1092, 1292, 1800,
2200, 2894, 3226, 3294, 3414, 3602,
6404. **VC12**: Weyhill *c.*3046, abundant
in roadside chalk-cutting, *GDF* 1984,
MFW 1989. Also 2244, 2844, 3660,
4828, 6852, 7042, 7638, 8236.

Matricaria recutita L.   Scented
Mayweed.   **C**   Frequent and locally
common   Map 391

An arable and waste-ground weed on
light soils; commonest on sandy loams,

more local on other soils. This is the
plant used in chamomile tea.

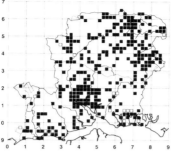

Map 391 Matricaria recutita

M. discoidea DC. (*M. matricarioides*
(Less.) Porter, *pro parte*)   Pineapple-
weed.   **C**   Very common

First record, E. F. Linton 1903, near
the mill, Christchurch 1593, VC11
(*Fl.Bmth App.1*).
   In muddy waysides, roadside verges
and fields and heavily-trodden gate-
ways. A native of Asia, naturalized in
N America, this plant was first
recorded in Britain in 1871. The fruits
have no pappus, but are distributed in
mud. The motor car, from 1900
onwards, was such an effective dispersal agent that it is now practically ubiquitous (E. J. Salisbury in *Ch.Fl.Brit.*,
p.135).

Tripleurospermum maritimum
(L.) KOCH (*T. maritimum* ssp. *maritimum*)   Sea Mayweed.   **N**   Locally
frequent   Map 392

On the strand-line, on shingle, muddy
seashores, and in the spray-zone on
cliffs; frequent to occasional along the
coast. Intermediates with *T. inodorum*
are found in arable behind shores
where the latter is present.
   VC11: In 1988, *RPB* found 16 sites

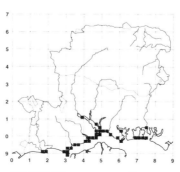

Map 392 Tripleurospermum maritimum

for *T. maritimum*, from Sturt Pond,
Keyhaven 2990, to Sinah Common
beach 6899. At Lisle Court shore 3595,
Browndown beach, Gosport 5898, and
Mengham sea-wall, Hayling Island
7399, plants were intermediate. At
Fort Gilkicker, Gosport 6097, plants
were slightly introgressed by *T. inodorum*. All det. *QK*.

T. inodorum (L.) SCH.BIP. (*T. mariti-
mum* ssp. *inodorum* (L.) Hyl. ex
Vaarama)   Scentless Mayweed.   **C**
Very common

A very common weed of arable and
waste land.

Cotula coronopifolia L.   Button-
weed.   **C**   Very rare

First record, D. P. J. Smith 1991,
Tipner, Portsmouth 6403, VC11, a few
plants on sandy shingle at the foot of
scrapyard slipway at drift-line in
harbour, probably from drifted seed,
det. *RPB & EJC*, Hb.RPB (*BSBI
News* 60: 35).

Senecio cineraria DC. (*S. bicolor*
(Willd.) Tod. ssp. *cineraria* (DC.)
Chater)   Silver Ragwort.   **H**   Very
rare

First record, J. Lamb 1915,
Christchurch, VC11 (*Suppl.Fl.Hants*,
p.58).
   Naturalized on the coast.
   VC11: Cliffs and shingle beaches at
Bournemouth 0890–1491, *MPY* 1966,
RPB 1978; Eastney 6798, *RMB* 1969,
Hb.RPB 1978; South Hayling 7198,
AB 1986; Needs Ore Point 4297, *RPB*
1993.

S. x albescens BURB. & COLGAN (*S.
cinerea* x *S. jacobaea*)   **H**   Very rare

VC11: Bournemouth 0990, cliff-top,
GHF 1986; Southbourne 1590, on
shingle, *RPB* 1978; Petersfield 7523,
Hb.RPB 1981, det. *CJ*; South Hayling
7198, Hb.AB 1983, det. *CJ*, now
destroyed. Also 1616, 2690.

S. fluviatilis WALLR.   Broad-leaved
Ragwort.   **H**   Very rare

On or near stream banks; generally
planted.
   VC11: St Cross 4727, roadside near
stream, *KC* 1981, (near the site of a
former nursery). **VC12**: Kings Worthy
4932, streamside-path, *RHJ* 1965,
gone by 1983 (*AB*). There are also
records for the site at Ashford 7326,
where, according to *Fl.Hants* (excl.sp.,

p.241, as *S. saracenicus* L. [*sic*.]), it was probably planted by the Revd J. Hawker.

S. jacobea L.   Common Ragwort.
N   Very common

First record, J. Goodyer 1659, 'Mr Tho. Bartar of Petersfeild... gathered this...on Ladle Hill' 4756, VC12 (*Early Brit.Bots*, p.194).

In neglected grassland on all soils, and on sandy and shingly beaches.

S. x ostenfeldii DRUCE (*S. jacobaea* x *S. aquaticus*)   **N**   Very rare or under-recorded

First record, J. F. Rayner 1922, Bassett, VC11 (*Rep.B.E.C.* for 1927, p.401).

VC8: Whitsbury Wood 1318, *JDG* 1960, det. *JEL* (*Suppl.Fl.Wilts*, p.31). VC11: Norleywood 3698, *AJS* 1980; Cadnam Green 2914, *MEY & AB* 1980; Crock Hill, Cadnam Common 2915, Hb.RPB 1985; Matley Passage 3307, *WFS c.*1970s, comm. *KC*; Worts Gutter, Furzey Lodge 3602, *GHF* 1990. VC12: Hollywater 8034, *AB* 1965, det. *JEL*.

S. aquaticus HILL   Marsh Ragwort.
N   Locally common   Map 393

In wet pastures, marshes, ponds, ditches and streamsides. Commonest in the New Forest, emphasizing its western affinity. On the chalk, it is only in the river valleys.

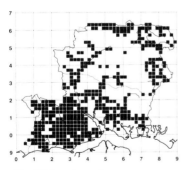

Map 393 Senecio aquaticus

S. erucifolius L.   Hoary Ragwort.
N   Locally common

First record, Gilbert White 1766, Fyfield, VC12 (*White's Jnls* 1: 206).

In scrub, borders of woods, rough pastures, banks and roadside verges. Common on the chalk and on heavy clay, local elsewhere.

S. squalidus L.   Oxford Ragwort.
H,C   Locally common   Map 394

First record, Miss L. C. Blake 1914, Great Western Station, Winchester 4729, VC12 (*Suppl.Fl.Hants*, p.57).

On railway banks, waste and bare ground, walls and pavings, bare banks, and shingle on the coast. Widespread and common in and around all large urban areas, and on some railways. Local and scattered elsewhere but still increasing.

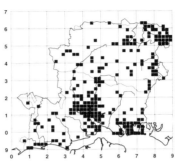

Map 394 Senecio squalidus

S. x baxteri DRUCE (*S. squalidus* x *S. vulgaris*)   **C**   Very rare or under-recorded

The F1 generation has been recorded at:
VC11: Southsea *c.*6498, *AWW* 1951; Millbrook, Southampton *c.*3912, Hb.AB 1971, det. *JEL*; Bedhampton Tip 7005, *ANHS* 1983, det. *AB*. VC12: New Road, Basingstoke 6351, *DEA* 1992.

S. x subnebrodensis SIMONK. (*S. x londinensis* Lousley; *S. squalidus* x *S. viscosus*)   **C**   Very rare

First record, A. W. Westrup 1958, Millbrook 3912, VC11, Hb.AWW.

VC11: South Hayling 7098, on shingle, Hb.AB 1975, det. *FR*; Sinah Common 6999, *GHF* 1980, Hb.RPB 1982, det. *CJ*; Bar End Road, Winchester 4828, *AJC* 1978; Calshot 4702, Hb.RPB 1974; Westfield Common, Hamble 4706, on shingle-heap behind beach, Hb.RPB 1985.

S. vulgaris L.   Groundsel.   **N?,C**
Abundant

A very common weed of arable, waste ground and gardens, occasionally on sand or shingle beaches.

var. **hibernicus** SYME (var. *radiatus* auct., non Koch)

The radiate form has been recorded

occasionally, particularly on the coast. There is evidence that this has arisen by introgression from *S. squalidus*. VC11: 19 ☐; VC12: 2 ☐.

S. sylvaticus L.   Heath Groundsel.
N   Locally common   Map 395

In disturbed or burnt heathland and acid woodland-clearings where it is fairly common. Occasionally on superficial soils on chalk.

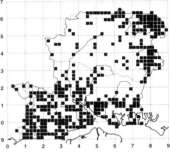

Map 395 Senecio sylvaticus

S. viscosus L.   Sticky Groundsel.
N,C   Locally frequent   Map 396

On railways, gravel-workings, bare waste-ground and roadside verges, coastal reclaimed-land and shingle. Widespread and locally frequent, especially along the network of existing and disused railways, and on the coast. It has much increased since *Fl.Hants* (p.221) which gave only two records, both in VC11.

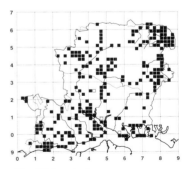

Map 396 Senecio viscosus

Tephroseris integrifolia (L.) HOLUB ssp. **integrifolia** (*Senecio integrifolius* (L.) Clairv.)   Field Fleawort.   **N** Rare   Map 397

First record, T. Yalden *c.*1770, 'on St Giles Hill, Winchester, near a chalk pit' 4829, VC12, Hb.BM (*Ray Syn. MS*, p.178).

On chalk downland, in short turf, often surviving on earthworks where the rest of the down has been ploughed. The map shows the distribution of this species following the same oblique belt through the downs as that of *Phyteuma orbiculare* (round-headed rampion) and the butterfly *Lysandra coridon* (Poda) (the chalk hill blue), though more sparsely, from War Down 7219 (where now non-extant) to Shipton Bellinger 2345. It is rather more frequent on the edge of Salisbury Plain.

VC8: Bokerley Ditch, Martin Down 0518, *RPB* 1964–93. **VC11**: Broughton Down 2832, 2833, plentiful, *PB & FR* 1986; Violet Hill 4127, *RPB* 1970; Beacon Hill, Warnford 6022, *FR* 1975–93. **VC12**: Ladle Hill 4756, *AB & FR* 1975–88; Shipton Bellinger 2345, *AB* 1981; Norn Hill, Basingstoke 6453, *NEGC c.*1942, site now built over.

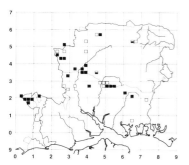

Map 397 Tephroseris integrifolia ssp. integrifolia

Sinacalia tangutica (MAXIM.) NORD. (*Senecio tanguticus* Maxim.)　Chinese Ragwort.　**H**　Very rare

This can establish itself on refuse-tips near water.

VC11: Casbrook Common tip 3525, *WFB* 1975. **VC12**: Sleaford tip　8038, *AB* 1966–68, now built upon.

Doronicum pardalianches L. Leopard's-bane.　**H**　Rare

First record, F. Browning 1929, Lithcot sand-pit, Petersfield, VC12 (*Suppl. Fl.Hants*, p.57).

An old-fashioned garden plant, to be found chiefly in places where it was once thrown out, e.g. old pits, roadsides, and wooded slopes below gardens, or where it has been naturalized. Gerard fancifully wrote: 'It is reported and affirmed, that it killeth Panthers, Swine, Wolves, and all kinds of wilde beasts, being given them with flesh.' (*Ger.Herb.*, p.759).

VC11: E side of A3057 Stockbridge 3534, *RPB* 1950. Also 1604, 2094, 2820. **VC12**: Bradshott Hill 7632, old Malmstone-pit, *AB* 1924–89; Isle of Wight Hill 2437, *DG* 1988. Also 4648, 4828, 7028, 7430, 8454.

D. plantagineum L.　Plantain-leaved Leopard's-bane.　**H**　Very rare

First confirmed record, Mrs A. Russell 1849, Sidmonton (*Phytologist* **3**: 716). This is Sydmonton chalk-pit 4962, VC12, *FR* 1973.

VC12: Highclere, *TJF* 1922, Hb.BM.

Tussilago farfara L.　Colt's-foot. **N,C**　Common

On bare or disturbed ground on banks, verges, riversides, cliffs, wasteland, and in old pits, especially where damp. It can be a troublesome garden weed. To this day, it is used by some for coughs and asthma.

Petasites hybridus (L.) P. GAERTN., B. MEY. & SCHERB.　Butterbur.　**N** Locally frequent　Map 398

First record, R. S. Hill 1836, banks of Basingstoke Canal, VC12 (*Fl.Hants*, p.228).

On banks of rivers and streams, marshy meadows; occasional on damp or even dry roadsides; fairly common on chalk, alluvial soils in the main valleys, very local or rare elsewhere. No female plants are known in Hants except for an introduced colony at Langstone Dairy Farm 7105, VC11. In former times it was evidently used for the same purpose as coltsfoot, for Gerard says it is 'is of great force against the suffocation [hysteria] of the mother' (*Ger.em.Johns.*, p.814.).

VC11: Bickton Mill 1412, *RPB* 1960–93; Emsworth 7506, E bank of millstream, *RPB* 1989. **VC12**: A31

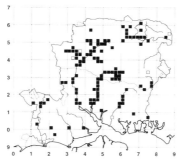

Map 398 Petasites hybridus

near Matterley Farm 5429, *RPB* 1968; Old Basing 6752; and Up Nately 6952, 7052, *CRH* 1992.

P. japonicus (SIEBOLD & ZUCC.) MAXIM.　Giant Butterbur.　**H**　Very rare

First record, R. P. Bowman 1966, Gully Copse, Curbridge 5212, VC11 (*Rep.S'ton N.H.S.*, p.12).

On marshy, shaded stream-banks.

VC11: R. Meon, West Meon 6423, *CDD* 1980. Also 3032, 4828, 6424.

P. albus (L.) GAERTNER　White Butterbur.　**H**　Very rare

First record, N. E. G. Cruttwell *c.*1940–45, Lychpit, Old Basing 6553, VC12, in chalky dell (*Fl.Bas.MS*, p.7). There has been much building in this area, but the habitat may still be intact.

P. fragrans (VILL.) C. PRESL　Winter Heliotrope.　**H**　Locally frequent

First record, J. Vaughan 1892, Portchester, VC11 (*Fl.Hants*, p.228)

A garden escape of remarkable permanence, now widely naturalized, especially on damp roadsides and near the coast. VC11: 86 □; VC12: 46 □.

Sigesbeckia serrata DC. (*S. jorullensis* auct., non Kunth)　Western St Paul's-wort, Indian-weed.　**H**　Very rare

First record, G. A. R. Watts 1935, fir plantation, Fleet 8054, VC12, 'probably introduced with poultry-food', Hb.RNG, det. *DLS* 1987 (*Watts MSS*, as *S. orientalis* L., in error; *Proc. B.S.B.I.* **7**: 19, as *S. cordifolia* H., B. & K. [Kunth in Humb., Bonpl. & Kunth]). However, it is not known in chicken-food but was a Victorian garden-curiosity which found its way to tips where, in sandy soil, the seeds were viable (E. J. Clement, pers. comm.).

This alien appears on rubbish-tips and disturbed soil around Aldershot, but the source is not known. The other records are:

VC12: Pondtail dump, Fleet 8253, *VL* 1958, Hb.RNG, det. *RKB*; same tip, *MMcC-W* 1960, Hb.K; Hazeley Heath dump 7558, *AB* 1967, det. *JEL*; Aldershot dump 8450, *DNT* 1969; Yateley Heath Wood 7958, and Hartfordbridge Flats 8058, plentiful on dumped earth, *EB & RCS* 1986, Hb.AB; Farnborough 8653, single plant on disturbed soil beside A325, *TD & ARGM* 1991, Hb.AB.

Rudbeckia hirta L. Bristly Cone-flower, Black-eyed-Susan. **H** Very rare

First records, Lady Anne Brewis 1982, South Hayling 7098, four plants well established on common, and F. Rose 1982, Tipner 6303, both VC11.

Galinsoga parviflora CAV. Gallant-soldier. **C** Very local
Map 399

First record, N. D. Simpson 1930, Southbourne, VC11, garden weed.

Probably spread from nurseries as a weed in gardens and waste ground. Mainly on the sand, about Bournemouth, Farnborough and Woolmer Forest, with a few other isolated records.

VC11: Western Docks, Southampton 3912, *WFB* 1962; Turkey Island, Shedfield 5612, weed in crop of marrows, Hb.RPB 1990. **VC12**: On rubbish dumped at Oakhanger Pond 7734, *PRy* 1984, det. *AB*; Farnborough Airfield 8451, *ARGM* 1986.

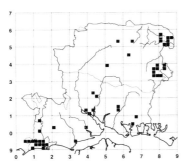

Map 399 Galinsoga parviflora

G. quadriradiata RUIZ & PAV. (*G. ciliata* (Raf.) S. F. Blake) Shaggy-soldier. **C** Very locally frequent
Map 400

First record, A. J. Maudsley 1943,

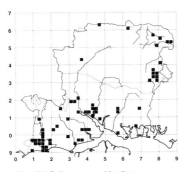

Map 400 Galinsoga quadriradiata

Hurn, VC11, comm. *AJW*, Hb.BM, (*Rep.B.E.C.* for 1943–44, p.730).

Probably also originating from nurseries as a garden and waste-ground weed, but slightly more frequent than *G. parviflora*.

VC11: Pikeshill, Lyndhurst 2909, weed on allotment, *AEB & JO* 1988; Mill Lane, Romsey 3421, abundant in neglected garden, *RMV* 1987; Norleywood 3597, in gardens, *MR* 1976. **VC12**: Hazeley Heath tip 7657, *RMB* 1968; Farnborough Airfield 8453, *ARGM* 1980; Hogmoor Road, Bordon 7835, cottage garden, *AB* 1962–80.

Bidens cernua L. Nodding Bur-marigold. **N** Locally frequent
Map 401

Beside marshy ponds and streams, meadow-ditches and wet gravel-pits; fairly common in the SW, infrequent in the NE, rare elsewhere, and mainly absent from calcareous wetlands.

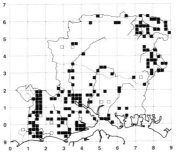

Map 401 Bidens cernua

B. tripartita L. Trifid Bur-marigold. **N** Locally common
Map 402

In very similar habitats to *B. cernua*, with which it often grows, but much the commoner in the SE and in the extreme NE.

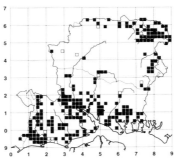

Map 402 Bidens tripartita

Eupatorium cannabinum L. Hemp-agrimony. **N** Locally common

First record, ?W. Bayley *c.*1570–72, 'In yᵉ dyche toward blak Bridge' Winchester, VC11 (ms note, believed to be by Dr Walter Bayley, under *Eupatorium Avicennae* on p.476 of a copy of Du Pinet's *Historia Plantarum* in Botany Library of BM(NH) (*Early Brit.Bots*, pp.235–236)).

In marshes, fens, stream-banks and wet, open woods. On the chalk, generally where the moisture is retained by Clay-with-flints or other chalk superficials; in hedges, woodland glades, and scrub on downs, and in old chalk-pits. Common in all but very acid wetland.

LILIIDAE (MONOCOTYLEDONS)

BUTOMACEAE

Butomus umbellatus L. Flowering-rush. **N** Very locally frequent
Map 403

First record, Miss C. R. May 1837, in a cut from the R. Avon, VC11 (*May Ptgs Cat.* no.787).

In rivers, streams and canals. Frequent throughout the R. Avon and R. Stour; rare elsewhere. It was once frequent by the Basingstoke Canal near Odiham, and at Crookham, Fleet and Aldershot, but was a casualty of the dredging, and is now much scarcer.

VC11: Lower Test, Nursling 3615, *RPB* 1955–88, 3614, colonizing newly-cut stream, *JWCP* 1990; Lymington River, Brockenhurst 3003, *PDG* 1978; R. Meon, Titchfield Haven 5302, drain in pasture close to river, *RPB* 1988. Formerly in Millers Pond, Sholing 4510, *RPB* 1958–65, but probably introduced. **VC12**: Basingstoke Canal, Ash Embankment 8851, three large clumps, *CRH* 1986–91, and one clump

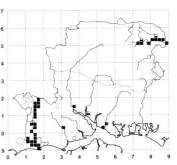

Map 403 Butomus umbellatus

near Queen's Parade 8652, *CRH* 1988–91. Surviving well on the canal at these sites, and may begin to recolonize others.

ALISMATACEAE

Sagittaria sagittifolia L.   Arrowhead.   **N**   Very locally frequent
Map 404

In rivers, streams and canals; on muddy substratum in slow-flowing or still water. Frequent in the Stour and Avon valleys, the Moors River and the Basingstoke Canal. Local in the lower Test Valley, and the Blackwater Valley in the NE.

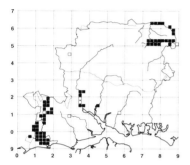

Map 404 Sagittaria sagittifolia

S. latifolia WILLD.   Duck-potato.
H   Very rare

First record, R. P. Bowman 1962, Coxford, Southampton 3914, VC11, swamp under willows, Hb.RPB, det. *EJC*, 1977 (*Rep.S'ton N.H.S.*, p.8).
   This aquatic plant of gardens can become established in swamps by ponds, and canals.
   VC11: Setley Pond 3099, Hb.RPB 1981, det. *EJC*. **VC12**: Basingstoke Canal, Fleet 8053, two plants, *CRH* 1986, since removed by dredging.

S. subulata (L.) BUCHENAU
Narrow-leaved Arrowhead.   **H**   Very rare

First record, D. N. & Mrs B. Turner 1962, Shortheath Pond 7736, VC12, Hb.AB 1974, det. *CDKC*.
   An aquarists' plant from eastern N America, now a dominant weed on the SE side of the pond. It was definitely present there several years before various aquatics were planted by the fishing club which has taken over the pond. The Oakhanger Angling Club have stated they did not introduce it, *AB* (*Watsonia* **10**: 411).

Baldellia ranunculoides (L.) PARL.
Lesser Water-plantain.   **N**   Local
Map 405

In clear, shallow edges of ponds, streams and ditches; formerly commoner and not so confined to the heathland areas as it almost entirely is today. Frequent in the New Forest; very rare, and decreasing in the NE.
   VC11: Near Hurn *c*.1397, *CDD* *c*.1970. **VC12**: Lodge Pond, Alice Holt Forest 8142, *VL* 1959, *AB* 1976; Fleet Pond 8155, 8254, abundant, *GARW* 1932 (*Watts MSS*), reappeared 8254 on digging dragonfly-pool, *CRH* 1989; Basingstoke Canal near Crookham, *RSH* 1859, Hb.BM; canal at Farnborough, *SNHS* 1975, later dredged, reappeared at Puckridge 8452, 1989, also 8552, *CRH* 1990, when water low during drought, but not since; Dogmersfield Lake 7551, on W shore, *CRH* 1987. Formerly, until 1930, at Oakhanger Pond 7734, *AB*.

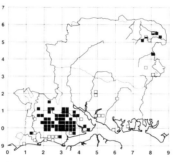

Map 405 Baldellia ranunculoides

[**Luronium natans** (L.) RAF.   Floating Water-plantain.   **H**   Very rare (Sched. 8)

Probably a deliberate introduction or an aquarists' throw-out, in pond opposite Furzey Cottage, South Weirs, Brockenhurst 2801, VC11, *AEB* 1985, a gradually increasing large patch, but rarely flowering, *RPB* 1994. Not native in S England.]

Alisma plantago-aquatica L.
Water-plantain.   **N**   Locally common

In ponds, ditches, slow-flowing, shallow rivers, streams and canals. Generally common, but scarce in chalk waters.

A. lanceolatum WITH.   Narrow-leaved Water-plantain.   **N**   Rare
Map 406

In rivers, lakes and canals. Frequent to

occasional in R. Stour and the Moors River; once common in the Basingstoke Canal around Fleet and Aldershot, but since the 1978 dredging, has been reduced to a few plants in each tetrad (*CRH* 1986). Rare elsewhere.
   VC11: R. Stour, near Jumpers Common 1394, Hb.RPB 1976, det. *FR*; Moors River 1099 or 1199, *MPY* *c*.1960. **VC12**: Sherborne St John *c*.6255, pond-margin, *NEGC c*.1940 (*Fl.Bas.MS*, p.18); Fleet Pond *c*.8254, *AHGA* 1930, Hb.BM, 8254, *MN* 1986; Foxlease 8256, in ditch, *ARGM & JK* 1978.

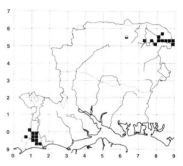

Map 406 Alisma lanceolatum

<**Damasonium alisma** MILL.
Starfruit.   **N**   Extinct (Sched. 8)

Formerly very rare on muddy or sandy shores of ponds; dependent on water-level falling in early summer. In Hants, the sites have been lost mainly through drainage or silting up of ponds. There are three old records:
   VC11: Pool about two miles from Christchurch on the Lyndhurst road, *JHu* (*in litt.* to *WAB*) 1849, Hb.WAB 1850 (*Fl.Hants*, p.403); Barton Common, *PSom* 1863 (*New Forest Hist. & Scen.*, p.295), *EWM*, *HG & JGr* 1876 (*loc.cit.*). **VC12**: Hook Common 7153, *GCD* 1910, Hb.BM, Hb.OXF (*Suppl.Fl.Hants*, p.111), last record at Hook, *GCD* 1917, Hb.RNG. The sheet in Hb.OXF consists of two large plants pulled up by the roots – *GCD* supplied most of the museums in like fashion. Its label says: 'this rare and somewhat erratic species I found in considerable quantity in the above locality'. The pond has since become overgrown but could be restored.>

HYDROCHARITACEAE

Hydrocharis morsus-ranae L.
Frogbit.   **N**   Rare   Map 407

Canals, drains and ponds, in peaty, very slow-flowing or still water. Rare in the lower Avon Valley where in 1995 it reappeared in a newly-cut drain. Numbers fluctuate in the Basingstoke Canal, where it was very common in the 1960s. It disappeared from around Odiham after dredging, and declined greatly at Farnborough, but survived abundantly until 1984 in the undredged canal through Fleet and Crookham. In disturbed water it seems to need the shelter of emergent vegetation. As boating and weed-cutting increased it declined rapidly until there was only a relic colony in Pondtail Flash, last seen *CRH* 1991.

VC11: Sowley Pond 3796, *RPB* 1953, no record since; Jockstrill Common, Sopley 1597, open water in drain, *HCC* 1986, *RPB* 1987, 1995. **VC12**: Kingsley Pond 7838, *AMM* 1962, but it has not so far reappeared since the pond was cleaned out; Fleet Pond and ditches 8154, 8254, *GARW c.* 1933 (*Watts MSS*), sparsely, *CRH* 1987; pond on Yateley Common 8359, *CRH* 1986.

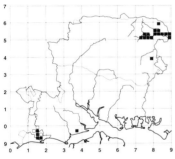

Map 407 Hydrocharis morsus-ranae

Stratiotes aloides L.   Water-soldier. **H**   Very rare

First records, M. E. Jakobson 1966, Basingstoke Canal, Eelmoor 8452, Farnborough 8552 and Aldershot 8652, 8851, VC12, locally abundant (*Survey, Bas.Canal*).

First noticed in the canal in the early 1950s, at Ash, Surrey, by *JEL* (who considered it an aquarists' introduction), it spread rapidly by vegetative reproduction until the canal was completely choked (*Fl.Surrey*, p.339). It then spread into Hampshire, where *SRD* in 1973 found it more or less dominant from the Surrey border to Norris Bridge. Despite its removal during the 1978 dredging, it began to recolonize, and in 1986 *CRH* found it in tetrads 8052, 8252, 8452, 8652. With

the advent of power-boating it is no longer able to choke the canal if, indeed, it can hold its own.

VC11: Moat at old gravel-pits, Fleetend 5005, six rosettes in shade, *RPB* 1988. **VC12**: Silchester pond 6462, *EAP* 1981.

Elodea canadensis MICHX
Canadian Waterweed.   **C**   Locally common   Map 408

First record, W. Borrer 1847 (the same year as the first English record), Leigh Park lake, Havant 7109, VC11 (*Fl. Hants*, p.405), where it had been introduced accidentally with American aquatics.

In rivers, streams, canals, lakes and ponds. Following its introduction, it spread rapidly until many watercourses and ponds were becoming choked. By the end of the nineteenth century there were indications of a gradual decline which probably continued into the 1930s. Since then it has appeared to stabilize, although more recently the equally aggressive *E. nuttallii* has been in competition with it and has supplanted it in places.

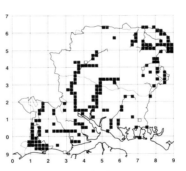

Map 408 Elodea canadensis

E. nuttallii (PLANCH.) H. ST JOHN
Nuttall's Waterweed.   **H**   Locally frequent   Map 409

First record, A. W. Westrup 1950, Sinah Common lagoon, Hayling Island 6999 (as *Egeria densa* Planch.).

This is another aquarists' introduction from N America, especially into fishing lakes. It is increasing rapidly, colonizing many ponds, streams and stretches of some rivers and appears likely to outdo *E. canadensis*. In ponds it can oust many more ecologically desirable and attractive plants.

VC12: R. Wey, Deadwater 8035; Yateley 8261, both Hb.AB, det. *EJC* (*Watsonia* 11: 401).

It is probably under-recorded due to

restricted access to most rivers, and to confusion with *E. canadensis*. In 1991, *E. canadensis* was recorded as frequent in the upper Test and local in the upper Itchen, but *E. nuttallii* was not found anywhere (*NRA Survey*).

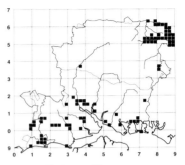

Map 409 Elodea nuttallii

<**E. callitrichoides** (RICH.) CASP. (*E. ernstiae* H. St John)   South American Waterweed.   **H**   Extinct

First record, Lady Anne Brewis 1967, Hammer Bottom, Bramshott 8632, VC12, in stream forming the boundary with Sussex, Hb.AB, det. *JGD* 1970 (*Watsonia* 10: 432), conf. *DAS* 1981.

This much rarer *Elodea* does not survive a hard winter, which is probably why it could not be found there in 1972.>

Lagarosiphon major (RIDL.) MOSS Curly Waterweed.   **H**   Rare

First record, S. R. Davey 1976, Gilkicker Point 6097, VC11, small pond on golf-course.

A commonly-used aquarists' weed which can dominate a small pond but does not seem to colonize streams.

VC8: 0812. **VC11**: Janesmoor Pond, Fritham 2413, *RPB* 1986; Titchfield Abbey fishpond 5406, *RPB* 1987. Also 1692, 2206, 2416, 2808, 3292, 3600, 4420, 5004, 5010, 5406. **VC12**: pond at Liss 7726, *AB* 1976, det. *EJC* (*Watsonia* 11: 401); pond in Alice Holt Forest 7942, *AB* 1983. Also 7232, 8652.

JUNCAGINACEAE

Triglochin palustre L.   Marsh Arrowgrass.   **N**   Locally frequent Map 410

In wet meadows, basic flushes and fens, and in the less saline grassy salt-marshes with *T. maritimum*. Widespread, and quite frequent in the New Forest and in some river valleys; otherwise very local.

VC11: Wick, Southbourne 1591, marshy margin of large dyke, *JOM* 1970; Stony Moors 2199, Hb.AWW 1963; Farlington Marshes 6805, *MB* 1979; Lovelocks Farm 6310, *JRw* 1991. **VC12**: Conford Moor 8232, *CL* 1952, *FR* 1987; Ashford Hill meadows 5662, *PB* 1983; Foxlease 8257, *CRH* 1985; Shepherds Spring meadow, Anton Lakes 3646, *ILR* 1991; by R. White-water 7150, *AJPB* 1990.

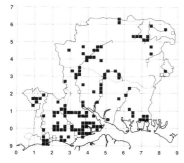

Map 410 Triglochin palustre

T. maritimum L.   Sea Arrowgrass. **N**   Locally common

In grassy coastal and estuarine salt-marshes, wet, brackish pastures and banks of tidal rivers. One remarkable inland site is at Holmsley 2300, VC11, in flushed turf on calcareous clay, *RPB* 1973–89, conf. *FR*. VC11: 72 □.

POTAMOGETONACEAE

Potamogeton natans L.   Broad-leaved Pondweed.   **N**   Locally common   Map 411

First record, Gilbert White 1766, Selborne, VC12 (*White's Jnls* **1**: 201).
    In slow-flowing rivers and streams, meadow drains and ponds. Common in most areas, but rare in chalk streams.

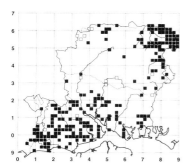

Map 411 Potamogeton natans

P. x fluitans ROTH (*P. natans* x *P. lucens*)   **N**   Very rare

First record, F. Townsend 1879, Moors River near Hurn Station, VC11, Hb.SLBI, det. *JED & GT* (*Proc.Hants Fld Club* **15**: 72).
    VC11: Moors River, near St Leonards 0901, *PMH* 1946; Palmer's Ford 0900, *PMH* 1939, det. *JED & GT* (*loc.cit.*). Still in the Moors River, St Leonard's Farm 0901 to Palmer's Ford 0900, abundantly, Hb.AB 1976; also at Hurn Bridge 1296, *RPB* 1977.

P. polygonifolius POURR.   Bog Pondweed.   **N**   Locally common   Map 412

Joint first British record, J. J. Dillenius *c*.1730, Petersfield, VC11/12, Hb.OXF. det. *GCD* (*Fl.Hants*, p.394; *Dill.Herb.*, p.142).
    In acid bog-pools, streams and ditches. Very common in the New Forest, Woolmer Forest and the NE heathland; local in other acid waters. **VC11**: Gomer Pond, Gosport 5899, *RPB* 1984; The Moors, Bishop's Waltham 5616, *FR* 1984, *PMHo* 1993, Hb.AB, Hb.RPB, Hb.RNG, det. *PMHo & CDPr*. The Bishop's Waltham population (originally iden-tified as *P. coloratus*, see below), which deceived several of us for some years, may correspond with forma *cancellatus* Fryer which has thin, translucent, finely reticulately-veined, submerged leaves. **VC12**: R. Blackwater, from 8855 to Farnborough North Station 8756, *JES* 1987.

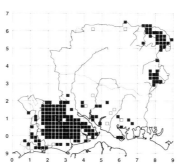

Map 412 Potamogeton polygonifolius

[**P. coloratus** HORNEM.   Fen Pondweed.

The record for The Moors, Bishop's Waltham 5616, VC11, (*Watsonia* **16**: 194) is an error. Fresh material, collected in 1993 from a calcareous stream and flushes at this site and cultivated by *PMHo*, has been redet.

PMHo & CDPr as *P. polygonifolius* (*q.v.*).]

P. nodosus POIR.   Loddon Pondweed.   **N**   Very rare or extinct

First record, I. MacDonald 1977, R. Blackwater, above Aldershot Military Sewage Works 8852, and Farnborough 8853, at gauging station, and below Sandhurst Sewage Works 8360, VC12.
    Late in 1980, a very worm-eaten specimen was found by *AB* at the first site which was confirmed by *FR*. The following year there was no trace of it. In 1987, during a survey of the R. Blackwater, *JES* could not find it at any of the sites. However, steps have been taken to re-introduce it in its former area.

P. lucens L.   Shining Pondweed.   **N** Local   Map 413

In slow- to swift-flowing rivers and streams, usually in calcareous waters. Frequent in the Avon and Test, more local in the Stour, the Moors River and lower Itchen. It has several times been claimed, but never expertly confirmed, for the Basingstoke Canal; these records seem to have been errors for *P. alpinus*.
    VC11: R. Itchen S of Bishopstoke 4617, *NTHH c*.1978. **VC12**: R. Alre 5832, *AB* 1963; in new pond on stream S of Forty Acres, Binsted 7640, valley-floor, *FR* 1989.

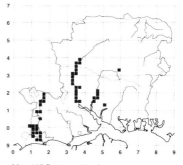

Map 413 Potamogeton lucens

P. x salicifolius WOLFG. (*P. lucens* x *P. perfoliatus*)   Willow-leaved Pondweed.   **N**   Very rare

VC11: Still in R. Avon, N of Christchurch at Knapp Mill 1593 (where recorded in *Fl.Bmth*, p.225, as *P. decipiens* Nolte) and Coward's Marsh 1594, Hb.RPB 1976, det. *RCLH* (leafy plants only); R. Avon near Sopley *c*.1496, *PMH* 1934, det.

JED & GT (*Proc.Hants Fld Club* **15**: 72); Avon Causeway Bridge 1497, *JEL* 1934.

<P. gramineus L.   Various-leaved Pondweed.   **N**   Extinct

Formerly in ponds. Not refound at Romsey (*Fl.Hants*, p.395, as *P. heterophyllus* Schreb.), Cadnam (*Suppl. Fl.Hants*, p.111), both VC11, or in Fleet Pond, VC12, *HCW* 1849, Hb.WARMS, det. *JED* 1965, last collected there, *CP* 1895. It is still in the Basingstoke Canal at Mytchett, just in Surrey, but there is no extant site in Hants.>

P. alpinus BALB.   Red Pondweed. **N**   Very local   Map 414

In slow-flowing, non-calcareous rivers, ditches, canals and lakes; rare, but locally plentiful.
   VC11: R. Stour 1393, *MPY c.*1960, det. *JGD*; Beaulieu River, Buck Hill 3804, 3805, *RPB* 1976, 3706, *NAS* 1987; Lymington River, Boldre Bridge 3198, 3298, *AEB* 1980, 3198, *AEB & RPB* 1990. **VC12**: Basingstoke Canal, Winchfield 7753, Hb.AB 1975, det. *JED* (*Watsonia* **11**:401). Formerly plentiful in the Basingstoke Canal, it decreased as the canal silted up until by 1970 there were only four small patches, from Odiham to Puckridge. It then thrived on the disturbance of the dredging, until in 1986 it extended its range and was abundant from North Warnborough to Puckridge, especially at Fleet. After this date turbidity increased from Odiham to Fleet. In 1992 it was still widespread, surviving best in the shallower canal-margins (*CRH*); it remains to be seen if it will survive increasing numbers of motor-boats clouding the water. It is also in a fishing lake at Farnborough 8853, *AB* 1980, and Hawley Lake 8457, *CRH* 1989.

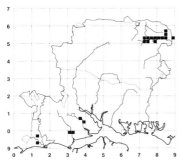

Map 414 Potamogeton alpinus

[**P. x griffithii** A. BENN. (*P. alpinus* x *P. praelongus* Wulfen)

A record for Odiham, VC12, *GCD* 1929 (*Suppl.Fl.Hants*, p.111) is unconfirmed. *P. praelongus* is unknown in Hants and the hybrid is reported only from Wales and Scotland by J. E. Dandy (*Hybr.Fl.Brit.Is.*, p.453).]

P. perfoliatus L.   Perfoliate Pondweed.   **N**   Local   Map 415

In rivers, streams and canals, usually in calcareous, still to medium-flow waters. In VC11 frequent in the Rivers Stour, Avon and the lower Test. In VC12 it is commonest in the Loddon, but is also in the Whitewater, the Wey, and the Basingstoke Canal. Otherwise rare, but possibly under-recorded, due to restricted access to fishing rivers.
   VC11: Bickton Mill 1412, Hb.RPB 1975, det. *JED*. **VC12**: Basingstoke Canal 8253, 8353, 8452, *CRH* 1988.

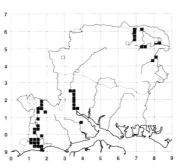

Map 415 Potamogeton perfoliatus

<P. friesii RUPR.   Flat-stalked Pondweed.   **N**   Extinct

First record, B. King 1880, Basingstoke Canal, Broad Oak, Odiham *c.*7552, VC12, det. *JED*.
   Formerly in canals and rivers. Last record: Basingstoke Canal at Odiham *c.*7451, *PMH & GARW* 1933, det. *WHP* (*Proc.Hants Fld Club* **12**: 297). There are older records for R. Stour, Christchurch, VC11, C. Waterfall 1899, Hb.BM, det. *JED*, and the canal at Aldershot, VC12, W. H. Beeby 1881 (*Fl.Hants*, p.397), det. *JED*.>

P. pusillus L.   Lesser Pondweed. **N**   Rare   Map 416

In ponds, especially those in gravel-pits, and in canals. Liable to confusion with *P. berchtoldii*, but apparently rare.
   VC11: Lee Lane gravel-pit, Romsey 3617, *RPB* 1975, Hb.BM, conf. *JED*, 3517, Hb.RPB 1976, det. *CDPr* 1990;

Timsbury 3424, ditches in gravel-pit, Hb.RPB 1976, det. *CDPr* 1990; Mudeford 1892, pool on upper beach, *JEL* 1934, det. *JED & GT* (*Proc.Hants Fld Club* **15**: 72); Southampton Common 4114, *CDD* 1957, boating lake, Hb.RPB 1991, det. *CDPr*; Black Water, Needs Ore Point 4197, in brackish drain, Hb.*RPB* 1993. **VC12**: Wellington Country Park 7362, flooded gravel-pit, *WMK* 1976; Yateley 8261, flooded gravel-pit, *AB* 1976, det. *CDPr* 1991; Basingstoke Canal, near Colt Hill 7451, *JEL* 1954, Hb.RNG; Blackbushe Airfield 8059, small pond, *AB* 1983; NE side of Fleet Pond 8255, *GARW & PMH* 1932 (*Proc.Hants Fld Club* **12**: 297), *ARGM* 1976, det. *AB*, gone by 1984; R. Blackwater 8855–8658, *JES* 1987.

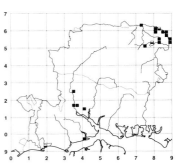

Map 416 Potamogeton pusillus

P. obtusifolius MERT. & KOCH Blunt-leaved Pondweed.   **N**   Very local   Map 417

In lakes, ponds and canals; frequent in the Aldershot area, otherwise rare.
   VC11: Hatchet Pond 3601, *AEB & ERB* 1989; Pitts Deep 3795, *RPB* 1972; Sowley Pond 3796, *AEB c.*1978; Biddenfield Pond 5412, Hb.AWW 1958; Woodington sand-pit, East Wellow 3120, Hb.RPB 1975, det. *JED*; Langstone 7105, former millstream,

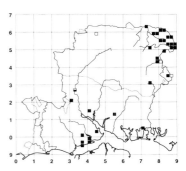

Map 417 Potamogeton obtusifolius

EAP 1984. VC12: Waggoners Wells 8534, *AB* 1976; The Kennels Pond, Alice Holt Forest 7942, *WEW* 1975, Hb.AB; Empshott Grange 7530, pond, *AB* 1977; Hawley Lake 8457, *GHF* 1981; Fleet Pond 8154, *CRH* 1987; Wellington Country Park 7362, flooded gravel-pit, *AB* 1977, *CRH* 1986.

P. berchtoldii FIEBER   Small Pondweed.   N   Locally frequent
Map 418

First record, Miss C. E. Palmer 1893, R. Whitewater, Hook *c.*7354, VC12, det. *JED & GT* (*J.Bot.* 78: 49–66). It was not recorded by Townsend who apparently included it under *P. pusillus* in *Fl. Hants* (p.397).

In streams, canals and ponds; fairly widespread.

VC11: R. Avon, Christchurch 1594, *NTHH* 1978; Titchfield Abbey 5406, Hb.AWW 1959, det. *JED*; Itchen Valley, Mans Bridge 4415, Hb.RPB 1975, conf. *JED*; Farlington Marshes 6803, *EAP* 1986. VC12: New Alresford 5832, newly-made fish-pond, *ACJ* 1975; Yateley 8161, flooded gravel-pit, *ARGM* 1987; Eelmoor 8452, pond, *ARGM* 1983, det. *CDPr*; Basingstoke Canal, after dredging, tetrads 7250, 8252, 8652, *CRH* 1986.

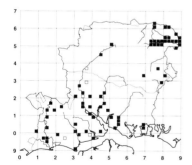

Map 418 Potamogeton berchtoldii

P. trichoides CHAM. & SCHLTDL. Hair-like Pondweed.   N   Very rare

First record, R. P. Bowman 1975, Mans Bridge 4415, VC11, in old reservoir fishing lake, Hb.RPB, conf. *JED* (*Watsonia* 16: 194). An earlier record, Fleet Pond, *PMH & GARW* 1932 or 1933 (*Proc.Hants Fld Club* 12: 292, 297) was subsequently withdrawn by *PMH* on the grounds that *WHP*'s identification was based on inadequate material and that he (*PMH*) was unable to rediscover the species at this site (*Proc.Hants Fld Club* 15: 78).

VC12: Plentiful at one end of the pond beside the R. Blackwater at Hawley 8559, *CRH* 1991, Hb.AB, conf. *CDPr & NTHH* (*Watsonia* 19: 151); pond by R. Blackwater, Aldershot 8851, *CRH* 1992, conf. *CDPr*.

<P. acutifolius LINK   Sharp-leaved Pondweed.   N   Extinct

Only record, R. Meinertzhagen 1898, Mottisfont, VC11, in four inches of muddy water, Hb.BM, conf. *JED & GT* 1939 (*Proc.Hants Fld Club* 15: 73). Not refound.>

P. crispus L.   Curled Pondweed.   N Locally common   Map 419

First British record, J. Goodyer 1621, fish-ponds adjoining Durford Abbey 7723, VC11 (*Early Brit.Bots*, pp.123–126).

In ponds, rivers and streams; widespread and fairly common.

VC11: R. Avon, Moortown 1404, *RPB* 1976; Wallington River, near North Fareham Farm 5808, Hb.AWW 1952. VC12: R. Test at Leckford 3738, *RPB* 1968; Yateley Green 8161, village pond, *ARGM* 1987.

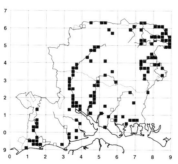

Map 419 Potamogeton crispus

P. pectinatus L.   Fennel Pondweed. N   Very locally common   Map 420

In nutrient-rich alkaline rivers and streams, and brackish ponds and drains near the coast; rarely, in ponds inland. Common throughout the Avon; in the Stour, Loddon and Blackwater, and locally in the lower Test. The R. Blackwater, however, is a puzzle. From its source in Aldershot, it flows through miles of acid country, never apparently receiving any alkaline water until it is joined by the R. Whitewater in 7463, yet in every tetrad from Aldershot (*CRH* 1992) to the Whitewater junction *P. pectinatus* occurs. Following pollution, *P. pectinatus* increases at

the expense of *Ranunculus penicillatus*, of which there is certainly none in the Blackwater. R. M. Walls, formerly of W Hampshire Water Co. (pers.comm), has pointed out that, at Farnborough, the chalk immediately underlies the gravel and sand, and that the town's water is probably abstracted from it. This might account for early records (sites no longer extant) from Fleet Pond and 'near Farnborough' (*HCW* 1860). According to R. A. Sweeting of the National Rivers Authority (pers.comm.), the R. Blackwater, before meeting the R. Whitewater, now receives effluent from six sewage works, catering for a very large population. Through this, considerable amounts of calcium carbonate are introduced into the river, so its chemistry no longer reflects the local geology. Although the R. Avon is not polluted, *Ranunculus penicillatus* is rather more sparsely distributed in that river than in the Rivers Test, Itchen and Meon; however, as Walls suggests, this could be accounted for by the amount of acid water brought in from the New Forest.

VC11: Woodington 3120, pond in sand-pit, Hb.RPB 1975, conf. *JED*; Farlington Marshes 6804, Hb.AWW 1957. VC12: R. Test, Laverstoke 4848, *EAB* 1968; Fleet Pond, *PMH* 1934, not seen since; Basingstoke Canal, Odiham 7451, *CL* 1958, 7552, *CRH* 1989, increasing 1991; R. Loddon, Sherfield on Loddon 6858, *IMcD* 1971.

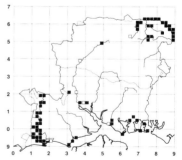

Map 420 Potamogeton pectinatus

Groenlandia densa (L.) FOURR. Opposite-leaved Pondweed.   N Local   Map 421

First British record, J. Goodyer 1621, 'abundantly in the river by Droxford', *c.*6018, VC11 (*Ger.em.Johns.*, p.824; Goodyer MSS fol.120a, fol.122 in *Early Brit.Bots*, p.126).

In rivers, streams, canals, drains and pools, usually in very clear calcareous water. There is evidence that it has declined since the last century. In 1991 it was found in only three 1km squares in the Itchen, VC11 (*NRA Survey*). The rivers where it is now most plentiful are the Meon, Alre, Lyde, and the Whitewater.

VC11: Moors River, Wools Bridge 0904 or 1004, *RPB* 1977; Timsbury 3523, old canal, *RPB* 1975; Mill Stream, Bedhampton 7006, *AWW* 1956, *RPB* 1990. **VC12**: Basingstoke Canal, Odiham 7451, *ACJ* 1975, Hb.BM, not since dredging in 1976; Micheldever Stream 5139, *AB* 1977; R. Whitewater, Hook 7354, *PDG* 1978.

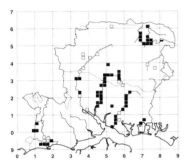

Map 421 Groenlandia densa

RUPPIACEAE

Ruppia maritima L.   Beaked Tasselweed.   **N**   Rare   Map 422

First record, Mrs M. A. T. Robinson 1847, Gomer ditch near Stokes Bay, VC11, Hb.BM, (*Fl.Hants*, p.399, as *R. rostellata* Koch).

In brackish drains and ponds on the coast.

VC11: Dibden Bay 4108, *RPB* 1975; Farlington Marshes 6804, Hb.AWW 1951.

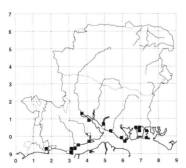

Map 422 Ruppia maritima

R. cirrhosa (PETAGNA) GRANDE (*R. spiralis* L. ex Dumort.)   Spiral Tasselweed.   **N**   Very rare

In brackish ponds and drains on the coast.

VC11: Keyhaven Marshes 3192, *GH* 1968; Pennington Marshes 3292, Hb.RPB 1976, conf. *FR*; Pennington, tetrad 3094, recorded 1944; Gomer, Gosport 5899, *MB* 1976; Eight Acre Pond, Normandy 3293, *SRD* 1976; Tourner Bury Marsh, Hayling Island 7399, 7300, *FR* 1980; Hythe 4108, in ditch, *RMV* 1986, Hb.RPB; Hilsea *c*.6602, in boating lake, *FB* 1957, Hb.BM.

ZANNICHELLIACEAE

Zannichellia palustris L.   Horned Pondweed.   **N**   Locally common   Map 423

In rivers, streams, canals, ditches and ponds. In slightly-brackish and calcareous to slightly-acid water. Common in the larger rivers, but quite local elsewhere. In 1991 it was found to be frequent and often in great abundance, particularly in the Test and the lower reaches of the Itchen. Records strongly suggest a fairly recent expansion in its range, and several river-keepers have commented on the increased occurrence of this pondweed. It is likely this may be due to widespread deposition of silt in shallow water as a result of lower river-flows. The pondweed readily colonizes silt and, once established, accumulates fresh silt which becomes stabilized by its roots (*NRA Survey*).

VC11: Rushbush Stream, Dibden Bottom 3806, *RPB* 1951; Farlington Marshes 6804, small brackish pond, *RMV* 1987. **VC12**: Basingstoke Canal 7451, *ACJ* 1975, Hb.BM; Longmoor 8031, new pool on airstrip, *AB* 1988.

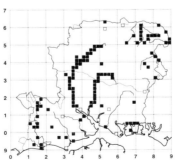

Map 423 Zannichellia palustris

ZOSTERACEAE

Much of the information in this section is derived from papers by C. R. Tubbs and J. M. Tubbs (*Aquat. Bot.* (1983) **15**:

223–239), Mrs S. M. Turk (*Botanical Cornwall* No.3 (1989): 10–12) and C. R. Tubbs (*Brit. Wildlife* (1995) **6**: 351–355).

Zostera marina L.   Eelgrass.   **N**   Rare   Map 424

First record, S. Doody 1724, as '*Potamogeiton marinum*', Portsea Island at 'Gatham [Gatcombe] Haven' [later the Great Salterns] 6701, VC11 (*Ray Syn.*, p.53).

Growing on relatively exposed shores, on firm sand sometimes mixed with flint-gravel, below low tide, and exposed only at extreme low-water spring tides. In 1904, this plant was described as 'common' (*Fl.Hants*, p.399), but from about 1933 until the 1950s, along with *Z. angustifolia* and *Z. noltii*, it decreased all round the coasts. The decline of this species was the result of a 'wasting disease' possibly caused by *Labyrinthula macrocystis*, a micro-organism allied to slime-moulds, but the reason for the simultaneous decline of the other two species, which in Hants subsequently made a greater recovery, is more complex, but it may be partly attributable to the same pathogen. In Cornwall it would seem that they are again all in decline. However, in Southampton Water and Portsmouth Harbour, destruction of habitat caused by the building of docks and dredging of channels also contributed to its decrease. Similarly at Hayling – where it was 'in plenty' (*ESM* 1900, Hb.BM), and where *AB* remembers it being washed up in quantity at Hayling Bay in 1919 and the 1920s – a great deal of sand was dredged up for building; it is now rare, and confined to small patches.

VC11: Pennington Marshes 3292, *NDS* 1937, Hb.BM; off Sowley Marsh 3795, *DSR* 1966; Thorns Beach 3996, *CRT & JMT* 1979–80; Lepe Beach

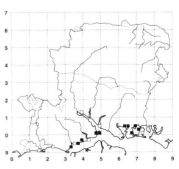

Map 424 Zostera marina

4498, great quantity cast up on high-water mark, but it is not known from which beds they came, *RPB* 1976; Stanswood Bay 4700, *CRT & JMT* 1979–80; Calshot Beach 4801, *RPB* 1975; Eight Acre Pond, Normandy 3293, *SRD* 1976; Bury Marsh, Eling 3711, drifted plants on shore of estuary, *RPB* 1985; Langstone Harbour 6700, *DSR* 1958; South Binness Island 7003, Hb.AWW 1951, *DSR* 1967. Formerly in Paulsgrove Lake 6204, *PMH* 1934; and Ports Creek, Cosham, *JS* 1934.

Z. angustifolia (HORNEM.) RCHB.
Narrow-leaved Eelgrass.   **N**   Very locally abundant   Map 425

First record, S. Doody 1724, as '*Alga angustifolia vitrariorum*', Portsea Island at 'Gatham [Gatcombe] Haven' [later the Great Salterns] 6701, VC11 (*Ray Syn.*, p.53). *Fl.Hants* (p.400) places this record here (as *Z. marina* var. β *angustifolia* Hornem.) but notes that it may refer to *Z. noltii*.

On soft to relatively firm mud, in estuaries and shallow water, from half to low tide-mark. It grows in association with *Z. noltii*, occupying softer muds and wet hollows among the *Z. noltii* beds on the firmer muds. *Z. angustifolia* also occurs in dense beds in creeks penetrating the upper shore, and in hollows among degenerate *Spartina* marsh. From about 1960 onwards, these two eelgrasses made a recovery in the three eastern harbours of Portsmouth, Langstone and Chichester. From 1969–79, these harbours were surveyed by *RMT*, Portsmouth Polytechnic, *FNH, CRT & JMT*. In 1979 they esti-mated *c.*280ha (692 acres) of these two species of eelgrass in Langstone Harbour and by 1987, *CRT* recorded *c.*340ha of 'eelgrass meadows' on inter-tidal mudflats. The spread occurred rather suddenly, and coincided in each harbour with increased discharges of both treated and untreated effluent – the period of most rapid spread corre-sponding with the steepest increase in effluent–discharge. Nevertheless, *CRT* does not consider the connection proven. In the late 1980s the 'wasting disease' recurred on both sides of the Atlantic but by 1994 the new epidemic, which in North America was conclus-ively shown to have been caused by a species of *Labyrinthula*, appeared to be over, suggesting that the disease is a cyclical phenomenon.

VC11: Little Horsea Island *c.*6304, *JV c.*1886, Hb.OXF, det. *TGT*; North Binness Island 6904, *DSR* 1956; *BSBI*

1993; Long Island 7003, *BSBI* 1993; Sinah, South Hayling, *PMH* 1934; Tye, North Hayling 7201, *FR* 1986; S of Farlington Marshes 6803, 6802, on mud in runnels, *RMV* 1987; Cams Bay, Fareham 5905, drifted plants on salt-marsh shore, *RPB* 1988. Formerly at Bournemouth beach, *WMR* 1889 (*Fl.Hants*, p.400); Hengistbury Head 1690, estuary, *JEL* 1927, Hb.RNG.

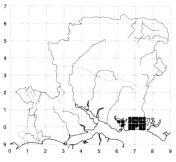

Map 425 Zostera angustifolia

Z. noltii HORNEM.   Dwarf Eelgrass.
N   Very locally abundant   Map 426

First record, W. Borrer 1856, Emsworth Creek, VC11 (*Fl.Vect.*, p.537).

Generally in firm mud or sand, from low-water, spring-tide to low-water, neap-tide levels; in the eastern harbours, however, in soft to relatively firm sand or mud, up to the upper-shore levels.

VC11: Stanswood Bay 4700, Hook 4804, Brownwich 5103, Lee-on-the-Solent 5600, Browndown 5699, Emsworth 7404, all *CRT & JMT* 1979–80 (*Aquat.Bot.* **15**: 224, fig.1); Sinah, South Hayling, *PMH* 1934; North Binness Island 6904, *DSR* 1956, *BSBI* 1993; Long Island 7003, *BSBI* 1993; South Langstone Harbour 6700, *DSR* 1967. Formerly from Christ-church Harbour to Southampton.

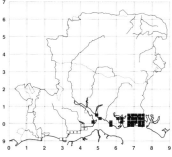

Map 426 Zostera noltii

ARACEAE

Acorus calamus L.   Sweet-flag.   **D** Rare

First record, W. Browne *c.*1650–56, '*non procul...Hedly...Comitati Hamp-tonis*' [near Headley in the County of Hampshire], VC12 (How's ms note in his copy of *Phyt. Brit.*, Magdalen College Library, Oxford (*Early Brit.Bots*, p.302)), but erroneously attributed to Surrey in *Merr.Pin.* (p.2). As it had been 'introduced into Europe by 1557, and recorded as naturalized in England by 1660' (*Fl.Brit.Is.*, p.1051), it would seem likely that it became established in Hants at about that date.

Sweet-flag was largely grown in the marshy fringes of lakes, ponds and rivers for strewing on the floors of great houses to counteract unpleasant smells, so records tend to be associated with such places. Gerard, who grew it in his garden, stated that in his time it had never flowered in England (*Ger. Herb.*, p.57).

VC11: Paultons Park lake, Ower 3116, *RPB* 1956; Roydon Woods 3102, damp patch in rough pasture, *AEB* 1980; R. Itchen, S of Eastleigh 4617, *NTHH* 1978; Leigh Park lake, Havant 7109, *AB* 1978. Also 1000, 2200, 3696, 4828, 5802, 6404, 6604, 6610, 6898, 7098. **VC12**: Winnall meadows, *RSH* 1863, abundant in all three fishing lakes, *JWCP* 1990; Ewhurst Lake 5757, *WEW* 1958; Headley Park 8138, *HMNHS* 1954; Frensham Great Pond 8440, *AB* 1975 (once cultivated for Farnham Castle); Milford Lake 4560, *AB* 1976. Also 5844, 7646, 8238, 8240.

Lysichiton americanus HULTÉN & H. ST JOHN   American Skunk-cabbage.   **H**   Rare

First record, L. G. Stimson 1957, the Millhouse millpond, Minstead 2909, VC11, in muddy willow-swamp (prob-ably escaped from Furzey Gardens).

In willow holts and other wet woods along streams; naturalized plentifully in a few places, after being carried downstream from water-gardens.

VC11: Burton Common 1995, *GDF* 1991; Long Aldermoor 2709, *RPB, FR & JHL* 1973–84; Hurn Forest 1001, *RPB & RMW* 1985; Lymington River N of Lower Buckland 3297, frequent over 150m in swampy carr, *RPB* 1989; Hollybrook, Southampton 3914, *RMV & RPB* 1990; Marlhill Copse, Southampton 4515, *WP* 1975; Brook-lands Farm, Lower Swanwick 4908, *KW* 1985; The Lakes, Chandler's Ford 4421, *JG c.*1975. **VC12**: Newtown

Gully 4763, *CL* 1960–64, *NFC* 1981 (escape from Newtown Grange); Yateley 8261, edge of flooded gravel-pit, *ARGM & DBr* 1987.

Arum maculatum L.   Lords-and-Ladies.   **N**   Common

Woodland and hedgebanks; common throughout Hants, but avoiding very acid soils, and sparse or absent in most unenclosed New Forest woods. A variant with yellow veins grows on a roadside at Wheatham Hill 7427, *AB*.

A. italicum MILL.   Italian Lords-and-Ladies.

ssp. **neglectum** (TOWNS.) PRIME   **N** Very locally abundant   Map 427

First record, E. H. White 1909, woods near Langrish (Bordean Hanger) *c.*7024, VC12 (his annotated copy of *Fl.Hants*).

In damp but well-drained woodland on calcareous soils, especially on the loamy, consolidated screes at the foot of escarpments, or in valley-bottoms, often growing amongst nettles. Very local, but commonly along the base of the Wealden Edge hangers on chalk, W from Buriton to Langrish and East Meon, then N more or less continuously to Selborne. On Malmstone at Dorton, Selborne, near Empshott, and South Hay, near Binsted. This Oceanic-southern species probably attains its greatest abundance in Britain in E Hants.

VC11: East Meon churchyard 6822, *PMH* 1938, Hb.BM, *RPB* 1974; Rookham Copse, Langrish 6923, *RPB* 1974; Duncoombe Wood 6721, *RPB* 1974; Appleton's Copse, Buriton 7319, *DPJS & JMC* 1988. **VC12**: The Warren, Hawkley 7228, 7328, abundant, *AB* 1964, *DBa* 1989; Wheatham Hill 7427, *AB* 1964, 1994; Empshott Green 7431, *AB* 1990; Selborne

Hanger, especially Coneycroft Bottom 7333, *AB & RPB* 1960; South Hay, in Kiln Hanger and Reynolds Hanger 7739, *AB* 1964, *FR* 1989, the northernmost site in England.

ssp. **italicum**   **D,H**   Rare

First record, L. Beeching Hall 1944, Mudeford Church, VC11, *RPB* 1991.

Planted for its beautiful foliage and also formerly as an aphrodisiac, it has escaped into a few shady verges, hedges and streamsides.

VC11: Lepe 4498, *CDD* 1959, *RPB* 1992; St.Cross, Winchester 4727, under trees on stream-bank, *RPB* 1974. Also 1496, 1406, 1418, 2890, 3094, 3222, 3802, 4428, 4824, 5024, 5424, 6204. **VC12**: Wherwell 3840, in lane, spreading from garden, *AB* 1973; outside Broadhanger, Froxfield 7125, one plant on roadside verge, *AB* 1979; Greatham 7730, under hedge outside old cottage, *AB* 1963, 1988.

LEMNACEAE

Spirodela polyrhiza (L.) SCHLEID. (*Lemna polyrhiza* L.)   Greater Duckweed.   **N**   Very local   Map 428

First record, W. A. Bromfield 1838, near Petersfield, VC11/12 (*Fl.Hants*, p.393).

Slow-flowing rivers, ponds and ditches, in clear, alkaline to neutral water. Very locally common in the Stour and lower Avon, and formerly so in the Basingstoke Canal before it was dredged. Otherwise, scattered in a few ponds.

VC11: R. Avon, Coward's Marsh 1595, *CDD* 1976; Avon Castle 1303, in ornamental pond, *GH* 1984; Butlocks Heath 4709, old reservoir, *MS* 1975. **VC12**: Pondtail Flash 8253, *CRH* 1984–90; pond at Eversley Cross 7961, *CRH* 1988; W of Frensham Great Pond 8340, by the dam, *AB* 1975.

Lemna gibba L.   Fat Duckweed.   **N**   Very local   Map 429

In clean, usually base-rich, freshwater ponds, brackish ditches and slow-flowing streams. Rare, except in the Avon Valley.

VC11: Wick 1591, streams in meadows, *CEP* 1970; South Charford, Breamore 1619, *RPB* 1966; Dibden Bay 4108, in brackish drain, *RPB* 1972. **VC12**: Finchampstead Bridge 7962, *WEW* 1959; Bishops Sutton 6131, *ANHS* 1982; Basingstoke Canal 7851, *AB* 1975 (*Watsonia* 11: 402); Froyle 7542, *CL* 1959.

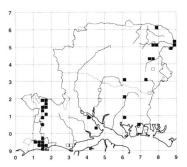

Map 429 Lemna gibba

L. minor L.   Common Duckweed.   **N**   Locally abundant

In slow-flowing streams, drains and ponds, frequently blanketing very stagnant and shaded surfaces; also in water tanks and flood-puddles, and tolerating a certain degree of pollution.

L. trisulca L.   Ivy-leaved Duckweed.   **N**   Locally frequent   Map 430

In slow-flowing stretches or backwaters of rivers and streams, ditches and ponds, and tolerating more brackish conditions than some other species. Frequent along the major rivers, but much decreased in the Basingstoke

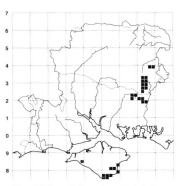

Map 427 Arum italicum ssp. neglectum

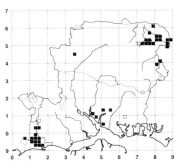

Map 428 Spirodela polyrhiza

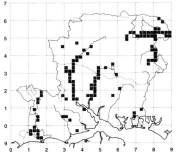

Map 430 Lemna trisulca

Cana¹ except in undisturbed stretches; rare and scattered elsewhere.

VC11: Purewell, Christchurch 1692, in stream, *RMW* 1989; Ladycross Pond 3303, *AEB* 1990; East End 3697, pond in old gravel-pit, *RPB* 1976. **VC12**: Pillhill Brook 2945, *MFW* 1989; pool by R. Blackwater 8559, *JES* 1987; Hackwood Park 6448, *HJMB* 1984.

L. minuta KUNTH (*L. minuscula* Herter)   Least Duckweed.   **C** Local, but rapidly spreading

First record, E. G. Philp 1983, R. Test at Leckford 3737, VC12 (*Watsonia* **15**: 404).

In 1991, this alien was found to be very frequent throughout much of the R. Test and frequent in the lower reaches of the R. Itchen; the lowest reaches of both rivers, however, were not covered (*NRA Survey*). It has also been found in the Rivers Avon, Alre, Whitewater and Blackwater, as well as the Basingstoke Canal, and is probably in other waters waiting to be found.

VC11: R. Avon: Moortown Farm, Ringwood 1403, in millstream, *GH* 1984, Hb.LANC, det. *ACL* (*Watsonia* **17**: 195); Jockstrill Common, Sopley 1597, in drain, *RPB* 1987, det. *ACL*; Ham Common 1498, in drain and edge of river, *AJB & RPB* 1987. R. Test: Horsebridge 3430, *JAM* 1984, det. *ACL* (*loc.cit.*). **VC12**: R. Test: Chilbolton Common 3840, *AJB* 1989. R. Itchen: Itchen Abbas 5332, *HJMB* 1988; Winnall Moors 4830, and Kings Worthy 4932, *AJB* 1989. R. Alre: Alresford Pond 5833, *ARGM* 1988. R. Whitewater: Greywell 7151, *CRH* 1987. R. Blackwater: pool at 8559, *JES* 1987. Basingstoke Canal: Odiham Castle 7251, *CRH* 1987.

JUNCACEAE

Juncus squarrosus L.   Heath Rush. **N**   Locally common   Map 431

Common on wet or dry, acid heaths, especially in bare, trampled or sparsely-vegetated areas. More rarely in bogs, where it grows taller, as in a spur-bog near Furzey Lodge 3602, VC11, *RPB* 1989.

J. tenuis WILLD.   Slender Rush.   **C** Locally common   Map 432

First record, J. F. Rayner 1910, Southampton Common 4114, VC11 (*Suppl.Fl.Hants*, p.109).

On dry or damp, sandy and gravelly heaths, especially along tracks, roadside

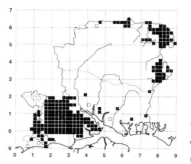

Map 431 Juncus squarrosus

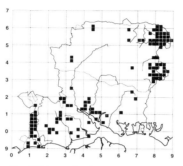

Map 432 Juncus tenuis

verges, pond-margins, and in plantation rides. This N American rush has now spread widely on acid soil, and travels on the tyres of motor vehicles. In E and NE Hants it is associated with military training areas, whence it has spread, through the agency of British army vehicles, to Germany.

VC11: East Meon 6622, *FE* 1932; Netley Common 4711, by track, *BRB* 1963; Fleetend, Warsash 5005, old gravel-pits, *RPB* 1988. **VC12**: Fleet Pond *c*.8154, on dry bed, *ECW* 1941; Highclere Park *c*.4458, *NFC* 1973; entrance to Chawton Park Wood 6736, *DEA* 1984; concrete ride, Eastover Copse 3242, *ILR* 1991, conf. *FR*; now common throughout Woolmer Forest, *FR* 1994.

J. compressus JACQ.   Round-fruited Rush.   **N**   Very rare   Map 433

In marshy water-meadows on base-rich soil, and fen pastures. It has always been rare in Hants and, with the 'improvement' of water-meadows, has become rarer still.

VC11: R. Avon, Ham Common 1498, damp, short turf in flood-plain, frequent in a small area, *CC* 1986, conf. *AJB & RPB* 1987 (*Watsonia* **17**: 194–195); near R. Avon, Winkton Common 1595, *JRw* 1994, Hb.RPB;

near Wallop Brook, Broughton 3132, *BRB* 1959, 3231 *GDF* 1972. **VC12**: North Warnborough 7351, fen pasture, *PMH & ECW* 1941, Hb.BM, abundant, *RJT* 1987, 7352, *AJPB* 1990; Micheldever 5039, sparsely in water-meadow, Hb.AB 1968, conf. *JGD*, meadow later 'improved'; Winnall Moors 4829, *AB* 1982, not seen 1989.

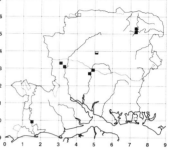

Map 433 Juncus compressus

J. gerardii LOISEL.   Saltmarsh Rush. **N**   Locally abundant   Map 434

Around the coast and in estuaries, in grassy and muddy salt-marshes, brackish marsh pastures; rarely in coastal gravel-pits.

VC11: Pennington Common 3095, *MR* 1976; Nursling gravel-pit 3515, 3615, *RPB* 1962, later filled in.

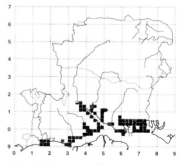

Map 434 Juncus gerardii

J. bufonius L. *sensu lato*

The following three segregates are now recognized:

J. foliosus DESF.   Leafy Rush.   **N** Locally frequent

First record, H. E. Coates 1896, Bournemouth, VC11, Hb.BM, det. *TAC & CAS*, comm. *TAC* 1982.

On wet sand, muddy sides of streams, and around springs in constantly wet places; apparently quite frequent on the Tertiaries of the SW, though in smaller numbers in the NE, but work on its distribution is incomplete.

VC8: West Wellow Common 2819, trodden mud by stream, *RPB* 1986. Also 0812. **VC11**: Near Hatchet Pond 3601, in wet flush, *DEG* 1981, Hb.RPB, det. *CAS*; North Gorley 1611, Hb.RPB 1981, det. *CAS*. Also 1296, 1408, 1608, 1614, 1616, 1800, 1818, 2000, 2098, 2214, 2602, 2800, 3002, 3404, 3408, 3696, 3698, 3602, 3608, 3806, 4006, 4098, 4200, 4202, 4400, 6408. **VC12**: Fleet Pond 8254, sandy bay, 12 plants at water's edge, *CRH* 1985; wet track near Tweseldown, Church Crookham 8252, *CRH* 1985–91. Also 8054, 8250, 8450, 8452.

J. bufonius L. *sensu stricto*   Toad Rush.   **N**   Frequent and locally very common

In muddy places in marshes, edges of ponds, winter flood-hollows, trackruts, damp paths, wet fields and woodland rides. Very common, though only sporadic on chalk.

J. ambiguus GUSS. (*J. ranarius* Nees ex Songeon & E. P. Perrier)   Frog Rush.   **N**   Very local

First record, H. Trimen 1862, Southsea, VC11, Hb.BM, det. and comm. *TAC* 1982.

In grassy, open, brackish places and salt-marshes, especially where trodden; known in a few coastal and estuarine sites and one inland, but may well be more widespread.

VC11: Barton on Sea, *EFL* 1903, Hb.LIV, det. *TAC*; Lymington, *EFL* 1893, Hb.BM, det. and comm. *TAC* 1982; Stanpit Marsh 1692, Lower Test, Nursling 3614, and Sinah Common golf-links 6999, Hb.RPB 1985 (*Watsonia* **16**: 449); Common Marsh, Stockbridge 3534 and Mill Stream, Bedhampton 7005, Hb.RPB 1990, all det. *CAS*. Also 2292, 2692, 2890, 3090, 3694, 3802, 4602.

J. subnodulosus SCHRANK   Blunt-flowered Rush.   **N**   Very local   Map 435

In fens, marshes, and meadow-ditches on base-rich peat soils; mainly in the larger river-valleys, especially along the Test, Whitewater, Lyde and Loddon; also near the coast.

VC11: Priory Marsh, Stanpit 1692, *PJW & RMW* c.1989; Pitts Deep 3795, *RPB* 1967, *AEB* 1990; Stanswood

4600, *RPB* 1966; Lye Heath, Southwick 6408, Hb.AWW 1957, *FR* 1990. **VC12**: Chilbolton Common 3840, *RBG* 1979; Greywell Moors 7150, *FR* 1994; Winnall Moors 4830, *MRe* 1985; Beggars Bridge Marsh 6161, *ReNHS* 1967; Pondtail Heath 8253, in small pool linked by a channel to Basingstoke Canal, *CRH* 1983, det. *FR*; bank of Basingstoke Canal, 8352, 8452, 8552, *CRH* 1989, det. *CAS*; these last two records on acid soil indicate the influence of basic water from the canal.

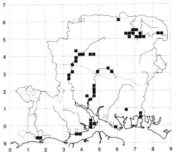

Map 435 Juncus subnodulosus

J. articulatus L.   Jointed Rush.   **N**   Locally common

In marshes, wet meadows, pond-margins, ditches and less-acid bogs.

J. x surrejanus DRUCE ex STACE & LAMBINON (*J. articulatus* x *J. acutiflorus*)   **N**   Under-recorded

First record, T. Moir 1939, Matley Passage 3307, VC11, wet grassland by roadside, det. *EWT & ARC* (*New Phytol.* **39**: 7,16).

Reported as common in some areas of Britain, so perhaps overlooked by Hants recorders. It may be expected where both parents grow together. Other records, as yet unconfirmed: **VC11**: Stanpit 1692, *JHL* 1960. **VC12**: Ancells Farm 8256, around pool, *CRH* 1989; lake near Aldershot 8852, *AJB & CRH* 1989; near Norris Hill 8353, and other unconfirmed records around Aldershot, *CRH* 1989.

J. acutiflorus EHRH. ex HOFFM.   Sharp-flowered Rush.   **N**   Locally abundant   Map 436

In wet meadows, wet heathland, valley bogs and wet, open woods on acid soils.

J. bulbosus L. (incl. *J. kochii* F. W. Schultz)   Bulbous Rush.   **N**   Locally common

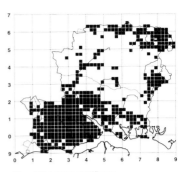

Map 436 Juncus acutiflorus

On wet heaths, in bogs, ditches, and flood hollows; in ponds, both on margins and fully aquatic; in muddy, woodland rides. Very common on acid soils.

J. maritimus LAM.   Sea Rush.   **N**   Locally common

First record, H. Trimen 1818, Portsea Island, VC11, Hb.BM.

On salt-marshes, banks of tidal rivers, creeks, ditches in brackish pastures; common on the coast and in estuaries. VC11: 45 ☐.

J. acutus L.   Sharp Rush.   **N**   Very rare

Dune-slack hollows on the coast; now only at Sandy Point, Hayling Island 7498, VC11, eight plants, *PHC* 1983 (*Watsonia* **16**: 194), *FR* 1994. First noticed there by Miss M. T. Hillard 1922 (*Suppl.Fl.Hants*, p.109), although the earliest record for Hayling Island (unlocalized), was 1886 (*Fl.Hants*, p.442). There is also an old record for Portsea, 'pond in a meadow belonging to High Grove', 1846–48, (*Maj.Smith MS Cat.*).

J. inflexus L.   Hard Rush.   **N**   Locally common

Common in marshes, fens, wet meadows, streamsides and damp grass-heaths; the commonest rush on heavy, basic soil.

J. x diffusus HOPPE (*J. inflexus* x *J. effusus*)   **N**   Probably under-recorded

VC12: Disused railway, Liss 7726, *AB* 1968; Hazeley Heath 7558, *CRH* 1991, conf. *FR*.

J. effusus L.   Soft Rush.   **N**   Locally abundant

In neglected, wet pastures, marshes,

valley bogs, wet, open woods and carr; very common on acid soil but only locally on chalk superficials.

J. conglomeratus L.   Compact Rush.   **N**   Locally common

In wet meadows, marshes, fens, less-acid valley-bogs, ditches and damp, open woods.

Luzula forsteri (SM.) DC.   Southern Wood-rush.   **N**   Locally frequent   Map 437

Associated with ancient woodland, old hedgebanks, boundary banks, and sunken lanes. On a variety of soils (except the very acid), but prefers good drainage and on the poorer soils tends mostly to be on banks. Commonest in the Beaulieu River valley, the Forest of Bere, the western Weald and the E Hants Hangers.
    VC11: Moorcourt Copse 3417, roadside bank, *RMV* 1986. **VC12**: Leeches Copse 7850, *CRH* 1989.

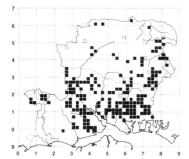

Map 437 Luzula forsteri

L. x borreri BROMF. ex BAB. (*L. forsteri* x *L. pilosa*)   **N**   Rare, or under-recorded

VC8: 0616. **VC11**: 1210, 1218, 3608, 3618, 5812, 6818. **VC12**: 6838, 7832.

L. pilosa (L.) WILLD.   Hairy Wood-rush.   **N**   Locally common   Map 438

In woods, copses and shady hedge-banks; common except on the most acid soils. Townsend's opinion that *L. pilosa* (*Fl.Hants*, p.440, as *L.vernalis* DC.) was less common than *L. forsteri* is no longer supported by their respective distribution maps which show that *L. forsteri* is now more local.

L. sylvatica (HUDS.) GAUDIN   Great Wood-rush.   **N**   Very local and rare   Map 439

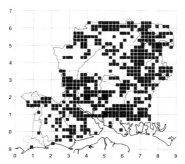

Map 438 Luzula pilosa

In ancient woodland on sandy or loamy, rather acid soils, including those of the chalk superficials.
    VC8: Boulsbury Wood 0715, 0815, *AB, WI & FR* 1976. **VC11**: Sandy Balls, Godshill 1614, *RPB* 1957, *HCC* 1986; Hale 1918, *RPB* 1983; near Sandleheath 1215, *RMV* 1986; Ampfield Wood 4124, *ME* 1968, *RMV* 1987; Crab Wood 4329, *CDD* 1960; Mustercombe Copse, Langrish 7123, Hb.AWW 1963, *FR* 1994; Cranbury Park woods 4423, 4523, *FR* 1972; Knowle Copse 5610, *JRw* 1991. **VC12**: Aldershot 8350, around spring on Caesar's Camp, *BFD* 1975, *ARGM* 1989; Fusney Copse 7950, *CRH* 1989; Bramshill Common 7461, along ride, *CRH* 1989.

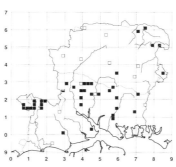

Map 439 Luzula sylvatica

L. luzuloides (LAM.) DANDY & WILMOTT   White Wood-rush.   **H**   Very rare

VC12: Wyeford Farm Wood, Pamber Green 5959, *WEW* 1957.

L. campestris (L.) DC.   Field Wood-rush.   **N**   Frequent and locally common

In old, dry grassland and lawns; on all soils.

L. multiflora (EHRH.) LEJ.   Heath Wood-rush.   **N**   Locally common

On heaths, acid pastures and open, heathy woods. Ssp. *multiflora* and ssp. *congesta* (Thuill.) Arcang. have both been recorded a few times, the latter mainly in the New Forest where (as the form *congesta*) it is stated in *Fl.Hants* (p.442) to be very common, but their respective distributions are largely unknown.

CYPERACEAE

Eriophorum angustifolium HONCK.   Common Cottongrass.   **N**   Locally common   Map 440

In bogs, wet heathland, and old, wet meadows, on both acid and alkaline peat; abundant in the New Forest, and often dominant in valley bogs; frequent on the northern and eastern heathland; now rare in meadows, due to drainage and 'improvement'.
    VC11: Flexford 4221, *RPB* 1982. **VC12**: Bransbury Common 4141, 4142, *RPB* 1974–86; Ashford Hill meadows 5662, *FR* 1983.

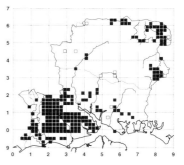

Map 440 Eriophorum angustifolium

E. latifolium HOPPE   Broad-leaved Cottongrass.   **N**   Rare   Map 441

In calcareous or base-rich valley-mires and wet meadows; very local to rare in several scattered sites on the Headon or Barton clays in the southern New Forest; also in the Lyde Valley and Greywell Moors, and at Conford Moor in a mire fed by water from the calcareous Sandgate Beds. Decreasing, with very few plants at most sites.
    VC11: Upper Pennington Common 2995, *RPB* 1976–92; Highcliffe *c.*2092, 1878, Hb.OXF. **VC12**: Stockbridge North Fen 3535, *FR* 1986.

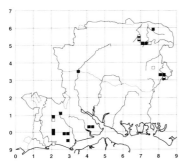

Map 441 Eriophorum latifolium

E. gracile KOCH ex ROTH   Slender
Cottongrass.   **N**   Very rare (Sched.
8)

Very wet, moderately acid valley-bogs
in the reed-zone bordering on alder
carr.

VC11: Widden Bottom, Sway 2899,
40 plants, *RPB* 1987 (*Watsonia* **17**:
195), only four in flower *HWi*, *AJPB
& NAS* 1994; Fort Bog, Matley 3308,
locally plentiful, *RPB* 1956, 1984,
Hb.AWW, 1000–1500 plants, *HWi*,
AJPB & NAS 1994; E of Thorney
Hill Holms 2100, and Wilverley Bog
2497, *FR* 1967, 1969, scarce at both
and no recent record; not refound at
Week Common 1399, *JEL* n.d. and
Holmsley Bog 2300, last seen *MPY &
AB* 1968. Recorded in *Fl.Hants* (p.457)
at Shappen Bottom 2101 or 2102, in
1885, White Moor 3108 and Denny
Bog (where it was again reported in
1968); recorded in *Fl.Bmth* (p.233)
'one to two miles N of Hurn Station, in
a moist hollow between the railway and
the meadows'. There is a recent record
for Stony Moors 2199, unconfirmed.
VC12: North Warnborough marsh
*c.*7352, *CP* 1899, Hb.OXF; Greywell
Moors 7150, *ECW* 1936, last seen
MPY 1967. Believed extinct in N
Hants.

E. vaginatum L.   Hare's-tail
Cottongrass.   **N**   Very local   Map
442

On wet heaths, with *Trichophorum
cespitosum* and *Erica tetralix*, often at
the base of slopes rising above valley
bogs. Rare, but locally plentiful in the
lower Avon Valley, NW New Forest,
and the Folkestone Sands heathland of
Woolmer Forest.

VC11: Black Barrow, Linwood
1810, *FR & NAS* 1990; Half Moon
Common 2916, 2917, *RPB & RMV*
1984; near Matley Passage 3307,
Hb.AWW 1960, *RPB* 1990–94. **VC12**:

Blackmoor golf-course 7834, *AB* 1974,
FR 1994; Cranmer Bottom 7932, *HCC*
1987; Great Dean Bottom, Longmoor
7829, *HCC* 1987, *FR* 1994. There is a
specimen in Hb.OXF from Shapley
Heath 7554, 1884.

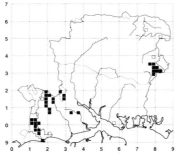

Map 442 Eriophorum vaginatum

Trichophorum cespitosum (L.)
HARTM. ssp. **germanicum** (PALLA)
HEGI (*Scirpus cespitosus* L.)   Deer-
grass.   **N**   Locally common   Map
443

On wet heaths, often on bare peat or
with sparse *Erica tetralix*, *Sphagnum
tenellum* and *S. compactum*. Common
on the New Forest and Avon Valley
heaths; local on the Folkestone Sands
about Woolmer Forest, and on the
Bagshot Sands in the NE.

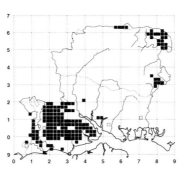

Map 443 Trichophorum cespitosum ssp.
germanicum

Eleocharis palustris (L.) ROEM. &
SCHULT.   Common Spike-rush.   **N**
Locally common

In freshwater marshes, shallow ponds
and ditches, wet meadows. Also occasionally in brackish marshes with *E.
uniglumis*, but replaced by *E. multicaulis* in acid bogs. The common plant
in Britain is ssp. *vulgaris* Walters,
whilst ssp. *palustris* (ssp. *microcarpa*
Walters) is more local. The distribu-

tion of both in Hants is scantily known,
but S. M. Walters has determined the
following two voucher specimens:

ssp. **vulgaris** WALTERS

VC11: Culverley Green, Brockenhurst
2902, Hb.RPB 1985.

ssp. **palustris**

VC11: Roydon Woods 3100, in marshy
pond, Hb.RPB 1985.

E. uniglumis (LINK) SCHULT.   Slender Spike-rush.   **N**   Rare   Map 444

First record, H. Trimen 1862, Gomer
Pond 5899, VC11 (*Fl.Hants*, p.450).

Estuarine and coastal brackish grassland, where very local. Inland in base-
rich, wet, alluvial pastures, rare but
perhaps overlooked. Usually in short
turf.

VC8: Plaitford 2720, marshy
meadow S of church, Hb.RPB 1991,
det. *ACJ*. **VC11**: Holmsley 2300, in
base-rich flush near *Triglochin maritimum*, a frequent associate in its brackish habitats, Hb.RPB 1984; Langstone
7105, *FR* 1983; The Moors, Bishop's
Waltham 5616, *FR & AOC* 1985.
VC12: Chilbolton Common 3840,
RBG 1979; Warnborough Greens
*c.*7252, *FR* 1983 (both *Watsonia* **15**:
404).

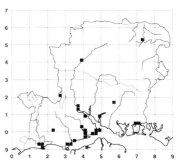

Map 444 Eleocharis uniglumis

E. multicaulis (SM.) DESV.   Many-
stalked Spike-rush.   **N**   Locally
common   Map 445

In wet hollows and pools of acid valley-
bogs on heaths. Very common in the
New Forest, frequent on the Bagshot
Sands in the NE.

VC8: Lopshill Common 0913, *RPB*
1989. **VC11**: Shedfield Common 5613,
Hb.RPB 1990; Browndown Common
5899, Hb.AWW 1957. **VC12**: Eelmoor
Marsh 8352, *ARGM* 1977–90; Hawley
Common 8357, *CRH* 1987; Silchester

Common 6262, *FR & ECW* 1975; Liphook golf-course 8330, *FR* 1992; rare in Woolmer Forest area.

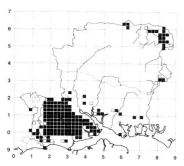

Map 445 Eleocharis multicaulis

E. quinqueflora (HARTMANN) O. SCHWARZ Few-flowered Spike-rush. N Very local and rare Map 446

In flushed sites in short swards of sedge on calcareous or base-rich fens. Frequent in the New Forest, where the Headon Beds or other calcareous strata outcrop on the valley sides; very rare elsewhere.

VC8: Lopshill Common 0913, *JDG* 1957, Hb.JDG (*Fl.Wilts*, p.584). VC11: Hatchet Pond 3601, Hb.RPB 1966, det. *ECW*; Stony Moors 2199, *FR* 1983; Acres Down 2708, *FR* 1984. VC12: Conford Moor, *ECW* 1932, 8133 *FR* 1988; Bransbury Common 4141, *FR & AOC* 1984.

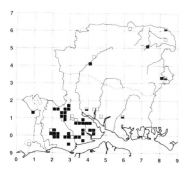

Map 446 Eleocharis quinqueflora

E. acicularis (L.) ROEM. & SCHULT. Needle Spike-rush. N Rare Map 447

On muddy or sandy beds of lakes and their open shores where submerged in winter. Rare, but forms an extensive sward revealed only on drying-out or drainage of lakes and reservoirs.

VC8: Furzley Common 2816, at spring in valley bog, *MES* 1991,

Hb.RPB. VC11: Greenmoor 3399, marl-pit pond, *AEB* 1988; East Boldre 3699, Hb.RPB 1976; Hatchet Pond 3601, Hb.RPB 1983, det. *SMW*. VC12: Hollywater Pond 8033, *CRH* 1990, det. *FR*; Fleet Pond, dried bed 8254, *ECW* 1941, Hb.BM, in newly-dug marginal pond 8255, *CRH* 1989; Duns Mere, Highclere 4560, *AB* 1976; Hawley Lake 8257, *AB* 1976, *CRH* 1989; Bourley Bottom Reservoir 8250, *RPB* 1973, abundant when drained, *ARGM* 1985; Basingstoke Canal 8652, Hb.RPB 1973, 8353–8652 *CRH* 1990.

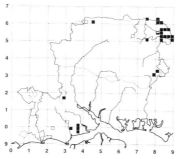

Map 447 Eleocharis acicularis

E. parvula (ROEM. & SCHULT.) LINK ex BLUFF, NEES & SCHAUER Dwarf Spike-rush. N Very rare

First British record, G. E. Smith 1835, Lymington 3394, VC11, Hb.BM (*Phytologist* 1: 310).

Forming short swards on estuarine sand or mud that is regularly submerged in brackish water.

VC11: Beaulieu 3802, tidal millpond, *BW* 1955, Hb.BM, *FR* 1985, *RPB* 1994; Stanpit Marsh 1692, Hb.RPB 1976, det. *FR*, *PJW* 1985; *RPB* 1994. Formerly also at Mudeford. Elsewhere in Britain known only in Dorset, Devon and N Wales.

Bolboschoenus maritimus (L.) PALLA (*Scirpus maritimus* L.) Sea Club-rush. N Locally common Map 448

In non-tidal, brackish marshes, ditches and ponds within sea-walls; also in the upper, less saline reaches of tidal estuaries and rivers. Rarely around gravel-pit ponds inland.

VC11: Fields Heath, Fawley 4502, *RPB* 1975; St Leonards 4098, *RPB* 1965; Bursledon old brickworks 5010, *RMV* 1988; also formerly Nursling 3515, flooded gravel-pit, *RPB* 1972.

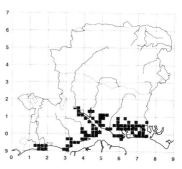

Map 448 Bolboschoenus maritimus

Scirpus sylvaticus L. Wood Club-rush. N Locally frequent Map 449

In acid, swampy valley-woodland, and in very wet, neglected pastures bordering woods and streams. Very shade-tolerant, and usually in somewhat-flushed sites. Often dominant and forming extensive beds. Local in the New Forest, more frequent on the Tertiaries between Plaitford and Boarhunt, and in two areas of the Thames Basin. Common on the Lower Greensand and Gault clay.

VC11: Near Penerley Wood, Beaulieu 3704, *RPB* 1967; Tile Barn, Brockenhurst 2901, *AEB* 1988. VC12: Abundant in swampy woods beside R. Blackwater, Yateley 8261, *ARGM* 1987; Peat Gully Copse, Beaurepaire Farm 6257, *ILR* 1991.

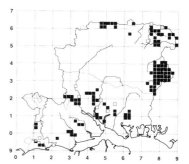

Map 449 Scirpus sylvaticus

<Scirpoides holoschoenus (L.) SOJÁK (*Scirpus holoschoenus* L., *Holoschoenus vulgaris* Link) Round-headed Club-rush. N Extinct

Formerly in damp, sandy places on the coast, VC11. '*In agro Hantoniensi detexit D. Sherard*', 1699 (*Morison Hist.* pt.3, p.232), presumably referring to Dr William Sherard. Sir J. E. Smith says 'Hudson has observed it in Hampshire' (*Eng.Bot.*, pl.1612, Jun. 1, 1806) but this was evidently based on a misreading of earlier books. Townsend accepted it as a native of the county, but extinct (*Fl. Hants*, p.454).>

Schoenoplectus lacustris (L.) PALLA (*Scirpus lacustris* L.)   Bulrush, Common Club-rush.   N   Locally frequent   Map 450

In the major freshwater rivers: Stour, Avon, Test, Itchen, and Loddon. Frequent and locally plentiful, usually only as tall stands in shallows, fringes and backwaters; more often non-flowering and bent over in swift-flowing currents. Rarely, in scattered freshwater ponds, as given below.
VC11: Town Copse gravel-pits 3419, *RPB* 1984; Emer Bog 3921, *RPB* 1985. **VC12**: The Wylds Lake, Liss 7828, *AB* 1965.

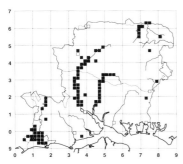

Map 450 Schoenoplectus lacustris

S. tabernaemontani (C. C. GMEL.) PALLA (*Scirpus tabernaemontani* C. C. Gmel.)   Glaucous Bulrush, Grey Club-rush.   N   Locally frequent   Map 451

Fringing the upper tidal reaches of rivers, and also in brackish pools and ditches in salt-marshes, and behind beaches and sea-walls. Rarely in fresh-water ponds, as given below.

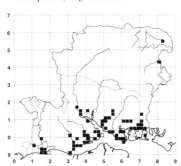

Map 451 Schoenoplectus tabernaemontani

VC11: Upper Crockford Bottom 3499, old marl-pit pools, *RPB* 1970; Roydon Woods 3100, marshy pond, *IB* 1978; Manor Farm pond, Boarhunt 6008, *RPB* 1979. **VC12**: Fleet Pond 8255, *VL* 1951, *ARGM* 1975, not refound since; Lodge Pond, Alice Holt Forest 8142, Hb.AB 1964.

Isolepis setacea (L.) R. BR. (*Scirpus setaceus* L.)   Bristle Club-rush.   N   Locally frequent   Map 452

On bare, sandy or muddy places, inundated in winter; watersides, trodden ground in marshes, shallow ditches, heathland and woodland tracks; common in the New Forest and on other acid soils. Local in some basic wet meadows; on chalk, confined to a few tracks on superficial deposits.
VC11: Warblington 7305, wet meadow, *EAP* 1982; Pennington Marshes 3292, *MR* 1976. **VC12**: Ashford Hill meadows 5662, *PB* 1983; Upper Clatford 3543, *GDF* 1983; Mabbotts Farm, Hawkley 7529, 'unimproved' meadow, *HR* 1985; ditch below Bricksbury Hill 8249, *ARGM* 1985.

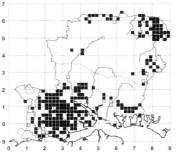

Map 452 Isolepis setacea

I. cernua (VAHL) ROEM. & SCHULT. (*Scirpus cernuus* Vahl)   Slender Club-rush.   N   Very local   Map 453

Mud and open turf in the upper salt-

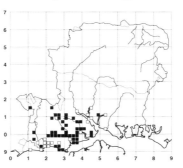

Map 453 Isolepis cernua

marshes of the W Solent, and in flushed turf around basic springs, in old marl-pits and sides of runnels in central and southern New Forest. Most frequent on the Headon Beds.
VC11: R. Hamble, beside Catland Copse 4910, on mud pan, *RPB* 1968; Acres Down 2708, *FR* 1984.

Eleogiton fluitans (L.) LINK (*Scirpus fluitans* L.)   Floating Club-rush.   N   Locally common   Map 454

Peaty water in ponds; ditches and streams draining valley bogs and wet heaths. Abundant in the New Forest; frequent in the lower Avon Valley, and on the Lower Greensand and NE Bagshot Sands; rare in the SE.
VC11: Hamble Common 4806, *RPB* 1976; Upper Lake, Rowland's Castle 7110, *HCC* 1985; Creech Pond, Denmead 6510, *JRw* 1991. **VC12**: Basingstoke Canal 8353–8652, abundant before 1978–79 dredging, seriously depleted since (*RAE Survey*, 1991); Cranmer Pond 7932, *JW* 1981.

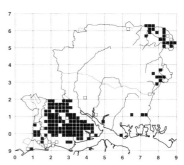

Map 454 Eleogiton fluitans

Blysmus compressus (L.) PANZ. ex LINK   Flat-sedge.   N   Rare   Map 455

Among short grass or sedge-swards, in calcareous fens and old, 'unimproved'

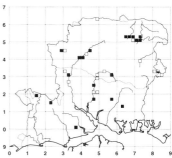

Map 455 Blysmus compressus

meadows; rare and decreasing. Mainly in the chalk-spring areas along the N edge of the chalk in N Hants. An isolated New Forest site in turf and sphagnum bog, flushed by a chalybeate spring.

VC11: Howen Bottom 2214, 2315, Hb.RPB 1964, still in two sites, *RPB* 1992; Breamore Marsh 1518, ponds, Hb.AWW 1963; The Moors, Bishop's Waltham 5616, *PJW* 1986. **VC12**: East Aston meadows 4444, *FR* 1986; Warnborough Greens 7352, *FR* 1983, 7351, *ARGM* 1990; Mapledurwell Fen 6752, *FR* 1973, *AJPB & CRH* 1992; Chilbolton Common 3940, *FR* 1984.

Cyperus longus L.   Galingale.
H,D,N?   Very rare

Said to have been planted at one time for strewing on floors; more often an escape from water-gardens. It could possibly have been native in wet flushes in the SW (e.g. Highcliffe cliffs), as it still is in Dorset.

VC11: Mudeford, *LBH* 1921, cliffs at Highcliffe, *GF* n.d., *KG* 1951, Hb.AB, comm. *JEL* (*Watsonia*, **1**: 259); Lymington, *TRG-P* 1926 (*Rep.B.E.C.* for 1926, p.137); Walhampton 3395, *RPB* 1954. Introduced at: Linwood 1809, *LWF* 1960; Ladycross Pond 3303, *AEB* 1986, conf. *RPB*; Gaters Mill, West End 4515, on river-bank, *DWG* 1980, Hb.BM, det. *JMM*; Itchen Navigation, Shawford 4724, *KC* 1978. **VC12**: Probably introduced at: Kings Worthy 4932, *WB* 1927 (*Suppl. Fl.Hants*, p.112), *RHJ* 1965, not seen *AB* 1979; Oakley 5650, roadside pond, *HJMB* 1984; Basingstoke Canal 8053, *CRH* 1987; New Buildings, Hartley Mauditt 7536, roadside pond, *FR* 1994.

C. fuscus L.   Brown Galingale.   **N** Very rare (Sched. 8)   Plate XI

On bare, muddy or stony shores of acidic ponds, below the winter water-level, particularly where geese are present. It can be abundant in drier summers when water-levels recede rapidly but in wet summers is often choked by rank herbage and scarce.

VC11: Breamore Marsh 1518, *BG* 1934, Hb.BM, *JO & FR* 1983; Breamore Marsh 1517, *MPY* 1965, *RPB* 1976, 1992; Kingston North Common 1503, small pond, *AJB, RAF & JNBM* 1983, large proportion of plants lost when site partly infilled, *RPB* 1989; Haskell's Pond 1402, *RPB* 1995. Probably lost at Blashford, where

it was first recorded by *WRL* in 1893 (*J.Bot.* **31**: 369).

Schoenus nigricans L.   Black Bog-rush.   **N   Rare   Map 456**

In flushed fens with open vegetation, central zones of valley-bottom mires fed by base-rich water, mainly from the Headon Beds.

VC11: Locally abundant in the New Forest, concentrated on Vales Moor 1903, 1904, Cranes Moor 1802, Shirley Common 1999, Common Moor 2004, Holmsley Bog system 2101–2301, and Stony Moors 2199. Isolated populations at: Dibden Bottom 3906; Crockford Bridge 3499, *RPB* 1975; Netley Hill 4811, *PHC* 1984, *RPB* 1994; near Wick Wood, Acres Down 2609, a few small plants, *PAB* 1984; Woodford Bottom 1911, *PS* 1989.

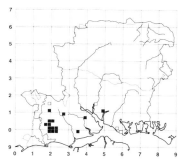

Map 456 Schoenus nigricans

Rhynchospora alba (L.) VAHL White Beak-sedge.   **N   Locally common   Map 457**

First record, T. Yalden *c.*1770, 'Forest of Bere, opposite Ashlands' *c.*6110, VC11 (*Ray Syn.MS*, p.256).

Wet heaths on open peat, the wetter hollows of valley bogs, and in the transitional zone between. Abundant in the New Forest (which has the largest

population in S Britain); still frequent in the lower Avon Valley, and occasional about Aldershot and Hazeley Heath on the NE Bagshot Sands. Some sites have been destroyed in Woolmer Forest by drainage, but it is still to be found in plenty in very wet, abandoned old rides.

VC8: Lopshill Common 0913, *RPB* 1989. **VC11**: Upper Pennington Common 2995, *SNHS* 1968; Acres Down 2608, *FR* 1984. **VC12**: Hawley Lake 8357, *CRH* 1983; Woolmer Forest 8033, old wet rides in local abundance and in the remaining bogs, *AB, FR & PLeB* 1985; the Slab 7834, *FR* 1989; Cranmer Bottom 7932, *HCC* 1987, *FR* 1994; Yateley Common 8359, *CRH* 1985; Eelmoor Marsh 8353 *ARGM & FR* 1994.

R. fusca (L.) W. T. AITON   Brown Beak-sedge.   **N   Very local   Map 458**

First British record, J. Petiver 1716, 'between Southampton and Limington', VC11 (*Conc.Gram.*, no.148).

Wet heaths on open peat fringing valley bog, especially along wet cattle- and pony-tracks, and on flushed peat; just penetrating into open vegetation of bogs. Frequent in S and C New Forest (where there is more than in the rest of S England); often with *R. alba* but never as abundant and more sporadic in flowering; extending to the lower Avon Valley, where it is rare.

VC8: Plaitford Common 2718, *AEB* 1983, *FR* 1991. **VC11**: Sopley Common 1397, *RMW c.*1980; Avon Common 1298 and Town Common 1496, *MAS* 1971; St Leonards 1003, *JRW* 1979; W of Burley 1803 and W of Cranes Moor 1802, *FR* 1984; N of Matley Wood 3308, *FR* 1979; Dark Water, Holbury Purlieu 4204, abundant, *RPB* 1954; Yew Tree Heath 3706, 3707, widespread as a colonizer of wet heath, burnt in 1976, *RPB* 1987, 1994.

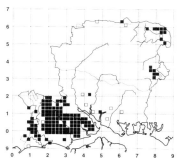

Map 457 Rhynchospora alba

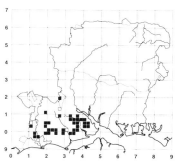

Map 458 Rhynchospora fusca

Cladium mariscus (L.) POHL
Great Fen-sedge. **N** Very rare

In tall, fen vegetation on alkaline peat. Seems now to have gone from everywhere except the first three VC11 sites noted.

VC11: Sowley Pond 3796, two clumps on N shore, *DCW* 1990, comm. *AEB*; Gomer Pond 5899, moderately plentiful but decreasing, *FR* 1980, flourishing following thinning of scrub, *RPB* 1989; Gilkicker Point 6097, *RPB* 1986 (*Watsonia* **17**: 196). Probably lost at: Rudley Mill 6212, *EHW* 1945, Hb.BM; Bishop's Waltham 5516, millpond, *AWW* 1960. **VC12**: Greywell Moors, *ECW* 1936, since shaded out.

Carex paniculata L. Greater Tussock-sedge. **N** Locally common Map 459

In alkaline to moderately-acid fens and carr, often on very wet peat. Common along most river valleys, particularly those of the Avon, Test and Itchen and those on the Tertiary sands and Lower Greensand. Typical of swampy alder- or willow-carr in the central flow-line of valley bogs, even in remote branch valleys. In some open sites it may be a relic of former fen or carr habitats.

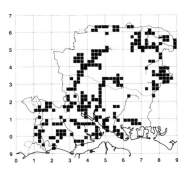

Map 459 Carex paniculata

C. x boenninghauseniana WEIHE (*C. paniculata* x *C. remota*) **N** Very rare

VC11: St Leonards Peat South 1000, *AJB & RWD* 1986, comm. *RMW*. **VC12**: Hazeley Heath *c.*7658, *JCDa* 1929, Hb.OXF (*Suppl.Fl.Hants*, p.114); marshy copse E of Purdies Farm 7658, *GARW* 1935 (*Watts MSS*), probably the same as the previous site. Unconfirmed record for Winchfield Hurst 7753, *DEB* 1963.

C. diandra SCHRANK Lesser Tussock-sedge. **N** Very rare

In wet fens, where competition is not too great. Now found only in three places in VC12. *Fl.Hants* (p. 460, under *C. teretiuscula* Gooden.) listed five localities in VC11 and three in VC12. A relic of more extensive, ancient fens.

VC11: By ditch near Pussex Farm, Hurn 1297, *TBS* (*Fl.Bmth App.2*, p.323); Portchester, *MTH* (*Suppl.Fl. Hants*, p.114). Neither refound. **VC12**: Bransbury Common 4141, Hb.RPB 1970, *FR* 1986; Greywell Moors 7150, 7251, *FR* 1973, *FR & CRH* 1991; Stockbridge North Fen 3535, plentiful, *FR* 1986–90; 'on left bank of Itchen ½ mile W of Easton', *GARW* 1935 (*Watts MSS*), site now destroyed, *NAS* 1991.

C. otrubae PODP. False Fox-sedge. **N** Locally common Map 460

In marshy meadows and ditches, on mineral soils rather than peat, and in brackish pastures near the coast. Locally common on the Tertiary clays and the Gault; rare on sand, and almost absent from the New Forest, where grazing may be the reason.

Recorded under *C. vulpina* L. in *Fl.Hants* (pp.461–462) but that species is unknown in Hants.

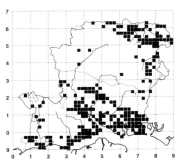

Map 460 Carex otrubae

C. x pseudoaxillaris K. RICHT. (*C. otrubae* x *C. remota*) Axillary Sedge. **N** Very rare

VC11: Three records in *Fl.Hants* (p.464), four in *Suppl.Fl.Hants* (p.114), none since. **VC12**: Dogmersfield *c.*7751, *EAB* 1966.

C. spicata HUDS. Spiked Sedge. **N** Frequent

First record, P. M. Hall & E. C. Wallace 1937, Greywell, VC12, Hb.BM, conf. *RWD*.

In dry grassland, verges, hedge- and ditch-banks, old gravel-pits, scrub-

borders; on gravel, sand, clay and the chalk-superficial loams. More tolerant of basic soils than *C. muricata* ssp. *lamprocarpa*. Not recorded in *Fl.Hants*, but evidently many records of this species were included under *C. muricata*.

C. muricata L. ssp. **lamprocarpa** ČELAK. (*C. pairii* F. W. Schultz) Prickly Sedge. **N** Locally frequent Map 461

First record, A. B. Jackson 1896, Highclere VC12, Hb.BM, det. *RWD*.

In dry grassland, verges, banks of pits and grassy sea-walls, on acidic sand or gravel. Distribution imperfectly known, but it is very frequent in the mid-Avon Valley, apparently frequent in Woolmer Forest and widespread but local on the NE Bagshot Sands.

VC8: Near Pinns Farm, Wellow 2920, *BW* 1947, det. *RWD*, bank N side of road E of farm, *RMV* 1986. **VC11**: Milford on Sea, *EM-R* 1950, Hb.K, det. *RWD*; B3347, Avon 1498, Hb.RPB 1978, det.*RWD*; Needs Ore Point 4297, Hb.RPB 1964, det. *RWD*. **VC12**: SW of Tadley 5858, *WEW* 1956, det. *ECW*; roadside near Liphook, *PMH & ECW* 1937; Longmoor airstrip 8030, *AB* 1982, *FR* 1988; Harewood Forest 4045, *RMV* 1982, conf. *RWD*; Hazeley Heath tip 7657, *CRH* 1989; Warren Bottom Copse 5554, *ILR* 1991.

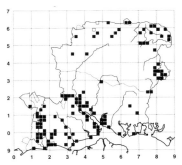

Map 461 Carex muricata ssp. lamprocarpa

C. divulsa STOKES Grey Sedge.

ssp. **divulsa** **N** Frequent and locally common

On dry hedgebanks, grass verges, borders of woods, on both basic and acidic sandy or gravelly soil.

ssp. **leersii** (KNEUCK.) W. KOCH (*C. polyphylla* Kar. & Kir.) **N** Locally frequent but under-recorded   Map 462

First record, A. B. Jackson 1912, Combe 3660 (Berks), VC12, dry hedge-bank, Hb.BM, det. *RWD*.

On hedgebanks and verges, dry grassland, woodland rides and borders, nearly always on chalk and other basic soils. Widespread but overlooked.

VC11: Breamore Wood 1419, *RMV* 1982, det. *RWD*; Sparsholt 4330, road-side, *RWD* 1976; Northney, North Hayling 7203, Hb.RPB 1983, det. *RWD*. **VC12**: Quarley Hill 2642, *FHP* 1957, Hb.CGE, det. *RWD*; Michelde-ver Wood 5337, verge of Broad Walk, *RMV* 1987; Butter Wood 7052, *ECW* 1939, Hb.BM, det. *RWD*; lane near Swarraton 5636, *AB* 1991, det. *FR*.

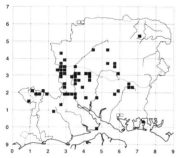

Map 462 Carex divulsa ssp. leersii

C. arenaria L.   Sand Sedge.   **N**
Locally frequent   Map 463

On sand-dunes and stabilized, sandy shingle along the coast, where fairly common; inland on sandy heaths in the Avon Valley and Woolmer Forest, where locally plentiful; rarely in New Forest, on roadside verges.

VC11: B3056 Lyndhurst 3107, 3207, *RPB* 1966–89; Jockstrill Common 1597 and Ham Common 1498, *HCC* 1986. **VC12**: Shortheath Common 7736, *AB* 1983, *FR* 1993.

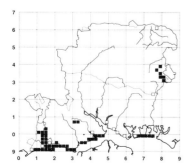

Map 463 Carex arenaria

C. disticha HUDS.   Brown Sedge.
N   Locally frequent   Map 464

In fen-meadows and alluvial, grazed marshes on basic soil. Common along the main river-systems, and occasional elsewhere. One unusual site on slipped clay:

VC11: Barton Cliff 2392, Hb.RPB 1977, det. *FR*.

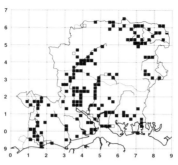

Map 464 Carex disticha

C. divisa HUDS.   Divided Sedge.   **N**
Very locally frequent   Map 465

First record, T. Yalden *c.*1770, 'in the meadow below Itchin Ferry, near Southampton' *c.*4310, VC11 (*Ray Syn.MS*, p.423).

In brackish pastures, especially along drains, grassy salt-marshes and inner sea-walls. Always near the sea or in estuaries, where frequent to abundant.

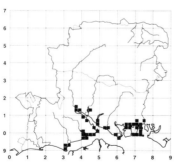

Map 465 Carex divisa

C. remota L.   Remote Sedge.   **N**
Locally abundant   Map 466

In wet woodland, in rides, flushes and carrs; shaded banks of streams and ditches. Very common on all moder-ately-acid soils or on peat; occasional on more basic soils.

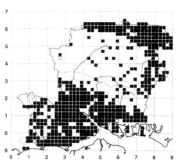

Map 466 Carex remota

C. ovalis GOODEN.   Oval Sedge.   **N**
Locally very common

On grassy heathland, old, acidic mead-ows and woodland glades or rides. Common on all acid soils; occcasional on chalk superficials.

C. echinata MURRAY   Star Sedge.
N   Locally common   Map 467

In bogs and waterlogged, wet heaths, acid marshes and wet meadows. Excep-tionally inside boggy willow-carr. Common in the New Forest, and on the Lower Greensand and NE Tertiaries.

VC11: Shedfield Common 5613, Hb.AWW 1956, *FR* 1984; Common Marsh, Stockbridge 3533, *RPB* 1976. **VC12**: Netherton Bottom 3656, *CL* 1962; Bransbury Common 4141, *FR* 1971; Tichborne 5731, *RPB* 1964, *FR* 1994.

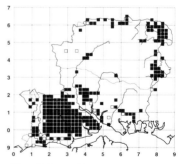

Map 467 Carex echinata

C. dioica L.   Dioecious Sedge.   **N**
Very rare

In short, calcareous fen-vegetation among other small sedges, especially on a spongy moss-carpet. In S England, now restricted to N Hants and E Dorset.

VC12: Now only on Bransbury Common 4141, *FR & PB* 1986 and at

Mapledurwell Fen 6752, *FR & PB* 1982. Lost at Conford 8232, through drainage and conifer planting, last seen *RAB & FR c*.1957; destroyed at Mapledurwell 6852, by the M3; lost from Tichborne, *GCD* (*Suppl.Fl. Hants*, p.113). A record in *Proc.Hants Fld Club* (**15**: 73), 'Near Weaver's Down, Liphook', *ECW* 1937, probably refers to the Conford site.

C. elongata L.   Elongated Sedge, Gingerbread Sedge.   **N**   Very rare

First record G. C. Druce 1897, 'a tuft or two' in VC12 near R. Blackwater, 'between Finchampstead and Jouldern's ford [Joulding's Ford 7563], rather more plentiful on Berks side near Thatcher's ford', 7463 (*J.Bot.* **35**: 313); not refound in 1930s *PMH & ECW* (*Proc.Hants Fld Club* **15**: 74), or by *FR* 1984.

   In very wet, acid, willow- and alder-carr, beside very wet ditches and edges of rivers, and often in them. Confined to the Moors River and to the R. Blackwater which forms the boundary with Berks and with Surrey; still also occurs a few metres into those counties.

VC11: Moors River, Fillybrook, Hurn Forest 1298, Hb.RMW 1985, det. *AOC*, Hb.RPB; St Leonards Peat South, Hurn Forest 1000, Hb.RMW 1985, det. *AOC* (*Watsonia* **16**: 451); St Leonards Peat North, Hurn Forest 1001, *RMW* 1985. **VC12**: R. Blackwater, Aldershot 8851, just in Hants, *CRH* 1990 (*Watsonia* **18**: 435). Prior to the destruction of this site in 1994 for road building, a tuft was removed and divided into plantlets, some of which were kept in cultivation. Of these, six were planted out under willows on a lake-margin about 300m. away in Surrey in 1993, and five were thriving in 1994, *CRH* (pers.comm.).

C. curta GOODEN.   White Sedge. **N**   Very locally frequent   Map 468

In wet sphagnum-bogs and swamp, where there is little lateral water-flow; sometimes inside wet willow-carr. Frequent in Woolmer Forest on the Folkestone Sands, and about Aldershot on the Bagshot Sands; very local in the Avon Valley, on the New Forest borders, and in a few sites within it.

   VC8: Plaitford Common 2718, *FR* 1983. **VC11**: Emer Bog 3921, *RPB* 1961; Sherfield English 2922, *RBG* 1984; Haskell's Pond, Kingston North Common 1402, *NAS* 1986, Hb.RPB, det. *AOC & RWD*; White Moor, Hincheslea 2701, 2801, *RPB* 1980.

VC12: Shortheath Pond 7736, *AB* 1973, *FR* 1993; Liss Forest 7828, *FR* 1970; Zebon Copse, Crookham 7951, *CRH* 1987; Alder Copse, Eversley 7860, *AJB* 1989.

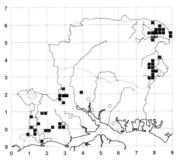

Map 468 Carex curta

C. hirta L.   Hairy Sedge.   **N** Frequent and locally common

In dry-to-wet grassland, especially where irregularly grazed, in meadows, drier fens, marshes, pond-margins, scrub-borders and roadside banks. Common generally, on all but very acid or very alkaline soil.

C. lasiocarpa EHRH.   Slender Sedge. **N**   Very rare   Map 469

Almost confined to the central zone of wet, rather base-rich valley-bogs along the Avon Water in the New Forest. Very locally plentiful in dense reed-swamp or with *C. limosa.*

   VC11: Holmsley Station 2300, *RPB* 1961, Hb.AWW, *FR* 1988; Wilverley Bog 2400, *GH* 1967, Hb.LANC, *FR* 1987, 2499, *RPB* 1961. One outlier along the Mill Lawn Brook at Common Moor, Burley 2004, *RPB* 1960, 1987.

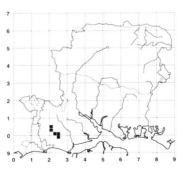

Map 469 Carex lasiocarpa

C. acutiformis EHRH.   Lesser Pond-sedge.   **N**   Locally common   Map 470

Watersides, marshes, wet meadows and moist woods, locally forming pure stands in alder- or willow-carr, where not too waterlogged. Commoner and more general than *C. riparia*, and occasional in the New Forest.

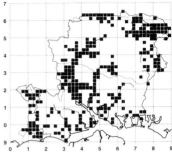

Map 470 Carex acutiformis

C. x ducellieri BEAUVERD (*C. acutiformis* x *C. vesicaria*)   **N**   Very rare

First British record, R. P. Bowman 1986, Ebblake, Ringwood Forest 1006, VC11, in acid, wet carr, Hb.BM, det. *AOC & RWD* (*Watsonia* 17: 196).

C. riparia CURTIS   Greater Pond-sedge.   **N**   Locally common   Map 471

Beside rivers, ponds and ditches; in marshes where there is little peat-formation. Absent from the New Forest, possibly due to grazing, but common along the main river-valleys, and scattered elsewhere in suitable habitats.

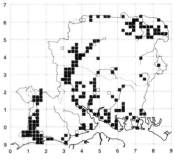

Map 471 Carex riparia

C. pseudocyperus L.   Cyperus Sedge.   **N**   Local   Map 472

In swamps, on pond-margins, wet gravel-pits, freshwater ditches, rivers and swampy alder-carr; usually over the less acidic mineral soils. Locally frequent in the SW and the lower Test

Valley, commoner in the Thames Basin; otherwise rare.

VC11: Moors River near Hurn 1298, *JHL* 1970; Barnes Lane, Milford on Sea 2893, *MAS* 1971; Brockenhurst 2901, wooded, old marl-pits, *AEB* 1988; Ridge Copse 3418, *RPB* 1984; Browndown 5899, Hb.AWW 1952. **VC12**: Highclere Park 4560, *AB* 1976; Dogmersfield Lake 7552, *CRH* 1987; Knox's Pond, Bordon 8034, *AB* 1985; R. Blackwater 8658, *CRH* 1989.

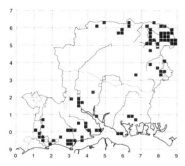

Map 472 Carex pseudocyperus

C. rostrata STOKES   Bottle Sedge. **N**   Locally frequent   Map 473

In very wet, acid, peaty swamps and calcareous fens. Frequent, and often dominant in the reed-zone of New Forest bogs, in Woolmer Forest and other sandy districts. Also in the Basing–Greywell fens; rare and scattered elsewhere; a pioneer colonist of open, peaty water.

VC8: Plaitford Common 2718, 2719, *FR* 1983. **VC11**: Holmsley Bog 2300, Hb.AWW 1962; Denny Bog 3405, *EAP* 1983; Emer Bog 3921, *RPB* 1960; Woodington 3020, *RPB* 1963; Nursling gravel-pit 3516, *RPB* 1963, since lost. **VC12**: Stockbridge North Fen 3535, *FR* 1986; Highclere Park 4560, *AB* 1976; Swelling Hill Pond, Four Marks 6632, *MB* 1969, since

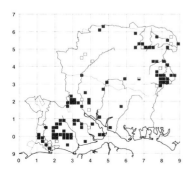

Map 473 Carex rostrata

cleaned out; Greywell Moors 7150, *FR* 1975, 1994; Alexandra Park, Bordon 8035, *PHC* 1983; Fleet Pond 8254, 8255, *ARGM* 1980, *CRH* 1991.

C. x involuta (BAB.) SYME (*C. rostrata* x *C. vesicaria*)   **N**   Very rare

VC11: Moors River, Fillybrook 1298, Hb.RMW 1985, specimen seen *RPB*; Moors River 1199, Hb.RMW 1987, det. *RWD*.

C. vesicaria L.   Bladder Sedge.   **N** Very local   Map 474

In swamps, ditches and ponds, open or shaded, on mineral soils. Now rather rare; mostly in the Avon Valley, the New Forest and the Tertiaries of the Thames Basin.

VC11: Moors River, Fillybrook 1298, *RMW* 1985; Longdown Inclosure 3508, Hb.RPB 1966; Lymington River, Roydon Woods 3102, *RJT* 1982; East End 3697, marl-pits, *AEB* 1982; Park Pale, Petty Priest Copse 4123, *RPB* 1986. **VC12**: Bransbury Common 4141, in marshy ground, *ECW c.*1955; Baughurst 5758, dried-up roadside pond, *WEW* 1956, *BRB* 1964; Fleet Pond 8254, *GARW* 1933, *ARGM & CRH* 1989; Ashford Hill meadows 5662, *PB* 1982, 1992; R. Blackwater 8460, in meadows, Hb.AWW 1962, *CRH* 1988.

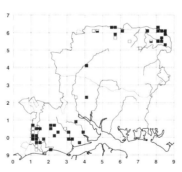

Map 474 Carex vesicaria

C. pendula HUDS.   Pendulous Sedge. **N,H**   Locally common Map 475

In damp woodland, especially on heavy soils of the London Clay, Barton Clay and Gault, often close to spring-lines or runnels. Locally common in C and SE Hants; rare in the New Forest and on the chalk. Some records are of garden escapes.

VC11: Lymington River, Heywood Mill 3199, *RPB* 1956, Sandleheath 1215, *MPY & ESH* 1964; Rolles-

brook, Southampton 4112, *WFB* 1965; Curbridge 5211, *RPB* 1966. **VC12**: Winnall Moors 4830, *YD* 1982; Brockbridge 7632, *AB* 1982; Hampage Wood 5430, *FR* 1985; Butter Wood 7253, *AJPB* 1986; Over Wallop 2838, *GDF* 1982; Plastow Green 5261, *PB* 1984.

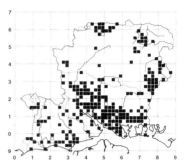

Map 475 Carex pendula

C. sylvatica HUDS.   Wood-sedge. **N**   Frequent and locally common

In woodland, especially on the less acid soil and on old hedgebanks. Generally common, except near the sea.

C. strigosa HUDS.   Thin-spiked Wood-sedge. **N**   Locally frequent Map 476

In old, moist woodland, on base-rich soil, both in valley flushes and in wet rides, preferring clay and Upper Greensand. On these soils it has a distribution along the S edge of the chalk, from Plaitford eastwards to the Wealden Hangers and Gault woods. It occurs too on the Tertiary clays in the far N of Hants. It prefers wet, squelchy conditions, such as a land-spring or 'lavant'*. Very rare in the SW.

VC8: Park Water, Plaitford Copse 2620, *RPB* 1966. **VC11**: Roydon Woods 3101, *IB* 1978; Drove Copse, Mottisfont 3026, Hb.RPB 1966; Marwell 5021, *RHJ* 1975; Grub Coppice, Boarhunt 6009, *HCC* 1980–87, *EAP* 1990; Great Copse, Leigh Park 7108, above E bank of stream, *HCC* 1980–87, *EAP* 1990. **VC12**: Hawkley, lavant below The Warren 7328, *AB* 1983; Round Copse, Binstead 7840, spring-line on Gault, *FR* 1989; Fishpond Copse, NE of

*   The first recorded use of the term is found in White's Selborne, letter xix of 26 Feb. 1774 to Daines Barrington, in which he wrote 'The land-springs, which we call *lavants* break out much on the downs of Sussex, Hampshire and Wiltshire'. (*O.E.D.*)

Bentley 8045, *CRH* 1985; Butter Wood 7051, *EAB* 1968, 800 plants, *CRH* 1986; near Hartley Wintney 7658, *UR* 1966; Redlands Copse 5661, *PB* 1989; Stafford Copse, Hollington 4361, *RJH & NFC* 1985.

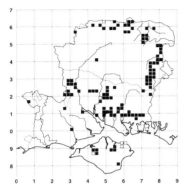

Map 476 Carex strigosa

C. flacca SCHREB. Glaucous Sedge. **N** Frequent and locally common

In chalk grassland, meadows, drier parts of fens, basic bogs and old marl-pits. The commonest sedge in Hants, found throughout the county.

C. panicea L. Carnation Sedge. **N** Locally common Map 477

Flushed areas in bogs, fens and wet meadows, always where there is some basic water-enrichment, and always in short vegetation. Very common in the New Forest, in the Tertiary and Lower Greensand areas, and in what remains of the old base-rich meadows of the river valleys. Also, more rarely, in short turf on a few chalk-down slopes.

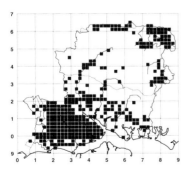

Map 477 Carex panicea

[**C. depauperata** CURTIS ex WITH. Starved Wood-sedge (Sched. 8).

An undoubted specimen of this very rare sedge was collected from a hedge-bank between Cranborne and Damer-ham, probably in the 1920s, by Mrs E. M. Haines. It was in the collection of H. H. Haines, now incorporated in Hb.LTR. The identity was confirmed by *CAS & RJG* in 1984. The locality may have been in either Dorset (VC9) or that part of Hants transferred from Wilts (VC8). Both sides of the county boundary were searched for it without success by *RPB* in June 1984 but, as there is still suitable habitat, there is a possibility that it may eventually be refound as it was in 1992 in Surrey after a 20-year interval.]

C. laevigata SM. Smooth-stalked Sedge. **N** Locally frequent Map 478

In acidic flushes and flushed rides in old woodland, especially alder carr, often with *Chrysosplenium oppositi-folium*; also in acid marshes, formerly woodland. Frequent and locally common in the N and E New Forest, and woods on the S Tertiaries from East Tytherley to Rowland's Castle; occasional on the Lower Greensand and the N Tertiaries from Highclere to Aldershot. It avoids the basic sub-strates on Gault and Upper Greensand that *Carex strigosa* favours.

VC11: Hale 1818, *JO* 1983; Tile Barn, Brockenhurst 2901, *AEB* 1988; Bere Farm, Boarhunt 5909, Hb.AWW 1957. **VC12**: Ashford Hill meadows 5662, *FR* 1983; Old Moor, Greatham 7731, *AB* 1980; Ewshot meadows 8150, *PB* 1984.

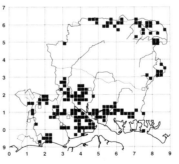

Map 478 Carex laevigata

C. binervis SM. Green-ribbed Sedge. **N** Locally frequent

On dry or damp heathland and heathy woodland rides. Common in the New Forest, NW of Southampton and on the NE Tertiaries. More local in the SE, and scarce in Woolmer Forest.

VC11: Buttsash 4105, *AEB* 1983;

Wickham 5912, Hb.AWW 1956. **VC12**: Near A343, 4361, *WMK* 1981; Silchester Common 6162, *HJMB* 1983; Conford 8232, *FR* 1982.

C. distans L. Distant Sedge. **N** Local Map 479

In grassy salt-marshes and wet, brack-ish pastures near the coast, and saline hollows behind beaches, frequent; inland, widespread in moist, calcareous 'unimproved' meadows, but very local and decreasing through 'improve-ment'. Sometimes confused with *C. hostiana*, though the two species are rarely found together.

VC11: Holmsley Station 2300, road-side verge, Hb.RPB 1981, det. *RWD*; Keyhaven Marshes 3191, abundant, *RPB* 1976; Sinah Common golf-links 6999, Hb.AWW 1960, *FR* 1981. **VC12**: Warnborough Greens 7252, *FR* 1983; Greywell 7151, *GHF* 1977; Bransbury Common 4141, *FR* 1984; Eelmoor 8353, *FR & ARGM* 1994.

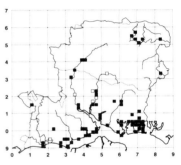

Map 479 Carex distans

C. x muelleriana F. W. SCHULTZ (*C. distans* x *C. hostiana*) **N** Very rare

VC12: Conford 8232, *ECW* 1940, det. *EN*; Ellis Farm, near Sherfield on Loddon 6956, *ECW* 1941, det. *EN*.

C. punctata GAUDIN Dotted Sedge. **N** Rare Map 480

In damp, open, sandy or shingly depressions in brackish grassland behind beaches and sea-walls; rare and very local, with few plants at most sites. One exceptional inland site has been found recently in the New Forest in an untypical but suitable habitat. No extant sites are known in Britain E of Hayling Island.

VC11: Keyhaven Marshes 3191, *JCDa* 1941, *RPB* 1977; Pennington Marshes 3292, *MR* 1976, *RPB* 1994; Stokes Bay 6097, *MB* 1976, *RPB* 1987;

Sinah Common 6999, *PMH* 1934, Hb.BM, Hb.RPB 1976. Newly recorded by A35 Vinney Ridge 2605, Hb.RPB 1990, conf. *RWD & AOC*; Oxey Marsh 3393, *MEY* 1977; N of Stansore Point 4699, *MR* 1976, *RPB* 1985; Sandy Point, Hayling Island 7498, *AB, EAP & FR* 1980, *FR* 1992. Presumed lost at Milford and Northney, North Hayling, site destroyed *c*.1970. Portchester, *AWW* 1960, comm. *RWD*, but not refound by the latter nor confirmed (*Watsonia* 13: 319).

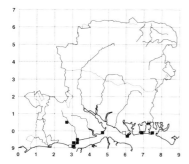

Map 480 Carex punctata

C. extensa GOODEN.　Long-bracted Sedge.　**N**　Rare　Map 481

In rather sandy, upper, tidal saltmarshes, and on banks of drains in brackish grassland within sea-walls.

VC11: Hengistbury 1790, *c*.200 plants, *MAS* 1971, two plants only, *SRD* 1976; Beaulieu River N of Bailey's Hard 3901, *NAS* 1989; Eastern Road, Portsmouth 6703, Hb.AWW 1959; Ports Creek, Hilsea Lines 6604, *RPB* 1990; Conigar Point 7305, *RPB* 1982; Sandy Point, Hayling Island 7498, *AB, EAP & FR* 1980; Tipner Ranges 6303, *EAP & FR* 1981, site since infilled.

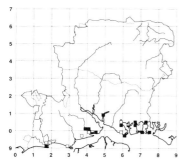

Map 481 Carex extensa

C. hostiana DC.　Tawny Sedge.　**N** Locally frequent　Map 482

On wet grass-heaths on the Headon Beds and Barton Clay, where flushed or flooded in winter, and fringes of valley bog; calcareous or basic, flushed mires and old meadows. Frequent and often common in the New Forest, and locally so in the upper Test Valley, and about Greywell. In scattered sites elsewhere, but decreasing through drainage. Interestingly, with *Juncus subnodulosus*, it has been carried down by the Basingstoke Canal from the area of the R. Whitewater to the acid Aldershot area.

VC11: Acres Down 2609, *FR* 1984; Rockbourne 1216, Hb.RPB 1979, det. *ACJ*; near Hooper's Farm, King's Somborne 3532, Hb.AWW 1962, conf. *ECW*; The Moors, Bishop's Waltham 5616, Hb.AWW 1963, *FR* 1983. **VC12**: Conford Moor 8232, *AB* 1982, *FR* 1994; Red House Field, Highclere 4360, *MEd* 1984; Bransbury Common 4141, *FR* 1971, 1986; Tichborne Common 5731, *FR* 1975, Hb.AB; Greywell Moors 7150, *FR* 1975, 1992; Pondtail 8253, *VL* 1960, *CRH* 1986.

Map 482 Carex hostiana

C. x fulva GOODEN. (*C. hostiana* x *C. viridula* ssp. *brachyrrhyncha*)　**N** Very rare

VC12: Tichborne 5731, *FR* 1978; Greywell 7150, *PMH* 1937, Hb.BM, det. *EN*, *FR* 1975, 1988.

C. hostiana x C. viridula ssp. **oedocarpa**　**N**　Very rare

VC11: Grass-heath near Bignell Wood 2813, Hb.RPB 1966, det. *ECW*. **VC12**: Conford 8232, *ECW* 1938, Hb.RNG, *FR* 1994.

C. x alsatica ZAHN (*C. x pieperiana* Junge; *C. flava* x *C. viridula* ssp. *brachyrrhyncha*)　**N**　Very rare

VC12: Greywell Moors, one large tuft, *FR* 1980, Hb.BM, conf. *AOC, HFG* 1992. This indicates that *Carex flava*

L. (large yellow-sedge) was once in Hants.

C. viridula MICHX ssp. **brachyrrhyncha** (CELAK.) B. SCHMID (*C. lepidocarpa* Tausch ssp. *lepidocarpa*) Long-stalked Yellow-sedge.　**N**　Rare Map 483

In fen-meadows and open calcareous mires; rare, but locally frequent in the upper Test Valley and near R. Whitewater. Elsewhere in scattered sites by chalk springs.

VC8: Damerham South End 1015, *RPB* 1977, det. *FR*. **VC11**: Rockbourne 1216, *RPB* 1979, det. *ACJ*; The Moors, Bishop's Waltham 5616, Hb.AWW 1960, *FR* 1984. **VC12**: Bransbury Common 4141, *FR* 1978, 1986; Stockbridge North Fen 3535, *FR* 1986; Tichborne Common 5731, *FR* 1975, Hb.AB; North Warnborough 7252, *FR* 1982; particularly abundant in former cress-beds at Anton Lakes 3647, *JRw* 1991.

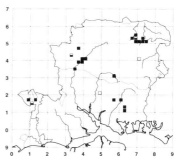

Map 483 Carex viridula ssp. brachyrrhyncha

ssp. **oedocarpa** (ANDERSSON) B. SCHMID (*C. demissa* Hornem.) Common Yellow-sedge.　**N**　Locally common　Map 484

In wet hollows of sphagnum bogs, heathland pond-margins and ditches,

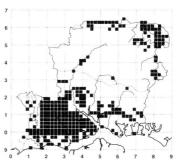

Map 484 Carex viridula ssp. oedocarpa

on wet, acidic, woodland rides, often on bare peat; also in old wet meadows and fens, from acidic to slightly calcareous. Abundant in the New Forest; frequent in suitable habitats elsewhere. In fen at Conford, where ssp. *brachyrrhyncha* is absent.

ssp. **viridula** (*C. serotina* Mérat) Small-fruited Yellow-sedge. **N** Very rare

On bare, sandy or stony shores of large acidic ponds, below winter water-level. Extant in only three New Forest sites, and one on the NE Bagshot Sands.

VC11: Hatchet Pond 3601, *JEL* 1929, Hb.RPB 1983; Burley Moor 2004, *RSS* 1913, Hb.BM, *AWW* 1961; Crockford Bridge 3598, *AEB* 1986, conf. *RPB*. **VC12**: Fleet Pond 8254, *JEL* 1935, Hb.RNG, one plant only, *ECW & WEW* 1970, since lost; Bourley Bottom 8250, *FR* 1978, 300–400 on W side of reservoir, *CRH* 1987, abundant on E edge when water-level was low, *CRH* 1992.

C. pallescens L. Pale Sedge. **N** Locally frequent Map 485

Clearings and rides in old, damp woodlands, including those replanted with conifers, and in old, 'unimproved' meadows; on acid-to-neutral soil, but local and sporadic. Fairly frequent in and around the New Forest, thinning out eastward and northward, with a few sites on the chalk superficials.

VC8: Boulsbury Wood 0715, *FR* 1976. **VC11**: Sowley Copse 3696, *MR* 1976; Ampfield Wood 4124, *RMV* 1987; Hookheath 6407, *RPB & EAP* 1983. **VC12**: Great Pen Wood 4462, *NFC* 1968; Ron Ward's Meadow, Tadley 6060, *PB* 1983; Fishpond Copse, NE of Bentley 8045, *ARGM* 1985; Coombe Wood, Ewshot 8149, *CRH* 1985; wood near Marsh House, Bentley 7944, *VL* 1959, *AB* 1969.

C. humilis LEYSS. Dwarf Sedge. **N** Rare Map 486

In short turf on the chalk downs extending into Hants at the SE edge of Salisbury Plain; very locally abundant, and dominant in sheep-grazed areas and on earthworks, but it is suppressed where rank grasses invade. The occurrence in SW England of this C European species is strange; on the Continent it is usually found with *C. ericetorum* Pollich.

VC8: Martin Down 0419, *PMH* 1933, Hb.BM, *RWD* 1978; Tidpit Common Down 0617, *PMH* 1933, Hb.BM, *RWD* 1978; Toyd Down 0819, *RPB* 1966; Martin Drove End 0421, *RPB* 1989. **VC11**: Mizmaze, Breamore 1420, Hb.AWW 1960, *RWD* 1978; Grim's Ditch, Gallows Hill 1320, Hb.AWW 1960, *RWD* 1978; N of Bokerley Dyke Plantation 0918, *RPB* 1979, conf. *RWD*; S of Rockbourne Down 1020, in verges of grass road, *RPB* 1989.

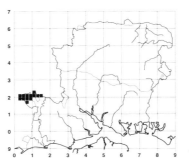

Map 486 Carex humilis

C. caryophyllea LATOURR. Spring-sedge. **N** Locally frequent Map 487

In well-grazed, chalk turf on the downs, and on grassy heaths and pastures on sand and clay, often on the

fine soil of ant-mounds; not found on the very acid soils tolerated by *C. pilulifera*; occasional in open, woodland rides. Frequent in the New Forest, general and locally frequent on the chalk and in other grassland.

C. montana L. Soft-leaved Sedge. **N** Very local Map 488

On flat or gently-sloping grassy heaths, woodland rides and adjacent ditch-banks, and in old marl-pits. Now confined to, but widespread and fairly frequent in, the New Forest; a constituent of the compact turf in the open-heath bracken-community, associated with *Anemone nemorosa*, *Hyacinthoides non-scripta* and *Gladiolus illyricus*. Usually on loams and clays of the calcareous Headon Beds or the Barton Beds, and sometimes coincident with seams of clay exposed in gullies. Populations are usually quite small, but several extensive ones have been found during recent surveys. The New Forest holds the greatest number of sites (but not the largest overall population) of this species in Britain, where it is at the NW limit of its continental range (*Watsonia* 11: 377).

VC11: Upper Pennington Common 2995, *FR* 1973, *MEY* 1991; Dawkins Bottom 3100, *RWD* 1976; Cunninger Bottom 1916, *RPB* 1976, 1994; Keeping Copse, SE of Bailey's Hard 3901, *AEB* 1980; Blackwell Common 4301, *RPB* 1984.

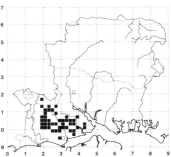

Map 488 Carex montana

C. pilulifera L. Pill Sedge. **N** Locally common Map 489

On dry heathland, often beneath bracken, acid grassland, heathland rides in woods. Common on all the sand and gravel of Hants, occasionally on Clay-with-flints overlying the chalk.

VC8: Martin Down 0518, *PET & RPB* 1990, det. *RWD & AOC*. **VC11**: Shedfield Common 5613, *PMH* 1937,

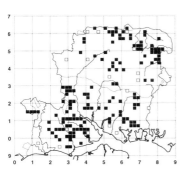

Map 485 Carex pallescens

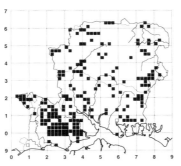

Map 487 Carex caryophyllea

Hb.BM, *RPB* 1990; Browndown Common 5899, Hb.AWW *c*.1960; Hyden Woods 6818, 6918, possibly from dormant seed after 1987 gale opened up a clearing, *JRw* 1991. **VC12**: Cheriton Wood 6129, *RPB* 1969; Bransbury Common 4141, *FR* 1971; Micheldever Wood 5338, *JRw* 1991.

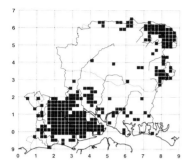

Map 489 Carex pilulifera

C. limosa L. Bog Sedge. **N** Very rare Map 490 Plate XII

In very wet hollows or standing water in the central reed-zone of valley bogs, often with *Dactylorhiza incarnata* and *Drosera anglica*. Very local in about six sites in the SW New Forest, but truly abundant at only three. A northern species, confined in S England to Hants and Dorset; and Norfolk (?now gone).

VC11: Bagnum Bog, Cranes Moor 1802, *MAS* 1980, *RPB* 1982, abundant, *FR* 1986; Holmsley Bog 2201, Hb.RPB 1956, *FR* 1987; Wilverley Bog 2499, *RPB* 1957; 2400, abundant, *FR* 1987; 2699, *RPB* 1979; Hincheslea Bog 2700, *AEB & FR* 1990, 2800, Hb.AWW 1963; E Denny Bog 3504, *LBH* 1937, Hb.BM, habitat presumed destroyed by drainage in 1968–70.

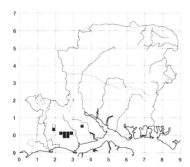

Map 490 Carex limosa

C. acuta L. Slender Tufted-sedge. **N** Very local Map 491

Streamsides, drains and marshes in wet meadows; widespread but very local or rare. Chiefly concentrated in the lower Avon Valley, but thinly scattered elsewhere.

VC11: Avon meadows N of Christchurch 1594, *RMW* 1986, Hb.RPB, det. *AOC & RWD*; near Moors River, St Leonards 1000, Hb.RMW 1985; Ebblake Stream, Ringwood Forest 1006, abundant in willow carr, Hb.RPB 1985, det. *AOC & RWD*; Hurst Common, Ringwood 1404, *HCC* 1986; Lower Test 3614, *PJW & MRe* 1986; S of Tadburn, Ampfield 3922, *NAS c*.1988; not refound at Holmsley *c*.2300, *LBH* 1930; Brownwich Haven 5103, Hb.AWW 1959, *RPB* 1984, det. *AOC, RWD & ACJ*; The Moors, Bishop's Waltham 5616, Hb.AWW 1963. **VC12**: Winnall Moors 4830, *AB* 1982, conf. *FR*; Ewhurst 5757, *WEW* 1957; Bramley Training Area 6658, *CRH* 1989; R. Blackwater W of Eversley 7462 or 7463, *PMH & ECW* 1937, Hb.BM; Fleet Pond 8254, *AWW c*.1959.

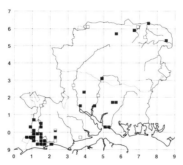

Map 491 Carex acuta

C. acuta x C. nigra (?*C*. x *elytroides* Fr.) **N**

VC11: Recorded 'on good authority' (*Hybr.Fl.Brit.Is.*, p.530).

C. nigra (L.) REICHARD Common Sedge. **N** Locally common

In marshes, fens, wet meadows and less-acid, frequently-flushed bogs. Common, especially in the SW and NE.

C. x turfosa FR. (*C. nigra* x *C. elata*) **N**

VC11: Recorded near Winchester (*Hybr.Fl.Brit.Is.*, p.529).

C. elata ALL. Tufted-sedge. **N** Very rare

On drains and streamsides in old water-meadows, and edges of ponds. Very

rare, but locally plentiful in the mid-Itchen Valley. Surprisingly absent from the N Hants calcareous fen-meadows.

VC11: Pylewell Park 3596 and Pylewell Lake 3695, *HCC* 1986; Sowley Brooms, near Sowley Pond 3696, Hb.RPB 1986–87, det. *RWD*; Mopley Pond 4501, Hb.RPB 1976, det. *RWD*; St Cross 4828, *JEL* 1934, *RPB* 1977. Not refound at Hockley *c*.4727, *PMH* 1939, Hb.BM, nor at Rudley *c*.6212, *GCD* 1929 (*Suppl.Fl.Hants*, p.114). **VC12**: Hyde Meadows 4829 and Winnall Moors 4830, *AB* 1982; R. Itchen, '¾ mile W of Easton, locally plentiful', *GARW* 1935 (*Watts MSS*), site now destroyed, *NAS* 1991.

C. pulicaris L. Flea Sedge. **N** Locally frequent Map 492

In base-rich fens, old, moist meadows, turfy, wet heaths, old marl-pits, valley mires flushed by calcareous to mildly-acid springs. Very frequent in the New Forest, especially on the Headon Beds; in a few widely-scattered sites elsewhere, at least one of them on dry, chalk turf.

VC11: Stony Moors 2199, Hb.AWW 1963; Common Marsh, Stockbridge 3534, *RPB* 1956; The Moors, Bishop's Waltham 5616, Hb.AWW 1963, *FR* 1984; Lye Heath Marsh 6408, Hb.AWW 1951. **VC12**: Conford Moor 8232, abundant, *FR* 1988; Eelmoor Marsh 8352, *ARGM* 1975–92; Greywell Moors 7251, *FR* 1982–90; Ashford Hill meadows 5662, *PB* 1983; Red House Field, Highclere 4360, *HRo* 1984; Bransbury Common 4141, Hb.AWW 1962, *FR* 1975; Noar Hill 7431, old chalk-pit at foot of slope, *AB* to 1993.

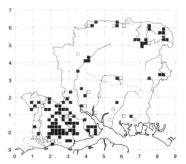

Map 492 Carex pulicaris

POACEAE

Sasa palmata (BURB.) E. G. CAMUS Broad-leaved Bamboo. **H** Very rare or under-recorded

Spreading in a few places, generally near water, from bamboo brakes in gardens.

VC11: Brambridge 4622, *RPB* 1977, det. *DMcC*. **VC12**: R. Deadwater, Walldown, Bordon 8034, *AB* 1978; near Fleet Pond 8154, *CRH* 1992, Hb.BM, conf. *DMcC*.

Sasaella ramosa (MAKINO) MAKINO & SHIBATA (*Arundinaria vagans* Gamble) Hairy Bamboo. **H**

VC12: Tweseldown Racecourse 8252, *CRH* 1983–95, Hb. BM, conf. *DMcC*; scrub near The Foresters' Public House 8252, *CRH* 1992–95.

Leersia oryzoides (L.) SW. Cut-grass. **N** Very rare or extinct

On river- and stream-banks in the New Forest. Early records were for Bisterne and Sopley; more recent ones were on the Highland Water, the Black Water and the Ober Water. It is probable that at all these sites it became over shaded or destroyed by grazing. The re-routeing in a new cutting of part of the Black Water could also be a cause of extinction. The last record was by *DEC* who in 1955 took plants from a meander of the Black Water at 2504 (where it had been reported 'in abundance' in 1928 (*Suppl.Fl.Hants*, p.117)) and propagated them at Cambridge University Botanic Garden. In 1988, *CRB* transplanted some of these back to the Ober Water but they seem to be grazed down every year.

Nardus stricta L. Mat-grass. **N** Locally common Map 493

On dry or damp grass-heaths, and where the heather is sparse; usually on thin peat and frequently in flushed but not waterlogged turf. Common in the SW and NE; very local elsewhere,

VC11: Shelley Common, Ower

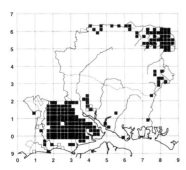

Map 493 Nardus stricta

3218, old meadow, *RMV* 1990; Baddesley Common 3921, wet meadow, *RMV* 1986. **VC12**: Ashford Hill meadows 5662, *PB* 1983.

Milium effusum L. Wood Millet. **N** Locally common Map 494

In old woods and copses, especially oak-with-hazel coppice, by sunken lanes and beech-woods; on humus-rich loam, clay, Malmstone, or chalk soils. Common, but very local in the SW.

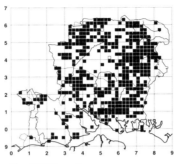

Map 494 Milium effusum

Festuca pratensis HUDS. Meadow Fescue. **N,D** Frequent and locally common

In meadows, pastures and verges; common on fertile, moist and heavy soils; often abundant in 'unimproved' grassland in water-meadows, but also frequently sown in leys, several different strains being used.

F. arundinacea SCHREB. Tall Fescue. **N** Frequent and locally common

In moist, unkempt meadows, riverside marshes, brackish grassland, on clay sea-cliffs and roadside verges on drier ground. Generally common, but infrequent in the SW and on parts of the N central chalk.

F. gigantea (L.) VILL. Giant Fescue. **N** Frequent and locally common

In damp woods, shady hedgerows and streamsides on more basic soils; widespread and common except in the New Forest and treeless areas.

F. heterophylla LAM. Various-leaved Fescue. **D** Very rare or under-recorded

First record, E. S. Marshall 1889, under trees near Bentworth House,

near Alton, VC12 (*Fl.Hants*, p.506).

A component of Victorian grass-seed mixtures, to be found in woodland rides, tree-belts, lawns and gardens, whence it spreads into the countryside.

VC11: Between Lyndhurst and Brockenhurst *c*.3004, spinney near the road, *SAT* 1938, det. *WOH* (*Rep. B.E.C.* for 1938, p.65); Curbridge 5313, Hb.AWW 1963; Hen Wood, West Meon 6522, frequent along shady ride, *JAN* 1987, det. *PJOT*. **VC12**: Blackmoor House grounds 7732, *AB* 1960, det. *JEL*; Newtown 4662, *CL* 1964. Also 7832, 7836.

F. arenaria OSBECK (*F. juncifolia* St-Amans) Rush-leaved Fescue. **N** Very rare

First records, W. Moyle Rogers 1900, Alum Chine, Bournemouth 0790 and E. F. Linton 1900, Mudeford *c*.1892, both VC11 (*Fl.Bmth*, p.258, as *F. rubra* var. *arenaria* (Osbeck) Syme). No specimens seen.

Coastal sand-dunes or sandy shingle.

VC11: Barton on Sea *c*.2392, sand-dune, in association with marram (*Ammophila arenaria*), *TCEW* 1957, Hb.ABRN, det. *AM* 1965, habitat probably eroded since then; Boscombe 1291, cliff-top, and Hengistbury 1891, abundant on sand over shingle, with marram, Hb.RPB 1992, det. *CAS*.

F. rubra L. ssp. **rubra** Red Fescue. **N,D** Common

Old grassland in pastures, in open woods, on verges, heathland, dunes and in brackish marshes. It is one of the commonest grasses on all soils. It is also sown in grass-seed mixtures.

ssp. **juncea** (HACK.) K. RICHT. (ssp. *pruinosa* (Hack.) Piper) **N** Under-recorded

A constituent of short turf on sandy and shingle beaches and cliff-tops, probably frequent, but rarely recorded.

VC11: Hengistbury Head 1690, *RMW* 1988, det. *AAl-B*, Hb.RPB 1989; Browndown Point 5799, Hb.RPB 1989, det. *CAS*.

ssp. **commutata** GAUDIN (*F. nigrescens* Lam.) Chewings Fescue. **N,D** Under-recorded

First record, A. W. Westrup 1950, Gilkicker Point 6097, VC11.

Prefers dry soils, for which reason it is frequently sown on verges, lawns, etc.

VC12: Beech 6838, *ANHS* 1983;

Hook Common 7153, *EAB* 1966; Headley Down 8335, *AB* 1970. Also 6040, 7030, 7238, 7836, 8038, 8236.

F. ovina L.   Sheep's-fescue.   **N** Locally common   Map 495

Old, dry grassland on the chalk, and on other not-too-acid soils, including coastal sand and shingle. Common on the remaining unploughed downs, where it provides the habitat for many orchids and other downland specialities. It responds vigorously to grazing but, if ungrazed, yields to coarser grasses and the habitat is destroyed. Largely replaced by *F. filiformis* on very acid soils.

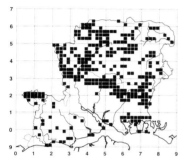

Map 495 Festuca ovina

ssp. **hirtula** (HACK. ex TRAVIS) M. J. WILK.

VC11: Ashley Hole 2015, on imported chalk, and Hook, Warsash 4904, on fixed shingle behind beach, Hb.RPB 1992, conf. *CAS*. **VC12**: Micheldever Spoil Heaps 5244, *RMV* 1990, conf. *PJOT*.
    The two other segregates, ssp. *ovina* and ssp. *ophioliticola* (Kerguélen) M. J. Wilk., have not yet been formally recorded, but the latter is likely to be common in chalk grassland; the map is of the aggregate species.

F. filiformis POURR. (*F. tenuifolia* Sibth.)   Fine-leaved Sheep's-fescue.   **N** Locally common   Map 496

First record, W. L. Notcutt 1844, Fareham Common, VC11 (*Fl.Hants*, p.505).
    On heaths, in open, acid woodland and heathy pastures; common in the New Forest and on the NE Tertiaries and Lower Greensand.

F. brevipila TRACEY (*F. longifolia* sensu C. E. Hubb. et auct., non Thuill.)   Hard Fescue.   **D**   Very rare

First record, Lady Anne Brewis 1975,

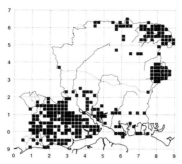

Map 496 Festuca filiformis

Sinah Common golf-links 6999, VC11, Hb.AB, det. *PJOT* 1990.
    Introduced as a turf-grass species.
    VC12: Farnborough Airfield 8654, near Dairy Gate, quite plentiful on slope with *F. filiformis*, *CRH* 1993, det. *PJOT*.

X Festulolium loliaceum (HUDS.) P. FOURN. (*Festuca pratensis* x *Lolium perenne*)   **N**   Local

In damp grassland, especially in water-meadows. VC11: 17 □; VC12: 29 □.
    VC11: Emsworth 7506, Hb.AWW 1951; Bickton Mill 1412, water-meadow, Hb.RPB 1959, det. *K*; Shirley 4012, *WFB* 1975, det. *RDT*. **VC12**: Riseley Ford 7463, *ECW & WEW* 1961; Bidden 7049, *MRA* 1970; Stockbridge North Fen 3535, Hb.RPB 1986.

X F. braunii (K. RICHT.) A. CAMUS (*Festuca pratensis* x *Lolium multiflorum*)   **D?**   Very rare

VC11: West Lane, Hayling Island 7101, Hb.AWW 1960.

X F. holmbergii (DÖRFL.) P. FOURN. (*Festuca arundinacea* x *Lolium perenne*) **N?**

Recorded for VC11 in *Hybr.Fl.Brit.Is.*, p.549, det. *AM* or *CEH*.

X F. brinkmannii (A. BRAUN) ASCH. & GRAEBN. (*Festuca gigantea* x *Lolium perenne*)   **N?**   Very rare

VC11: Casbrook Common tip 3524, *WFB* 1975, det. *RDT*.

X Festulpia hubbardii STACE & R. COTTON (*Festuca rubra* x *Vulpia fasciculata*)   **N**   Very rare

First record, Wild Flower Society field meeting 1986, Gunner Point, Hayling Island 6999, VC11, sand-dune near

fence of golf-links, det. *AJS*, comm. *EAP*.

Lolium perenne L.   Perennial Rye-grass.   **N,D**   Abundant

In grassland on all soils; universal. Extensively sown as a monoculture in reseeded pastures and also, for its resistance to trampling, in playing fields.

L. multiflorum LAM. (*L. perenne* ssp. *multiflorum* (Lam.) Husn.)   Italian Rye-grass.   **D**   Common

Like *L. perenne*, commonly sown in leys from which it frequently spreads to disturbed roadsides, arable and waste ground. The hybrid between the two has been recorded, and is also said to be frequently sown.

L. temulentum L.   Darnel.   **C** Very rare

First record, R. S. Hill 1863, field near Silchester, VC12 (*Fl.Hants*, p.515).
    A weed of arable fields, and on refuse tips. By the time of Townsend, it had become a rare cornfield weed – he had only six records for the mainland. Nowadays it is more often found on rubbish heaps where, according to J. E. Lousley (*Fl.Surrey*, p.385), it is not rare. There are about ten more recent Hants records but, without specimens, they cannot all be cited because of possible confusion with the recent alien *L. rigidum* Gaudin.
    John Gerard wrote that 'Among the hurtful weedes, Darnell is the first... The new bread wherein Darnel is, eaten hot, causeth drunkennesse: in like manner doth beere or ale wherein the seed is fallen, or put into the Malt' (*Ger.em.Johns.*, pp.78,79).
    VC11: Stanpit 1692, *KG c.*1960, Hb.AB, conf. *EJC*; Swaythling tips 4415, Hb.AWW 1958; Casbrook Common 3525, on tip, *WFB* 1968. **VC12**: Sheet 7524, *AB* 1970.

Vulpia fasciculata (FORSSK.) FRITSCH (*V. membranacea* auct., non (L.) Dumort.)   Dune Fescue.   **N** Very rare

On dunes, and beaches of sand and shingle. Almost confined to the SE coast, where it is locally frequent.
    VC11: Hengistbury sand-spit 1891, Hb.RPB 1992; Sinah Common dunes 6998, *PMH* 1936, Hb.BM, *RPB* 1972, *FR* 1994; Black Point, Hayling Island 7598, *RPB* 1972; Lepe 4598, roadside behind beach, *MR* 1977. Also 3090, 6698, 7098.

V. bromoides (L.) GRAY   Squirrel-tail Fescue.   **N,C**   Locally common

On dry, bare ground and short turf on banks, verges, commons, dunes, walls, railways, and in old pits. Common on sandy and gravelly soils, local and occasional elsewhere.

V. myuros (L.) C. C. GMEL. (*V. megalura* (Nutt.) Rydb.)   Rat's-tail Fescue.   **N,C**   Locally frequent   Map 497

On dry, bare ground or banks, coastal, reclaimed land and shingle, waysides, old walls, gravel-pits, and especially associated with railways. Occasional to locally frequent (in the SW and in the Woolmer Forest military area), but absent from many other districts.
   VC11: Dibden Bay 4008, 4108, banks and tracks over 1km, *MR* 1977. **VC12:** Longmoor 7931, plentiful in old station yard, Hb.AB 1973, det. *CEH* 1987 (as *V. megalura*) (*Watsonia* **10**: 434).

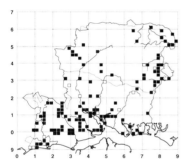

Map 497 Vulpia myuros

V. ciliata DUMORT. ssp. **ambigua** (LE GALL) STACE & AUQUIER (*V. ambigua* (Le Gall) More)   Bearded Fescue.   **N,C**   Rare

First record, G. C. Druce 1919, Hayling Island, VC11 (*Rep.B.E.C.* for 1919, p.690, as *Festuca danthonii* Asch. & Graebn. var. *ambigua* (Le Gall) Druce).
   Native on coastal sands; a colonist along bare heathland roadsides in the New Forest and Woolmer Forest; also occurs as a casual in waste places.
   VC11: Markway Hill 2402, track of old road, *RMW* 1987, Hb.RPB 1988; B3056 Matley 3307 and Yew Tree Heath 3606, old camp-site, Hb.RPB 1990, all det. *CAS*; Millbrook *c.*3812, *AWW* 1958; Sinah Common 6999, *FR* 1978; along 1km of coast 6998, 7098, *SRD* 1978; Black Point and Sandy Point, Hayling Island 7598, Hb.RPB 1989, det. *CAS*. **VC12:** Farnborough

8656, *RHJ* 1968; Woolmer Road, E of Greatham 7831, sandy NE verge, *FR* 1992.

V. unilateralis (L.) STACE (*Nardurus maritimus* (L.) Murb.)   Mat-grass Fescue.   **N**   Very rare

First record, E. C. Wallace & W. E. Warren 1955, Micheldever Spoil Heaps 5143, VC12, Hb.RNG (*Proc.B.S.B.I.* **4**: 252).
   On bare chalk and grassy tracks; confined, very sparsely, to the chalk around Winchester.
   VC11: Farley Mount 4129, with typical chalk flora by old bomb-craters, *WMB* 1956, 1960, Hb.OXF (*loc.cit.*). **VC12:** Micheldever Spoil Heaps 5144, 5244, *JEL & ECW* 1956, Hb.BM, *HFG* 1991; Lower Abbotstone Wood 5836, grassy track in recently planted beech–larch wood, *EM-R* 1957, Hb.K.

Cynosurus cristatus L.   Crested Dog's-tail.   **N,D**   Common

Well-drained old grassland in meadows, roadside verges, on chalk downs, and in drier parts of fens; also on acid ground, and sometimes included in grass-seed mixtures.

C. echinatus L.   Rough Dog's-tail.   **C**   Very rare

First record, J. F. Rayner 1916, Chandler's Ford, VC11, by path in cornfield (*Proc.IoW N.H.S.* **1**: 272).
   A colonist, established at Bournemouth, and formerly on Hayling Island where it persisted for at least 30 years.
   VC11: East Cliff, Bournemouth 0991, in cliff-top grassland, *WFS* 1989, comm. *GHF* (*Wild Fl.Mag.* **1990**: 11), Hb.RPB 1990; Southampton New Docks *c.*4111, Hb.EST 1935; South Hayling, *TJF* 1922, Hb.BM; Hayling Island, in several places, *MTH* 1922 (*Rep.B.E.C.* for 1922, p.753); Sinah Common golf-links 6999, and Eastoke 7398, Hb.AWW 1950; Sinah Common beach, *AB* 1952, where coastline since eroded.

Puccinellia maritima (HUDS.) PARL.   Common Saltmarsh-grass.   **N**   Locally frequent

Salt-marshes, both on tidal mud and inside sea-walls; also in brackish pastures. VC11: 48 ☐.

P. x hybrida HOLMB. (*P. maritima* x *P. distans*)   **N**

VC11: Hayling Island, *GCD* 1929

(*Suppl.Fl.Hants*, p.121, as *Glyceria maritima* Mert. & Koch x *G. distans* Wahlb.).

P. x krusemaniana JANSEN & WACHT. (*P. maritima* x *P. rupestris*)   **N**   Probably extinct

VC11: R. Test, Nursling 3614, tidal mudbank, Hb.RPB 1977, det. *AM* (*Watsonia* **16**: 197). Lost through erosion. The only previous record for the British Isles was in Chichester Harbour (VC13), in 1920 (*Hybr.Fl. Brit.Is.*, p.559).

P. distans (JACQ.) PARL. ssp. **distans** Reflexed Saltmarsh-grass.   **N,C** Very locally frequent   Map 498

On rather bare, brackish, non-tidal mud, and by tracks and drains inside sea-walls. Frequent in Portsmouth, Langstone and Chichester harbours, otherwise rare, although increasingly being found as a salt adventive on inland roadsides.
   VC11: Beaulieu millpond 3802, *RPB* 1963, 1994; Normandy Marsh 3294, Hb.RPB 1977, det.*AM*; Tipner 6303, *EAP & FR* 1981; adventive on A3 at 7014, 7015, 7116, *AB* 1986. **VC12:** Laffan's Plain, Aldershot 8453, adventive on manure heap, *JEL*, *ECW & PMH* 1936, Hb.BM; adventive on A303 at 5242, and at M3 roundabout 7252, *GK* 1981.

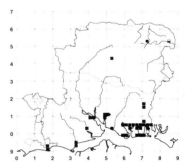

Map 498 Puccinellia distans ssp. distans

P. fasciculata (TORR.) E. P. BICK-NELL   Borrer's Saltmarsh-grass.   **N** Very locally frequent   Map 499

On bare mud or shingle in salt-marshes, especially on non-tidal flats and on coastal, reclaimed land. Locally frequent in Southampton Water, the Hamble estuary, and the SE harbours, otherwise rare.
   VC11: Pennington Marshes 3292, *AW* 1939; Hook, Warsash 4805,

Hb.RPB 1978, det. *AM*; Browndown Point 5799, *RPB, EJC & EAP* 1989.

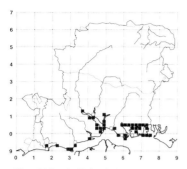

Map 499 Puccinellia fasciculata

P. rupestris (WITH.) FERNALD & WEATH.   Stiff Saltmarsh-grass.   **N**   Very locally frequent   Map 500

On firm, bare mud in upper, non-tidal, salt-marshes, sea-walls, reclaimed land and tidal river-banks. Locally frequent in Southampton Water and the SE harbours.

VC11: Hythe Spartina Marsh 4307, *RPB* 1975; Mengham, Hayling Island 7399, sea-wall, Hb.RPB 1977; Farlington Marshes 6804, *RMV* 1988. Formerly at Blackfield, Fawley 4402, in wet gravel-pit, *RPB* 1966.

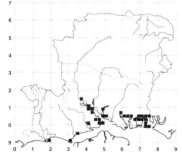

Map 500 Puccinellia rupestris

Briza media L.   Quaking-grass.   **N,D**   Frequent and locally common

In old grassland not dominated by coarse grasses; meadows, chalk downs, roadside verges and drier parts of fens. Common on the chalk and other base-rich soils; sown in grass-seed mixtures on more acid land.

B. minor L.   Lesser Quaking-grass.   **C**   Rare   Map 501

In unsprayed cornfields and bare, disturbed ground. A cornfield weed probably introduced a long time ago

and established in a few places on rather acid sandy or gravelly soils.

VC11: Sowley 3695, 3696, 3796, in cornfields over a wide area, *AEB & RPB* 1980–85; Sowley Lane 3696, *RPB* 1994; Dilton 3300, *AEB* 1980; Gardeners Lane 3319 and Roke Manor Farm, near Romsey 3423, in winter wheat, *GC* 1987. **VC12**: Cornfield near Pamber Green 5959, Hb.AWW 1962, last seen *AJS* 1974; Tadley 6061, waste ground, *PB* 1979, built over 1980 (possibly *RSH*'s 1859 site 'near Tadley Church' in *Fl.Hants* (p.503)).

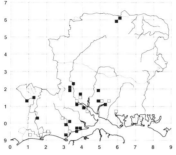

Map 501 Briza minor

B. maxima L.   Great Quaking-grass.   **H**   Very rare

Sandy cliff-tops, banks and verges not far from gardens, from which it presumably originated; open waste-ground.

VC11: Large patch under pines in Redhill Avenue, Bournemouth 0895, just within the boundary, *DEA* 1985; established on cliff-top, East Cliff, Bournemouth 0990, *DEA* 1985; Boscombe 1091, 1191, sandy banks along cliff-top path, *RPB* 1990. **VC12**: Near St Mary Bourne 4150, in relict chalk-grassland, a small population in an apparently naturalized situation, *ILR* 1991, conf. *FR*.

[**Poa infirma** KUNTH   Early Meadow-grass.

VC11: Hengistbury Head 1690, in short turf on S shore of harbour with *P. bulbosa* and *Trifolium suffocatum*, Hb.FAW, (*BSBI News* **65**: 15). Specimens from this site in Hb.RPB were referred to *P. annua* by *PJOT* 1993.

Specimens of a dwarf annual *Poa* in Hb.RPB from six other S Hants coastal sites and one in Hb.RMW collected in 1993 (together with those from Hengistbury) have been examined by *JRE* who remarks that none can be said to be 'typical' *P. infirma*. However,

they differ so markedly from *P. annua* that he is reluctant to conclude that they are merely extreme forms of that species. Without accurate measurement of the length of the anthers, and as *P. annua* is now known to be an allopolyploid of hybrid origin (the parents being *P. infirma* and *P. supina* Schrad.), the identity of this dwarf coastal *Poa* may perhaps be satisfactorily determined only by carrying out chromosome counts.]

P. annua L.   Annual Meadow-grass.   **N**   Abundant

In open grassland, arable and waste ground, roadsides and woodland paths, especially in thin turf and bare, heavily trodden soil; universal.

P. trivialis L.   Rough Meadow-grass.   **N**   Very common

In damp pastures and woods, shady places, verges, arable and waste ground.

P. humilis EHRH. ex HOFFM. (*P. subcaerulea* Sm.)   Spreading Meadow-grass.   **N**   Local, but under-recorded

Short grassland in damp meadows, brackish pastures, open woods, sandy heathland and dunes. Frequent about Woolmer Forest, and locally on the coast and in estuaries, with a few other scattered records, but probably overlooked. VC11: 24 □; VC12: 18 □.

VC11: R. Test, Nursling 3614, brackish pasture, Hb.RPB 1959, det. *CEH*; Stanpit Marsh 1691, *RMW & PJW* 1986, Hb.RPB. **VC12**: Warnborough Greens 7252, *FR* 1983; N of Blackbushe Airfield 8059, *AJB* 1986.

P. pratensis L.   Smooth Meadow-grass.   **N**   Very common

In pastures, on verges, arable and waste ground, and walls; very common except in wetter grassland, where *P. trivialis* replaces it.

P. angustifolia L.   Narrow-leaved Meadow-grass.   **N**   Locally frequent

In dry places, on walls and in chalk grassland. Commonest on the central chalk, especially under beeches. VC11: 23 □; VC12: 36 □.

VC11: Near Nursling gravel-pit 3516, Hb.RPB 1977; Broughton Down 2734, N corner, *RMV* 1988. **VC12**: Basing 6652, old walls, *FR* 1978, *AB* 1989.

P. chaixii VILL. Broad-leaved Meadow-grass. **H** Very rare

First record, G. C. Druce 1931, Vernham Dean Rectory *c*.3456, VC12, growing among planted shrubs, Hb.BM.

Included in Victorian grass-seed mixture for growing under trees.

VC11: Catland Copse 4910, well naturalized, *FR* 1981. **VC12**: Wood SE of Pardown, Basingstoke 5848, *TBR* 1962; Dogmersfield Park 7751, *AJSt* 1966; Blackmoor House 7732, under trees, *AB* 1960–80, lost after these were cut down.

P. compressa L. Flattened Meadow-grass. **N** Very locally frequent Map 502

In dry places on chalk, sand or gravel, on old walls and waste ground. Generally rather rare, but frequent in the NW and fairly frequent in the NE.

VC11: Beaulieu old airfield 3400, 3501, Hb.RPB 1990; Calshot 4702, large patch on reclaimed land, *RPB & AJG* 1987; Portchester Castle 6204, *EAP* 1981; Merdon Castle, Hursley 4226, roadside at foot of wall, *RPB* 1987. **VC12**: Smannell 3849, old wall, *GDF* 1983; Whitchurch 4647, flint wall by Methodist church, *RPB* 1969; Arford Common 8336, pathside, *CRH* 1989, conf. *AB* 1990; wall between church and Froyle Place 7542, *ANHS* 1991.

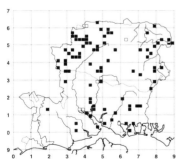

Map 502 Poa compressa

P. palustris L. Swamp Meadow-grass. **H** Very rare or extinct

First record, Miss E. S. Todd 1929, waste ground near Southampton West Station (now Southampton Station) *c*.4112, VC11, Hb.EST, det. *GCD*.

An alien, which used to be sown in wet places.

VC11/12: River bank at Winchester, *NEGC c*.1940 (*Fl.Bas.MS*, p.19). **VC12**: Edge of Fleet Pond 8254, *JEL* 1933. When the pond was drained for

the 1939–45 war, *PMH & ECW* found it abundantly over the dried bed. By 1950, it was confined to the edge (teste *JEL*), where it was last seen by *WEW, ECW & EJC* 1970. In 1987, the pond was so silted-up and invaded by reeds around the margins that *PJOT & AB* could not find it. Bank of R. Blackwater near Yateley 8161, *ECW* 1961, Hb.RNG. A record for Milford Lake, Highclere 4560, *AB & WMK* 1976, Hb.AB (*Watsonia* 11: 403) was later found to be an error.

P. nemoralis L. Wood Meadow-grass. **N,H** Locally common Map 503

In woods, on shady banks, lanes and streamsides. Widespread, and apparently much commoner in the N. It seems to be absent from the Wealden Edge Hangers. It is probably also occasionally sown under trees and in shelter belts, but it has not been possible to separate these records.

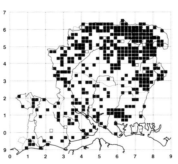

Map 503 Poa nemoralis

P. bulbosa L. Bulbous Meadow-grass. **N** Very rare

First record, J. Staley 1932, South Hayling, VC11 (*Proc.Hants Fld Club* 12: 297).

On sand-and-shingle dunes at the coast, and on a sandy path in one place inland. Once plentiful on the dunes of Sinah Common before the erosion phase, then it largely vanished but is now increasing again on S coast of Hayling Island.

VC11: Southbourne 1391, on cliff-top, *RMW* 1993; Stanpit Marsh 1691, sandy edge of harbour, *RMW* 1978, 1982, conf. *RPB* 1986; Hengistbury Head 1691, short turf on S shore of harbour, *RMW & FAW* 1987; Little Haven, Mudeford 1891, gravelly car park area, *FAW* 1991; dune-path outside Sinah Common golf-links 6899, 6999, Hb.AWW 1950, *AB* 1963; on one

sand-and-shingle dune near South Hayling car-park 7098, *FR & SRD* 1978, also Hb.AWW, 7198, abundant in several places on fixed shingle, *FR* 1993; N of Heath Pond, Petersfield 7522, path by tennis courts (non-flowering), *FR* 1977, perhaps now lost following maintenance work, 1988.

Dactylis glomerata L. Cock's-foot. **N,D** Very common

In pastures, roadside verges, borders of fields and waste places; an abundant constituent of rank grassland, and often sown in pastures.

Catabrosa aquatica (L.) P. BEAUV. Whorl-grass. **N** Local Map 504

In choked drains of water-meadows, swampy streams and pond-margins, and around chalk springs. Most frequent along the Avon, lower Test and NE wetlands. Otherwise very local in alkaline to moderately-acid and also brackish waters.

VC11: Wood Crates 2708, in alder carr, *FR* 1973, *RPB* 1994; The Furlongs, Redbridge 3613, *RPB* 1955; Lisle Court, Lymington 3495, brackish marsh, *AEB* 1986; ditch by Wickham Common 5810, *JRw* 1985. **VC12**: Side of Pillhill Brook 2945, *MFW* 1989; Cut Pound, Alton 7139, (R. Wey), *JLSL* 1978; R. Loddon, Basingstoke to Basing, 6552, 6652, *NEGC c*.1940 (*Fl.Bas.MS*, p.19); Waggoners Wells 8534, 8634, *JEL* 1933, Hb.BM, *AB* 1968; Darby Green 8360, *WEW* 1957, *ARGM* 1987; particularly abundant in water-cress beds, Bishops Sutton 6032, *AB* 1991.

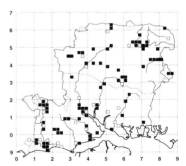

Map 504 Catabrosa aquatica

Catapodium rigidum (L.) C. E. HUBB. (*Desmazeria rigida* (L.) Tutin) Fern-grass. **N** Frequent to occasional

On dry, bare ground on chalk, gravel

or sand; also on disused railways, rubble and old walls; widespread but not very frequent. VC8: 1 □; VC11: 71 □; VC12: 48 □.

VC11: R. Hamble, Curbridge 5111, *SNHS* 1989; Portchester Castle 6204, Hb.AWW *c*.1950. VC12: Old Burgh-clere Lime Quarry 4757, *PB* 1984; Froyle Place 7542, wall of kitchen-garden, *CL* (*in litt*)., *ANHS* 1991; Noar Hill 7331, chalk-pit, *ARGM & DBr* 1991.

C. marinum (L.) C. E. Hubb.
(*Desmazeria marina* (L.) Druce)   Sea Fern-grass.   **N**   Locally frequent   Map 505

Coastal, on shingle, fixed sand-dunes, sea-walls, rubble and masonry.

VC11: Barton on Sea 2392, below cliffs, *RPB* 1986; South Hayling 7198, shingle among beach huts, *SRD* 1978, *FR* 1993; Calshot Castle 4802, *RPB* 1985.

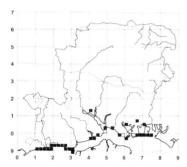

Map 505 Catapodium marinum

Parapholis strigosa (Dumort.) C. E. Hubb.   Hard-grass.   **N**   Locally frequent   Map 506

On firm mud and in short turf in upper salt-marshes; also on bare, reclaimed land and along sea-walls. Common in estuaries and on much of the coastline.

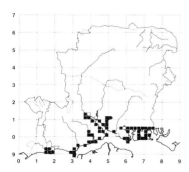

Map 506 Parapholis strigosa

P. incurva (L.) C. E. Hubb.   Curved Hard-grass.   **N**   Rare

On firm clay below cliffs, sandy shingle-spits, and on bare, gravelly ground and dry mud along and on top of sea-walls on the coast. Rare, but easily over-looked.

VC11: Farlington Marshes 6804, on sea-wall, Hb.AWW 1958; Calshot 4801, *MEY* 1977, Hb.RPB 1978, conf. *AM*; Taddiford Gap, near Hordle Cliff 2692, on dry, slipped clay, Hb.RPB 1977, conf. *AM*; Northney, North Hayling 7303; Gutner, Hayling Island 7301 (with *P. strigosa*), *RPB* 1989; Lepe Beach 4598, *RPB* 1989; Penning-ton, Hb.CGE 1952; Milford on Sea, *CEH* n.d., Hb.K (probably the basis of a pre-1930 record for SZ29 in *Atlas Brit.Fl.* (p.404) and therefore the first record for Hants). Also 2292, 2492, 2690, 2890, 3292, 3494, 3694, 3894.

Glyceria maxima (Hartm.) Holmb.   Reed Sweet-grass.   **N**   Locally abun-dant   Map 507

In marshes, wet meadows, ponds, slug-gish streams, river-margins and canals; common in the large river-valleys and in the NE wetlands. Often dominant, completely choking some watercourses, causing rapid silting-up of mud and debris.

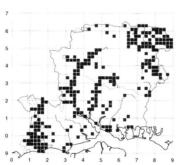

Map 507 Glyceria maxima

G. fluitans (L.) R. Br.   Floating Sweet-grass.   **N**   Locally very common

In shallow ponds, choked ditches and streams, boggy pastures and swampy woods; very common in acid-to-neutral waters, but very local in most chalk wetlands.

G. fluitans x G. declinata   N

VC11: There are field records for tetrads 1816, 3004.

G. x pedicellata F. Towns. (*G. flui-tans* x *G. notata*)   Hybrid Sweet-grass.   **N**   Occasional, but under-recorded

In similar habitats to both parents, but can often occur alone; widespread but often overlooked. VC8: 1 □; VC11: 26 □; VC12: 19 □.

G. declinata Bréb.   Small Sweet-grass.   **N**   Locally common   Map 508

First British record, F. Townsend *c*.1872, by roadside opposite Shedfield House 5513, VC11 (*Fl.Hants*, p.499).

In boggy ditches and streamsides on heathland, muddy woodland-rides, marshy acid pastures; common in the New Forest and NE heathlands, very local in base-rich situations.

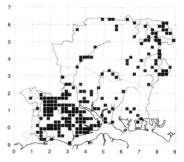

Map 508 Glyceria declinata

G. notata Chevall. (*G. plicata* (Fr.) Fr.)   Plicate Sweet-grass.   **N**   Locally common   Map 509

In drains in water-meadows, swamps, sluggish streams, pond-margins and chalk springs; common in the chalk river-valleys, where it largely replaces *G. fluitans*, but also frequent in other waters except markedly acid ones.

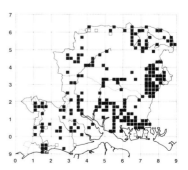

Map 509 Glyceria notata

Melica uniflora RETZ. Wood Melick. **N** Frequent and locally common

In woods, copses and shady hedge-banks; common on all except acid soils, but very local in the SW and the New Forest; grazing soon eliminates it.

Helictotrichon pubescens (HUDS.) PILG. (*Avenula pubescens* (Huds.) Dumort.) Downy Oat-grass. **N** Locally common Map 510

Common in chalk grassland, and some-times in dry or damp meadows and roadside verges on other basic soils.

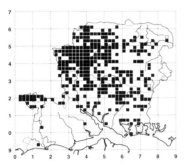

Map 510 Helictotrichon pubescens

H. pratense (L.) BESSER (*Avenula pratensis* (L.) Dumort.) Meadow Oat-grass. **N** Locally frequent Map 511

In short, dry chalk-grassland; fairly common on the remaining downs, but decreasing where ungrazed; elsewhere, rarely, in imported turf.
VC12: Long Sutton 7444, hedge-bank, *CRH* 1990.

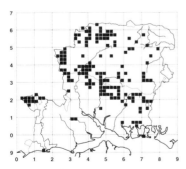

Map 511 Helictotrichon pratense

Arrhenatherum elatius (L.) P. BEAUV. ex J. PRESL & C. PRESL False Oat-grass. **N** Abundant

In rank grassland everywhere, and a great encroacher on the ungrazed

downs, spreading below ground and coming up in the middle of the *Festuca* sward and smothering it; grazing, however, discourages it.
Both *Fl.Hants* (p.495) and *Suppl.Fl. Hants* (p.120) contain records of var. *bulbosum* (Willd.) St.-Amans, and *AB* remembers it in the 1920s at Black-moor and Noar Hill. The only known recent record is from Longwood Warren 5227, VC11, in cornfield border, *HFG* 1993.

Avena strigosa SCHREB. Bristle Oat. **C** Very rare

Casual weed of arable and waste places.
VC11: Ringwood, *LBH* 1930.
VC12: 7234, 7630, 7834, 7836, 8236.

A. fatua L. Wild-oat. **C** Locally frequent

In borders of fields, verges and waste ground. It infests many arable crops, especially in the NW.

A. sterilis L. ssp. **ludoviciana** (DURIEU) NYMAN (*A. ludoviciana* Durieu) Winter Wild-oat. **C** Very rare

First record, Ms J. M. Thurston 1951, Survey of Wild Oats (*Ann.Appl.Biol.* **41**: 619).
A cornfield weed which favours heavy soil. According to *CEH*, the first British records were in 1914 (Fal-mouth Docks, Cornwall), 1917 (Hythe Quay, Colchester, Essex), and 1926 (Abingdon, Berks). However, in her 1951 survey, J. M. Thurston concluded that it appeared to have spread out from Oxfordshire, being commonest in Beds, Berks and Bucks, and scarcer in the neighbouring coun-ties. She received four samples from Hants, probably all from centrads SU45 and 65, but localities were not specified. The authors know of six records:
VC11: NE Denmead *c*.6612, *AWW* 1963. **VC12**: Haw Bridge 7441, *AWW* 1963; Clay's Farm, Alton 7439, *AB* 1968; Bentley Station 7842, *AWW* 1963; Odiham 7450, *AJSt c*.1964; SE of Fleet, *c*.8250, *VL* 1959.

Gaudinia fragilis (L.) P. BEAUV. French Oat-grass. **C** Very rare

First record, J. Rowe 1993, Curdridge 5213, VC11, old meadow grazed by horses, Hb. HCMS, conf. *FR* (*Watsonia* **20**: 300).

Trisetum flavescens (L.) P. BEAUV. Yellow Oat-grass. **N,D** Locally common

Old grassland in pastures, on chalk downs, banks and roadside verges. Also included in sown grass-mixtures on a great variety of dry soils.

Koeleria macrantha (LEDEB.) SCHULT. (*K. cristata* auct., non (L.) Pers.) Crested Hair-grass. **N** Locally frequent Map 512

In short, chalk grassland. Fairly common on the downs, though greatly reduced locally by lack of grazing. Rarely, elsewhere, on verges of grass-heaths and golf-courses.
VC11: Lyndhurst 3008, golf-course, *RPB* 1966; B3056, near Pig Bush 3605, *RPB* 1983; B3080, near Bramshaw Telegraph 2216, *RPB* 1988. **VC12**: The Chase, Woolton Hill 4462, disused railway, *VF* 1982.

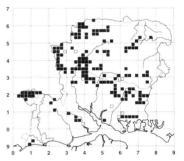

Map 512 Koeleria macrantha

Deschampsia cespitosa (L.) P. BEAUV. Tufted Hair-grass. **N** Common

In rough pastures, marshes, roadside verges and open, damp woods on heavy soils waterlogged in winter; generally common, except in intensively-farmed, dry, chalk areas.
Ssp. *parviflora* (Thuill.) Dumort. has been collected at three sites in VC11, *RMV* 1989, but, according to H. J. M. Bowen, the British authority, both this subspecies and ssp. *cespitosa* are poorly characterized and the former does not merit recognition even as a variety.

D. setacea (HUDS.) HACK. Bog Hair-grass. **N** Very local Map 513

First record, H. C. Watson 1869, 'Fleet Pond...growing in the swamp' *c*.8155, VC12, Hb.BM (*J.Bot.* **7**: 281). The specimen is labelled 'in swampy spots, south and west sides of Fleet Pond'. Watson's account mentions that *D. setacea* was quickly found on leaving the railway station (which was further W than the modern station). *CRH* considers it likely that this locality was in The Flash on the W side of the pond, since infilled and now the site of an industrial estate.

In turfy flood-hollows on wet heaths, margins of bogs and pools. Though still in Surrey, this elegant grass is now gone from VC12, and, in Hants, is virtually confined to the New Forest, where most populations are of restricted extent.

VC11: Near Home Farm, Sopley 1700, *NAS* 1989; B3080 Bramshaw Telegraph 2216, grassy pits and hollows, *RPB* 1989; Greenmoor 3399, *AJB* 1986; Janesmoor Plain 2413, *JCDa* 1936, *RPB* 1989; Setley 2899, *RPB* 1985; Dibden Bottom 3806, *RPB* 1962–94; Whitten Bottom 2001; Bagshot Moor 3600, *RPB* 1970; Hatchet Pond 3601, *RPB* 1971; near Fawley Inclosure 4005, *RPB* 1963, 1993; Peaked Bottom 3599, *RPB* 1984; heathland N of Hurn Airport *c*.1099, *CDD* 1962, Hb.AWW, conf. *RPB*. **VC12**: Margin of Hawley Pond, abundant, *FT c*.1870; wet bog on E margin of Fleet Pond 8254, abundant, *FT* 1873, Hb.SLBI (both *Fl.Hants*, p.492, as *D. discolor* Roem. & Schult.), *JGr* 1892, Hb.BM, and last record, at SE end 8254, *GARW* 1938 (*Watts MSS*).

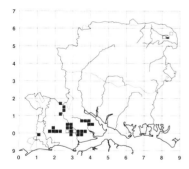

Map 513 Deschampsia setacea

D. flexuosa (L.) TRIN. Wavy Hair-grass. **N** Locally common

On dry grass-heaths, commons, open, acid woods and shady moss-covered banks on gravel or sand. Confined to acid soil, therefore reliable records on the chalk e.g. Pill Heath 3552, VC12, must be on superficials.

Holcus lanatus L. Yorkshire-fog. **N** Very common

In pastures, verges, waste ground and open woods; universal on all soils. Often very invasive in resown grass-land on poor soils.

H. mollis L. Creeping Soft-grass. **N** Locally very common

This likes shadier places than *H. lanatus* such as woods, although it can persist for some time in the open after scrub clearance. On the chalk, it is found only on superficial acid soils.

Aira caryophyllea L. Silver Hair-grass. **N** Locally frequent

On dry, bare, gravelly or sandy places on banks, tracks, verges, heaths and wall-tops; fairly common, with a similar distribution to *A. praecox*, but less frequent.

A. praecox L. Early Hair-grass. **N** Locally very common   Map 514

On dry, open, sandy or gravelly places on banks, heaths, pastures, verges, shores, cliff-tops, paths, and in old pits. Also around mossy tree-roots in open woodland. Very common on acid soil. In contrast to Townsend's statement (*Fl.Hants* p.493) that it is 'common, particularly on the chalk', it is now found on the chalk only on ant-hills and on superficial soils.

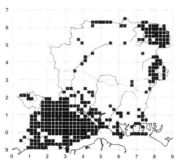

Map 514 Aira praecox

Anthoxanthum odoratum L. Sweet Vernal-grass. **N,D** Very common

In pastures, on banks, grass heaths and open woods. At one time, included in hay-seed mixtures.

<A. aristatum BOISS. (*A. puelii* Lecoq & Lamotte) Annual Vernal-grass. **C** Extinct

Formerly a rare alien of sandy and gravelly fields. Two VC11 records in *Fl.Hants* (p.481); none since.>

Phalaris arundinacea L. Reed Canary-grass. **N** Locally abundant

On riversides, ditches, pond-margins, marshes and swampy woods, where it is common.

P. canariensis L. Canary-grass. **C** Locally frequent

On disturbed roadsides, waste ground and refuse tips; frequent and usually transient, mainly as a bird-seed alien.

Agrostis capillaris L. (*A. tenuis* Sibth.) Common Bent. **N,D** Frequent and locally very common

Old grassland in pastures, verges, on heaths, arable and waste ground, and in open woods. Very common on dry or damp, acid soil; on chalk grassland only on acid superficials. On account of its fine texture, it is also imported from abroad for seeding putting- and bowl-ing-greens.

A. gigantea ROTH Black Bent. **N,C** Frequent

A rampant weed in unsprayed corn-fields and neglected arable land, especially on light soils; also on waste ground, borders of fields and woods, and in clearings. Widespread and fairly common.

A. stolonifera L. Creeping Bent. **N,C,D** Frequent and locally abundant

Widespread in grassland, especially in damp places in pastures, brackish marshes and waste ground. It is much more common on the chalk than other bents – often, in fact, being the only one on the downs. Dwarf varieties are used in lawns.

A. curtisii KERGUÉLEN (*A. setacea* Curtis, non Vill.) Bristle Bent. **N** Locally very common   Map 515

On dry heaths, commons and open, acid woodland on the poorest gravel and sand. Abundant on the SW Tertiaries; more local in the SE and NE. Bromfield recorded it from Woolmer Forest, but there is no specimen and it has not been seen since.

VC8: Whitsbury Wood 1318, *JDG* 1960 (*Suppl.Fl.Wilts*, p.65). **VC11**: Netley Hill 4811 and Hamble Common 4805, *FR c*.1985; Browndown 5799, Hb.AWW *c*.1960; Peel Common 5602, *FR* 1976; Shedfield Common 5612, *FR* 1984; Warsash churchyard 5005, *RPB* 1988; Southleigh Forest 7308, *AWW*

1952. **VC12**: Yateley Heath Wood 8057, *AB* 1980; Aldershot 8751, railway depot, *GHF* 1981 (since built over); Eversley Common 7959, *PLeB* 1970, *CRH* 1987, destroyed by gravel-quarry soon after; Silchester Common 6262, *PB* 1980; Bourley, Aldershot 8350, 8351, 8450; also Farnborough Airfield 8453, *CRH & ARGM* 1986, *RAE Survey* 1991); Ludshott Common 8534, *NAS* 1987, conf. *FR* 1991, *PleB* 1993.

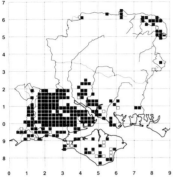

Map 515 Agrostis curtisii

A. canina L.   Velvet Bent.   **N,D** Locally common

On wet heaths, in neglected, marshy pastures, ditches, pond-margins and damp tracks in open woods. Common on acid soil, local elsewhere. It has been used as a lawn grass.

A. vinealis SCHREB. (*A. canina* ssp. *montana* (Hartm.) Hartm.)   Brown Bent.   **N,D**   Under-recorded

First record, F. Escombe 1928, North Stoneham, VC11, wet heathy ground, Hb.HGS.

According to the literature, this grass is found on dry, heathy ground, but in Hants it can occur on both dry and damp heathland, on sand, gravel or clay; it can be a drought-resistant lawn grass. There are a few confirmed records:
VC11: Hengistbury Head 1790, on firm sand below slope, Hb.RPB 1989, det. *HJMB*; Three Beech Bottom, Setley 2999, damp heath, *RPB* 1985, det. *ADB*; Setley Common, Roydon Woods 3000, clay turf along ride, *RPB* 1985, det. *ADB*. **VC12**: Woolmer Forest 7932, on disturbed sand, very dwarf, *AB* 1965, 7831, in a very dry place, with *A. capillaris*, *AB* 1985; Conford 8232, *AB* 1969; Chawton Park Wood 6836, in ride, on Clay-with-flints, *AB* 1980, det. *PJOT* 1990;

Woolmer Forest and S of Longmoor Camp *c*.7930, *FR* 1986; Longmoor 7931, old railway, *FR* 1990.

A. scabra WILLD. (*A. hyemalis* sensu Philipson et auct., non (Walter) Britton, Sterns & Poggenb.)   Rough Bent. **C**   Very rare or extinct

First record, E. C. Wallace 1941, Fleet Pond, VC12, on drained bed, det. *CEH* (*Watsonia* 1: 59).

Occurred in artificial situations, such as railways.

VC12: Bordon military railway 7836, profusely, *JLM & EJC* 1966, Hb.AB (*Watsonia* 10: 434), but did not survive destruction of railway in 1976; Sleaford 8038, refuse tip, *AB* 1969, det. *JEL*.

X Agropogon littoralis (SM.) C. E. HUBB. (*Agrostis stolonifera* x *Polypogon monspeliensis*)   Perennial Beard-grass. **N**   Very rare

First British record, T. Johnson 1641, 'Prope castrum South-Sea-Castle', VC11 (*Merc.Bot.*, pt.ii, p.24).

VC11: First discovered at Farlington Marshes 6804 by *PMH & EHW* 1931. In 1990, six plants were refound here by *FR & EAP* growing with *Polypogon monspeliensis* (L.) Desf. in a small hollow in brackish grassland; Calshot 4801, *MEY* 1977, Hb.RPB, *AJG*, *JOM & RPB* 1987; Dibden Bay 4109, brackish seepage-channel behind estuary-wall, abundant amongst the parents, Hb.RPB 1988, still present, *PJOT & RPB* 1993.

Calamagrostis epigejos (L.) ROTH Wood Small-reed. **N** Local Map 516

In damp, open woods and clearings, fens, rough, bushy pastures, including drier brackish zones; widespread but local, mostly on clay soils in the S and NE, otherwise rare.

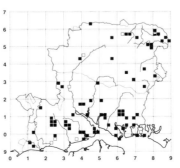

Map 516 Calamagrostis epigejos

VC11: Park Ground Inclosure 3006, *RPB* 1977; Botley Wood 5310, *DEA* 1979; Gilkicker Point 6097, *AWW* 1950, *JF* 1986. **VC12**: Great Pen Wood 4462, *NFC* 1968; Hartley Wood 7536, *GHF* 1987; Bramley Ammunition Depot 6557, *FR* 1980; Gullet Lane, Soldridge 6434, *AAB* 1981; Itchel Mill Springs 7849, *CRH* 1991; Conford Moor 8232, *FR* 1980–94.

C. canescens (F. H. WIGG.) ROTH Purple Small-reed. **N** Very rare

In boggy alder-carr and other wet woods and fens.

VC11: Shepton Water, Bishop's Dyke 3504, *RPB* 1957, det. *TGT*; White Moor, Matley Heath 3208, *RPB* 1963; Gomer Pond, Gosport 5899, fen along stream, *AWW & RPB* 1963; Chark Common 5701, *MB* 1970, 1976; Sowley Brooms 3696, open conifer-plantation, *RPB* 1977; near R. Avon, Week Common 1399, *RPB* 1978; near Holmsley Station 2300, boggy wood, *LBH c*.1930. Not refound in VC12 (three localities in *Fl.Hants*, p.490).

[**X Calammophila baltica** (FLÜGGÉ ex SCHRAD.) BRAND (*Calamagrostis epigejos* x *Ammophila arenaria*)

Planted mistakenly for marram (*A. arenaria*), to counteract coastal erosion in several places on and under a shingle cliff at Rook Cliff, Milford on Sea 2891, originating from a native population at Winterton-on-Sea, E Norfolk, VC27. Date of introduction unknown but transplants were flowering profusely, *JRR & AJG* 1979, since when they appear to have declined (*Watsonia* 18: 370,376).]

Ammophila arenaria (L.) LINK Marram. **N,D** Local Map 517

On sand-dunes and beaches; widespread but local. Follows *Elytrigia*

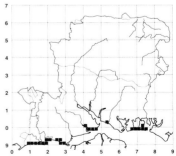

Map 517 Ammophila arenaria

juncea as a primary colonizer of new dunes. Sometimes planted to counter erosion.

Gastridium ventricosum (GOUAN) SCHINZ & THELL. Nit-grass. N,C Very rare Map 518

In unsprayed cornfields, especially headlands of winter wheat, and adjacent waste places close to the coast. Now very rare, but can be abundant in certain fields when crop conditions allow it to germinate, whilst quite absent from adjacent fields that are sprayed or used for root crops and legumes. Formerly widespread but local along the coast and some way inland.

VC11: Barton on Sea *c.*2392, waste ground in garden near cliff-edge, *TCEW* 1957, Hb.ABRN (a habitat similar to that of extant native sites in Dorset, except that it is not over limestone); Tanners Lane, East End 3695, barnyard, cornfield and beach, *JEL & LWF* 1946, *PJOT* 1980, *RAF & PJW* 1985; Sowley Lane 3696, 3796, border of wheat-field, *RPB* 1994; Sowley Farm, East End 3796, headlands of wheat-field with *Briza minor*, *AEB & PJOT* 1980; Beck Farm, East End 3897, arable, *NCC* 1980; Thorns 3896, *KG* n.d., Hb.AB; Ringwood *c.*1604, *WBW* 1950; Manor Road, South Hayling 7199 or 7100, 'garden ground', *PMH* 1936, Hb.BM.

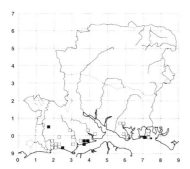

Map 518 Gastridium ventricosum

Lagurus ovatus L. Hare's-tail. C,H Very rare

First record, E. Chambers 1950, Stanpit 1692, VC11, conf. *KG*, Hb.AB (*Proc.Bmth N.S.S.* **49**: 73), *RMW* 1979.

Usually a casual from gardens, near the sea.

VC11: Southbourne 1491, several large patches on cliff-top in disturbed, sandy soil, *RPB* 1990; Black Point,

Hayling Island 7598, one plant on bank of sand-dune, *RPB* 1989, three plants, *RS* 1991, abundant, *WFS & HFG* 1995; Alverstoke 6098, rough ground near the sea, *MB* 1975 (landscaped 1976).

Apera spica-venti (L.) P. BEAUV. Loose Silky-bent. C,N? Very local Map 519

Although considered by C. E. Hubbard to be a doubtful native, P. J. O. Trist (*Fl.Breck.*, p.104) considers it native in the Breckland because it can infest sandy fields, as it once did the fields around Aldershot (*Fl.Hants*, p.487), in which area it is still most frequent. Generally transient, on disturbed, sandy ground, roadsides and waste ground. However, the soil must contain abundant seed in places, as at Coldharbour, Kingsley 7838, VC12, where it appeared in thousands following the reopening of a choked track through fields in connection with roadworks (*AB* 1987).

VC11: Fryern Court, Fordingbridge 1416, 20–30 plants on arable, *JO* 1987, Hb.RPB (*Watsonia* **17**: 198); E of Godshill Inclosure 1716, 1816, on disturbed soil over newly-laid water main, *JO* 1989. **VC12**: Winchfield *c.*7652, cornfield on clay, *ECW* 1937, Hb.BM; E of Winchfield 7654 and N of Winchfield Hurst 7754, plentiful in several fields, *CRH* 1991; Hare's Farm, Hartley Wintney 7757, *HJMB* 1988.

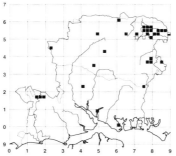

Map 519 Apera spica-venti

<A. interrupta (L.) P. BEAUV. Dense Silky-bent. C Extinct

VC12: One tuft on corner of Queen's Avenue and Duke of Connaught's Road, Aldershot 8753, *RCP* 1980, Hb.AB, conf. *TGT* (*Watsonia* 14: 433), site later destroyed.>

Polypogon monspeliensis (L.) DESF. Annual Beard-grass. N,C Rare Map 520

Joint first British record, R. Garth *c.*1595, '*proxime salinas et antiquas aedes* [very near saltworks and old buildings] Drayton' *c.*6704, VC11 (*Stirp.Adv. Nova*, pt.2, p.469)

In wet, brackish hollows on coastal marshes; firm, bare mud on polders and banks, and on dredged shingle on reclaimed, coastal land; also in disused gravel-pits near the coast. Inland it is an alien, possibly becoming established. Rare, although once locally abundant on the W side of Southampton Water, but declining as the polders become grassed over. Now very rare in Portsmouth and Langstone harbours, as some of the marshes were drained due to the presence of the mosquito, *Anopheles atroparvus* van Thiel, the chief source of the benign tertian form of malaria which once occurred in Britain and was commonly called 'ague' (*Nat.Hdbk 14*, p.6).

VC11: Dibden Bay 4008, 4009, *RPB* 1959, 4109, *RPB & PJOT* 1993; Calshot 4801, *RPB* 1972; Badminston Common, Fawley 4501, levelled disused gravel-pit and banks of pond, plentiful, *RPB* 1988; Hamble 4706, former construction site, *PS* 1991; Tipner 6403, *DPJS* 1991; Farlington Marshes 6804, *PMH* 1931, Hb.BM, Hb.AWW 1954, still there, *MB, FR & EAP* 1990. **VC12**: Hawley Hill 8458, close to dumped soil, *CRH* 1991; Bramshill Common 7561, scattered tufts near tip, *HFG* 1993.

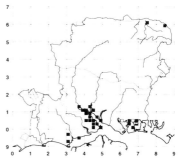

Map 520 Polypogon monspeliensis

P. viridis (GOUAN) BREISTR. Water Bent. C Very rare

First record, N. M. Rumens & Mrs M. D. Thomas 1992, Albion Place, Southampton 4111, VC11, damp patch at base of arches of old city wall, a few plants, Hb.RPB, conf. *TAC*.

Alopecurus pratensis L. Meadow Foxtail. **N,D** Common

In old pastures and meadows, marshes, and on roadside verges. Common, especially in damp lowlands. Also sown agriculturally.

A. x brachystylus PETERM. (*A. x hybridus* Wimm.; *A. pratensis* x *A. geniculatus*) **N** Very rare or over-looked

VC11: Lower Test, Nursling 3614, *RPB* 1980, det. *PJOT*. **VC12**: R. Blackwater, Eversley Cross 7962, *AHGA & NYS* 1937.

A. geniculatus L. Marsh Foxtail. **N** Locally common

In wet pastures, marshes, on muddy ditch- and streamsides, pond-margins. Common on acid-to-neutral soils; local in chalk wetlands.

A. x plettkei MATTF. (*A. geniculatus* x *A. bulbosus*) **N** Very rare

First record, R. P. Bowman 1978, Lower Test, Nursling 3614, VC11, Hb.K, Hb.RPB, det. *TAC* 1980 (*Watsonia* 16: 198).

This has since been located at two other sites on the Lower Test close to *A. bulbosus* though usually occurring at a slightly higher level in the brackish zone. It seems to compete aggressively with the less vigorous parent which has a shorter flowering season and little vegetative spread.

VC11: Wick Meads 1592, 1692, *RMW* 1991; Stanpit Marsh 1691, 1692, Hb.RPB 1985–86, det. *PJOT*; Keyhaven 3091, *RPB* 1986, det. *PJOT*; The Furlongs, Lower Test 3613, *RPB* 1986, det. *PJOT*; Farlington Marshes 6804, *EAP* 1980.

A. bulbosus GOUAN Bulbous Foxtail. **N** Very rare Map 521

In wet, brackish pastures, usually subject to tidal flooding. Now very rare, although some extant populations are fairly large.

VC11: Lower Test 3613, 3614, *RPB* 1954, 1984; Farlington Marshes 6804, *JS* 1934, Hb.BM, *EAP* 1990; Stanpit Marsh 1692, 1791, 1792, *RMW et al.* 1978–83; South Marsh 1691, brackish marsh-grassland, *RPB* 1986, conf. *PJOT*; Wick Meads 1592, 1692, abundant, *RMW* 1991; Keyhaven 3091, small brackish pasture, *SRD c.*1980, *RPB* 1986. *AB* remembers finding it at Stokes Bay *c.*5998, *c.*1947, near the

high-tide level, but the area was subsequently 'cleared up'. Not refound at West Lane, Hayling Island *c.*7100, *JS* 1935, Hb.BM (*Proc.Hants Fld Club* 15: 74). Formerly known in four other sites (*Fl.Hants*, p.484).

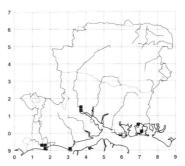

Map 521 Alopecurus bulbosus

A. aequalis SOBOL. Orange Foxtail. **N** Very rare

Pond-margins and ditches. Confined to the extreme NE corner of VC12, and not refound in VC11 (last record 1908), although there are more recent but dubious records for tetrads 1692 and 4216.

VC12: Near Heckfield, *VEM* 1921, Hb.RDG; drained bed of Fleet Pond, *PMH & ECW* 1941, Hb.BM, Hb.RNG; near Bramshill Common, edge of pond, *AMS* 1960, Hb.RDG; Bramshill *c.*7362, *AMS* 1963; Bramshill *c.*7460, *PH* 1967; Wilk's Water, Basingstoke Canal 7552, 'till 1962', *AJSt & WEW*; Tundry Pond, Dogmersfield 7752, Hb.AB 1976, *ARGM* 1982, not seen, *CRH* 1992.

A. myosuroides HUDS. Black-grass, Black Twitch. **C** Locally common Map 522

An arable weed, mainly on the chalk. Still frequent in spite of crop-spraying,

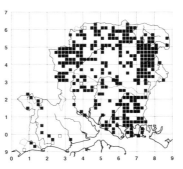

Map 522 Alopecurus myosuroides

but rare in the SW. The distribution map reflects the paucity of recorders covering grasses, particularly in the central area.

Phleum pratense L. Timothy. **N,D** Common

In pastures, borders of fields, roadside verges and waste ground. An important fodder grass, sown on a large scale.

P. bertolonii DC. (*P. pratense* ssp. *bertolonii* (DC.) Bornm.) Smaller Cat's-tail. **N,D** Frequent and locally common

In old grassland on the chalk downs, in meadows and on verges. Common, but less frequent in the SW. Like *P. pratense*, often cultivated for fodder.

P. arenarium L. Sand Cat's-tail. **N** Very rare

Principally inhabits sand-dunes which are scarce in Hampshire as most of the coast is mud or shingle. It has been found nowhere in the county except the S of Hayling Island and Southsea, although it can be plentiful in these few sites.

VC11: Fort Cumberland 6798, shingle beach, Hb.AWW 1960; South Hayling 6899, near ferry, *PMH* 1934, Hb.BM; Sinah Common dunes 6999, *RPB* 1972, *FR* 1994; South Hayling 7198, *SRD* 1977; Sandy Point, Hayling Island 7498, *FR*, *AB & EAP* 1984, *FR* 1994; Black Point, Hayling Island 7598, *RPB* 1972.

<Bromus arvensis L. Field Brome. **C** Extinct

This was a rare cornfield weed in the days of Townsend. It was last found in this habitat at Broad Lane, Christchurch, Hb.HGS 1917, and in a cultivated field, Swaythling, *JFR* 1918 (*Proc.IoW N.H.S.* 1: 273), both VC11. In 1970, *DEB* found a large patch of this grass at Well 7546, VC12, on disturbed ground following road-widening and the installation of a gas-main. It persisted for three years, Hb.AB, det. *CEH*.>

B. commutatus SCHRAD. Meadow Brome. **N** Occasional Map 523

As *B. racemosus*, in damp meadows and, like that species, being displaced by meadow 'improvement' to verges, borders of fields and tracks.

VC11: R. Avon, Moortown 1404, hay meadows, Hb.RPB 1976, det. *AM*;

Bishop's Waltham 5616, meadows, locally plentiful, *FR* 1991; Farlington Marshes 6804, *AWW* 1951, *AJS* 1986. **VC12**: West Stratton 5240, by field-track, *AB* 1969; damp patch in cornfield below Noar Hill 7532, *AB* 1983 (var. *pubens* H. C. Watson det. *CEH*).

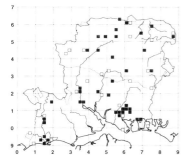

Map 523 Bromus commutatus

B. racemosus L.   Smooth Brome. **N**   Occasional   Map 524

Unimproved grassland in damp hayfields and water-meadows, usually on alluvial soils. As the meadows were 'improved' it became confined to odd corners, where it was frequent on the clay and Malmstone of the western Weald in the 1960s, but it is now as rare there as it is elsewhere.

VC11: Lower Test, Nursling 3615, *RPB* 1977; Frenchmoor 2728, old meadows, Hb.RPB 1984. **VC12**: Ashford Hill meadows 5662, *FR* 1986; Stratfield Saye 7063, Hb.AWW 1959; North Warnborough 7251, *GDF* 1977; Burhunt Valley 7432, *IM* 1986; Itchen Stoke 5533, roadside verge, *AB* 1991.

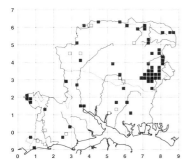

Map 524 Bromus racemosus

B. hordeaceus L. ssp. **hordeaceus** (*B. mollis* L.)   Soft-brome.   **N** Common

In meadows, verges and waste ground.

ssp. **ferronii** (MABILLE) P. M. SM. (*B. ferronii* Mabille)   Least Soft-brome. **N**   Very rare

First record, C. D. Drake 1975, Hordle 2692, cliff-top, Hb.AB, det. *AM*.

In exposed places by the sea, on cliff-tops, sand and shingle.

VC11: South Hayling car-park 7098, *FR* 1976; Needs Ore Point 4297, *FR* 1978; Gunner Point, Hayling Island 6999, turf of stabilized sand-dune, Hb.RPB 1988, det. *PJOT*; Sandy Point, Hayling Island 7498, *FR* 1980.

ssp. **thominei** (HARDOUIN) BRAUN-BLANQ. (*B. thominei* Hardouin)   **N** Very rare or overlooked

First confirmed records, E. A. Pratt 1977, Sinah Common 6999, det. *FR*, and Lady Anne Brewis 1977, Eastoke, Hayling Island 7498, det. *PJOT*, both VC11.

On coastal dunes and other sandy places. There are a number of inland records of this plant but, in the opinion of P. M. Smith (*Watsonia* 6: 327), these are probably all referable to *B. x pseudothominei* P. M. Sm. (*q.v.*). They have accordingly been withheld.

VC11: Beckton Bunny 2592, cliff-top, Hb.RPB 1989 and Stansore Point, Lepe 4698, *RPB* 1986, both det. *PJOT*; Hordle Cliff 2791, Hb.RPB 1993.

B. x pseudothominei P. M. SM. (*B. x thominei* sensu Tutin et auct., non Hardouin; *B. hordeaceus* x *B. lepidus*)   Lesser Soft-brome.   **C**   Probably frequent

First records, A. W. Westrup 1960, Stephen's Castle Down, Upham 5521 and Funtley Bridge 5508, field by R. Meon; both VC11, Hb.AWW, det. *PJOT*.

'Improved' meadows, lawns, road-sides and waste places. According to P. M. Smith (*Watsonia* 6: 340–341), the alien *B. lepidus*, an impurity of grass-seed, has interbred, either before or after introduction, with *B. hordeaceus* ssp. *hordeaceus* to form a hybrid almost indistinguishable from *B. lepidus* and now apparently much more common than the latter.

B. lepidus HOLMB.   Slender Soft-brome.   **C**   Rare or overlooked

First record, L. Beeching Hall 1929, between Keyhaven and Lymington,

VC11. *NDS* grew the seeds in his garden in Bournemouth, and distrib-uted plants in 1930, Hb.BM.

In waste places, on roadsides and arable land. VC11: 9 □; VC12: 6 □.

VC11: Beaulieu old airfield 3401, bed of former runway, Hb.RPB 1987, det. *PJOT* (the only recent Hants record); Marchwood, on land reclaimed from the sea, *HJG* 1935, Hb.K (*Rep.B.E.C.* for 1935, p.48); West Meon *c.*6423, recently-felled wood S of village, *PGT* 1946, Hb.K; Soake House, Denmead 6611, Hb.AWW 1959, det. *PJOT*; Weston Farm, Buriton 7221, manure heaps, Hb.AWW 1960, det.*PJOT*; Old Winchester Hill 6420, Hb.AWW 1960, det.*PJOT*; Funtley Bridge 5508, field by R. Meon, Hb.AWW 1960, det. *PJOT*; Cheesefoot Head, weed on arable, *CEH* 1954, Hb.K. **VC12**: Blackbushe Airport 8058, sandy soil at roadside, *BLB* 1950, Hb.K; Noar Hill, Selborne 7432, cultivated field, *NYS* 1954, Hb.K; Burghclere *c.*4658, corner of waste ground, *MMcC-W* 1957, Hb.BM; roadside between Ashmans-worth and Hurstbourne Tarrant 4055, *JFH & PCH* 1957, Hb.BM; Southside Farm, Longparish 4443, unploughed corner, Hb.AWW 1962, det. *PJOT*; Dogmersfield Park 7751, *WEW* 1967.

<B. interruptus (HACK.) DRUCE Interrupted Brome.   **N,C**   Extinct

Formerly endemic to Britain and characteristic of sainfoin and clover fields. There are seven old records, of which the most recent are two speci-mens dated 1906, one from Totton, VC11, and one from Sydmonton, VC12, in Hb.HGS.>

B. secalinus L.   Rye Brome.   **C** Very rare

This cornfield weed was fairly frequent in Townsend's time, but is now very rare.

VC11: Parley Green 1097, *NDS & LBH* 1924 (*Suppl.Fl.Hants*, p.123); Compton, in barley-field, *PMH* 1939, Hb.BM. **VC12**: Roadside from Blounce Farm to Humbly Grove Farm, near South Warnborough 7145, Hb.JBM 1942.

<B. pseudosecalinus P. M. SM. Smith's Brome.   **C**   Extinct

First and only record, C. B. Clarke 1890, Andover, VC12, Hb.K, det. *PMS.*>

Bromopsis ramosa (HUDS.) HOLUB (*Bromus ramosus* Huds.) Hairy-brome. **N** Frequent and locally very common

In woods, scrub, shady waysides and hedgerows; common, except on acid soils in the SW and NE.

B. erecta (HUDS.) FOURR. (*Bromus erectus* Huds.) Upright Brome. **N,D** Locally abundant Map 525

In chalk grassland, where often dominant to the exclusion of fine-leaved grasses and dwarf herbaceous species. Occasionally on roadside verges off the chalk, as on the A31, A35 and A338, VC11.

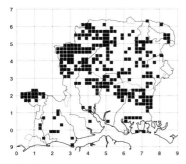

Map 525 Bromopsis erecta

B. inermis (LEYSS.) HOLUB ssp. **inermis** (*Bromus inermis* Leyss.) Hungarian Brome. **D** Rare

First record, R. P. Bowman 1963, B3333 Browndown 5899, roadside verge outside military training camp, Hb.RPB, det. *CEH*.

It has been grown as fodder and, being drought-resistant, is also sown on dry verges.

VC11: Up Somborne 4132, 4030, hedgerow, *AB* 1968; Knowle Lane, Fair Oak 5018, shady W verge, Hb.RPB 1990; Nelson Hill, Southampton 4112, *EJC, ALG & PAH* 1991, Hb.RPB; Farlington Marshes 6803, resown on top of sea-wall, *MB* 1985; Gilkicker Point 6097, Hb.JF 1986. **VC12**: W of Apsley Farm, Faccombe 3859, *RPB* 1969; A325 at Greatham 7831, 7731, Hb.AB 1968, det. *CEH* (*Watsonia* 10: 434); B3002 verges at Passfield Oak 8233, Hogmoor Road 7834 and Forest Centre, Bordon 8033, *AB* 1980–88; Monks Wood, Alton 7439, border of field, *AB* 1968, det. *CEH*; Sotherington Farm, Selborne 7533, *AB* 1991; Wherwell 3941, along path, *PS* 1992.

Anisantha diandra (ROTH) TUTIN ex TZVELEV (*Bromus diandrus* Roth) Great Brome. **C** Rare Map 526

First record, Miss M. T. Hillard 1920, Great Salterns *c.*6701, VC11 (*Suppl.Fl. Hants*, p.123, as *B. maximus* Desf.).

On sandy waste-ground, banks, tips and disturbed roadside verges. This species, as well as *A. rigida* and *A. madritensis*, belong to the Mediterranean flora, and seem to cling to the coast.

VC11: Still on and near the cliffs of Bournemouth 0890–1491, *AB & RPB* 1977–78; Southampton 4210, 4417, *PS* 1991; Fareham–Portchester, abundant for half a mile by widened road, *PMH* 1935, Hb.BM (*Proc.Hants Fld Club* 15: 75, as *B. gussonei* Parl.); Wallington 5807, *RPB* 1988.

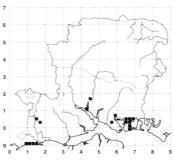

Map 526 Anisantha diandra

A. rigida (ROTH) HYL. (*Bromus rigidus* Roth) Ripgut Brome. **N?,C** Very rare

First record, J. F. Rayner 1923, Knap Mill, Christchurch 1593, VC11 (*Suppl.Fl.Hants*, p.123, as *B. rigens* L. var. *rigidus* (Roth) Rayner).

In Hants, as in France and Jersey where it is native, this grass is found on sand-dunes, and also in other coastal habitats, in at least one of which it has persisted for 80 years. In the Breckland, however, it is a rare cornfield weed (*Fl.Breck.*, p.101).

VC11: Boscombe, Bournemouth, sandy cliffs, *HNR* 1942, Hb.K, *KG* 1954, 0990, 1091, Hb.RPB 1990; Gunner Point, Hayling Island 6999 and South Hayling 7098, sparsely-vegetated sand-dunes, large patches in each site, Hb.RPB 1988, det. *PJOT* (*Watsonia* 17: 485); Cams Bay, Fareham 5905, two small patches on shore, *RPB* 1991; B3333 Browndown 5899, bare soil on roadside, *RPB* 1989; IBM North Harbour, Cosham 6404, on

reclaimed land, *RBa* 1990, Hb.RPB, det. *FR*.

A. sterilis (L.) NEVSKI (*Bromus sterilis* L.) Barren Brome. **N** Common

On waysides, borders of fields, waste ground, and along walls, etc.

A. tectorum (L.) NEVSKI (*Bromus tectorum* L.) Drooping Brome. **C** Very rare

First record, F. H. C. Pack 1926, Sholing *c.*4410, VC11, Hb.HGS (*Suppl.Fl. Hants*, p.123).

VC11: Dibden Bay 4109, two patches on reclaimed land, Hb.RPB 1987, det. *PJOT* (var. *hirsutus* Regel) (*Watsonia* 17: 197), still plentiful, *RPB* 1992; West End, Southampton 4814, 70 plants over 30m of new road, *PS* 1990, Hb.RPB (*Watsonia* 18: 435). **VC12**: Ewshot 8048, three plants on bank newly sown with grass, *AduSB* 1960.

A. madritensis (L.) NEVSKI (*Bromus madritensis* L.) Compact Brome. **C** Very rare

First record, J. Sowerby 1806, walls at Southampton and on Netley Abbey, VC11 (*Sowerby MS*; *Fl.Hants*, p.509).

On bare waste-ground, roadside verges and old walls. Though very rare it has persisted for 180 years at Southampton and Netley Abbey.

VC11: Millbrook 3812, *AWW c.*1958; Mayflower Park and Castle Way, Southampton 4111, *WFB* 1962; Town Quay 4210, *PS* 1991; R. Itchen, Southampton 4311, *DMcC* 1980; Belvidere 4312, gravel at foot of wall, *PS* 1991; Netley Abbey *c.*4508, Hb.HGS 1907, 1925, *JO* 1948; A31, Ringwood 1405, new road, *AB* 1977; Bishop's Waltham *c.*5517, *EM-R c.*1950, Hb.K; Calshot Spit 4801, *RPB* 1985, det. *PJOT*; Dibden Bay 4109, scrapyard, *AB* 1988, *RPB* 1992.

<**A. rubens** (L.) NEVSKI (*Bromus rubens* L.) Foxtail Brome. **C** Extinct

VC11: Mill Spit, Christchurch, Hb.HGS 1923, det. *PJOT* 1993 (as var. *rubens*). A casual originating from the Mediterranean and SW Europe.>

Ceratochloa carinata (HOOK. & ARN.) TUTIN (*Bromus carinatus* Hook. & Arn.) California Brome. **C** Very rare

First record, Mrs C. Hora 1986, footpath near Greywell Tunnel 7151, VC12, Hb.RNG, det. *HJMB* (*Watsonia* **18**: 228).

VC11: Belvidere, Southampton 4312, sandy roadside verge, *PS* 1991, Hb.RPB, det. *PJOT* (*Watsonia* **19**: 154). **VC12**: Grassy area around King John's Castle, Basingstoke Canal 7251, *CH* 1989, Hb.AB, det. *AB* (*Watsonia* **18**: 228).

C. cathartica (VAHL) HERTER (*Bromus willdenowii* Kunth; *B. unioloides* (Willd.) Kunth)   Rescue Brome. **C**   Very rare

First record, J. F. Rayner 1915, Millbrook Station 3912, VC11, reclaimed land (*Proc.Hants Fld Club* **10**: 102,116).
VC11: Near Sandy Lane, Shedfield 5514, E side of farm-track, established over several metres, *EAP* 1992, det. *EJC*; by Danes Stream, Milford on Sea 2991, side of footpath SE of carpark, *VS* 1992, det. *PJOT* (both *Watsonia* **20**: 300). **VC12**: Shipton Bellinger 2345, *GDF* 1982, det. *PJOT*.

Brachypodium pinnatum (L.) P. BEAUV.   Tor-grass. **N**   Very local Map 527

In rank chalk-grassland. Usually specific to chalk, but sometimes on calcareous clay, or on verges or railways which contain lime. This vigorous encroacher is mercifully infrequent in Hants, except in the NW and the edge of Salisbury Plain.
VC11: Inchmery 4398, old marl-pit, *RPB* 1972; Holmsley Station 2300, *RPB* 1972; Ramsdean Down 7020, *ECW* 1939, Hb.BM, not seen for many years, *FR*. **VC12**: Bransbury Common 4141, *FR* 1978.

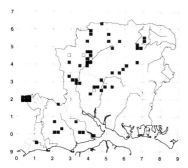
Map 527 Brachypodium pinnatum

B. sylvaticum (HUDS.) P. BEAUV. False Brome. **N**   Very common

In woods, scrub and undergrazed chalk-grassland, shady hedgebanks and roadside verges; very common except on the poorest acid soils. Where open areas are invaded by scrub, *B. sylvaticum* generally follows beneath and is then difficult to eradicate.

Elymus caninus (L.) L. (*Agropyron caninum* (L.) P. Beauv.)   Bearded Couch. **N**   Locally common   Map 528

In woods, scrub and shady hedgerows and roadsides. Common on the chalk, especially in the NW, on riverside alluvium and most other basic soils, and in woodland on the banks of the R. Rother near Liss, VC12. Quite rare in the SW.
VC11: Lower Test, Nursling 3614, *RPB* 1978; Nursted House, Buriton 7421, *FR* 1983. **VC12**: South Tidworth 2446, *MFW* 1989; Ashford Hill 5562, meadows by stream, *PB* 1983; Hare's Farm, Hartley Wintney 7657, *HJMB* 1988; Medstead 6436, *ANHS* 1982.

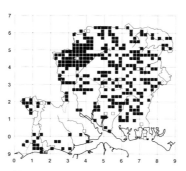
Map 528 Elymus caninus

X Elyhordeum macounii (VASEY) BARKWORTH & D. R. DEWEY (X *Agrohordeum macounii* (Vasey) Lepage; *Elymus trachycaulus* (Link) Gould ex Shinners x *Hordeum jubatum*)   **C**

An obscure N American hybrid which probably arrived in a grass-seed mixture. The identification is provisional.
VC11: Calshot 4801, sown grassland on reclaimed land behind the beach, *RPB* 1978, Hb.EJC, det. *EJC*.

Elytrigia repens (L.) DESV. ex NEVSKI ssp. **repens** (*Elymus repens* (L.) Gould; *Agropyron repens* (L.) P. Beauv.) Common Couch. **N,C**   Common

On arable and waste ground, borders of fields, roadsides, gardens, and behind seashores. Universally abundant and invasive.

E. x oliveri (DRUCE) KERGUÉLEN ex CARRERAS MART. (*Agropyron* x *oliveri* Druce; *E. repens* x *E. atherica*)   **N**   Very rare or overlooked

VC11: Eling 3612, S edge of creek at junction with estuary, Hb.ACL 1986 (*Watsonia* **17**: 197).

E. x laxa (FR.) KERGUÉLEN (*Agropyron* x *laxum* (Fr.) Tutin; *E. repens* x *E. juncea*)   **N**   Very rare

VC11: Eastoke, Hayling Island *c*.7498, *PMH* 1935, Hb.BM.

E. atherica (LINK) KERGUÉLEN ex CARRERAS MART. (*Elymus pycnanthus* (Godr.) Melderis; *Agropyron pungens* auct., non (Pers.) Roem. & Schult.) Sea Couch. **N**   Locally common Map 529

On drier, upper zones of salt-marshes, banks of tidal rivers and creeks, shingle beaches and sea-walls.

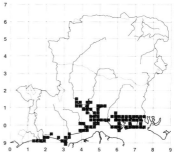
Map 529 Elytrigia atherica

E. x obtusiuscula (LANGE) HYL. (*Agropyron* x *obtusiusculum* Lange; *E. atherica* x *E. juncea*)   **N**   Very rare or overlooked

VC11: Christchurch Harbour shore, tetrad 1690 or 1890, Hb.EST 1921, det. *GCD*; Thorns Beach 3895, *RPB* 1965; Eastney 6898, Hb.RPB 1978, det. *AM*.

E. juncea (L.) NEVSKI ssp. **boreoatlantica** (SIMONET & GUIN.) HYL. (*Elymus farctus* (Viv.) Runemark ex Melderis; *Agropyron junceiforme* (A. Löve & D. Löve) A. Löve & D. Löve) Sand Couch. **N**   Local   Map 530

On sand-dunes and beaches, occasionally in turf on shingle. Widespread, but local. A primary colonist of young dunes, followed by marram.
VC11: Park Shore, Beaulieu 4096,

RPB 1963; Calshot Spit 4802, colonizing recently-accreted sand over shingle, *RPB* 1988.

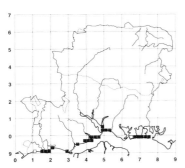

Map 530 Elytrigia juncea ssp. boreoatlantica

Leymus arenarius (L.) HOCHST. (*Elymus arenarius* L.) Lyme-grass. **N,D** Very local Map 531

On sand-dunes and beaches of shingly sand; locally scattered, and usually of small extent. Sometimes planted as an effective sand-binder to counter erosion, as at Stansore Point 4698 in 1966, and probably also at Taddiford Gap 2692 and a few other places.

VC11: Native on Sinah Common dunes 6999, 7098, rather plentiful, *RPB* 1972, *FR* 1994; Sandy Point, Hayling Island 7498, *FR* 1989. It appeared spontaneously 1km from the coast in a lawn under fruit-trees at Hook Cottage, Warsash 5004, and, much further inland, in a water-meadow at Warnford 6222, both records *CSS* 1966.

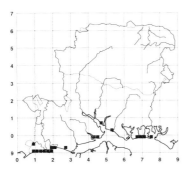

Map 531 Leymus arenarius

Hordelymus europaeus (L.) JESS. Wood Barley. **N** Very rare

First British record, C. Merrett 1666, 'In the woods a mile west from Petersfield', VC11/12, probably citing a record by J. Goodyer (*Merr.Pin.*, p.57).

In woods, usually of beech, on the

chalk; a declining species in Hants.

VC11: Hockham, East Meon 6720, *RPB* 1961; Pillinch Copse, near Hursley 4026, small beech-wood, *RPB* 1969, 1974; The Hangers, Hambledon 6515, abundant, *APNH* 1980, *FR* 1984. Not refound at Butlers Copse, Bury Lodge 6414, *WAB* 1850 (*Fl.Hants*, p.516), or Ditcham Park, *RSA* 1924 (*Proc.Hants Fld Club* 9: 353). VC12: Not refound since the original records given in *Fl.Hants* at Hurstbourne Hanger, Old Alresford and Chawton Park, nor at Ackender Wood, Alton (last record, *JV* 1887), where the habitat has since been ruined by forestry.

Hordeum murinum L. ssp. **murinum** Wall Barley. **N** Locally very common, but under-recorded

On waysides, along walls and pavements, borders of arable fields, and disturbed waste-ground. Very common in dry places in and around urban areas, but infrequently recorded in open countryside.

H. jubatum L. Foxtail Barley. **C,D** Very rare

First record, Miss M. T. Hillard 1920, Hayling, VC11 (*Proc.IoW N.H.S.* 1: 273–274).

Native in N America and E Asia. Introduced in sown grassland, or on waste ground; does not usually persist in a close sward.

VC11: Calshot 4801, reclaimed area, Hb.RPB 1973, det. *AM*; Calshot Spit 4802, sparse turf on shingle, *RPB* 1990; IBM North Harbour, Cosham 6404, brackish, reclaimed land, *RJB* 1991; Ports Creek, Hilsea 6704, *DPJS* 1991; Northney, North Hayling 7203, *AB* 1975; Sinah Common golf-links 6998, *RPB* 1976, conf. *AB*. VC12: Aldershot 8852, on waste ground, *TD* 1979, Hb.AB, conf. *EJC* (*Watsonia* 13: 342); Farnborough 8654, *ARGM* 1980 (*RAE Survey*).

H. secalinum SCHREB. Meadow Barley. **N** Locally frequent Map 532

Old grassland in meadows and brackish pastures, mainly on the clay. Fairly common in the SE, and locally so along the Stour, the lower Test and in the NE. Almost absent from the NW.

VC11: Lower Test 3614, E of tidal river, *RMV* 1990; Dibden Bay 4010, dominant on edge of polder, *RPB*

1986; IBM North Harbour, Cosham 6405, *RBa & RJB* 1990; Petersfield Meadow, opposite The Spain* 7423, *AB* 1985. VC12: Sherfield on Loddon 6858, unimproved pasture, *MEd* 1984; North Warnborough 7250, *AB* 1976; Ashford Hill meadows 5662, *PB* 1987; Roman Silchester 6462, *PB* 1982.

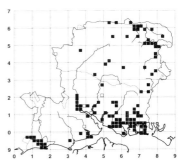

Map 532 Hordeum secalinum

H. marinum HUDS. Sea Barley. **N** Very rare

On earthen sea-walls and sandy ground on the coast. The progressive restructuring and strengthening of sea-walls has meant the destruction of much of this plant.

VC11: Now only at three sites: Farlington Marshes sea-wall 6803, *RPB* 1976, *RMV* 1987, 6804, plentiful on bare mud around pastures, *BSBI* field meeting, 1993; Sinah Common 6999, *FR* 1978; and Dibden Bay 4109, *RPB* 1986. Not refound at Normandy, Lymington 3293, 3294, *RPB* 1953, nor Keyhaven to Hurst 3090, *LWF* 1946.

Secale cereale L. Rye. **C,D** Very rare or under-recorded

A casual from straw, and also sown as food for pheasants.

VC11: Cadnam roundabout 2813, *AB* 1975; A31 Ringwood 1605, new road, *AB* 1977; Ocknell 2410, *RPB* 1979. VC12: 7036, 7232.

Danthonia decumbens (L.) DC. (*Sieglingia decumbens* (L.) Bernh.) Heath-grass. **N** Locally common Map 533

On wet or dry grass-heaths and acidic pastures. Very common in the New Forest, but less so on other acid soils. Very local on chalk grassland,

* A square in Petersfield alongside which stands John Goodyer's house, still a private residence, which bears a commemorative plaque.

especially on leached slopes, but occurs on pure chalk soils at Buster Hill 7120, VC11, *FR* 1991, as it does in Dorset.

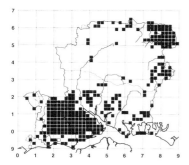

Map 533 Danthonia decumbens

Cortaderia selloana (SCHULT. & SCHULT. fil.) ASCH. & GRAEBN. Pampas-grass.   **H**   Very rare

Established amongst native vegetation in a few sites on the coast, probably originating from thrown-out garden refuse as it is a commonly-grown ornamental.

VC11: Southbourne 1391, sandy sea-cliff, *RPB* 1989; N of West Cliff, Dibden Bay 4108, in rank grassland on polder, single male tussock, apparently self-sown, Hb.RPB 1991. Also 3292, 6404.

Molinia caerulea (L.) MOENCH Purple Moor-grass.   **N**   Locally abundant   Map 534

On wet heaths, bogs, damp, acid pastures and open, heathy woods. Invasive on bogs if they dry out or are ungrazed, driving out other plants. Very common and often dominant in the New Forest (where, however, it is effectively controlled by pony-grazing in winter), and on the acid soils of the Lower Greensand and NE Tertiaries.

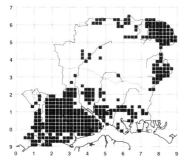

Map 534 Molinia caerulea

Rare in the chalk valleys of the upper Test and Anton, and at Tichborne.

Ssp. *caerulea* and, probably, ssp. *arundinacea* (Schrank) K. Richt. occur in Hants but have not been studied individually.

Phragmites australis (CAV.) TRIN. ex STEUDEL (*P. communis* Trin.) Common Reed.   **N**   Locally abundant

In watercourses, ponds, fresh and brackish tidal marshes, wet woods, valley bogs, on landslips and at bases of sea-cliffs. Common in such places, except in the E. The more extensive reedbeds are on estuary-mud in the lower Test Valley, the Avon Water at Keyhaven, the lower Lymington River, at Titchfield Haven and Farlington Marshes. At Keyhaven and on the Lower Test, where there is strong historical evidence of a large increase in extent of the reeds in modern times, a small percentage is still cut commercially for thatching. In the New Forest, a remarkable dwarf form no more than 20cm high occurs in seasonal flood-hollows and even on elevated heaths.

Eragrostis curvula (SCHRAD.) NEES African Love-grass.   **C**   Very rare

First record, E. J. Clement & A. L. Grenfell 1989, near Mayflower Park, Southampton 4111, VC11, disused railway at entrance to docks, Hb.RPB, det. *TAC* 1991 (*Watsonia* **19**: 153).

A native of tropical and southern Africa. There are *c*.50 plants, possibly 10–20 years old, with tufts up to 20cm at the base (*loc.cit.*).

Cynodon dactylon (L.) PERS. Bermuda-grass.   **C**   Very rare

First record, J. F. Rayner 1924, shore, Eling, VC11, well established (*Proc.IoW N.H.S.* **1**: 272).

A mat-forming perennial from warmer climates, but occasionally its underground rhizomes enable it to survive many winters near the coast. We cannot equal Cornwall's record of 300 years, but *C. dactylon* has certainly been at Eling Tide mill 3612 for about 70 years, from *JFR* 1924 to *RPB* 1994. It was also recorded from Bournemouth in *c*.1929 (*Suppl.Fl.Hants*, p.120), and at Durley Chine, Bournemouth 0790, *KG* 1950, Hb.AB; and at Poole (Dorset) in 1945, seen by *FR*. Its continued presence in this area is confirmed by a record for East Cliff, Bournemouth 0990, *WFS* field meeting 1987, comm. *GHF*.

Spartina SCHREBER   Cord-grasses.

Some introduction is required to the occurrence of this interesting genus in Hampshire.

Until the early 19th century, there was only one species of *Spartina* native in Britain, *S. maritima* (chromosome number 2n=60), which was apparently common in consolidated tidal salt-marshes around small depressions or pans, through much of S England. At some date prior to 1816, the common native *Spartina* of the salt-marshes of the NE of the USA, *S. alterniflora* (2n=62), became introduced into Southampton Water, no doubt by ship movements from the USA. The first definite record was by W. Borrer in 1829 (see below for details) but *Fl.Hants* (p.480) reported that a labourer had told W. A. Bromfield of its existence since about 1816. In 1815, the sterile hybrid between the native *S. maritima* and *S. alterniflora* was detected by F. A. Edelstein for the first time on the banks of the River Itchen, and specimens are in Hb.BM.

Not until 1870, however, does it seem to have been noticed again. In that year, R. S. Hill observed it at Hythe, and it was described as a new taxon *S.* x *townsendii* by H. Groves and J. Groves (*Rep.B.E.C.* for 1880, p.37). It may have arisen by hybridization on more than one occasion; in any case it proved to be far more vigorous than either of its parents. *S.* x *townsendii* has the chromosome number of 2n=62, the two supernumeraries having come over to the hybrid.

For many years, the *Spartina* which spread vigorously (and was clearly fertile) through the salt-marshes of Hants (and along much of the coast of S England) was thought to be all *S.* x *townsendii*, and confusion arose when the chromosomes were first counted in these populations. 2n was found to be 120 or 124, and for a number of years *S.* x *townsendii* was believed to be the fertile tetraploid hybrid of *S. maritima* and *S. alterniflora*, derived by hybridization which involved also chromosome set doubling – a situation which made normal pollen-formation and sexual reproduction possible. Only much later, in 1957, did the eminent Kew botanist and world authority on grasses, C. E. Hubbard, realize that there were two morphologically distinct taxa present in Hants:
(i) the sterile hybrid, *S.* x *townsendii* H. & J. Groves, with 2n=62, and
(ii) the fertile hybrid, with 2n=120 or 124.

The latter plant Hubbard called *S. anglica* in his Penguin book *Grasses*, edn 2, in 1968, but it was not formally published (with Latin diagnosis) until 1978 (*J.Linn.Soc.Bot.* 76: 364–365). It is the fertile (ii), not the sterile (i), hybrid that has spread so widely and universally in the salt-marshes of southern England, both naturally and as a result of introductions made by man to help bind the loose mud in estuaries. It can grow lower down the mud-flats than the latter and is thus much more useful for land reclamation. It has been found by C. J. Marchant forming two different back-crosses with *S.* x *townsendii* near Hythe, Hants.

During this century, *S. anglica* has spread greatly, and both *S.* x *townsendii* and *S. maritima* have declined through competition from this vigorous species that has taken over their habitats. Today, *S.* x *townsendii* is a rarity, and *S. maritima* has also become so rare that it is in danger of extinction in England.

Also in the latter part of this century, *S. anglica* has in many places suffered much 'die-back' for reasons not perfectly understood (see *Biol.Fl.*, no.716; *J.Ecol.* 57: 285) but possibly due to infection or to changes in the hydrology.

S. alterniflora also became introduced into SW France early last century and formed hybrids with *S. maritima* just as in England.

Spartina maritima (CURTIS) FERNALD   Small Cord-grass. N Rare   Map 535

First record, T. Yalden *c.*1770, 'in the mud near the hospital at Portsmouth', VC11 (*Ray Syn.MS*, p.393).

In tidal salt-marsh and mud-flats on the upper shore, and behind sea-walls. The original *Spartina* of our mud-flats, *S. maritima* has probably now been reduced to six or seven small patches in the creeks of Hayling Island where sites continue to be lost due to erosion or reclamation.

VC11: Keyhaven Marshes 3191, Hb.RPB 1976, det. *AM*, conf. *AJG* 1992; Normandy Marsh 3393, Hb.RPB 1973, det. *AM*, conf. *AJG* 1992, site lost through excavation of scrape *c.*1990; by A2030, Great Salterns Lake, Portsmouth 6701, up to 50 plants, *DPJS* 1991, Hb.RPB, det. *PJOT*; Northney 7204, *GHF* 1979, conf. *AJG & JDT* 1988; Tourner Bury 7399, *FR* 1980; Mengham Salterns, Hayling Island 7399, Hb.RPB 1976, det. *AM*,

conf. *AJG* 1992; Gutner Peninsula 7301, *FR* 1986. Now extinct in Southampton Water, and last collected from the Beaulieu Estuary at Gilbury Hard 4100, Hb.HGS 1907.

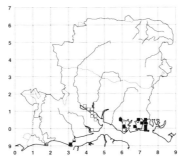

Map 535 Spartina maritima

S. x townsendii H. GROVES & J. GROVES (*S. maritima* x *S. alterniflora*) Townsend's Cord-grass. **C,N** Very rare   Map 536

First record, F. A. Edelstein 1815, banks of the Itchen (Southampton) VC11, Hb.BM, det. *MDH* 1973.

In tidal salt-marsh and mud-flats, chiefly on the landward fringe of swards of *S. anglica*.

VC11: Keyhaven Marshes 3191, 1986, on dissected, eroding marsh above shingle *AJG* 1986; Hythe 431075 southwards, in good numbers, and also sparsely near the Esso refinery, Fawley *c.*4505, where it had been planted along with some *S. anglica*, both *AJG* 1990; Needs Ore Point 4297, *FR & RPB* 1991, and Sinah Warren 6999 (though with some *S. maritima* characters – ?hybrid), *FR & RPB* 1989, both det. *AJG*.

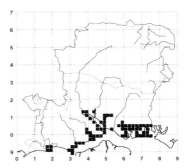

Map 536 Spartina anglica (incl. S. x townsendii)

S. anglica C. E. HUBB.   Common Cord-grass. **C,N** Locally very common   Map 536

First record, R. P. Murray 1887, Redbridge, Southampton, VC11, Hb.BM, det. *MDH* 1973.

This is now the almost universal *Spartina* species of the British coasts. It colonizes the shores of Hants for most of their extent, wherever there is mud. It can grow lower down the mud-flats than could *S.* x *townsendii*, and is therefore even more useful for land reclamation.

S. alterniflora LOISEL. (*S. glabra* Mühl ex Bigelow)   Smooth Cord-grass. **C** Very rare

First British record, W. Borrer 1829, R. Itchen, (Southampton), VC11, Hb.K (*Comp.Bot.Mag.* 2: 254).

On estuarine, tidal mud-flats. It was said to be used for thatching at Hythe. A native of N America, it has been planted in Essex and in the Cromarty Firth.

Described in *Fl.Hants* (p.480) as abundant at intervals along both sides of Southampton Water and down to Hill Head. Now, of the only two remaining sites, one (possibly accidentally introduced in ship's ballast) is at Bury Marsh, Eling 3711 where in 1963 it dominated roughly 20ha (50 acres) of mud-flats. Since the 1970s it has been greatly reduced by dredging for the Southampton Container Dock. The front of the site carries a healthy sward, intermixed with *S. anglica*, in deeply-dissected marsh (*AJG* 1990, in litt.). A large clump at 'Sylvan Villa', Hythe Spartina Marsh 4307, on landward side of the marsh, known there for at least 30 years by *JCEH*, was rediscovered by *JCEH, CC & HWi* in 1993.

A small outlier on Eling shore 3712, composed of a single large clump, planted by S Mangham in 1923 (in litt.), and seen *FWO* 1924, is the basis of the record for *S. glabra* (*Suppl.Wild Fl. Guide*, p.48). Recorded here by *WFB* 1963, Hb.RPB, det. *CEH*, as *S. alterniflora*, and by *AJG* 1986 (see D. H. Kent, *Watsonia* 8: 163–164). Another small clump, discovered in Dibden Bay in 1961, was destroyed by reclamation work in 1963 (*Biol.Fl.*, no.716).

S. pectinata BOSC ex LINK   Prairie Cord-grass. **C** Very rare

First record, C. R. Hall & A. R. G. Mundell 1986, near R. Blackwater, Farnborough 8757, VC12, on edge of former gravel-working used as a slurry-pond, Hb.BM, det. *JMM*.

A grass of the American prairies, not a salt-marsh plant. One huge clump, its origin a mystery and probably spreading vegetatively, still present 1991.

Setaria pumila (Poir.) Roem. & Schult. (*S. lutescens* (Weig.) F. T. Hubb.; *S. glauca* auct., non (L.) P. Beauv.) Yellow Bristle-grass. **C** Very rare

VC12: Thoroughly established in a garden in Fleet 8152, *DBr* 1981–91.

S. viridis (L.) P. Beauv. Green Bristle-grass. **C** Very rare

VC11: Dock Gate 8, Southampton 4111, producing a dominant sward in rough grassland, *NMR & MDT* 1992, Hb.RPB, conf. *TAC*. **VC12**: Though normally a birdseed or wool–alien casual, it has become ineradicable in a cottage garden in Benhams Lane, Greatham 7831, where there was once an aviary, *AB* 1963–90.

<**Digitaria ischaemum** (Schreb. ex Schweigg.) Mühl. Smooth Finger-grass. **N?,C** Extinct

Once a very rare infester of sandy fields.

VC11: Fields N of Christchurch on the Wimborne road in abundance, commencing from the allotment gardens, Hb.WAB 1850. Portchester, *JV c.*1929, Hb.OXF (*Suppl.Fl.Hants*, p.116, as *Panicum lineare* Krocker), was probably an alien casual, as also Southbourne, *KG* 1951.>

D. sanguinalis (L.) Scop. Hairy Finger-grass. **C** Very rare

VC12: Established for at least five years on ballast at Fleet railway station 8155, *ARGM & DBr* 1988–92.

SPARGANIACEAE

Sparganium erectum L. (*S. ramosum* Huds.) Branched Bur-reed. **N** Locally very common Map 537

First record, Gilbert White 1766, Selborne, VC12 (*White's Jnls* 1: 205).

In ponds, ditches, rivers and canals, which it often chokes. For this reason, much has recently been removed by Water Authorities from rivers and canals by dredging. It is thus now difficult to find enough ripe fruit to map the four subspecies accurately, but a start has been made.

ssp. **erectum** Rare or under-recorded

First records, R. P. Bowman 1975,

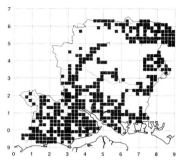

Map 537 Sparganium erectum

R. Itchen at Mans Bridge 4415, VC11, and Lady Anne Brewis 1975, R. Hart at Hartfordbridge 7757, VC12.

VC11: Timsbury 3423, old canal, *RPB* 1975; Nursling 3516, *RPB* 1975, det. *FR*. Also 0800, 1496, 4618, 6622, 6820. **VC12**: R. Blackwater, Frogmore 8460, *AB* 1978, det. *FR*. Also 6450, 6856, 7658, 7856, 8256.

ssp. **microcarpum** (Neuman) Domin Local

First record, J. Comber 1914, by the Danes Stream, Milford on Sea, VC11, det. *ESM* (*Rep.B.E.C.* for 1914, p.165).

Dispersed over E Hants, the Moors River 0900, and the Basingstoke Canal (once choked with all four subspecies).

VC11: Titchfield Haven 5302, *RPB* 1975, det. *FR*. Also 5406, 5408, 5416, 5812, 6008, 6020, 6208, 6408. **VC12**: Basingstoke Canal, Winchfield 7652, *AB* 1975, det. *CDKC*. Also 7234, 7238, 7436, 7440, 7442, 7450, 7452, 7828, 7830, 7842, 7850, 7852, 8042, 8044, 8260, 8650, 8652, 8656.

ssp. **neglectum** (Beeby) Schinz & Thell. Locally common

First record, R. P. Murray 1886, 'Hants South' (*J.Bot.* 24: 143).

This is much the commonest subspecies in Hants, and probably accounts for nine-tenths of the population.

VC11: R. Itchen, St.Cross 4828, *AB* 1975, det. *CDKC*. **VC12**: R. Slea at Grooms Farm 8138, *AB* 1975.

ssp. **oocarpum** (Čelak.) Domin Very local

First record, Lady Anne Brewis 1973, Fleet Pond 8254, VC12, det. *CDKC*. Frequent in the NE corner of Hants, and also in the Moors River. It has a degree of infertility, suggesting that it

is a hybrid of ssp. *neglectum* with either ssp. *erectum* or ssp. *microcarpum*.

VC11: Moors River, St Leonard's Farm 0901, with the other subspecies, in profusion, *AB* 1976; Wallington River 6408, *AB c.*1976; R. Meon, Exton 6120, *AB c.*1976. **VC12**: Steep 7425, flooded sand-pit, *AB* 1983; Nutkin Farm, Kingsclere 5259, *AB* 1976. Also 6860, 7050, 7240, 7250, 7252, 7440, 7442, 7450, 7626, 7850, 7856, 8056, 8260, 8438, 8440, 8634, 8650, 8652, 8654, 8656, 8852.

S. emersum Rehmann Unbranched Bur-reed. **N** Locally frequent Map 538

First record, H. E. Lowe 1832, Bishops Sutton 6131, VC12, Hb.WARMS.

In slow-flowing rivers and streams, lakes and ponds; locally common in the S, especially the New Forest, and in the NE; otherwise rare.

VC11: Tanner's Brook, Old Shirley 3914, *RPB* 1962, rare after concreting of banks; Dockens Water, Rakes Brakes Bottom 2212, *SNHS* 1987; Wallington River near Bere Farm 5909, *RPB* 1988. **VC12**: R. Loddon at Sherfield 6858, *IMcD* 1971; R. Blackwater 8853–8559, abundant, *CRH* 1989; Oakhanger Stream, Oakhanger Farm 7736–7836, *NRCB* 1985–87.

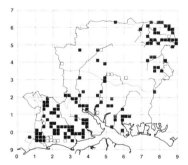

Map 538 Sparganium emersum

S. angustifolium Michx Floating Bur-reed. **N** Very rare

First record, R. P. Bowman & F. E. W. Venning 1952, near Hatchet Pond 3601, VC11, Hb.RPB, Hb.BM, conf. *CDKC* 1958, *c.*20 leafy plants, *RPB* 1992, a few producing flowers and fruit, 1994.

In an acid, peaty gravel-pit pond, where it is thought to have been deposited by migrant wildfowl. This is the only known site in S England.

S. natans L. (*S. minimum* Wallr.) Least Bur-reed. **N** Very rare

In peaty pools and ditches where the water is somewhat calcareous; now confined to a few sites in the SW of the New Forest, in water apparently derived from the Headon Beds. Persistent, even when overshadowed by bushes.

VC11: Pilley Bailey 3399, *AEB* 1979; Crockford Bridge 3498, *AEB* 1979; 3598 *AEB* 1982; Marlborough Deep 2298, *AEB* 1983; Upper Pennington Common 3095, small pool in dense scrub, Hb.RPB 1968, not refound since. There are two very old records: moor near Petersfield *c.*7522 (*Fl.Hants*, p.360), and Milton Glen *c.*2294 (*Suppl.Fl.Hants*, p.110).

TYPHACEAE

Typha latifolia L. Great Reedmace (erroneously Bulrush). **N** Frequent and locally common

First record, Gilbert White 1768, Fyfield, VC12 (*White's Jnls* 1: 246).

River- and stream-banks, canals, ditches, ponds and swamps, especially on muddy substrates; often in pure stands of varying extent, causing silting-up in some watercourses and ponds. The seeds can blow for miles or travel through underground drains to start fresh colonies.

T. x glauca GODR. (*T. latifolia* x *T. angustifolia*) **N** Very rare

In a very few sites where the parents occur together.

VC11: Nursling 3516, flooded gravel-pit, *RPB* 1956, now infilled; R. Avon, S of Coward's Marsh 1594, Hb.RPB 1976, conf. *FR*; Lymington River, Boldre 3297, *RPB* 1983. Also 1094, 3494, 4400, 4806. **VC12**: Crondall 8048, old clay-pit, *AB* 1970, conf. *ECW*, now infilled.

T. angustifolia L. Lesser Reedmace **N,H** Local Map 539

In lakes and ponds, marshy riversides and wet marl-pits; locally frequent in the S, often near the coast, and sometimes in brackish water; also along the NE border; rare elsewhere. Sometimes planted, especially in the NE. Becoming over-collected for commercial dried-flower arrangements.

VC11: Beaulieu River, Black Bridge 3803, *RPB* 1956, 1985; Mopley Pond, Fawley 4501, *RPB* 1952, 1990; Heath Pond, Petersfield 7522, *RMB* 1969. **VC12**: Fleet Pond 8154, 8155, 8254, 8255, *ARF* 1975, *CRH* 1983–91;

Hawley 8858, *CRH* 1983; Wellington Country Park 7362, *CRH* 1985; Longmoor airstrip 8030, *SP* 1988.

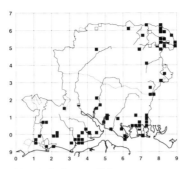

Map 539 Typha angustifolia

PONTEDERIACEAE

[**Pontederia cordata** L. Pickerelweed. **H** Very rare

A native of N America; established in a small gravel-pit pond near Hatchet Pond 3601, VC11, but probably planted, *AJCB* 1980, det. *EJC* (*BSBI News* 26: 18), patch of plants extending, *RPB* 1989–94. Also planted in a few other New Forest ponds but not surviving.]

LILIACEAE

Narthecium ossifragum (L.) HUDS. Bog Asphodel. **N** Locally common Map 540

First record, T. Johnson 1634, 'It growes in a bogge on a heath in the mid-way betweene Sarisbury and Southampton', VC11 (*Merc.Bot.*, [pt.i], pp.21,22).

In valley bogs and flushed, wet heaths where there is some peat-formation, frequently dominant where it occurs. Common in the New Forest, more local in the Avon Valley and on

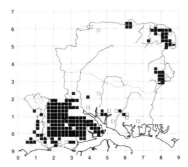

Map 540 Narthecium ossifragum

the NE Tertiary heathlands, and in Woolmer Forest; rare in a few relic populations on the SE Tertiaries.

VC8: Lopshill Common 2913, *ET* 1954–56 (*Fl.Wilts*, p.560), *RPB* 1989. **VC11**: S of Netley Hill 4811, *RPB* 1985; Wickham Common 5910, *RPB* 1989. **VC12**: Hook Common 7253, *HJMB* 1986; Silchester Common 6262, *PB* 1980.

<**Simethis planifolia** (L.) GREN. Kerry Lily. **C** Extinct

Recorded by Miss Ricardo 1915 at Mudeford, VC11 (J. E. Kelsall's annotated *Fl.Hants* referred to in *Suppl.Fl.Hants*, p.107). Possibly brought in with imported *Pinus pinaster*, as was the population formerly naturalized in Branksome Chine, Bournemouth, VC9.>

Colchicum autumnale L. Meadow Saffron. **N,H** Very rare

In grassy rides of woods and copses, usually on clay or loam soils of drift deposits overlying the chalk. Formerly also in old meadows, but eradicated as it was poisonous to cattle. The remaining native sites all appear to be near the border with Wilts, where it is relatively frequent. Many have disappeared since the time of Townsend, probably due to changes in woodland management.

VC8: Boulsbury Wood 0614, *WI* 1976; near Damerham, *c.*120 plants, *JWA* 1954 (*Proc.Hants Fld Club* 19: 306), perhaps the same as the previous site. **VC11**: Probably introduced near Home Covert, Nursling 3716, *RPB* 1953, now gone. **VC12**: Appleshaw 3048, large wood opposite church, *RPB* 1952; Appleshaw, near Lambourne's Hill 2949, 2950, Cunneys Down Copse 2949, and Hillfield Copse 2950, all *ILR* 1991; Bilgrove Copse, Enham Alamein 3649, *RPB* 1967; Hampshire Gate 3354, rough grass-ride of valley-floor wood, *GDF* 1981; wood near Vernham Dean, tetrad 3244 or 3246, *PMH* 1934. Probably introduced at Longstock Park 3638, *SS* 1960.

There is no connection between this plant and *Crocus nudiflorus* Sm. from which the comestible saffron is produced. In fact, Gerard observed that 'those which have eaten of the common medow Saffron must drinke the milke of a cow, or els death presently ensueth...[the roots] being eaten kill by choaking...as Mushromes do' (*Ger.em.Johns.*, p. 164).

Gagea lutea (L.) KER GAWL.   Yellow Star-of-Bethlehem.   **N**   Very rare

First record, H. Purefoy Fitzgerald 1884, Inham's Copse, Moundsmere, VC12, Hb.BM (*Fl.Hants*, p.434).

In woods on moist, basic, loamy soil. **VC11**: Beaulieu, Miss Moore 1908 (*Suppl.Fl.Hants*, p.108), not refound; Moot Lane, Hale to Downton 1719, both sides of Wilts/Hants border, *BG* 1935, refound in Hants, Rye Hill Copse, Hale 1819, *JO* 1987. **VC12**: Still in Inham's Copse 6143, *PS* 1989; this is a 'bluebell wood' and the non-flowering plants of *G. lutea* are surprisingly hard to distinguish from young plants of *Hyacinthoides non-scripta*.

Tulipa sylvestris L.   Wild Tulip. **H**   Very rare

Old orchards, remains of old gardens and adjoining woods and chalk-pits. **VC11**: Known for 200 years at Portchester, where a plant had been taken into a garden from marshy grassland outside but was reported to have disappeared some time prior to 1979. Red House, Brickhill, Rockbourne 1215, old orchard around stream, *AW* in litt. to *PMH* 1937. **VC12**: Island in moat behind Sherfield Court 6758, *EAB* 1965; 'Quarry Bottom', Froyle 7642, two flowers in old chalk-pit, *CL* 1957–58, incorporated into A31 *c.*1960. Established in the park of The Wakes, Selborne 7432, possibly from Gilbert White's time, as he used to plant out his old tulip bulbs in the park. Prof. T. Bell, who bought The Wakes in 1844 (the only intervening occupier since White being the latter's niece), exhibited *T. sylvestris* at the Linnean Society on 2 June 1870 (*Proc.Linn.Soc.* **1869–70**: 116), saying that at The Wakes park there was 'a patch about three feet diameter...undoubtedly wild', and that it occurred also at Froyle, and near Theddon Grange, Alton. The owners of The Wakes, up to and including the present owners – The Wakes Museum, have periodically divided the bulbs after they have ceased to flower and brought them back into flowering condition. Flourishing and conserved, *AB* 1989.

Fritillaria meleagris L.   Fritillary. **N?,H**   Very rare

Old alluvial meadows.
VC12: The plant's last site in Hants is in a field adjoining the famous colony on the Duke of Wellington's estate at Stratfield Saye, Berks, where it is now carefully conserved. Sadly, from what-

ever cause, the fritillaries on the Hants site have dwindled until, in 1982, *PB* could find only four plants. However in 1986, the Duke began scattering *Fritillaria* seed there which has raised hopes of a recovery; the most recent records are of eight plants, *CRH* 1990, still present *PB* 1993. It was clearly plentiful on both the Berks and Hants sides of the river in 1850 when Bromfield wrote 'In all the woods around Stratfield Saye, but in more abundance in the Park. Here the Fritillary grows in tens of thousands in the wet pasture and meadowland, scattered over a vast acreage of the Park, but most abundantly towards the north end [i.e. Stanford End 7062 or 7063], and in the wet meadows beyond it, on the other side of the road...' (*Phytologist* 3: 964–965).

There are several old records elsewhere, e.g. Mottisfont, VC11, in meadowland, *RMz* 1898, Hb.BM; near Tadley, VC12, till recent years, *PB*. It is also known to have been introduced in several localities, among them Chilworth churchyard 4018, VC11, *RPB* 1988, 1995.

Lilium martagon L.   Martagon Lily.   **H**   Very rare

First record, C. Robinson, *c.*1794, Durley Wood, VC11, in some abundance; searched for by *WAB* 1849, without success (*Phytologist* 3: 968).

An introduction in woods.
VC11: Ashley 3830, tree-belt S of church, *SS* 1966, *RPB* 1984; Stanmore Wood, a mile E of Kilmeston, *GAT* 1911 and 1917 (*Proc.IoW N.H.S.* **1**: 269), probably the same site as Broom Wood, Kilmeston 6026, *JD* 1975, comm. *JRW*. **VC12**: Laverstoke Park 4849, by path near roadway, *ARo* 1958; Heath End, East Woodhay 4162, wooded hedgebank, *WMK* 1974; Lilley's Copse, Preston Candover 5942, formerly in abundance, *NEGC* *c.*1940 (*Fl.Bas.MS*, p.17), *AWW &* *EAB* 1962, one plant *MB* 1967, when coniferized.

Convallaria majalis L.   Lily-of-the-valley.   **N,H**   Very local   Map 541

Native on dry grass-heaths in open bracken, or with isolated holly and birch, on the acid gravels and clays of the New Forest plateaux; also in moist oak-woods on the Tertiary sands and clays; rarely, under oak or beech on humus-rich chalk soil. Local in the N of the New Forest and in the Pamber Forest area, otherwise rare. We have

tried to exclude garden escapes from the map.
VC8: Martin Wood 0616, *WI* 1976. **VC11**: Ocknell Plain 2311, *SS* 1951; Spearywell Wood 3128, *RMV* 1989; Lord's Wood 3916, 3917, *RPB* 1953; Hanging Wood 3829, *RPB* 1962; Crab Wood 4329, *WMB* 1979. **VC12**: Redlands Copse, Ashford Hill 5662, *VF* 1982; Silchester Common 6262, *PB* 1980; Micheldever Great Wood *c.*5238, *AWW* 1963; Newtown *c.*4662, *CL* 1964.

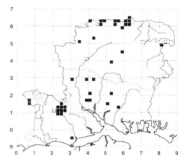

Map 541 Convallaria majalis

Polygonatum multiflorum (L.) ALL.   Solomon's-seal.   **N,H** Locally abundant   Map 542

First record, J. Gerard 1597, 'in Odiham parke in Hampshire', VC12 (*Ger.Herb.*, p.758).

In woods, copses and hedgebanks, mainly on the chalk and Malmstone, where it is more abundant than in any other English county; more local on clay, and rarely on calcareous sand. It has also been known in alder carr. Virtually absent only from the SW and from Ports Down southwards.

VC11: Near Brockenhurst, *NDS* 1931 (probably introduced); Parker's Moor, Ashfield 3719, in dry alder-carr (Bracklesham Beds), and The Hangers, Hambledon 6515, *RPB* 1985; Rakefield Hanger 7121, *DBa & FR* 1991. **VC12**: Truncheants Farm *c.*7236 (Malmstone), *AB* 1965; lane near Bramshott Flour Mill 8333 (Bargate Beds), *AWW* 1960; Huntingford *c.*8238 (Sandgate Beds), *RCS* 1988; Pamber Forest 6262 (London Clay), *PB* 1991; lane leading to Bradshott Mill 7732 (Gault), Lord Selborne (*Fl.Hants*, p.430), *AB* 1989.

'The root of Solomons seale stamped while it is fresh and greene, and applied, taketh away in one night, or two at the most, any bruise, blacke or blew spots gotten by fals or womens wilfulness, in stumbling upon their hasty husbands fists, or such like.

Galen saith, that neither herb nor root hereof is to be given inwardly: but note what experience hath found out, and of late dayes, especially among the vulgar sort of people in Hampshire...That if any...chance to have any bones broken...their refuge is to stampe the roots hereof, and give it unto the patient in ale to drinke: which sodoreth and glues together the bones in very short space...Moreover, the said people do give it in like manner unto their cattell...which they do also stampe and apply outwardly in manner of a pultesse.' (*Ger.em.Johns.*, p.906).

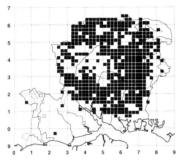

Map 542 Polygonatum multiflorum

P. x hybridum BRÜGGER (*P. multi-florum* x *P. odoratum*)   Garden Solomon's-seal.   **H**

First record, E. A. Pratt 1983, S of Creech Farm, Southwick 6309, 6310, VC11, in several places on W side of road.

VC11: Milton Road, Waterlooville 6810, in rough grassland, *RBa* 1992. **VC12**: Bramshott Common 8532, naturalized, probably from plantings at former Canadian wartime camp, *AB* 1992.

P. odoratum (MILL.) DRUCE   Angular Solomon's-seal.   **N**   Very rare

VC11: The site at Hart Hill, where it was first found in 1892 (*Fl.Hants*, p.430), is probably identical with the site on the S verge of the A31 W of Ocknell Arch 2410, *RPB* 1955, from which the few plants had to be rescued when road alterations were carried out. Subsequently, some were replanted in the A31 verge NE of Spreading Oak, and some 30 plants were noted in 1975. A few years later, when the road was converted to dual carriageway, these had to be removed again, but plants taken into cultivation at Southampton University pending transplantation to a suitable site did not survive. Small

transplants to Woodfidley Passage 3405, Great Hat 2199, and later to Marlborough Deep 2298, and in streamside carr NW of Wootton Bridge *c*.2300 have all apparently died out. A few barren stems in Goatspen Plain gravel-pits 2201, *RPB* 1971–73, were possibly transplants too, but did not survive. However, after diligent search, a very small group of leafy plants was discovered close to the original site, on N side of the A31 at Winding Stonard, on SE edge of the wood, *HFG* 1994. These appear to be native and *JHL* confirms that none were transplanted there during previous rescue operations. Other, unconfirmed, sites are Burley Street 2002, *ECh* 1952 (*Proc.Bmth N.S.S.* **41**: 34)), and Ridley Plain area 2006, *MPY c*.1964. **VC12**: Old records for Chawton Park, Alton 7036, J. Woods *c*.1802 (*Fl.Hants*, p.430); and woods at Rotherfield Park, East Tisted *c*.6932, Miss Scott 1850 (*Phytologist* **3**: 960), have never been confirmed.

Paris quadrifolia L.   Herb-Paris. **N**   Very locally frequent   Map 543

First record, J. Goodyer 1618, 'I sawe some with 5 leaves and some with 6 leaves at Chawton', VC12 (*Early Brit. Bots*, p.110).

In moist woods and copses on calcareous soil. Frequent, and locally abundant in the Wealden Edge scarp, on chalk, Gault and Malmstone, where it is present at the base of almost every hanger; more local on the NW chalk, but rare elsewhere, and totally absent from the S.

VC11: Timsbury Manor 3423, carr by old canal, *RPB* 1975 (also recorded in *Suppl.Fl.Hants*, p.108); Deacon Hill, Chilcomb 5027, *JRw* 1992; Clanfield Road, Hambledon 6615, Hb.AWW 1957. **VC12**: Damp wood beside R. Loddon 6653, *FR* 1980; Hobb's Copse, Sydmonton 4859, *NFC* 1971; Combe Wood 3558, *PB* 1984; Bradley Wood

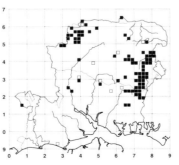

Map 543 Paris quadrifolia

6441, *ANHS* 1987; Fishpond and Lawns Copses, NE of Bentley 8045 (Gault), *FR & AB* 1985; The Warren, Hawkley 7328, *ECW* 1941, *AB* 1988; Bushy Leaze Wood, Alton 6838, *JPE* 1984; Cheesecombe Lane, Hawkley 7428, *FR* 1994.

Ornithogalum pyrenaicum L. Spiked Star-of-Bethlehem.   **H?**

There is only one record, and it is of doubtful status: G. W. Pierce 1930, near Marwell *c*.5020, VC11, in long grass in private grounds, a single plant (*Proc.Hants Fld Club* **10**: 299).

O. angustifolium BOREAU (*O. umbellatum* auct., non L.)   Star-of-Bethlehem.   **H**   Locally frequent and occasional

Probably a garden escape in every case, though it can spread and persist far from houses. On grassy borders of fields, lanes, greens, banks, and in open woods. In W Hants it has a strong affinity with churchyards; in E Hants it will often spread down the ditches of lanes, and flower periodically. VC8: 4 □; VC11: 26 □; VC12: 42 □.

VC8: Townsend Lane, Martin 0519, in plenty in grass border, *CDD* 1952, *RPB* 1984–94; Martin Down 0519, a few plants in rank grass, *PET* 1982, *RPB* 1989. Records for Martin, *HJG* 1937 (*Proc.Hants Fld Club* **15**: 71), and *JHL* 1965 may be the same sites. Knoll Farm, Damerham 1017, two plants under beeches on verge of wheat-field, *JO* 1987. **VC11**: East Tytherley churchyard 2929, *RPB* 1983. **VC12**: Tichborne 5630, *c*.50 plants on border of field, *RPB* 1967, 1975; Duck Street 3249, on grassy island at cross-roads, *GDF* 1981; Yateley, *BG* 1964, 8061, *ARGM* 1987; Norris Hill 8353, known 10 years, *TD* 1979. At intervals all along the ditch of Benhams Lane 7731, 7831, *AB* 1989; also along the roadside ditch through Kingsley 7737, 7837, where first shown to *AB* by *ECW* in 1963, until *c*.1990 when the ditch was piped.

O. nutans L.   Drooping Star-of-Bethlehem.   **H**   Very rare

First record, Miss N. Thorpe 1943, Mapledurwell, VC12, large patch in small copse (*Rep.B.E.C.* for 1943–44, p.759), later destroyed, *EAB*.

VC12: Thoroughly established and increasing along a hedgerow and its bank at Oakhanger 7734, *AB* 1959–94; between Coldharbour and Malthouse Farm, Kingsley 7938, in several places along the road, *AB* 1977.

Hyacinthoides non-scripta (L.) CHOUARD ex ROTHM. (*Endymion non-scriptus* (L.) Garcke) Bluebell. **N** Common

In Hants, the bluebell has three main types of habitat: ancient woodland and the relics thereof, where they are noticeably more prolific on the Malmstone hangers than on the drier chalk; grass-heaths under bracken, as in the New Forest, VC11, and at Linchborough Park, Woolmer Forest 8033, VC12, *AB* 1988; and sand-dunes and cliff-top headlands, as at Southbourne 1590, 1690, VC11, *RPB* 1975. Largely absent from riverain woods along the Rother and Wey, VC12.

H. non-scripta x H. hispanica H? Under-recorded

VC8: North Allenford, Damerham 0817, grassy roadside near stream, Hb.RPB 1994. **VC12**: Recorded only in tetrads 6436, 7238, *ANHS* 1982, but probably more frequent.

H. hispanica (MILL.) ROTHM. (*Endymion hispanicus* (Mill.) Chouard) Spanish Bluebell. **H** Frequent or perhaps over-recorded

This cultivated bluebell is now commonly naturalized on roadside verges, shady stream-banks, edges of commons, grassy waste-ground, and in scrub. None of those recorded appear to have been critically determined, so many records may be referable to the hybrid or intermediates, which are said to be commoner in gardens than this parent.

Muscari armeniacum LEICHTLIN ex BAKER Garden Grape-hyacinth. **H** Occasional

A garden escape, increasingly appearing in grassy places, usually as isolated groups which do not persist. All records of *Muscari* have been placed here.
VC11: 3416, 3414, 3032, 4206, 4618. **VC12**: 4050, 5042, 7860, 8052, 8252.

Allium roseum L. Rosy Garlic. **H** Very rare

First record, R. M. Walls *c*.1985, Stanpit Marsh 1692, VC11, bank on shore of harbour.
VC11: Keyhaven 3091, dry, grassy bank by road, *GY & MEY* 1988; Stanpit 1692, bank at corner of golf-course (formerly a tip), Hb.RPB 1990.

A. triquetrum L. Three-cornered Garlic. **H** Very rare

First record, Lady J. C. Davy 1940, Keyhaven 3091, VC11 (annotated *Fl.Hants* in *RPB*'s possession), still there on grassy, roadside bank, *RPB* 1995.
A garden escape, generally in shady, grassy places by the sea.
VC11: Middle Chine, Bournemouth 0790, *MPY* 1960, *RPB* 1978; Alum Chine and Durley Chine 0790, *FAW* 1992; near Lymington Harbour 3294, roadside, *KBu* 1961; Warsash 4905, *PE* 1961; East Wellow 3020, one plant under roadside elms, *SS* 1974; Winchester 4828, College meadows on river-bank, *KC* 1986; Crab Wood 4229, *SAL* 1985; Ferry Road, Sinah Common 6999, 7099, *RPB* 1990; Marlpit Oak 2899, slope in wooded pit, *VS* 1993.

A. paradoxum (M. BIEB.) G. DON Few-flowered Garlic. **H** Very rare

First record, Mrs F. Finucane 1962, Chiltley Lane, Liphook 8430, VC12, a garden escape which has since spread along the lane.
VC11: Hambledon 6414, three clumps naturalized away from gardens on roadside verge below wall, *PS* 1995. **VC12**: In a wood near Fleet Pond 8154, *CWa & ARGM* 1983, persisting and spreading, *CRH* 1991.

A. ursinum L. Ramsons. **N** Locally abundant Map 544

First record, Gilbert White 1766, Selborne, VC12 (*White's Jnls* 1: 193).
In moist woods and copses; wooded banks of streams, roads and hedges. On base-rich soil, often where there is seasonal flushing. Common on the SE and E chalk, often dominant on the Malmstone hangers, but more local in the NW; elsewhere more restricted to silted stream-banks and alder carr; rare in the SW.
Where this is abundant, few other plant species occur; it may secrete some antibiotic factor.
VC11: Avon Water, Wilverley Bog

to Mead End 2499–2698, *RPB* 1956, still at Mead End, *RPB* 1995. **VC12**: Sarson Wood 2942, *MFW* 1989.

A. oleraceum L. Field Garlic. **N** Very rare

In grassy field-borders, with a preference for the chalk.
VC11: The last known record was Dean Hill, *HLG* (*Suppl.Fl.Hants*, p.107). **VC12**: Near New Barn Farm, Laverstoke 4845, along grassy track, *RPB* 1967, not seen 1991; Clanville 3249, hedgebank at road junction, *GDF* 1969, not seen 1981. Norn Hill, Basingstoke 6453, roadside, *NEGC c*.1940 (*Fl.Bas.MS*, p.17), now built over; Micheldever Station 5043, *c*.10 plants on path between railway and cornfield, *MBJ* 1984, Hb.AB; Abbots Ann 3243, comes up most years in rough grass in garden, *JRM* 1994.

A. ampeloprasum L. var. **babingtonii** (BORRER) SYME (*A. babingtonii* Borrer) Babington's Leek. **H** Very rare

First record, R. A. Barrett 1991, Green Lane, Clanfield 7016, VC11, 14 plants on roadside, Hb.RPB, det. *EJC* (*BSBI News* 60: 35).

A. vineale L. Wild Onion, Crow Garlic. **N** Frequent and locally common Map 545

On grass verges, banks, pastures, borders of arable fields, railways, sand-dunes and sea-walls; common, especially on the chalk or by the sea. It is usually bulbiferous, only occasionally producing flowers with the bulbils. Gerard, quoting from Galen, states that 'crow Garlicke is stronger and of more force than the garden garlicke' (*Ger.em.Johns*, p.180). All forms of garlic have great medicinal properties.

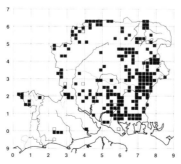

Map 544 *Allium ursinum*

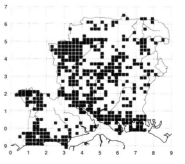

Map 545 *Allium vineale*

A. nigrum L.   Broad-leaved Onion.
H Very rare

First record, A. R. G. Mundell 1983, Farnborough Airfield 8653, VC12, eight spikes in long grass, det. *ALG* (*BSBI News* **39**: 9). Naturalized with 45 spikes, *CRH & ARGM* 1993, Hb.RPB.

The dried seed-heads are sometimes used as a floral decoration; as the site is used for temporary, tented trade-stands for the biennial Farnborough Airshow, held in September, these may well be the source.

Leucojum aestivum L.   Summer Snowflake, Loddon Lily.   **H,N**   Rare

First record, Miss Russell 1892, Southwick, VC11, in a damp wood, Hb.BM, *EHW* 1930. Wallington River, NW of Southwick 6109, probably the same locality, 13 clumps, *NAS* 1985, 18 clumps, *RPB* 1994.

In wet woodland on river- and stream-sides. Mostly a naturalized garden-escape but now considered native along the Loddon and Avon, although *RPB* doubts its native status in Hants. Records have not been segre-gated into ssp. *aestivum* and ssp. *pulchellum* (Salisb.) Briq., as they are doubtfully distinct.

VC11: R. Avon S of Wattons Ford 1301, dominant over *c*.55 x 60m in wet alder-willow carr on W bank, Hb.RPB 1995, probably where recorded un-localized in this tetrad, *KK c*.1965; Meon Navigation, Titchfield Haven 5303, wet willow-holt, *RPB* 1962, 1993;   R. Meon, Droxford 6018, in pasture, *RPB* 1984, 1994; Monks Brook, Eastleigh 4418, *RPB* 1985; Avon Valley, Ringwood *c*.1404, boggy copse, *JCBa & PWJF* 1968; Emsworth 7505, ditch S of new A27, just in Hants, *GHF* 1985. Also 1492, 3298, 3299, 3414, 4400, 4402, 4502, 7416. **VC12**: Reported from Sherfield and Basing, *NEGC c*.1940 (*Fl.Bas. MS*, p.16); R. Loddon, Basing 6653, two plants in damp wood, *ARGM* 1977, three plants elsewhere in same wood *PB, FR & ARGM* 1980.

Galanthus nivalis L.   Snowdrop.
H Locally frequent

First record, Miss C. R. May 1832, lanes near Fordingbridge, VC11 (*May Ptgs Cat.*, no.823).

Not native, but escapes out of gardens and churchyards down road-sides and lanes, and is frequently fully naturalized in copses, woods and thick-ets, especially along streams.

VC11: East Wellow 2921, 3020, frequent along streams, *RPB* 1957–93. **VC12**: Long Copse, Selborne 7434, *EV* 1871, Hb.BM, *AB* 1970.

Narcissus x medioluteus MILL.. (*N. x biflorus* Curtis; *N. tazetta* L. x *N. poeticus* L. agg.)   Primrose-peerless.
H Very rare

This relic of old-fashioned gardens barely survives.

VC12: Coldhayes, Liss 7526, in a copse, Lord Selborne 1877 (*Bell's Selb.* **2**: 371), the patch still had one or two flowers in 1932, but none in 1960, *AB*; Cliddesden *c*.6248, *EAB* 1966.

N. pseudonarcissus L. ssp. **pseudonarcissus**   Wild Daffodil.
N,H Locally frequent   Map 546

First record, Gilbert White 1766, Selborne, VC12 (*White's Jnls* **1**: 192).

In woods, copses, spinneys, old hedgebanks and shady meadows on fertile loams and clays. In the western Weald, nearly always on the Malm-stone hangers. Locally common, espe-cially on well-drained slopes of wooded valleys, and beside their streams. Quite abundant in certain districts, although numbers dwindling in neglected wood-land and where light has let in bram-bles. The map includes only native records, so far as is known, and not feral plants from gardens.

VC11: Near Sandleheath 1315, deciduous woodland near stream, *RMV* 1986; Sherfield English 2921, 2823, 3023, in many copses, *RPB* 1957; Walkford Brook 2294, *FR* 1964; Rookesbury Park, Wickham 5811, *AWW* 1963. **VC12**: Worldham Hill 7538, once abundant, but sadly decreased, *AB* 1970; The Chase, Woolton Hill 4462, *NFC* 1975; Park-field Copse, Elvetham 7855, plentiful, *GARW* 1943 (*Watts MSS*), *DPD* 1978;

Adhurst St Mary 7625, on Lower Greensand, abundant, *FR* 1982; wood NE of Tundry Pond, Dogmersfield 7752, *ARGM* 1974–91.

Asparagus officinalis L. ssp. **offici-nalis**   Garden Asparagus.   **D**   Rare

Well established on some shores and banks by the sea, and on waste land as a garden escape. VC11: 16 □; VC12: 7 □.

VC11: Mengham sea-wall, Hayling Island 7399, *RPB* 1977; Frater Lake, Gosport 5903, scrub on bank of creek, *RPB* 1987. **VC12**: Bordon–Kingsley disused railway 7836, *AB* 1981.

Ruscus aculeatus L.   Butcher's-broom.   **N,H**   Locally common
Map 547

First record, Gilbert White 1766, Selborne, VC12 (*White's Jnls* **1**: 192).

A sign of ancient woodland, it can be native in any dry wood, scrub or hedgerow, but is especially common in the New Forest. Sites near houses should be discounted, for it is easily bird-sown from gardens. Very rare on the N chalk, the Malmstone, and the Thames Basin.

VC11: Upper Noads Copse 2532, *VW* 1987. **VC12**: Longmead Copse, Hawkley 7428 (Malmstone), *FR* 1988; Abbotts Wood Inclosure, Alice Holt Forest 8139 (Gault), several patches, *JH* 1977; Heckfield Heath 7260, old boundary-bank, *CRH* 1988.

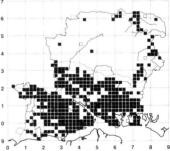

Map 547 Ruscus aculeatus

IRIDACEAE

Genus **Sisyrinchium**

All occurrences in the wild in England are of escapes of the many cultivated species. They arrive spontaneously in damp places, and are probably spread by birds.

S. bermudiana L.   Blue-eyed-grass.
H   Very rare

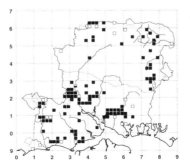

Map 546 Narcissus pseudonarcissus ssp. pseudonarcissus

First confirmed record, Mrs C. Darter 1992, Bramshott Common 8532, VC12, frequent over small area, Hb.AB, conf. AB.

All previous records of *S. bermudiana* are probably referable to *S. montanum*.

S. montanum GREENE (*S. bermudiana* auct., non L.)   American Blue-eyed-grass.   **H**   Very rare

First record, W. R. Ward 1871, near Christchurch, VC11, 'in a wood about half a mile from the coast...near a small running stream...in one spot, and pretty abundant there' (*Gdnrs'Chron.* 15 July 1871, p.901).

There are three specimens in Hb.BM, all collected by *WRW*, 1871, 1872, 'three miles E of Christchurch in wet spongy soil', all det. *JMM* 1990.

VC11: School Road, Wellow *c*.2919, *GWP* 1931 (*Proc.Hants Fld Club* **12**: 84); Brockenhurst, roadside, *HS* 1939, comm. *WAP* (*Rep. B.E.C.* for 1939–40, p.296, as *S. angustifolium* Mill.); Burley Road, Wilverley Plain 2501, grass verge, *RPB* 1956; Swaythling 4415, 'made ground' in cemetery, *WP* 1969; Little Park Farm, Swanwick 5208, several strong clumps in a derelict arable field, *PMH* 1934, Hb.BM, det. *JMM* 1990; West Walk, Wickham 5912, Hb.AWW 1958, det. *RPB* 1988, probably identical with West Walk, Forest of Bere, *VMC* 1946, Hb.BM, det. *JMM* 1990; Heath Pond, Petersfield *c*.7523, bare gravel and short turf on N shore, few clumps, *APHo* 1972, *PHa* 1976, comm. *AB*, det. *JMM* 1991 (from colour slides). **VC12**: On the 'rough' of the old Aldershot Command golf-course 8653, '200 yards from the club-house, which has no garden, abundant in a patch of 10–15 yards', *CCF* 1931, Hb.BM, det. *JMM* 1990; Norris Hill, near Fleet 8353, *ARGM* 1987–92; Farnborough Airfield 8453, *c*.10 plants, *ARGM* 1988. The last two are perhaps the only sites still extant.

S. californicum (KER GAWL.) DRYAND.   Yellow-eyed-grass.   **H** Very rare or extinct

VC11: Catisfield 5506, on waste ground, *MBU* 1956–59.

S. laxum OTTO ex SIMS (*S. iridifolium* Kunth ssp. *valdivianum* (Phil.) Ravenna)   Veined Yellow-eyed-grass.   **H**   Very rare

A patch of numerous plants amongst very wet, short grass on Farnborough

Airfield 8653, VC12, was shown to *ARGM* in 1984 by an airfield worker who had known it for many years, det. *ALG*. It thrived until the site was destroyed by development in 1989; seed was rescued and sown elsewhere on the airfield, but no plants found, *ARGM* 1992. Also known on Jersey, the origin of this S American plant is obscure as it is rarely grown in gardens, but it seeds profusely and is well naturalized in New Zealand.

Iris germanica L.   Bearded Iris.   **H** Very rare

VC12: A garden escape. Stoke 4050, established above old chalk-pit, *GDF* 1984.

I. sibirica L.   Siberian Iris.   **H** Very rare

VC12: A garden escape, near Fleet Pond 8255, *CRH* 1983–92, det. *KWP*.

I. pseudacorus L.   Yellow Iris.   **N** Locally common

First record, Gilbert White 1766, Selborne, VC12 (*White's Jnls* **1**: 204).

In marshes, wet meadows, pond-margins, streamsides, ditches and wet, open woods.

I. foetidissima L.   Stinking Iris. **N,H**   Local   Map 548

In woods, scrub, shady hedge- and road-banks on the chalk, on Headon clays, and along the coast, where it occurs on wooded shores of the W Solent and Hayling Island. Frequent also as an escape or throw-out from gardens, and much planted in churchyards. Known or suspected introductions have not been mapped.

VC11: Gilbury Hard 4100, *RPB* 1952; Peak Copse, Upham 5420, *RPB* 1975. **VC12**: Near Wolverton 5457, *BS & ARGM* 1977; still in hedge of

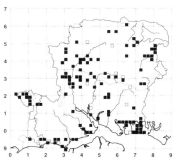

Map 548 Iris foetidissima

Norton Farm, Selborne 7334, where Gilbert White described it as a probable garden discard, *AB* 1989; Butter Wood 7051, *AJPB* 1986; Herriard Common 6543, *HCC* 1989.

Crocus vernus (L.) HILL (*C. purpureus* Weston)   Spring Crocus. **H**   Very rare

First record, Lord Selborne 1877, 'Holywater', near the brook, VC12 (*Bell's Selb.* **2**: 369), *PMH* 1933, Hb.BM. The meadow at Hollywater, Bordon 8033, has now been partly 'improved', and the remainder, with its 'wild' crocuses, incorporated in a private garden, *AB* 1985.

Present-day garden plants, more or less naturalized in churchyards, grass verges and on stream-banks, appear to be the larger-flowered strains and hybrids now cultivated, but most recorders have not distinguished them from *C. vernus*.

VC11: Southampton Cemetery 4113, spreading in grass, *CDD* 1951–58; Stanpit 1692, a few plants on landscaped tip, *RPB* 1980–85. Also 2002, 2202, 3000, 3224, 4014. **VC12**: In enclosure wall of turf around old ranger's cottage, Woolmer Pond 7832, *AB* 1980.

Gladiolus illyricus KOCH   Wild Gladiolus.   **N**   Very local   (Sched. 8) Map 549

First British record, W. H. Lucas 1856, New Forest, VC11 (*Ann.Nat.Hist.* **20**: 815).

On grass-heaths, beneath the canopy of bracken, frequently associated with *Anemone nemorosa*, *Conopodium majus*, *Carex montana* and *Hyacinthoides non-scripta* on brown ranker soils, the less acid sands and clays. In the British Isles, restricted now to the New Forest where it is widespread but local. Some populations are quite large, but in recent years a considerable decline in numbers has been evident at several sites, compared with the result of surveys between 1964–71. Factors influencing this decline include scrub and heather encroachment but, in at least some sites, past attempts to eradicate bracken to improve grazing and, more recently, indiscriminate heath-burning are directly responsible for losses. *G. illyricus*, one of the most beautiful and prized species in Hants, is specially protected, like several other of the county's wild plants, under the Wildlife and Countryside Act 1981, which makes it illegal to pick, uproot, destroy or sell such species. It is polli-nated chiefly by the butterfly *Oclodes venata* (Bremer & Grey) (the large skipper) (*Ecol.Wild Gladiolus*, p.35). Numbers of plants flowering from year to year vary greatly in each individual population.

There is one overlooked old record, believed to be native, near Ensbury, Bournemouth, VC9, 'where there was much growing on the site of a hedge-bank adjoining a newly broken-up piece of heathland, amongst bracken, under the same conditions as those of the New Forest plant', J. H. Austen before 1874 (*Fl.Dorset*, p.262). Formerly also in Isle of Wight.

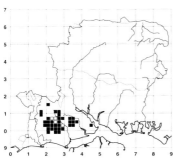

Map 549 Gladiolus illyricus

G. communis L. ssp. **byzantinus** (MILL.) A. P. HAM. (*G. byzantinus* Mill.)   Eastern Gladiolus.   **H** Very rare

First record, A. G. Leutscher 1964, near Lyndhurst, VC11, Hb.BM, det. *APH*.

An occasional escape from culti-vation, usually transient.

VC11: East Cliff, Bournemouth 0990, a few plants on cliff-top bank, *RPB* 1990. Also 2200.

Crocosmia x crocosmiiflora (LEMOINE ex BURB. & DEAN) N. E. BR. (*Tritonia* x *crocosmiiflora* (Lemoine ex Burb. & Dean) G. Nicholson; *C. pottsii* (Macnab ex Baker) N. E. Br. x *C. aurea* (Hook.) Planch.))   Mont-bretia.   **H** Locally frequent

First record, A. W. Westrup 1956, Stubbington 5503, VC11.

An artificial hybrid, long cultivated, now increasingly naturalized on waste ground, edges of woods, verges, streamsides, and below sea-cliffs, but avoiding the chalk. Obviously discarded from gardens in most cases, but can also be carried down streams during flooding. Capable of rapid

multiplication by bulb offsets, it can be difficult to eradicate.

VC11: Beckton Bunny 2592, damp, sandy stream-bank, *RPB* 1985.

DIOSCOREACEAE

Tamus communis L.   Black Bryony.   **N** Common

First record, J. Goodyer 1621, [Hants] (*Ger.em.Johns.*, p.871).

Very common in woods, scrub and hedges, except on very acid soils.

ORCHIDACEAE

Cephalanthera damasonium (MILL.) DRUCE   White Helleborine. **N** Locally frequent   Map 550

In chalk woodland, especially younger beech-woods where there is little other ground flora; extending also into chalk scrub. Frequent to locally common on the shallow rendzina soils of the chalk districts; absent elsewhere. Not on the Ports Down chalk.

VC11: Galley Down 5718, abundant in young beech plantation, *MB* 1975. **VC12**: Baroda Road, Tidworth Barracks 2147–2247, frequent in grass under avenue of planted beeches and limes, *RPB* 1985; N of The Dower House, near Upton Grey 6848, small beech-plantation by road, *MO* 1980, *CRH* 1990.

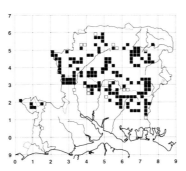

Map 550 Cephalanthera damasonium

C. x schulzei CAMUS, BERGON & A. CAMUS (*C. damasonium* x *C. longifolia*) **N** Very rare

VC11: Chappetts Copse, West Meon 6523, *MB* 1955, *RPB* 1985; Drayton, East Meon 6723, *RPB* 1973; Queen Elizabeth Forest 7319, *MW & JRLB* 1983.

C. longifolia (L.) FRITSCH   Narrow-leaved Helleborine.   **N** Rare   Map 551

In open beech-woods and scrub on chalk, preferring a combination of some light, shelter, and light ground-cover.   Locally frequent to locally abundant in the E, from near Bishop's Waltham to SE of Basingstoke; most frequent near West Meon, and on the hangers N of Petersfield. More plenti-ful in Hants than anywhere else in the British Isles, although more wide-spread near coast of W Scotland.

VC11: Galley Down 5718, *JRW & FR* 1978, *AJB* 1990; Chappetts Copse, West Meon 6523, *MB* 1955, *AJB* 1990, *RPB* 1994. **VC12**: Oakshott Hanger 7327, in chalk scrub, *FR* 1982–92; Herriard Park 6747, *NEGC* 1942 (*Fl.Bas.MS*, p.14), *FR & AB* 1976, *PB* 1988. One casual record in Woolmer Forest 7931, on Folkestone Sands (but near the railway), *PLeB* 1973, not seen again.

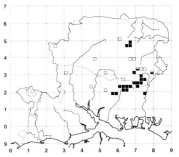

Map 551 Cephalanthera longifolia

C. rubra (L.) RICH. Red Helleborine. **N** Very rare (Sched. 8) Plate XIII

First record, Miss E. M. Williams 1926, Upper Test Catchment, VC12 (as District VI(1) in *Suppl.Fl.Hants*, p.99; *Proc.Hants Fld Club* 10: 78). Miss Williams was thoroughly reliable, but no further details can be found, such was the secrecy kept. In 1986, however, K. Turner and J. R. W. Hollins found one beautifully-flowering spike, in rather deep shade, in a beech–yew wood on a NW-facing slope in VC12 (*Watsonia* 17: 195). At least nine non-flowering shoots were present over some 50m of the bank. It is thought that sufficient light to stimulate the rhizomes had been let into this very dark wood by the felling of a few trees higher up the bank. It has also flowered in subsequent years, but not in 1992 or 1994. Heavy thinning of the trees at this site has recently been undertaken as, to judge from its behaviour elsewhere, this species clearly requires a certain level of light to promote the formation of inflorescences.

Epipactis palustris (L.) CRANTZ Marsh Helleborine. **N** Rare Map 552

First record, J. Goodyer 1633, '*Palma Christi, radice repente*','within a mile of...Peters-field, in a moist medow named Wood-mead, neere the path leading from Peters-field towards Beryton [Buriton]' *c*.7421, VC11 (*Ger.em.Johns.*, p.227).

In calcareous fens and wet meadows, especially in flushed areas where the vegetation is not very rank. Scattered through Hants; most frequent in fens along the spring-line N of the chalk, from Bransbury to Odiham, with a very few sites in the SW of the New Forest; also on the Sandgate Beds at Conford, and in several sites in alluvial meadows by chalk rivers. More frequent in Hants than in any other English county except Norfolk.

VC11: The Moors, Bishop's Waltham 5616, *AWW c*.1960, *FR* 1992. No longer at Flexford 4221, *JG* 1953, grazing having ceased. **VC12**: Stockbridge North Fen 3535, abundant, *IM & FR* 1985–90; Greywell 7251, including var. *ochroleuca* Barla, *FR* to 1992; Marndell [Marnel Dell] 6354, *RSH* 1835, Hb.BM, refound *AWW* 1960, but site destroyed 1962; Eelmoor Marsh, Farnborough 8352, *c*.15 spikes on ground flushed by calcareous water from Basingstoke Canal, *ARGM* 1977–92, *c*.80 spikes, *FR* 1994.

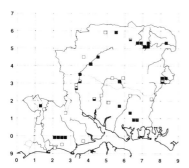

Map 552 Epipactis palustris

E. purpurata SM. Violet Helleborine. **N** Local Map 553

In woodland of beech, oak or hazel, usually in heavy shade with little other ground flora; especially on Clay-with-flints over chalk. Locally frequent in the NE from Petersfield to Odiham and Ewshot; rare elsewhere.

VC11: Spearywell 3127, *RPB* 1964–92; 3128, *GDF* 1968, *RPB* 1985–92; Pound Lane, Ampfield 4022, *PS* 1990, *RPB* 1994; Funtley 5507, wooded banks of old railway, *DPJS & JMC* 1988; The Hangers, Hambledon 6615, *PHC & APNH* 1978. **VC12**: Selborne Hanger 7333, *FT* 1873 (*Fl.Hants*, p.419), *SP* 1988; Old Litten Lane, Wheatham Hill 7327, *FR* 1982–94; King John's Hill 7537, *IM* 1986; Rowledge churchyard 8043, *RCS* 1986; Freemantle Park Wood, Kingsclere 5356, *FT* 1882 (*loc.cit.*), *WGH* 1984. **VC22**: N edge of Fifty Acre Piece 6365, S side of road, *PB* 1983.

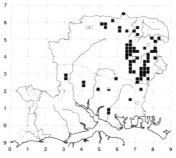

Map 553 Epipactis purpurata

E. x schulzei P. FOURN. (*E. purpurata* x *E. helleborine*) **N** Very rare

First British record, M. J. Godfery & P. M. Hall 1931, Selborne Common, VC12 (*Rep.B.E.C.* for 1931, p.724).

E. helleborine (L.) CRANTZ Broadleaved Helleborine. **N** Locally common Map 554

First record, Gilbert White 1766, Selborne, VC12 (*White's Jnls* 1: 214–215).

In shady woodland, especially on chalk but also on clays, loams and less-acidic sands, where most often along wooded roadsides and stream-banks. Generally frequent to common, but rather rare in the W New Forest, the SE, and the treeless chalk uplands.

VC11: Hengistbury Head 1790, scarce, *LW* 1980; Stansore Point 4699, on bare shingle amongst willows, *RPB* 1973–86. **VC12**: Worthy Down 4534, in beech-belts, *EAP* 1982; The Mount, Highclere 4360, *NFC* 1978; Yateley Common 8159, *CRH* 1986.

E. leptochila (GODFERY) GODFERY Narrow-lipped Helleborine. **N** Very rare

First record, A. Roseweir 1954, Southlynch Plantation, Hursley 4226, VC11, det. *DPY*, Hb.K (*Watsonia* 5: 127).

In beech-woods on chalk. The Hursley site was coniferized *c*.1963 and a few plants were last seen there in 1974, *RPB*.

VC11: Hedgemoor Copse, West Tytherley 2631, *ARo & DPY* 1956, Hb.K (*loc.cit.*). This beech-wood was partly felled in 1966, but the plant was refound in 1987 by *VW*, and shown to *RPB*, who counted 15 spikes (*Watsonia* 17: 195), and in 1989 *FR* found four more spikes nearby. However, in 1992 there were none, and only two in 1993.

E. phyllanthes G. E. SM. Green-flowered Helleborine. **N** Local Map 555

First record, F. Townsend 1860, Andover, VC12, Hb.SLBI (as *E. media* auct.) (*Watsonia* 2: 127).

In shady woods and tree-belts, especially of beech, and in willow holts, usually amongst ivy. On chalk, sand or clay, and on alluvium in river valleys. Occasional to locally frequent across central and N Hants; almost absent further S. All four varieties have been

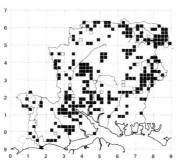

Map 554 Epipactis helleborine

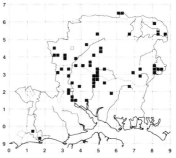

Map 555 Epipactis phyllanthes

recorded, the localities sometimes producing more than one. Intermediates do occur; perhaps the varieties are of little taxonomic value.

var. **phyllanthes**

VC11: A27 near Shootash, Wellow 3221, *MHo* 1951, Hb.K (*Watsonia* 2: 271), *RPB* 1994. **VC12**: Conford 8232, in various places in the alder-wood, *EABr & DMi c.*1970, det. *DPY* (*Watsonia* 5: 138), *ANHS* 1989, det. *FR*; near Norris Bridge, Basingstoke Canal 8353, *ARGM* 1977, det. *JLSL*, destroyed by work on towpath in 1985.

var. **vectensis** (T. STEPHENSON & T. A. STEPHENSON) D. P. YOUNG

VC11: R. Test, Nursling 3615, *RPB* 1950, Hb.K, det. *DPY* (*Proc. B.S.B.I* 1: 63), *RPB* 1992; Stanpit Marsh 1692, *RPB* 1963, det. *DPY*, *MNJ* 1989; Michelmersh 3424, old chalk-pit, *AJRa* 1978–90, det. *RPB*; Ramsdown, Hurn 1297, *LW* 1985, det. *MNJ & RPB*, *MNJ* 1991. **VC12**: Quarley Down Farm 2441, *BSBI* 1968, Hb.BM, det. *DPY*; Selborne Hanger 7333, *PMH & MJG* 1931 (as *E. leptochila*), Hb.BM, det. *DPY* 1951 (*Watsonia* 2: 272), *SP* 1978–93; S of Freefolk Wood 5043, *ARo & RPB* 1974.

var. **degenera** D. P. YOUNG

VC11: Chilbolton Avenue, Winchester 4629, *GWP & GGP* 1949, Hb.BM, det. *DPY* (*Watsonia* 2: 272); Wood Mill, Southampton 4315, on tidal mud-bank, *RPB* 1962, Hb.K, det. *DPY*, *EAP* 1985; Itchen Navigation, Otterbourne 4622, *JG* 1959, det. *DPY* (*Watsonia* 5: 138). **VC12**: Fulling mills, Easton 4932, under trees by stream, *MJ* 1951, Hb.BM, Hb.AWW 1962; B3420, Crawley Down 4436, *GGP & EWC* 1951 (*Watsonia* 2: 272); Hollywater Road, Bordon 8034, under trees in garden, *CWa* 1986, det.*FR*, all down same road, *CWa* 1991.

var. **pendula** D. P. YOUNG

VC12: Stonybrow Wood, East Tisted 6830, N roadside under beech, *ARo c.*1957, det. *DPY* (*Watsonia* 5: 138); copse E of Shipton Bellinger 2445, *GDF* 1977, det. *FR*. **VC22**: Side of Welshman's Road by Benyon's Inclosure 6164, 6264, 30 plants, *PB* 1980, det. *FR* (as 'probable').

Neottia nidus-avis (L.) RICH.
Bird's-nest Orchid.   **N**   Locally frequent   Map 556

First record, Gilbert White 1774, 'in the long Lythe...& also amongst some bushes on Dorton' 7434, VC12 (*White's Jnls* 2: 36–37).

A saprophyte, in deep humus in shady woodland, concentrated mainly in beech-woods on chalk, but also locally under oak, ash and hazel on other types of soil. It disappears when light is let into a wood, as at Noar Hill.

VC11: Galley Down *c.*5718, *c.*1000 plants in young beech-wood, *MB* 1975; Roydon Woods 3102, *IB* 1978; Pitts Deep 3795, *RPB* 1972–89. **VC12**: Abundant in beech-plantation N of The Dower House, near Upton Grey 6848, *MO & SO* 1980; Isle of Wight Hill 2437, *GDF* 1988; Shipton Plantation 2345, 2445, numerous, *MFW* 1989; Butter Wood 7151, *AJPB* 1988; The Warren, Hawkley 7328, 14–18 plants, *DBa* 1989; Woolmer Forest 8133, under oaks, *JH* 1973–74; Micheldever Spoil Heaps 5244, *HFG* 1991, conf. *AJB*.

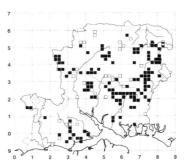
Map 556 Neottia nidus-avis

Listera ovata (L.) R.BR.   Common Twayblade.   **N**   Frequent and locally common

First record, Gilbert White 1766, Selborne, VC12 (*White's Jnls* 1: 197).

In woodland on calcareous to weakly-acid soil, on chalk, clay and sand, under various tree species; also in long grassland on chalk and clay soils. On Noar Hill, VC12, in 1920, there was only one small patch near the wood but, since the grazing ceased, it has increased enormously.

L. cordata (L.) R.BR.   Lesser Twayblade.   **N?**   Very rare or extinct

First record, R. Findlay 1927, near Brockenhurst, VC11, 'five plants in open heath amongst heather, some 200 yards from a plantation of pine', two plants in 1930, none thereafter, Hb.K (*Rep.B.E.C.* for 1932, p.226).

VC11: One other, more recent but unconfirmed record is suspected of being a deliberate introduction: W of Slufters Inclosure, old, boggy sand-pit, *c.*1980, comm. to *PS* 1987, original recorder uncertain. Searches in 1981 and 1987 revealed none, but three plants of *Pinguicula vulgaris* that appeared to have been planted were seen, casting doubt on the status of *L. cordata*. Two old records may relate to a single or to two different sites, apparently in VC9, Dorset: 'near Branksome Chine', in 1895, and 'near Bournemouth', in 1853 (*Fl.Bmth*, p.205; *Fl.Hants*, p.416). However, E. F. Linton (*Fl.Bmth App.1*, p.299) reported that the plant gathered by Revd H. Roberts in 1853 was 'on table land between Bournemouth and Boscombe Chine'. If correct, this would put the site in VC11 and indeed constitute the first record for Hants, as cited by Townsend.

Spiranthes spiralis (L.) CHEVALL.
Autumn Lady's-tresses.   **N**   Locally frequent   Map 557

First record, Gilbert White 1765, 'on the Lythe', Selborne, VC12 (*White's Jnls* 1: 162).

In old, short, dry grassland, especially on chalk, but also on the Headon Beds of the New Forest, on sands and on gravels. Locally frequent in S and E Hants, very rare in the N and NW. Occasionally it appears in lawns made from downland turf or even in seeded lawns. Requires very short grass to grow in, and has therefore declined badly on the downs since grazing ceased. It fluctuates, being best suited by a hot summer, with rain just before flowering time.

VC11: Eastley, Wootton 2498, abundant on grass-heath, *RPB* 1970; Hurst Castle 3189, on stable shingle, *SNHS* 1968, *MR* 1976; Poulner 1706,

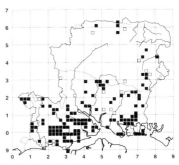
Map 557 Spiranthes spiralis

hundreds in pasture, *MNJ* 1982; Ports Down 6206, 6306, still in several places, *ARGM & CRH* 1990. **VC12**: Noar Hill 7431, though greatly reduced from the former multitude, *AB* 1988; Oxdrove, Burghclere 4661, *NFC* 1982.

<S. aestivalis (POIR.) RICH. Summer Lady's-tresses.   N   Extinct

Formerly amongst sphagnum in three or four valley bogs near Lyndhurst in the New Forest, VC11, to which it was confined in Great Britain: N of A35 near New Forest Gate, 1840 to *c*.1959; at Gritnam to *c*.1938, and a bog near Brick Kiln Inclosure up to *c*.1940, when the habitat was temporarily destroyed by drainage. For some years after 1900 it was abundant at one site, the bog being 'white' with flower spikes, and at another some 200 plants were seen. By about 1940, only a few plants remained in two sites and none have been seen at the original site since the last record in 1959. Persistent collecting may well have contributed to its extermination, as herbaria show that numerous botanists collected a whole sheet of plants with roots. Although two sites are still very wet, drainage may also have contributed to its final loss, as well as overshading by trees or scrub, and invasion of the habitat by coarse vegetation through natural succession.>

Hammarbya paludosa (L.) KUNTZE Bog Orchid.   N   Very local   Map 558   Plate XIV

First record, C. Merrett 1667, 'on the bogs betwixt Southton and Rownhams' *c*.3915, VC11 (*Merr.Pin.*, p.86).

In flushed parts of open, sphagnum bogs, often with *Pinguicula lusitanica, Rhynchospora alba* and *Sphagnum auriculatum*. Local in the S of New Forest; more isolated and rare in the N. Typi-

cally, a single population may consist of up to 50 spikes, often far fewer, sometimes in clusters of spikes together; a few of the larger populations may reach 200 plants in a good year. Now unknown elsewhere in Hants (except for one specimen, evidently planted, on Silchester Common, VC12, 1984). With the exception of parts of the W Highlands of Scotland, the New Forest currently has the largest concentration of populations of the species in western Europe.

VC11: East Boldre 3600, *c*.150 plants, *FR* 1978; Acres Down 2708, *RPB* 1984; W of Long Beech Inclosure 2412, *FR* 1982–94.

Herminium monorchis (L.) R.BR. Musk Orchid.   N   Rare   Map 559

In chalk grassland amongst short *Festuca* turf. 'Rare' in *Fl.Hants* (p.422), it is now even scarcer for only about eight sites remain, each, with the exception of Noar Hill, VC12, with very few plants.

VC11: Twyford Down 4827, *MNJ* 1981–92; Droxford 6017, *JB* 1984; Head Down 7319, *MW* 1979; Oxenbourne Down 7118, *MM* 1980–83 survey; Buriton 7320, lime-pit, *MM* 1980–83 survey. **VC12**: Hampshire Gate 3354, *GDF* 1981; Highclere, Bull 1932, Hb.RDG, probably same as, or near, Ladle Hill 4756, *WGH c*.1970; Noar Hill (High Common) 7431 and adjacent squares, generally many thousands (though now suffering from trampling), *AB, FR* to 1994.

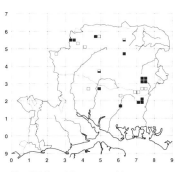

Map 559 Herminium monorchis

Platanthera chlorantha (CUSTER) RCHB.   Greater Butterfly-orchid.   N   Locally frequent   Map 560

In woodland and scrubby grassland on chalk and basic clay. It responds to coppicing, and disappears when a wood gets dark. Fairly common on the chalk of C, E and N Hants, but absent from

the New Forest, the SE and the extreme NE.

VC11: Batchley, Everton 2995, in dense coppice-woodland, *AEB* 1988, nine spikes *MEY* 1990; East Wellow 2921, numerous after coppicing, *RPB* 1961; Farley Mount 4229, *MNJ* 1964–81; Dundridge 5718, abundant in felled wood, *AB* 1985. **VC12**: Stoke 3952, abundant on rough bank, *GVD* 1975; Pamber Forest 6160, *PB* 1982; Happersnapper Hanger 7328, 16 plants in chalk grassland, *DBa* 1989; House Lands Plantation, Noar Hill 7331, *DPJS & JMC* 1989.

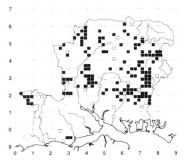

Map 560 Platanthera chlorantha

P. bifolia (L.) RICH.   Lesser Butterfly-orchid.   N   Locally frequent   Map 561

First record, Gilbert White 1761, 'in the hollow shady part of Newton-lane, just beyond the cross', Newton Valence, VC12 (*White's Jnls* 1: 105).

There are two distinct forms of this species:

i) the form with ovate leaves is frequent in bogs and wet heaths in the New Forest, but rare or gone from Tertiary heaths near Aldershot, and no longer in Woolmer Forest where it was known to the Haslemere NHS 1920–30.

VC11: Boundway Hill 2698, *FR* 1983, *RPB* 1992; Dibden Bottom 3806, *RPB* 1951–92. **VC12**: Pondtail Heath, Fleet 8253, large colony, *ARGM c*.1958–62, now gone; Foxlease, Hawley 8356, one plant in boggy heath, *JK & ARGM* 1978, not found since.

ii) The form with elliptical-lanceolate leaves is scattered across C and N Hants in woodland and scrub, and on open downs, on basic soils, with a preference for Clay-with-flints. It also occurs in bracken on dry grass-heaths in the New Forest, sometimes with *Gladiolus illyricus*.

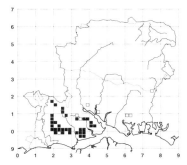

Map 558 Hammarbya paludosa

VC11: Holmsley Station 2300, under bracken, *RPB* 1971; Boundway Hill 2698, boggy heath, *FR* 1980–93; Fletchwood Meadows 3311, *AB* 1985; Punchbowl, Exton 5921, chalk-grassland slope, *RPB* 1968. **VC12**: Stoneybrow Wood 6730, *FR* 1983; Selborne Common 7332, *JLSL c.*1970, *SP* 1983; Weston Common 6844, 12 plants in clearing made for conifers, *ETu* 1986; Micheldever Spoil Heaps 5144, *HFG* 1991, conf. *AJB*.

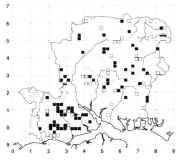

Map 561 Platanthera bifolia

Anacamptis pyramidalis (L.) RICH. Pyramidal Orchid.   **N**   Locally frequent   Map 562

First record, Gilbert White 1766, Selborne, VC12 (*White's Jnls* 1: 212).

In chalk grassland, old meadows on the chalk and, exceptionally, off it.

VC11: R. Avon, Breamore Mill 1617, ten spikes, *RPB* 1979; Hengistbury Head 1691, three spikes in grass verge, *MNJ* 1983; Pauncefoot Hill, Romsey 3420, in central reservation of A31, *RPB* 1991; Peartree Green, Itchen 4311, *PS* 1993; The Hampshire Centre, Bournemouth 1194, *FAW* 1986, 200+ *FAW* 1990, site scheduled for development so some plants transplanted to three other sites in Bournemouth; Sandy Point, Hayling Island 7498, *AP* 1990, det. *EAP*.

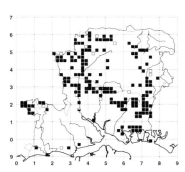

Map 562 Anacamptis pyramidalis

X Gymnanacamptis anacamptis (F. WILMS) ASCH. & GRAEBN. (*Anacamptis pyramidalis* x *Gymnadenia conopsea*)

VC11/12: Recorded in *Hybr.Fl.Brit. Is.*, p. 487.

[**Chamorchis alpina** (L.) RICH. False Orchid.

Reported in 1976 from the New Forest area, VC11 (*Orch.Brit.*, p.152). An alpine species of damp, calcareous soils in mountain pastures and, if correct, doubtless introduced.]

[**Pseudorchis albida** (L.)   A. LÖVE & D. LÖVE (*Leucorchis albida* (L.) E. Mey.)   Small-white Orchid.

There is one published record for near Chandler's Ford, Maj. Robertson 1919 (*Rep.B.E.C.* for 1919, p.681). Although listed for VC11 in *Druce Com.Fl.*, it is excluded from the *Atlas Brit.Fl.* (App. II, p.417), as suspected or known to have been recorded in error. No other details of this record are available and no specimen or photograph is known, so the occurrence of this predominantly northern orchid cannot be confirmed.]

Gymnadenia conopsea (L.) R. BR. ssp. **conopsea**   Fragrant Orchid.   **N** Locally frequent   Map 563

First record, Gilbert White 1769, Selborne, VC12 (*White's Jnls* 1: 289).

In old chalk-grassland and occasionally in fens. Far less common than formerly, because of ploughing and 'improvement' of chalk grassland, but still widespread across the centre of Hants, and along the N chalk scarp near Kingsclere.

VC11: Beacon Hill, Warnford 6022, *FR* to 1993. **VC12**: Noar Hill 7431, *AB, FR* to 1994.

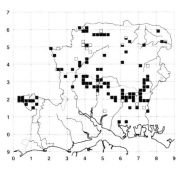

Map 563 Gymnadenia conopsea ssp. conopsea

ssp. **densiflora** (WAHLENB.) CAMUS, BERGON & A. CAMUS   **N**   Rare Map 564

In calcareous meadows and fens, often with *Epipactis palustris* and usually in small numbers; reduced by drainage at some sites.

VC8: South End, Damerham 1015, fen-meadow, 40+ spikes, with ssp. *conopsea*, *RPB* 1977–81, gradually destroyed by drainage, pond-excavation and a tree-nursery. **VC11**: Rockbourne 1216, *RPB* 1977; The Moors, Bishop's Waltham 5616, *AWW c.*1960, *FR* 1992. **VC12**: Bransbury Common 4141, abundant, *FR* 1984; Conford 8233, *ECW & PMH* 1938, *FR* 1985–91; Stockbridge North Fen 3535, *IM* 1985–89, *FR* 1992; Mapledurwell Fen 6752, *FR* to 1992; Greywell 7251, *FR* to 1988. It can also occur on chalk downs, e.g. Button's Brow, Goleigh 7330, *GL* 1966, 1968, det. *FR* (eventually choked by long grass).

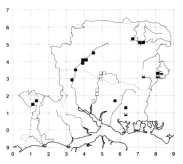

Map 564 Gymnadenia conopsea ssp. densiflora

ssp. **conopsea** x ssp. **densiflora**

VC12: Bransbury Common 4141, with the parents, *FR* 1984, conf. *AOC*.

ssp. **borealis** (DRUCE) F. ROSE   **N** Rare   Map 565   Plate XV

In basic-to-calcareous flushes and hollows on grass-heaths; on the Headon Beds and other base-rich clays in the New Forest only, but locally frequent there. This taxon is the prevailing form of *G. conopsea sensu lato* in the hill-pastures of N and W Britain, and is known otherwise in SE England only in Ashdown Forest and near Lewes, Sussex (on chalk grassland).

VC11: Stony Moors 2199, *RPB* 1971, *FR* 1983; Boundway Hill 2698, over 100 plants, *RPB, AEB & FR* 1985, 1993; Marlpit Oak 2899, in damp grass-heath with *Carex montana*, *AEB & FR* 1981–91; near Crow's Nest

Bottom 2415, 16 plants by roadside, *GLo & PEth c.*1985–91; W Dibden Bottom 3806, *RPB* 1956–92.

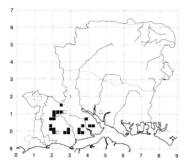

Map 565 *Gymnadenia conopsea* ssp. borealis

The essential differences between these three subspecies are in the shape of the lip and wings, in the scent and in the normal flowering period, viz:

ssp. **conopsea**
Lip about as wide as long
Wings linear, somewhat deflexed
Scent slightly rancid
Flowering mid-June to early July

ssp. **densiflora**
Lip nearly twice as broad as long, with 'shoulders'
Wings linear, held horizontally, with rounded to truncate tips
Sweet carnation scent
Flowering mid-July to early August

ssp. **borealis**
Lip narrow, with hardly any lobes
Wings oval-lanceolate, pointed, deflexed
Sweet carnation scent
Flowering third week of June to early July

X Gymnaglossum jacksonii
(QUIRK) ROLFE (*Gymnadenia conopsea* x *Coeloglossum viride*)

First British record, R. Quirk 1911, near Winchester, VC11/12 (*Rep.Winch. Coll.N.H.S.*, **1909–1911**: 5–6).
VC11: Above Winchester Downs (Shawford), *RMz* 1945, Hb.BM. **VC11/12**: Cheesefoot Head *c.*5327, in sunken track running E–W, *JCD* n.d., submitted to *GWP*, Hb.BM.

X Dactylodenia st-quintinii
(GODFERY) J. DUVIGN. (X *Dactylogymnadenia cookei* (J. Heslop-Harrison)

Soó; *Gymnadenia conopsea* x *Dactylorhiza fuchsii*)

VC11: Rudley Mill 6212, *PMH* 1931 (*Rep.Winch.Coll.N.H.S.* **1927–1931**: 9) (presumably *D. fuchsii* x *G. conopsea* ssp. *densiflora*); Beacon Hill, Warnford 6022, *ARGM* 1981. **VC11/12**: Cheesefoot Head *c.*5228, *RLMS* 1930 (*loc. cit.*), 11 plants, *RQ* 1932. **VC12**: Noar Hill 7431, *SP* 1982 (the latter three presumably x ssp. *conopsea*).

X D. legrandiana (CAMUS) PEITZ (X *Dactylogymnadenia legrandiana* (Camus) Soó; *Gymnadenia conopsea* x *Dactylorhiza maculata*)

VC11: Howen Bottom 2415, two spikes, *RPB* 1955; Dibden Bottom 3806, *RPB* 1951, *MNJ* 1985; Boundway Hill 2698, *RPB* 1992, conf. *FR* (all presumably *D. maculata* x *G. conopsea* ssp. *borealis*).

X D. wintoni (DRUCE) PEITZ (X *Dactylogymnadenia wintoni* (Druce) Soó; *Gymnadenia conopsea* x *Dactylorhiza praetermissa*)

VC11: Near Southwick, marshy meadow, three spikes, *PMH* 1931, det. *MJG* (*Rep.Winch.Coll.N.H.S.* **1927–1931**: 8–9) (presumably *D. praetermissa* x *G. conopsea* ssp. *densiflora*). **VC11/12**: Cheesefoot Head *c.*5228, *RQ* 1932. **VC12**: Greywell Pumping Station 7251, *DMT-E* 1981–82.

Coeloglossum viride (L.) HARTM. Frog Orchid. N Local Map 566

In chalk grassland, usually in short turf; frequent on E Cranborne Chase downs, and in N and C Hants. Varies very much from year to year.
 VC8: Martin Down 0319, 0419, *RPB* 1981. **VC11**: Broughton Down 2832, *FR* 1985; Beacon Hill, Warnford 6022, *FR* 1982; by A333 Ports Down 6406, edges of old chalk-ride, *CJo*

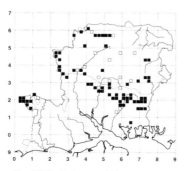

Map 566 *Coeloglossum viride*

comm. *JSt* 1987; Oxenbourne Down 7118, *MM* 1980–83 survey; Butser Hill 7120, common, *FR* to 1993. **VC12**: Noar Hill 7431, *AB*, abundant in 1978 and 1991; Ladle Hill 4656, *NFC* 1979, *FR* 1987; Harrow Way 5151, *WEW* 1957, *FR* 1990; East Woodhay 4060, chalk-pit, *WMK* 1979; Watership Down 4857, *NFC* 1974.

X Dactyloglossum mixtum (ASCH. & GRAEBN.) RAUSCHERT (*Coeloglossum viride* x *Dactylorhiza fuchsii*)

VC11: Near Winchester, *MSp* n.d., Hb.BM; Longwood Warren 5227, *EAP* 1981. **VC12**: Noar Hill 7431, *JM* 1968, *JC* 1978, *AB* 1980.

Dactylorhiza fuchsii (DRUCE) SOÓ Common Spotted-orchid. N Frequent and locally common

In woodland, chalk grassland, roadside verges, old meadows (both wet and dry), fens, and less acid parts of heaths and marshes. It frequently colonizes abandoned gravel-pits, often in profusion. Probably our commonest orchid, it hybridizes readily with the other *Dactylorhiza* species and is very variable. At one extreme an anthocyanin-rich form occurs with a uniform, deep-red labellum, and the leaves entirely covered in purple anthocyanin. Found at Beacon Hill, Warnford, VC11, by *FR* 1979, this has been newly named var. *rhodochila* Turner-Ettl. At the other extreme, pure white-flowered, faintly-scented spikes with unspotted leaves occur as individuals in some populations – not to be confused with var. *okellyi*.

[**D. fuchsii** var. **okellyi** (DRUCE) BATEMAN & DENHOLM

Recorded by G. C. Druce (*Rep.B.E.C.* for 1928, p. 761, as *Orchis okellyi* Druce) as having been collected by himself and *PMH* on chalk downs at Cheesefoot Head, VC11, but this taxon is now known to be restricted to W Ireland, W Scotland and the Isle of Man.]

D. maculata (L.) SOÓ ssp. **ericetorum** (E. F. LINTON) P. F. HUNT & SUMMERH. Heath Spotted-orchid. N Locally common Map 567

On heathland, especially wet heaths, bogs and acid grassland. Frequent locally, and common in the New Forest.

VC11: Sagles Spring, Rockbourne 1216, in fen, *MNJ* 1983; Baddesley Common 3921, *RMV* 1986; Lower Beckford Farm 6310, *EAP* 1983.
VC12: Bransbury Common 4141, 4142, (peat on chalk), *MB* 1960, *RPB* 1988; Newtown church 4763, damp meadow, *NFC* 1974; Wolverton 5458, meadow, *PB* 1984; Mabbotts Farm, Hawkley 7529, *HCC* 1985; Passfield Common 8133, *FR* 1955–88; Eelmoor Marsh 8353, 8453, *ARGM* 1975–94; Silchester Common 6262, *PB* 1980.

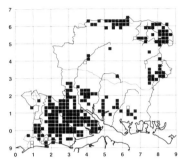

Map 567 *Dactylorhiza maculata* ssp. ericetorum

D. incarnata (L.) Soó   Early Marsh-orchid.

ssp. **incarnata   N   Very local   Map 568**

In calcareous fens and wet, alluvial meadows. Now rather rare and decreasing through agricultural changes.
    VC11: Winkton Common 1595, *MNJ* 1983; Acres Down 2708, *FR* 1993 (with ssp. *pulchella* in flush); South Charford 1619, *RPB* 1990; Lye Heath, Southwick 6408, *RPB* 1985; Lower Test 3614, *RPB* 1980, *JWCP* 1990–92. **VC12**: Stockbridge North Fen 3535, *FR* 1989; Ashford Hill

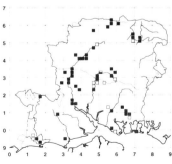

Map 568 *Dactylorhiza incarnata* ssp. incarnata

meadows 5662, *PB* 1982; Warnborough Greens 7352, *FR & PB* 1987; Goodworth Clatford 3642, *AO* 1979.

ssp. **pulchella** (DRUCE) Soó   **N**   Local   Map 569

In valley bogs and acid marshes. Frequent in the New Forest but rare elsewhere, and more or less confined to the Aldershot area. White-flowered plants often occur with the purple ones.
    VC9: Kinson Common 0696, *CEP* 1986. **VC11**: Foulford Bottom 1805, *MNJ* 1981, 1994; Holmhill Bog 2602, *RPB* 1980; Moorgreen, West End 4714, *RPB* 1955. **VC12**: Ancells Farm, Fleet 8255, *ARGM* 1983, two sites, one destroyed by new road 1986, the other surviving in a boggy ditch but decreased, *CRH* 1991; Eelmoor Marsh 8352, *ARGM* 1977–94; Farnborough Airfield 8453, *ARGM* 1979, site since destroyed; Farnborough 8552, army golf-course, few, *ARGM c.*1980, *CRH* 1987.

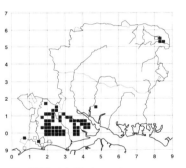

Map 569 *Dactylorhiza incarnata* ssp. pulchella

D. praetermissa (DRUCE) Soó   Southern Marsh-orchid.   **N   Locally common   Map 570**

    In fens, less-acid parts of bogs, wet meadows and marshy gravel-pits. Still fairly common and locally plentiful, especially along the main river-valleys, though decreasing through drainage.
    Very occasionally it occurs on chalkdown slopes and in old chalk-quarries, e.g.: **VC8**: Martin Down 0518, *RMV* 1984. **VC11**: Cheesefoot Head 5327, *PMH* 1930, Hb.BM; down between Exton and Beacon Hill 6021, *PMH* 1930, Hb.BM; Broughton Down 2932, *RPB* 1965; Farley Mount 4229, *RMV* 1986; Old Winchester Hill 6420, *JB* 1981. **VC12**: Noar Hill 7431, *AAB* 1982, det. *JLSL*; downland near Tidworth 2546, *MFW* 1989; Shoulder

of Mutton Hill 7326, *DBa* 1988; Greywell Pumping Station 7251, *DMT-E* 1989–90, a white-flowered variant.
    D. praetermissa hybridizes with *D. fuchsii* and *D. maculata*, and less often with *D. incarnata*.

var. **junialis** (VERM.) SENGHAS (*Orchis pardalina* Pugsley)

This plant, with ring-spots on the leaves and double, crimson loops on the lip, occurs in several places in Hants, in fens, meadows, and even on chalk grassland. It is unlikely to be the hybrid *D. praetermissa* x *fuchsii* as it is often found without *D. fuchsii* and lacks the hybrid vigour of the cross.
    VC12: Tichborne Common 5630, *FR* 1978; Stockbridge North Fen 3535, *FR* 1986; Greywell Moors 7250, *FR & AOC* 1983; Beacon Hill, Old Burghclere 4557, on chalk, *FR & PB* 1983; Warren Hill 2446, *FR* 1981.

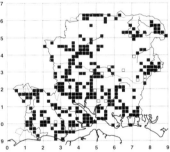

Map 570 *Dactylorhiza praetermissa*

D. purpurella (T. STEPHENSON & T. A. STEPHENSON) Soó   Northern Marsh-orchid.   **N?**   Very rare or extinct

First record, A. Roseweir 1955, Moorgreen, Southampton 4714, VC11, det. *VSS*.
    This northern species is suspected of having been introduced in Hants, where it has occurred in two slightly-acid marsh areas near Moorgreen 4714, 4814. The habitat was partly destroyed during construction of the M27, and the plants that remain are mostly hybrids. The pure species last seen, one spike only, *MNJ* 1986.

D. traunsteineri (SAUT. ex RCHB.) Soó   Narrow-leaved Marsh-orchid.   **N   Very rare**

First record, H. W. Pugsley 1937, Greywell Marsh, VC12, Hb.BM.

(Only its apparent hybrid with *D. praetermissa* remains).

VC11: West Common, Exbury 4400, *RPB* 1984, *FR* 1991, det. *FR* (*Watsonia* **19**: 152). This population has recently been described as a var. nov. under the name var. *bowmanii* M. N. Jenk. (*Watsonia* **20**: 263–273). **VC12**: Mapledurwell Fen 6752, *FR* 1971 (*Watsonia* **10**: 433), a small population, still reasonably pure, in a calcareous fen, six plants *FR* 1986, *c*.30 good plants, *FR* 1992; The Old House, Wonston 4739, water-meadow, Hb.AB 1981, det. *FR*.

The continued presence in several sites of its probable hybrids suggests that it once occurred more widely.

Dactylorhiza hybrids

It is probable that hybrids in the genus *Dactylorhiza* are relatively uncommon, except for the *praetermissa-fuchsii* cross, but, as the species have a great range of 'intermediate' types, it is impossible to distinguish them with certainty (F. R.). Thus, although there are records of putative hybrids of the following, it is not proposed to treat them in any detail:

D. fuchsii x *D. traunsteineri*
D. fuchsii x *D. maculata*
D. fuchsii x *D. incarnata*
D. fuchsii x *D. incarnata* x *D. praetermissa*
D. fuchsii x *D. praetermissa*
D. fuchsii x *D. purpurella*
D. maculata x *D. praetermissa*
D. maculata x *D. purpurella*
D. incarnata x *D. maculata*
D. incarnata ssp. *incarnata* x *D. praetermissa*
D. incarnata ssp. *pulchella* x *D. praetermissa*
D. incarnata x *D. purpurella*
D. incarnata x *D. praetermissa* x *D. traunsteineri*
D. praetermissa x *D. purpurella*
D. praetermissa x *D. traunsteineri*

[**Orchis laxiflora** LAM. Loose-flowered Orchid.

Marshes at Kettlebrook, VC12?, an undoubted specimen, but probably planted, *FBr* 1926 (*Suppl.Fl.Hants*, p.101).]

O. mascula (L.) L. Early-purple Orchid. N Locally common Map 571

In old woodland and scrub on moderately-basic to calcareous soil; less often in old meadows and chalk grassland. On Noar Hill it has increased with the lack of grazing, and favours the parts where moss has grown up under the grass. Still fairly common in much of Hants but, due to heavy grazing, rare in the few suitable, unenclosed, New Forest woodlands such as thickets in old marl-pits.

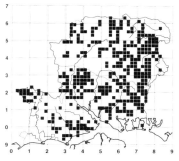

Map 571 Orchis mascula

O. morio L. Green-winged Orchid. N Locally frequent and occasional Map 572

In old pastures, on dry chalk, on damper, clay meadows, on sand-dunes and in gravel-pits. Like *O. ustulata*, it has suffered a tragic decline; from being very common, it is now rather sparsely scattered in those habitats that have escaped 'improvement', and can also be found in a few churchyards and lawns.

VC11: Fletchwood Meadows 3311, *AB* 1985; Hinton Admiral 2195, plentiful in churchyard, *KK* 1976; St Leonards Hospital 1002, huge colony, *MNJ* 1982; Sinah Common golf-links 6999, in plenty, *AB* 1975, *c*.500 spikes on sand-dunes, *RPB* 1985. **VC12**: Headley 5162, very fine in old gravel pits, *FR* 1985; Farnborough Airfield

8453, *ARGM* 1974–91, counted annually with up to 4,000 (*RAE Survey*); Boyneswood Road, Four Marks 6735, in garden lawn, *AAB* 1980, since increased; Hall's Farm, Bramshill 7462, hundreds in unimproved meadow, *PB* 1983, 600–700 plants, *CRH* 1988; Ewshot 8149, 20 plants in meadow, *CRH* 1983; Woolton Hill 4261, in churchyard and two gardens, *NFC* 1976.

O. ustulata L. Burnt Orchid. N Very rare Map 573 Plate XVI

First record, T. Garnier 1799, Flower Down, Winchester 4632, VC12 (*Hants Repos.* **1**: 121).

In old, short, chalk-grassland. The distribution map of this plant is depressing, with its accumulation of hollow symbols all marking former colonies now ploughed up, overgrown or planted over. Those that remain are generally sparse. They consist (as in Sussex) of two forms (which in Germany are given subspecific status as ssp. *ustulata* and ssp. *aestivalis* Kümpel & Mrkvicka) (*Watsonia* **19**: 121–126):

i) the 'normal' form, with a broad lip (*c*.1mm across the 'waist') and a hood which pales at maturity, flowering in late May and early June. This is still on Martin Down 0419, VC8, in plenty in some years (e.g. over 1,300, *PET* 1988); very scarce on Tidworth Golf Course, Dunch Hill 2148, *AO* 1979, and Danebury Hill 3732, *FR* 1983–88, both VC12.

ii) The late form, with a narrower lip (*c*.0.5mm wide across the 'waist') and a hood which remains purple at maturity, flowering from mid-July to mid-August. This occurs in a few places along the chalk scarp in VC12, from Old Burghclere to

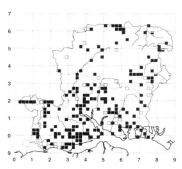

Map 572 Orchis morio

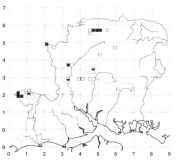

Map 573 Orchis ustulata

Cannon Heath Down: Ladle Hill 4756, *WMK* 1974 (*Watsonia* **11**: 402), on the ancient earthworks, *FR & ARGM* 1978, 66 counted *CRH & ARGM* 1991; Ashley Warren 4856, *PB* 1980; Watership Down 4956, *SRD* 1979, *BMe* 1982; Cannon Heath Down 5156, one plant, *SRD* 1979. It was also at Bossington 3328, VC11, in a meadow on chalk alluvium, until this was planted with poplars, *RPB* 1953–62.

Aceras anthropophorum (L.) W. T. AITON   Man Orchid.   N   Very rare   Map 574

In chalk grassland, especially on banks. Due to disturbance and being shaded out by scrub, it seems to have disappeared from three of the known sites and at the other sites there has been a decline in numbers of spikes.

VC8: Martin Down, *c.*20 plants, *PET* 1983, two only, *RPB* 1992, about six spikes, *FR* 1994. **VC11**: Beacon Hill, Warnford 6022, a few plants, *RPB* 1971, *FR* 1987; White Way, Exton 6021, 70 spikes, *RPB* 1973, since declined to only a few, with none in some years but, following scrub clearance by *HWT* the previous winter, five spikes appeared on the E bank, *GCMR* 1994; Old Winchester Hill, *CWMB* 1950 (*Watsonia* **2**: 207), *RJC* 1989; not recently reported at Oxenbourne 7019, *AWW c.*1960, or at Rake Bottom, Ramsden Down 7020, *MB* 1969; Telegraph Hill 5228, last seen *c.*1969; Stephen's Castle Down 5521, road verges, *ARo* 1955, last seen *RPB* 1975; Chalton Down *c.*7315, S end near stand of *Juniperus*, *AGT* 1925 (*J.Ecol.* **13**: 188), comm. *MM* 1989, not refound *EAP* 1990. **VC12**: SW of East Tisted 6931, chalk cutting of disused railway, five spikes, *DPJS* 1988, not refound, *FR* 1991.

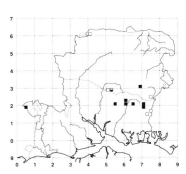
Map 574 Aceras anthropophorum

Himantoglossum hircinum (L.) SPRENG.   Lizard Orchid.   N   Very rare   (Sched. 8)

First record, A. Shrubbs 1884, hills beyond Cove Common, Aldershot, VC12, Hb.CGE.

In chalk grassland, roadside verges, and chalk-pits. Very rare indeed, and rarely established for long. From the following chronological list of occurrences at each site, it can be seen that there was a long chain of records through the 1920s and '30s petering out in the 1950s. There were then no further records till 1985–86, and then a gap of six years before the most recent record.   **1925**: Roadside near Stockbridge, VC12, schoolgirls E. Hatcher & S. Lobb, conf. Mrs Wilde (*Suppl.Fl. Hants*, p.100), doubtless the same site as *EFC* 1944 (*Proc.Hants Fld Club* **16**: 194), 'one plant at Leckford, first observed in 1925 by two schoolgirls'; Shalden Dock, Alton 6941, VC12, in a shallow chalk-pit (now filled in), *GWW*, which evidently survived for some years because in 1950 *EHW* found two here, and *KAC* (in her catalogue of Alton plants at the Curtis Museum) recorded that a plant came up every year till the pit was overgrown. The last occasion was 1955. A specimen is in Hb.HCMS. **1926**: Winchester, foot of St Catherine's Hill, VC11, found by a pupil of the County Girls' School (*Suppl.Fl.Hants*, p.100). **1928**: Ropley railway cutting, VC12, schoolgirl Peggy Bampton, conf. Mrs Chapman, (*loc.cit.*), Hb.HCMS. **1930**: Hill Farm, Morestead, VC11, *SD* comm. *GWP*, Hb.BM, doubtless the same as Owslebury, where it occurred three times in four years in a hayfield, *GWP & GGP* (*Wild Orchids Hants*); roadside on chalk between Whitchurch and Litchfield, near Whitchurch, VC12, one plant, anon, Hb.OXF. **1931**: One plant in the parish of Exton, VC11, *FE* (*Proc.Hants Fld Club* **12**: 83); 'Branshley, near Romsey [VC11], schoolchild', ex *HTB* (*Rep.B.E.C.* for 1931, p.670). **1935**: Odiham, VC12, photographs deposited by *LKAG* in Hb.BM and Hb.RDG, with no further comment. **1942**: Ropley 6331, one plant on grassy roadside-bank, schoolgirl Ann Rossiter, Hb.HCMS, road since widened. **1943**: One plant in Cheesefoot Head area, *c.*5327, VC11/12, *CJM* (*Proc.Hants Fld Club* **16**: 61). **1985–86**: Old Burghclere Lime Quarry 4757, VC12, *PB*. **1993**: On dry grassland within the Test Valley, VC12, *JHT*.

Most occurrences in England have been of single plants which often do not reappear; however, on fixed dunes in E Sussex and E Kent it is much more constant. For a detailed discussion by R. Good of reasons for the increase of *H. hircinum* in the earlier part of the century and its possible relationship to a milder climate-phase, see *New Phytol.* **35**: 142–170.

Ophrys insectifera L.   Fly Orchid.   N   Local   Map 575

In open woods, chalk-pits, scrub and grassland; on chalk. Widespread but concentrated mainly in the Meon Valley and the hangers, although it has decreased. It likes the half-shade at the edges of woods and therefore often becomes overgrown.

VC8: Martin Down *c.*0418, *JHL* 1965. **VC11**: Farlington, Ports Down 6806, *MB* 1979, 45 plants *EAP* 1981; Crab Wood 4329, many plants, *SP* 1983. **VC12**: Micheldever Spoil Heaps 5143, 5144, *RPB* 1950, 3000–4000 plants 1969, *HFG* 1991; Upper Oakshott 7327, *FR* 1986; Old Burghclere Lime Quarry 4757, many plants, *PB* to 1990, peloric form, with lip of same size and form as petals, *JBW* 1982, *DMT-E* 1984; Noar Hill 7431, form without brown pigmentation, *JOc* 1990.

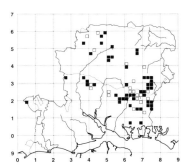
Map 575 Ophrys insectifera

O. sphegodes MILL.   Early Spider-orchid.   N   Very rare or extinct   (Sched. 8)

First record, D. Cockerton 1883, Bullington, VC12, abundant (*Fl.Hants*, p.414).

In short, calcareous grassland.

Never refound at Bullington, nor at the following sites in recent years: **VC11**: Owslebury Cricket Down, *HW*, a schoolgirl, 1930, comm. *GWP*, Hb.BM (*Proc.Hants.Fld Club* **10**: 299);

The White Way, Exton *c*.6021, *PMH* 1937, Hb.BM; Stansore Point, Lepe, in coastal turf, *VM* 1959, *SRD* 1970–78, not seen since.

O. apifera HUDS.   Bee Orchid.   **N**
Locally frequent   Map 576

First record, Gilbert White 1770, Selborne, VC12 (*White's Jnls* **1**: 327).

Grassland, banks and scrub on chalk. Frequent to locally common on the E downs, scarcer in the W, fluctuating from year to year; appears sporadically elsewhere, in verges, gravel-pits, waste ground, old railways, or on sparsely-vegetated, reclaimed land, generally indicating the presence of lime.

VC11: Holmsley 2300, *JHL c.*1975, *RPB* 1977–94; Southampton Common 4114, *AJRa* 1984; Paulsgrove, Ports Down 6306, *ETR* 1981; Gravel Hill, Queen Elizabeth Country Park 7218, *MW* 1993. **VC12**: Old Burghclere 4657, disused railway, *PB* 1982, 1988; Stoner reservoir 7325, *DBa* 1989; Noar Hill 7431, rather scarce, *AB* to 1988, more plentiful, *FR* 1994; Hazeley Heath 7657, landscaped tip, *CRH* 1987—88; East Woodhay 3861, *RPB* 1973; Treloar Hospital lawn, Alton 7038, *SP* 1983; Farnborough Airfield, at numerous widely-scattered sites but usually for only a few years in one spot, *ARGM* 1977–90, (*RAE Survey*); Danebury Down 3237, *MO* 1976.

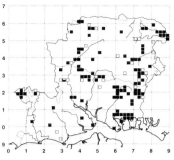

Map 576 Ophrys apifera

CHAPTER XI

THE LICHEN FLORA

K. A. SANDELL AND FRANCIS ROSE

The lichen flora of Hampshire comprises an overall total of 590 species, made up of 564 taxa recorded in the period 1967–95, and a further 26 reliable older records of species not seen since the turn of the century or earlier, mostly backed by herbarium specimens. Although this is a rich lichen flora for a lowland county, this richness is largely due to the presence within the county of the ancient woodlands and the extensive *Calluna* heaths of the New Forest. The Forest alone has 335 epiphytic lichen taxa within its boundaries, and a further 21 species on the heaths. In comparison, Sussex has records of 580 lichen species, of which 511 have been seen since *c.*1960. Apart from the New Forest, much of Hampshire is highly agricultural with a rather unexceptional lichen flora. However, although there are no natural, hard, rock-outcrops, the churchyards contain a wealth of lichen species. Some chalk grasslands are quite rich, especially Butser Hill and Isle of Wight Hill, as are also the few ancient parklands such as Hurstbourne and Highclere. Scattered around the county there are also a few, quite rich, ancient woodlands.

Rarer species of particular note in the Hampshire lichen flora include the following:

Agonimia octospora †
Anaptychia ciliaris
Arthonia astroidestra †
A. ilicina
A. invadens
A. leucopellaea
Bacidia circumspecta
Bactrospora corticola
Biatora sphaeroides
Buellia erubescens †
B. schaereri
Caloplaca atroflava
C. cirrochroa
C. herbidella
Catillaria laureri *
Catinaria papillosa †
Cetrelia olivetorum
Chaenotheca stemonea
Cladonia cariosa
C. convoluta
C. incrassata
C. strepsilis
Collema fragrans †
Cryptolechia carneolutea †
Degelia plumbea
Enterographa elaborata (elsewhere in the British Isles only in N. Ireland)
E. sorediata †
Heterodermia obscurata
Hypocenomyce sorophora †
Lecanactis amylacea †
Lecanora pruinosa †
L. quercicola

Leptogium plicatile
Lobaria amplissima
L. virens
Megalaria grossa
Megalospora tuberculosa †
Ochrolechia inversa
Opegrapha fumosa †
O. prosodea
Pannaria conoplea
P. mediterranea
Parmelia crinita
P. disjuncta
P. horrescens
P. laevigata
Parmelia minarum †
P. sinuosa
P. taylorensis
Parmeliopsis hyperopta
Pertusaria velata †
Phyllopsora rosei †
Pyrenula nitida †
Ramonia nigra
Rinodina isidioides †
Sphaerophorus globosus
Sticta limbata
Strangospora ochrophora
Strigula stigmatella *
Thelopsis rubella †
Tomasellia lactea †
Trapelia corticola
Usnea articulata
Wadeana dendrographa †
Zamenhofia coralloidea †

Z. hibernica †
Z. rosei †

* confined to Hampshire (the New Forest) in the British Isles
† more plentiful in Hampshire (especially the New Forest) than elsewhere in the British Isles.

Notes

(i) For the list below, and uniquely in Hampshire, 10km squares can be and are specified by only two digits, i.e. with the leading SZ(40) or SU(41) omitted. In this section, the term 'square' always refers to a 10km square rather than to a tetrad. Records in 100km square SZ(40) are cited first.

(ii) Space does not permit the inclusion of distribution maps for all lichen species. Nevertheless, two maps, showing distribution on a tetrad basis, are given for representative species confined to ancient woodlands: *Lobaria pulmonaria* and *Thelotrema lepadinum*.

(iii) The abbreviations N (north), S (south), etc., refer to the county of Hampshire rather than Britain. See p.86 for explanation of square [ ] and angle < > brackets in this flora.

(iv) In most cases, where a recorder and date are not given for specific site records, the species has generally been seen there by one of the authors.

(v) The nomenclature is that of *Checklist of Lichens of Great Britain and Ireland*, O. W. Purvis, B. J. Coppins & P. W. James, British Lichen Society, Bulletin No.72 (Supplement), 1993. Author citations of species included in that work are omitted.

(vi) The format and arrangement of the records in the following sections on Lichens and Bryophytes differ; this is because lichens are traditionally listed alphabetically and are recorded on a 10km-square basis, whereas bryophytes are usually listed in taxonomic sequence and recording has historically been based on the vice-county system.

Absconditella delutula   Rare. On clayey soil on roadside embankment NW of Basingstoke 55, *KS* 1990, det. *BJC*. Probably overlooked elsewhere.

A. lignicola VĚZDA & PIŠÚT (1984) Very rare. On an oak at Ladycross Inclosure, New Forest 30, *NAS* 1993, det. *BJC*.

A. pauxilla   Rare. On horizontal, sawn conifer-stump, Appleslade Inclosure, New Forest 10, *RW* 1990, det. *BJC*. Probably overlooked elsewhere.

A. trivialis   Rare. On clayey soil of roadside embankment NW of Basingstoke 55, *KS* 1990, det. *BJC*. Probably overlooked.

Acarospora fuscata   Common. On acid, saxicolous, nitrophilous substrates, especially horizontal surfaces of siliceous gravestones. Appears to be commoner in the more polluted areas of the county. 31 squares.

A. heppii   Rare. On flint pebble on track in Woolmer Forest near Liss 72, *FR & KS* 1988. Probably overlooked.

A. smaragdula   Rare. On granite gravestones in a very few churchyards, e.g. Ashford Hill Church 56, *KS* 1985. Also 19, 21.

Acrocordia conoidea   Rare. On hard limestone. Netley Abbey 40, *FR* 1993. Also 29, 65.

A. gemmata   Widespread but not

generally common. On trunks of mature, mainly wayside and parkland trees. Commonest in the New Forest. 28 squares.

A. salweyi   Widespread but occasional. On mortar of old walls. Possibly under-recorded. 19, 30, 32, 42, 50, 60, 61, 64, 65, 72.

Agonimia allobata (*Polyblastia allobata*) Rare. On mossy trunks, mainly in the New Forest, e.g. Ladycross Inclosure 30; Bramble Hill Walk, Great Wood 21; on tree-roots at Dockens Water 11, *KS* 1990; by Beaulieu River and Brockenhurst Park 30 and Hincheslea Wood 20, *NAS* 1990. Also 63.

A. octospora   Widespread and rather frequent in the New Forest but very rare elsewhere. Mainly on mature *Quercus* trunks in sheltered sites. Kilmeston Severals 52 is the only Hants site known outside the New Forest. Rarely found fertile. 10, 11, 20, 21, 30, 31, 52.

A. tristicula   Widespread and probably quite common. On moss in shaded places on stonework and brickwork of churches and old walls. Probably under-recorded. 09, 23, 42, 53, 62, 65, 71, 72, 73, 76.

Anaptychia ciliaris   Widespread but rather rare. Many former sites were on *Ulmus*; at present known on *Fraxinus*, *Acer* and *Quercus* trunks in open, wayside or parkland situations, e.g. Appleshaw 34, Bishop's Waltham Moors 51, Stratton House 54, Armsworth 63. On *Quercus* in open area in the New Forest W of Brook 21. On calcareous tombstone, Lyndhurst churchyard 30. 27 squares, but may no longer exist in some.

Anisomeridium biforme   Widespread, but common only in the New Forest and around Liss. Corticolous, especially on *Fagus*. May be overlooked elsewhere. 16 squares.

A. nyssaegenum (*A. juistense*)   Probably widespread and common, but seriously under-recorded. Mostly on *Sambucus* in shaded, secondary habitats. 21, 30, 33, 35, 45, 54, 63, 64, 72.

<*Arthonia anglica*   Formerly on *Ilex* near Lyndhurst, New Forest, *JMCr* 1868, Hb.BM.>

A. astroidestra (not *A. stellaris* as

thought earlier, teste *BJC*).   Known only from New Forest where local on *Ilex*. Mark Ash Wood 20, *PWJ & FR* 1969, Hb.BM; Eyeworth Wood 21, *FR* 1968, Hb.BM; Busketts Wood 31, *NAS* 1991. Also 10, 30.

A. cinnabarina (*A. tumidula*)   Scattered throughout the S and E, principally on *Corylus*; most frequent in the hangers and parts of the New Forest where *Corylus* occurs, and also there on old *Fagus*. 10, 20, 21, 30, 31, 50, 60, 61, 72, 73, 83.

A. didyma   Widespread but not common. On *Quercus* and *Corylus*. Possibly overlooked. 10, 11, 20, 29, 30, 31, 39, 42, 46, 51, 60, 61, 70, 83, 84.

A. elegans   Widespread but rare. On *Corylus*. Mostly in the S, e.g. Upper Hamble Country Park 51, *FR* 1987; Forest of Bere 61, *FR* 1988. Also 21, 30, 39, 54, 72.

A. ilicina (*Arthothelium ilicinum*) Confined to the New Forest where rather frequent. Mostly on *Ilex* trunks; also, rarely, on *Fagus*. 10, 11, 20, 21, 31.

A. impolita   Widespread but not common. Rare in the New Forest. On dry bark of old *Quercus* in parklands and waysides, often in *Lecanactis premnea* community. 17 squares.

A. invadens   On *Schismatomma decolorans* on *Quercus*. Rare in New Forest. Brinken Wood 20, *BJC & FR* 1971; Wood Crates 20, *NAS* 1991; Rockram Wood 21, *NAS* 1992.

A. lapidicola   Very rare but possibly overlooked. Usually on stonework flushed with heavy metal run-off. Recorded for 64, *CJBH* 1984, and for 62.

A. leucopellaea   Quite rare. On *Quercus* and *Fagus* trunks. Only in the New Forest where local, e.g. Frame Wood 30; Stricknage 21. Also 10, 20.

A. muscigena (*A. leucodontis*)   Rare, but possibly overlooked. On *Sambucus* near Cheriton 52, *KS* 1988, det. *BJC*.

A. punctiformis   Quite frequent. In areas where known, very common on second-year twigs, mostly of *Quercus*. Probably overlooked in many areas. 17 squares.

A. radiata   Widespread and common

in the New Forest but infrequent elsewhere. Mainly on smooth bark of *Fagus* and *Corylus* in quite lightly-shaded sites. 34 squares.

A. spadicea   Widespread and very common in established woodlands. Mostly on trunks of *Quercus* in shade. 40 squares.

[*A. stellaris*   All Hants records referable to *A. astroidestra* (*q.v.*).]

A. vinosa   Uncommon but found throughout the county wherever there is suitable old woodland. Mostly on *Quercus*. Commonest in the New Forest. 30 squares.

<*A. zwackhii*   Formerly on *Fagus*, Vinney Ridge 20, *CLa* 1873, det. *BJC*, Hb.BM.>

Arthopyrenia antecellans   Confined to the New Forest where frequent, mainly on *Ilex*. Possibly overlooked elsewhere. 10, 11, 20, 21, 30, 31, 39.

A. cerasi   Very rare, if identification correct. Reported from Great Wood, Bramshaw 21.

A. cinereopruinosa   One record on *Corylus* from Baker's Copse, Roydon 30, *NAS* 1994, det. *BJC*.

A. lapponina   Widespread but uncommon. On thin branches. Primarily in the New Forest but some other scattered records. Probably overlooked. 10, 20, 21, 30, 31, 39, 42, 44, 51, 72.

<*A. nitescens*   Formerly on *Ilex*, New Forest, *TS* 19th century, Hb.BM.>

A. punctiformis   Occasional. On smooth bark and on older twigs than *Arthonia punctiformis*. Primarily in the New Forest, with a few other scattered sites. Probably overlooked. 10, 11, 19, 20, 21, 30, 31, 46, 61, 75, 84.

A. ranunculospora   Widespread and quite frequent in ancient woodland. On *Quercus*, *Fraxinus* and *Fagus* trunks. Commonest in the New Forest. 21 squares.

A. viridescens   One record on *Corylus* from Baker's Copse, Roydon 30, *NAS* 1994, det. *BJC*.

Aspicilia caesiocinerea   Very rare. Milford Churchyard 29, *FR* 1993; Hamble Church 40, *FR* 1994; Tich-borne Church 53, *FR* 1994; Heckfield 76, *FR* 1992.

A. calcarea   Very common throughout the county. Found in most churchyards on flat, calcareous tombstones. 49 squares.

A. contorta   Rather less common than the previous species, but found in similar habitats. May be overlooked, as generally in smaller quantity than *A. calcarea*. 36 squares.

A. subcircinata   Ellingham Churchyard 10, *FR* 1994; old brick-wall, Michelmersh 32, *FR & KS* 1995.

Bacidia absistens   Very rare. On bark, Kilmeston Severals 52, *FR* 1975.

B. arceutina   Apparently rare, though may be overlooked. In established woodland, on smooth bark of youngish *Fraxinus* trunks. Scattered sites are known at present, e.g. Waltham Trinleys 54. Also 21, 24, 30.

B. arnoldiana   Rare, but probably much overlooked. On shaded *Sambucus* branch, Basingstoke Golf Course 54, *KS* 1986, det. *BJC*; Bignell Wood 21, *BJC*.

B. bagliettoana (*B. muscorum*)   Widespread but not common. On moss in short, chalk grassland. 10, 21, 23, 24, 42, 45, 54, 64, 65, 71, 72, 73.

B. biatorina   Widespread and frequent in the New Forest but found scattered throughout the county where suitable habitats occur. An old woodland species found mostly on *Quercus*. 10, 20, 21, 30, 31, 35, 40, 42, 46, 51, 61, 63.

B. circumspecta   Very rare. Found only in the New Forest, e.g. on *Fagus*, Rushpole Wood 30; Bramshaw Wood 21.

B. delicata   Apparently very rare. On moss on shaded wall, Steep 72, *BJC* 1972.

B. friesiana   Very rare. On basic bark of *Acer campestre*, near Cheriton 52, *KS* 1988, det. *BJC*; N of Petersfield 72, *BJC* 1972.

B. herbarum   Very rare. On mossy, chalk stones. Isle of Wight Hill 23, *PWJ* c.1975; Butser Hill 71, *BJC* 1973.

B. incompta   Much rarer now than records indicate as mostly on *Ulmus*. It survives in sap-seepages on old New Forest *Fagus* and inside hollow *Ilex*. Records for 01, 10, 19, 20, 21, 29, 30, 32, 44, 45, 55, 75, but probably now lost from some sites.

B. laurocerasi   Uncommon. Mainly in the S, especially in the New Forest. Rare in N. On basic bark of *Acer* and *Fraxinus* in open situations. Not particularly a species of old woodland. 19, 20, 21, 29, 30, 32, 35, 52, 72.

B. naegelii   Scattered throughout the county but nowhere common. On basic bark of *Sambucus* and *Acer*. May be overlooked. 29, 39, 42, 43, 44, 45, 52, 53, 54, 62, 71, 72.

B. phacodes   Scattered and occasional in the S, rare in the N. On basic bark, especially of *Sambucus* and *Acer campestre* in quite shaded sites. 01, 20, 21, 29, 30, 32, 44, 49, 62, 64, 72.

<*B. polychroa*   Formerly near Stoney Cross, New Forest 21, but probably not in ancient woodland areas, *JMCr* 1869.>

B. rubella   Widespread but nowhere common. Not found in the most polluted areas. On basic bark of *Sambucus*, *Fraxinus* and *Acer campestre*. 25 squares.

B. sabuletorum   Common throughout the county. Characteristic of moss on undisturbed, chalk-rich soils but also frequent on moss on calcareous tombstones. Formerly on mossy *Ulmus*. 33 squares.

<*B. subturgidula*   Formerly on decorticate *Ilex*, near Lyndhurst, *JMCr* 1868 and *CLa* 1873.>

B. vezdae   Widespread but not common. In established woodland throughout the county, mainly on *Quercus* trunks. 29 squares.

B. viridifarinosa   Quite frequent in the New Forest but rare elsewhere. On mature *Fagus* and *Quercus* bark. Records of this recently-described species may well increase. Alice Holt Forest 84, *FR* 1988. Also 10, 20, 21, 30, 31.

Bactrospora corticola   Very rare. Known only on old *Quercus* at Hurstbourne Park 44, *PWJ*, *BJC & FR* 1971.

Baeomyces roseus Rare. On peaty banks in the New Forest. 10, 11, 20.

B. rufus Occasional in heathy areas in SW and NE. Most frequent on the New Forest heaths on bare, sandy or clay soil of banks and tracksides. 10, 11, 19, 20, 21, 30, 31, 32, 55, 65, 72, 73, 75, 76, 83.

Belonia nidarosiensis (*Clathroporina calcarea*) Common, but formerly under-recorded. On sheltered church-walls, especially on N aspects, e.g. Brockenhurst 30, *PWJ* Bramshaw 21, *KS & VJG* 1990. Now known in 38 squares and probably present in all.

Biatora epixanthoides (*Bacidia epixanthoides*) Rather rare. Only in ancient woodlands of the New Forest and on *Quercus* in Combe Wood 35, *FR*. Also 10, 21, 30.

B. sphaeroides (*Catillaria sphaeroides*) Occasional but widespread in New Forest woodlands. On old, mossy *Quercus* and *Fagus* trunks. 10, 20, 21, 30.

Bryoria fuscescens Rare. Eyeworth Wood 21, on *Crataegus*, *FR* 1968; Nutley Wood 64, on *Quercus*, *FR & PWJ* 1975.

B. subcana Very rare. On scrub, Irons Well near Eyeworth Wood 21, *FR* from 1968, det. *DLH*.

Buellia aethalea Widespread and common. In churchyards, where frequent on granite gravestones and memorials; less common on sandstone and brickwork. 50 squares.

B. disciformis Occasional. In the New Forest, mostly on old *Fagus*. 20, 21, 30, 31.

B. erubescens Rare. In the New Forest, on old *Fagus*. 10, 20, 21.

B. griseovirens Widespread but apparently not common. May be under-recorded due to identification problems. Mainly towards the base of trees on more or less smooth bark but sometimes lignicolous. 17 squares.

B. ocellata (*B. verruculosa*) Widespread and common. In similar habitats to *B. aethalea* but extending more on to sandstone. 47 squares.

B. punctata Very common throughout. On nutrient-enriched bark of a variety of trees and less commonly on walls and acid gravestones. 52 squares.

B. schaereri Very rare. On old *Quercus*. Stubbs/Frame Wood 30.

B. stellulata Rare. In similar places to *B. aethalea*, but normally maritime. There is much confusion between the two and some of the records are in need of confirmation. 01, 40, 50, 64, 65.

Byssoloma leucoblepharum Very rare. On tree stump, The Noads, 3.5km NE of Beaulieu, 30, *BJC & FR* 1972, det. *ESé*. Only three other sites known in British Isles.

<*Calicium adspersum* Extinct. 'New Forest', Hb.BM, 19th century.>

C. glaucellum Occasional. Scattered records throughout on old conifers and *Fagus* or *Quercus* lignum. Most records are from the New Forest, e.g. Burley Old Inclosure 20. Also 21, 23, 30, 31, 35, 44, 63, 73.

<*C. lenticulare* (*C. subquercinum*) Formerly at Lyndhurst, New Forest, on hollow, putrid *Quercus*, *JMCr* 1869, Hb.BM, det. *LT*.>

C. salicinum Widespread but infrequent, mainly in the W. In old woodlands and parks, mostly on old, dry *Quercus* trunks in open sites. 11, 20, 21, 30, 31, 42, 44, 45, 46, 55, 73.

C. viride Widespread and locally common. In wooded areas on trunks of a variety of mature trees. 34 squares.

Caloplaca atroflava Very rare. On flint pebbles, Butser Hill 71, *BJC* 1973.

C. aurantia Widespread and common, especially near the coast. Mainly on S sides of limestone churches; less common on gravestones. Much less common than *C. flavescens*. 34 squares.

C. cerina Rare and scattered. On basic bark of *Acer* and *Fraxinus* in open situations, e.g. Old Burghclere 45. Also 23, 29, 33, 53, 62, 63.

C. cirrochroa Very rare. On mediaeval wall (S) of ruins of Abbey Church, Beaulieu 30, *FR* 1995.

C. citrina Abundant throughout on basic, saxicolous substrates; less

common on nutrient-enriched bark. 55 squares.

C. crenularia (*C. festiva*) Occasional. In churchyards, generally on flat gravestones, but also on old walls. On weakly-acid to basic stonework but not on limestone. May be under-recorded or increasing. 01, 11, 34, 38, 44, 46, 55, 71, 72, 83.

C. dalmatica Locally very frequent in C and S Hants on ancient, vertical, S-facing calcareous stonework, especially of mediaeval churches. 29 squares. Old records for *C. ochracea* may all be referable to this species.

C. decipiens Occasional and nowhere common. On basic, saxicolous substrates. On tops of brick-walls in Basingstoke 65. Also 11, 32, 35, 43, 53, 54, 55, 69, 76.

C. ferruginea Rare. On old trees in the New Forest, e.g. Bramshaw Wood 21, on *Quercus*; Wood Crates 20, on *Fagus*; Busketts Wood 31, on *Fagus*, *FR* 1991.

C. flavescens (*C. heppiana*) Very common. On walls, churches and tombstones, especially on calcareous stone but also on brickwork influenced by mortar. 54 squares.

<*C. flavorubescens* Formerly recorded on trees at Lymington 39, *PWJ c.*1960.>

C. flavovirescens Occasional, scattered records mainly in the S. On tiled roofs, brickwork and sandstone. May be under-recorded. 11, 19, 22, 29, 32, 46, 49, 50, 54.

C. herbidella Rare. Bramshaw and South Ocknell 21, on *Quercus*, *FR* 1971; Hurstbourne Park 44, on *Fraxinus*, *FR* 1985.

C. holocarpa Probably very common but under-recorded and may be a complex of several closely-related species. On a wide range of basic, saxicolous substrates. 35 squares.

C. isidiigera Occasional. On granite, brickwork and limestone. In Hants, seems to be confined to the NW though may be overlooked elsewhere. Goodworth Clatford 34, *KS* 1988; Old Burghclere 45, *KS* 1986. Also 01, 55.

C. lactea Very rare. On limestone

chest-tomb at Milford on Sea 29, *KS* 1990.

C. luteoalba (Sched. 8) Possibly extinct as all former sites on old *Ulmus*. Blashford 10; near Lymington 29. Also 74. May still occur on other nutrient-enriched trunks.

C. marina Rare. On coastal rocks. Its apparent rarity may be due to lack of suitable substrates but lichens are under-recorded for coastal areas of Hants. Needs Ore 49; Hayling Island 79. Also 19.

C. obscurella (*C. sarcopisioides*) Rare. On basic bark of branches rather than trunks, mostly *Sambucus*. Probably overlooked. Armsworth Park 63, *BJC & FR* 1972; Hollands Wood 30, *FR* c.1972; Mark Ash 20, *BJC* 1993. Also 29, 62.

[*C. ochracea* There are several unconfirmed old records, but it is now thought that all records refer to *C. dalmatica*.]

C. saxicola Common throughout. In similar habitats to *C. flavescens* but generally less common, especially on tombstones. More common on asbestos roofs, and flints of old walls. May be over-recorded as confusible with *C. flavescens*. 37 squares.

C. teicholyta Very common. On old church-walls and gravestones on basic rocks; less common on brickwork with mortar influence. Rarely fertile, e.g. East Stratton 54. 49 squares.

C. ulcerosa Rare. On *Ulmus*, Laverstoke Park 44, *BJC* 1971; on *Fraxinus*, East Stratton Park 54, *KS* 1988; on old *Fagus*, Howen Bushes 21, *NAS* 1992; Wormstall Wood 39, *NAS* 1993; on *Juglans*, Brockenhurst Park 30, *NAS* 1993. Probably somewhat under-recorded.

C. variabilis Rather rare. On chest-tombs in churchyards, e.g. Easton Church 53, *FR* 1994. Also 40, 42, 43, 44, 62.

C. virescens Rare. On basic bark. *Acer campestre* near Cheriton 52, *KS* det. *BJC* 1988; old *Ulmus*, Armsworth Park 63, *BJC & FR* 1973, Hb.BM. Probably under-recorded.

Candelaria concolor Scattered and nowhere frequent. On rather nutrient-enriched bark in parkland, mostly in central Hants. 01, 11, 19, 22, 33, 43, 44, 52, 53, 61, 62, 71, 72.

Candelariella aurella Very frequent and probably commoner than records suggest. Mainly on concrete. 35 squares.

C. coralliza Rare. Coastal rocks at Hengistbury Head 19, *VJG* 1989. Plants on rough granite memorials inland may in some cases be this species, but more research is needed before one can be definite about this.

C. medians Frequent to common. On basic, nutrient-enriched stonework, mostly church-walls and gravestones. 43 squares.

C. reflexa Frequent. On basic bark, mainly of *Sambucus* in open situations. 29 squares.

C. vitellina Very common. On slightly-acid, nutrient-enriched substrates, both saxicolous and corticolous. 55 squares.

C. xanthostigma Occasional. Apparently, mainly in a belt across the centre of the county on dry bark of old parkland trees. 17 squares.

Catapyrenium squamulosum Rare. On chalky soil. Porton Down 23, *FR & PWJ* 1975; Old Burghclere Lime Quarry 45, *KS* 1985; Butser Hill 71, 72, *OLG* 1991; roadside W of Basingstoke 55, *KS* 1986. Also Ports Down 60, *FR* 1977. (Mostly recorded in the past as *C. lachneum*, but the species of the southern chalklands is almost certainly all *C. squamulosum*.)

Catillaria atomarioides Very rare. On ironstone, Hengistbury Head 19, *VJG & KS* 1991.

C. atropurpurea Frequent in the New Forest; widespread but occasional elsewhere. An old woodland species mainly on *Quercus* but also on *Fraxinus*. 22 squares.

C. chalybeia Occasional to common, with scattered records. On acid, saxicolous substrates mainly of smooth brickwork and acid gravestones. Probably overlooked. 28 squares.

C. laureri (*Catinaria laureri*) (Sched. 8) Very rare. Confined in Britain to the New Forest. On a few old *Fagus*.

Mark Ash and Knightwood Inclosure 20; Busketts Wood 31; Rushpole Wood 30, *NAS* 1993. Recorded from 25 *Fagus* trees in 1993–94 *NAS*. Also Bignell Wood 21 and Wood Crates 20, *NAS* 1994.

C. lenticularis Common on calcareous stonework. 31 squares.

C. pulverea Confined to the New Forest where occasional. Mostly on *Salix* in wet carrs. 10, 20, 21, 30, 31, 39.

Catinaria papillosa Coppins in ed. Very rare. On *Fagus* near Wood Crates 20, *VJG* 1983.

Celothelium ischnobelum (*Leptorhaphis ischnobela*) Rare and scattered. On smooth bark of *Corylus*, e.g. Waggoners Wells 83, *FR* 1975. Also 20, 21, 35.

Cetraria chlorophylla Widespread but infrequent. On a variety of trees, especially on branches and young trunks. 16 squares.

Cetrelia olivetorum Rare. In the New Forest, on old *Fagus*. Wood Crates, S of Acres Down 20; Mark Ash 20.

Chaenotheca brachypoda (*Coniocybe sulphurea*) Rare. Inside old, hollow *Fraxinus* trunk, South Brinken Wood 20, *NAS* 1989. Also 21.

C. brunneola Occasional. On dry bark of old *Quercus* and lignum, mainly in the New Forest, e.g. Red Shoot Wood 10, *BLS* field meeting 1990. Also 11, 20, 21, 30, 39, 45, 46, 83.

C. chrysocephala Occasional. In the New Forest, on *Quercus* and *Betula*, e.g. North Ocknell 21. Also 20, 30, 31.

C. ferruginea Widespread and quite frequent. On *Quercus*, especially in secondary woodlands. Occasional on worked timber. 34 squares.

C. furfuracea (*Coniocybe furfuracea*) Rare. In the New Forest, in crevices of roots of old trees. 20, 21.

C. hispidula Rather rare. In dry crevices of old *Quercus*. In the New Forest 20, 21, 30, and Forest of Bere 61.

C. stemonea Very rare. In crevices of old *Quercus* in pasture. Downlands Court, Liphook 82, *KS & FR* 1990, det. *BJC*; Denny Wood 30, *DSR* 1960; Lyndhurst, *JMCr* 1906.

C. trichialis   Quite rare. In crevices of old, dry *Quercus* bark. Hurstbourne Park 44, Pylewell Park 39, *NAS & KS* 1990; and in the New Forest, e.g. Stricknage Wood 21, 20, 30.

Chaenothecopsis pusilla   Rare. On *Fagus* lignum, Queen Bower 20, *KS* 1989.

Chromatochlamys muscorum (*Microglaena muscorum*)   Rare. On moss in chalk turf. Isle of Wight Hill 23; Farley Mount Country Park 42.

Chrysothrix candelaris   Widespread and frequent. In established woodland, mainly in dry crevices of *Quercus*. 38 squares.

C. chrysophthalma   Fairly common. On acid-barked trees, especially *Quercus* and conifers. Little-recorded until recently, partly because of identification difficulties; however, it seems to be spreading rapidly. 11, 20, 21, 30, 31, 50, 51, 61, 63, 66, 73, 83.

Cladonia arbuscula   Occasional. On heaths in the New Forest, where rare and local, and E Hants, e.g. Woolmer Forest 83, locally common. Also 10, 11, 19, 20, 21, 30, 72, 73.

C. caespiticia   Occasional. Mainly in the New Forest, on mossy trunks and stumps. 10, 20, 21, 29, 30, 31, 61, 72, 74.

C. cariosa   Rare. On clayey, basic soil on roadside embankment NW of Basingstoke 55, *KS* 1986, det. *BJC*. The specimen contains atranorin and fumarprotocetraric acid of the form found on Cornish mine-spoil heaps, proving that it is this rather critical species.

C. cervicornis ssp. *cervicornis*   Scattered and occasional, mainly in the S. In open, dry, basic habitats. 19, 20, 30, 38, 54, 59, 71, 72, 79.

ssp. *verticillata*   Occasional. On New Forest and E Hants heaths. 10, 19, 20, 21, 30, 72, 73, 83.

C. chlorophaea sensu lato   Frequent. On peaty soils and bark. 45 squares. We have not attempted to separate the segregates, as they are of doubtful value.

C. ciliata var. *tenuis*   Occasional. Mainly on New Forest heaths but also scattered on other heathland, e.g. Woolmer Forest 83. Also 11, 20, 21, 23, 30, 31, 39, 56, 59, 72.

C. coccifera sensu lato   Frequent. On heathlands. Most records are probably *C. diversa* teste *BJC*. 20 squares.

C. coniocraea   Very common. On bark, lignum and peaty soils. 51 squares.

C. convoluta   Very rare. On dry, S-facing chalk-turf on Butser Hill 72, *SRD* 1972, flourishing, *OLG* 1991. A southern-continental species, rare in Britain.

C. crispata var. *cetrariiformis*   Occasional to frequent. On heathlands. 18 squares.

C. digitata   Widespread but occasional. In established woodland on stumps, lignum, and decaying acid bark. 19 squares.

C. diversa   See *C. coccifera*.

C. fimbriata   Widespread and quite common. Mostly on moss on gravestones or basic walls. May be over-recorded. 32 squares.

C. floerkeana   Frequent. On heathlands and rotting wood. Generally commoner than *C. coccifera* which usually occurs in the same habitats. 23 squares.

C. foliacea   Occasional. In chalk turf or on sand-dunes. Most sites are coastal but also inland at Butser Hill 71, *OLG* 1991; Isle of Wight Hill 23, *PWJ & FR* 1975; Noar Hill 73 *FR* 1972. Occasional also in the New Forest on disturbed and base-enriched heaths 30. Also 19, 20, 39, 49, 59, 79.

C. furcata   Frequent. Mainly on heathlands but also on more basic soils. 27 squares.

C. glauca   Rare. On heathlands, but may be overlooked. 10, 21, 73.

C. gracilis   Occasional in the New Forest and rare elsewhere on heaths. Locally frequent at Woolmer Forest 73, 83. Also 11, 19, 20, 21, 30.

C. humilis (*C. conoidea*)   Occasional. On light, mainly chalky soils or on

sand-dunes or sea-walls, e.g. Hayling Island 79. Also 23, 60, 70, 72.

C. incrassata   Rather rare. On damp bank on heath, Black Barrow 11, *FR & NAS* 1993; steep, sandy banks above seepage step-mires, Foulford Bottom 10 and Acres Down 20, *NAS* 1988; on peaty soil, Woolmer Forest 73, *FR* 1993; on *Betula* roots and peaty soil, Waggoners Wells 83, *FR* 1975. Overlooked until very recently. Also 19.

C. macilenta (*C. bacillaris*) Frequent. In woodlands, on bark and lignum; also on acid soil on heaths. 33 squares.

C. ochrochlora   Occasional and scattered but most frequent in the New Forest. On rotting stumps and logs. 16 squares.

C. parasitica   Occasional and scattered but commonest in the New Forest. On rotting lignum especially of *Quercus*. 10, 11, 20, 21, 29, 30, 31, 39, 44, 50, 51, 52, 61, 64, 83.

C. pocillum   Widespread and quite frequent, especially in chalk turf and on wall-tops. 21 squares.

C. polydactyla   Quite frequent in the New Forest and scattered elsewhere. Mainly on soft lignum. 17 squares.

C. portentosa   Common to locally abundant on heathlands. Also on *Quercus* branches in humid sites in the New Forest. 25 squares.

C. pyxidata   Widespread and quite frequent, especially on tree-bases. 20 squares.

C. ramulosa (*C. anomaea*)   Occasional and scattered. In *Calluna* heath and on tree-bases, mainly in the New Forest. 10, 19, 20, 21, 30, 31, 32, 62, 71, 75, 83, 84.

C. rangiformis   Widespread and quite frequent on basic soil. 27 squares.

C. scabriuscula   Very rare. On heath, Woolmer Forest 73, *FR* 1989.

C. squamosa   Widespread and quite frequent on peaty soils and rotting wood. 20 squares.

var. *subsquamosa*   Occasional. Mainly on SW heaths. 11, 19, 20, 21, 30, 39.

C. strepsilis   Local on wet heaths. Quite frequent in the New Forest, rare on NE heaths, e.g. Yateley Common 85. Also 10, 11, 19, 20, 21, 30, 40, 66, 75, 84. A stunted, sorediate form, which may be a new taxon, occurs on heathland in the Shappen Hill area of the New Forest, 20.

C. subrangiformis (*C. furcata* ssp. *subrangiformis*)   Widespread but occasional. In short chalk-turf e.g. Butser Hill 71, 72; Isle of Wight Hill 23. Also 01, 23, 24, 32, 33, 42, 54, 55, 60, 62, 73, 74.

C. subulata   Rare. On heaths, mainly in the New Forest, but also Hazeley Heath 75. Also 10, 11, 20, 30.

C. uncialis ssp. *biuncialis*   Occasional to frequent. On New Forest and NE heaths. 10, 11, 19, 20, 21, 29, 30, 39, 40, 59, 72, 73, 83, 85.

<*C. zopfii*   Formerly on heaths S of Bramshaw Wood 21, *HMLi & RGLi* 1910.>

Clauzadea immersa (*Lecidea immersa*) Very rare. On chalk pebbles. Butser Hill 72, *OLG* 1991. Also 19, 62.

C. metzleri (*Lecidea metzleri*)   Rare. On chalk pebbles. Butser Hill 71, 72, *OLG* 1991; Noar Hill 73, *KS* 1988. Also 32.

C. monticola (*Lecidea monticola*) Widespread and quite common. On limestone walls, gravestones and chalk pebbles. 30 squares.

Cliostomum griffithii   Common throughout. On neutral to acid bark in a wide variety of situations. 45 squares.

Coelocaulon aculeatum   Widespread but occasional. On heathlands and sandy or shingly shores in the S and E. 18 squares.

C. muricatum   Rare or overlooked for the previous species. On heaths and sandy or shingly shores in the S. 20, 30, 51, 73, 79.

Collema auriforme (*C. auriculatum*) Widespread and frequent. On basic soils, walls and limestone gravestones. Common in some churchyards but seems to be less frequent near the coast. 30 squares.

C. crispum   Widespread and fre-

quent. On limestone walls, flat tombs and compacted, chalk soils. 29 squares.

<*C. fasciculare*   Formerly amongst mosses in shaded cavity of *Fagus* trunk, New Forest, *CLy* 1806.>

<*C. flaccidum*   Old, unlocalized, literature record for 'New Forest', teste *PWJ*; no details available.>

C. fragrans   Rare. Formerly on old *Ulmus*. Until 1971, on *Ulmus* at Hurstbourne Park; now (1992–94) only on *Fagus* in the New Forest. 20, 21, 30, 31, 32, 44.

C. fuscovirens   Very rare. On chesttomb, East Wellow churchyard 32, *FR* 1995.

C. limosum   Rare. On consolidated, chalky soils. Hawkley 72, *BJC* 1972; Basingstoke 65, *KS* 1990. Probably a transient species and under-recorded.

C. occultatum   Very rare. On *Acer campestre*, Ivy Wood 30, *FR* 1972.

C. subflaccidum   Rare. On old *Fraxinus*, Wood Crates 20, *FR* 1972; Sloden Wood and Ashley Lodge 21, *FR* 1975.

C. tenax   Frequent. On basic soil, and mortar of old walls. Apparently commonest in the NW. 29 squares.

var. *ceranoides*   Widespread but local. On rather compacted, basic soils. May be under-recorded. 01, 23, 24, 33, 39, 54, 55, 60, 61, 64, 65, 71, 73.

Cryptolechia carneolutea   Now very rare. Formerly on old *Ulmus* in the S, but the only recent records are all on *Fagus* at Wood Crates 20, *VJG* 1987; Mark Ash 20, *NAS* 1994; and Bramshaw Woods 21, *NAS* 1993. Previous records before 1975 on *Ulmus* at 29, 39, 49.

Cyphelium inquinans   Widespread but local. On old fence-rails and post-tops. Common at some sites. 18 squares.

C. sessile   Rare and scattered. On *Pertusaria coccodes*. 20, 63, 71.

C. tigillare   Very rare and probably now extinct. On wooden post, Whitley Wood 20, *PWJ* 1971, same site as 'near Brockenhurst 30, *PWJ & ECW* 1971' (Whitley Wood spans the grid line).

Degelia plumbea (*Parmeliella plumbea*) Very rare. On old *Fraxinus* overhanging Lymington River, N end of Roydon Woods 30, *FR* 1984.

Dimerella lutea   Occasional. On *Quercus* in ancient woodlands of the New Forest. 10, 20, 21, 30, 31, 39.

D. pineti (*D. diluta*)   Widespread and frequent. On trunks of rough-barked trees, mainly *Quercus* in established woodlands. May be spreading. 27 squares.

Diploicia canescens   Very common. On basic rocks, especially in churchyards, and nutrient-enriched tree-bases, mainly of *Quercus*, *Acer* and *Fraxinus*, on farmland. 53 squares.

Diploschistes muscorum   Occasional. On *Cladonia* on wall-tops. May be under-recorded as confusible with *D. scruposus*. 46, 61, 62, 65, 72, 74.

D. scruposus   Widespread and frequent. On brickwork and tiles; common at some sites, especially in N. 29 squares.

Diplotomma alboatrum   Widespread and locally common. On basic rocks and mortar of church-walls, much less common on gravestones and other walls; formerly on *Ulmus* trunks. 39 squares.

Dirina massiliensis f. *sorediata* Frequent. On shaded, basic church-walls; on the N side of the majority of old parish churches. 35 squares.

Enterographa crassa   Frequent. On fairly-smooth, shaded bark; commonest in old woodlands. 45 squares.

E. elaborata   Very rare. In the New Forest, Hb. CRK ex Hb.IC 1815, *CLy* 1849. Refound on one *Fagus*, Busketts Wood 31, *NAS* 1993.

E. sorediata   Rare. On *Quercus* in New Forest ancient woodlands. Frame Wood and Hollands Wood 30; Great Wood and Bramshaw Wood 21; Pylewell Park 39, *NAS* 1990, det. *FR*.

Eopyrenula grandicula   Very rare. On old *Corylus*, Ivy Wood and Baker's Copse, Roydon 30, *NAS* 1994.

Evernia prunastri   Very common. On bark of a wide variety of trees in open situations; also on fences and, rarely, old walls. 54 squares.

Fellhanera subtilis Rare. On fence-post, Downlands Court, Liphook 82, *KS & FR* 1990, det. *BJC*.

Fuscidea lightfootii Quite frequent in the New Forest; rare elsewhere. On twigs, mostly of *Salix*, in damp situations. 10, 11, 20, 21, 30, 31, 39, 64, 83.

F. viridis Very rare. On *Fagus* in Rushpole Wood 30, *NAS* 1992.

Graphina anguina Rare. On smooth bark. New Forest 20, 21, and N of Havant 70, *BJC* 1972.

<**G. ruiziana** 19th-century record from 'Lymington', Hb.BM, but no details known.>

Graphis elegans Frequent. On smooth bark of *Fagus*, *Corylus* and *Ilex*; commonest in established woodlands in the least-polluted areas. 43 squares.

G. scripta Commoner than the previous species, in similar situations. 44 squares.

Gyalecta derivata Rare. On *Fraxinus* in the New Forest. 21, 31.

G. flotowii Rare. On *Fraxinus* (and formerly on *Ulmus*) in the New Forest 10, 20, 30, and Hurstbourne Park 44.

G. jenensis Rare. On shaded, rather damp limestone. Ellisfield Church 64; Bramshaw Church 21; Michelmersh Church 32; Netley Abbey 40, *FR* 1993; Droxford churchyard 61, *FR* 1994; Upham churchyard 52, *TCh & FR* 1994.

G. truncigena Occasional but wide-spread. Mainly on *Quercus* and *Fraxinus* in old woodlands. 10, 11, 20, 21, 22, 30, 33, 35, 42, 63, 72, 73, 74.

Gyalideopsis anastomosans Wide-spread and probably under-recorded. On more-or-less smooth bark of branches and trunks. 20, 21, 30, 31, 35, 39, 53, 61, 62, 63, 64, 66, 72, 83.

Haematomma ochroleucum var. **porphyrium** Widespread but infre-quent. On basic stonework of church-walls and on gravestones but nowhere in large quantity. 32 squares.

Heterodermia obscurata Very rare. On *Fagus* at Busketts Wood, New Forest 31.

[**Hymenelia lacustris** Only one record (*Census Cat.Brit.Lichens* (1953)) and presumed an error.]

H. prevostii Rare. On calcareous memorials. Bramshaw Church 21, *KS & VJG* 1990, det. *BJC*; Droxford churchyard 61, *FR* 1994; Upham churchyard 52, *TCh & FR* 1994. May be overlooked.

Hyperphyscia adglutinata (*Physciopsis adglutinata*) Widespread but infre-quent. On moderately nutrient-enriched bark of wayside trees, mainly *Fraxinus* and *Acer*, and on limestone memorials. May be decreasing due to agricultural pollution. 34 squares.

Hypocenomyce caradocensis Rare. On very acid bark or lignum. Norley Wood 39, *FR & BJC* 1973; Forest of Bere 51, *FR* 1989; Isle of Wight Hill 23 *PWJ* 1975. Also 11.

H. scalaris Frequent. Mainly on worked timber but occasionally on acid stones and trunks. 34 squares.

H. sorophora Very rare. On large, decorticate tree-trunk, North Ocknell 21, *KS* 1990, det. *BJC*. First British record.

Hypogymnia physodes Abundant. On bark, old, worked timber, heather stems and peaty soil. Generally, rarely found fertile but more often so in the New Forest. 56 squares.

H. tubulosa Widespread but much less common than the previous species. Mainly on horizontal branches and twigs. 36 squares.

Icmadophila ericetorum Rare or overlooked. On peat W of Holmsley Passage 20, *FR & NAS* 1989, conf. *BJC*.

Imshaugia aleurites (*Parmeliopsis aleurites*) Occasional on sunlit lignum in the New Forest. 10, 20, 21, 29, 30, 31.

Lecanactis abietina Common to locally abundant. On dry, acid, shaded bark in quite dense *Quercus* woodland; rare on trees on chalk soils. 36 squares.

L. amylacea Rare. In the New Forest, on old *Quercus* in dry crevices

at the base. Allum Green 20; Stubbs Wood and Mallard Wood 30; Busketts Wood 31; Pinnick Wood 10; Strick-nage Wood 21, all 1975–93, *FR*, *PWJ*.

L. lyncea Scarce but locally frequent. On dry bark of ancient *Quercus*, mainly in the New Forest, but also Highclere Park 46, *FR* 1970; Hurstbourne Park 44, *FR* 1983; Pylewell Park 39, *NAS & KS* 1990. Also 10, 20, 21, 30, 31, 32.

L. premnea Widespread but occa-sional, except in the New Forest where locally common. On ancient, dry *Quercus* trunks in old parkland; also old *Taxus* in churchyards. 24 squares.

L. subabietina Occasional. On old, dry *Quercus* trunks towards the base. Confined to the S and commonest in the New Forest. 10, 19, 20, 21, 30, 39, 41, 50, 51, 79.

Lecania cyrtella Widespread and probably common. On nutrient-rich bark of *Sambucus* and *Acer campestre* in open sites. Overlooked. 23 squares.

L. cyrtellina Very rare. On *Acer* at Ivy Wood 30, *FR* 1975, det. *BJC*. Probably overlooked elsewhere.

L. erysibe (incl. f. *sorediata*) Com-mon. On nutrient-enriched rock and man-made substrates, especially tops of gravestones. The records probably also include some for *L. rabenhorstii* (not yet recorded but probably await-ing discovery as it is in Sussex) and *L. turicensis*. 40 squares. The sorediate form is occasional on man-made sub-strates and much less recorded than the fertile form. 42, 52, 53, 64, 72, 73, 74.

<**L. fuscella** Formerly on *Populus* trunks near Brockenhurst and near Stoney Cross, *JMCr* 1869, Hb.BM.>

L. hutchinsiae (*Catillaria littorella*) Rare. On coastal pebbles. Hurst Castle spit 38, *VJG c*.1980.

L. turicensis Local, on old stone-work, especially near the coast. Alver-stoke Church 69, *FR* 1995; Netley Abbey 40, *FR* 1994; Winchester Cathedral 42, *FR* 1994; Headbourne Worthy 43, *FR* 1995; Chilcomb Church 32, *FR* 1994; Portchester Castle 60, *FR* 1993; Corhampton 62, *FR* 1993; Wield Church 63, *FR* 1994; Ropley Church 63, *FR* 1994; South Hayling 70, *PWJ* 1992.

Lecanora actophila   Rare. On coastal rocks. Hurst Castle spit 38, *VJG* c.1980.

L. aitema   Rare but probably overlooked. On fences, e.g. Farleigh Wallop Church 64, *KS* 1983, det. *BJC*. Also 21.

L. albescens   Common. On limestone gravestones and church-walls. 29 squares.

L. argentata (*L. subfuscata*)   Very rare. Bramshaw 21, and an old record on trunks of trees near Lyndhurst, *JMCr* 1869, Hb.BM.

L. campestris   Very common. On churches, gravestones and walls on basic rocks. 52 squares.

L. carpinea   Rather rare. On smooth, basic bark, especially on horizontal branches, but possibly overlooked. 01, 11, 20, 30, 45, 53, 61, 62.

L. chlarotera   Very common. On smooth bark of trees in open woodland and parkland; most frequent on *Fagus* and *Fraxinus*. 50 squares.

L. conferta   Very rare (or overlooked?). On vertical limestone or plastered walls of ancient churches. Winchester Cathedral 42, *TCh & FR* 1994; east end of St Cross Church, Winchester, 42, *FR & KS* 1995; Droxford Church 61, *FR & TCh* 1994. More than one taxon may be involved.

L. confusa   Occasional to locally common. On smooth bark of branches and saplings in open sites in SW, e.g. on *Salix*, Hengistbury Head 19. Also 01, 20, 21, 29, 30, 31, 39, 40, 41, 49, 50.

L. conizaeoides   Abundant. On acid bark, acid rock, brickwork and worked timber; rare on tree-trunks in old woodlands, e.g. the New Forest. 57 squares.

L. crenulata   Frequent. In small quantities on limestone of church-walls. 37 squares.

L. dispersa   Very common. On basic bark, rocks and man-made substrates. 55 squares.

L. expallens   Very common. On bark of wayside and open-woodland trees. A similar-looking crust is common on siliceous church-walls and gravestones;

this may be a different species but is recorded here as *L. expallens*. See also *Pertusaria flavicans*, p.319. 56 squares.

L. intumescens   Occasional. On smooth bark, mainly in the New Forest but also at Martin Down 01, on *Fraxinus*, *FR & KS* 1991. Also 10, 20, 21, 30, 31.

L. jamesii   Occasional. Mostly on *Salix* twigs in New Forest carrs. Also on roadside *Fraxinus* near Cheriton 52, *KS* 1988, det. *PWJ*. Also 10, 11, 20, 21, 30, 31, 39.

L. muralis   Common, especially in the N. On slightly nutrient-enriched rocks and man-made substrates, often on paths or flagstones. It has probably increased recently. 42 squares.

L. orosthea (*Lecidea orosthea*)   Scattered and very occasional. On siliceous gravestones 19, 20, 43, 45, 64, 74, 75.

L. pallida   Scattered and occasional but most frequent in the New Forest. On smooth, acid bark of branches and twigs in woodlands on acid soil. 16 squares.

L. piniperda   Very rare. Only in the New Forest, on *Fagus*, Mark Ash 20, *FR & PWJ* 1972.

L. polytropa   Frequent on granite tombstones. Commonest in the NE and probably increasing. 35 squares.

L. pruinosa   Rare (but probably overlooked, as thought to be extinct in Britain until a few years ago). On vertical limestone stonework or buttresses of ancient churches; also on a mediaeval brick-wall. North Stoneham Church 41, *KP* 1994; Winchester Cathedral 42, frequent on N side and on chest-tombs, *FR, KS & TCh* 1994; St Cross Church, Winchester 42, E end of church and ancient brick-wall, *FR & KS* 1995; Headbourne Worthy Church 43, Romsey Abbey 32, Barton Stacey Church 44, East Meon Church 62, Farley Chamberlayne Church 32, all *FR* 1995.

L. pulicaris   Occasional, but probably overlooked outside New Forest. Found on smooth bark of young trees and twigs, and also on old fence-posts. 10, 11, 19, 20, 21, 30, 31, 33, 35, 52, 53, 66, 70, 75.

L. quercicola   Rare. On old *Quercus*,

scattered in the New Forest, and Hurstbourne Park 44; Cranbury Park 42, *FR & SRD* 1975. Also 10, 20, 21, 30.

L. saligna   Rare, on fence-posts. Alton 73, *MMG* 1986; Old Winchester Hill 62, *BJC* 1972; Headbourne Worthy churchyard 43, *FR* 1995.

<*L. sarcopisioides*   Formerly on old posts near Brockenhurst, *JMCr*, Hb.BM. Believed extinct.>

L. soralifera   Very rare. On acid stonework. Selborne Church 73, *KP* 1990.

L. sublivescens (*Lecidea sublivescens*)   Rare. On old, dry *Quercus* in old, open woodlands and parklands. Frame Wood 30, *FR* c.1980; Hurstbourne Park 44, *FR* 1983; Bramshill Park 75, *BJC* c.1972.

L. sulphurea (*Lecidea sulphurea*)   Frequent. On acid gravestones, acid stonework and old brick-walls. Often overgrowing thalli of *Tephromela atra*. 37 squares.

L. symmicta   Scattered and probably quite frequent in less polluted areas. On worked timber and nutrient-enriched branches. 19 squares.

L. varia   Occasional. On worked timber. 20, 21, 33, 50, 51, 60, 62, 71, 72, 73.

[*Lecidea cinnabarina*   Erroneously recorded, as confused in the past with *Pertusaria pupillaris* and *Schismatomma quercicola* (*qq.v.*, pp.319 and 321). *L. cinnabarina* is probably not correctly recorded for Great Britain.]

L. doliiformis   Rare. Only in the New Forest. Red Shoot Wood 10, *RW* 1987; by Beaulieu River 30, *NAS* 1990; The Noads 30, *NAS* 1990; Howen Bushes 21, *NAS* 1992; Mark Ash 20, *NAS* 1993; Amie's Wood 10, *NAS* 1991.

L. fuscoatra   Widespread and locally frequent, especially in the N. On acid, nutrient-enriched gravestones and brick walls. 21 squares.

L. lichenicola   Rare. On chalk pebbles, Stockbridge Down 33, *KS* 1988; Frequent, Butser Hill 72, *OLG* 1991.

L. turgidula   Very rare. On bark, Mark Ash 20, *BJC* c.1972.

L. uliginosa See under **Placynthi-ella uliginosa** (p.320).

Lecidella elaeochroma Widespread. On smooth, basic bark in open situations. Locally frequent, but rare or absent in the polluted areas of the extreme NE, and a casualty of agricultural pollution in rural areas. 42 squares.

L. scabra Common. On brick walls and siliceous tombs. Slightly under-recorded as rarely fertile. 33 squares.

L. stigmatea Frequent on limestone walls mainly of churches. 44 squares.

Lempholemma polyanthes Very rare. On damp base of limestone chest-tomb, Barton Stacey churchyard 44, *FR* 1995.

Lepraria incana sensu lato Abundant. Mainly on sheltered bark and rock. Records for *Lepraria* spp. need clarifying, but *L. incana* is likely to prove very common (with *L. lobificans*, *L. lesdainii* and *L. umbricola*, as well as *L. nivalis* which, though not yet recorded, is very likely to be present). Recorded in 57 squares as *L. incana* sensu lato.

L. lesdainii In deeply shaded wall-crevices. Droxford churchyard 61, *TCh & FR* 1994.

L. lobificans Frequent in the New Forest, *NAS* 1994; and in old church-yards.

L. umbricola Rare. On *Fagus*, Wood Crates 20, *OWP* 1994. Also 21, 30.

[**Leproloma membranaceum** See *L. vouauxii* below.]

L. vouauxii Quite frequent. On limestone gravestones and church-walls; also on mortar of old walls. On *Quercus* in Highland Water Inclosure. Most pre-1989 records of this species were made under the name of *Lepraria membranacea* = *Leproloma membranaceum*. As this is an acidophilous, mainly upland species, it is unlikely to occur in Hants. (Other spp. of *Leproloma* may occur.) Approximately 26 squares.

Leproplaca chrysodeta Occasional but probably widespread. In small quantity near the base of sheltered church-walls on limestone; mostly

recorded at present in the N. 33, 34, 40, 44, 54, 55, 64, 74, 75.

L. xantholyta Quite rare. On sheltered, limestone church-walls and tombs. Less common than the previous species and in less shaded sites, e.g on tombstone, Hursley churchyard 42, *FR* 1972. Also 11, 22, 33, 34, 40, 42, 45, 64, 76.

Leptogium biatorinum (*L. cretaceum*) Rare. On recently-disturbed chalk soils. Roadside near Wolverton 55, *KS* 1986, det. *BJC*. Probably under-recorded. Also 65, 75.

<*L. coralloideum* (*L. palmatum*) Formerly near Stoney Cross 21, *EMHo* 1930, Hb.BM.>

L. gelatinosum (*L. sinuatum*) Rare. In thin chalk-turf, and on old limestone memorials. Broughton Down 23; Martin Down 01; Micheldever Spoil Heaps 54; Hackwood 64; Butser Hill 72, *OLG* 1991; Beaulieu churchyard 30, *FR* 1995.

L. lichenoides Rare. Amongst mosses on smooth bark of *Fagus* and *Fraxinus*, in the New Forest only. 20, 21, 30, 31.

L. plicatile Locally rather frequent. Ropley churchyard 63, *BJC* 1973. Also 32, 33, 41, 42, 43, 44, 53, 54, 61, 62, 72, 83.

L. schraderi Widespread and occasional to locally frequent. In thin chalk-turf, and mortar of old walls. 20 squares.

<*L. tenuissimum* Old literature record for New Forest, teste *PWJ*, no details available.>

L. teretiusculum Rare. On old *Fraxinus* and *Quercus* in ancient New Forest woods, e.g. Mark Ash 20; on flint, Butser Hill 72, *OLG* 1991. Also 21, 30, 31, 40.

L. turgidum Rare. Fertile on a marble memorial, Burghclere churchyard, 45, *KS* 1985, det. *BJC*; on limestone, Wootton St Lawrence Church 55, *KS* 1985. Also 30, 83.

Leptorhaphis epidermidis Rare. On *Betula*, mainly in the New Forest, but also Butser 72, *FR* 1982, det. *BJC*. Also 20, 21, 30, 63.

L. maggiana Probably a common species in the New Forest. On young

Corylus twigs, Ivy Wood and several other New Forest woods 30, *NAS* 1994; Kings Copse 40, *NAS* 1994.

Lobaria amplissima Very rare. In New Forest ancient woodlands. On *Fagus* at Bramshaw 21; on *Quercus*, South Ocknell 21; *Quercus* bough, Frame Wood 30; fragment on *Fagus*, Mark Ash 20. Also, until 1969, on *Quercus*, Vinney Ridge 20.

L. pulmonaria (Map 577) Rare and confined to the ancient New Forest woodlands where it is, however, occasional. On *Fagus*, *Fraxinus* and *Quercus*. About 150 host-trees are known. 10, 20, 21, 30, 31.

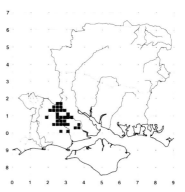

Map 577 Lobaria pulmonaria

<*L. scrobiculata* Formerly near Lyndhurst, *JMCr*, Hb.BM, and Kemp-shott Woods 65, *VCH Hants* 1: 78.>

L. virens (*L. laetevirens*) Rare; confined to the ancient New Forest woodlands where it is local on *Fagus*, *Fraxinus* and *Quercus*. About 70 host-trees are known. 10, 20, 21, 30.

Loxospora elatina (*Haematomma elatinum*) Common in the New Forest on acid-barked trees in sheltered sites; rare elsewhere in ancient woodlands, e.g. Forest of Bere 51, *FR* 1988. 10, 11, 20, 21, 30, 31, 39, 72.

Macentina stigonemoides Probably widespread and frequent. Amongst mosses on *Sambucus* in moderate shade. Near Linkenholt 35, *KS* 1989, det. *BJC*. There are, as yet, few records of this recently-described species. 33, 45, 62.

Megalaria grossa (*Catinaria grossa*) Very rare. On old trees in the New Forest. On *Fagus*, Wood Crates 20; on

Fraxinus, South Ocknell 21; on *Fagus*, Mark Ash 20, *NAS* 1993.

Megalospora tuberculosa (*Bombyliospora pachycarpa*) Occasional, but sterile, in the New Forest. In ancient woodlands on old *Quercus* and *Fagus*. 10, 20, 21, 30, 31.

Melaspilea lentiginosa Rare. In the New Forest. On thallus of *Phaeographis dendritica* on *Ilex*, Bramshaw 21. Also 20.

M. ochrothalamia Rare, in the SW only. On *Ilex* at Vinney Ridge, old woodland N of Burley New Inclosure, and Mark Ash 20. Also 10, 21, 31, 42.

<*Menegazzia terebrata* In 19th century, on trees near Lyndhurst, *JMCr*, Hb.BM. May yet be refound in New Forest carr.>

Micarea botryoides Rare. On clay boundary-bank at Wood Crates 20, *KS* 1987.

M. cinerea Very rare. On *Quercus*, Red Shoot Wood 10, *BJC & NAS*, 1994.

M. denigrata Scattered. On worked timber, mainly tops of fence-posts. Probably commoner than records suggest. 21, 33, 51, 52, 54, 55, 61, 62, 64, 65, 73, 75, 83.

M. erratica (*Lecidea erratica*) Occasional but probably frequent and overlooked. On siliceous pebbles on heaths and open, grassy areas, and on flints in old church walls. 11, 19, 20, 21, 30, 71, 72, 75, 76.

M. lignaria Very rare. On flat stones, Lyndhurst Moor, *JMCr* 1869, Hb.BM. Now on peat in the New Forest, teste *PWJ*.

M. melaena Rare. On top of gatepost, Bramshaw Wood 21, *BJC* 1968, Hb.E. Also 20, 30, 83.

M. misella Rare. On dry lignum, Yateley Common 85, *KS* 1988, det. *BJC*.

M. myriocarpa Rare. On pebbles in sandy soil at base of uprooted tree, North Ocknell 21, *KS* 1990, det. *BJC*. Probably overlooked elsewhere.

M. nitschkeana Occasional. On

twigs. *Juniperus* scrub, Stockbridge Down 33. Also 21, 30, 51.

M. peliocarpa Occasional. In the New Forest, on acid bark. 10, 20, 21, 30, 31. Also on fence-rail at Farleigh Wallop 64, *MMG*, det. *BJC*.

M. prasina Widespread and frequent. On acid bark and damp lignum in established woodland. Commonest in the New Forest. 31 squares.

M. pycnidiophora Occasional. On shaded, smooth bark in the S; commonest in the New Forest; also Forest of Bere 51, 61, Upper Hamble Country Park 41 and Waggoner's Wells 83, *NAS* 1994. Also 10, 20, 21, 30, 31, 64.

Microcalicium ahlneri Rare. On rather soft lignum in the New Forest. High Corner Wood 11, *NAS*; South Brinken 20, *KS & NAS*; Parkhill Copse 30, *NAS*; Great Stubby Hat 31, *NAS* 1994.

Mniacea jungermanniae Rare. On clay soil of trackside embankment, Appleslade Inclosure 10, *RW*. Recently found in other New Forest sites by *HM*.

Moelleropsis humida (*Biatora humida*) Rare. On bare, clayey soil on roadside embankment NW of Basingstoke 55, *KS* 1990, det. *BJC*. A pioneer species; it could occur more widely in a sterile state.

Mycoblastus caesius (*Haematomma caesium*) Locally common in the New Forest. On more or less smooth bark of *Betula*, *Fagus* and *Ilex*. 10, 20, 21, 30, 31.

M. sterilis Scattered and probably quite frequent. On acid trunks and branches. Commonest in the New Forest. 19 squares.

Mycocalicium subtile Very rare. On *Quercus* in the New Forest. Old woodland N of Burley New Inclosure 20. Also 30.

Mycoglaena myricae Common on *Myrica* in the New Forest but underrecorded; not yet looked for on *Myrica* elsewhere. 11, 20, 21, 30, 31, 40, *NAS* 1993–94.

[*Mycomicrothelia confusa* Records for this species are referable to *Kirsch-*

steiniothelia aethiops (Berk. & M. A. Curtis) D.Hawksw., a non-lichenized fungus, which should not therefore be further considered here.]

Mycoporum quercus Widespread. On twigs, especially of *Quercus*. Most records are from the S of the county. 19 squares.

Nephroma laevigatum Very rare and now possibly extinct. On one old *Quercus*, Vinney Ridge 20, *FR* 1967 to *c.*1985.

Normandina pulchella Widespread but occasional, except in the New Forest where locally common. On mossy trunks in old woodlands. 28 squares.

Ochrolechia androgyna Widespread and quite frequent. On acid bark, especially in the New Forest. 35 squares.

O. inversa Occasional in the New Forest. On *Fagus*, *Quercus* and *Betula*. 10, 11, 20, 21, 30, 31.

O. parella Frequent. Generally in small quantity on old brick, flint or siliceous walls; occasionally on gravestones. Dominant on N wall of Burghclere Church 46, *KS* 1985. 43 squares.

O. subviridis Common. On basic bark, usually in open situations, mainly on *Fraxinus* and *Quercus*. 46 squares.

<*O. tartarea* In 19th century, near Cadnam, New Forest, *JMCr*, Hb.BM.>

O. turneri Widespread but occasional. On more-or-less acid bark. 37 squares.

***Omphalina* spp.** Rare. In the New Forest. Most of the records have not been reliably determined to species level, except for those detailed below. 20, 21, 30, 31.

Omphalina hudsoniana (*Coriscium viride*) Rare. In the New Forest on peaty soil. Mark Ash 20. Also 21.

Opegrapha atra Widespread. Frequent in the S but apparently rare in the N. On smooth bark of *Fagus*, *Corylus* and *Fraxinus*, often on quite small trunks. 21 squares.

O. calcarea*, *O. chevallieri* and *O. conferta See *O. saxatalis* below.

O. corticola   Occasional. On rough bark of old trees in ancient woodlands; mainly in the New Forest but also Hurstbourne Park 44, *FR*; Highclere Park 46, *FR*; Kilmeston Severals 52. Also 10, 11, 20, 21, 29, 30, 31, 39.

O. fumosa   Occasional. Locally frequent in the New Forest on *Quercus*, e.g. Stricknage Wood 21, *BJC & FR* 1984; Hollands Wood 30, *BJC* 1984; Anses Wood and Bramshaw Wood 21; Red Shoot Wood 10; Whitley Wood 30, *NAS* 1992.

O. herbarum   Scattered and generally rather rare. On shaded bark. Most records are from the New Forest where it is frequent; also found in parklands. May be overlooked. 10, 20, 21, 30, 31, 35, 39, 44, 46, 53, 62, 71, 72.

O. lichenoides   See *O. varia* below.

O. mougeotii   Very rare. On limestone wall, Old Burghclere Church 45, *KS* 1985.

O. multipuncta   Apparently rare. Local in sap-runs on old *Fagus* in the New Forest. Mark Ash Wood 20, on *Fagus*, *NAS* 1993; Gritnam Wood 20, *NAS* 1992; Shave Wood and E of Rufus Stone 21, *NAS* 1993.

O. niveoatra   Rare or overlooked. On rather shaded, more or less smooth trunks on bark or lignum. 20, 42.

O. ochrocheila   Infrequent. On shaded, decorticate parts of standing trunks and bark in old woodland. Mainly in the New Forest but also Danebury 33; and Rotherfield Park 63. Also 10, 20, 21, 29, 30.

O. prosodea   Scattered and occasional. On ancient *Quercus* or *Taxus*; rare in the New Forest. Also on ancient *Taxus* in churchyards in the S of the county, e.g. Warblington 70; Brockenhurst churchyard 30. *O. prosodea* has the most southerly distribution of any lichen species in Britain.

O. rufescens   Rare and scattered. Mostly on *Fraxinus* in open woodland; also on *Quercus*, King's Hat 30, *NAS* 1991; and *Ilex*, Hive Garn Bottom 11, *NAS* 1994. 10, 20, 53, 71, 72, 73.

O. saxatilis (incl. *O. calcarea*, *O. chevallieri* and *O. conferta*)   Widespread but only occasional and locally frequent, especially in the S. Usually low down on calcareous, N walls of old churches. 28 squares.

O. sorediifera   Widespread but infrequent. On bark in established woodland. Most common in the New Forest. 19 squares.

O. varia (incl. *O. lichenoides*)   Widespread and quite frequent. On nutrient-rich bark of old *Quercus* and on basic bark of *Fraxinus* and *Acer*. Formerly on *Ulmus*. 31 squares.

O. vermicellifera   Scattered. On nutrient-rich bark of *Fraxinus* and *Acer* on dry, shaded sides of trees; commonest in the New Forest. 20, 21, 29, 30, 34, 39, 44, 46, 50, 52, 60, 63, 73.

O. viridis   Rare. In the New Forest on *Fagus* at Burley Old Inclosure 20; Hollands Wood 30. Also 21. Old record from Hayling Island *c*.79, ex Hb.CLa 1911.

O. vulgata (*O. cinerea*)   Widespread and frequent. On rather shaded, more-or-less smooth trunks on bark or lignum. The commonest *Opegrapha* species in the county. 40 squares.

O. xerica   Very rare (or overlooked?). On ancient *Taxus* in churchyards. Farringdon 73, *FR* 1993; Long Sutton 74, *FR* 1995.

Pachyphiale carneola (*P. cornea*) Widespread but really common only in the New Forest; absent from more polluted areas. On bark in old woodlands and parklands, and in the New Forest in mature *Quercus* plantations. 33 squares.

Pannaria conoplea   Now rare and decreasing. In the New Forest on mossy *Quercus* or *Fagus*, e.g. South Ocknell, Great Wood and Stricknage Wood 21; Busketts Wood 31; Amie's Wood 10. Also 20.

P. mediterranea   Very rare. In the New Forest on one old roadside *Quercus*, Shave Wood 21 *FR & PJW* 1972, 1993.

<*P. rubiginosa*   One old literature record for the New Forest, teste *PJW*.>

P. sampaiana   Very rare and probably now extinct. In the New Forest on *Fraxinus*, South Ocknell 21, *FR* 1971–81, not refound 1990.

Parmelia acetabulum   Scattered and occasional, mostly in the N. On wayside trees, now mainly *Acer* and *Fraxinus*. It may have declined due to Dutch elm disease and agricultural pollution. 24, 34, 39, 52, 53, 55, 62, 65, 72, 73, 74, 75.

P. arnoldii   Very rare. In the New Forest on branches of trees, especially *Quercus*, in damp situations. Stricknage Wood 21; Shave Wood 21, *BJC & FR* 1971; Wood Crates 20, *FR & SRD* 1971, Hb.BM.

P. borreri   Widespread but occasional. On nutrient-rich bark in open sites in generally less-polluted areas. 23 squares.

P. caperata   Very common except in urban areas where occasional only. On trunks and large branches of a wide variety of trees; occasional on fences and stonework. 53 squares.

P. conspersa   On granite memorial, Ellingham churchyard 10, *FR* 1994.

P. crinita   Confined to the New Forest where frequent. Mainly on mature *Fagus* but also on *Quercus* boles. 10, 11, 20, 21, 29, 30, 31.

P. disjuncta   Very rare. On granite, Copythorne churchyard 31, *PWJ* 1972; Bishop's Waltham churchyard 51, *FR* 1992; West Tisted churchyard 62, *FR* 1993.

P. elegantula   Scattered and occasional. On nutrient-rich trunks and branches on wayside and parkland trees; not in the New Forest woodlands. 22, 30, 32, 44, 45, 46, 53, 55, 61, 62, 65, 72, 75, 85.

P. exasperata   Old record from Lyndhurst, *JMCr*, Hb.BM; Sandy Point, Hayling Island 79, on *Quercus*, *FR & KS* 1993.

P. exasperatula   Rare or overlooked. On nutrient-rich bark in parkland. 62, 73.

P. glabratula ssp. *glabratula*   Very common. On bark and wood; occasional on nutrient-enriched rock; rarely fertile. 54 squares.

ssp. *fuliginosa*   Frequent on nutrient-enriched, acid tombstones. Rare on bark. 27 squares.

P. horrescens Occasional. On bark in sheltered sites in the New Forest, mainly on *Fagus*, but also on *Ilex* and *Alnus*, e.g. Red Shoot Wood 10; Wood Crates 20; Mallard Wood 30; Busketts 31; Shave Wood 21. Otherwise in Britain only in SW England and North Wales.

P. laciniatula Widespread. On basic trunks and branches of wayside and parkland trees, mainly in the N and E on *Fraxinus*; very rare in the New Forest. 19 squares.

P. laevigata Very rare. In the New Forest on moist acid bark of *Alnus*, *Ilex*, *Salix*, *Betula* and *Fagus* in very wet carr. Mark Ash 20, *FR* 1992. Formerly at Wood Crates 20, to 1975. An oceanic species at its eastern limit in the British Isles in the New Forest.

P. minarum (Sched. 8) Rare to locally frequent. On mature *Fagus* in the New Forest. Apart from W Cornwall, known nowhere else in the British Isles. Busketts 31; Wood Crates, Mark Ash, Hincheslea Wood and Gritnam Wood 20; Shave Wood, Rockram Wood and Stricknage Wood 21. Recorded from 49 trees in 1993/94, *NAS*.

P. mougeotii Common. On siliceous graves, especially granite chippings, and less commonly on brickwork or hard lignum. This species has increased in recent years and is probably still spreading. 41 squares.

P. pastillifera Occasional. On trees in open situations. Due to past confusion with *P. tiliacea*, records need checking but probably more frequent in Hants than that species. Recorded in 01, 02, 12, 34, 45, 52, 53, 54, 61, 62, 72, 73, 74.

P. perlata Widespread. On a variety of trees in open woodlands. Common in the New Forest but less common elsewhere, and on basic-barked trees in polluted areas. Less common than *P. caperata* but increasing as air pollution by SO₂ decreases in and around towns. 44 squares.

<P. quercina Probably now extinct. Last recorded on *Fraxinus* near Lymington 39, *PWJ* 1960.>

P. reddenda Frequent in the New Forest but scattered elsewhere. On *Quercus* and *Fagus* in sheltered, old woodland. 17 squares.

P. reticulata Widespread. Frequent in the New Forest and occasional elsewhere. On *Quercus*, *Fagus* and *Fraxinus* in open, old woodlands and in pastures. More abundant than *P. perlata* in much of the New Forest. 28 squares.

P. revoluta Frequent. On trunks and branches of broad-leaved woodland trees; occasional on nutrient-enriched, sandstone gravestones. 48 squares.

P. saxatilis Very common. On acid bark and siliceous rocks. 52 squares.

P. sinuosa Very rare. Only in the New Forest. On *Ilex* in carr, Stinking Edge 20, *PWJ* 1972; on the upper boughs of fallen *Fagus*, Shave Wood 21, *BJC* 1972. An oceanic species at its eastern limit.

P. soredians Occasional. On trunks and branches in dry, sunny situations, mainly in the SE. A Mediterranean species. 10, 31, 32, 42, 52, 53, 60, 61, 70, 71, 72, 79.

P. subaurifera Frequent. On branches of broad-leaved trees; less commonly on nutrient-rich trunks of small trees, wood and gravestones. 43 squares.

P. subrudecta Very common. On wayside and woodland trees but occasionally on fences. 52 squares.

P. sulcata Very common. On wayside and woodland trees everywhere; occasional on fences and siliceous, nutrient-enriched gravestones. Probably commoner than *P. saxatilis*. 57 squares.

P. taylorensis Very rare. Only in the New Forest. On four *Fagus*, Anses Wood 21, *PWJ & FR*, 1972, 1989.

P. tiliacea Apparently rare. On old *Acer*, near Ladle Hill 45, *KS & FR* 1985. Confusible with *P. pastillifera* (*q.v.*).

P. verruculifera Widespread and frequent. On mainly flat, siliceous or granite gravestones. 27 squares.

Parmeliella testacea Very rare and possibly extinct. On old *Fraxinus*, South Ocknell 21, *BJC, FR & SRD* 1971, det. *PMJ*. Not refound in 1990.

Parmeliopsis ambigua (*Foraminella ambigua*) Widespread but infrequent.

On more or less acid bark. It has spread in recent years. 22 squares.

P. hyperopta (*Foraminella hyperopta*) Rare on acid bark in the New Forest 20, 21, 29, 30, 31. Otherwise a species of the Caledonian pine-forests.

Peltigera canina Apparently very rare. On grass heath with slight base-enrichment in New Forest, Stoney Cross 21, *NAS* 1992; Hatchet Pond 30, *NAS, KS & FR* 1993; Ocknell Wood 21, *NAS* 1993.

P. didactyla (*P. spuria*) Occasional. On bare, sandy or clay soils, generally in rather disturbed sites, e.g. roadsides near Kingsclere 55; old gravel-working, Bramshill Plantation 76. Also 19, 21, 23, 32, 42, 72, 86.

P. horizontalis Occasional. On mossy trunks in old woodlands, especially in the New Forest, e.g. Stricknage Wood 21. Also Hurstbourne Park 44, *FR* 1971; Combe Wood 35, *FR* 1972. Also 20, 30, 31.

P. lactucifolia (*P. hymenina*) Scattered and occasional, usually on bare soils and tree-bases. Mainly in the New Forest area. 11, 20, 21, 23, 29, 30, 31, 46, 62, 72.

P. membranacea Scattered and occasional. Amongst mosses on soil and fallen trees. Most frequent in the New Forest. 19, 20, 21, 23, 29, 30, 31, 33, 38, 49, 50, 56, 70, 72, 73, 83. Some of these may be *P. canina*, which has only recently been distinguished in Hants.

P. neckeri Very rare but probably overlooked. On gravel path, Newtown churchyard 46, *KS* 1985, det. *BJC*.

P. praetextata Scattered and occasional, except in the New Forest where it is frequent. On mossy trunks and roots. 21, 23, 29, 30, 31, 35, 44, 64, 73, 83.

P. rufescens Scattered and occasional. On thin soils, generally over chalk or clay. 19, 20, 23, 24, 32, 38, 42, 44, 45, 51, 64, 71, 72, 73.

Pertusaria albescens Widespread (except in highly-polluted areas) but rather infrequent. On woodland and parkland trees. 37 squares.

var. *corallina* Widespread and more

frequent than the nominate variety; in the same habitats. 40 squares.

P. amara   Very common on wayside and woodland trees. Occasional on siliceous gravestones and worked timber. The commonest *Pertusaria* species; f. *pulvinata* is frequent in the New Forest. 54 squares.

P. coccodes   Frequent on waysides and open-woodland trees. Occasional on worked timber. Fertile at Warren Bottom Copse 55. 41 squares.

P. coronata   Very rare. Only in the New Forest. On *Fraxinus*, Red Shoot Wood 10, *FR* 1978, det. *PWJ*; Vinney Ridge 20, *FR* 1995.

P. flavicans   Apparently rare or overlooked. On north walls of churches. South Hayling 70, *FR* 1992. Some saxicolous records of *Lecanora expallens* (*q.v.*, p.314) may belong here.

P. flavida   Widespread but occasional. On trees in waysides or open woodland, especially common in the New Forest. 27 squares.

P. hemisphaerica   Frequent. On rough bark of mature trees in open woodland situations, mainly on *Quercus*. 39 squares.

P. hymenea   Common. On bark of woodland trees. 48 squares.

P. leioplaca   Widespread and quite frequent. On smooth bark of small trees or coppice-poles, especially *Corylus*, in rather dense woodland. 34 squares.

P. multipuncta   Widespread and frequent in the S, especially the New Forest. Occasional in the N. On smooth bark in old woodlands. 19 squares.

P. pertusa   Common. On wayside and woodland trees, rarely on stonework. 50 squares.

P. pupillaris (erroneously reported in past as *Lecidea cinnabarina* (*q.v.*, p.314)) Rare. In eastern woodlands only. Plash Wood, Rotherfield Park 63, *NAS* 1990; Oakshott Hanger 72. Also 64, 83.

P. pustulata   Rare. On trunks of *Fagus* in the New Forest and at Downlands, near Liphook 83, *KS & FR* 1990, conf. *BJC*; Amie's Wood 10; Emery Down and Mark Ash 20. Also 21.

P. velata   Occasional. On smooth bark of old trees in ancient New Forest woodland. Commonest on *Fagus* but also on *Quercus* and *Fraxinus*. 20, 21, 30, 31. The New Forest is its headquarters in Britain.

Petractis clausa   Rare. On chalk pebbles, Butser Hill 71, *BJC* 1973; 72, *OLG* 1991; limestone capping on bridge, Bournemouth 09, *KS & VJG* 1991.

Phaeographis dendritica   Occasional to locally frequent. On smooth bark in old woodlands, mainly in the S and W, and commonest in the New Forest. 10, 11, 20, 21, 23, 30, 31, 32, 33, 39, 42, 50, 51, 70, 73.

P. inusta   Occasional. On smooth bark in old woodlands, mainly in the New Forest, but also the Forest of Bere 51, 61, *FR* 1988; and Alice Holt Forest 84, *FR* 1987. Also 10, 20, 21, 30.

P. lyellii   Occasional. On smooth bark in the New Forest. Roe Inclosure, Red Shoot Wood 10, *BJC & FR* 1971; Frame Wood 30. Also 20, 21, 31, 39, 40.

P. smithii   Very rare. On *Carpinus* in the New Forest. Bakers Copse, Roydon Woods 30, *PWJ* 1982.

Phaeophyscia endophoenicea   Very rare. On several *Quercus* by Long Beech Inclosure, New Forest 21, *NAS* 1993.

P. nigricans   Occasional. On concrete or brickwork, e.g. Winchester 42, *SRD* 1972; Liss Railway Station 72, *FR* 1972. Probably somewhat overlooked. Also 32, 43.

P. orbicularis   Abundant. On nutrient-rich bark, rock and man-made substrates. 52 squares.

Phlyctis agelaea   Very rare. On *Acer campestre*, Ivy Wood 30, *VJG & FR* 1974.

P. argena   Common on acid bark in woodlands and parklands. Rare on sandstone gravestones. 49 squares.

Phyllopsora rosei   Occasional to locally frequent in the New Forest. On *Fagus* and *Quercus*, sometimes fertile. Wood Crates 20; Stricknage Wood 21; Frame Wood 30; Busketts Wood 31.

Physcia adscendens   Very common. On bark and rock in a wide range of nutrient-enriched sites. 56 squares.

P. aipolia   Frequent. On sunlit, nutrient-enriched bark, especially *Sambucus* and *Fraxinus*. 30 squares.

P. caesia   Very common on calcareous rocks and man-made substrates, especially tops of limestone gravestones. Occasional on nutrient-enriched lignum. 51 squares.

<*P. clementei*   19th-century record at Southampton, Hb.BM.>

P. dubia   Widespread but occasional. On nutrient-enriched siliceous rocks, generally in graveyards. May be overlooked. 20, 33, 35, 42, 53, 54, 55, 64, 72, 74, 76.

[*P. semipinnata*   Recorded in *Census Cat.Brit.Lichens* (1953); no other record.]

P. stellaris   Sandy Point, Hayling Island 79, on *Quercus*, *FR & KS* 1993.

P. tenella   Common. On nutrient-rich, sunlit bark and rocks. 44 squares.

P. tribacia   Occasional to locally frequent. On very nutrient-rich bark of wayside trees, *Acer* and *Fraxinus*, and on old walls in churchyards. 26 squares.

<*P. tribacioides* (Sched. 8)   Old record, fruit-trees, Lymington, Hb.BM ex Hb.JMCr, det. *RMo* 1972.>

Physconia distorta (*P. pulverulacea*) Widespread but rather infrequent. On sunlit, nutrient-rich bark of mature trees. Not found in the most polluted areas or the New Forest woodlands; may also have suffered from agricultural pollution. 34 squares.

P. enteroxantha   Apparently only occasional. On nutrient-rich bark of wayside trees; most frequent in the N. 35, 42, 45, 51, 52, 55, 63, 65.

P. grisea   Very common. On nutrient-rich bark and calcareous rocks. 50 squares.

P. perisidiosa   Widespread. On nutrient-rich bark of wayside trees. 28 squares.

Placynthiella icmalea (see also *P. oligotropha* and *P. uliginosa*) Frequent. On bark, moss on walls, and lignum, including worked timber. 41 squares.

P. oligotropha (*Lecidea oligotropha*) Apparently rare. On bare peat in the New Forest. Some records of *P. icmalea* may belong here. 30.

P. uliginosa (*Lecidea uliginosa*) Occasional. On bare peat in the New Forest and NE heaths. Likely to be much commoner than records suggest, and some records of *P. icmalea* may belong here. 19, 20, 21, 30, 75.

Placynthium nigrum Frequent. On calcareous gravestones, especially chest-tombs, but not in all church-yards. Also occasionally on chalk stones. 42 squares.

P. tantaleum Very rare. On chalk stones. Butser Hill 71, *BJC* 1973.

P. tremniacum Very rare. 32, *TWO c.*1978. Possibly referable to *P. nigrum*.

Platismatia glauca Common on acid bark, especially of branches. Occasional on wood. Much less common near the coast. 43 squares.

Polyblastia albida Very rare. On chalk pebbles. Butser Hill 71, *BJC* 1973; Noar Hill 73, *KS* 1988.

P. dermatodes Very rare. On chalk stones. Butser Hill 71, *BJC* 1973; 72, *OLG* 1991.

P. gelatinosa Occasional. On thin, chalky soil, e.g. Butser Hill 71, *BJC* 1973; Butser Hill 72, *OLG* 1991; Old Burghclere Lime Quarry 45, *KS* 1985; roadside W of Basingstoke 55; Martin Down 01, *VJG* 1991; Broughton Down 23, *KS* 1986. Probably overlooked.

Polysporina simplex Occasional. On rough, granite gravestones, mainly in the N and W, though may be over-looked as it tends to occur in small quantity. 01, 21, 33, 34, 42, 43, 56, 65.

Porina aenea Widespread and quite frequent. On shaded smooth bark of mainly young stems of *Fraxinus* and *Corylus*. 24 squares.

P. borreri Occasional. In the New Forest on *Quercus* and *Ilex*, e.g. Shave Wood 21; High Corner Wood 11, *NAS* 1993. Also 10, 20, 30, 31.

P. chlorotica Rare. On flint pebbles near acid streams of the New Forest. Highland Water 21. Also 20.

P. leptalea Occasional. On smooth bark of *Fagus* and *Carpinus*. Forest of Bere 61; Frobury Park Copse, near Ecchinswell 55. Also 20, 21, 30, 31, 46.

P. linearis Very rare or overlooked. On limestone gravestone, Winchfield 75, *KS* 1985.

Porpidia cinereoatra Very rare. On acid stonework. Burley churchyard 20, *FR* 1995; Tichborne churchyard 53, Droxford churchyard 61, both *FR* 1994.

P. crustulata (*Huilia crustulata*) Occasional. On brick and acid pebbles; probably under-recorded. 20, 23, 31, 55, 65, 71.

[*P. macrocarpa* (*Huilia macrocarpa*) The only record (*Census Cat. Brit. Lichens* (1953)) is probably an error.]

P. soredizodes (*Huilia soredizodes*) Rare or overlooked. Droxford church-yard 61, *TCh & FR* 1994.

P. tuberculosa (*Huilia tuberculosa*) Very common. On sandstone and gran-ite gravestones, and on smooth brick-walls. 41 squares.

Protoblastenia calva Very rare. On limestone stonework, e.g. Winchester Cathedral 42, *FR* 1994.

P. incrustans Rare on calcareous stonework. Droxford churchyard 61, *TCh & FR* 1994.

P. rupestris Frequent. On calcareous walls and tombs throughout the county, also on flints and chalk pebbles in chalk grassland. 50 squares.

Pseudevernia furfuracea Very rare. On acid bark. Plash Wood, Rotherfield Park 63, *KS & NAS* 1990; tiles, Medstead Church 63, *FR* 1994. Also 20, 53. Records of this and the follow-ing taxon have not always been distin-guished.

var. *ceratea* Very rare. On *Quercus*, Farleigh Wallop 64, *KS* 1983; Eyeworth Wood and South Ocknell Wood 21, *FR & PWJ* 1971.

<*Pseudocyphellaria aurata* Early 19th-century record for the New Forest, Miss Hardy, formerly in Hb.WBo, now Hb.K.>

Psilolechia leprosa Rare or over-

looked. On church-wall subject to copper influence, e.g. near lightning-conductors. Longstock Church 33, *KS* 1988; Herriard Church 64, *OWP & KS* 1987.

P. lucida Very common. On shel-tered walls and vertical, siliceous gravestones. 45 squares.

Psora decipiens Very rare. On com-pacted, chalk soil, Isle of Wight Hill 23, *FR & PWJ* 1975.

Pycnothelia papillaria Occasional in the New Forest; rare elsewhere. On moist heaths. Yateley Common 85, *FR*, 1988; Shedfield Common 51, *BJC* 1972. Also 10, 11, 20, 21, 29, 30, 40.

Pyrenocollema monense (*Arthropyre-nia monensis*) Occasional. On chalk pebbles in rather shaded sites; probably overlooked. Near Linkenholt 35, *KS* 1989; Noar Hill 73, *KS* 1990; Butser Hill 72, *OLG* 1991; Danebury hill-fort 33, and near Litchfield 45, both *KS* 1989.

Pyrenula chlorospila Frequent in the New Forest on smooth bark, especially *Fagus*. Occasional elsewhere on *Acer* and *Fraxinus*. 16 squares.

P. macrospora Frequent in the New Forest; rare elsewhere. On smooth bark. 10, 20, 21, 29, 30, 31, 32, 42, 44, 60, 63, 73.

P. nitida Rare. In the New Forest, on smooth bark of *Fagus*, e.g. Mallard Wood 30; Wood Crates 20; Busketts 31.

Pyrrhospora quernea Common. On neutral bark of wayside and open-woodland trees. Only occasionally fer-tile. 52 squares.

Ramalina calicaris Rare. On sunlit trees. Scrubby area near Exbury 49, *SRD c.*1972; on *Ulmus*, West Tyther-ley 22, *FR & SRD* 1972. Also 64.

R. canariensis (*R. baltica*) Scattered and occasional. On nutrient-enriched, wayside trees; rarely, on sheltered church-walls. 01, 02, 11, 12, 22, 29, 39, 45, 49, 53, 61, 62, 63, 72, 79.

R. farinacea Very common. On sunlit tree-trunks and branches. 52 squares.

R. fastigiata Frequent. On sunlit, nutrient-enriched trunks and branches. 38 squares.

R. fraxinea   Rare. On sunlit, nutrient-enriched trees. Mainly coastal and decreasing. 12, 19, 29, 39, 49, 79.

R. lacera (*R. duriaei*)   Very rare. Boldre Church 39, *FR* 1993.

Ramonia chrysophaea   Occasional. On old, rather damp *Quercus* trunks. Forest of Bere 61, *FR*; Great Wood, Anses Wood, North Ocknell 21, *NAS*; Brinken, Mark Ash 20, *NAS*; Pinnick Wood, Amie's Wood 10; Rushpole Wood, Busketts Wood 31; High Corner Wood 11, *NAS*, most over period 1988–94. On *Ulmus*, Laverstoke Park 44, *BJC* 1971.

R. dictyospora   Very rare. On *Quercus* bough, Stricknage Wood 21, *BJC* 1984; on lignum from inside a hollow *Ilex*, Busketts Wood 31, *NAS* 1992; Shappen Burley 20, *NAS* 1993..

R. nigra   Rare. Only in the New Forest, on lignum inside trunks of old trees. Dead *Fagus*, Wood Crates 20, *VJG* 1990; Long Beech 21, *FR & NAS* 1991. Also on base-enriched bark of *Quercus*, Irons Well and Great Wood, Bramshaw 21, and on lignum inside a hollow *Fraxinus*, Lucas Castle 21, both *NAS c.*1990.

Rhizocarpon concentricum   Rare. On flints on basic soils. Isle of Wight Hill 23; Butser Hill 72, *OLG* 1991; Martin Down 01, *VJG* 1991. Also 71.

R. distinctum   Very rare. On siliceous stonework. Rough granite memorial, Ropley Church 63, *BJC* 1973; Chalton Church 71, *BJC* 1973.

R. geographicum   Scattered and occasional. On brick, tile and slate roofs, flint stonework and siliceous gravestones. 11, 20, 21, 46, 53, 63, 64, 65, 73.

R. obscuratum   Frequent. On siliceous gravestones and flint pebbles on clay soils. 37 squares.

Rinodina aspersa (*Buellia aspersa*) Very rare. On pebbles. Isle of Wight Hill 23, *PWJ* 1975; Lyndhurst Moor, *JMCr* 1906. Probably to be found on coastal shingle-beaches.

R. colobinoides   Very rare. On one *Acer* tree, Brockenhurst Park 30, *NAS* 1994.

R. efflorescens   Occasional. On bark in damp sites, e.g. on *Quercus*, Sutton

Park Wood 62, *BJC* 1973; Wood Crates 20, *FR & ESé* 1984; Pamber Forest 66, *FR* 1990. Also 21, 31, 61.

R. exigua   Scattered and occasional. On *Quercus* trunks; formerly on *Ulmus*. 19, 29, 32, 39, 40, 42, 63, 75.

R. gennarii   Widespread and locally frequent. On basic, sunlit walls; on many old churches but rarely on gravestones. 35 squares.

R. isidioides   Occasional, in the New Forest only. On *Quercus* trunks, e.g. fertile at Bramshaw and South Bentley 21; Stubbs Wood 30; Red Shoot Wood 10; Queen Bower 20, *FR* 1967–92. Except for one record in Wiltshire (Savernake Forest), otherwise unknown in southern Britain E of Exmoor and Herefordshire.

R. roboris   Widespread and locally plentiful, but rather infrequent. On mature *Quercus* and *Fagus* trunks in open woodland and parkland, especially in the New Forest and SE Hants. 30 squares.

R. sophodes   Apparently rare, but may be under-recorded. On twigs. Sutton Scotney 44, *KS* 1989. Also 01.

R. teichophila   Rare. On stonework with some nutrient enrichment, e.g. on brick steps and church-walls, Old Burghclere 45, *KS & MMG* 1986. Also 11, 35, 61.

Roccella phycopsis   Portchester Church 60, *Macnight* 1836; still plentiful, *KS & FR* 1991; South Hayling Church 70, *HM* 1992.

Sarcogyne regularis   Widespread but only locally frequent. On calcareous rocks and mortar of old walls. 24 squares.

Sarcopyrenia gibba   Rare or overlooked. On chest-tombs, e.g. Winchester Cathedral 42, *TCh, FR & KS* 1994; Droxford churchyard 61, *TCh & FR* 1994; now known in several other sites.

Sarcosagium campestre   Rare. On loose, chalk soils in quite disturbed places. Near Deane 55, *KS* 1985, det. *OLG*; Butser Hill 72, *OLG* 1991.

Schismatomma cretaceum (*S. virgineum*)   Occasional in the New Forest, rare elsewhere. Scattered on dry, old *Quercus* trunks in woodland. Adbury

Park, Newtown 46, *KS*; Kilmeston Severals 52, *FR* 1973; Forest of Bere 61, *FR* 1988; High Corner Wood 11, *FR* 1992. Also 10, 20, 21, 30, 83.

S. decolorans   Frequent. On dry bark of mature trees; generally on *Quercus* but also *Fagus*, *Ilex* and *Carpinus*. 45 squares.

S. niveum   Locally frequent in the New Forest but only occasional elsewhere. On sheltered bark of mature *Fagus* and *Quercus* in old woodlands. 10, 11, 20, 21, 30, 31, 32, 39, 40, 46, 51, 60, 61, 62, 65.

S. quercicola   Widespread in old woodlands in the S; very rare in the N. Mainly on *Quercus* and *Fagus*, especially in the New Forest where it is frequent. 10, 11, 20, 21, 30, 31, 39, 40, 41, 51, 61, 63, 84.

Scoliciosporum chlorococcum   Scattered and occasional. On twigs; probably overlooked and much commoner than records suggest, as rarely fertile. 01, 20, 30, 33, 35, 39, 40, 60, 62, 64, 73.

S. pruinosum   Widespread but occasional. On more or less rough bark in rather dense woodland; mainly on young *Quercus* in bark crevices. 23 squares.

S. umbrinum   Widespread. On slightly nutrient-enriched, sandstone graves; probably commoner than records suggest. 22 squares.

Solenopsora candicans   Scattered and occasional. On calcareous stonework, mainly in the W; most frequent on drip-courses but also on memorials. It appears to be spreading eastwards in the county at present. 01, 11, 12, 19, 21, 22, 24, 32, 33, 35, 38, 41, 42, 43, 50, 53, 55, 60, 61, 70, 75.

Sphaerophorus globosus   Very rare. In the New Forest, on a few old, acid-barked *Quercus*. Great Wood 21, FR.

<*Sphinctrina tubiformis*   Old record, near Brockenhurst, *JMCr*, Hb.BM.>

S. turbinata   Rare, but probably under-recorded. Usually on *Pertusaria* species. Downlands Court, Liphook 83, *FR* 1990. Also 20, 50.

Staurothele hymenogonia   Occasional. On chalk pebbles in open, grassland sites. Butser Hill 71, *BJC* 1973; Noar Hill 73, *KS* 1988; W of Basingstoke 55, *KS* 1990. Also 32, 65, 72.

Steinia geophana Rare. On compacted, chalk soil in rather disturbed sites. Basingstoke town-centre 65 *KS* 1986; Danebury Hill 33, *KS* 1989; Butser Hill 72, *OLG* 1991. Also 45.

Stenocybe pullatula Occasional in the New Forest; very rare elsewhere. On *Alnus* twigs in very wet sites. Waggoners Wells 83, *FR* 1973. Also 20, 21, 30, 31.

S. septata Common in the New Forest; occasional elsewhere. In old woods on *Ilex*, rarely, on *Quercus* and *Betula*. 18 squares.

Stereocaulon pileatum Occasional. On brick walls by roadsides, and on clinker at Micheldever Station 54, *KS* 1991. Under-recorded because of its polluted habitat, and probably spreading in the county. Also 42, 65, 72, 75.

S. vesuvianum var. *symphycheileoides* Rare. In similar sites to the previous species. Basingstoke 65, *KS* 1987. Probably a recent arrival in the county.

Sticta limbata Rare. In the New Forest on old, mossy trunks, e.g. Vinney Ridge 20; Bramshaw Wood, and South Ocknell 21; on *Fraxinus*, Roydon Woods 30; on *Fagus*, Busketts Wood 31. Much decreased in the last ten years.

Strangospora moriformis Rare. On lignum. On gate-post, Westbury Forest, East Meon 62, *BJC* 1972, Hb.BM. Wood of *Ilex* in shade, Wood Crates 20, *BJC & FR* 1972, Hb.BM.

S. ochrophora Rare. On *Quercus* and *Fagus* in old woodland, mainly in the New Forest. Combe Wood 35, *FR* 1972; on *Fraxinus*, Burnt Grove 32, *NAS*, 1992. Also 20, 21, 30.

S. pinicola Very rare or overlooked. On old *Fraxinus* S of Chappetts Farm 62, *BJC* 1972.

Strigula stigmatella Very rare. In the New Forest, on *Quercus*, Great Wood 21, *FR* 1970, det *TDVS*. Only recent British record.

S. taylorii Rare. In the New Forest

on *Fagus*. Bramshaw 21, *FR* 1983; Hincheslea Wood 20, *KS* 1990.

<Teloschistes flavicans (Sched. 8) Old records only: on *Crataegus* at Brockenhurst, JMCr 1906; Knight Wood, JMa 1879.>

Tephromela atra (*Lecanora atra*) Common. On churches, gravestones and old brick-walls; on non-calcareous substrates. Very rare on trees; on *Fagus*, Vinney Ridge 20. 48 squares.

Thelidium decipiens Very rare. On limestone, Priors Dean Church 72, *BJC* 1971.

T. incavatum Rare. On hard chalk. Butser Hill 71, *BJC* 1973; 72, *OLG* 1991; Ropley Church 63, *BJC* 1973; Martin Down 01, *FR & KS* 1991. Also 42.

T. minutulum (*T. mesotropum*) Widespread and rather rare, but overlooked. On chalk pebbles in uncultivated, but sometimes disturbed, chalk areas; also on stone. Less common than *T. zwackhii*. 21, *BJC* 1972. Also 33, 45, 65, 72, 75.

T. zwackhii (*T. microcarpum*) Widespread and occasional, but overlooked. On chalk nodules, often in shade, and thin, chalk soils in uncultivated areas. 23, 24, 33, 45, 52, 54, 55, 62, 65, 71, 72, 73.

Thelocarpon lichenicola Very rare. On sandy soil of upturned root-plate, Mark Ash 20, *KS* 1989, det. *BJC*.

T. ?olivaceum Very rare. On chalk pebble near Litchfield 45, *KS* 1989. There is some uncertainty over this record – the small specimen, which was tentatively identified thus by *BJC*, was not really adequate for determination, and further searches were unsuccessful.

T. pallidum Very rare. On chalk pebbles, Butser Hill 72, *OLG* 1991.

Thelopsis rubella Widespread and frequent in the New Forest, but occasional elsewhere. On old, mossy trunks in old woodlands, mainly of *Quercus* and *Fagus*. Highclere Park 46; Hurstbourne Park 44; Kilmeston Severals 52; Waggoners Wells 83; Alice Holt Forest 74, 84, all *FR*. On old *Fraxinus*, Buriton village green 71, *NAS* 1994. Also 10, 11, 20, 21, 30, 31, 32, 63.

Thelotrema lepadinum (Map 578) Frequent. In old woodlands, generally on mossy trunks; more common in the New Forest, and here especially on *Ilex*. 32 squares.

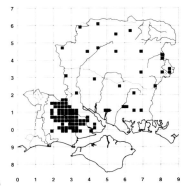

Map 578 *Thelotrema lepadinum*

Tomasellia gelatinosa Rare. On *Corylus* in the New Forest, and at Highclere Park 45, *FR c.*1975. Also 11, 30.

T. lactea Widespread and locally frequent on old *Ilex* in the New Forest. Very rare in England generally. 10, 11, 20, 21, 30, 31.

Toninia aromatica Common. On old, calcareous walls, mainly of churches, but occasionally on tombstones. It prefers three-dimensional to plane surfaces. 45 squares.

T. lobulata Very rare. On chalk soil, Old Burghclere Lime Quarry 45, *KS* 1985.

T. sedifolia (*T. caeruleonigricans*) Rare. In thin chalk-turf. Isle of Wight Hill and Broughton Down 23, *SRD c.*1975; Old Burghclere Lime Quarry 45, and Micheldever Spoil Heaps 54, both *KS* 1985; Ports Down 60, *FR* 1977.

Trapelia coarctata Frequent to locally common. On neutral to acid, slightly nutrient-enriched stonework, brickwork and gravestones. 30 squares.

T. corticola Occasional. In the New Forest, generally on bark of *Quercus*. Wormstall Wood 39, *NAS*; Red Shoot 10, *FR* 1992; Pitts Wood 11, *NAS*; Mark Ash, and on *Fraxinus* at Wood Crates 20, 1992, Stricknage and Long Beech 21, 1991, Mallard Wood 30, 1995, all *FR*.

T. involuta   Occasional. In similar habitats to *T. coarctata*. May be under-recorded. 40, 42, 52, 55, 72, 74, 76.

T. obtegens   Very rare. In similar habitats to *T. coarctata*. 40, *MRDS* 1981; Droxford churchyard 61, *TCh & FR* 1994.

T. placodioides   Occasional. On brick walls and sandstone graves, generally on horizontal surfaces. May be under-recorded. 45, 46, 55, 71, 72, 73, 84.

Trapeliopsis flexuosa (*Lecidea aeruginosa*)   Widespread and quite frequent. On damp lignum and old, worked timber. Probably under-recorded until recently for *T. granulosa*. 11, 21, 24, 33, 39, 45, 46, 52, 54, 55, 65, 66, 73, 75.

T. gelatinosa (*Lecidea gelatinosa*)   Very rare. On sandy soil by track, South Bentley Wood 21, *KS* 1987.

T. granulosa (*Lecidea granulosa*)   Very common. On peat in heathland areas; less common on lignum and worked timber. Some records are probably for *T. flexuosa*. 44 squares.

T. pseudogranulosa   Rare or overlooked. On damp peat, sandy banks, and mossy tree-stumps. Likely to prove frequent. 20, 21, 64, 75.

Usnea articulata   Rare. In the New Forest on branches. Some records are for wind-blown fragments. Gritnam Wood 20, *FR & SRD* 1975; Crows Nest 21, *FR & SRD* 1972; Hollands Wood, Stubbs Wood and Frame Wood 30, *FR*, all 1974–90.

U. ceratina   Widespread in established woodlands, mainly in the S. Occasional, except in the New Forest where common. On trunks of mature *Quercus*, *Betula* and *Fagus*, in open woodland. 24 squares.

U. cornuta (*U. inflata*)   Widespread and locally frequent. In established woodland on trunks of mature trees. 26 squares.

U. flammea   Rare. Local in the New Forest on old *Betula* trunks; also on *Fagus*. Mallard Wood 30, *PWJ* 1986. Also 20, 21, 31.

U. florida   Widespread but occasional. On branches of large trees, especially in the New Forest. 18 squares.

U. fulvoreagens   Very rare. In the New Forest. Queen Bower 20, *PWJ c.*1978.

U. hirta   Rare. On acid-barked trees, especially *Pinus* and *Betula*. Waggoners Wells 83, *FR* 1972. Also 20, 30.

U. rubicunda   Occasional in the S, especially in the New Forest. On trunks of mature trees in established woodlands. 10, 20, 21, 30, 31, 42, 51, 70.

U. subfloridana   Frequent to common. On bark in all but the most polluted areas; occasional on worked timber. Mainly on branches and twigs of acid-barked trees. 46 squares.

Verrucaria aquatilis   Rare. On stone in stream E of Stroudbridge Farm, Petersfield 72, *BJC* 1972.

V. baldensis   Frequent. On limestone gravestones. 29 squares.

V. bryoctona   Rare. On disturbed, chalky soil, Basingstoke 65, *KS* 1986, det. *AOr*.

V. dolosa (incl. *V. mutabilis*)   Apparently rare. On chalk pebbles and flints in chalk grassland. Probably overlooked. Butser Hill 71, *BJC* 1973; Butser Hill 72, *OLG* 1991. Also 23, 61.

V. dufourii   Rare. On chalk pebbles. Butser Hill 72, *OLG* 1991; 32, *TWO c.*1978.

V. elaeomeleana   Rare or overlooked on flints in stream-beds. Hurstbourne Tarrant 35, *OLG* 1993; St. Mary Bourne 45, *OLG* 1993.

V. glaucina   Frequent. On limestone gravestones and walls. 39 squares.

V. hochstetteri   Common. On limestone graves, walls and on chalk pebbles. 46 squares.

V. hydrela   Very rare. On stones in stream, Bramshaw Wood 21, *BJC* 1968.

V. macrostoma (incl. f. *furfuracea*; and *V. viridula* f. *tectorum* (*q.v.*))   Scattered and occasional. On limestone church-walls. 01, 11, 40, 42, 50, 51, 52, 53, 55, 60, 64, 70, 71, 74.

V. margacea   Very rare. On stones in stream S of Busketts Wood 31, *PWJ* 1972.

V. maura   Rare. On coastal rocks. Hurst Spit 38, *VJG* 1985.

V. mucosa   Rare. On coastal rocks. Hurst Spit 38, *VJG* 1985.

V. muralis   Very common. On calcareous rocks of gravestones and walls, also on mortar and chalk pebbles. 47 squares.

V. murina   Apparently confined to the area around Petersfield, but may be under-recorded. On chalk pebbles, Butser Hill 71, *BJC* 1973; Butser Hill 72, *OLG* 1991. Also 62, 73.

V. mutabilis   See *V. dolosa* above.

V. nigrescens   Very common. On basic rocks and mortar-influenced brickwork, also on flints in chalk grassland. 52 squares.

V. rheitrophila (*V. kernstockii*)   Rare or overlooked on submerged flints and bricks in clear, chalk streams. R. Test near Overton 55; near Whitchurch 44; R. Dever, Wonston 43; all *OLG* 1993.

V. viridula   Very common. On calcareous walls and gravestones, and on flints. Some records probably refer to *V. macrostoma*. 46 squares.

Vezdaea aestivalis   On moss on sarcophagus, Winchester Cathedral 42, *TCh, FR & KS* 1994.

V. leprosa   Rare. On soil under galvanized-wire fence, Butser Hill 72, *OLG* 1991.

Wadeana dendrographa   Occasional. Mainly on old *Fraxinus* in the New Forest. Wood Crates and Bratley 20; Bramshaw, Eyeworth, Sloden and South Ocknell 21; Frame Wood (on *Quercus*) and Roydon Woods 30.

W. minuta   Very rare. On *Quercus* in Tantany Wood 30, *FR* 1980.

Xanthoria calcicola   Quite frequent. On nutrient-rich, limestone gravestones. 44 squares.

X. candelaria   Frequent. On nutrient-rich, sunlit, siliceous rocks; less frequent on flints and mortar in walls, and on nutrient-rich bark and worked timber. 38 squares.

X. elegans   Scattered and occasional. On nutrient-rich man-made substrates such as wall-capping and concrete. 11, 39, 43, 50, 65, 66.

X. parietina   Abundant. On nutrient-rich trunks, rocks, wood and man-made substrates. 56 squares.

X. polycarpa   Widespread and locally frequent. On nutrient-rich bark of branches and small trunks, and on lignum. 32 squares.

Xylographa vitiligo   Very rare. On lignum in the New Forest. Whitley Wood 20, *PWJ c*.1975.

Zamenhofia coralloidea (*Porina coralloidea*)   Widespread in the New Forest ancient woodlands on mossy *Quercus* trunks. Rare elsewhere; Pit Wood 11, *NAS* 1993; Hurstbourne Park 44, *FR c*.1972; Kilmeston Severals 52, *FR c*.1978. Also 10, 20, 21, 30, 31, 39.

Z. hibernica (*Porina hibernica*)   Widespread but occasional in the New Forest ancient woodlands. On *Quercus* and rarely on *Fagus*. 10, 20, 21, 30, 31.

Z. rosei   Rare, but frequent in the New Forest on *Quercus*. Red Shoot Wood 10; old woodland N of Burley New Inclosure 20; South Bentley Inclosure 21; Hollands Wood 30; Busketts Wood 31. Many more sites have been found by *NAS* in 1992, 1993.

CHAPTER XII

THE BRYOPHYTE FLORA

A. C. CRUNDWELL AND FRANCIS ROSE

A full bryophyte flora of South Hampshire, VC11, by Mrs J. A. Paton (*Bry.Fl.S.Hants*), was published by the British Bryological Society in 1961. Data are at present being collected for a similar treatment of the bryophytes of North Hampshire, VC12. This account, however, is brief, details of localities being given only for the rarer species, but all recorded species have been included.

North Hampshire has for many years been comparatively neglected. It lacks the obvious attraction of the New Forest, and is farther from London than Surrey. Of the earlier collectors, the most important were R. S. Hill, M.D., of Basingstoke, the Revd W. L. W. Eyre of Swarraton (better known as a mycologist), and A. B. Jackson of Newbury (better known for his work on conifers). Many common species were, however, quite unknown from the vice-county until the time of E. C. Wallace, who did about as much fieldwork in it as all his predecessors put together. Some dubious VC12 records of taxa rare or unknown elsewhere in Hampshire, from W. Ingham's *Census Cat.Brit.Mosses*, edn 1, although lacking data and

supporting herbarium specimens, have been included. In recent years, much additional field work has been done by R. C. Stern.

We are greatly indebted to Mrs Paton not only for her bryophyte flora of South Hampshire, which has been an invaluable aid in the preparation of this account, but also for much additional information on work done by herself and others since her flora was published. That work included a historical survey of bryological work in VC11. All undated *JAP* records in this account are derived from her flora and are therefore pre-1961. Recording has continued since its publication, particularly in the New Forest and in other forests and woodlands, mainly by F. Rose and R. C. Stern.

The arrangement and nomenclature follows that of *Distribution of bryophytes in the British Isles*, M. F. V. Corley & M. O. Hill, 1981. Author citations of species included in that work are omitted.

Notes (i), (iii) and (iv) under 'The Lichen Flora' (p.306) relating to grid references, abbreviations and use of brackets also apply to this account.

ANTHOCEROTAE

Anthoceros agrestis **VC11,12:** Uncommon and diminishing. Arable fields and waste ground on non-calcareous soils.

A. punctatus **VC11:** Rare. On bare moist soil. In a few locations in the S part of the New Forest and elsewhere.

Phaeoceros laevis **VC11:** Rare. On wet clay of trackways and bare soil in the New Forest and elsewhere.

HEPATICAE

Sphaerocarpos texanus **VC12:** Very rare. On sandy loam in field near Liss 72, *FR* 1982, 1992; edge of arable field, Fair Oak, near Kingsclere 56, *RDP*

1992; in gravel-workings, Headley by Kingsclere 56, *PB* 1985.

Targionia hypophylla **VC11:** Formerly intermixed with *Reboulia* in the New Forest, *CLy* (*Eng.Fl.Crypt.*), now presumably extinct in this VC. **VC12:** On roadside banks and walls at Headley by Bordon 83 first seen *CPH* 1919, and Arford 83, locally abundant, *ACC* 1991. Formerly at Silchester 66, *RSH* 1861, and Liss 72, *JSG* 1908. Apart from small populations at Churt, Surrey, and Chithurst, near Midhurst, Sussex, these are now the only records of this species in SE England.

Reboulia hemisphaerica **VC11,12:** Uncommon but sometimes plentiful on sheltered, sandy lane-banks. Occasional in the New Forest; frequent on the Lower Greensand (especially

the Bargate Beds) from Liss to NE of Headley; rare on the NE Tertiaries. Silchester Common 66, *PB & ACC* 1984; formerly in lane near Eversley 76, *RSH* 1868.

Conocephalum conicum **VC11,12:** Frequent on damp concrete and brick-work by streams and rivers, and on earth-banks of woodland streams.

Lunularia cruciata **VC11,12:** Common on damp soil on lane-banks, in churchyards and gardens, and on the banks of rivers and streams.

Preissia quadrata **VC11:** Rare. Only in the New Forest in calcareous flushes; Stony Moors 29, *FR* 1951–95; Gritnam Wood 20, in flush, *FR* 1984; N of King's Copse Inclosure 40, *FR &*

NAS 1988; below Crockford Bridge 39, *ABo c*.1985.

Marchantia polymorpha **VC11,12:** Locally frequent on damp soil in churchyards and gardens, on river banks, on sites of fires, and on sawdust in woodlands.

Ricciocarpos natans **VC12:** Greywell Moors 75. Isolated thalli are also seen from time to time in the Basingstoke Canal from Greywell to Winchfield, and in Fleet Pond 85, *CRH* 1986.

Riccia cavernosa (*R. crystallina* in *Bry.Fl.S.Hants*) **VC11:** Rare. On exposed mud at dried-up pools. Buriton 72, 1957, and Rockbourne 11, *JAP*; Burley, *CCT*.

R. fluitans **VC11,12:** Occasional in ponds and in backwaters of rivers.

R. glauca **VC11,12:** Frequent in stubble fields and woodland rides on non-calcareous clay and loam soils.

R. subbifurca CROZ. (*R. warnstorfii* in *Bry.Fl.S.Hants* and in *Distr. Bryophytes*)) **VC11:** Uncommon. On damp soil in the New Forest: Michelmersh Wood 32, Brockwood 62, and six further squares, all *JAP*. **VC12:** Edge of arable field, Fair Oak, near Kingsclere 56, *RDP* 1992.

R. sorocarpa **VC11,12:** Common in stubble fields and on woodland rides, often with *R. glauca* but occasionally on slightly more basic soils.

Metzgeria fruticulosa **VC11,12:** Uncommon but widely scattered on the bark of *Sambucus* and, less frequently, *Salix* and *Fraxinus*.

M. temperata **VC11,12:** In similar habitats to those of *M. fruticulosa* but commoner, and on the bark of a wider range of trees.

M. furcata **VC11,12:** Very common on a wide range of tree species.

Aneura pinguis **VC11,12:** Frequent in flushes in bogs, in damp calcareous grassland and on woodland rides.

Cryptothallus mirabilis **VC11:** Islands Thorns Inclosure 21, New Forest, *RCS* 1992. **VC12:** Among *Molinia* and beneath *Sphagnum* at the edges of bogs at Silchester 66, *JHDi*

1964, and at Woolmer Forest 73, *NYS* 1956, *FR & ECW* 1985.

Riccardia multifida **VC11,12:** In several bogs and calcareous fens in the New Forest; very rare elsewhere.

R. chamedryfolia **VC11,12:** Commoner than *R. multifida*. In bogs, old sand-pits and woodland rides.

R. incurvata **VC11:** Very rare. Sandy waste-ground by Holmsley airfield 20, *JAP*; E of Millyford Bridge 20, *JAP* 1973.

R. palmata **VC11:** On rotten logs, only from carr NW of Knowles Hill, Wood Crates 20, *FR* 1973.

R. latifrons On *Sphagnum* in bogs and on wet, peaty banks. **VC11:** Locally frequent in the New Forest. **VC12:** Only in bog by Queens Road, Woolmer Forest 83, *FR* 1983.

Pellia epiphylla **VC11,12:** Very common. On damp rides and by streams and ditches on base-poor soils.

P. neesiana In similar habitats to the last but very rare. **VC11:** Near Millyford Bridge 20, *JAP* 1973; Islands Thorns Inclosure 21, *RCS* 1992. **VC12:** Sandford Wood, Kingsclere 55, *JApp* 1964; Silchester Common 66, *BBS* 1975.

P. endiviifolia **VC11,12:** A calcicole species, common along rivers and streams, in flushes and springs, and on damp basic soils.

Pallavicinia lyellii **VC11:** Very rare. In the New Forest only: Cadnam Bog 21, *CLy* 1814, *FR* 1991, on *Alnus* roots in carr; Wood Crates 20, *FR* 1973; S of Burley 20, on old railway-cutting, *AEB & FR c*.1978.

Blasia pusilla Very rare. On damp acid soil on banks. **VC11:** New Forest, *AEB*. **VC12:** Woolmer Forest 83, *RAB & ECW* 1954; Spring Lakes, Aldershot 85, *CRH & ACC* 1992; Liss Forest 72, *FR* 1986; near Conford 83, *FR* 1975.

Fossombronia foveolata **VC11,12:** Rare, on damp, sandy and peaty ground. Occasional on New Forest moist heaths.

F. maritima (PATON) PATON **VC11:**

In one site only. New Forest, Wood Crates 20, *JAP* 1973.

F. pusilla **VC11,12:** On damp, acid soils. Frequent on woodland rides, more rare in arable fields.

F. wondraczekii **VC11,12:** In habitats similar to those of *F. pusilla* but slightly less frequent.

F. incurva **VC12:** Rare, but small and perhaps overlooked. On soil in scrubby woodland, Bramshott Common 83, *ACC* 1991; on bank in old encampment, Broxhead Common 83, *ACC* 1993.

<***Haplomitrium hookeri*** **VC11:** Formerly on side of ditch, road from Cadnam to Paultons Park 21, *CLy* 1812 and 1815. Not seen since, presumed extinct.>

Barbilophozia attenuata Surprisingly very rare in Hants, as it is locally frequent in Sussex. On sandy peat-banks. St Catherine's Hill, Christchurch 19, *MCFP* 1952, *JAP* 1958. **VC12:** Newtown Common 46, *FR & PB* 1982, *JWB & ACC* 1988.

Lophozia ventricosa var. *ventricosa* **VC11,12:** Common in the New Forest, occasional elsewhere on Lower Greensand and NE Tertiaries. On moist and sandy banks in woodlands and heaths.

var. *silvicola* **VC11:** Apparently rare. On damp sand or peat in woods or among *Calluna*, rarely, on *Sphagnum*.

L. excisa **VC11:** Rare. On sandy soil. Burley 20, *JAP*. **VC12:** Woolmer Forest 73, *ACC* 1986; Newtown churchyard 46, *ACC & JWB* 1988.

L. capitata **VC11:** Originally described from the New Forest (bog near Lyndhurst Race Course 30, *CLy* 1813, and Cadnam Bog 21, *CLy* 1814) but not seen since. **VC12:** Silchester Common 66, *ECW* 1961; Yateley Heath Wood 85, *ECW & ACC* 1985.

L. incisa **VC11:** Only in Rhinefield Bog, New Forest 20, *EFW* 1956.

L. bicrenata **VC11,12:** Uncommon. On damp sand in *Calluna* heaths in the New Forest and elsewhere.

L. herzogiana E. A. HODGS. & GROLLE **VC12:** In small quantity in Callunetum by Woolmer Pond 73,

ACC 1986 and seen there for several years subsequently. However, the habitat has since been destroyed by burial under muddy sand excavated from the pond. The species must therefore be deemed provisionally to be extinct, though there are many nearby areas of Callunetum where it may yet be found. This was the only locality for this species outside New Zealand, and it was presumably an introduction.

Leiocolea turbinata VC11,12: Rather frequent on damp, chalky soil in downland, and on bare chalk in old quarries. On malmstone N of Hawkley 72, *FR*.

L. badensis VC12: Only twice recorded. Old chalk-workings, Wheatham Hill 72, *ECW* 1950; chalk-pit, Sydmonton Court, Ecchinswell 45, *RCS* 1979.

Gymnocolea inflata VC11,12: Frequent in suitable habitats. On wet heaths and on damp sand in old workings.

Sphenolobus minutus VC11: Only once recorded. Sandy soil among *Calluna* in sheltered valley, St Catherine's Hill 19, Christchurch, *MCFP* 1954.

Tritomaria exsectiformis VC11,12: Rare. New Forest (four sites known) and NE Hants. On damp, sandy soil in woods, and in *Calluna* heaths; on a railway bank, Winchfield 75.

Mylia anomala VC11,12: Common in the New Forest, frequent on the Lower Greensand and Tertiary heaths. With *Sphagnum* in bogs and wet heaths.

Jungermannia atrovirens VC12: Only twice recorded. On damp, chalky, open waste-ground. Wheatham Hill 72, *ECW* 1957; Micheldever Spoil Heaps 54, *FR, ECW, JCG & JES* 1969.

J. pumila VC12: In one site only. On outcrops of Upper Greensand in *Fraxinus* wood on hanger, Long Copse, Selborne 73, *FR* 1988.

J. gracillima VC11,12: Common in the New Forest, widespread but less common elsewhere. On woodland rides on acid soils, on heathland tracks and on banks of streams and ditches.

J. hyalina VC11,12: Widely distributed but uncommon. On woodland rides on wet, acid soils.

<**J. paroica** VC12: Formerly on bank of ditch, Ewshot 84, *ACC* 1981. The habitat has unfortunately since been destroyed by road-widening. The nearest known locality for this species is in Somerset.>

Nardia scalaris VC11,12: Uncommon. On sandy heaths, occasionally on woodland rides and banks.

N. geoscyphus Uncommon (or overlooked?). On sandy and peaty banks, sometimes where under water for part of the year. VC11: Near Christchurch 19, *JAP* 1960. VC12: Kingsley Common 73, *DHD* 1956, *FR* 1989; Bramshill Plantation 76, *ACC* 1982; near Liss Forest 72, *ACC* 1985; Woolmer Forest 73, *FR* 1985.

Plagiochila porelloides VC11,12: Frequent in woodland on neutral and basic soils; occasional on lane-banks and in N-facing chalk-grassland.

P. asplenioides VC11,12: In similar habitats to *P. porelloides* but a little more frequent in the N of the county, less so in the S.

P. killarniensis VC11: Rufus Stone, New Forest 21, *CLy* 1812 (published as *P. spinulosa*). Refound there on leaning trunk of beech on *BBS* excursion in 1992. Formerly in East Sussex, but there are no other records from SE England.

Lophocolea bidentata VC11,12: Common, but usually sterile and difficult to distinguish from *L. cuspidata*. Among grass on ditch-banks, in woodland and in damp meadows.

L. cuspidata VC11,12: Very common, frequently with perianths. On the bark of trees, on rotting wood, on woodland soils, and amongst grass.

L. heterophylla VC11,12: Almost ubiquitous and the commonest liverwort in the county. On the bark of trees, on rotting wood and on sandy banks.

Chiloscyphus polyanthos VC11,12: Frequent in the New Forest, scattered localities elsewhere, mostly in non-calcareous habitats. On soil, on tree-roots and decaying wood in wet places, and on stones in streams.

C. pallescens VC11,12: In similar habitats to those of *C. polyanthos* but less frequent and favouring basic, often less wet soils; common on the boulders of the Upper Greensand scarp.

Saccogyna viticulosa VC11: Occasional in old New Forest woodlands. On moist banks, especially on *Leucobryum* carpets. First found near the Rufus Stone 21, *JAP* 1953. Now known from at least five other sites (e.g. Holm Hill Inclosure, *FR* 1954; Stricknage Wood and Bramshaw Wood, *FR* 1965–92. The only other records in SE England of this highly oceanic species are from East Sussex.

Diplophyllum albicans VC11,12: Where present, usually abundant, but absent from large tracts of the county where the soils are chalky. On acid, sandy banks in woodland, and by sunken lanes.

D. obtusifolium VC11: Certainly rare, but easily overlooked. On bare, gravelly soil, Hen Wood 62, near West Meon, *RCS* 1981.

Scapania curta VC12: Very rare. By path in Doles Wood, Hurstbourne Tarrant 35, *ECW* 1951. There is poor material that may be this from Silchester Common 66, and Long Copse, Selborne 73 *FR* 1988.

S. nemorosa VC11,12: Frequent in the New Forest, but elsewhere rather uncommon, though widely distributed. On acid soil on damp woodland rides; also recorded from tracks in heathland, and from decaying wood.

S. irrigua VC11,12: Frequent in the New Forest; in scattered localities elsewhere. On acid soils on damp paths, tracks and woodland rides.

S. compacta VC11: Rare, and only in the New Forest, where known from five localities on clay or gravel on woodland banks and also in the open.

S. undulata VC11: Occasional. On stones and roots in streams, and on shaded stream-banks. VC12: Very rare. Stream entering Fleet Pond 85, *ECW* 1956; Bourley Bottom, near Church Crookham 85, *CRH* 1978, det. *FR*.

S. aspera Rare. On N-facing banks

in chalk grassland. **VC11**: Butser Hill 72, *JAP* 1939, *FR* 1993; Mount Down 42, *JAP & PFH* 1958. **VC12**: Isle of Wight Hill 23, *ECW & FR* 1971.

S. gracilis   **VC11**: Very rare. On decaying *Betula* logs in old New Forest woodlands. Frame Wood 30, *FR* 1974–80; Highland Water Inclosure 20, *RCS* 1991.

Odontoschisma sphagni   **VC11,12**: Frequent, sometimes abundant, on the bryologically richer *Sphagnum* bogs throughout the county.

O. denudatum   **VC11,12**: Scattered throughout the county, commoner in the S than the N. On damp sand or peat under *Calluna*, in ditches and on banks.

Cephaloziella elachista   Apparently very rare. In *Sphagnum* bogs. **VC11**: In tuft of *Mylia anomala* in valley mire, Shatterford Bottom 30, *RPHW* 1981. **VC12**: Among *Drepanocladus fluitans* in bog, Shortheath Common 73, *ACC* 1951.

C. subdentata   **VC12**: Apparently very rare but easily overlooked. Among *Sphagnum* in bog, Shortheath Common 73, *ACC* 1951; Tadley Common 66, *BBS* excursions 1964 & 1975.

C. rubella   **VC11,12**: Widely scattered, certainly often overlooked. On damp, acid sand or peat in Calluneta, on ditch-banks and in sand-pits.

C. hampeana   **VC11,12**: In similar localities to *C. rubella*, but often also on less acid soils, and on woodland rides.

C. divaricata   **VC11,12**: Frequent on acid, peaty sand in heaths and sand-pits, on banks, and on woodland rides. Tolerant of somewhat drier conditions than the last two species, and perhaps a little more frequent.

C. turneri   **VC11**: Found only once. Side of ditch, near Brockenhurst 30, *DAJ, HHK & JBD* 1928.

[*C. integerrima*   Formerly listed by the *BBS* for VC11, but the specimen, teste *JAP*, is unnameable.]

Cephalozia bicuspidata ssp. *bicuspidata*   **VC11,12**: Widespread throughout the county. On acid soils, on woodland rides and sandy heaths, and on ditch- and stream-banks.

ssp. *lammersiana*   **VC11,12**: Much less common than ssp. *bicuspidata* but certainly under-recorded. In similar, though somewhat wetter, habitats.

C. connivens   **VC11,12**: Frequent in bogs, wet heaths and damp, acid woodland. On wet, peaty and sandy ground, and on rotting wood.

C. pleniceps   **VC11**: Found only once. Duckhole Bog, near Holmsley 20, *JAP* 1956. A northern species, otherwise known in SE England from E Sussex, and from Norfolk.

C. lunulifolia   **VC11,12**: Scattered throughout the county. On stumps and banks in woodland, occasionally also in *Sphagnum* bogs.

C. macrostachya   **VC11,12**: Common in the New Forest valley-mires; very local in Woolmer Forest 73, 83, and on the NE Tertiaries, 66, 75, 85. Among *Sphagnum* in bogs.

C. catenulata   **VC11**: Found once only. On rotten log, Mark Ash, New Forest 20, *FR* 1967.

Nowellia curvifolia   A suboceanic species, increasing in SE England but still very rare. On stumps and rotting logs. **VC11**: Stubbs Wood, W of Beaulieu 30, *FR & BdeF* 1979; Highland Water Inclosure 20, *RCS* 1992. **VC12**: Skyers Wood, Ramsdell 55, *RCS & PB* 1982; Foley Manor carr, near Liphook 83, *RD* 1985.

Cladopodiella francisci   **VC11,12**: Not common. Occasional in the New Forest, rare on NE Tertiaries. On damp, peaty banks and sides of ditches.

C. fluitans   **VC11,12**: Rather local. Common in the New Forest, rare in Woolmer Forest and NE Hants. Among *Sphagnum* in bogs, especially in pools.

Kurzia pauciflora   **VC11,12**: Common among *Sphagnum* in bogs, especially in the New Forest. Occasional on wet, peaty banks.

K. sylvatica   **VC11**: Only one confirmed record; often difficult to distinguish from the last species. Shaded ditch-bank, edge of Mark Ash Wood 20, New Forest, *JAP* 1977.

Lepidozia reptans   **VC11,12**: Common on acid, sandy and peaty banks.

Occasional on tree-stumps and tree-roots.

Bazzania trilobata   **VC11**: Only in the New Forest. Abundant in the woods to the E of the Rufus Stone 21 *JAP et al.* 1952, *FR* 1994; Rushpole Wood 30, on wet bank, *FR* 1971–89.

Calypogeia neesiana   **VC11**: Found once only but easily overlooked. Shaded bank of peaty sand, St Catherine's Hill, Christchurch 19, *JAP* 1958.

C. integristipula   **VC11**: Found once only, amongst *Cephalozia connivens*, damp woodland, Holmsley 20, *RPHW* 1981 (*Bull.Brit.Bryol.Soc.* **40**: 22).

C. muellerana   **VC11,12**: Occasional on acid sandy and peaty banks. Sometimes also among *Sphagnum* in bogs.

C. fissa   **VC11,12**: A very common calcifuge of damp soil in woodland, by streams and ditches, and among *Sphagnum* in bogs.

C. sphagnicola   A rare plant of *Sphagnum* bogs. **VC11**: Wilverley Bog 29, 1951; Cranes Moor 10, 1986; Mark Ash Wood 20, 1962, and Bramshaw Wood 21, 1972, all *FR*. **VC12**: Castle Bottom, Eversley 75, *FR* 1986.

C. arguta   **VC11,12**: Frequent, but often in small quantity. On damp, sheltered banks, and sides of streams or ditches, usually on clay soils. Calcifuge.

Trichocolea tomentella   Rare. On wet stream-banks, and flushes in woodland. **VC11**: A few localities in the New Forest. Wood E of Waterlooville 60, *NMB* 1944; The Moors, Bishop's Waltham 51, *FR & RCS* 1984; alder carr in Flexford NR 42, *NAS* 1987. **VC12**: Foley Manor, Liphook 83, *RD* 1985; wood NE of Kingsclere 56, *PRB c.*1982.

Ptilidium ciliare   **VC11,12**: Very local. Very rare in the New Forest, more frequent in Woolmer Forest. On heathy grassland and dampish heaths, usually among *Calluna*. Kingston Common 10, *NAS* 1989; Woolmer Forest, Shortheath, Kingsley Common and the Warren 73, *FR* 1980–92; Heckfield Heath 76, *ACC*.

P. pulcherrimum   **VC11,12**: Uncommon but widely scattered, mostly in the New Forest, and always in small quantity. On *Salix*, *Fraxinus*, *Acer*, *Betula*, *Quercus* and *Castanea*.

Radula complanata   **VC11,12**: Frequent throughout the county, especially on *Sambucus* and *Fraxinus* growing on calcareous soils.

Porella arboris-vitae   Very locally frequent on N-to NE-facing slopes in chalk turf. **VC11**: Butser Hill 72, *FR* 1954–93; Oxenbourne Down 71 *FR* to 1986; Old Winchester Hill 62, *JAP* 1941, *ECW* 1942, but no longer present. **VC12**: Old quarries, Noar Hill 73, *ECW & ACC* 1955, but now gone; epiphytic on *Fraxinus*, Wick Hill Hanger, Selborne 73, *FR* 1988.

P. platyphylla   **VC11,12**: Common in calcareous areas, much less so elsewhere. On the roots and boles of trees; less frequently on walls and stones.

P. cordaeana   **VC11**: Found only once, on silt-covered roots of a *Fraxinus* by Lymington River, Roydon Woods 30, *FR* 1980.

Frullania tamarisci   **VC11,12**: Common in the New Forest, uncommon but widespread elsewhere. Mainly epiphytic on *Quercus*, *Fraxinus* or *Fagus* in ancient woodland, but occasionally in chalk turf, e.g. Butser Hill 71, 72.

F. fragilifolia   **VC11**: Only in the New Forest, where frequent on *Quercus*, *Fagus* and *Fraxinus* in the ancient woodlands.

F. dilatata   **VC11,12**: A common epiphyte, especially on basic or neutral soils; also, rarely, on walls and gravestones.

Harpalejeunea ovata   **VC11**: In one locality only, on trunk of old *Fagus*, Stricknage Wood 21, New Forest, *FR* 1978, *RCS* 1992. A remarkable extension of the range for this oceanic species – the nearest other locality is in Devon.

Lejeunea cavifolia   **VC11,12**: Occasional in calcareous areas, usually on *Fraxinus*.

L. lamacerina   **VC11**: Only in the New Forest, where common on tree-roots, on decaying wood, and on soil on stream-banks. Largely calcifuge.

L. ulicina   **VC11,12**: A very common

epiphyte throughout the county, on a wide range of trees both in woodland and in sheltered parkland.

Cololejeunea minutissima   **VC11**: An epiphyte, most frequent in coastal districts. There are several records from the New Forest and old ones from Compton 42, near Winchester, and from Beacon Hill 62, near Meonstoke.

MUSCI

Sphagnum papillosum   **VC11,12**: Common in bogs and in boggy areas in wet heaths.

S. palustre   **VC11,12**: Common in wet woodlands, also at bog-margins and on flushed areas in wet heaths.

S. magellanicum   **VC11,12**: Frequent in bogs in the New Forest but rare elsewhere. Woolmer Forest (Cranmer Bog 73, *FR* 1984–93, and Queens Road Bog 83, *FR* 1983); Hazeley Heath 75, *JMi* 1964, *FR* 1984; Netley Common 41, *NAS* 1987.

S. squarrosum   **VC11,12**: Widely distributed but not common. A species of flushes in carr and wet woodland.

S. teres   **VC11**: Local. Known only from seven localities in the New Forest. In basic flushes in bogs.

S. fimbriatum   **VC11,12**: Common. In carr and wet woodland, and on banks of ditches, usually where there is some water-movement.

S. capillifolium   **VC11,12**: Common in the New Forest; elsewhere widely distributed but not always abundant, and sometimes unexpectedly absent. Forms hummocks and patches in bogs and wet heaths.

S. subnitens   **VC11,12**: Common in the New Forest, occasional elsewhere. On wet heaths and flushed areas of valley bogs; most often when not extremely base-poor.

S. molle   Rather rare. Mainly on wet heaths and bog-margins. **VC11**: Eight records in the New Forest. **VC12**: Silchester Common 66, *FIW* 1861; Eversley Common 75, *RCS* 1984; Hazeley Heath 75, in gravel-pit, *ACC* 1981, and on wet heath, *ACC & FR* 1991.

S. compactum   **VC11,12**: Common and abundant on all wet heaths; often associated with *Erica tetralix*.

S. auriculatum var. *auriculatum* **VC11,12**: The commonest *Sphagnum* in the county. Often submerged in ditches and pools, sometimes in bogs and wet heaths, but equally frequent in carr and wet woodland-rides.

var. *inundatum*   **VC11,12**: Apparently rare. Most records are from the New Forest. Submerged in pools and bogs.

S. subsecundum   **VC11**: Occasional in the New Forest in flushes in bogs. **VC12**: Aldershot 85, *WRS* 1900, conf. *MOH*.

S. contortum   **VC11**: Occasional in base-enriched valley-mires. Low hummocks in pools, Wilverley Bog 29, *FR* 1951, *NAS* 1992; Dibden Bottom 30, *NAS* 1992; Hinchelsea Bog 20, *NAS* 1992; Holmsley 20, *NAS* 1992.

S. cuspidatum   **VC11,12**: Generally distributed in suitable habitats; especially common in the New Forest. In pools and ditches on wet heaths and in bogs.

S. tenellum   **VC11,12**: A widespread species of wet heaths, where associated with *S. compactum* and *Erica tetralix*.

S. recurvum var. *amblyphyllum* **VC11,12**: Probably quite common. In several wet woods in the New Forest and elsewhere. Characteristic of wet woods and marshes, avoiding the more acid habitats of var. *mucronatum*. Most records do not distinguish between the two.

var. *mucronatum*   **VC11,12**: Very common. Characteristic of areas of bog and wet heath where there is at least some water-movement; also in wet woodland.

Tetraphis pellucida   **VC11,12**: Common on stumps and logs in moist, acid woodland; sometimes also on sandy banks. Fruit occasional, less rare in Hants than reported elsewhere.

Polytrichum longisetum   **VC11,12**: A rare plant of sandy or peaty ground, mainly in damp woodland. Sterile and usually stunted, though quite well grown in Highclere churchyard 46, *JWB & ACC* 1991.

P. formosum **VC11,12**: Widespread and often abundant. A woodland species; the only *Polytrichum* species found on soils that are only moderately acid.

P. commune var. *commune* **VC11,12**: Frequent and locally abundant in bogs, wet heaths and swampy woodland.

var. *perigoniale* **VC12**: Apparently very rare. On burnt heathland, Blackmoor 73, *ECW* 1951, and Oakhanger 73, *ECW* 1938.

[var. *humile* **VC12**: Recorded in *Census Cat.Brit.Mosses* (edn.1, 1907, as var. *minus*). A dubious record.]

P. piliferum **VC11,12**: Frequent in suitable habitats, but less common than *P. juniperinum*. A plant of very barren, bare, sandy or gravelly soils on heaths.

P. juniperinum **VC11,12**: Common on acid soils of heaths and roadside tracks, especially on peaty or organic substrates.

P. alpestre Apparently very rare. **VC11**: Bog E of Eyeworth Wood, New Forest 21, *FR* 1968. **VC12**: Bog on Shortheath Common 73, *ECW* 1971, *FR* 1987.

Pogonatum nanum **VC11,12**: A rare and declining species. There are a number of records from sandy banks and path-sides in the New Forest, and three old ones from the Tertiaries in the N.

P. aloides **VC11,12**: Widely distributed on acid, sandy banks. Frequent in the New Forest, and scattered in the N and E.

P. urnigerum A rare species of damp, open, sandy or stony soils. **VC11**: Three New Forest records. **VC12**: Chawton Park Wood 63, *JCG* 1980; Burghclere Rectory garden 45, *ABJ* 1906.

Atrichum tenellum **VC11**: Rare or overlooked. On clay in ride, Creech Walk, Denmead 61, *HM* 1986.

A. undulatum var. *undulatum* **VC11,12**: Very common, especially in woodland, but frequent also on roadside banks and in grassland. A calcifuge species which also avoids extremely poor soils.

var. *minus* **VC11**: Very rare, perhaps extinct. Formerly near Burley 20, *WRS* 1914.

Archidium alternifolium **VC11,12**: Occasional. Most records are from the New Forest or from the N and E of the county. A calcifuge of damp depressions in tracks on heaths and in woodlands.

Pleuridium acuminatum **VC11,12**: Fairly frequent on bare, acid, usually sandy, soil on banks and woodland rides.

P. subulatum **VC11,12**: Much less frequent than *P. acuminatum* but in similar habitats, although perhaps a little more often in fields.

Pseudephemerum nitidum **VC11,12**: Frequent, locally abundant. On moist, non-calcareous clayey or loamy soils. On woodland rides, especially on the sides of ruts, and on ditch- and stream-banks.

Ditrichum cylindricum **VC11,12**: A widespread, sometimes abundant plant of non-calcareous soils in open habitats liable to occasional disturbance, e.g. arable fields, woodland rides, gardens.

D. flexicaule British records of this species apply mostly to *D. crispatatissimum* (q.v.). There is only one confirmed record of *D. flexicaule* proper in Hants. **VC12**: Calcareous turf, Micheldever Spoil Heaps 54, *NAS & ACC* 1991.

D. crispatatissimum (C. MÜLL.) PARIS **VC11,12**: A calcicole, almost restricted to the chalk and to old marl-pits on the Headon Beds in the New Forest. Characteristic of short, grazed turf and of chalk-pits; has declined with the loss of chalk grassland.

D. heteromallum Very rare. Mainly on bare, sandy or gravelly ground in pits. **VC11**: Cadnam 21, New Forest, *WMB* 1956. **VC12**: Kingsley Common 73, *ACC* 1961; The Holt, *PB*; Headley near Kingsclere 56, *PB* 1985; Woolmer Forest 72, *FR* 1990.

Brachydontium trichodes **VC12**: Recorded only on one outcrop of Upper Greensand in a *Fraxinus* wood, Long Copse, Selborne 73, *FR & ACC* 1988.

Seligeria paucifolia **VC11,12**:

Common. On lumps of chalk in escarpment woodlands, and on chalk stones embedded in grassland.

S. calcarea **VC11,12**: Very rare. In chalk-pits near Winchester, *FYB* 1853, *ABJ* 1906; Kingsclere 55, *ABJ*; Ecchinswell 56, *ECW* 1974; tombstone in Hawley churchyard 85, *ACC* 1986.

S. recurvata **VC11,12**: Rare, requiring harder rock than the two previous species. On flint at S part of Butser Hill 71, *ACC* 1984. On Upper Greensand outcrops in roadside bank at Ashford Chace 72, *ECW* 1964, and on boulders in several hangers between there and Binsted, 72, 73, 74, *FR* 1983–92.

Ceratodon purpureus **VC11,12**: Abundant on non-calcareous soils on heaths, disturbed ground and waste places.

Dichodontium pellucidum **VC11**: Frequent in the W part of the New Forest and on Upper Greensand SW of Petersfield. **VC12**: Frequent on moist stones in rivulets in woods on the Upper Greensand scarp, *FR* 1972–74; on wall by Bramshott Church 83, *ACC & ECW* 1981; on half-buried brick on Whitmoor Hanger 83, *ACC* 1987; on a stone in damp woodland by the Roman Wall, Silchester 66, *ACC* 1990.

Dicranella schreberana **VC11,12**: Frequent on recently disturbed soils, usually but not always calcareous, e.g. arable fields, woodland rides, lane-banks.

D. rufescens **VC11,12**: Uncommon, on non-calcareous soils. Most records are from the New Forest. In woodland rides and sand-pits, and on stream- and ditch-banks.

D. varia **VC11,12**: Frequent on calcareous soils, most often when disturbed, e.g. chalk-pits, lane-banks and woodland rides. Occasional in non-calcareous habitats, as on Railroad Heath, Fleet 85, in abundance, fruiting freely, *RCS & ACC* 1984.

D. staphylina **VC11,12**: Common in arable fields, farm-tracks and woodland rides. Described in 1969; previously confused with *D. varia*.

D. cerviculata **VC11,12**: Not common. Gravel-pits, wet heaths and sides of peaty ditches. Easily overlooked and not identifiable sterile.

D. heteromalla **VC11,12:** A very common calcifuge of light woodland soils; also on stumps and tree-roots, on lane-banks and occasionally on heath-land.

Dicranoweisia cirrata **VC11,12:** One of the commonest epiphytes, more tolerant than most of atmospheric pol-lution and hence frequent in suburban areas but very rare in the interiors of the old New Forest woodlands. On the bark of trees, especially *Quercus*, also occasionally on wooden fences.

Dicranum polysetum **VC11:** In only two localities: among *Calluna*, Ashley Heath, W of Ringwood 10, *ECW* 1981; Turf Hill Inclosure 21, *RCS* 1992. A northern continental species at the limit of its range.

D. bonjeanii **VC11,12:** Frequent in the New Forest in flushes. Occasional in chalk grassland, as on Noar Hill 73, *ACC* 1984. In very acid turf in Woolton Hill churchyard 46, *ACC* 1988.

D. scoparium **VC11,12:** Very com-mon on heaths and in acid woodlands; also in smaller quantity on tree-trunks, on stumps and on rotting wood. A straight-leaved form is frequent on N-facing chalk-turf; this needs proper investigation.

D. majus **VC11,12:** Locally frequent in acid woodland and on sheltered lane-banks; mainly in the New Forest and in the N and E.

D. spurium Rare. On damp heaths. **VC11:** Locally frequent in the New Forest, 19, 20, 21, 29, 30, 31. **VC12:** Woolmer Forest 73, 83, *FR* 1986–94; Heath End 46, *JPMB* 1948; Tadley Common 66, *ECW* 1961—75, not seen since 1976 heath fire.

D. fuscescens **VC11:** Recorded from two districts only. Very rare on *Quercus* and logs in the New Forest. On *Sambucus* in coombe on Butser Hill 72, *DHD* 1952.

D. montanum **VC11,12:** This and the following two species are now increasing their range in the British Isles. On living and dead trees and branches, most often of *Betula*, less commonly of *Corylus*, *Quercus* or

Fagus. Frequent on old *Quercus* in the New Forest; occasional in the N and E.

D. flagellare **VC12:** Seen once only, on a *Betula* trunk, Stonybrow Wood, East Tisted 63, *ACC* 1986.

D. tauricum **VC11,12:** Not common. On old stumps and rotten logs; less often on living trees, including *Acer pseudoplatanus*, *Quercus* and *Crataegus*. First found in 1981, and now noted from 17 localities, all but two in VC12.

Dicranodontium denudatum **VC11:** Found once only, on soil under *Fagus*, Wood Crates 20, New Forest, *FR* 1972.

Campylopus subulatus **VC11:** Reported from only one locality, but very readily overlooked. Gravelly path, Appleslade Inclosure, New Forest 10, *JAP* 1958.

C. fragilis **VC11:** Rare and local, on acid, peaty and gravelly soils; occa-sional in the New Forest; very rare at Wickham Common 51, and on Hayling Island.

C. pyriformis var. *pyriformis* **VC11,12:** Very common on sandy and peaty soils, on heaths and in wood-lands. Occasional on stumps and rotting logs.

var. *azoricus* Rare but overlooked. In wet heaths and bogs. **VC11:** Stonyford Pond, Beaulieu Heath 40, *JAP*. **VC12:** Blackmoor 73, on old *Molinia* tussocks, *MFVC* 1972; Hollywater Green 83, *ACC* 1986; Hazeley Heath 75, *ACC & FR* 1991; Tadley Common 66, *ACC* 1987.

var. *fallaciosus* **VC12:** In damp heath, Tadley Common 66, *MFVC* 1973.

C. paradoxus (*C. flexuosus* (Hedw.) Brid.) **VC11,12:** Frequent on rotting wood, and on the ground in heathy woodlands, but much less common than *C. pyriformis*.

C. introflexus **VC11,12:** A largely tropical montane species of the south-ern hemisphere that has spread all over the British Isles. First Hants record 1953; now very common on heathland, sometimes even dominant, especially after fires; occasional on tree-stumps, roadside banks and church-roofs.

C. brevipilus **VC11,12:** Frequent in the New Forest and Christchurch regions. Rare in the N and E (five localities). On wet heaths, sometimes with *Sphagnum compactum*.

Leucobryum glaucum **VC11,12:** Frequent in suitable habitats. In heaths, bogs, and moist, acid wood-lands where it may be on rotting wood and coppice-stools as well as on the ground.

L. juniperoideum **VC11,12:** In Hants, restricted to ancient woodlands. Very common in the New Forest beech-woods, where formerly thought to be a different species, *L. albidum*. Rare elsewhere, e.g. Newtown Com-mon 46, *FR & PB* 1982; Waggoners Wells 83, *ACC* 1983.

Fissidens viridulus **VC11,12:** Widely scattered but rarely abundant. On calcareous soils, usually on banks of streams and lanes, and by woodland rides.

F. pusillus var. *pusillus* **VC11,12:** An uncommon plant of damp stones and brickwork; mainly in stream-beds and on retaining walls, known from about a dozen localities in Hants.

var. *tenuifolius* **VC11,12:** Common on lumps of chalk in woodland. Very frequent also on stones on the Upper Greensand hangers; occasional on churches and tombstones.

F. limbatus Reported from only four localities, but probably not as rare as this suggests. An inconspicuous and easily overlooked plant, first published as British in 1980. **VC11:** By streams on Purbrook Heath 60, *JAP* 1960. **VC12:** On earth over stone (Bargate) in lane-bank, Headley near Bordon 83, *ACC* 1990; on chalky soil, Highnam Copse, Froyle 74, *ACC* 1990; wood-land S of Tunworth 64, *ACC* 1993.

F. incurvus **VC11,12:** A widely-distributed calcicole of woodlands, downs and shaded banks. Probably under-recorded, as hardly nameable without capsules.

F. bryoides **VC11,12:** Very common on clay banks and heavy woodland soils, but infrequent on calcareous substrates.

F. crassipes A plant of stonework, brickwork and concrete, by rivers and

canals carrying calcareous water.
VC11: Locally common. **VC12**: Only from Itchen Stoke 53, *WMB* 1957, *ACC* 1990.

F. exilis **VC11,12**: Inconspicuous and under-recorded, but uncommon. On clay banks and rides in woods, often associated with *F. taxifolius*. Occasionally abundant, as in Itchen Wood 53, *ACC* 1984.

F. osmundoides **VC11**: Recorded only from one stream-bank where locally abundant, Wood Crates, New Forest 20, *FR* 1973. A western and northern species in Britain; the nearest locality to this is in Somerset.

F. taxifolius ssp. *taxifolius* **VC11,12**: Very common on clay banks, in woodlands, churchyards, grassland and occasionally in arable fields.

ssp. *pallidicaulis* **VC11**: Recorded from one locality only. Islands Thorns Inclosure 21, *HM & RCS* 1993.

F. cristatus **VC11,12**: An occasional plant of chalk grassland. Scattered throughout the county, but less common than *F. adianthoides* with which it is sometimes confused.

F. adianthoides **VC11,12**: A widespread species of chalk grassland; occasional also in marshes and basic flushes. In the field, not distinguishable with certainty from the previous species.

Encalypta vulgaris **VC12**: Very rare. On chalk soil, Isle of Wight Hill 23, *FR & ECW* 1974, *EWJ* 1989.

E. streptocarpa **VC11,12**: Widely distributed but uncommon. On chalky soils in beech-woods, on roadside banks, in chalk turf and in chalk-pits; less often on walls.

Tortula ruralis ssp. *ruralis* **VC11,12**: Commonest on little-used tarmac on footpaths and roadsides. Sometimes on roofs and walls, less often in chalk turf and on sandy banks. Generally distributed but mostly in small quantity.

ssp. *ruraliformis* **VC11,12**: On sandy ground by the sea, where uncommon. Sometimes also on inland sandy areas, as at Broxhead Common 83, *ACC* 1982, and on roadside verges and waste ground. There are occasional populations intermediate between this and ssp. *ruralis*.

T. intermedia **VC11,12**: Very common on walls, especially in churchyards.

T. virescens **VC12**: Rare, perhaps overlooked. On trunk of *Juglans* in farmyard, Cholderton 24, *ACC & RCS* 1994.

T. laevipila var. *laevipila* **VC11,12**: Uncommon. On the trunks and branches of well-lit trees, especially *Sambucus* and *Fraxinus*; rarely, on walls.

var. *laevipiliformis* **VC11,12**: In habitats similar to those of var. *laevipila* but less frequent and possibly only a form of the type.

T. muralis var. *muralis* **VC11,12**: Ubiquitous on walls, brickwork, stonework and concrete.

var. *aestiva* **VC12**: A rather ill-defined variety found occasionally on damp brickwork.

T. marginata **VC11,12**: Widely distributed and sometimes abundant on damp or very sheltered brickwork and stonework, as on church-walls near ground-level and on retaining walls. More lime-demanding than *T. muralis* and frequent on stones and natural outcrops of the Upper Greensand.

T. subulata var. *subulata* **VC11,12**: Uncommon, but widely distributed and locally abundant. On chalky banks by roadsides and in woodland.

var. *angustata* **VC11**: Found once only, on a roadside bank, Hursley 42, *JAP* 1958. **VC12**: Recorded in *Census Cat.Brit.Mosses* (edn 1, 1907).

T. papillosa Rare. **VC11**: Romsey churchyard 32, *CLy* 1818; New Forest, *WRS* 1926, *JAP* 1959; floodplain of R. Test at Testwood, *NAS* 1991. **VC12**: Six localities, usually on tree-trunks (*Acer*, *Fraxinus* and *Sambucus*) but once on concrete railway-buffers.

T. latifolia **VC11,12**: Not uncommon. Most plentiful on tree-roots by streams and rivers, and on bridges where liable to occasional submergence, but almost equally frequent on poorly-drained tarmac away from permanent water.

T. cuneifolia **VC11**: Found once

only, on a sandy bank, Lee-on-the-Solent 50, *JWH* 1956.

Aloina brevirostris **VC11**: Found once only, on bare chalk, Dean Hill 22, *JAP* 1957.

A. rigida **VC11**: Rare. On bare chalk. In a few places in SW Hants and on Ports Down 60, *JAP*.

A. aloides var. *aloides* **VC11,12**: An uncommon but widely-distributed plant of bare chalk and chalky soil on banks, paths and woodland rides. Confused in the past with the much less common var. *ambigua*.

var. *ambigua* **VC11**: In scattered localities. **VC12**: With var. *aloides* on roadside verge, Little Hampage Wood, near Winchester 52, *ACC* 1985.

[*Pterygoneurum ovatum* **VC12**: Recorded in *Census Cat.Brit.Mosses* (edn 1, 1907). A dubious record.]

Pottia caespitosa Very rare. On chalky soil. **VC11**: Twyford Down 42, 1958, and Ashley Down 32, *JAP*. **VC12**: Isle of Wight Hill 23, *EWJ* 1989.

P. starkeana ssp. *starkeana* **VC12**: Found once only. Isle of Wight Hill 23, *ECW* 1974.

ssp. *conica* **VC11,12**: Not separately recorded in the British Isles before 1978. In the same habitats as ssp. *minutula*, but rather less frequent.

ssp. *minutula* **VC11,12**: Calcicolous. Common in arable fields and woodland rides and on banks and paths.

P. wilsonii **VC11**: Found once only, on a sandy bank by the sea, Tanners Lane, S of East End 39, *FR* 1974.

P. crinita **VC11**: Rare. On cliff-bases and sandy banks near the sea, e.g. Milford 29, *EFW* 1956; Stanpit Marsh 19, and Netley 40, *JAP*.

P. lanceolata **VC11,12**: A rather rare plant of chalky soil in open habitats and sandy banks by the sea.

P. intermedia **VC11,12**: Much less common than *P. truncata*, for which it is often overlooked, but in similar habitats.

P. truncata **VC11,12**: Very common in arable fields, in gardens, on waste ground and woodland rides on all soils, except the extremely acid and extremely basic.

P. heimii VC11: Local. On salt-marshes and waste ground near the coast in and W of Southampton Water.

P. bryoides VC11,12: A rare plant (seven records only) of neutral to slightly basic soils, mainly at the sides of woodland rides and churchyard paths. Only detectable in winter, when there are capsules.

P. recta VC11,12: Frequent. On bare chalk and on calcareous soil; on the downs, in arable fields and on banks and tracks.

Phascum cuspidatum VC11,12: Common everywhere except on extremely acid soils. A plant of arable fields and other disturbed habitats.

var. *piliferum* VC11: Probably overlooked. Recorded once only, at Langstone Harbour 60 or 70, *HM* 1991.

P. curvicolle VC11,12: A rare calcicole, sometimes associated with *Pottia recta* on the chalk downs, and once only, on the Upper Greensand.

P. floerkeanum VC11,12: A rather rare calcicole of arable fields and banks.

Acaulon muticum VC11,12: Rare, but probably overlooked. Mostly on bare, more-or-less neutral soil in grassy glades in woodland.

Barbula convoluta var. *convoluta* VC11,12: Very common. In open, well-lit communities on calcareous to slightly acid soils; also occasionally on walls.

var. *commutata* VC11,12: Frequent in slightly damper, more sheltered situations, and perhaps no more than a luxuriant modification of the typical form.

B. unguiculata VC11,12: Very common. A plant of waste ground, roadsides, stubble-fields, especially on basic soils, and occasionally on walls.

B. hornschuchiana VC11,12: Throughout, but often in small quantity. On basic soils on roadside verges, paths and waste ground. Frequently associated with *B. convoluta*.

B. revoluta VC11,12: Frequent throughout, but often in very small quantity. On sheltered walls and tombstones.

B. acuta VC12: Very rare, but easily mistaken for *B. fallax*. In chalk grassland near Cholderton Park 24, *ACC* 1987, and below Spollycombe Copse, Holybourne 74, *ACC & RCS* 1990; both in very small quantity.

B. fallax VC11,12: Very common in chalk grassland, and on calcareous roadside banks and paths. Rare away from calcareous strata, and mainly on imported soil.

B. reflexa VC12: Known only from Micheldever Spoil Heaps 54, *ECW* 1941.

[*B. spadicea* VC12: Recorded in *Census Cat.Brit.Mosses* (edn 1, 1907). A dubious record.]

[*B. glauca*. Formerly recorded in error for *Trichostomopsis umbrosa* (*q.v.*).]

B. rigidula VC11,12: Widespread but usually in small quantity. On brickwork and stonework, especially in churchyards.

B. nicholsonii VC11,12: Uncommon but overlooked. Most abundant on brickwork by streams, but most records are from tarmac or stone surfaces that remain wet for some time after rain. A large-celled population with double the normal chromosome number is present on concrete rides in Harewood Forest 34, *ACC* 1985, *HM* 1993.

B. trifaria VC11,12: Common, especially in churchyards, but rarely abundant. On walls and hard, compacted ground, chiefly where calcareous.

B. tophacea VC11,12: Frequent but rarely in quantity. On damp calcareous ground, flushes on cliffs, railway bridges; occasionally on churches.

B. vinealis VC11,12: Common throughout on walls.

B. cylindrica VC11,12: Common on walls, especially where there is some accumulation of humus and silt, but also frequent on sheltered banks.

B. recurvirostra VC11,12: Common

on chalky woodland banks and *Fagus* roots; also on damp, sheltered walls.

Gyroweisia tenuis VC11,12: Widely distributed but rarely abundant. On damp brickwork and stonework, especially in churchyards and on railway bridges; also on outcrops of Upper Greensand.

Leptobarbula berica (DE NOT.) SCHIMP. VC12: Not published as British until 1985, and perhaps an introduction. The earliest Hants specimen dates from 1982. So far, it is known from 17 localities, all in VC12. On brickwork and stonework, most often church-walls and tombstones. On Upper Greensand stones in walls, but not on natural outcrops.

Eucladium verticillatum VC11,12: A rather rare calcicole of wet mortar on bridges by streams and rivers, sometimes also on railway bridges.

Weissia controversa VC11,12: Fairly common, on sandy lane-banks. Usually calcifuge but occasionally in mildly calcareous habitats.

W. rutilans VC11: Found twice only. Roydon Woods, Brockenhurst 30, *RCS* 1982. VC12: On ride, Stonehanger Copse, Abbotts Ann 34, *RCS & ACC* 1989.

W. tortilis VC11: Rare. In open chalk-turf and scree, usually on S aspects. Oxenbourne Down 71, *JAP* 1959, *FR* 1990; Old Winchester Hill 62, *JAP* 1960; Broughton Down 23, *FR* 1986; Butser Hill 72, *FR* 1991.

W. microstoma var. *microstoma* VC11,12: Confined to the chalk, where fairly frequent in bare patches in grassland and on banks.

var. *brachycarpa* VC11: Rare. On damp, basic clay of the Headon Beds in the southern parts of the New Forest, *JAP*.

W. sterilis VC11,12: Very rare. In chalk grassland. Butser Hill 72, *PMH & ECW* 1941, *FR* 1988; Broughton Down 23, *FR* 1986; Stockbridge Down 33, *ACC* 1986.

W. longifolia var. *angustifolia* VC11,12: Common. In short chalk-turf or on bare chalk.

Oxystegus sinuosus VC11,12: Very

frequent throughout on walls. Also common on the chalk on woodland soil and on *Fagus* roots.

Trichostomum crispulum **VC11,12:** Occasional in chalk grassland, especially on trackways; also in marl-pits and on calcareous, woodland rides.

T. brachydontium Very rare. **VC11:** Calcareous clay on wet heath N of Durns Town, Sway 29, *TL* 1952. **VC12:** In chalk turf, Sheephouse Copse, Well 74, *ACC* 1983.

Tortella tortuosa Rare. **VC11:** Known from four localities on the chalk, e.g. Butser Hill, 71 & 72, *FR et al.* **VC12:** On the Roman Wall at Silchester, very scanty, *FR & ACC* 1986; Isle of Wight Hill 23, *BBS* excursion 1989.

T. flavovirens var. *flavovirens* **VC11:** Very rare. On sandy ground by and near the coast, near Hurst Castle 38, *JAP*; Salternshill Copse 49, *JAP*.

T. inflexa **VC11:** S of Petersfield, common on lumps of chalk in woodland and, sometimes, in open grassland. **VC12:** Strangely absent from the hangers N of Petersfield, and recorded only from a fallow field near Shalden 64, *JES & ECW* 1967, and from chalk stones under scrub, Beacon Hill, Burghclere 45, *RDP* 1994.

Pleurochaete squarrosa **VC11:** Very rare. Between Holt Down and War Down 71, *JAP* 1958; S-facing bank, Butser Hill, *FR* 1991.

Trichostomopsis umbrosa Rare; perhaps introduced. On damp brickwork of railway bridges. **VC11:** Stanmore, Winchester 42, *JAP* 1958 (first British record); Otterbourne 42, *JAP* 1960; Ditcham 71, *RCS* 1987. **VC12:** Grateley 24, *ACC* 1990; Newnham 75, *ACC* 1985, 1993; Basing 65, *ACC* 1985; Micheldever 53, *ACC* 1993. Earlier gatherings were for some time misidentified as *Barbula glauca*, not yet found in Hants.

Leptodontium flexifolium Very rare. On sandy heathland. **VC11:** Chandler's Ford 42, *BGo* 1963. **VC12:** Headley Park, Headley, near Bordon 83, *RCS* 1979; heath N of Bordon 73, *ACC* 1990.

<*L. gemmascens* Formerly on

wooden roof, Romsey 32, VC11, *WEN* 1917.>

Cinclidotus fontinaloides **VC11:** In several localities on concrete sluices in flood-zone above normal water-level on the Rivers Avon, Test and Itchen.

C. mucronatus **VC11,12:** On masonry and tree-trunks by streams and rivers; locally frequent by the Rivers Stour, Test, Rother and Meon. Recorded by *JAP* also from dry habitats on exposed flint and brick walls on roadsides.

Schistidium apocarpum **VC11,12:** Widely distributed but much less common on walls than *Grimmia pulvinata*; rather frequent also on flat surfaces of stone and concrete, and on tarmac paths and roadsides.

Grimmia pulvinata **VC11,12:** Common and often abundant on walls and tombstones; also on flat surfaces of stone, brick and concrete; very rare as an epiphyte.

G. trichophylla **VC11,12:** Uncommon. Nine localities, on walls and, less often, tombstones, e.g. 29, 40, 49, 62, 73.

Racomitrium fasciculare Very rare. On tiled church-roofs. **VC11:** Bursledon 40, *KS & FR* 1994. **VC12:** North Waltham 54, *ECW* 1972, *ACC* 1984; Highclere 46, *JWB & ACC* 1991.

R. heterostichum Rare. On tiled church-roofs and walls. **VC11:** Buriton 72, *ACC & ECW* 1957. **VC12:** Chilbolton 34, *ECW* 1969; Bentworth 64, *JCG & ACC* 1981; Headley near Bordon 83, and Grayshott 83, both *ACC* 1983.

R. lanuginosum **VC11:** Local on wet heaths in the New Forest 10, 11, 19, 20, 21, 29, 30. Rare on N-facing chalk-grassland, e.g. at Butser Hill 71, 72, *ECW* 1939, *FR c.*1970, not since. **VC12:** Only from near Popham Beacons 54, *ECW* 1965.

R. ericoides (BRID.) BRID. **VC12:** Only one confirmed find, on floor of sand-pit, Sleaford, near Kingsley 83, *ACC* 1990. Records of *R. canescens* from the New Forest and from chalk grassland are probably based on this or the following species.

R. elongatum FRISVOLL Three

records only. **VC11:** Picket Hill near Ringwood 10, *ACC* 1946; near Long Cross, W of Bramshaw 21, *JAP* 1957. **VC12:** In grass, Shortheath Common 73, *ECW, FR & ACC* 1951.

Campylostelium saxicola **VC12:** Very local. Confined to Upper Greensand rocks and stones; not infrequent in the hangers from Petersfield to S of Bisted 72, 73, *FR & ACC*.

Funaria hygrometrica **VC11,12:** Very common. Especially characteristic of sites of fires in woodland, but widespread on disturbed and waste ground everywhere.

F. fascicularis **VC11,12:** Uncommon. Known from *c.*20 scattered localities on disturbed ground – arable fields, edges of paths and tracks – on slightly acid to slightly basic soil. Often in very small quantity.

F. obtusa **VC11:** Occasional on damp, sandy soil on ditch-sides and sheltered banks in and near the New Forest. **VC12:** Warren Heath, Eversley 75, *ECW* 1962.

Physcomitrium pyriforme **VC11,12:** Uncommon but widely distributed. Usually on disturbed soil on the banks of rivers and streams, occasionally by ditches, in meadows and on damp roadside verges.

Physcomitrella patens **VC11,12:** Rare. Six localities, on wet, neutral or basic clay, on woodland rides, pond-margins and water-meadows.

Ephemerum recurvifolium Rare. On calcareous soils in fields and woodlands. **VC11:** Lower Brook 32, *JAP* 1958; Broughton Down 23, *JAP*; picnic-site, Crab Wood, Sparsholt 42, *RCS* 1985. **VC12:** Near Hampshire Gate, Tangley 35, *RCS & ACC* 1991; near Vernham Dean 35, *ACC* 1986.

E. sessile **VC12:** On woodland rides. Only from Highnam Copse, Froyle 74, 1950, and Sheephouse Copse, Well 74, *ACC* 1985.

E. stellatum **VC11:** Stubble-field, Hayling Island, *HM & RCS* 1992. **VC12:** On a ride, Cheriton Wood 62, *RCS & ACC* 1984.

E. serratum **VC11,12:** Occasional on slightly acid soils on damp woodland rides; also in arable fields and, less often, on disturbed soil in pastures and churchyards. Most records refer to var. *minutissimum*.

Tetraplodon mnioides VC12: Found once only, on dung (of dog or possibly deer) in *Calluna* heath, Yateley Common 85, *FR* 1986. A most surprising find of a species that, in Britain, is largely confined to upland regions.

Splachnum ampullaceum VC11: Frequent, though perhaps less so than formerly, on dung in bogs and wet heaths in the New Forest. VC12: Only one, unlocalized, 19th-century record.

Schistostega pennata VC12: One locality only, on sandstone in pit by Mellow Farm, Headley 83, near Bordon, *ECW* 1982, *FR & PB* 1983.

Orthodontium lineare VC11,12: An introduced Southern Hemisphere plant, first found in Hants in 1950; now common throughout on stumps and, less frequently, boles of living trees and peaty banks.

Leptobryum pyriforme VC11,12: Uncommon on damp soil by ponds, in gardens and churchyards, and in flower-pots.

<*Pohlia elongata* VC11: Formerly at Southampton, *JFR* 1905, not seen since. A surprising occurrence of this northern species.>

P. nutans VC11,12: Very common on acid, sandy and peaty soils in heaths and woodlands; more rarely on stumps, roadside banks, church-roofs and thatch.

P. drummondii Very rare. On woodland footpaths. VC11: Appleslade Inclosure 10, *JAP*, and four other sites in the New Forest. VC12: Highnam Copse, near Froyle 74, *ACC* 1982.

P. annotina (HEDW.) LINDB. VC11,12: Rather uncommon. On damp waste ground, banks and paths, on slightly acid soils. Occasional populations with large solitary gemmae need further investigation.

P. camptotrachela VC11: One record only. Denny Wood 30, New Forest, *JAP* 1955.

P. lutescens VC11,12: Generally distributed, but uncommon and easily

overlooked. On lane-banks and woodland rides on acid soils.

P. lescuriana VC12: Apparently uncommon. In damp, woodland rides, ditch-and stream-banks, and damp, arable fields. Calcifuge, in slightly damper places than *P. lutescens*.

P. carnea VC11,12: Frequent, though usually in small quantity. Widespread on calcareous to slightly acid soils. On woodland rides, on damp soil among *Juncus*, on banks of lanes, streams and ditches, in chalk-pits and occasionally in arable fields.

P. wahlenbergii VC11,12: Frequent on basic or neutral soils, on damp, woodland rides and, occasionally, arable fields.

Epipterygium tozeri VC11: Uncommon. On shaded roadsides, stream- and ditch-banks. VC12: On sandy bank, Mellow Farm, Headley, near Bordon 83, *FR & PB* 1983; side of ditch, Abbotts Wood Hill, Dockenfield 83 (now in Surrey), *ACC* 1994.

Bryum pallens VC11,12: Rather uncommon. Mainly on chalky soil in turf and in old chalk-pits. Occasional on woodland rides and on damp heaths.

B. algovicum var. *rutheanum* VC11,12: In dune slacks, Sinah Common, Hayling 69, *JAP*. Rare elsewhere on waste ground in the New Forest and near Farnborough 85, *ACC* 1985; in quarry at Steep, Petersfield 72, *MFVC* 1966.

B. inclinatum VC11,12: Uncommon, but widely distributed on sandy ground and in gravel-pits; occasional also in chalk grassland.

B. intermedium Rare. On damp, calcareous ground. VC11: Heath W of Beaulieu Road Station 30; derelict masonry, Salternshill Copse 49; garden, Glen Eyre, Southampton 41; track through old lime-works, S of Buriton 71, all *JAP*. VC12: Shapley Heath, Winchfield 75, *ACC* 1988.

B. donianum VC12: In small quantities on calcareous or sandy lane-banks. East Worldham 73, *ACC* 1985; Over Wallop 23, *ACC* 1993; E of Liss 72, *FR c*.1975.

B. capillare VC11,12: Very common. On a wide range of woodland trees; also

on roofs, walls and on the ground, avoiding only extremely acid soils.

B. flaccidum VC11,12: Rare in areas of acid soils where *Sambucus* is infrequent, but common elsewhere. On *Sambucus* and, occasionally, *Fraxinus* and other trees, or on soil.

B. torquescens Very rare but probably overlooked. In calcareous grassland. VC11: Oxenbourne Down 71, *JAP* 1959; near Deanhill Wood 22, *JAP*. VC12: Isle of Wight Hill 23, *NGH* 1989.

B. creberrimum VC11: Recorded only from a path across dry heath, Rowbarrow, Denny 30, *JAP* 1957, and from waste ground near river, Salternshill Copse, Beaulieu 49, *JAP*.

B. pseudotriquetrum VC11,12: Occasional in wet, base-rich fen-vegetation; more rarely in chalk grassland, as on Noar Hill 73, *ACC & FR* 1988, or on wet, non-calcareous soils, as in Woolmer Forest 73, *RCS & ACC* 1988. The only fertile specimens (Matley Bog 30, *JAP*; gravel-workings, Headley, near Kingsclere 56, *ECW & ACC* 1985) are synoecious and thus belong to var. *bimum*.

B. caespiticium VC11,12: Common on highly calcareous to neutral substrates; on walls and less often on waste ground, chalk grassland and arable fields.

B. alpinum VC11: Rare. On damp, gravelly tracks in the New Forest. VC12: Peaty ground, Yateley Heath 75, *ACC* 1952; Bartley Heath Wood 75, *ACC* 1987.

B. bicolor VC11,12: Very common on waste ground on neutral or basic soils; often also on the mortar between kerbstones at roadsides, with *B. argenteum*.

B. gemmiferum VC12: In sand-pit near Kingsley 73, *ACC* 1951, not seen since.

B. dunense Mainly maritime in Britain, but the only three Hants records are on bare ground inland. VC12: By track W of Alton 63, 1990; Noar Hill 73, 1991; Bramshott Common 83, 1993, all *ACC*.

B. argenteum VC11,12: Almost ubiquitous on waste and cultivated ground, sides of paths and roads, walls and masonry. Usually present as var. *argenteum*, occasionally as the poorly-understood var. *lanatum*.

B. radiculosum **VC11,12**: Frequent on mortar of damp walls, churches and railway bridges; also, occasionally, on calcareous soil.

B. ruderale **VC11,12**: Frequent on basic or neutral soils. Often associated with *B. bicolor* (q.v.) at the sides of paths and farm tracks, on roadside verges and on waste ground; rarely, in arable fields.

B. violaceum **VC12**: Rather frequent. Often associated with *Phascum cuspidatum* (q.v.); in arable fields, lane-banks and tracksides on neutral to highly calcareous soils. Easily overlooked and not yet recorded for VC11 where it is very likely to occur.

B. klinggraeffii **VC11,12**: In very similar habitats to *B. violaceum* but possibly tolerant of slightly damper conditions and slightly commoner.

B. sauteri Very rare. On bare patches on woodland rides. **VC11**: Hen Wood, East Meon 62, *RCS* 1982. **VC12**: Doles Wood, Hurstbourne Tarrant 35, *RCS* 1980; Walker's Copse, Dummer Grange Farm 54, *ACC* 1993.

B. tenuisetum **VC11,12**: Uncommon. On woodland rides and paths on acid soils; occasionally on wet heaths and sand-dunes.

B. microerythrocarpum **VC11,12**: Not uncommon but confined to moderately acid soils. On woodland rides, banks and arable fields, more rarely on heaths.

B. bornholmense **VC11,12**: On peaty or sandy heathland soils. Recorded from ten localities, but likely to be more widespread.

B. rubens **VC11,12**: Very common on calcareous and neutral soils on disturbed ground. In arable fields, on woodland rides, on road-banks and on waste ground.

Rhodobryum roseum Very rare. Usually on ant-hills in chalk grassland. **VC11**: Old Winchester Hill 62, *ECW* 1941, *FR* 1960; Breamore Wood 11, *JHGP* 1945; Oxenbourne Down 71, *JAP*, *FR* 1985; Butser Hill 72, *FR &*

RCS 1992. **VC12**: Abbotstone Down 53, *ECW & FR* 1981.

Mnium hornum **VC11,12**: An abundant woodland species of soil and the boles and stumps of trees. Calcifuge, and confined in chalk areas to rotting wood or to acid humus at the bases of trees.

M. stellare Strongly calcicolous; on lane-banks and in woodland on the chalk and Upper Greensand. **VC11**: Nursted Rocks, S of Petersfield 72, *HM* 1985. **VC12**: Selborne 73, *ECW* 1955, *ACC* 1983, 1992; Wheatham Hill 72, *ECW* 1941, still plentiful, *FR* 1994; below Empshott Mill 73, *FR* 1992; Hartley Mauditt 73, *ECW* 1965. Also in Great Deane Wood near Oakley 55, *ACC* 1990, and on the bank of a stream from the chalk, Sydmonton Common 46, *ECW* 1985.

Rhizomnium punctatum **VC11,12**: Frequent in marshes and in damp woodland where sometimes on rotting branches and stumps. Also occurs as a persistent, brown protonema on stones in moist places by ponds and streams, in churchyards and woodland.

R. pseudopunctatum Very rare. In marshes and fens. **VC11**: Marlborough Deep, Holmsley 29, *ECG* 1953; marshy woodland NE of Holmsley Inclosure 20, *JAP* 1957; by old marl-pits, Forest Lodge 29, *JAP & ECW*. **VC12**: Greywell Moors 75, *FR* 1973, not seen since; Hawley Common 85, *E de VH* 1924.

<*Plagiomnium cuspidatum* **VC12**: Formerly recorded at Swarraton 53, *WLWE* (*Moss Fl.Hants*); Hackwood Park 64, *FYB* 1851, Hb.BM. An uncommon and declining plant in the British Isles generally.>

P. affine **VC11,12**: Frequent in woodlands on neutral or basic soils, and usually in drier habitats than *P. undulatum*.

P. elatum Local. In marshes and calcareous fens and flushes. **VC11**: Near Holmsley Station 20, *JAP* 1957; in valley SW of Holmsley Inclosure 29, *JAP*; Lye Heath marsh 60, *NAS* 1989. **VC12**: Abundant at Stockbridge North Fen 33, *FR, RCS & ACC* 1990, and at Greywell Moors 75, *FR* 1953, *ACC* 1990; Yateley 86, *ACC* 1983; Bullington 44, *ACC* 1991; Andwell, near Mapledurwell 65, *ECW* 1948. For-

merly at North Warnborough Marsh 75, *ECW 1941*, and Conford Moor 83, *FR*, not seen since 1982.

P. undulatum **VC11,12**: Common in damp grassland and in almost every rural churchyard. Frequent also in damp woodlands on slightly acid to strongly basic soils.

P. rostratum **VC11,12**: Rare and always in small quantity. On damp soil; rarely, on tree-roots or moist walls.

Aulacomnium palustre **VC11,12**: Frequent in bogs and wet heaths. However, in dry habitats on Newtown Common 46, among very tall *Calluna*, *JWB & ACC* 1988, and in *Betula* wood S of Greatham Moor 73, *ACC* 1994.

A. androgynum **VC11,12**: Frequent on sandy banks, rotting logs and stumps; also on trunks of *Sambucus* and *Salix*.

Bartramia pomiformis **VC11,12**: Frequent in the SW and not uncommon elsewhere on the Lower Greensand and the Tertiaries. Locally abundant on sandy, non-calcareous lane-banks.

Philonotis caespitosa **VC11**: A rather critical species, perhaps overlooked. Near Bournemouth, *WRS* 1922; stream bank SW of Holmsley Station 20, *MCFP* 1951; near Millyford Bridge 20, *JAP* 1960. Not seen recently.

P. fontana **VC11,12**: Frequent in the New Forest, uncommon elsewhere. On damp, gravelly paths and banks in woods and heaths; usually stunted and scanty.

P. calcarea **VC11**: In several localities in the New Forest in calcareous valley-fens, e.g. near Forest Lodge 29, *JAP*; Stoney Moors 29, *FR* 1954–83. **VC12**: Conford 83, *ECW* 1938, not seen recently and presumed lost.

Breutelia chrysocoma **VC11**: In one site only. New Forest, *HFP* 1898; in flushes on heath W of the Rufus Stone 21, *NAS* 1989.

Zygodon viridissimus var. *viridissimus* **VC11,12**: Common and often abundant on walls and most kinds of tree, especially *Sambucus*.

var. *stirtonii* **VC11**: Widely distributed and possibly overlooked. Numerous records from walls and one from an oak branch, *AJES*. **VC12**: On wall of Headbourne Worthy church 43, *ACC* 1993.

Z. baumgartneri **VC11,12**: Much less common than *Z. viridissimus* and only once found on a wall. Widely scattered on a wide range of trees, especially on old *Quercus* in ancient woodland and on *Acer* spp. but also on *Fagus, Betula, Tilia, Fraxinus, Aesculus, Ulmus* and *Sambucus*.

Z. conoideus **VC11,12**: Common as an epiphyte on *Sambucus*; in the New Forest most often on *Fagus*, but also recorded from *Quercus, Fraxinus, Betula, Salix* and *Acer*. Widespread, but by no means everywhere.

Z. forsteri (Sched. 8) **VC11**: On *Fagus* near the Rufus Stone 21, *MCFP* 1954, where seen on several trees, especially in wound-tracks and knot-holes, until 1992; Rockram Wood 21, *NAS* 1993.

Orthotrichum striatum **VC11**: 'Rare and usually in small quantity on roadside trees and sallows' (*Bry.Fl.S. Hants*); probably now rarer and in still smaller quantities. **VC12**: 'N. Hants, Hill herb.' (*Moss Fl.Hants*); base of tree by R. Test, NE of Wherwell 44, *HM* 1993.

O. lyellii **VC11,12**: Scattered throughout but nowhere common. Perhaps most frequent on *Fraxinus*, but also on *Quercus, Fagus, Ulmus, Salix, Acer* and *Sambucus*.

O. affine **VC11,12**: Very common throughout on a wide range of trees, especially *Sambucus* and *Salix*; more rarely on walls.

O. sprucei **VC11**: Rare. On *Alnus* and *Salix* by stream- and river-banks at flood-level.

O. anomalum **VC11,12**: Frequent on walls and tombstones; occasional on concrete.

O. cupulatum **VC11**: Flint wall, East Meon 62, *JAP* 1957. **VC12**: Uncommon. Noted from nine localities on walls and tombstones, a tarmac path and a garden urn.

O. stramineum **VC11,12**: Rare, but overlooked. Recorded from about 15 localities, often in ancient woodland, on a wide range of trees, e.g., *Fraxinus, Sambucus, Alnus, Betula* and *Acer*.

O. tenellum **VC11**: Very local, on a variety of trees.

O. diaphanum **VC11,12**: Abundant. Equally at home on walls and trees, especially *Sambucus*.

O. pulchellum **VC11,12**: A rare plant, small and usually in small quantity, hence easily overlooked. Reported from various species of tree in about ten localities.

Ulota coarctata **VC11**: In one locality only, on *Sambucus* in wood S of Beacon Hill 52, *JAP*. Formerly also in Sussex; the nearest present-day localities of this northern species are in Somerset and Norfolk.

U. crispa **VC11,12**: Widely distributed in damp woodlands on a wide range of trees, especially *Salix* and *Fraxinus*. Var. *crispa* is perhaps slightly more frequent than var. *norvegica* but they occur in similar habitats, sometimes together.

U. phyllantha **VC11,12**: Uncommon but scattered throughout, particularly near the coast, mainly on *Salix, Sambucus* and *Fraxinus*.

Fontinalis antipyretica var. *antipyretica* **VC11,12**: Frequent, but not always where it might be expected. Submerged on stones and brickwork in all the major rivers and several smaller streams, as well as the Basingstoke Canal and a few ponds.

var. *gigantea* **VC11**: Rhinefield Water 20, *EWJ* 1960.

Climacium dendroides **VC11,12**: Rather uncommon and declining because of drainage. In marshes and fens; also in two places on Noar Hill 73, in not particularly moist chalk-grassland, *ECW & ACC* 1955, *FR & ACC* 1991.

Cryphaea heteromalla **VC11,12**: Frequent, though sometimes very stunted and scanty; nearly always on *Sambucus* where this is abundant. Seen once each on *Salix, Acer campestre* (at Wheatham Hill 72, *FR* 1992), and on a tombstone (at Rowledge 84, *ACC* 1983).

Leucodon sciuroides **VC11,12**: Formerly quite frequent on the trunks of sunlit trees, especially *Ulmus*; now less so in this habitat due to both Dutch Elm Disease and increasing atmospheric pollution from traffic. Occasional on exposed walls and tombstones, though usually in small quantity.

[*Antitrichia curtipendula* **VC12**: Record of unknown origin in *Census Cat.Brit.Mosses* (edn 1, 1907, p.50).]

Pterogonium gracile **VC11**: Local on tree-trunks, especially frequent in some ancient woodlands in the New Forest and in a few parklands. **VC12**: Very rare. Formerly on fallen *Fagus* at Stonybrow Wood, East Tisted 63, *FR* 1980–87. When this tree was removed in 1989, efforts were made to transplant the moss to others but it has not been refound; on base of old *Quercus*, Hurstbourne Park 44, *FR* 1985; on *Fraxinus* trunk, almost horizontal after uprooting by wind, Noar Hill 73, *ACC* 1991; tree-trunk near Sidown Hill, Highclere 45 (*Moss Fl.Hants*).

Leptodon smithii **VC11,12**: In the S, occasional (formerly frequent) on trees, especially *Fagus* in the New Forest, and sometimes on walls. In the N, rare: in hedge at Tichborne 53, *ACC* 1985; Swarraton 53, *WLWE* (*Moss Fl.Hants*); on *Tilia*, Old Burghclere 45, *ACC* 1986; formerly on *Quercus ilex* (blown down in 1990), Highclere Park 46, *FR* 1978; on tombstone in Chawton churchyard 73, *FR* 1993.

Neckera crispa **VC11,12**: Widely distributed but uncommon and often stunted and scanty. Almost confined to the chalk, mainly on sides of terracettes in N-facing chalk-grassland. On two very old *Quercus*, Bramshaw Wood 21, *RPB* 1957, *FR* 1994; also on *Quercus*, Shave Wood 21, *FR* 1972.

N. pumila **VC11,12**: Quite frequent, especially in the S. On a wide range of trees; most often in woodland, rare on roadside trees.

N. complanata **VC11,12**: Common on the chalk and absent from the most acid soils. Mostly on shaded tree-trunks and roots; occasional in damp chalk-grassland.

Homalia trichomanoides **VC11,12**: Common on the roots and boles of trees on the chalk. Occasional also on shaded stream-banks and on trees in damp places.

Thamnobryum alopecurum
VC11,12: Very common in woodland and on lane-banks on basic soils. Elsewhere very rare, but sometimes present on damp walls and on brickwork by streams.

Hookeria lucens (Map 579) **VC11:** In the New Forest, frequent on stream-banks and on flushes in carrs; very local elsewhere, e.g. Flexford NR 42, *NAS* 1987; Bishops Waltham Moors 51, *FR & RCS* 1985; Marrelsmoor Coppice 60, *HWT* habitat assessment team 1987; Forest of Bere 61, *RCS* 1988. **VC12:** Very rare. Silchester Common 66, *EWJ* 1964, *PB & ACC* 1984; Moor Copse, Kingsclere 55, *FR* 1985; Foley Manor carr, Liphook 83, *RD* 1986.

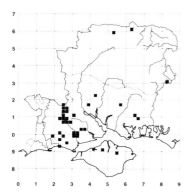

Map 579 Hookeria lucens

Leskea polycarpa **VC11,12:** Rather common in the S, less so in the N. Usually on trees by water, especially where liable to occasional flooding. Away from water, on *Acer* branch in hedge, Tichborne 53, *ACC* 1985.

Heterocladium heteropterum var. **flaccidum** **VC12:** On flints and on the ground. Combe Wood, Linkenholt 35, *PB & FR* 1984; under *Fagus* at head of coombe, The Warren 72, *ACC* 1992.

Anomodon viticulosus **VC11,12:** A calcicole. Frequent on the roots and boles of trees, sometimes also on sheltered banks; less commonly on shaded walls and brickwork by streams. Also on one old *Fagus*, Shave Wood 21, *FR* 1973–88.

Thuidium abietinum **VC11,12:** Occasional to very locally abundant. In short, open chalk-grassland and chalk-pits. Most plants belong to ssp. *hystricosum* but ssp. *abietinum* has been recorded from Noar Hill 73, and a few other localities in the N.

T. tamariscinum **VC11,12:** Very common in woodland, particularly on heavy soils; also, occasionally, in chalk grassland. Least common on extremely acid and extremely basic soils.

T. delicatulum **VC11:** Locally frequent in and near the New Forest on wet *Molinia* heath, on damp rides and roadside banks; occasional on marshy ground. **VC12:** Weavers Down 83, *ECW* 1937; Passfield Common 83, *ECW* 1954.

T. philibertii **VC11,12:** Rather rare (*c*.10 localities), in old chalk-turf, e.g. Noar Hill 73, *ACC & FR* 1990; Butser Hill 71, *FR* 1991.

Cratoneuron filicinum **VC11,12:** Common and mildly calcicolous. In damp, slightly basic soil, especially chalk-pits, springs, marshy turf and roadside verges; also on brickwork of bridges and by watercress-beds.

C. commutatum var. **commutatum** Very rare. Calcareous fens and flushes. **VC11:** Bishops Waltham, *FR* 1984–93. **VC12:** Greywell Moors 75, *ECW* 1952, *ACC* 1992; formerly at Mapledurwell Fen 65, *ECW* 1967.

var. **falcatum** **VC11:** Local in calcareous flushes and pools on the Headon Beds in the New Forest. **VC12:** Formerly at Greywell Moors 75, *ECW* 1963, and in Conford Moor 83, *ECW & ACC* 1955. Confirmation of its continued presence in the vice-county is desirable.

Campylium stellatum var. **stellatum** **VC11:** Occasional in the New Forest on wet, calcareous clay and in the less acid parts of many valley bogs; sandy lane, North Baddesley 32, *NAS* 1989. **VC12:** In fens and bogs. Greywell 75, *FR* 1965; Mapledurwell 65, *FR* 1990; Eelmoor Marsh 85, *FR & ECW* 1976; Stockbridge North Fen 33, *FR, RCS & ACC* 1990. Formerly at Conford 83, *ECW & ACC* 1955, North Warnborough 75, *ECW* 1969, and Hawley Pond 85, *ECW* 1934.

var. **protensum** **VC11,12:** More frequent than var. *stellatum*, in drier places and more restricted to basic soils. Widely distributed on chalky banks and in old chalk-pits; occasionally also on woodland rides.

C. chrysophyllum **VC11,12:** Rather more frequent than *C. stellatum* var. *protensum*, especially on the chalk downs, and in similar but drier habitats.

C. polygamum **VC11:** Only once recorded, on roadside near Shawford 42, *JAP* 1957.

C. elodes **VC11,12:** Rare. About the bases of *Alnus* in pools in the New Forest, or in turf on calcareous clay, *JAP*. Greywell Moors 75, *ECW* 1936; Stockbridge North Fen 33, *RCS, FR & ACC* 1990.

C. calcareum **VC11,12:** Rather rare, on flints and lumps of chalk; occasionally on soil and tree-roots in chalk woodland and on shaded banks.

Amblystegium serpens **VC11,12:** Very frequent on the branches of trees, especially *Sambucus*, and on walls, damp brickwork and shaded stones; less frequent on soil.

A. tenax **VC11,12:** Rare. On stone, brick and concrete by rivers, streams and canals where liable to occasional flooding.

A. varium **VC11,12:** Uncommon. Usually on wood or concrete by water where subject to periodic flooding; occasionally on the ground in wet meadows.

A. humile Rare; most often in fens and wet meadows. **VC11:** Purewell, Christchurch 19, *MCFP* 1960. **VC12:** Six localities.

A. riparium **VC11,12:** Very common. On wood or masonry by water and on decaying wood or rotting vegetation in wet carr.

Drepanocladus aduncus **VC11,12:** Occasional. On soil in clay-pits, pond-margins and ditches in slightly basic to slightly acidic habitats.

D. sendtneri **VC11:** Found only once, submerged in pool, Marlborough Deep 29, *MCFP* 1951.

D. lycopodioides **VC11:** Found only once, in boggy area in open moorland, Dibden Bottom 30, *TL* 1958, not seen since. **VC12**: Recorded in *Census Cat. Brit.Mosses* (edn 1 1907, p.57).

D. fluitans **VC11,12**: Frequent. In acid habitats on wet heaths, on peat, in shallow pools and in old gravel-pits. Var. *fluitans* and var. *falcatus* seem to be equally frequent and to have similar ecology.

D. exannulatus **VC11,12**: Frequent. On wet, boggy ground where liable to submergence in winter; often in shallow pools, gravel-pits and pond-margins. Var. *exannulatus* and the poorly-defined var. *rotae* are about equally frequent.

D. revolvens **VC11**: Almost confined to the New Forest, where occasional in flushes on the Headon Beds and in the less acid valley-bogs. **VC12**: Very rare. Eelmoor Marsh 85, *FR & ECW* 1976, *FR* 1994; Stockbridge North Fen 33, *FR* 1985. Formerly on Silchester Common 66, *?FIW* 19th century; Conford 83, *ECW & ACC* 1955, *FR* to 1970; and at Greywell 75, *ECW* 1936, *FR* to 1965, but extinct through dumping of soil by 1970.

D. vernicosus (Sched. 8) **VC11**: Very rare. In basic flushes in the New Forest. Greenberry Bridge, N of Holmsley Station 20, *JAP* 1958; N of King's Copse Inclosure 40, *NAS & FR* 1989; Widden Bottom 29, *NAS & FR* 1990.

D. uncinatus **VC11**: Very local. On moist, decaying logs and tree-roots in and about the New Forest.

Hygrohypnum luridum **VC11**: Boards by mill-stream, Brockenhurst 30, *HND* 1889. **VC12**: Rare; eight records, six of them from churchyards, in gutters or on flat, sunken tombstones where water stands after rain.

Scorpidium scorpioides **VC11**: Locally plentiful in flushes on margins of bogs in the New Forest, *JAP, FR* to 1994. **VC12**: Formerly at Fleet Pond 85, *ECW* 1934, not seen since.

Calliergon stramineum Among *Sphagnum* in slightly flushed but active bogs. **VC11**: Occasional in the New Forest. **VC12**: Local, with only six localities, mainly in Woolmer Forest.

C. cordifolium **VC11,12**: Rather local. In wet woodlands, in alder carr and around the borders of ponds.

C. giganteum **VC11**: As *C. cordifolium*, rather local and in similar habitats; also in wet ditches on calcareous soil, *JAP*. **VC12**: Very rare; in calcareous fens. Greywell Moors 75, *ECW* 1936, still there 1991; Stockbridge North Fen 33, *FR, RCS & ACC* 1990. Formerly at North Warnborough Marsh 75, *ECW* 1969.

C. cuspidatum **VC11,12**: Very common. In damp grassland, both acid and basic; also on woodland rides, in fens, marshes and around ponds, especially where the conditions are basic.

Isothecium myurum **VC11,12**: Widespread on tree-boles and roots but much less common than *I. myosuroides*. Favours damper conditions than that species and most frequent in calcareous habitats; also often at the base of trees whereas the latter can be higher up.

I. myosuroides **VC11,12**: Very abundant on the trunks and roots of trees; less often on stumps or on the soil. Less frequent in very basic or very acid habitats.

I. striatulum **VC11**: Highcliffe 19, on garden rockery, *MCFP* 1952; Hurst Castle 38, on stone and on gravel pathside, *JAP* 1958. **VC12**: Locally frequent on chalk on roots of *Fagus*, *Ulmus* and *Fraxinus*. Ashford Hill 72, *ECW & FR* 1978, *FR* to 1990; Bramdean Common 62, *ACC* 1991; Swarraton 53, *WLWE* (*Moss Fl.Hants*).

Scorpiurium circinatum **VC11**: Old limestone walls, Beaulieu Abbey 30, *JAP, FR* to 1995 and Netley Abbey 40, *JAP, FR* to 1993; Portchester Castle 60, *FR* 1993; St Cross Hospital, Winchester 42, on ancient walls, *FR* 1995.

Homalothecium sericeum **VC11,12**: Very common on basic walls, tombstones and sunlit tree-trunks and roots.

H. lutescens **VC11,12**: Very common in sunlit chalk-turf. Also at Bramshott 83, *ECW* 1948, presumably on Bargate Beds.

<H. nitens **VC11**: Sub-fossil (late Devensian) in peat, Church Moor, Mark Ash Wood, recorded by Clarke & Barber (see Introduction, p. 11).>

Brachythecium albicans **VC11,12**: Very common, especially on acid soils,

but occasional on basic ones. On light, sandy and gravelly soils on heaths, roadsides and waste ground when fully illuminated; sometimes also on concrete and on roofs.

B. glareosum **VC11,12**: Rather uncommon. Calcicolous and almost confined to the chalk; on bare soil, banks and pathsides in open woodland.

B. salebrosum Rare. **VC11**: On rotten trunk, Denny Wood 30, *EWJ* 1946. **VC12**: Fallen trunk in swamp, Barton Stacey 44, *JApp* 1964; Abbotstone Down 53, *FR* 1982; on branch of *Sambucus* in scrub, Thruxton Hill 24, *RCS & ACC* 1994.

B. mildeanum **VC11**: Rather rare. In and around the New Forest on damp, gravelly waste-ground, *JAP*. **VC12**: Edge of ride, Freefolk Wood 44, *ECW* 1941; Greywell Moors 75, *FR & ACC* 1990; edge of valley bog, Hazeley Heath 75, *FR & ACC* 1991.

B. rutabulum **VC11,12**: Very common throughout, but avoiding extremely acid soils. In woodlands, waste places and grassland on logs, shaded banks and walls.

B. rivulare **VC11,12**: Widespread in carr, flushes, marshes, and by streams and rivers, but not in very acid habitats.

B. velutinum **VC11,12**: Frequent on roots, boles and branches of several species of tree, especially *Sambucus*; also locally abundant on sandy banks, ranging from the slightly acid to the highly basic.

B. populeum Uncommon. On tree-roots and boles; also, occasionally, on walls and flints. **VC11**: Only in the New Forest region. **VC12**: All records from the chalk or Upper Greensand.

B. plumosum **VC11**: Very local, with ten sites on tree-roots on stream-banks, in and near the New Forest only.

Pseudoscleropodium purum **VC11,12**: Most abundant in chalk grassland, but common in all sorts of woodland and grassland as well as on heaths.

Scleropodium cespitans **VC11,12**: Occasional on the boles and roots of trees near water; quite frequent also on churchyard paths, on tarmac at the sides of drives, and on retaining walls.

S. tourettii   VC11: Very local on dry, gravelly soil on roadsides, *JAP*. VC12: Rare. Rides of Milford Wood, Highclere Park 46, *ABJ* (*Moss Fl.Hants*); hedgebanks, Liphook 83, *ECW* 1941, and Bramshott 83, *ECW* 1937; chalky soil under *Fagus*, Popham Beacons 54, *ECW* 1951; Farrow Hill, Hawkley 72, *FR* 1988.

Cirriphyllum piliferum   VC11,12: Common. In damp woodland, avoiding very acid soils; in slightly drier habitats on the chalk.

C. crassinervium   VC11,12: Typically on the chalk, especially on *Fagus* roots and on shady banks, where it is often abundant; also occasionally present on walls and tombstones away from the chalk.

Rhynchostegium riparioides VC11,12: Avoids extremely acid water but is common elsewhere. In streams and rivers, on walls and weirs submerged for all or most of the year.

R. murale   VC11,12: Occasional on damp, sheltered walls; also recorded from chalky soil and trees.

R. confertum   VC11,12: Very common on the boles and roots of trees, on branches of *Sambucus*, on stones in woodland, and on shaded walls, mainly on base-rich soils.

R. megapolitanum   VC11,12: Widespread along the coast on dunes and on gravelly soils, *JAP*. Rare elsewhere, on sandy banks and waste ground, especially on the Folkestone Sand strata of the Lower Greensand, e.g. Duckmead Lane, Liss 72, *FR* 1994; S of Oakhanger 73, *FR* 1994.

Eurhynchium striatum   VC11,12: Very common in woodland on the chalk and on sheltered lane-banks. Recorded almost throughout the county, but rare on acid soils.

E. pumilum   VC11,12: Frequent and generally distributed. On loamy or sandy soil, usually basic, in woodland and on hedgebanks; especially common on lanesides on the Bargate Beds in 72 and 73, *FR*.

E. praelongum var. *praelongum* VC11,12: Very common and abundant throughout, especially in woodland, but also on roadside banks, in grassland

and in marshes. Avoids extremely acid soils.

var. *stokesii*   VC11: *JAP* records numerous woodland localities for this poorly-defined variety. VC12: Greywell Moors 75, *RCS* 1992; The Warren 72, *ACC* 1992.

E. swartzii var. *swartzii*   VC11,12: Very common. On damp, bare soil in arable fields, farm tracks, chalk turf, woodland rides and waste ground. Also, as a better-grown plant, forming patches among grass in hedgebanks.

var. *rigidum*   A variety probably of little taxonomic value. VC11: Waste ground near Hurst Castle 38, *JAP* 1958. VC12: Noar Hill 73, *ECW* 1941.

E. schleicheri   VC11,12: Common, but easily passed by as *E. swartzii*. On slightly acid to very basic, light soils; on shaded banks by lanes or in woodland, commonest on Upper Greensand and the Bargate Beds.

E. speciosum   VC11,12: Rather rare. On soil and tree roots by streams and ponds, and in wet woodland. Probably under-recorded as easily overlooked for robust *E. swartzii*.

Rhynchostegiella tenella var. *tenella* VC11,12: Very common on damp walls and tombstones; also on flints in chalk woodland and other basic stones (Bargate, Upper Greensand) in shaded situations.

var. *litorea*   VC11: Rare. Recorded by *JAP* from the bases of shrubs and hedges in a few localities. VC12: On stone in bank, Hammer Lane, Barford 83, *ACC* 1994.

R. curviseta   VC11,12: Characteristic of the Upper Greensand, where it is frequent from Buriton 72, to Binsted 74, on stones outcropping in the hangers and in lane-banks. *JAP* also recorded it in VC11 from scattered sites near water on stone and concrete walls.

R. teesdalei   Very rare and not seen recently. VC11: Concrete wall of stream, Rockbourne 11, *JAP* 1959. VC12: Swarraton 53, *WLWE* (*Moss Fl.Hants*).

Entodon concinnus   VC11,12: An obligate calcicole, confined to the chalk. Rather local, appearing to have limited ability to colonize new sites.

Mainly in old chalk-grassland on southerly aspects; less common in chalk-pits, e.g. Butser Hill 71, 72, and Abbotstone Down 53, both *FR*. Now decreased through scrub-invasion of the Downs.

Plagiothecium latebricola   VC11,12: Rather rare. Typically on bases of *Alnus* and stools of *Carex paniculata* or ferns in *Alnus* swamps; occasionally also in dry situations on the stools of coppiced *Corylus* and *Castanea*, and on *Betula* stumps.

P. denticulatum   VC11,12: A calcifuge; widely distributed, but rare on the chalk. On rotting wood, woodland banks and carr.

P. ruthei   Very rare. VC11: Decaying log in marshy woodland, Nightingale Wood 31, near Romsey, *JAP* 1959. VC12: Yateley 86, *HWM* 1920.

P. curvifolium   VC11,12: Common except on the chalk, and rather commoner than *P. denticulatum* in the drier woodland habitats and on the most acid soils. A calcifuge of rotting wood and woodland soils.

P. laetum VC12: On *Corylus* stool, Highnam Copse, Froyle 74, *ACC* 1982.

P. succulentum   VC11,12: Widely distributed but nowhere as common as *P. nemorale*. On neutral woodland soils; rarely, on stumps and fallen tree-trunks.

P. nemorale   VC11,12: Very common. In woodlands and shaded lane-banks on soils ranging from the slightly acid to the slightly basic.

P. undulatum   VC11,12: Frequent and locally plentiful in the New Forest and in woods on the Lower Greensand and the Tertiaries; occasional in conifer plantations elsewhere. A calcifuge of sheltered woodland.

Herzogiella seligeri   VC11,12: Rather rare but increasing in SE England. First found in Hants in 1964 and now known from about a dozen localities. On stumps and rotting wood.

Isopterygium elegans   VC11,12: Common everywhere except on the chalk. A calcifuge of light woodland soils, shaded lane-banks and heaths; sometimes on rotting wood and on tree-roots. Fruit very rare, on sandy banks: in beech-wood, Holm Hills 83, *ACC* 1984; abundant in Woodland Lane, SE of Liss 72, *FR* 1994.

Taxiphyllum wissgrillii **VC11,12**: Very local. A calcicole of shaded places on the chalk and especially on the Upper Greensand; on stones, soil and tree-roots.

Platygyrium repens **VC12**: North-down Plantation, Steventon 54, *RCS & ACC* 1990, on a few adjacent trees of *Fraxinus* and *Acer campestre*; Grey-well Moors 75, on *Alnus*, *HM* 1992; on *Salix* and on *Fraxinus*, Forest Park, Dogmersfield 75, *ACC* 1992. Increasing in southern England and likely to be found in additional localities.

Hypnum cupressiforme var. *cupressiforme* **VC11,12**: Ubiquitous and very variable. Common on trees, roofs, walls and in turf.

var. *resupinatum* **VC11,12**: A common epiphyte on all kinds of deciduous tree; occasional also on rotting wood and on walls.

var. *lacunosum* **VC11,12**: Frequent in chalk grassland, on roadsides, waste ground and occasionally on walls and tombstones.

H. mammillatum **VC11,12**: A very common epiphyte, especially on *Quercus* and *Fagus*. Persists on fallen branches for many years.

H. jutlandicum **VC11,12**: Avoids the chalk, but common elsewhere in habitats too base-deficient for the previous two species. Very common in heaths and heathy woodland, and present in many bogs.

H. imponens **VC11,12**: Quite frequent in the bogs and wet heaths of the New Forest and in the Woolmer Forest neighbourhood; surprisingly, unrecorded from Silchester Common or from any of the bogs on the Tertiaries in the N.

H. lindbergii **VC11,12**: Frequent in the New Forest; rather common elsewhere. On damp, woodland rides, on neutral or slightly basic soils.

Ctenidium molluscum var. *molluscum* **VC11,12**: Common in chalk grassland and on chalky, roadside banks; in the New Forest, on shaded stream-banks on slightly basic soils and, on the Headon Beds, in calcareous fens. Also, rarely, on sheltered walls, and by lanesides on Upper Greensand.

A separate 'woodland taxon' (*Smith Moss Fl.*, p.661), not yet formally described, occurs on sheltered banks in woodlands on mildly acid clay and loam soils, scattered throughout Hants, especially in the New Forest and the Forest of Bere.

Hyocomium armoricum **VC11**: Very local. Confined to stream-banks at flood-level in the New Forest, e.g. Stricknage Wood 21, abundant, *FR* 1976–93; Highland Water Inclosure 21, *RCS* 1991; Ocknell Wood 21, *FR* 1971.

Rhytidiadelphus triquetrus **VC11,12**: Frequent in most of the county. Most abundant in chalk grassland; present also in non-calcareous woodlands but avoids wet habitats.

R. squarrosus **VC11,12**: Very common, often abundant. Almost always amongst grass, e.g. in lawns, turf, churchyards, lightly shaded woodland rides, and marshes.

R. loreus **VC11,12**: An uncommon species of woodlands, both acid and basic. A good indicator of ancient woodland, frequent in the New Forest, e.g. E of Rufus Stone and Stricknage Wood 21, *FR* 1992; it can also occur, as at Bordon 73, *ACC* 1985, in recently-developed woodland on former heath-land; present also in N-facing chalk-turf N of Butser 72, *FR* 1975.

Pleurozium schreberi **VC11,12**: A calcifuge commonly associated with *Calluna* on heathland and frequent also in open woodland under light shade. Unrecorded with capsules.

Hylocomium brevirostre **VC11,12**: Rare and apparently declining. Most records are from chalk scrub or glades in escarpment woodland, but also known on old woodland floors in the New Forest, e.g. E of Rufus Stone 21, *FR* to 1993.

H. splendens **VC11,12**: Widespread but patchy. In heaths and damp woodlands; also in deep turf in N-facing chalk-grassland.

APPENDIX I

LIST OF RECORDERS AND REFEREES, WITH ABBREVIATIONS

1. INDIVIDUALS

This list of individual recorders and referees, with the abbreviations of their names as used in the text, includes those making the first record of a plant in Hampshire, as well as others who have contributed records but are not specifically mentioned in the text.

Aberdeen, J. S.		Bailey, J. P.	JPB	Beeby, W. H.	
Abraham, Miss F.		Bailey, S.	SBa	Beeson, M.	
Adam, Dr P.		Bailey, W. G.		Bell, W.	WBe
Adams, Mrs J. M.		Baker, Miss D.		Bennett, A.	
Adamson, R. S.	RSA	Baker, Rt Hon. H. T.	HTB	Bennett, E. J.	
Aellen, Dr P.	PA	Baker, J. G.	JGB	Bennett, Miss -.	
Akeroyd, Dr J. R.	JRA	Balfour, J. H.		Bennians, Cmdr J.	JBe
Al-Bermani, A.-K.K.A.	AAl-B	Balfour-Browne, Miss E.	EB-Br	Benoit, P. M.	PMB
Allen, Dr D. E.	DEA	Ball, D.	DBa	Bentley, F.	FB
Allen, M.		Ball, Dr P. W.	PWB	Berens, Mrs A. du S.	AduSB
Allen, R.		Balme, O. E.		Berry, Dr P. M.	
Alston, A. H. G.	AHGA	Bampton, Miss P.		Berulter, Miss -.	
Andrews, C. E. A.	CEAA	Bangerter, E. B.	EBBa	Beswick, J. R. L.	JRLB
Andrews, F. W.		Banks, Mrs J.		Bevan, J.	JBev
Andrews, J.	JA	Banks, Mrs M.	MBa	Bickham, S. H.	
Antony, Mrs S.		Baring, Mrs O.		Bidmead, Miss H. A.	
Appleton, D.		Barker, Dr A. J.		Bigg, Miss -.	
Appleton, Revd R.		Barker, G.		Billett, D. F.	
Appleyard, Mrs J.	JApp	Barker, J. C.	JCBa	Billett, Mrs R. A.	RABi
Arnold, Revd F. H.		Barker, Mrs P. V. J.	PVJB	Bing, H.	
Arthern, M. R.	MRA	Baron, W. M. M.	WMB	Birkinshaw, C. R.	CRB
Arthure, B. F.		Barrett, G. E.	GEB	Birt, Miss M. E.	
Ash, G. M.	GMA	Barrett, R. A.	RBa	Bishop, E. B.	
Ash, Mrs J.		Barrington, M. D.		Black, Miss C.	
Ash, Mrs J. W.	JWA	Barter, Miss -.		Blaikley, Miss N. M.	NMB
Ash, S.	SA	Barton, W. C.	WCB	Blake, Mrs A.	
Ashby, Mrs R. C.	RCA	Bassett, Mrs B. J.		Bolland, -.	
Ashley-Harris, Dr H. C.	HCA-H	Batchelor, H. C.		Bolt, I. C.	IB
Ashton, Maj. C.		Bateman, R. M.		Bolton, Mrs A. E.	AEB
Ashton, Mrs C.		Bates, Dr J. W.	JWB	Boniface, Miss M.	MBo
Aston, A. H.	AHA	Bathe, -.		Boniface, R. A.	RAB
Aston, Mrs L.		Bathe, Mrs -.		Borrer, W.	WBo
Atkins, -.	Atk	?Bayley, Dr W.		Boswell-Syme, J. T. I.	
Austen, Revd J. H.		Bayton, Revd W. Stevens		Boucher, Mrs A. M.	AMB
Ayer, J.		Beale, Dr P. T. B.	PTBB	Boucher-West, Mrs -.	
		Beasley, J. A.	JAB	Boulger, G. E. S.	
Babington, Prof. C. C.		Becher, Mrs M.	MBec	Boulton, C.	
Bacon, Miss G.		Beckett, D. M. R.	DMRB	Bowden, Miss L. F.	
(later Foggitt, Mrs G., *q.v.*)		Beddington, Miss W. G.	WGB	Bowen, Dr H. J. M.	HJMB
Bacon, J.	JB	Beddow, Revd A. J. C.	AJCB	Bower, Miss S.	SB
Bacon, Mrs P. M.		Bedford, K.		Bowles, N. R. C.	NRCB

Bowman, E. F.		Butcher, W.	WB	Coombe, Dr D. E.	DEC
Bowman, R. P.	RPB	Butler, Miss H.		Coombe, J. E.	
Bowra, J. C.	JCB	Byfield, A. J.	AJB	Coombes, A. J.	AJC
Boxall, Mrs C.	CB			Cope, Dr T. A.	TAC
Boxall, M. R.	MRB	Cadbury, J.		Coppins, Dr B. J.	BJC
Boycott, Miss M. I.		Cadman, W. A.		Corfe, B. O.	
Boys, J. C. S.		Caesar, Miss J.		Corley, M. F. V.	MFVC
Bradfield, Miss -.		Calthorpe, Sir R.		Cornwallis, Ms V. M.	VMC
Bradshaw, A. D.	ADB	Campbell, Mrs A.		Cornwell, -.	
Bradshaw (later Proctor), Dr M. E.	MEB	Canham, Miss M. O.	MOC	Cottle, N. W.	
Branson, A. J. P.	AJPB	Cannon, J. F. M.		Cotton, C.	
Bratton, J. H.	JHBr	Cardew, R. M.		Cotton, T. A.	
Bray (formerly Hodgson), Mrs E.		Carpenter, Mrs J. M.		Cox, J. R.	JRC
Braybrooks, E. M.		Carpenter, R. J.	RJC	Cox, Mrs J. M.	JMC
Bree, T.		Carter, A. H.	AHC	Coxhead, Mrs K.	KC
Brenan, Prof. J. P. M.	JPMB	Carter, C.	CCa	Crabbe, J. A.	
Brewin, Mrs D.	DB	Carter, H.		Cragg-Barber, M.	MC-B
Brewis, Lady Anne	AB	Carter, Dr R. N.	RNC	Crane, A. J.	AJCr
Brickell, C. D.		Causton, Capt. L. P.		Cranston, Miss? L. E.	
Briggs, Mrs E. A.	EABr	Chadwick, Mrs B. K.		Crawford, G. F.	
Briggs, Mrs M.		Chadwick, N. L.		Crombie, J.M.	JMCr
Briggs, T. R. A.	TRAB	Chaffey, J.		Crosfield, A. J.	
Bristow, B. R.	BRB	Chambers, E.	ECh	Cross, W. J.	
Britton, C. E.		Chandler, Revd P. J.	PJC	Crosthwaite-Eyre, Mrs D.	
Brocas, F. Y.	FYB	Chapman, Dr S.		Crothall, Miss L.	LC
Bromet, Miss F. C.		Chapman, V. J.		Crundwell, A. C.	ACC
Bromfield, Dr W. A.	WAB	Chapple, J. F. G.		Cruttwell, Canon N. E. G.	NEGC
Brookman, Mrs D.	DBr	Chater, A. O.	AOC	Cryer, J.	JCr
Brooks, Mrs E. R.	ERB	Chatfield, Dr J.	JCh	Cumming, L.	LCu
Brough, Dr P. R.	PB	Chatters, C.	CC	Curtis, J.	
Brown, G. C.		Chawner, Miss E. F.	EFC	Cuthbert, C. R.	CRC
Brown(e), Revd W.		Cheke, A. S.	ASC		
Browning, F.	FBr	Chester, T.	TCh	Dack, J. M.	
Bruce, Miss H.	HBr	Childs, Miss K. A.	KAC	Daker, M. G.	MGD
Brummitt, Dr R. K.	RKB	Churches, Miss E. W.	EWC	Dalby, Dr D. H.	DHD
Brunning, Bro. D. E.	DEB	Clanchy, J.	JC	Dale, Dr J.	
Bryant, M.	MB	Clapham, Prof. A. R.	ARC	Dallas, C. C.	
Buchanan, R.	RB	Clarke, C. B.	CBC	Dampier-Child, E.	
Buchanan, Mrs -.		Clarke, M. J.		Dampney, D. J.	DJD
Buckell, F.	FBu	Clarke, Mrs S.		Dandy, J. E.	JED
Buckle, O.		Clayden, Lt-Col. C. N.		Daniels, R. E.	REDa
Buckle, Miss W. F.	WFB	Clement, E. J.	EJC	Dann, Capt. M. P.	
Bucknall, C.	CBu	Cleminshaw, E.		Darrah, G. V.	GVD
Budd, P. A.	PAB	Clough, R. I.		Darrah, J. H.	
Budgeon, E.	EB	Coates, H. E.		Darter, Mrs C.	CD
Bull, -.		Cobb, Mrs J. M.		Davey, S. R.	SRD
Bull, H.		Cobbe, Miss A. B.		David R. W.	RWD
Bull, K.	KBu	Cobbold, V.		Davidson, Miss C.	CDa
Bullard, G. E. S.	GESB	Cockerton, Revd D.		Davidson, Miss F.	
Bulloch, Mrs D. E.		Codling, A. N.		Davies, Lt -.	
Burden, R. F.		Cohen, E.	EC	Davis, R. G.	RD
Burford, Miss -.		Cole, M. J.	MJC	Davy, Lady J. C.	JCDa
Burges, R. C. L.		Cole, Miss T.	TC	Dawson, Dr F. H.	
Burkmar, Dr R. J.	RJB	Colebourn, P. H.	PHC	Dawson, Dr H. J.	HJD
Burnett, Dr J. H.	JHB	Collett, T. G.		Day, B. P.	BPD
Burnhill, Miss M. J.		Collins, P.		Day, F. M.	
Burrows, E. A.	EAB	Collinson, P.		Deahill, W. J.	
Burrows, Mrs P. H.	PHB	Colman, Sir Jeremiah, Bt	JCo	Deakin, R. H.	
Burton, C. W. Musgrave	CWMB	Colman, Lady -.		de Foucault, B.	BdeF
Burton, R. M.	RMB	Colston, A.		de Lobel, M. (or de L'Obel)	
Burtt, B. L.	BLB	Comber, J.		Denholm, Dr A. I.	
Bury, H.	HB	Combridge, P.		Derrick, S.	SD
Bush, R.		Conway, Prof. V. M.		Desprès, Miss Y. (later Eldridge,	YD
Butcher, Mrs A. A.	AAB	Cook, Prof. C. D. K.	CDKC	Mrs Y.)	
Butcher, Dr R. W.		Cook, R.	RC	Dicks, D.	

Dicks, Miss S.		Eyre, Revd W. L. W.	WLWE	Gerrans, Miss M. B.	
Dickson, Dr J. H.	JHDi			Giavarini, V. J.	VJG
Dickson, Revd R.		Fairfax-Ross, Miss? V.		Gibbons, Miss J.	
Dillenius, J. J.		Farmer, Miss J.		Gibbons, Dr R. B.	RBG
Dimmock, D. P.	DPD	Farmer, J. L.		Gibson, Mrs G. M.	GMG
Dingle, Mrs R. M.	RMD	Farre, F.		Gilbert, Dr O. L.	OLG
Ditmas, Mrs M.	MD	Farrell, Miss L.		Giles, N. R.	NRG
Dixon, H. N.	HND	Fawdry, Miss D. W.	DWF	Gillam, Miss B.	
Dodd, F.		Ferguson, Miss? C. M.		Gilmour, J. S. L.	JSLG
Dolman, Miss G. S.		Ferguson, Dr I. K.	IKF	Gilson, H. Cary	
Donald, D.		Ffennell, D. W. H.	DWHF	Goater, B.	BGo
Donaldson, K. S.	KSD	Field, G. D.	GDF	Goater, Mrs J.	JG
Dony, Mrs C. M.		Field, Miss V.	VF	Goddard, D.	
Dony, Dr J. G.	JGD	Filfilan, S. A.	SAF	Goddard, H. J.	HJG
Doody, S.		Filsar, Miss -.		Godfery, Col. M. J.	MJG
Douglas, Miss A. M.	AMD	Findlay, R.		Goodall, D. W.	DWG
Douglas, Miss J. M.	JMD	Findley, P. W. J.	PWJF	Goodall, J.	
Douglas, M.	MDo	Finnemore, M.		Goodall, Mrs M. A.	MAG
Dove, T.	TD	Finucane, Mrs F.	FF	Goodchild, R. F.	RFG
Dowdeswell, W. H.		Firbank, K.		Goodhart, Mrs M. S.	MSG
Downey, Mrs -.		Fisher, H.	HF	Goodliffe, F. D.	FDG
Drabble, Dr E.		Fisher, J.	JFi	Goodman, P. J.	PJG
Drake, C. D.	CDD	Fitter, R. S. R.		Goodway, Dr K. M.	KMG
Drake, Dr -.	DrD	Fitzgerald, H. Purefoy	HPF	Goodyer, John	
Draper, J. C.	JCD	Fitzgerald, Lady R. A.	RAF	Gordon, Miss V.	VG
Driver, G. R.		Flatt, Dr M. E. (née Scruby)		Gorings, P.	
Druce, Dr G. C.	GCD	Flower, N.	NF	Goriup, P. D.	PDG
Duncan, J. B.	JBD	Foggitt, Mrs G. (née Bacon)	GF	Gornall, R. J.	RJG
Duncan, Miss U. K.		Foggitt, J.		Gorringe, Miss E. K.	KG
Dupree, D.	DDu	Foggitt, T. J.	TJF	Gosling, M. M.	MMG
Durnell, P. R.		Fojt, Dr W.		Graham, Mrs E.	
Durran, J. H.		Foley, M. J. Y.		Graham, Revd G. G.	
Duthie, Mrs R. E.	RED	Follett, Mrs -.		Graham, R. A.	RAG
Dutton, Miss J.	JD	Foord-Kelcey, Mrs F. L.		Graiff, Mrs D.	DG
Dyce, J. W.		Forster, G. H.	GHF	Grant, Mrs -.	
		Foss, Lt-Col. C. C.	CCF	Graty, T. E. C.	
Eagle, Mrs P.	PE	Foster, S.	SF	Graves, W.	
Earle, Mrs M.	ME	Fourt, D.		Graveson, A. W.	
Earwood, J.	JE	Fowler, T. H.		Gray, Dr A. J.	AJG
Eaton, Dr D.		Fox, Miss D.		Gray, C. P.	
Edees, E. S.	ESE	Fraser, Dr A. R.	ARF	Gray, Revd J. D.	
Edelstein, F. A.		Fraser, J.		Greaves, Mrs R.	
Edgington, M.	MEd	Fraser-Jenkins, C. R.	CF-J	Green, D. E.	DEG
Edmonds, J. M.	JME	Freeman, E. F.		Green, E. C.	ECG
Edmondson, Dr J. R.	JRE	Frost, Miss L. W.	LWF	Green, G. G.	GGG
Edmunds, M.		Fryer, Miss -.		Green, Revd G. H.	
Edwards, B.	BE	Fryer, Mrs J. D.	JF	Green, Dr G. P.	
Edwards, P.		Furmage, D. B.	DBF	Green, H. L.	HLG
Egginton, J. P.	JPE			Green, I. P.	IG
Eldridge, Mrs Y. (née Desprès)		Gagg, A. N.		Green, P. R.	
Elkington, Dr T. T.	TTE	Gale, B. A.	BAG	Greenup, Miss B.	
English, R. D.		Gallagher, Miss M.		Greenwood, Mrs B. D.	
Ereaut, G.		Gambier-Parry, T. R.	TRG-P	Greenwood, C. W.	CWG
Escombe, F.	FE	Gamble J. S.	JSG	Gregory, Mrs E. S.	ESG
Etherington, P.	PEth	Ganf, Mrs E.	EG	Gregory, P. A.	
Evans, A. H.	AHE	Gardiner, J. C.	JCG	Grenfell, A. L.	ALG
Evans, H.		Gardner, M.		Grey, Miss -.	
Evans, Mrs H. D.		Gardner, Miss R. E.		Griffiths, S. N.	SNG
Evans, J. B.		Garner, Miss A.		Grinstead, K.	
Evans, J. G.		Garnier, Dean T.		Grontmij, -.	Gr
Evans, T. G.	TGE	Garry, F.		Groom, R. E.	
Evelyn, R.	RE	Garth, R.		Grose, Mrs I. M.	IMG
Everard, Mrs B.		Géhu, Prof. J. M.	JMG	Grose, J. D.	JDG
Everett, Miss S. J.	SJE	Gent, Mrs G. M.		Grossert, A.	AG
Exton, E.		Gerard, J.		Grove, L. K. A.	LKAG

Groves, H.	HG	Higgens, Fr J.		Jackson, Maj. J. P. A.	JPAJ
Groves, J.	JGr	Hill, Mrs –.		Jackson, P.	PJ
Groves, T.		Hill, C. F.		Jackson, R.	
Gullick, Miss B. (later Welch, Mrs B.) BG		Hill, J.		Jackson, Miss R. Hartas	RHJ
Gulliver, J.		Hill, Dr M. O.	MOH	Jakobson, M. E.	
		Hill, N.		James, P. W.	PWJ
Haes, E. C. M.		Hill, Dr R. S.	RSH	Janson, Mrs –.	
Haig, E.	EHa	Hillard, Miss M. T.	MTH	Jaques, Miss M.	MJ
Haines, Mrs E. M.	EMH	Hilliard, Miss E.		Jarvis, Mrs –.	
Haines, Miss E. S.	ESH	Hinde, Miss E. de V.	EdeVH	Jeffrey, C.	CJ
Haines, Miss G. M.	GMH	Hitch, Dr C. J. B.	CJBH	Jeffreys, E. M.	
Haines, H. H.		Hitchon, A.		Jeffries, R. L.	
Hale, Miss A. L.	ALH	Hoare, Miss. R.		Jenkins, Miss –.	
Hall, C. R.	CRH	Hodgetts, J. W.	JWH	Jenkinson, M. N.	MNJ
Hall, I. G.		Hodgetts, N. G.	NGH	Jennings, Mrs M. B.	MBJ
Hall, Mrs J. F.	JFH	Hodgson (later Bray), Mrs E.	EH	Jermy, A. C.	ACJ
Hall, L. Beeching	LBH	Hodgson, J.	JHo	Jewell, A. L.	ALJ
Hall, P. C.	PCH	Holland, P.		Jewell, H. M.	
Hall, P. M.	PMH	Hollingsworth, P. M.	PMHo	Jindbay, R.	
Halliday, Dr G.	GH	Hollins, J. R. W.	JRWH	Johnson, C.	CJo
Halliday, P.	PHa	Holliwell, A. P.	APHo	Johnson, T.	
Halliday, T.		Holmes, E. M.	EMHo	Johnstone, V. A.	VAJ
Hambler, Dr D. J.	DJHa	Holmes, J.	JH	Jollands, A.	
Hamilton, A. P.	APH	Holmes, Dr N. T. H.	NTHH	Jolly, Mrs M. A.	MAJ
Hamilton, E. A.		Holt, E.		Jones, A. W.	
Hammond, Mrs –.		Hook, O.		Jones, Mrs B.	
Hanbury, F. J.		Hooker, Sir Joseph D.		Jones, C.	
Hannam, B.		Hooper, Miss S. S.	SSH	Jones, D. A.	DAJ
Hannam, J.		Hope-Simpson, Dr J. F.	JFH-S	Jones, D. M.	
Hanson, C. G.		Hora, Mrs C.	CH	Jones, E.	EJ
Harding, Miss A.		Horlor, Miss M. D.	MDH	Jones, Dr E. W.	EWJ
Hardy, Miss –.		Hornby, Dr R. J.	RJH	Jones, J.	
Hare, A. D. R.	ADRH	Hoult, E.		Jones, J. M.	
Harley, Dr R. M.	RMH	House, A. P. N.	APNH	Jonsell, Prof. B. E.	BEJ
Harmes, P. A.	PAH	Howard, Miss E. M.		Jørgensen, Prof. P. M.	PMJ
Harold, Dr B.	BHa	Howard, Miss M.	MHo		
Harris, Miss A.	AH	Howard, W.		Kay, Dr Q. O. N.	QK
Harris, Revd B. G.		Howarth, Dr W. O.	WOH	Kearns, Miss –.	
Harris, P. M. P.	PMPH	Howe, J.	JHow	Keens, Miss W. M.	WMK
Hastings, Miss S. M.		Howitt, Mrs B.		Keith-Lucas, Dr M.	
Hatcher, Miss E.		Howitt, R. C. L.	RCLH	Kelcey, J. G.	
Hater, –.		Hubbard, Dr C. E.	CEH	Kelsall, Revd J. E.	JEK
Hatton, –.		Hubbard, Dr J. C. E.	JCEH	Kendall, N.	
Hawes, P. T. J.		Hughes, Mrs J.	JHug	Kent, D. H.	DHK
Hawkes, Revd H.		Hughes, M.	MHug	Kenyard, B.	
Hawkins, Mrs P.	PH	Hughes, Dr M. G.		Kerslake, Mrs V.	VK
Hawksworth, Prof. D. L.	DLH	Hunt, Mrs –.		Kibble, F. G.	FGK
Haworth, C. C.	CCH	Hunt, Dr D. J.	DJH	Kilderbee, Miss G. E.	
Haynes, F. N.	FNH	Hunt, D. R.		Killick, Mrs K. D.	KK
Hayward, K.		Hunt, Miss M. (later Soanes, Mrs M.)		King, B.	BK
Hayward, Mrs M. M.		Hunt, P. F.	PFH	King, M.	
Headley, –.		Hunter, Miss? J.		King, N.	
Hearn, Miss K. A.	KAH	Huntley, Capt. E.		Kingham, D.	
Heath, Revd D. M.		Hurst, C. P.	CPH	Kingsley, Miss R. G.	RK
Hedges, E.		Hussey, J.	JHu	Kingstone, Bro. –.	
Hedley, C. R. F.		Hussey, W.		Kirk, S.	SK
Helyar, W. G.	WGH	Hutchison, Miss A. M.		Kirkpatrick, Miss –.	
Hemsley, J. H.		Hylmö, B.	BH	Kitchener, G.	GK
Hensman, Miss P. E.	PEH	Hynd, W. R. B.	WRBH	Knight, H. H.	HHK
Hepper, F. N.				Knight, Dr J.	JK
Heppleston, Mrs P.		Ingram, A. J.		Knight, P.	
Heslop, M.		Ingram, W.	WI	Knights, N.	
Heslop-Harrison, Prof. J.		Irvine, Mrs J.		Knipe, P. R.	
Hesselgreaves, Miss J.	JHe			Knott, A.	
Hewett, Revd G. M. A.		Jackson, A. B.	ABJ	Knowlton, D.	

345

Krog, Prof. H.	HK	Mace, Mrs P.		Milne-Redhead, E. W. B. H.	EM-R
		Mace, P.		Milton, J. N. B.	JNBM
Lacey, Prof. W. S.	WSL	Macey, Mrs A.	AMa	Missen, Mrs D.	DMi
Lack, D.		McAllister, H. A.	HMcA	Mitchell, A. F.	AFM
Laflin, T.	TL	McCallum-Webster, Miss M.	MMcC-W	Mitchell, Dr R.	
Lamb, J.		McClintock, D. C.	DMcC	Moberg, Dr R.	RMo
Lambert, Dr J. M.		McCosh, D. J.	DJMcC	Mobsby, Mrs M.	
Lancaster, C. R.	CRL	MacDonald, I.	IMcD	Mobsby, P.	
Lang, D. C.		McIntyre, G. E.		Moggridge C. J.	CJM
Lang, Mrs D. K.		MacKeith, Miss M.	MMcK	Moir, T.	
Langdon-Davies, Mrs C. R. (née Scott)		Macklin, Mrs G.	GM	Mold, Miss S.	SM
Lange, A.		MacLeod, C.	CMcL	Monckton, H. W.	HWM
Langham, W.	WL	Macnight, -.		Money, Miss -.	
Langmead, Dr J.		McQuarrie, Miss M.		Moon, Dr J. R.	JRM
Langridge, C.	CL	McQuillin, Mrs I. J.		Moore, Miss -.	
Langton-Lockton, Dr -.	L-Lo	Macreight, Dr D. C.		Moore, Mrs J. A.	JAM
Lansley, Mrs J.		McSwiney, M. S. W.		Morgan, G. H.	
Lansley, J. L. S.	JLSL	Mahon, A.		Morgan, Mrs V.	VM
Larbalestier, C.	CLa	Makins, F. K.	FKM	Morris, Mrs -.	
Larter, L. N. H.	LNHL	Mangham, Prof. S.		Morris, L. E.	
Lavender, J. H.	JHL	Mansell-Pleydell, J. C.		Morrison, Mrs A.	AMo
Lawson, C.		Marchant, C. J.		Morton, Miss G. L.	
Leach, S. J.		Marchant, L. F.	LFM	Moss, Miss C.	CMo
Leadbitter, E. C. E.		Marks, Miss K. M.		Moss, C. E.	
Lean, Mrs A. S.		Marquand, C. V. B.		Moule, Revd G. W. H.	
Leather, Miss V. M.	VL	Marquand, E. W.	EWM	Mountford, J. O.	JOM
Le Brocq, P.	PLeB	Marr, M.	MM	Muirhead, Miss C. W.	
Lees, R. G.	RGL	Marren, P.		Mullin, J. M.	JMM
Le Pard, G. F.	GFLeP	Marriott, Mrs -.		Mummery, L.	LM
Le Rossignol, J. N.	JLeR	Marsden-Jones, E. M.	EMM-J	Mundell, A. R. G.	ARGM
Leslie, A. C.	ACL	Marshall, Revd E. S.	ESM	Murch, Mrs O.	
Leslie, Miss E.	EL	Marshall, I.	IM	Murphy, Miss R. J.	
Lester-Garland, L. V.		Marshall, J. Braybrooke	JBM	Murray, Revd R. P.	
Leutscher, A. G.	AGL	Martindale, J.	JMa	Murray, V. E.	VEM
Liddell, Miss -.		Mason, Dr J. L.	JLM		
Lightfoot, Revd J.		Matcham, H. W.	HM	Napper, D. M.	
Linton, Revd E. F.	EFL	Maton, G.		Nash, Miss -.	
Linton, Revd W. R.	WRL	Maton, Miss P. B.		Nelmes, E.	EN
Lister, C. A.		Matthews, C.	CM	Nelson, Dr G. A.	GAN
Lister, Mrs S. A.	SAL	Matthews, G. A.	GAM	Newbould, Prof. P. J.	
Little, J. E.		Maudsley, Capt. A. J.	AJM	Newcombe, Miss -.	
Littlebury, H. C.		Maxwell, Mrs D.	DMa	Newnham, W. O.	WON
Livens, H. M.	HMLi	Maxwell, J. F.		Newton, A.	AN
Livens, R. G.	RGLi	May, Miss C. R.	CRM	Newton, Mrs M.	MNe
Lloyd, J.		May, J.	JM	Nicholl, Miss E.	ENi
Loader, Miss F. M.	FML	Maycock, R.	RMa	Nicholson, W. E.	WEN
Lobb, Miss S.		Medhurst, Miss J. A.	JMe	Noble, M.	MNo
Lock, L.	LL	Meikle, R. D.	RDM	Nolder, Mrs J.	JN
Long, Mrs -.		Meinertzhagen, Col. R.	RMz	Noll, Miss C. F.	
Long, G.	GLo	Melderis, Dr A.	AM	Norman, Mrs E.	ENo
Long, J. W.		Melvill, Revd A. H.	AHM	North, M.	MN
Longden, Mrs -.		Melvill, Dr J. C.	JCM	Norton, G.	
Lousley, J. E.	JEL	Melville, Dr R.	RM	Norton, J. A.	JAN
Loveless, Dr A. R.	ARLo	Merrett, C.		Notcutt, W. L.	
Lowe, D.		Mesley, W. R.		Nott, Miss -.	
Lowe, Revd H. E.		Messenger, K. G.	KGM		
Lowe, P. R.		Meynell, Miss D.	DM	Oates, M.	MO
Lowe, R.	RL	Meyrick, B.	BMe	Oates, Mrs S.	SO
Lucas, Lady A. R.	ARL	Miles, Lady A. M.	AMM	Ockenden, J.	JOc
Lucas, Mrs B. E.	BL	Miles, B. A.	BAM	Ohlenschlager, Mrs A.	AO
Lucas, Mrs M. J.		Miles, Dr J.	JMi	Oliver, F. W.	FWO
Lucas, Revd W. H.		Miller, Mrs E.		Oppé, J.	JOp
Lyall, Mrs G.	GL	Mills, A. R.		Orange, A.	AOr
Lycett, Miss C.		Mills, Prof. J. N.	JNM	Orr, Mrs J.	
Lyell, C.	CLy	Mills, W. H.	WHM	Orr, Sqn-Ldr N. W.	

Ottley, Mrs B. A.	BAO	Piggott, Mrs -. Pemberton		Ricardo, Miss -.	
Ottley, Dr T. W.	TWO	Pigott, Prof. C. D.	CDP	Rice, D. C.	
Ounsted, J.	JO	Piquet, J.		Rich, T. C. G.	TCGR
		Pitman, P. B.		Richards, Dr A. J.	AJR
Pack, F. H. C.	FHCP	Pitman, Mrs S.	SPi	Richards, Mrs F. D.	FDR
Packham, C. G.		Platten, G.		Ricketts, I. A.	
Padwick, Miss -.		Playfair, D. T.		Riddelsdell, Revd H. J.	HJR
Padwick, Mrs A. G.		Pogson, Dr C. I.		Ridley, H. N.	HNR
Padwick, C. J.		Poingdestre, J.	JPo	Rihan, J. R.	JRR
Page, Dr C. N.	CNP	Polkey, A.		Riley, L. A. M.	LAMR
Page, J.		Ponsonby, Hon. L.	LPo	Rob, Miss C. M.	
Page, K. W.	KWP	Pope, Dr C. R.	CRP	Roberts, A.	
Page, P. W. K.	PWKP	Porley, Dr R. D.	RDP	Roberts, Dr E. T.	ETR
Pain, J. W. C.	JWCP	Povey, S. M.	SP	Roberts, G. C. M.	GCMR
Palmer, Miss C. E.	CP	Powell, Miss A. C.		Roberts, R. H.	RHR
Palmer, Hon. E. R.		Poyner, -.		Robertson, Maj. -.	
Palmer, J. R.	JRP	Poynton, J. B.		Robinson, Capt. C.	
Palmer, K.	KP	Pratt, Revd E. A.	EAP	Robinson, F.	
Palmer, Hon. L.	LP	Prentice, H.		Robinson, Mrs J.	JRo
Palmer, Hon. R.	RP	Press, J. R.	JRPr	Robinson, Mrs M. A. T.	
Palmer, R. C.	RCP	Preston, C. D.	CDPr	Robson, Dr N. K. B.	NKBR
Palmer, Hon. W. J. L.	WJLP	Primavesi, Revd A. L.	ALP	Rogers, E.	ERo
Pamplin, W.		Prime, Dr C. T.		Rogers, F. A.	FAR
Pankhurst, Dr R. J.	RJP	Prior, P. N.		Rogers, Mrs M. A.	MAR
Pardy, V.		Pritchard, Dr N. M.	NP	Rogers, Revd W. Moyle	WMR
Parfitt, A.	AP	Probyn, Mrs F. M.		Rollinson, Mrs E. J. B.	JR
Parkes, H. M.		Proctor, Dr M. C. F.	MCFP	Rollinson, P. H.	PHR
Parkinson, J.		Proctor, Dr M. E. (née		Rooke, K. B.	
Parsons, Dr H. F.	HFP	Bradshaw)		Rooke, Miss S. G.	
Parsons, J. R.	JP	Pryor, R. A.		Rooke, Col T. E.	TER
Partridge, F.	FP	Pugsley, H. W.	HWP	Roper, Miss -.	
Partridge, Mrs F. C.		Pulfrey, Dr W.	WP	Roper, P.	
Paterson, A. P.		Pullan, Mrs G. H.		Rose, Dr F.	FR
Paton, Mrs J. A.	JAP	Pulteney, R.		Roseweir, A.	ARo
Patrick, K.	KPa	Purvis, Dr O. W.	OWP	Rossiter, Miss A.	
Pattenden, M. T.				Rostański, Prof. K.	KR
Paul, Mrs -.		Quirk, Revd R.	RQ	Rothwell, Mrs E.	ER
Paul, Miss A. M.	AMP			Rowe, J.	JRw
Payn, Lt-Col. W. A.	WAP	Rackham, A. J.	AJRa	Rowe, M. W.	
Payne, E. F.	EFP	Rackham, Mrs B. M.		Rowen, J.	
Payne, R. M.		Radcliffe-Smith, A.	AR-S	Rowlatt, Dr U.	UR
Pearce, W. A.		Ralphs, I. I.	ILR	Roycroft, Miss H.	HRo
Pearman, D. A.	DAP	Rand, M. W.	MR	Rudolf, Miss J.	
Pearsall, W. H.	WHP	Rand, R.		Rudolph, Miss G.	
Peck, Miss U.	UP	Randall, R. D.	RDR	Ruffell, J.	JRu
Pemberton, G. W. S.	GWSP	Randall, R. E.	RER	Rumens, N. M.	NMR
Pemberton, Miss H.		Ranwell, D. S.	DSR	Rumsey, F. J.	FJR
Penney, Mrs L. P. C.	LPCP	Ratcliffe, D.		Runnells, A. M.	
Pepin, C. E.	CEP	Raven, Canon C. E.		Rushforth, H.	HR
Perkins, Miss -.		Raven, J. E.		Russell, -.	
Perkins, D.		Raven, Prof. P. H.		Russell, Miss -.	
Perring, Dr F. H.	FHP	Ray, J.		Russell, Mrs A.	
Peterken, Dr G. F.	GFP	Raybould, A.		Russell, Mrs B. H. S.	BHSR
Peterken, J. H. G.	JHGP	Rayner, J. F.	JFR	Russell, Mrs E. M. P.	
Peterson, C. J.		Read, Mrs G. H.		Rutherford, Miss A.	AR
Peterson, Miss L. J.		Reddie, J. A.	JAR	Rycroft, Sir Richard N., Bt	
Petiver, J.		Reed, Miss M.	MRe	Rye, Mrs P.	PRy
Phelps, Mrs R. C.	RCPh	Reeks, H.		Ryle, G. B.	
Philipson, Dr W. R.		Reese, A. R.		Ryves, T. B.	TBR
Philp, E. G.	EGP	Reeves, Revd J. W.	JWR		
Pickard, J. F.	JFP	Reeves, W. W.	WWR	Sadler, H. G.	HGS
Pickard, Miss K.		Reid, C.		Salisbury, Sir Edward J.	
Pickering, V. H.	VHP	Renvoiz, P.		Salmon, C. E.	
Pierce, G. G.	GGP	Renyard, B. W.		Salmon, Miss H. M.	HMS
Pierce, G. W.	GWP	Reynolds, P. J.	PJR	Salter, J. H.	

Salter, Dr T. Bell	TBS	Smith, Miss M.		Swan, G. A.	GAS
Salwey, T.	TS	Smith, Mrs M.	MS	Swann, E. L.	
Sandell, K. A.	KS	Smith, N.	NS	Swinscow, Dr T. D. V.	TDVS
Sandell, R. E.		Smith, P. M.	PMS	Symes, H.	HS
Sandels, Mrs A. M.	AMS	Smith, R.	RSm	Symons, -.	
Sanders, -.		Smith, R. E. N.		Synge, R. L. M.	RLMS
Sanderson, N. A.	NAS	Smith, Miss S.			
Sandwith, Mrs C. I.		Smythe, W.	WSm	Talbot-Ponsonby, Miss C. E.	
Sandwith, N. Y.	NYS	Snow, Mrs J.	JSn	Tanner, H.	HTa
Saunders, J.		Snudden, P.		Tansley, Sir Arthur G.	AGT
Sayer, R. C. L.		Soanes, Mrs M. (née Hunt)		Taplin, Mrs G.	
Schulz, Mrs? D. L.	DLS	Soar, Miss E. C.		Taschereau, Dr P. M.	
Scott, A.		Somerfeld, Mrs -.		Tate, Dr G. R.	
Scott, Miss C. R. (later		Somerset-Ward, Mrs M.	MS-W	Tatum, E. J.	
Langdon-Davies, Mrs C. R.)		Somerville, Revd P.	PSom	Taverner, J. H.	JHT
Scott, Dr D. H.	DHS	Somes, R.		Taylor, B.	BT
Scott, M.		Southam, M. J.	MJS	Taylor, Sir George	GT
Scott, Mrs S. P.		Southwell, S. S.	SS	Taylor, Mrs M.	MT
Scott, Mrs V.	VS	Southwood, Mrs P.	PSo	Taylor, P. G.	PGT
Scruby (later Flatt) Dr M. E.	MES	Sowerby, J.		Taylor, S. A.	SAT
Seagrief, Mrs M. S.		Sperling, -.		Teesdale, J. M.	
Seaward, Prof. M. R. D.	MRDS	Spicer, W. W.		Thomas, Revd H.	HT
Selborne, Lord, later 1st Earl of		Spittal, M. K.		Thomas, Mrs M. D.	MDT
Selby, P. J.	PJSe	Spittall, Miss -.		Thompson, H. S.	
Sell, P. D.	PDS	Sprague, Dr T. A.		Thompson, J. D.	JDT
Sennitt, B. F. C.	BFCS	Spreadbury, W. H.	WHS	Thompson, N.	
Sérusiaux, Dr E.	ESé	Sprigg, M.	MSp	Thomson, Mrs -.	
Sevier, Miss A.		Squiresland, -.		Thomson, S.	
Sewell, P.		Stace, Prof. C. A.	CAS	Thorpe, Miss N.	NT
Shackleton, J.		Stafford, P. J.	PJS	Thurston, Ms J. M.	
Sharland, R. E.		Staley, C.		Thwaites, G. H. K.	
Shaw, Mrs B.	BS	Staley, J.	JS	Tibell, Dr L.	LT
Sheasby, P. G.		Standen, R. S.	RSS	Timm, E. W.	EWT
Shepard, B.		Stanley, P. D.	PS	Timms, M.	
Sherlock, R.	RS	Starck, Mr & Mrs -.		Timperley, Mrs E.	ET
Sherrin, W. R.	WRS	Stearn, L. F.	LFS	Timperley, H. W.	HWTi
Sherring, R. V.		Stern, R. C.	RCS	Tindall, Mrs -.	
Showler, A. J.	AJSh	Sterry, P.		Tirrard, B.	
Shrubbs, A.		Stevens, A. J.	AJSt	Titt, R. A.	RAT
Sibley, Miss E.		Stevens, Miss D.		Tittensor, R. M.	RMT
Sick, E.	ES	Stewart, M. A.	MAS	Tobins, Miss J. M.	
Sidebottom, Mrs -.		Stewart, Mrs M. E.		Todd, Miss E. S.	EST
Silverside, Dr A. J.	AJS	Stewart, Mrs O. M.	OMS	Tolman, T. W.	
Simmonds, Mrs A. M.	AMS	Stewart, S. A.		Townsend, C. C.	CCT
Simmonds, P.	PSi	Stidston, Mrs A. H.		Townsend, F.	FT
Simmons, Mrs -.		Still, A. L.	ALS	Toynton, P. E.	PET
Simpson, D. A.	DAS	Still, K.		Trist, P. J. O.	PJOT
Simpson, N. Douglas	NDS	Stilwell, J. B. L.	JBLS	Trueblood, A.	
Simpson, W.	WS	Stimson, L. G.		Tubbs, C. R.	CRT
Sims, T. A.	TAS	Stoate, C.	CS	Tubbs, Mrs J. M.	JMT
Sivell, P.		Stokes, J.	JSt	Tullis, G. A.	GAT
Skinner, J. F.		Stone, Mrs? E. A.		Tunnah, Mrs E.	ETu
Sladen, E. M.		Stopher, W. I.		Turk, Mrs S. M.	
Slater, F. M.		Strachan, Mrs I.		Turner, Mrs B.	
Sledge, Dr W. A.	WAS	Stranack, Dr F. R.	FRS	Turner, D. N.	DNT
Sleep, Dr A.	ASl	Stratton, F.		Turner, K.	
Smith, Maj. -.		Streatfield, Revd G. S.		Turner, R.	RT
Smith, Dr A. J. E.	AJES	Struthers, F. M.		Turner-Ettlinger, D. M.	DMT-E
Smith, C. F.		Styles, Dr B. T.		Turnock, Mrs A. M.	
Smith, D.	DS	Suffern, Dr C. S.	CSS	Turrill, Dr W. B.	WBT
Smith, D. P. J.	DPJS	Summerhayes, V. S.	VSS	Tuson, Mrs M.	MTu
Smith, Revd G. E.		Sumner, G. Heywood M.	GHMS	Tutin, Prof. T. G.	TGT
Smith, Mrs J. E.	JES	Surplice, J.		Tweed, R. D.	RDT
Smith, J. M.		Sutton, Dr -.		Tyas, C. J.	CJT
Smith, Miss K.		Swain, H. E.		Tyler, R. J.	RJT

Tyler, Mrs S. W.		Watts, Lt-Col. G. A. R.	GARW	Wilkinson, Revd H. M.	HMWi
		Watts, H. W.		Wilkinson, P. R.	
Ubsdell, Dr R. A. E. (later Dr F.)		Way, Mrs W. E. C.		Willan, V.	
Ullman, R. B.		Wayles, Mrs F. J. P.	FJPW	Willé, J. E.	JEW
Usher, M. B.	MBU	Wearing, M.	MW	Williams, Miss E. M.	
		Webb, Prof. D. A.	DAW	Williams, I. A.	
Vaile, Mrs Y.		Webb, F. B.		Williams, L. H. J.	
Valentine, Prof. D. H.		Webb, G.		Williams, Mrs L. J.	
Vannerom, H.		Webb, Miss I.	IW	Williams, Mrs V. A.	VW
Vardy, B. J.		Webb, N. P.		Willis, G. W.	GWW
Vaughan, Mrs E.	EV	Webster, B. J.		Wills, E.	
Vaughan, Mrs I. M.		Webster, P. J.		Wills, J.	
Vaughan, Canon J.	JV	Webster, Dr S. D.	SDW	Wilmott, A. J.	AJW
Veall, Dr R. M.	RMV	Wedgwood, Mrs M. L.	MLW	Wilson, G.	
Venner, J. P. F.	JPFV	Weightman, Miss A.		Wilson, J. B.	JBW
Venning, Brig. F. E. W.	FEWV	Welch, Mrs B. (née Gullick)	BW	Wilson, M.	
Venning, Miss J.		Wells, R. V.	RVW	Wilson, Dr P. J.	PJW
Verdcourt, Dr B.		Wells, T. C. E.	TCEW	Winch, Mrs –.	
Vesey-Fitzgerald, B.		Welsh, Dr R. P. H.	RPHW	Winship, Mrs H. R.	HWi
Vorse, J.		Welstead, A. R.	ARW	Winsland, D. C.	DCW
		Welstead, Mrs N. I.	NIW	Winterbottom, J. E.	
Wade, A. E.		West, Dr C.	CW	Wise, J. R.	
Wadlow, H. J.	HJW	Westerhoff, Mrs D. V.	DVW	Wolfenden, Mrs D.	DW
Wain, Dr C.	CWa	Westrup, A. W.	AWW	Wolley-Dod, Lt-Col. A. H.	AHW-D
Walker, –.		Westwood, S.	SW	Wood, Ms E.	
Wallace, E. C.	ECW	Wettstein, R. von	RvW	Woodhead, Mrs F. A.	FAW
Wallis, A.		Wheeldon, A.	AWh	Woodhouse, Miss A.	
Walls, R. M.	RMW	Wheeler, H.	HWh	Woods, H.	
Walter, –.		Whitaker, Miss –.		Woods, J.	
Walters, Miss –.		Whitcombe, Mrs B.	BWh	Woods, J. J.	
Walters, Dr S. M.	SMW	White, Mrs A.	AW	Woods, R. G.	RW
Warburg, Dr E. F.	EFW	White, A. D.		Woodvine, Mrs –.	
Ward, C. M.		White, Mrs D. H. S.		Wormald, Dr –.	
Ward, R.	RWa	White, E. H.	EHW	Wright, C. A.	
Ward, W. R.	WRW	White, Revd Gilbert		Wright, J.	
Warner, F. I.	FIW	White, G. M.		Wyatt, Mrs H. M.	
Warner, R.		White, H. T.	HTW	Wyatt, J. W.	JWW
Warner, S. A.		White J. L.	JLW	Wylie, Mrs A. E.	AEWy
Warren, J. B. L.		White, J. R.	JRW		
Warren, W. E.	WEW	White, K. M. W.		Yalden, T.	
Warwick, T.	TWa	White, Thomas		Yeatts, J.	
Warwick-Haller, A.		White, Miss T.		Yeldham, Mrs –.	
Warwick-Haller, Mrs G.		Whitefoord, Miss C.	CWh	Yeo, Dr P. F.	PFY
Waterfall, C.		Whitehead, Dr B.	BWhi	Yonge, Miss C. M.	
Waters, J.	JW	Whitehead, Mrs L. E.	LEW	Young, Dr D. P.	DPY
Watson, H. C.	HCW	Whiteman, P.		Young, Miss M. E.	MEY
Watson, K.	KW	Whittaker, Miss H.	HW	Young, Mrs G.	GY
Watson, Mrs L.	LW	Wickham, W.		Yule, Mrs M. P.	MPY
Watson, W. C. R.	WCRW	Wilde, Mrs –.			
Watt, Mrs W. Boyd	WBW	Wildish, M. F.	MFW		

2. CORPORATE BODIES

This list includes societies and other organizations which have contributed (many as the result of field meetings) or determined plant records for the Flora.

Alton Museum Records Centre		British Lichen Society	BLS
Alton Natural History Society	ANHS	British Museum (Natural History)	
Andover Natural History Society	AVNHS	(now Natural History Museum)	BM
Biological Records Centre	BRC	British Pteridological Society	
Botanical Society of the British Isles	BSBI	Dorset Trust for Nature Conservation	
Bournemouth Natural Science Society	BNSS	English Nature (part of former NCC)	
British Bryological Society	BBS	Game Conservancy (arable weeds survey)	GC

Hampshire County Council (habitat assessment team)	HCC	Nature Conservancy Council (survey)	NCC
		Newbury Field Club	NFC
Hampshire Field Club and Archaeological Society	HFC	Portsmouth & District Natural History Society	
Hampshire Flora Group	HFG	Portsmouth Polytechnic	
Hampshire Ornithological Society	HOS	Reading Natural History Society	ReNHS
Hampshire & Isle of Wight Wildlife Trust	HWT	Ringwood Natural History Society	
Haslemere Natural History Society	HMNHS	Royal Horticultural Society Gardens, Wisley	RHS
Kew, Royal Botanic Gardens	K		
Liverpool University (survey)		Salisbury & District Natural History Society	
London Natural History Society			
Lord Wandsworth College		Southampton Natural History Society	SNHS
Manpower Services Commission team	MSC	Sussex Botanical Recording Society	
Moors River Survey team		Wild Flower Society	WFS
National Rivers Authority	NRA	Winchester College Natural History Society	WCNHS

ABBREVIATIONS FOR HERBARIA

The following abbreviations are cited in the systematic accounts

Hb.AB   Lady Anne Brewis (incorporates herbarium of Miss E. K. Gorringe)

Hb.ABD   University of Aberdeen

Hb.ABRN   Monks Wood Experimental Station, Abbots Ripton

Hb.ACL   A. C. Leslie

Hb.AJS   A. J. Silverside

Hb.ALT   Herbarium, Curtis Museum, Alton (now held by Hampshire County Council Museums Service, Winchester (Hb.HCMS, *q.v.*))

Hb.AMB   Mrs A. M. Boucher

Hb.AWW   A. W. Westrup (now held by Hampshire County Council Museums Service, Winchester (Hb.HCMS, *q.v.*))

Hb.BIRM   University of Birmingham

Hb.BM   British Museum (Natural History) (now known as The Natural History Museum, London) (incorporates herbaria of J. M. Crombie, J. F. Pickard, J. W. Reeves and H. Trimen, and part of those of T. J. Foggitt and N. D. Simpson)

Hb.BMH   Museum of the Bournemouth Natural Science Society

Hb.BRIST   University of Bristol (at City Museum, Bristol, but held separately)

Hb.BRISTM   City Museum, Bristol

Hb.CGE   University of Cambridge

Hb.CRK   University College, Cork, Ireland (incorporates herbarium of I. Carroll)

Hb.DJMcC   D. J. McCosh

Hb.DMH   University of Durham

Hb.DZS   Museum of the Wiltshire Archaeological & Natural History Society, Devizes (holds separately herbarium of J. Donald Grose (Hb.JDG, *q.v.*)

Hb.E   Royal Botanic Garden, Edinburgh

Hb.EST   Miss E. S. Todd (at Swindon Museum & Art Gallery)

Hb.FAW   Mrs F. A. Woodhead

Hb.GF   Mrs G. Foggitt (now held, with part of herbarium of T. J. Foggitt (Hb.GF/TJF) at Tolson Memorial Museum, Huddersfield, West Yorkshire (Hb.HDD, *q.v.*))

Hb.GL   University of Glasgow

Hb.HCMS   Hampshire County Council Museums Service, Chilcomb House, Winchester (holds the herbarium formerly at Curtis Museum, Alton (Hb.ALT), and also the herbaria of Canon N. E. G. Cruttwell, J. Braybrooke Marshall (Hb.JBM), Mrs E. Rothwell, H. G. Sadler (Hb.HGS) and A. W. Westrup (Hb.AWW))

Hb.HDD   Tolson Memorial Museum, Huddersfield, West Yorkshire (holds herbaria of T. J. Foggitt (part) and of Mrs G. Foggitt)

Hb.HGS   H. G. Sadler (now held by Hampshire County Council Museums Service, Winchester (Hb.HCMS, *q.v.*))

Hb.HME   Haslemere Educational Museum

Hb.HWB   Butler Museum, Harrow School, Middlesex

Hb.JBM   J. Braybrooke Marshall (formerly held in Curtis Museum, Alton; now held by Hampshire County Council Museums Service, Winchester (Hb.HCMS, *q.v.*))

Hb.JDG   J. Donald Grose (in Hb.DZS, but held separately)

Hb.JF   Mrs J. D. Fryer

Hb.JJD   J. J. Dillenius, 'Herbarium of the Synopsis', University of Oxford

Hb.JTIBS   J. T. I. Boswell-Syme (in Hb.BM, but held separately)

Hb.K   Royal Botanic Gardens, Kew

Hb.KTU   Silesian University, Katowice, Poland

Hb.LANC   University of Lancaster

Hb.LIV   Liverpool Museum

Hb.LTR   University of Leicester

Hb.MANCH	Manchester Museum
Hb.MNE	Maidstone Museum & Art Gallery
Hb.NDS	N. Douglas Simpson (in Hb.BM, but mainly held separately)
Hb.NMW	National Museum of Wales, Cardiff
Hb.OXF	Druce-Fielding Herbarium, University of Oxford (the British Collection is known as 'the Druce Herbarium')
Hb.PFY	P. F. Yeo
Hb.QMC	Queen Mary College, University of London
Hb.RDG	Reading Museum & Art Gallery
Hb.RDR	R. D. Randall
Hb.RMV	R. M. Veall
Hb.RMW	R. M. Walls
Hb.RNG	University of Reading (incorporates herbaria of J. E. Lousley and E. C. Wallace)
Hb.RPB	R. P. Bowman
Hb.SLBI	South London Botanical Institute, Norwood (incorporates some of F. Townsend's specimens)
Hb.SPN	University of Southampton
Hb.TJF	T. J. Foggitt (now held in part by Hb.BM, but mainly with that of Mrs G. Foggitt (Hb.GF/TJF) in herbarium at Tolson Memorial Museum, Huddersfield, West Yorkshire (Hb.HDD, *q.v.*))
Hb.VG	Miss V. Gordon
Hb.WARMS	Warwickshire Museum, Warwick (incorporates herbarium of Warwick Archaeological & Natural History Society)
Hb.WAB	W. A. Bromfield (held by B. Shepard, Newport, Isle of Wight)

GENERAL ABBREVIATIONS, TERMS AND SYMBOLS

agg.	aggregate
auct.	*auctorum* (of other authors)
AWVPs	ancient woodland vascular plants (as indicators)
BP	before present
C	central
C	colonist (see p.85)
c.	*circa* (about, around)
cm	centimetre(s)
comm.	communicated by
conf.	confirmed by
D	denizen (see p.85)
det.	determined by
E	east
ed., eds	editor(s)
edn	edition
et al.	*et alii* (and other authors)
excl.sp.	excluded species (given in F. Townsend's *Flora of Hampshire*)
f.	*forma* (form)
fig.	figure
fil.	*filius* (son of)
fol.	folio
H	hortal (see p.85)
ha	hectare(s) (1ha = 100 × 100m = 2.47 acres)
in litt.	*in littera* (in a letter)
incl.	including
indet.	indeterminate
km	kilometre(s)
loc.cit.	*loco citato*, in the place cited (above)
m	metre(s)
mm	millimetre(s)
ms, mss, MS, MSS	manuscript(s) – lower case indicates notes and letters, upper case major works
N	native (see p.85)
N, NE, NW	north, north-east, north-west
n.d.	no date
nothomorph	a term formerly used to define a hybrid between two infra-specific taxa
nothossp.	nothosubspecies, a hybrid between two subspecies
nv.	nothovariety, a hybrid between two varieties
pers.comm.	personal communication to the author(s)
pers.obs.	personal observation (of the author(s))
pH	hydrogen potential
pl., pls	plate(s)
R.	River
redet.	redetermined by
S, SE, SW	south, south-east, south-west
sensu lato	in the broad sense
sensu stricto	in the narrow sense
sp., spp.	species, species (plural)
sq.km, sq.m	square kilometre(s), square metre(s)
ssp., sspp.	subspecies, subspecies (plural)
var.	variety
VC3	Vice-county 3, S. Devon
VC7	Vice-county 7, N. Wilts.
VC8	Vice-county 8, S. Wilts.
VC9	Vice-county 9, Dorset
VC10	Vice-county 10, Isle of Wight
VC11	Vice-county 11, S. Hants.
VC12	Vice-county 12, N. Hants.
VC13	Vice-county 13, W. Sussex
VC17	Vice-county 17, Surrey
VC18	Vice-county 18, S. Essex
VC21	Vice-county 21, Middlesex
VC22	Vice-county 22, Berks.
W	west
X, x	prefix for hybrid
<··· ···>	extinct species (see p.86)
[··· ···]	excluded species (see p.86)
□	tetrad (2km × 2km squares) (see p.84)

BOOKS, PERIODICALS AND UNPUBLISHED MSS CITED IN THE SYSTEMATIC ACCOUNTS

Listed by abbreviations given in parentheses in the text; titles of books and journals are given in italics. Further details of some standard works are given in the select bibliography at the end of this book.

Alien Pl.Brit.Is. – *Alien Plants of the British Isles*, by E. J. Clement & M. C. Foster, 1994.

Ann.Appl.Biol. – *Annals of Applied Biology*, Vol. 1, No. 1→, 1914→, Cambridge. [Bi-monthly, now published by Horticulture Research International, Welles-bourne, Warwickshire.]

Ann.Nat.Hist. – *Annals and Maga-zine of Natural History including Zoology, Botany and Geology.* Series 1, Vol. 6 – series 13, Vol. 9, 1841–1967; continued as *Journal of Natural History.*

Aquat.Bot. – *Aquatic Botany*, Vols 1→, 1975→.

Atlas Brit.Fl. – *Atlas of the British Flora*, ed. F. H. Perring & S. M. Walters, edn 2, 1976.

Atlas Brit.Fl.Crit.Suppl. – *Critical Supplement to the Atlas of the British Flora*, ed. F. H. Perring, 1968.

Atlas Kent Fl. – *Atlas of the Kent Flora*, by E. G. Philp, 1982.

Aubrey N.H.Wilts – *Natural History of Wiltshire*, by J. Aubrey, 1656–1691, ed. J. Britton, from MS volume in library of The Royal Society, 1847. Reprinted 1969.

Bell's Selb. – *The Natural History and Antiquities of Selborne, in the County of Southampton*, by Gilbert White, ed. Thomas Bell, 2 vols, 1877.

Biol.Fl. – Biological Flora of the British Isles, a series published in *J. Ecol.* **29**(2) →, 1940→.

Bladder Camp. – *The Bladder Camp-ions*, by E. M. Marsden-Jones & W. B. Turrill, 1957.

Book of Gorley – *The Book of Gorley*, by G. Heywood M. Sumner, edited version 1910. [Facsimile edn: *Cuckoo Hill: the book of Gorley*, Heywood Sumner, with introduction by Margot Coatts, 1987.]

Bot.Cornwall – *Botanical Cornwall Newsletter*, an occasional publica-tion of the Cornish Biological Records Unit, Nos 1–5, 1987–91. [Further issues are being published by Institute of Cornish Studies, University of Exeter.]

Bot.Guide – *The Botanist's Guide through England and Wales*, by Dawson Turner and Lewis Weston Dillwyn, 2 vols, 1805.

Bot.J.Linn.Soc. – *Journal of the Proceedings of the Linnean Society, London*, Vols 1–8, 1855–65; continued as *Journal of the Linnean Society of London. Botany*, Vols 9–61, 1867–1968; continued as *Botanical Journal of the Linnean Society*, Vols 66→, 1969→.

Brambles Brit.Is. – *Brambles of the British Isles*, by E. S. Edees & A. Newton. Ray Society, 1988.

Brit.Wildlife – *British Wildlife*, Vol. 1→, 1989→.

Bull.Brit.Bryol.Soc. – *Bulletin of the British Bryological Society*, No. 1→, 1963→.

Brit.Phaen.Bot. – *British Phaeno-gamous Botany, etc.*, by W. Baxter, 6 vols, 1832–43.

Bry.Fl.S.Hants – A Bryophyte Flora of South Hants, by Jean A. Paton, in *Transactions of the British Bryological Society*, 1961, **4**: 1–83.

BSBI Hdbk 3 – *Docks and Knotweeds of the British Isles*, by J. E. Lousley & D. H. Kent, 1981. BSBI Hand-book No. 3.

BSBI Hdbk 4 – *Willows and Poplars of Great Britain and Ireland*, by R. D. Meikle, 1984. BSBI Hand-book No. 4.

BSBI News – *The Newsletter of the Botanical Society of the British Isles*, No. 1→, 1975→.

Census Cat.Brit.Lichens – *Census Catalogue of British Lichens*, by W. Watson, 1953.

Census Cat.Brit.Mosses – *A Census Catalogue of British Mosses*, by W. Ingham, edn 1, 1907.

Ch.Fl.Brit. – *The Changing Flora of Britain*, ed. J. E. Lousley. Botani-cal Society of the British Isles, 1953.

Comp.Bot.Mag. – *Companion to the Botanical Magazine*, by W. J. Hooker, Vol. 1, 1835; Vol. 2, 1836.

Conc.Gram. – *Graminum, Muscorum, Fungorum...Britannicorum concor-dia. A methodical concordance of British Grasses, etc.*, by James Petiver, [1716].

Dill.Herb. – *The Dillenian Herbaria. An account of the Dillenian collec-tions in the Herbarium of the University of Oxford*, by G. C. Druce (ed. S. H. Vines), 1907.

Distr.Bryophytes – *Distribution of Bryophytes in the British Isles*, by

M. F. V. Corley and M. O. Hill. British Bryological Society, 1981.

Druce Com.Fl. – *The Comital Flora of the British Isles* (*Flora comitalis Britannicae: Fl.com.Brit.*), by George Claridge Druce, 1932.

Early Brit.Bots – *Early British Botanists and their Gardens, etc.*, by R. W. T. Gunther, 1922.

Ecol.Wild Gladiolus – *The Ecology of the Wild Gladiolus* (*Gladiolus illyricus*) *in the New Forest, Hampshire*, by J. Stokes, 1987.

Eng.Bot. – *English Botany; or Coloured Figures of British Plants, with their essential characters, synonyms, and places of growth, etc.*, by James Edward Smith, the figures by James Sowerby, 36 vols, 1790–1814. Edn 3, ed. J. T. Boswell-Syme, 12 vols, 1864–89.

Eng.Bot.Suppl. – *Supplement to English Botany etc.*, by W. J. Hooker *et al.*, plates by J. Sowerby and J. W. Salter, 5 vols [plates consecutively numbered from edn 1], 1831–65.

Eng.Fl.Crypt. – *English Flora. Cryptogamma*, by W. J. Hooker, **5** (1): 1–132, 1844.

Engl.Fl. – *The Englishman's Flora*, by Geoffrey Grigson, 1955.

Exper.Taxon.Veronica – *Experimental Taxonomy of Veronica section Beccabungae Griseb*, by N. G. Marchant, Ph.D. thesis, University of Cambridge, 1970.

Fern Atlas – *Atlas of Ferns of the British Isles*, by A. C. Jermy *et al.*, 1978.

Fern Gaz. – *Fern Gazette* [*British Fern Gazette* (*Br.Fern Gaz.*) before 1974], Vol. 1→, 1909→.

Fl.Bas.MS – *Flora of Basingstoke*, by N. E. G. Cruttwell, unpublished ms, 1940–45.

Fl.Bmth – *Flora of Bournemouth*, by E. F. Linton, [1900].

Fl.Bmth App.1 – *Appendix 1 to Flora of Bournemouth*, by E. F. Linton, 1919.

Fl.Bmth App.2 – *Appendix 2 to Flora of Bournemouth*, by E. F. Linton, 1925.

Fl.Breck. – *An Ecological Flora of Breckland*, by P. J. O. Trist, 1979.

Fl.Brit.Is. – *Flora of the British Isles*, by A. R. Clapham, T. G. Tutin & E. F. Warburg, edn 2, 1962.

Fl.Christchurch – *Flora of the Christchurch Area*, by Felicity Woodhead, 1994.

Fl.Dorset – *Flora of Dorset*, by J. C. Mansel-Pleydell, edn 2, 1895.

Fl.Hants – *Flora of Hampshire, including the Isle of Wight*, by Frederick Townsend, edn 2, 1904.

Fl.IoW – *Flora of the Isle of Wight*, by J. H. Bevis, R. E. Kettell & B. Shepard, 1978.

Fl.Londin. – *Flora Londinensis: or Plates and Descriptions of such Plants as grow wild in the Environs of London, etc.*, by William Curtis, 6 Fasciculi, 1775–98.

Fl.Surrey – *Flora of Surrey*, by J. E. Lousley, 1976.

Fl.Sussex – *The Flora of Sussex*, ed. A. H. Wolley-Dod, 1937.

Fl.Vect. – *Flora Vectensis*, by W. A. Bromfield, 1856.

Fl.Wilts – *The Flora of Wiltshire*, by J. D. Grose, 1957, reprinted 1979.

Gdnrs'Chron. – *Gardeners' Chronicle and Agricultural Gazette*, 1841–1968.

Ger.em.Johns. – *The Herball or generall Historie of Plantes*, by John Gerard, emaculated by T. Johnson, 1633, reprinted 1636. Facsimile reprint of 1633 edn, 1975; abridged edn, 1985.

Ger.Herb. – *The Herball or generall Historie of Plantes*, by John Gerard, 1597.

Hants Chron. – *The Hampshire Chronicle*. [A weekly journal, published in Winchester since 1772 without interruption.]

Hants Repos. – *The Annual Hampshire Repository*, by Dean Garnier & Revd Poulter, Vol. 1, 1799.

Herb Guide – *The Herb User's Guide*, by D. Hoffman, 1987, [now *The Thorson's Guide to Medical Herbalism*].

Hist.Countryside – *The History of the Countryside*, by Oliver Rackham, 1986.

Hybr.Fl.Brit.Is. – *Hybridization and the Flora of the British Isles*, by C. A. Stace, 1975.

IBM List – IBM [International Business Machines] North Harbour

Wildlife Group. Wild vascular plant list, by R. A. Barrett, 1991.

J.Bot. – *Journal of Botany, British and Foreign*, Vols 1–80, 1863–1942. London.

J.Ecol. – *Journal of Ecology*, British Ecological Society, Vol. 1→, 1913→.

J.Portsmth & Dist.N.H.S. – *Journal of Portsmouth & District Natural History Society*, Vol. 1→, 1961→ [an infrequent and irregular publication]

Keble's Parishes – *John Keble's Parishes: a history of Hursley and Otterborne*, by C. M. Yonge, 1898.

List Flg.Pl.Andvr – *A List of Flowering Plants in the immediate Neighbourhood of Andover*, by C. B. Clarke, 1866.

Lobel Stirp.Illus. – *Stirpium Illustrationes, Accurante G. How* by Matthias de L'Obel. Published posthumously, 1655.

Maj.Smith MS Cat. – Six mss bound together, including 'Alphabetical list of native plants found in Portsea Island at different times since September 1846' and 'Alphabetical list of British plants [found] in the neighbourhood of Gosport with a few exceptions from June to first week in September 1848'. Bound volume in Botany Library, Natural History Museum, London, catalogued as *British Plants* under 'Smith, Major'.

May Ptgs Cat. – Caroline May Flower Paintings Catalogue. MS list of Miss C. R. May's dated paintings of wild flowers from the early 19th century in 5 vols (including 237 paintings of Hampshire flora, each numbered separately in the catalogue), now in private hands.

Merc.Bot. – *Mercurius Botanicus; sive Plantarum graia suscepti itineris ... ...cum earum nomiibus Latinis & Anglicis, etc*, by Thomas Johnson, 2 parts, 1634, 1641.

Merr.Pin. – *Pinax Rerum, naturalium Britannicarum, continens Vegetabilia, Animalia et Fossilia in hac Insula reperta inchoatus, etc.*, by C. Merrett, 1666.

Milf.Rec.Soc. – *Notes on the Botany of Milford*, by Revd A. H. Melvill,

1910, and The wild plants found in and near Milford on Sea, by P. T. B. Beale, published together in *Milford-on-Sea Record Society* 4(2), June 1928.

Morison Hist. – Plantarum Historiae Universalis Oxoniensis, etc., by Robert Morison. Part 2, 1680; Part 3, ed. Jacob Bobart, 1699; [Part 1 was never published].

Moss Fl.Hants – Moss Flora of Hampshire and the Isle of Wight, by A. B. Jackson, in *Proc.Hants Fld Club* [*q.v.*] 6: 29–40.

Nat.Hdbk 14 – Mosquitoes, by K. R. Snow, Naturalists' Handbook No. 14, 1990.

Nat.Wld – *Natural World*, the national magazine of the Wildlife Trusts, Royal Society for Nature Conservation (3 issues per annum), No. 1→, Spring 1981→.

New Bot.Guide – *The New Botanists' Guide to the Localities of the Rarer Plants of Britain, etc.*, by H. C. Watson, Vol. 1, 1835, Vol. 2, 1837.

New Fl. – *New Flora of the British Isles*, by C. A. Stace, 1991.

New Forest Hist.& Scen. – *The New Forest, its History and its Scenery*, by J. R. de C. Wise, 1863 [1862]. Edn 2, 1867.

New Phytol. – *New Phytologist*, Vol. 1→, 1902→.

Newsletter S'ton NHS – Newsletter of the Southampton Natural History Society, 1994.

NRA Survey – *Rivers Test and Itchen Macrophyte Survey* by L. E. Cranston & C. M. Ferguson. National Rivers Authority, 1991.

OED – *The Oxford English Dictionary -A New English Dictionary on Historical Principles*, reissued in 12 vols, 1933. Reprinted as compact edition in 2 vols, 1979.

Orch.Brit. – *Orchids of Britain*, by D. C. Lang, 1980.

Phyt.Brit. – *Phytologia Britannica. Natales exhibens indigenarium Stirpium sponte emergentium*, by W. How, 1650. [How's own copy in library of Magdalen College, Oxford, with ms annotations in his own hand.]

Phytologist N.S. – *The Phytologist. A Botanical Journal*, [New Series], ed. A. Irvine, 6 vols, 1855–63.

Phytologist – The Phytologist; a popular botanical miscellany, conducted by George Luxford [and latterly E. Newman], 5 vols [the last incomplete], 1841–54. [W. A. Bromfield regularly wrote 'Notes and occasional observations on some of the rare British plants growing wild in Hampshire' which appeared in *Phytologist* **3**: 205, 260, 269, 332, 363 (1849); 401, 490, 519, 555, 571, 593, 617, 653, 685, 741 (1850); 745, 793, 817, 821, 882, 951, 1002, 1025, 1061, 1089; **4**: 9, 21 (1851). These were bound together as '*Flora Hantoniensis*', with ms annotations by the author; in library of the Herbarium, Royal Botanic Gardens, Kew.]

Pl.Crib – *Plant Crib*, by T. C. G. Rich & M. D. B. Rich. Botanical Society of the British Isles, 1988.

Proc.Bmth N.S.S. – *Proceedings of the Bournemouth Natural Science Society*, Vol. 1→, 1908→.

Proc.B.S.B.I. – *Proceedings of the Botanical Society of the British Isles*, Vols 1–7, 1954–1969 [see also *Watsonia*].

Proc.Hants Fld Club – *Proceedings of the Hampshire Field Club & Archaeological Society*, Vols 1–3, 1885–1900 (as *Proceedings of the Hampshire Field Club*), Vols 4→, 1901→.

Proc.IoW N.H.S. – The alien and adventive Flora of Hampshire and the Isle of Wight by J. F. Rayner, in *Proceedings of the Isle of Wight Natural History Society*, **1** (4): 166–175, 1924; **1** (5): 229–274, 1925.

Proc.Linn.Soc. – *Proceedings of the Linnean Society of London*, Vols 1–179, [1838] 1839–1968; continued as the *Biological Journal of the Linnean Society*, Vol. 1→, 1969→, with Proceedings of the Society in the December issues until 1982, after which Proceedings published separately in *Newsletter and Proceedings of the Linnean Society of London*, Vol. 1→, 1984→.

RAE Survey – *Revised List of Flowering Plants and Ferns for RAE* [Royal Aircraft Establishment] & *Aldershot/Bourley, 1973–90*, by A. R. G. Mundell, 1991.

Ray Syn. – *Synopsis Methodica Stirpium Britannicarum, in qua tum Notae Generum Characteristicae traduntur, tum Species singulae breviter describuntur, etc.* by John Ray, 1690, edn 3, ed. J. J. Dillenius, 1724.

Ray Syn.MS – ms notes by J. Lightfoot in a copy of John Ray's *Synopsis*, formerly in the Oxford Botanic Garden Library, now in Department of Plant Science, University of Oxford.

Rep.B.E.C. – *Report. Botanical Exchange Club*. London, 1877–78; continued as *Report. Botanical Exchange Club of the British Isles*. Manchester, 1879–1900; continued as *Report. Botanical Exchange Club and Society of the British Isles*. Manchester, 1901–13; continued as *Report. Botanical Society and Exchange Club of the British Isles*. Arbroath, 1914–1947.

Rep.S'ton N.H.S. – *Records of the Southampton Natural History Society*, 1956–61; continued as *Annual Reports of the Southampton Natural History Society*, 1962→.

Rep.Watson B.E.C. – *Report of the Watson Botanical Exchange Club*, London, 1884–1934.

Rep.Winch.Coll.N.H.S. – *Reports of the Winchester College Natural History Society*. An occasional publication.

Rubi Hdbk – *Handbook of the Rubi of Great Britain and Ireland*, by W. C. R. Watson, 1958.

Silva – *Silva, or a discourse on forest trees*, by John Evelyn, 1664 edn, edited by A. Hunter M.D. 1776. [Facsimile reprint 1973.]

Smith Moss Fl. – *The moss flora of Britain and Ireland*, by A. J. E. Smith, 1978.

Sowerby MS – *Additions to the Flora of Hampshire*, by J. Sowerby; ms notes, in handwriting of the elder Sowerby, dated 3, 4, 5 and 6 June, 1806. Botany Department, The Natural History Museum, London.

Stirp.Adv.Nova – *Stirpium Adversaria Nova perfacilis vestigatio, luculentaque accessio ad priscorum, presertim Dioscoridis & recentiorum, materiam medica, etc.*, by P. Pena &

M. de Lobel, 1570. Edn 2, entitled *Nova Stirpium Adversaria ... quibus accessit Appendix, etc.*, 1576.

Suppl.Fl.Hants – *A Supplement to Frederick Townsend's Flora of Hampshire and the Isle of Wight*, by J. F. Rayner, 1929.

Suppl.Fl.Surrey – *Flora of Surrey Supplement and Checklist*, by A. C. Leslie, 1987.

Suppl.Fl.Wilts – *Supplement to the Flora of Wiltshire*, by L. F. Stearn, 1975.

Suppl.Wild Fl.Guide – *Supplement to the Pocket Guide to Wild Flowers*, by David McClintock. Privately published, 1957.

Survey Bas.Canal – A survey of the Basingstoke Canal, by M. E. Jakobson, MSc thesis, London University, 1966.

Theatrum Bot. – *Theatrum Botanicum: The Theater of Plants; or an Herball of large extent, etc.*, by John Parkinson, 1640.

Top.Bot. – *Topographical Botany. Being local and personal records towards shewing the distribution of British Plants traced through the 112 counties and vice counties of England and Scotland*, by H. C. Watson, 2

pts, 1873–74.

Trans.Linn.Soc. – *Transactions of the Linnean Society* [of London], Vols 1–30, 1791–1875; continued as *Transactions of the Linnean Society of London. Botany*, Series 2, Vols 1–9, 1875–1922; continued as *Transactions of the Linnean Society of London*, Series 3, Vol. 1→, 1939→.

Turn.Bot.– *Botanologia, The British Physician: or, The Nature and Vertues of English Plants, etc.*, by R. Turner, 1664.

Turn.Herb. – *The first and seconde partes of the Herbal of W. Turner... corrected and enlarged with the third parte, lately gathered, etc.*, by William Turner, 1586.

Vascular Pl.Brit.Is. – *List of Vascular Plants of the British Isles*, by D. H. Kent, 1992.

VCH Hants – *Victoria History of Hampshire and the Isle of Wight*, Vol. 3, 1908 (Victoria Histories of the Counties of England series, ed. Page, W., *q.v.* in Select Bibliography).

Watsonia – *Watsonia. Journal of the Botanical Society of the British Isles*, Vols 1–7, London, 1949–69;

Watsonia. Journal and Proceedings of the Botanical Society of the British Isles, Vols 8→, 1970→.

Watts MSS – Lt-Col. G. A. R. Watts' unpublished notebooks, in Botany Library, Natural History Museum, London.

Weeds & Aliens – *Weeds and Aliens*, by E. J. Salisbury. New Naturalist Library No. 43, 1961.

White's Jnls. – *The Journals of Gilbert White*, ed. Francesca Greenoak from Gilbert White's *MSS*, 1751–93, comprising *Flora Selborniensis* (1766–67) and *Garden Kalendar* (1751–73) (in Vol. 1) and *Naturalist's Journal* (1768–93) (in Vols 1–3), 3 vols, 1986–89.

White's Selb. – *The Natural History of Selborne, the naturalists's calendar and miscellaneous observations, extracted from his* [Gilbert White's] *papers, etc.*, 2 vols, 1802.

Wilts.Fl. – *The Wiltshire Flora*, ed. B. Gillam, 1993.

Wild Fl.Mag. – *The Wild Flower Magazine. Journal of the Wild Flower Society*, 1921→.

Wild Orchids Hants – Wild Orchids of Hampshire, by G. W. & G. G. Pierce, in *Hampshire Review*, 1953.

REFERENCES & SELECT BIBLIOGRAPHY

Listing works cited in the introductory chapters and consulted in the preparation of this work as well as others of general interest to users of *The Flora of Hampshire*.

Allen, D. E., 1986. *Flora of the Isle of Man*, 250 pp. Manx Museum and National Trust, Douglas.

Barber, K. E. (ed.), 1987. *Wessex and the Isle of Wight – Field Guide*. Quaternary Research Association, Cambridge.

—— & Clarke, M. J., 1987. Cranes Moor, New Forest: palynology and macrofossil stratigraphy. *In* Barber, K. E. (ed.) *Wessex and the Isle of Wight – Field Guide*, pp. 33–44. Quaternary Research Association, Cambridge.

Bevis, J. H., Kettell, R. E. & Shepard, B., with geological chapter by Insole, A. (ed. Fraser, O. H.), 1978. *Flora of the Isle of Wight*, 114 pp. Isle of Wight Natural History & Archaeological Society, Newport, IoW.

Blackwood, J. W. & Tubbs, C. R., 1970. A quantitative survey of chalk grassland in England. *Biological Conservation* 3(1): 1–5.

Bowen, H. J. M., 1968. *The Flora of Berkshire*, 389 pp. incl. 10 figs, 570 maps. Privately published, [Reading].

Briggs, M., 1990. *Sussex Plant Atlas (Selected Supplement)*, 32pp., 85 maps. Booth Museum of Natural History, Brighton.

British Red Data Book: 1 – *Vascular Plants*. (See Perring & Farrell, below).

Bromfield, W. A., 1848–50. *Flora Hantoniensis*, serialized in *The Phytologist* [see Appendix IV].

——, 1856 (ed. Hooker, W. J. & Salter, T. B.). *Flora Vectensis – being a systematic description of the phaenogamous ... plants and ferns indigenous to the Isle of Wight*. xxxv, 678 pp. 1 portrait, 1 map. William Pamplin, London.

Brough, P., Gibbons, R. & Pope, C., 1986. *The Nature of Hampshire and the Isle of Wight*, 176 pp, many b/w illustrations, 9 col. pls, 5 maps. Barracuda Books, Buckingham.

Brummitt, R. K. & Powell, C. E., (eds) 1992. *Authors of Plant Names*, [iv], 732 pp. Royal Botanic Gardens, Kew.

Catt, J. A., 1979. Distribution of loess in Britain. *Proceedings of the Geologists' Association* 90: 93–95.

Clapham, A. R., Tutin, T. G. & Warburg, E. F., 1962. *Flora of the British Isles* (edn 2). xlviii, 1269 pp. Cambridge University Press, Cambridge.

——, —— & Moore, D. M. 1987. *Flora of the British Isles* (edn 3). xxvii, 688 pp. Cambridge University Press, Cambridge.

Clarke, M. J. & Barber, K. E., 1987. Mire development from the Devensian Lateglacial to the present at Church Moor, Hampshire. *In* Barber, K. E., (ed.) *Wessex and the Isle of Wight – Field Guide*, pp. 23–32. Quaternary Research Association, Cambridge.

Clement, E. J. & Foster, M. C., 1994. *Alien Plants of the British Isles*, xviii, 590 pp. Botanical Society of the British Isles, London.

Collins, M. A., 1982. *Some evidence for the influence of land use on distribution of non-calcareous soils on the Chalk Downs of southern England*. PhD thesis, King's College, University of London.

Corley, M. F. V. & Hill, M. O., 1981. *Distribution of bryophytes in the British Isles. A census catalogue of their occurrence in vice-counties*, 160 pp. British Bryological Society, Cardiff.

Dandy, J. E., 1958. *List of British Vascular Plants*, xvi, 176 pp. British Museum (Natural History), London.

——, 1969. *Watsonian vice-counties of Great Britain*. 38 pp, 2 folding maps. Ray Society, London.

Darwin, Charles R., 1875. *Insectivorous Plants* (edn 2), x, 462 pp. John Murray, London.

Dony, J. G., Jury S. L. & Perring, F. H., 1986. *English Names of Wild Flowers* (edn 2), viii, 117 pp. Botanical Society of the British Isles, [London].

Druce, G. C., 1897. *The Flora of Berkshire*, being a topographical and historical account of flowering plants and ferns found in the county, cxcix, [i], 644 pp. Clarendon Press, Oxford.

——, 1917. John Goodyer of Mapledurham, Hampshire. *Report for 1916 of the Botanical Society & Exchange Club of the British Isles* 4: 523–550.

Du Pinet, A. 1561. *Historia Plantarum Earum imagines, nomenclaturae, qualitates, & natale solum* [from P. A. Matthioli, P. Dioscorides and others]. *Quibus accessere simplicium medicamentoru facultates, secundum locos et genera, ex Dioscoride*. [2 pts in 1 vol.] Lugduni [Lyons].

Ellis, R. Gwynn, 1993. *Index to Clive Stace's New Flora of the British Isles*, 110 pp. Department of Botany, National Museum of Wales, Cardiff.

Evelyn, John, 1664. *Silva, or a discourse on forest trees, and the propagation of timber, etc.* Revised edn, 1776, with notes by A. Hunter, M.D., [liv], 649, [xii] pp., engraved portrait by Bartolozzi, 40 (incl. 1 folding) engravings of trees, 1 folding table. Privately published, York.

Fisher, G. C., 1971. Brickearth and its influence on the character of soils in the south-east New Forest. *Proceedings of the Hampshire Field Club and Archaeological Society* **28**: 99–109.

Garrard, I. & Streeter, D., 1983. *The Wild Flowers of the British Isles*, 295 pp., about 1400 col. illus. Macmillan, London. [The text is by D. Streeter, the illustrations by I. Garrard.]

Gerard, J. (revised and ed. Johnson, T.), 1633. *The herball or generall historie of plantes*, [xxxviii], 1631, [xlvi] pp. London. [Also complete in a facsimile edition, 1975, with publishers' note, viii pp. Dover Publications, New York.]

Gillam, B. (ed.), 1993. *The Wiltshire Flora*, x, 386 pp. incl. 615 maps, 8 col. pls, 12 figs. The Nature Conservation Bureau, Newbury.

Godwin, H., 1975. *The History of the British Flora* (edn 2), ix, 541 pp. Cambridge University Press, Cambridge.

Gordon, P. & Shakesby, R., 1973. Molluscan fauna of Rake Bottom: a study of valley infill, Rake Bottom, Butser Hill, Hants. *South Hampshire Geographer* **6**: 10–20.

Graham, G. G. & Primavesi, A. L., 1993. *Roses of Great Britain and Ireland*, 208 pp., b/w illustrations, 32 maps. BSBI Handbook No. 7. Botanical Society of the British Isles, London.

Grose, J. D., 1957. *The Flora of Wiltshire*, iv, 824 pp. incl. 34 maps, 11 b/w pls. Wiltshire Archaeological and Natural History Society, Devizes.

Gunther, R. W. T., 1922. *Early British Botanists and their gardens, based on unpublished writings of Goodyer, Tradescant and others*, vi, 417 pp., 9 pls. Oxford University Press, Oxford.

Hall, P. C., 1980. *The Sussex Plant Atlas*, 179 pp. incl. 969 maps. Booth Museum of Natural History, Brighton.

Hoffman, D., 1987. *The Thorson's Guide to Medical Herbalism*, 240 pp. HarperCollins (Thorsons), London.

Hubbard, C. E., 1984. *Grasses* (edn 3), 463 pp. Penguin Books, Harmondsworth.

Jermy, A. C., Chater, A. O. & David, R. W., 1982. *Sedges of the British Isles* (edn 2), 268 pp., b/w illustrations, 60 maps. BSBI Handbook No. 1. Botanical Society of the British Isles, London.

Jones, D. K. C., 1981. *Southeast and Southern England*, x, 332 pp. incl. table & figs in text (in series *The Geomorphology of the British Isles*). Methuen, London.

Kent, D. H., 1992. *List of vascular plants of the British Isles*, xvi, 384 pp. Botanical Society of the British Isles, London.

Linton, E. F., 1900. *Flora of Bournemouth, including the Isle of Purbeck ...*, vii, 290 pp., 1 map. Privately published, Bournemouth.

Lousley, J. E., 1961. A census list of wool aliens found in Britain 1946–60. *Proc. B.S.B.I.* **4**: 221–247.

——, 1976. *Flora of Surrey*, 475 pp. incl. 504 maps, 3 col. pls, 32 b/w pls, 1 portrait. David & Charles, Newton Abbot.

—— & Kent, D. H., 1981. *Docks and Knotweeds of the British Isles*, 197 pp., b/w illustrations. BSBI Handbook No. 3. Botanical Society of the British Isles, London.

Mabberley, D. J., 1987. *The Plant-Book – a portable dictionary of the larger plants*, xii, 706 pp. Cambridge University Press, Cambridge.

Mansel-Pleydell, J. C., 1895. *Flora of Dorsetshire or a catalogue of plants found in the county of Dorset* (edn 2), xxxviii, 345, xxv pp, 1 map. Whittaker, Dorchester.

Marren, P., 1992. *The Wild Woods – a regional Guide to Britain's ancient Woodland*, 256 pp., 50 col., 15 b/w pls. David & Charles, Newton Abbot.

Matthews, J. R., 1937. The geographical relationships of the British flora. *J. Ecol.* **25**: 1–90. London.

Meikle, R. D., 1984. *Willows and Poplars of Great Britain and Ireland*, 198 pp., b/w illustrations. BSBI Handbook No. 4. Botanical Society of the British Isles, London.

Melville, R. N. & Freshney, E. C., 1982. *The Hampshire Basin and adjoining areas* (edn 4), vii, 146 pp., 17 pls (some coloured). British Regional Geology Handbook, HMSO, London.

Meteorological Office, 1977. *Average annual rainfall; international standard period 1941–1970*. Map (2 sheets), Meteorological Office, Bracknell.

Mitchell, A. [F.], 1978. *A Field Guide to the Trees of Britain and Northern Europe*, 416 pp. incl. 640 line drawings, 40 col. pls. Collins, London.

Munby, J. (ed.), 1982. *Domesday Book 4. Hampshire* [unpaginated]. Phillimore, Chichester.

Nicholls, R. J., 1987. Evolution of the upper reaches of the Solent River and the formation of Poole and Christchurch Bays. *In* Barber, K. E. (ed.) *Wessex and the Isle of Wight – field guide*, pp. 99–114. Quaternary Research Association, Cambridge.

Ordnance Survey Maps covering Hampshire, 1810–1817, edn 1, comprising sheets 77: Devizes (1817); 78: Basingstoke & Newbury (1817); 79: Dorking & Kingston (1816); 85: Salisbury & New Forest (1811); 86: Winchester & the Solent (1810); 87: Brighton & Chichester (1813); 93: Poole & Isle of Purbeck (1811); 94: Isle of Wight (and part of Hampshire) (1810). Ordnance Survey, London. [Facsimile edition, 1970, David & Charles, Newton Abbot].

Page, C. N., 1982. *The Ferns of Great Britain and Ireland*, xii, 447 pp., numerous b/w illustrations, maps. Cambridge University Press, Cambridge.

Page, W. (ed.), 1904–11. *Victoria History of Hampshire and the Isle of Wight*, Vols 1–5. Victoria Histories of the Counties of England series. Constable, London.

Paton, J. A., 1965. *Census Catalogue of British Hepatics* (edn 4), British Bryological Society.

Perring, F. H., 1968. *Critical supplement to the atlas of the British Flora*, viii, 159 pp. (incl. 390 maps). Botanical Society of the British Isles, London.

—— & Walters, S. M., 1976. *Atlas of the British Flora* (edn 2), xxiv, 432 pp. (incl. 1623 maps). Botanical Society of the British Isles, London.

—— & Farrell, L., 1983. *British Red Data Books: 1 – Vascular Plants* (edn 2), [ii], xxviii, 100 pp. Royal Society for Nature Conservation, Lincoln.

Philp, E. G., 1982. *Atlas of the Kent Flora*, xii, 211 pp., incl. 970 maps. Kent Field Club, Maidstone.

Purvis, O. W., Coppins, B. J. & James, P. W., 1993. *Check list of lichens of Great Britain and Ireland*, 75 pp. British Lichen Society, Bulletin No. 72 (Supplement).

Rackham, O., 1980. *Ancient Woodland: its history, vegetation and uses in England*, xii, 402pp. Edward Arnold, London.

Raven, C. E., 1950. *John Ray, Naturalist – his life and works*, xx, 506 pp., 1 portrait. Cambridge University Press, Cambridge. (Paperback edition, 1986)

Ray, John, 1660. *Catalogus Plantarum circa Cantabrigiam nascentium ...*, xxx, 182, [103] pp. John Field, Cambridge.

Rayner, J. F., 1929. *A Supplement to Frederick Townsend's Flora of Hampshire and the Isle of Wight*, xix, 132 pp. Privately published, Southampton.

Rich, T. C. G., 1991. *Crucifers of Great Britain and Ireland*, 336 pp., b/w illustrations, 60 maps. BSBI Handbook No. 6. Botanical Society of the British Isles, London.

Rose, F., 1976. Lichenological indicators of age and environmental continuity in woodlands. In *Lichenology: progress and problems*, eds Brown, D. H., Hawksworth, D. L. & Bailey, R. H., pp. 279–308, 7 tables, 1 fig. Systematics Association Special Volume No. 8, Academic Press, London.

——, 1981. *The Wild Flower Key*, 480pp. (incl. *c.*1000 col. illus.). (edn. 1) Warne, London. Edn 2 [1988].

——, 1989. *Colour Identification Guide to Grasses, Sedges, Rushes and Ferns of the British Isles and north-western Europe*, 240 pp., 62 col. pls. Viking Penguin, London.

——, Stern, R. C., Matcham, H. W. & Coppins, B. J., 1991. *Atlas of Sussex Mosses, Liverworts and Lichens*, 135 pp. incl. 447 maps. Booth Museum of Natural History, Brighton.

Ryves, T. B., 1975. Notes on wool-alien species of *Crassula* from Blackmoor, North Hants., 1970–74. *Watsonia* **10**: 391–393.

——, 1976. Notes on some wool-alien Malvaceae. *Watsonia* **11**: 70–71.

——, 1977. Notes on wool-alien species of *Lepidium* in the British Isles. *Watsonia* **11**: 367–372.

Seymour, W. A., 1980. *A History of the Ordnance Survey*, xviii, 394 pp., 27 pls. Dawson, Folkestone.

Simpson, N. D., 1960. *A bibliographical Index of the British Flora*, xix, 429 pp. Privately published, Bournemouth.

Stace, C. A. (ed.), 1975. *Hybridization and the Flora of the British Isles*, xiii, 626 pp. Academic Press, London, in collaboration with the Botanical Society of the British Isles.

——, 1991. *New Flora of the British Isles*, viii, 1226 pp. Cambridge University Press, Cambridge.

Stearn, W. T., 1992. *Botanical Latin – history, grammar, syntax, terminology and vocabulary* (edn 4, revised), xiv, 566 pp. David & Charles, Newton Abbot.

Stewart, A., Pearman, D. A. & Preston, C. D. (eds), 1994. *Scarce Plants in Britain*, 515 pp. incl. 254 maps, 16 tables, 49 figs. Joint Nature Conservation Committee, Peterborough.

Tansley, A. G., 1939 [reissued 1953 in 2 vols, continuously paginated]. *The British Islands and their vegetation*, 930 pp, 162 pls. Cambridge University Press, Cambridge.

Taverner, John, 1566. *The Book of Survey*. Public Record Office MS, Chancery Lane, London.

Townsend, F., 1883 [1884]. *Flora of Hampshire, including the Isle of Wight; or a list of the flowering plants and ferns found in the County of Southampton ...*, xxiv, 524 pp., 2 pls (one coloured), 1 map. Lovell Reeve, London.

——, 1904. *Flora of Hampshire including the Isle of Wight...* (edn 2), xl, 658 pp., 2 pls (one coloured), 1 map. Lovell Reeve, London.

Tubbs, C. R., 1968. *The New Forest: An Ecological History*, 248pp., 16 pp. of b/w half-tones, 6 figs. David & Charles, Newton Abbot.

——, 1986. *The New Forest* (New Naturalist Library No. 73), 300 pp., 20 col. pls. Collins, London.

—— & Dimbleby, G. W., 1965. Early Agriculture in the New Forest. *Advancement of Science* **22**: 88–97.

Tutin, T. G., 1980. *Umbellifers of the British Isles*, 197 pp., b/w illustrations. BSBI Handbook No. 2. Botanical Society of the British Isles, London.

——, Heywood, V. H., Burges, N. A., Moore, D. M., Valentine, D. H., Walters, S. M., Webb, D. A. (eds), 1964–80. *Flora Europaea* **1**: Lycopodiaceae to Platanaceae, xxxii, 464 pp., 5 maps; **2**: Rosaceae to Umbelliferae, xxvii, 455 pp., 5 maps; **3**: Diapensiaceae to Myoporaceae, xxix, 370 pp., 5 maps; **4**: Plantaginaceae to Compositae (and Rubiaceae), xxix, 505 pp., 5 maps; **5**: Alismataceae to Orchidaceae, xxxvi, 452 pp., 5 maps. Cambridge University Press, Cambridge. [Edn 2 (with additional eds, Chater, A. O. and Edmondson, J. R.) in progress, Vol. 1: Psilotaceae to Platanaceae, xlvi, 581 pp., 5 maps, 1993]

Waton, P. V., 1982. *A palynological study of the impact of man on the landscape of central southern England, with special reference to the chalklands*. 428 pp. PhD thesis, University of Southampton.

Watson, H. C., 1852. *Cybele Britannica* **3**: 524–528.

Webb, J., Quail, S., Haskell, P. & Riley, R., 1989. *The Spirit of Portsmouth: a History*, [viii], 212 pp. incl. 42 b/w illustrations. Phillimore, Chichester.

White, G., [MSS 1768–93] as *The Journals of Gilbert White*, ed. Francesca Greenoak, 1986–89, in 3 vols. Century Hutchinson, London.

—, 1789. *The Natural History and Antiquities of Selborne in the county of Southampton*, v, 468 [13] pp., 9 pls. B. White & Son, London.

—, 1789. *The Natural History of Selborne*, ed. R. Mabey, 256 pp., with engravings (nine coloured), 1 col. map. Century Hutchinson, London. 1988. [The text of this new bicentenary edition, which includes a complete bibliography of previous editions, follows that of the first edition of 1789, supplemented by Gilbert White's own corrections.]

—, 1813. *The Natural History and Antiquities of Selborne in the county of Southampton to which are added the Natural-ist's Calendar, miscellaneous observations and poems* (edn 3), x[2], 588 pp., 12 pls. White, Cochrane & Co., etc., London. [One of the most important and complete editions, in facsimile with xxxi pp. new introduction by P. G. M. Foster, 1993. Ray Society, London.]

Wilson, A. (ed.), 1930. *A Census Catalogue of British Hepatics*, edn 3.

Wolley-Dod, A. H. (ed.), 1937. *The Flora of Sussex*, lxxiii, 571 pp., 6 pls., 2 maps. Saville, Hastings.

Woodhead, F., 1994. *Flora of the Christchurch area*, 120 pp. incl. 650 maps, 10 figs, 4 col. pls. Privately published, Bournemouth.

INDEX TO THE VASCULAR FLORA

Current generic and specific names are in **bold type**; synonyms are in *italics*. Family names are in **bold capitals**; those of higher taxa are in light capitals. English names are in Roman type. Page numbers of principal entries in the Vascular Flora (Chapter X) are in **bold**.

Current generic and specific names are in **bold type**; synonyms are in *italics*. Page numbers of principal entries in the Lichen Flora (Chapter XI) are in **bold** followed by map number where relevant.

INDEX TO THE BRYOPHYTE FLORA

Current generic and specific names are in **bold type**; synonyms are in *italics*. Higher taxa are in light capitals. Page numbers of principal entries in the Bryophyte Flora (Chapter XII) are in **bold** followed by map number where relevant.